Total Correction to apply to Obs. Alt. ☉ to obtain T												
Seasonal Correction	Jan. +0'.3	Feb. +0'.2	Mar. +0'.1	April 0'.0	May − 0'.2	June − 0'.2	July − 0'.2	Aug. −0'...				

☉	H.E. in Feet					☉	H.E. in Feet					☉	H.E. in Feet				
	10	15	20	25	30		35	40	45	50	55		60	65	70	80	90
6°	4.5	3.8	3.2	2.7	2.2	6°	1.8	1.4	1.0	0.6	0.3	6°					
6½	5.1	4.4	3.8	3.3	2.8	6½	2.4	2.0	1.6	1.2	0.9	6½	0.6	0.3	0.0		
7	5.7	5.0	4.4	3.8	3.4	7	2.9	2.5	2.2	1.8	1.5	7	1.1	0.8	0.5		
7½	6.1	5.4	4.8	4.3	3.8	7½	3.4	3.0	2.6	2.2	1.9	7½	1.6	1.3	1.0	0.4	
8	6.5	5.8	5.2	4.7	4.2	8	3.8	3.4	3.0	2.6	2.3	8	2.0	1.7	1.4	0.8	0.3
8½	6.9	6.2	5.6	5.1	4.6	8½	4.2	3.8	3.4	3.0	2.7	8½	2.4	2.0	1.7	1.2	0.6
9	7.2	6.5	5.9	5.4	4.9	9	4.5	4.1	3.7	3.4	3.0	9	2.7	2.4	2.1	1.5	0.9
9½	7.5	6.8	6.2	5.7	5.2	9½	4.8	4.4	4.0	3.7	3.3	9½	3.0	2.7	2.4	1.8	1.2
10	7.8	7.1	6.5	6.0	5.5	10	5.1	4.7	4.3	4.0	3.6	10	3.3	3.0	2.6	2.1	1.5
11	8.3	7.6	7.0	6.4	6.0	11	5.5	5.1	4.8	4.4	4.1	11	3.7	3.4	3.1	2.5	2.0
12	8.7	7.9	7.4	6.8	6.4	12	5.9	5.5	5.2	4.8	4.5	12	4.1	3.8	3.5	2.9	2.4
13	9.0	8.3	7.7	7.2	6.7	13	6.3	5.9	5.5	5.1	4.8	13	4.5	4.2	3.9	3.3	2.8
14	9.3	8.6	8.0	7.5	7.0	14	6.6	6.2	5.8	5.4	5.1	14	4.8	4.5	4.2	3.6	3.1
15	9.5	8.8	8.3	7.7	7.3	15	6.8	6.4	6.1	5.7	5.3	15	5.0	4.7	4.4	3.8	3.3
16	9.8	9.0	8.5	7.9	7.5	16	7.1	6.7	6.3	5.9	5.6	16	5.3	4.9	4.6	4.1	3.6
17	10.0	9.3	8.7	8.2	7.7	17	7.3	6.9	6.5	6.1	5.8	17	5.5	5.1	4.8	4.3	3.8
18	10.2	9.4	8.9	8.4	7.9	18	7.4	7.0	6.7	6.3	6.0	18	5.7	5.3	5.0	4.5	3.9
19	10.3	9.6	9.0	8.5	8.0	19	7.6	7.2	6.8	6.5	6.1	19	5.8	5.5	5.2	4.6	4.1
20	10.5	9.8	9.2	8.7	8.2	20	7.8	7.4	7.0	6.7	6.3	20	6.0	5.6	5.3	4.8	4.2
23	10.8	10.1	9.5	9.0	8.5	23	8.1	7.7	7.3	7.0	6.6	23	6.3	6.0	5.7	5.1	4.6
26	11.1	10.4	9.8	9.3	8.8	26	8.4	8.0	7.6	7.3	6.9	26	6.6	6.3	5.9	5.4	4.9
30	11.4	10.7	10.1	9.6	9.1	30	8.7	8.3	7.9	7.6	7.2	30	6.9	6.6	6.3	5.7	5.2
35	11.7	11.0	10.4	9.9	9.4	35	9.0	8.6	8.2	7.9	7.5	35	7.2	6.9	6.6	6.0	5.5
40	11.9	11.2	10.6	10.1	9.6	40	9.2	8.8	8.4	8.1	7.7	40	7.4	7.1	6.8	6.2	5.7
45	12.1	11.4	10.8	10.3	9.8	45	9.4	9.0	8.6	8.2	7.9	45	7.6	7.3	7.0	6.4	5.9
50	12.2	11.5	10.9	10.4	9.9	50	9.5	9.1	8.7	8.4	8.0	50	7.7	7.4	7.1	6.5	6.0
60	12.4	11.7	11.1	10.6	10.2	60	9.7	9.3	9.0	8.6	8.3	60	8.0	7.6	7.3	6.8	6.2
70	12.6	11.9	11.3	10.8	10.4	70	9.9	9.5	9.2	8.8	8.5	70	8.1	7.8	7.5	7.0	6.4
80	12.8	12.1	11.5	11.0	10.5	80	10.1	9.7	9.3	8.9	8.6	80	8.3	8.0	7.7	7.1	6.6
90	12.9	12.2	11.6	11.1	10.6	90	10.2	9.8	9.4	9.1	8.7	90	8.4	8.1	7.8	7.2	6.7

Total Correction to apply to Obs. Alt. ★ to obtain True Alt. SUBTRACTIVE

★	H.E. in Feet					★	H.E. in Feet					★	H.E. in Foot				
	10	15	20	25	30		35	40	45	50	55		60	65	70	80	90
7	10.5	11.2	11.8	12.3	12.8	7	13.2	13.6	14.0	14.4	14.7	7	15.1	15.4	15.7	16.3	16.8
7½	10.0	10.7	11.3	11.9	12.3	7½	12.8	13.2	13.6	13.9	14.3	7½	14.6	14.9	15.2	15.8	16.3
8	9.6	10.3	10.9	11.5	11.9	8	12.4	12.8	13.2	13.5	13.9	8	14.2	14.5	14.8	15.4	15.9
8½	9.3	10.0	10.6	11.1	11.5	8½	12.0	12.4	12.8	13.1	13.5	8½	13.8	14.1	14.4	15.0	15.5
9	9.0	9.7	10.3	10.8	11.2	9	11.7	12.1	12.4	12.8	13.2	9	13.5	13.8	14.1	14.7	15.2
9½	8.7	9.4	10.0	10.5	10.9	9½	11.4	11.8	12.1	12.5	12.9	9½	13.2	13.5	13.8	14.4	14.9
10	8.4	9.1	9.7	10.2	10.7	10	11.1	11.5	11.9	12.2	12.6	10	12.9	13.2	13.5	14.1	14.6
11	7.9	8.6	9.2	9.7	10.2	11	10.6	11.0	11.4	11.7	12.1	11	12.4	12.7	13.0	13.6	14.2
12	7.5	8.2	8.8	9.3	9.8	12	10.2	10.6	11.0	11.4	11.7	12	12.0	12.3	12.6	13.2	13.8
13	7.2	7.9	8.5	9.0	9.4	13	9.9	10.3	10.7	11.0	11.4	13	11.7	12.0	12.3	12.9	13.4
14	6.9	7.6	8.2	8.7	9.1	14	9.6	10.0	10.4	10.7	11.1	14	11.4	11.7	12.0	12.6	13.1
15	6.6	7.3	7.9	8.4	8.9	15	9.3	9.7	10.1	10.5	10.8	15	11.1	11.4	11.7	12.3	12.8
16	6.4	7.1	7.7	8.2	8.7	16	9.1	9.5	9.9	10.2	10.6	16	10.9	11.2	11.5	12.1	12.6
17	6.2	6.9	7.5	8.0	8.5	17	8.9	9.3	9.7	10.0	10.4	17	10.7	11.0	11.3	11.9	12.4
18	6.0	6.7	7.3	7.8	8.3	18	8.7	9.1	9.5	9.8	10.2	18	10.5	10.8	11.1	11.7	12.2
19	5.9	6.5	7.1	7.6	8.1	19	8.5	9.0	9.3	9.7	10.0	19	10.3	10.7	11.0	11.5	12.1
20	5.7	6.4	7.0	7.5	8.0	20	8.4	8.8	9.2	9.4	9.9	20	10.2	10.5	10.8	11.4	11.9
23	5.3	6.0	6.6	7.1	7.6	23	8.0	8.4	8.8	9.2	9.5	23	9.8	10.1	10.4	11.0	11.5
26	5.0	5.7	6.3	6.8	7.3	26	7.7	8.1	8.5	8.9	9.2	26	9.5	9.8	10.1	10.7	11.2
30	4.7	5.4	6.0	6.5	7.0	30	7.4	7.8	8.2	8.6	8.9	30	9.2	9.5	9.8	10.4	10.9
35	4.4	5.1	5.7	6.3	6.7	35	7.1	7.5	7.9	8.3	8.6	35	8.9	9.2	9.5	10.1	10.6
40	4.2	4.9	5.5	6.0	6.5	40	6.9	7.3	7.7	8.1	8.4	40	8.7	9.0	9.3	9.9	10.4
45	4.0	4.7	5.3	5.8	6.3	45	6.7	7.1	7.5	7.9	8.2	45	8.5	8.8	9.1	9.7	10.2
50	3.9	4.6	5.2	5.7	6.2	50	6.6	7.0	7.4	7.7	8.1	50	8.4	8.7	9.0	9.6	10.1
60	3.7	4.4	4.9	5.5	5.9	60	6.4	6.8	7.1	7.5	7.8	60	8.1	8.5	8.8	9.3	9.9
70	3.5	4.2	4.7	5.3	5.7	70	6.2	6.6	6.9	7.3	7.6	70	7.9	8.3	8.6	9.1	9.7
80	3.3	4.0	4.5	5.1	5.5	80	6.0	6.4	6.7	7.1	7.4	80	7.7	8.1	8.4	8.9	9.5
90	3.1	3.8	4.4	4.9	5.4	90	5.8	6.2	6.6	6.9	7.3	90	7.6	7.9	8.2	8.8	9.3

A SET OF

NAUTICAL TABLES

FOR GENERAL NAVIGATIONAL PURPOSES

COMPILED BY THE LATE
STEPHEN M. BURTON
Master Mariner

REVISED AND EDITED BY THE LATE
GILBERT F. CUNNINGHAM, B.A., Ph.D.
formerly Staff Navigator, R.A.F.V.R.

SEVENTH EDITION
(THIRD IMPRESSION)

THE MARITIME PRESS LIMITED
13 LONG ACRE, LONDON, W.C.2

FIRST PUBLISHED 1934
by Burton's Navigational Publications Limited

SEVENTH EDITION (REVISED) © 1967
SECOND IMPRESSION © 1968
THIRD IMPRESSION © 1970
THE MARITIME PRESS LIMITED

Printed in Great Britain by
Lowe & Brydone (Printers) Ltd., London

SBN 540 00188 0

PREFACE

TO THE SEVENTH EDITION

THE DEATH of Stephen Merceron Burton on 3rd January 1966 removed a notable figure from the world of navigation. During his years as a practising navigator with the Merchant Marine he conceived the idea of compiling a set of nautical tables which would be at once concise and comprehensive, and when he left the sea his ingenuity and perseverance enabled him to place his tables on the market in a remarkably short space of time. Their success was immediate, and the first edition, published in 1934, was sold out within a year. The number of successive editions and impressions are a tribute to the qualities of the tables. Captain Burton's original aims of securing the maximum ease, speed and accuracy have always been the first consideration, and it is hoped that the improvements in this new edition will help the volume to maintain even more worthily these high standards.

I would like to add a note of personal appreciation; during over thirty years of association with the late Captain Burton I learned a great deal from him regarding the navigator's craft, and I hope that, although now unhappily deprived of the benefit of his advice, I may be able to continue the Burton tradition.

The most important changes in the seventh edition are the introduction of negative characteristics for logarithms and the remodelling of the Haversine Table. The first of these changes has been made to suit the modern method of teaching in schools and nautical colleges and to provide continuity when changing from ordinary schooling to nautical training. For the benefit of those who are accustomed to the older convention the former positive characteristics have been retained, in square brackets. The revision of the Haversine Table has simplified it by getting rid of the time indexing, no longer required when all almanacs use G.H.A. A Conversion Table for time and arc has been added, and one or two minor improvements have been made.

The checking of masses of figures is an onerous duty, and while every effort has been made to secure complete accuracy, printers are only human, and sometimes mistakes slip through. In this connexion we are most grateful to those users who have drawn our attention to errors and ambiguities, and we always appreciate communications on such matters.

May 1967   GILBERT F. CUNNINGHAM

CONTENTS

NOTES ON THE TABLES

GENERAL. An extensive investigation into the degree of accuracy normally obtained in the practice of astronomical position-finding at sea has indicated that the average inaccuracy in a position line produced by the average observer is 0'.7, and that one in twenty such position lines may be as much as 3'.0 in error. It would seem, therefore, that while every care should be taken to guard against actual blunders, to be over-meticulous about the degree of accuracy in the calculations connected with astronomical navigation is more likely to be misleading than useful.*

TABLES 1, 1a and 2 (inside front cover). **G.H.A. Sun, Planets and Aries,** tables for accelerating, and proportional parts for adjusting G.H.A. and Dec. of planets. These are simply tables of proportional parts corresponding to minutes and seconds for a given hourly difference of G.H.A. For the Sun and Aries the hourly differences are, as will be seen, respectively, 15° 00' and 15° 02'.46. For the planets the hourly difference is 15° 00' ± a quantity " v " printed at the foot of the planet's day-column in the almanac. This v being comparatively small, it is sufficient to take the proportion corresponding to the nearest minute. Except sometimes in the case of Venus this v proportion is always additive. (See also notes on Table 10.)

Examples:

	SUN.	JUPITER.	ARIES.
Given G.H.A. at 14 hrs.	267°15'.6	105°12'.2	09°15'.7
		v 3 .6	
			h. m. s.
Required accelerated G.H.A.'s for each at G.M.T. - - - -			14 43 23

	SUN.	JUPITER.	ARIES.
for 14 hrs. - - - - -	267°15'.6	105°12'.2	09°15'.7
,, 43 m. - - - - -	10 45 .0	10 45 .0	10 46 .8
,, 23 s. - - - - -	5 .8	5 .8	5 .8
,, v 3.6 - - - -		2 .5	
	278 06 .4	116 05 .5	20 08 .3

TABLE 3—pp. 2-91. **Traverse Table.** This table was originally taken, by permission of Messrs. J. D. Potter, from Raper's Tables.

It may perhaps be as well to remind navigators that since all quantities printed in the Traverse Table under any particular course bear the same proportion to each other, the range of availability of the table may be indefinitely increased by multiplying and dividing the quantities to be dealt with (other than the course).

Example—Given D. Lat. 467.2 and Dep. 958.2, required the course and distance.

By halving these quantities we get—

$$\left.\begin{array}{l} \text{D. Lat. } 233.6 \\ \text{Dep. } 479.1 \end{array}\right\} = \text{Co. } 64°, \text{ Dist. } 533 \text{ M.}$$

The required results are therefore: course 64°, distance 533 × 2 = 1066 M.†

Formulae for computing Traverse Table—

D. Lat. = Dist. Cos. Co., and Dep. = Dist. Sin. Co.

TABLE 4—pp. 92-99. **Meridional Parts.** The figures for Table 4 have been taken, with the permission of the Controller of H.M. Stationery Office and the Hydrographer of the Navy, from the " Table of Meridional Parts for the Terrestrial Spheroid", by John W. Atherton. This book is printed, by order of the Lords Commissioners of the Admiralty, for use in the Hydrographic Office; and upon it all British charts are now, and have been for some seventy-five years past, constructed.

Mercator Sailing. The original conception of the unit of distance which was denominated the " nautical mile " was the length of a minute of arc on the

* See "The Accuracy of Astronomical Observations at Sea". *The Journal of the Institute of Navigation*, Vol. X, 1957 pp. 223ff.　　　　　　　　† Symbol of nautical mile.

Earth's surface subtending a minute of angle at the Earth's centre: and the adoption of this unit was intended to simplify astronomical navigation. Owing to the non-spherical shape of the Earth, however, the nautical mile varies in length from $6046\frac{1}{2}$ feet at the equator to 6108 feet at the poles and must, in fact, be considered as the length of an arc subtending a minute, not at the Earth's centre, but at the centre of curvature of the place. In order to overcome the inconvenience of having a varying unit of distance the figure of 6080 feet has been adopted as the " British standard nautical mile ", and it is this distance which is generally meant when the nautical mile is referred to. The distance which emerges from a calculation by Mercator Sailing is not a distance in any standard nautical mile, but in what might be called " natural nautical miles ". It is the number of natural nautical miles or minutes intervening between the places between which the so-called distance has been calculated. No table at present exists for converting natural nautical miles into British standard nautical miles, but the difference seldom amounts to as much as $\frac{1}{2}\%$ and may therefore be considered as unimportant in the practice of navigation.

TABLE 4a—p. 100. **Correction to be applied to the Mean Latitude to obtain Middle Latitude.** As demonstrated in text books, Cos.Mid.Lat. = D. Lat. D.M.P. This table gives the correction to be applied to the mean latitude in order to convert it to the Middle Latitude. By using the Middle Latitude, as distinct from the mean latitude, courses and distances calculated by the Middle Latitude Sailing formulae are made to give the same results as they would give if calculated by the Mercator method, but such results are not in any " standard " nautical mile, as explained in the Note on Table 4 above.

It is to be noted that the table does not go to less than 11° Mean Lat. This is because, owing to the shape of the Earth, D.M.P. is less than D. Lat. in the band of latitudes between 11° 30' N. and 11° 30' S. (as inspection of the Table of Meridional Parts, or of any equatorial chart, will reveal). In these latitudes minutes of longitude are actually slightly greater in length than minutes of latitude and departure may be assumed to be the same as D. Long. for practical purposes.

TABLES 5, 6 and 9—pp. 101-111. **Sun, Star, and Moon's Total Corrections.** True alt. = Obs. alt. − Dip − Ref. ± S.D. + Pax.-in-alt. The appropriate refraction is that for apparent altitude* (i.e. Obs. alt. — Dip). The Sun's correction is for semi-diameter 16', lower limb. A small subsidiary correction to adjust the total correction for other semi-diameters is included in the Sun table as an inset. To correct a Sun observation for upper limb: to the FULL diameter (i.e. semi-diameter × 2) add 1'.2 and subtract this total from the observed altitude. The remainder should then be corrected in the ordinary way by the Total Correction table. (The 1'.2 is introduced to allow for the phenomenon of irradiation.)

The star table is compiled for dip and refraction only, semi-diameter and parallax being negligible quantities in their case.

The corrections for the Moon's observed altitude are the same as for the Sun, but certain refinements have to be introduced owing to the comparative proximity of the former body to the Earth. Thus, the semi-diameter requires to be augmented, and the parallax-in-altitude calculated from the formula Pax.-in-alt. = H.P. Cos. alt. The table here given was calculated for height of eye 100 feet. By using this height of eye the subsidiary correction for that variant, which it is important not to forget, is rendered always additive.

Examples:

	SUN.	STAR.	MOON.
	June 15th. Obs. alt. ☉ 28° 15'.5 H.E. 32 ft. =	Obs. alt. star 47° 15' H.E. 43 ft.	Obs. alt. ☾ 39° 19' H.E. 49 ft. H.P. (from almanac) 57'.2

SUN.		STAR.		MOON.	
Obs. alt.	28° 15'.5	Obs. alt.	47° 15'.0	Obs. alt. ☾	39° 19'.0
Corr.	+8 .6 (8.8—0.2)	Corr.	− 7 .3	Main Corr.	+ 17 .8
				For H.E.	+ 2 .9
True alt.	28 24 .1	True alt.	47 07 .7	True alt.	39 39 .7

* Of the limb observed.

vi

TABLES 7 and 7a—p. 103. **Sun's Semi-diameter and Parallax-in-Altitude of Sun and Planets.** Pax.-in-alt. = H.P. Cos. alt. The horizontal parallax and semi-diameter are taken from the Nautical Almanac.

TABLE 8—p. 103. **Equation of Time.** This quantity is the amount in time by which the hour angle of the (imaginary) Mean Sun differs from that of the (visible) True Sun. Although not now used directly in normal navigational calculations, it is sometimes necessary to apply Equation of Time to either the Mean or the Apparent Time to convert from one to the other. Equation of Time is given in the almanac, but as it is generally only needed to the nearest minute, and it changes little over the years, it may be found convenient to have this table here.

The signs are for application to Apparent Time to obtain Mean Time, and must therefore be reversed for application to Mean Time.

TABLE 10—pp. 112-115. **G.H.A. and Dec., Moon, Acceleration and adjustment of.** The principle which the Nautical Almanac adopts for dealing with those heavenly bodies whose G.H.A. acceleration is not uniform is to give a value, denominated " v ", by which the acceleration exceeds an adopted minimum. For the Moon this adopted minimum is 14° 19′ per hour and the quantity against each hour in the Moon's v column is the amount by which the G.H.A. difference between this hour and the succeeding hour exceeds 14° 19′. In this table, sub-tables 1 and 2 give the proportional parts for minutes and seconds respectively for an hourly acceleration of 14° 19′, and sub-table 3 gives the proportional parts for minutes for the v (or variation from 14° 19′), as given at the head of each column of the sub-table. This proportional part table is also available for use in correcting the declination.

Example:

Given almanac tabulation as	G.M.T.	G.H.A.	v	Dec.	d
	10	122°52′.5	14′.8	N.16°53′.8	11′.6
	11	137 26 .3	14 .8	16 42 .2	11 .6
	12	152 00 .1	14 .9	16 30 .6	11 .7

Required G.H.A. and Dec. for (1) 10h.52m.11s.
(2) 11 09 56

(1) For 10 hrs. G.H.A. 122°52′.5   v 14.8   Dec. N. 16°53′.8   d 11′.6 —
„ 52 m.   12 24 .5
„ 11 s.   2 .6
„ v and d   12 .8   —10 .1
                ‾‾‾‾‾‾‾‾‾   ‾‾‾‾‾‾‾‾‾
              135 32 .4   N. 16 43 .7

(2) For 11 hrs. G.H.A. 137°26′.3   v 14.8   Dec. N. 16°42′.2   d 11′.6 —
„ 9 m.   2 08 .9
„ 56 s.   13 .4
„ v and d   2 .5   — 2 .0
                ‾‾‾‾‾‾‾‾‾   ‾‾‾‾‾‾‾‾‾
              139 51 .1   16 40 .2

TABLE 10a—p. 116. **Bubble Sextant, corrections for.** The only corrections which it is proper to apply to an observation by bubble sextant are those for refraction and parallax; but in view of the fact that under the most favourable conditions a bubble sextant observation cannot be relied upon to within some minutes, it would seem superfluous to take the Sun's parallax-in-altitude into account, and parallax is always negligible in the case of the planets and stars. The case of the Moon is different, and a table is given in two parts by which the Moon's main lower limb table is made available for correcting bubble sextant observations of the Moon. The first part of the table extracts the dip and semi-diameter components from the main lower limb table term, and the second part obliterates the augmentation element.

Example:

$$\begin{array}{lrr}
\text{Obs. alt.: Moon, bubble sextant} & 52°00'.0 & \text{H.P. } 58'.8 \\
\text{Table 9} & + 41.8 \\
\hline
\text{Table 10a } 6.2 & 52\ 41.8 \\
.2 & -\ \ 6.4 \\
\hline
\text{True alt.} & 52\ 35.4 \\
\end{array}$$

TABLE 11—p. 117. **Augmentation of Moon's Semi-diameter.** From the formula—Augmentation = 2s Cos. (z − ½p) Sin. ½p Cosec. (z − p) where s = horizontal semi-diameter, z = zenith distance, and p = parallax-in-altitude.

TABLE 12—p. 117. **Reduction of Moon's Equatorial Parallax for Figure of the Earth.** Assuming r, ratio of earth's polar to equatorial radius = .9966 (Clarke), H.P. for Lat. 90° = Eql. Pax. × r, and Reduction = Eql. Pax. − Polar Pax. Reduction for other latitudes = Sin.² Lat. × reduction for Polar Pax. (of that lat.).

TABLE 13—p. 117. **Correction for the Moon's Meridian Passage.** Correction = $\dfrac{\text{Retardation} \times \text{Long.}}{360}$ The time of the Moon's meridian passage is to be taken from the almanac. The retardation for any particular day is the difference between the time of transit on that day and the
$$\begin{cases} \text{preceding day for East longitude,} \\ \text{following day for West longitude.} \end{cases}$$
The table is only required when preparing to observe the meridian altitude of the Moon, in which case it is necessary to know (a) the Ship's Time of transit, for observing, and (b) the G.M.T. of transit for correcting the body's declination, etc.

Example:

Given, Moon's meridian passage at Greenwich.
$$\begin{cases} \text{June 11th, 16h. 08m.} \\ \text{June 12th, 17h. 02m.} \end{cases} 55\text{m. Diff.}$$

Required, L.M.T. and G.M.T. of Moon's meridian transit on June 12th in Long. 103°E.

Transit at Greenwich, 12th,	- -	- 17h. 02m.	
Ret. 55m. and Long. 103°E = Corr.	-	15.8	− because Long. E.
Transit at ship, L.M.T., 12th,	- -	- 16 46.2	
Long. in time,	- -	- 6 52.0	
Transit at ship, G.M.T., 12th,	- -	- 9 54.2	

TABLE 14—p. 118. **Dip of the Sea Horizon.** From the formula—Dip (in minutes) = .97√Height of eye in feet.

TABLES 15 and 16—pp. 118-119. **Mean Refraction and Additional Altitude Corrections for Non-standard Conditions of Refraction.** On the advice of Mr W. A. Scott, B.Sc., F.I.N., of H.M. Nautical Almanac Office, these refraction tables have been compiled from Garfinkel's work, which is now considered to be the most satisfactory treatment of the subject available. It is to be noted that the corrections in Table 16 are intended to be applied as additional altitude corrections, and not as corrections to the mean refraction (although they could, in fact, be treated as algebraic additions to the mean refraction).

TABLE 17—p. 120. **Dip of the Shore Horizon.** From the formula—Dip (in minutes) = $1146\dfrac{h}{d}$ + .0002d, where h = height of eye in feet and d = distance in yards.

TABLE 18—pp. 121-136. **Logarithms.** These are common logarithms to the base 10. As usual, only the mantissae are tabulated, the characteristic or index being supplied by the calculator. The rules for supplying the latter are as follows.

(a) If the number contains integers the characteristic is positive and is one less than the number of the digits preceding the decimal point, e.g.

$$\text{log. } 475.1 = 2.67679 \qquad \text{log. } 4.751 = 0.67679$$

(b) If the number is wholly decimal the characteristic is negative and one greater than the number of zeros between the decimal point and the first significant figure (or, if preferred, the same as the number of places from the decimal point to that occupied by the first significant figure), e.g.

$$\text{log. } .4751 = \bar{1}.67679 \qquad \text{log. } .004751 = \bar{3}.67679$$

When combining logarithms in the course of multiplication and division it must be remembered that the mantissa is **always positive**. The beginner may find it easier to deal with the characteristics and mantissae separately and then to take their algebraic sum to obtain the answer, e.g.

$17.51 \times .00763$	log. 17.51	1	.24329
	log. .00763	$\bar{3}$	.88252
		$\bar{2}$ 1.12581	$= \bar{1}.12581$

= 0.13360 (correct to five significant figures)

When subtracting, the characteristics can readily be set down in what is seen to be the most convenient form, e.g.

$17.51 \div .00763$	log. 17.51		1.24329
	log. .00763	$\bar{3}$	.88252
		3 .36077	$= 3.36077$

= 2295 (correct to four significant figures)

In navigation it was for many years customary to use positive characteristics throughout, by taking the difference between the negative characteristic and 10 (e.g. $\bar{3}$ becomes 7) and rejecting multiples of 10 in the result or adding 10 to keep the result positive. Since many books still use this method, and for the convenience of those navigators who prefer it, in the tables of logarithmic functions in this book the positive characteristics are printed in square brackets at head and foot of column following the standard negative ones. The following shows the working of the second example above by this method.

log. 17.51	(1)1.24329
log. .00763	7.88252
	3.36077

The logarithms of numbers up to four significant figures are tabulated. That for a number containing five significant figures can be found to a degree of accuracy sufficient for practical purposes from the difference column, together with an approximation for a sixth figure if required, e.g.

| log. 3.7296 | log. 3.729 | = 1.57159 |
| | diff. for 6 = | 7 = 1.57166 |

| log. 0.0349673 | log. 0.03496 | $\bar{2}.54357$ |
| | diff. for 73 = | 94 = $\bar{2}.543664$ |

TABLE 19—pp. 137-166. **Logarithmic Functions (of the angle),** i.e., **Log. Sines, Cosines, etc.** It so happens that (i) it is always more convenient to have an all downward-reading table where possible; and (ii) the only functions of the angle (other than the haversine) which come into general use in modern navigation are the cosine, secant, and tangent. Thus, for the " St. Hilaire " method we use two cosines, for the " longitude " method two secants; and when working courses and distances all three of these functions variously, as will be seen from the following formulae used in the three " sailings ".

Mercator.	Mid. Lat.	Parallel.
$\dfrac{\text{D. Long.}}{\text{D.M.P.}}$ = Tan. Co.	D. Long. Cos. Mid. lat. = Dep.	D. Long. = Dep. Sec. Lat.
Dist. = D. Lat. Sec. Co.	$\dfrac{\text{Dep.}}{\text{D. Lat.}}$ = Tan. Co.	Dep. = D. Long. Cos. Lat.
	Dist. = D. Lat. Sec. Co.	

Bearing in mind these facts the table has been arranged in such a manner that the degrees at the top of the page read continuously from 0° to 90°, and under each degree is tabulated the logs. cosine, secant, and tangent. For these three functions we therefore have an all downward-reading table.

There remain the other functions to be provided for. But it follows from the arrangement described above that if the table be read from the bottom up the degrees will read continuously from 90° to 0°, and over each degree will be tabulated the remaining three functions, namely, logs. sine, cosecant and co-tangent. Hence all workers and all purposes are accommodated with maximum convenience in a table contained within 30 pages.

Whole minute intervals are used throughout the table; it being sufficient for practical purposes to take out logs. cosine and secant for latitude and declination to the nearest minute only. On the other hand it is considered desirable that altitudes be always read and corrected to the nearest half minute, and that half minutes of latitude and declination be otherwise used in the calculations; for although, as stated above, these fractions do not appreciably affect the logs. cosine and secant, they are nevertheless liable to make a whole minute difference in the quantity " Lat. ± Dec." in connection with which a sensitive natural function is employed. Stray half minutes in this term (and the z-dist.) are in any case no inconvenience, since they are provided for in the Haversine Table.

Finally, where for academic purposes, or with abnormally high latitudes and/or declinations, interpolation is deemed necessary, the process will be found to be greatly simplified by the use of five-figure logarithms. With the assistance of the " D " column, halves may generally be read off at sight, care being taken to observe in which direction the function is increasing. For tenths, proceed by proportion, as in the examples below. (It is assumed that seconds of angle are no longer used in navigation.)

The table has been indexed for time from the bottom up, to provide for the formula Sin. Az. = Sin. H.A. Cos. Dec. Sec. Alt.

47°			
/	**Cos.**	**D.**	**Sec.**
	$\overline{1}.$ [9]		0.
..	.....		.....
..	.....		.....
14	83188		16812
15	83174	14	16826
16	83161	13	16839
17	83147	14	16853

Examples :

Log. Cos. 47°14′.6 = $\overline{1}$.83188 − (.6 × 14) = $\overline{1}$.83188 − 8/4 = $\overline{1}$.83180
Log. Sec. 47°15′.3 = 0.16826 + (.3 × 13) = 0.16826 + 3/9 = 0.16830

Angle for—

Log. Cos. $\overline{1}$.83180 = 47°15′ − $\dfrac{6}{14}$ = 47°15′ − .43 = 47°14′.6

Log. Sec. 0.16848 = 47°16′ + $\dfrac{9}{14}$ = 47°16′ + .64 = 47°16′.6

See also sight examples under Haversine Table.

Note—The sine of an angle is the sine of its supplement and the cosine of its complement, and similarly for the numerical values of other functions.*

Thus, Sin. 96° 16′ = $\left\{ \begin{array}{l} \text{Sin.} (180° − 96° 16′) = \text{Sin. } 83° 44' \\ = \text{Cos. } 6° 16' \quad . \quad . \quad . \quad . \end{array} \right\}$ Log. $\overline{1}$.99740

Tan. 137° 12′ = $\left\{ \begin{array}{l} \text{Tan.} (180° − 137°12′) = \text{Tan. } 42°48' \\ = \text{Cot. } 47°12' \quad . \quad . \quad . \quad . \end{array} \right\}$ Log. $\overline{1}$.96662

*Algebraically the *signs* of the functions change with the quadrants in accordance with the mnemonic All/Sin/Tan/Cos, i.e. these functions and their reciprocals (All/Cosec/Cot/Sec) are positive in the first, second, third and fourth quadrants respectively, and negative elsewhere.

TABLE 20—pp. 167-216. **Haversines.** A half minute of arc interval of tabulation has been adopted in this table because it is found that a whole minute interval, despite its greater ease of use, would not always give a degree of accuracy adequate for navigational purposes without interpolation.

The general arrangement of the table scarcely requires particular notice. Certain innovations have been introduced in order to relieve eye-strain, such as the omission of half-minute indications in the "Arc" column, and the semi-skeletonized arrangement of the matter printed in the body of the page. It will be found convenient to "double-read" the quantities for half minutes; thus, the middle term of the figures here printed should be read "069—23069". In various other ways the table will be found considerably more easy and comfortable to use than a second-interval table.

23060
069
23079

Examples:

At 10.48 a.m.   D.R. 33° 16′ N. 26° 59′ E.   True alt. 63° 12½′

G.H.A. 315° 00′.0,   Dec. 12° 06½′ N.

	"St. Hilaire"			**"Longitude"**			
G.H.A. -	315° 00′.0		True alt. -	63° 12½′			
Long. -	26 59 .0E.						
			Z. dist. -	26 47½		Nat.	05367
L.H.A. -	341 59 .0		Lat. -	33 16 N.	Sec. 0.07773		
		L. Hav. 2̄.33946	Dec. -	12 06½N.	Sec. 0.00976		
Lat. 33° 16′ N.	Cos. 1̄.92227						
Dec. 12 06½N.	Cos. 1̄.99024		(Lat. – Dec.)	21 09½		Nat.	03371
		L. Hav. 2̄.30197			L. Hav. 2̄.30019	Nat.	01996
		Nat. 02004			L. Hav. 2̄.38768		
(Lat. – Dec.) 21 09½	.........Nat. 03371				L.H.A. 342° 01′		
		Nat. 05375			G.H.A. 315 00		
		26° 48½′			Long. 27 01E.		
True alt. -	63° 12½′						
True Z. dist.	26 47½						
Calc. ,,	26 48½						
Intercept - -	1 to						

Note—It will be found convenient when working either of these methods to take out the two cosines, or the two secants, as the case may be, first. The remainder of the problem is then finished in the Haversine Table.

TABLES 21, 22, 23 and 24—pp. 217-235. **Ex-Meridian Tables I to IV.** When a celestial body is on the observer's meridian its zenith distance is (Lat. + Dec.), or 180°—(Lat. + Dec.) if on the inferior meridian. If it is near the upper meridian its altitude is slightly lower (slightly higher on the lower meridian) than at its meridian passage. The latter altitude can be arrived at almost by mental arithmetic, and since the Ex-Meridian Tables provide a rapid method of finding the "reduction", i.e. the above difference, such a sight can be worked out very quickly. It must be realised, however, that an ex-meridian sight does not, as sometimes stated, give the observer's latitude. Unless the body is almost on the meridian itself, the azimuth should always be calculated and the intercept plotted to obtain a position line, as in the examples below.

From the basic formulae it can be shown that the reduction, in minutes of arc, is equal to:

$$\frac{1.9635 \text{ Cos. Lat. Cos. Dec.}}{\text{Sin. Mer. Zenith Dist.}} \times \frac{(\text{L.H.A. in minutes of time})^2}{60}$$

Since three arguments are involved, two steps are necessary. Table I is entered with arguments Lat. and Dec. to obtain factor F, which is the first term of the above product; care should be taken to select the appropriate page according as Lat. and Dec. are of **same** or **contrary** names. For sights below pole, although Lat. and Dec. are necessarily of the same name, F must be found from the lower section of the **Contrary** pages, as clearly noted there. Table II is then entered with L.H.A. and F from Table I, and from it the reduction is obtained, in parts

xi

as necessary. If the reduction is applied, as shown in the examples, to the Meridional Zenith Distance (Lat. + Dec.) for ordinary sights and to the Meridional Altitude (Lat. + Dec.) − 90° for ˜sights below pole, it will always be **added**, thus leading to easier working.

By the application of a " Second Correction " the availability of the ex-meridian method may be somewhat increased. The formula for this correction is:

$$\frac{\text{First Correction}^2}{2} \text{ Tan. Alt. Sin. } 1'$$

the result being in minutes of arc. It is ascertained from Table III which is entered with first correction at top and meridional altitude at side, although, except for high altitudes, the observed altitude may be used. This correction is **subtractive** to the first correction, except in the case of sights below pole, where it can be neglected as small, although theoretically additive.

Table IV is a guide to the limits within which the ex-meridian method is suitable. They correspond roughly to the period during which the bearing of the body is within 15° of the meridian.

Examples of ex-meridian working:

Example (i)	Example (ii)	Example (iii)	Example (iv)
		Given—	
		L.A.T. 11h 27m 40s	Given—
		= L.H.A.	
Given—	Given—	(Ely) 32 20	
			L.H.A.164°15′ = 63m from Inferior meridian
L.H.A. 349° 15′	L.H.A. 1° 15′	D.R.Lat. 47° 40′ N	
D.R. Lat. 52 10 N	D.R. Lat. 9 54 S	Dec. 11 32 S	
Dec. 8 18 N	Dec. 5 06 S	☉ 30 03.5	D.R.Lat. 53° 10 N
☉ 45 12.0	☉ 84 47.6	Corr. 8.8	Dec. 45 55 N
Corr. 9.0	Corr. 9.7		Obs. alt. ✶ 10 18
			Corr. 10
F = 1.72	F = 23.2	F = 1.51	
Lat. 52° 10′.0 N	Lat. 9° 54′.0 S	Lat. 47° 40′.0 N	Below Pole—
Dec. 8 18.0 N	Dec. 5 06.0 S	Dec. 11 32.0 S	Lat. = Mer. alt. + P. Dist.
			∴ Mer. alt. = Lat. − P. Dist.
Mer.Z.D. 43 52.0	Mer.Z.D. 4 48.0	Mer.Z.D. 59 12.0	F = .83
Red. 1 30.8	Red. 23 9.6	Red. 1 17.4	
.7 21.6	.2 .1	.5 8.7	Lat. 53° 10′.0
.02 .6		.01 .2	P. Dist. 44 05.0
	4 57.7		
44 45.0	Table III .2	59 38.3	Mer. alt. 9 05.0
Table III .4		Table III .1	Red. .8 52.9
	C.Z.D. 4 57.5		.03 2.0
C.Z.D. 44 44.6		C.Z.D. 59 38.2	
	C.A. 85 02.5		9 59.9
C.A. 45 15.4	T.A. 84 57.3	C.A. 30 21.8	
T.A. 45 21.0		T.A. 30 12.3	T.A. 10 08.0
Intercept 5.6 to	Intercept 5.2 away	Intercept 9.5 away	Intercept 8.1 to
A = 6.99 +	A = 8.00 +	A = 7.73 +	A = 4.73 −
B = .78 −	B = 4.09 −	B = 1.45 +	B = 3.80 −
C = 6.21 +	C = 3.91 +	C = 9.18	C = 8.53 −
Bg. 165½°	Bg. 345½°	Bg. 171°	Bg. 349°
90	90	90	90
P.L. 075½	P.L. 255½	P.L. 081	P.L. 259

N.B.—It is important to understand that the ex-meridian method does not give the latitude in the "absolute" sense. It is simply a way of obtaining a calculated altitude without the use of logs. It will be obvious, however, that when the bearing of the body is within a few degrees of the meridian and the D.R. longitude is not suspected of serious error, the intercept may be taken as indicating the approximate latitude.

TABLE 25—pp. 236-239. **Altitude Change in One Minute of Time.**
There sometimes arise occasions in navigation when it may be necessary or convenient to adjust an altitude for a given time-interval. Thus an altitude may have been pre-computed for a particular instant and the actual observation not obtained until a minute or so later; or, a number of star sights having been

taken, it may be considered more convenient to adjust one or more of the altitudes to a common time in preference to calculating each from a different D.R.

In figure, E = D.R. position and XL a position-line.

From E drop EJ perpendicular to XL. Then EJ becomes an intercept or altitude-difference, and XEJ is the azimuth.

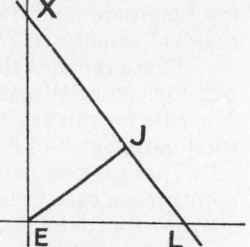

Now, EL is clearly a D. Long., and may therefore be expressed as a time-interval.

If EL = 1 minute (in time), then, by Parallel Sailing, it is also 15′ Cos. Lat. (in miles).

∴ EJ (Altitude Change) = 15′ Cos. Lat. Sin. Az.

Example:

Lat. D.R. 49°N.
G.M.T. 9h. 45m. 00s.
Computed altitude 47°18′
Azimuth 120°

Actual (corrected) observation obtained at
9h. 47m. 14s.   47° 46′.5

Required the intercept at G.M.T.
9h. 45m. 00s.

From Table 25, altitude change per minute
for Lat. 49° Az. 120° = 8.5′
Time diff. 2m. 14s. = 2.23m.
True altitude   -   47° 46′.5 (Body rising)
Adjustment 2.23 × 8.5 —   19 .0
                         _____
Adjusted alt.   - 47   27 .5
Computed alt.   - 47   18 .0
                         _____
Intercept at   9 .5 to
G.M.T. 9h. 45m. 00s.

It may be as well to point out that although the data given in the table is correct, the **method,** as here exemplified, takes no account of the fact that the azimuth is continually changing; besides also assuming the observer to be stationary. The method is, in fact, only suitable for use with short time-intervals not exceeding from 2 to 10 minutes, according, respectively, to whether the bearing is near the meridian and changing rapidly, or near the Prime Vertical and changing slowly.* Also, to get correct results, it is necessary to transfer the position-line for run, when appreciable. It might be worth mentioning that if the azimuth is in the upper two lines of the azimuth numerals at the top of the page the body is Eastward and rising, and if it is in the lower two lines it is Westward and declining.

TABLE 26—p. 240. **Stars and the Meridian.** A star will be on the meridian when its Sidereal Hour Angle (S.H.A.) is the same as the Sidereal Hour Angle of the (local) Meridian (S.H.A.M.). It will be obvious, then, that if the S.H.A.M. at any particular moment is known, inspection of a list of these S.H.A.'s will at once reveal the position of all the stars with respect to the meridian at that moment.

If we assume that Aries travels at the same rate as the Mean Sun it can be demonstrated diagramatically that

$$\text{S.H.A.M.} = \text{M.P.}\Upsilon - \text{L.M.T.}$$

but as, in fact, Aries accelerates on the Mean Sun by 4m. in each day, this simple equation is liable to give results up to several minutes in error unless certain adjustments are made.

Part of this maximum error is due to the fact that the S.H.A's of the stars, when converted into time at 15 degrees to the hour, come out in sidereal time instead of Mean (solar) Time. To convert these periods it is necessary to add to the S.H.A.'s 4m. − 1/6 (S.H.A. in hours). The other part of possible error is concerned with longitude. The L.M.T. of Aries' transit over the meridian in East longitude is later than the corresponding transit at Greenwich, and in West longitude it is earlier. The amount of this difference is

$$\frac{4 \times \text{Longitude}}{360} \text{ minutes.}$$

In Table 26 the stars' S.H.A.'s are given in Mean Solar Time intervals, which

*It is thus when the altitude change per minute is *smallest* that caution is most necessary, especially with high altitudes.

automatically annuls the first source of error and makes the simple equation above yield results correct to within 2m. This is near enough for the purpose of the table, and for the general purposes of navigation. But a table of corrections for longitude is also given across the foot of the page by the use of which the residual liability to 2m. error may be avoided.

There remains the question as to which day Mer. Pass. Aries should be taken out for, especially as it is not necessarily that of the actual Greenwich date. The rule for this is that if M.P.♈ is less than L.M.T. use M.P.♈ (+ 24 hrs.) for the local date, but if M.P.♈ is greater than L.M.T. use M.P.♈ for the preceding day.

There is one particular case in which ambiguity can arise as to which is the appropriate date to use for M.P.♈. Thus, the L.M.T. (of civil twilight) is in general only an approximate, or " guessed " time. When, therefore, M.P.♈ and L.M.T. are of about the same value, giving an S.H.A.M. of nearly 0000 hrs., too early a choice of L.M.T. will result in the stars crossing the meridian 4m. earlier than expected. This danger can be guarded against by always using M.P.♈ for the local date in these circumstances.

It is to be noted that the twilight times given in the almanac are G.M.T., which may be taken for practical purposes as L.M.T. If the time kept on the ship's clocks is either Zone Time or Apparent Time (L.A.T.), adjustments must be made accordingly. In the latter case the Table of Equation of Time (Table 8, p. 103) may be found convenient.

Examples:

On June 14 it is estimated that civil twilight will occur at L.M.T. 0715. Required stars suitably placed for sights about that time.

M.P.♈	06 37	(Greenwich date June 14)
L.M.T.	07 15	
S.H.A.M.	23 22	

Table 26 shows that at this time Schedar would be crossing the meridian, followed 3m. later by Diphda. Whether suitable for observation or not would, of course, depend on the relation between the latitude and their declinations. Stars below this in the table would be to the Eastward and rising, and stars above (Nos. 2, 1, 57, 56, etc.) would be to the Westward.

On October 20 it is estimated that evening twilight will occur at 1840.

M.P.♈ 19th	22 01	(Greenwich date October 19)
L.M.T.	18 40	
S.H.A.M.	03 21	

Table 26 shows that at this time Deneb will have passed the meridian by a minute or two. Stars below this in the table (Nos. 54, 55, etc.) will be to the Eastward and rising, and those above in the table will be to the Westward.

TABLE 27—p. 241. Hour Angle Change in One Minute of Altitude
From figure in notes on Table 25 (p. xiii)—
EL = EJ Cosec. Az.

but EL = D. Long, or H.A. change
= H.A. change in arc. Cos. Lat. (from Parallel Sailing).

∴ H.A. change = Cosec. Az. Sec. Lat. 4
(the 4 being introduced to convert from arc to time).

TABLE 28—pp. 242-245. Amplitudes, True, in Time and Arc. The Time Amplitude is the interval of time between the instant of rising or setting and 6 hours or 18 hours and the Bearing Amplitude is the difference between the bearing at rising or setting and 90° or 180°.

Formulae:
Arc: Sin. Amp. = Sin. Dec. Sec. Lat.
Time: Cos. H.A. = Tan. Lat. Tan. Dec.
Amp. = 6 hrs. (or 18 hrs.) ∼ H.A.

Owing to refraction, at the moment of true amplitude the Sun's centre appears to be elevated about 33′ above the horizon. In tropic latitudes the difference between the true and apparent amplitudes is negligible, since the Sun rises and sets nearly perpendicular to the horizon. In the higher latitudes, however, the difference may amount to as much as 3°, and for this reason it is probably better under these circumstances to use timed observations only for compass checks. In the case of the Moon the position is reversed. As a consequence of the Moon's large parallax that body is actually not visible at the moment of its true amplitude, its upper limb being then about 1′ below the horizon. Its availability for amplitude purposes is therefore restricted to latitudes within about 30° of its declination, when it will rise and set near the perpendicular.

TABLES 29 and 30—pp. 246-319, A, B, and C Tables.

A = Cot. H.A. Tan. Lat.   B = Cosec. H.A. Tan. Dec.   C = Cot. Az. Sec. Lat.

The ABC Tables provide one of the quickest and most convenient means of finding the azimuth; and also provide, with equal facility, great-circle courses and the "Longitude Correction".

Table 29 contains the values designated "A" and "B", corresponding to the arguments H.A. and Lat., and H.A. and Dec. respectively, which values, when combined according to their appropriate signs, form "C", which is, in fact, the "Longitude Correction", and which, by means of Table C (Table 30), produces azimuths and great-circle courses. Table C is indexed for the arguments Azimuth and Latitude. When in search of azimuth the table is entered with latitude and value C (not value C and latitude). The eye is run horizontally across the pages opposite the latitude until value C is picked up, when the azimuth will be found at the head of the page.

Examples:

Time Azimuth.

H.A. 84°   Lat. 6°30′S. Dec. 1°18′N.

H.A. 84° { Lat. 6°30′S., A = .012 +
          { Dec. 1 18N., B = .023 +

C = .035 +

Then in Table C, with Lat. 6½°, Az. = 272°

Note.—Except when value C is small (less than .2) two decimal places are sufficient.

Time Azimuth.

H.A. 235°   Lat. 71°20′N. Dec. 62°10′N

H.A. 235° { Lat. 71°20′N., A = 2.07 −
          { Dec. 62 10N., B = 2.31 −

C = 4.38 −

Then in Table C, with Lat. 71°20′, Az. = 035°

For Great-Circle Courses—

D. Long. = Hour angle.
From Lat. = Latitude.
To Lat.   = Declination.

Example of Great-Circle Course :—

From Lat. 58° 10′N. Long.   5° 20′W.
To Lat.   20° 05′N. Long. 61° 35′W.

56° 15′W D. Long.

With H.A. 56¼° { Lat. 58° 10′N., A = 1.09 +
               { Dec. 20° 05′N., B = .44 −

C = .65 +

Then in Table C, with Lat. 58°, Az. = 251° = Course required.

When D. Long. is E. it would be proper to subtract it from 360° in order to make the precepts at the head of Table C yield correct advice for naming the course. This, however, need not be done if it is remembered to name the course as for "Body RISING" which, as the course will be easterly, should present no difficulty.

Longitude Correction—
"C" (the combination of the values A and B) is the error of longitude corresponding to an error of one minute in the latitude. It must, of course, be multiplied by the total error of latitude to obtain the total error of longitude.

To determine which way to apply the correction. The position-line runs at right-angles to the bearing of the body observed. Draw a short line to represent the bearing of the body, according to quadrant, and across the appropriate end of this line draw a second line to indicate the position-line. Thus, supposing the body bore S.E., then by sketch it is obvious that the position-line runs N.E. and S.W.—which means that the further the observer is to the North, the further he will be to the East, or the further to the South the further to the West.

Example:

At 07.12 L.A.T., Lat. D.R. 22° 12′N.   Long. obs. 37° 42′W.   Sun in N.E. quadt.   Dec. 18° 55′N

Now, L.A.T. 07.12 = H.A. 4h. 48m.

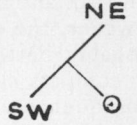

With H.A. 4h. 48m. and $\begin{cases} \text{Lat.} & 22°\ 12′N., \\ \text{Dec.} & 18°\ 55′N., \end{cases}$ A = .13 +

B = .36 −

Therefore, Long. Corr.   (C) = .23 −

At noon, when the above sight brought forward gave Lat. D.R. 23°05′N. Long. obs. 37°13′W., the latitude was found by meridian altitude to be 23°13′N. Then since the D.R. latitude, with which the sight was worked, is 8M. in error, it is obvious that the observed longitude must also be in error. The true latitude being more northerly, the sketch indicates that the true longitude will be further to the West—by the amount 8 × .23 = 1′.84.

Long. obs. (for D.R. Lat.)   -   -   37° 13′ W.

Corr.   -   -   1.8 W.

Long. obs. (for True Lat.),   -   -   37° 14.8 W.

The correct noon position is therefore Lat. 23° 13′N. Long. 37° 14′.8W.

Note—Two decimal places are always sufficient for the Longitude Correction, for which purpose the sign of C is immaterial.

TABLE 31—pp. 321-325.   **Vertical Sextant Angles.** $\dfrac{\text{Height}}{\text{Dist.}} = \text{Tan. Angle.}$

The table is for plane right-angled triangles only, which means that the point at sea-level vertically below the object observed must be within the observers' horizon (as defined by Table 44). The angle to be observed is that which subtends the crest of the object and its sea-level base point. Consequently, when a long fore-shore intervenes, guesswork has to be resorted to and the result should be accepted with caution.

The datum level for heights on British charts is High Water Ordinary Spring Tides. When the range of tide bears a considerable proportion to the height of the object (which may be the case with a sea-rock lighthouse) too small a distance may result. For lights the height given on the charts is that of the focal plane; but here also observations of the summit of the 'house give distances on the safe side—EXCEPT WHEN PASSING INSIDE A SUNKEN DANGER.

The space at the head of the table will be found convenient for pencilling in the heights of frequently used lighthouses, etc.

TABLE 37—p. 344. **Co-logarithms of Steaming Time.** The co-log. of a number is the log. of its reciprocal, and its usefulness is that it enables division to be performed by adding. Co-logs. of times from 23 to 25 hours are tabulated here, and provide a quick method of arriving at the speed of the day's run by means of the precept

Log. Dist. + Co-Log. Time = Log. Speed.

Only the mantissae are necessary; the position of the decimal point will always be obvious. Example:

Distance 441'	Log. Distance	.64444
Times 23 h. 38 m.	Co-Log. Time	.62648
	Log Speed	.27092

Speed = 18.66 knots

TABLE 38—p. 345. **Correction to be applied to W/T D.F. bearing to obtain Mercator bearing,** i.e. Half-Convergency Table.

$$\text{Formula: Corr.} = \frac{\text{D. Long. Sin. Mid. Lat.}}{2}$$

This formula is not exact, but is that usually used and considered sufficiently accurate for this purpose.

All " rule of thumb " precepts for applying this correction are liable to be extremely confusing, since they are reversed—(i) according to which side of the meridian the distant station is on; (ii) according to which hemisphere the ship is in; and (iii) according to whether the D.F. station is the ship station or the distant station. It will be found most satisfactory to lay the parallel rulers on the chart roughly according to the uncorrected bearing, and then, pivoting them on the D.F. station, note which way they need to be moved to make the position-line lie nearer to the equator. (See remarks on this subject in *The Art of Astronomical Navigation.*)

Aircraft navigators should note that when using Modified Polyconic, Cassini's, Lambert's or Transverse Mercator projections, either full or no convergency should be applied, as under:

Aircraft taking bearing, use full convergency (i.e. tabulated value × 2).
W/T (Ground) Station taking bearing, use no convergency.

TABLE 39—p. 346. **Distance to the Radar Horizon.** The figures for this table have been taken from Admiralty Chart No. 5028 with the permission of the Controller of H.M. Stationery Office and the Hydrographer of the Navy. Its purpose and method of use are explained and demonstrated on the table itself. It may, however, be re-emphasised here that the figures have been calculated for a radar wavelength of 3 cm. and for a " standard atmosphere ". The expression " standard " as used here is not to be taken as meaning " normal ". " In some parts of the world propagation conditions may be non-standard for weeks on end and, on occasions, for several consecutive months."[*]

TABLE 42—p. 349. **Factors for Running Fix.** Factor = Sin. Bow-angle × Cosec. Change × Sin. (Bow-angle + Change). The table is entered with the angle between the first bearing and the Course **made good** at the top, and the change of bearing at the side. The resulting factor, when multiplied by the distance made good **over the ground** between bearings, gives the distance the ship **should** pass off abeam. It is preferable for these purposes to reckon the distance run by the time interval rather than by log.

When course is altered between bearings, or, which amounts to the same thing, a cross-current has to be allowed for, the method is not applicable.

TABLE 43—p. 350. **Conversion of Time to Arc and Arc to Time.** This concise table can be entered either with Time (bold figures) or Arc (roman figures). It gives intervals of 2 minutes time and $\frac{1}{2}°$ arc; while the side table provides figures for fractions of this interval for every second of time = 15″ arc. At the same time it may be mentioned that the conversion can be very simply performed by the use of the factors below, without recourse to a table.

[*]From a paper by Lieut.-Comdr. P. G. Satow in the *Journal of the Institute of Navigation*, Vol. III, No. 3, July 1950.

To convert arc to time, × 4 ÷ 60
time to arc, × 60 ÷ 4

Examples:

| Arc | 18° 43′ | Time | 2h. 43m. 12s. |

Arc   18° 43′
           4
60) 74 52
    1h. 14m. 52s. time

Time   2h. 43m. 12s.
           60
4) 163 12
    40° 48′ arc

Arc   127° 19′
           4
60) 509 16
    8h. 29m. 16s. time

Time   21h. 33m. 19s.
           60
4) 1293 19
    323° 19¾′ arc

TABLE 44—(facing back cover). **Speed, Distance, and Time Table** (for intervals up to 65 minutes). Although not generally included in nautical tables in the past, the great convenience of this table when navigating a coast in tidal waters will be found completely to justify its inclusion here. In addition to its obvious use, that of determining the distance run for a given speed and time, it is equally handy for ascertaining the speed or the time required to run a given distance. Thus, suppose the ship has made 10.2 miles between bearings in 46 minutes, then, running the eye across the table horizontally at 46 minutes, we see that 10.2 corresponds to a speed of 13¼ knots. Again, assuming we have 4.2 miles to run to reach an alter-course position and are making 11½ knots, then, running the eye down 11½ knots till we come to 4.2, we see that it will take 22 minutes.

TABLE 45.—(facing back cover). **Distance of Sea Horizon.**

From the formula, Dist. (M.)$=1.17\sqrt{\text{Height of eye in feet}}$.

The table may be used for ascertaining the maximum distance at which an object of known height should be visible.

Example:—Given, height of eye 33 feet; height of object, 280 feet. Required maximum distance at which object should be sighted.

For height 33 feet distance = 6.7 M.
    ,,   280   ,,   ,,   = 19.6 M.

Required distance, 26.3 M.

(See also Table 46 and footnote thereto.)

TABLE 46—(inside back cover). **Rising and Dipping Distances.** The value of this table lies in the fact that it sometimes saves a minute or two in the blinding light of the chart-room when navigating in coastal waters at night-time. The quantities in the body of the page are the distances at which objects of stated heights would be visible in a clear atmosphere under normal conditions of refraction. It has been compiled by simply adding together the two distances corresponding to height of eye and height of object, as defined by the formula given for Table 45. In the case of lights, only those of ample **power** should be considered eligible for the method. Attention is drawn to the warning contained in the footnote to the table itself.

TABLES

Table 3 — TRAVERSE TABLE*

1°

* Also for conversion of D. Long., Dep., etc.

D Lon / Dist.	Dep / D. Lat.	Dep.	D Lon / Dist.	Dep / D. Lat.	Dep.	D Lon / Dist.	Dep / D. Lat.	Dep.	D Lon / Dist.	Dep / D. Lat.	Dep.	D Lon / Dist.	Dep / D. Lat.	Dep.
Hyp.	Adj.	Opp.	Hyp.	Adj.	Opp.	Hyp.	Adj.	Opp.	Hyp.	Adj.	Opp.	Hyp.	Adj.	Opp.
1	1.0	0.0	61	61.0	1.1	121	121.0	2.1	181	181.0	3.2	241	241.0	4.2
2	2.0	0.0	62	62.0	1.1	122	122.0	2.1	182	182.0	3.2	242	242.0	4.2
3	3.0	0.1	63	63.0	1.1	123	123.0	2.1	183	183.0	3.2	243	243.0	4.2
4	4.0	0.1	64	64.0	1.1	124	124.0	2.2	184	184.0	3.2	244	244.0	4.3
5	5.0	0.1	65	65.0	1.1	125	125.0	2.2	185	185.0	3.2	245	245.0	4.3
6	6.0	0.1	66	66.0	1.2	126	126.0	2.2	186	186.0	3.2	246	246.0	4.3
7	7.0	0.1	67	67.0	1.2	127	127.0	2.2	187	187.0	3.3	247	247.0	4.3
8	8.0	0.1	68	68.0	1.2	128	128.0	2.2	188	188.0	3.3	248	248.0	4.3
9	9.0	0.2	69	69.0	1.2	129	129.0	2.3	189	189.0	3.3	249	249.0	4.3
10	10.0	0.2	70	70.0	1.2	130	130.0	2.3	190	190.0	3.3	250	250.0	4.4
11	11.0	0.2	71	71.0	1.2	131	131.0	2.3	191	191.0	3.3	251	251.0	4.4
12	12.0	0.2	72	72.0	1.3	132	132.0	2.3	192	192.0	3.4	252	252.0	4.4
13	13.0	0.2	73	73.0	1.3	133	133.0	2.3	193	193.0	3.4	253	253.0	4.4
14	14.0	0.2	74	74.0	1.3	134	134.0	2.3	194	194.0	3.4	254	254.0	4.4
15	15.0	0.3	75	75.0	1.3	135	135.0	2.4	195	195.0	3.4	255	255.0	4.5
16	16.0	0.3	76	76.0	1.3	136	136.0	2.4	196	196.0	3.4	256	256.0	4.5
17	17.0	0.3	77	77.0	1.3	137	137.0	2.4	197	197.0	3.4	257	257.0	4.5
18	18.0	0.3	78	78.0	1.4	138	138.0	2.4	198	198.0	3.5	258	258.0	4.5
19	19.0	0.3	79	79.0	1.4	139	139.0	2.4	199	199.0	3.5	259	259.0	4.5
20	20.0	0.3	80	80.0	1.4	140	140.0	2.4	200	200.0	3.5	260	260.0	4.5
21	21.0	0.4	81	81.0	1.4	141	141.0	2.5	201	201.0	3.5	261	261.0	4.6
22	22.0	0.4	82	82.0	1.4	142	142.0	2.5	202	202.0	3.5	262	262.0	4.6
23	23.0	0.4	83	83.0	1.4	143	143.0	2.5	203	203.0	3.5	263	263.0	4.6
24	24.0	0.4	84	84.0	1.5	144	144.0	2.5	204	204.0	3.6	264	264.0	4.6
25	25.0	0.4	85	85.0	1.5	145	145.0	2.5	205	205.0	3.6	265	265.0	4.6
26	26.0	0.5	86	86.0	1.5	146	146.0	2.5	206	206.0	3.6	266	266.0	4.6
27	27.0	0.5	87	87.0	1.5	147	147.0	2.6	207	207.0	3.6	267	267.0	4.7
28	28.0	0.5	88	88.0	1.5	148	148.0	2.6	208	208.0	3.6	268	268.0	4.7
29	29.0	0.5	89	89.0	1.6	149	149.0	2.6	209	209.0	3.6	269	269.0	4.7
30	30.0	0.5	90	90.0	1.6	150	150.0	2.6	210	210.0	3.7	270	270.0	4.7
31	31.0	0.5	91	91.0	1.6	151	151.0	2.6	211	211.0	3.7	271	271.0	4.7
32	32.0	0.6	92	92.0	1.6	152	152.0	2.7	212	212.0	3.7	272	272.0	4.7
33	33.0	0.6	93	93.0	1.6	153	153.0	2.7	213	213.0	3.7	273	273.0	4.8
34	34.0	0.6	94	94.0	1.6	154	154.0	2.7	214	214.0	3.7	274	274.0	4.8
35	35.0	0.6	95	95.0	1.7	155	155.0	2.7	215	215.0	3.8	275	275.0	4.8
36	36.0	0.6	96	96.0	1.7	156	156.0	2.7	216	216.0	3.8	276	276.0	4.8
37	37.0	0.6	97	97.0	1.7	157	157.0	2.7	217	217.0	3.8	277	277.0	4.8
38	38.0	0.7	98	98.0	1.7	158	158.0	2.8	218	218.0	3.8	278	278.0	4.9
39	39.0	0.7	99	99.0	1.7	159	159.0	2.8	219	219.0	3.8	279	279.0	4.9
40	40.0	0.7	100	100.0	1.7	160	160.0	2.8	220	220.0	3.8	280	280.0	4.9
41	41.0	0.7	101	101.0	1.8	161	161.0	2.8	221	221.0	3.9	281	281.0	4.9
42	42.0	0.7	102	102.0	1.8	162	162.0	2.8	222	222.0	3.9	282	282.0	4.9
43	43.0	0.8	103	103.0	1.8	163	163.0	2.8	223	223.0	3.9	283	283.0	4.9
44	44.0	0.8	104	104.0	1.8	164	164.0	2.9	224	224.0	3.9	284	284.0	5.0
45	45.0	0.8	105	105.0	1.8	165	165.0	2.9	225	225.0	3.9	285	285.0	5.0
46	46.0	0.8	106	106.0	1.8	166	166.0	2.9	226	226.0	3.9	286	286.0	5.0
47	47.0	0.8	107	107.0	1.9	167	167.0	2.9	227	227.0	4.0	287	287.0	5.0
48	48.0	0.8	108	108.0	1.9	168	168.0	2.9	228	228.0	4.0	288	288.0	5.0
49	49.0	0.9	109	109.0	1.9	169	169.0	2.9	229	229.0	4.0	289	289.0	5.0
50	50.0	0.9	110	110.0	1.9	170	170.0	3.0	230	230.0	4.0	290	290.0	5.1
51	51.0	0.9	111	111.0	1.9	171	171.0	3.0	231	231.0	4.0	291	291.0	5.1
52	52.0	0.9	112	112.0	2.0	172	172.0	3.0	232	232.0	4.0	292	292.0	5.1
53	53.0	0.9	113	113.0	2.0	173	173.0	3.0	233	233.0	4.1	293	293.0	5.1
54	54.0	0.9	114	114.0	2.0	174	174.0	3.0	234	234.0	4.1	294	294.0	5.1
55	55.0	1.0	115	115.0	2.0	175	175.0	3.1	235	235.0	4.1	295	295.0	5.1
56	56.0	1.0	116	116.0	2.0	176	176.0	3.1	236	236.0	4.1	296	296.0	5.2
57	57.0	1.0	117	117.0	2.0	177	177.0	3.1	237	237.0	4.1	297	297.0	5.2
58	58.0	1.0	118	118.0	2.1	178	178.0	3.1	238	238.0	4.2	298	298.0	5.2
59	59.0	1.0	119	119.0	2.1	179	179.0	3.1	239	239.0	4.2	299	299.0	5.2
60	60.0	1.0	120	120.0	2.1	180	180.0	3.1	240	240.0	4.2	300	300.0	5.2
Hyp.	Opp.	Adj.	Hyp.	Opp.	Adj.	Hyp.	Opp.	Adj.	Hyp.	Opp.	Adj.	Hyp.	Opp.	Adj.
Dist. / D Lon	Dep.	D. Lat. / Dep	Dist. / D Lon	Dep.	D. Lat. / Dep	Dist. / D Lon	Dep.	D. Lat. / Dep	Dist. / D Lon	Dep.	D. Lat. / Dep	Dist. / D Lon	Dep.	D. Lat. / Dep

89°

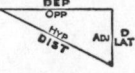

D. Long. = Dep. Sec. Lat.
(Hyp.) (Adj.) (Angle)

89°

Table 3

TRAVERSE TABLE

1°

1°

D Lon Dist.	Dep D. Lat.	Dep	D Lon Dist.	Dep D. Lat.	Dep	D Lon Dist.	Dep D. Lat.	Dep	D Lon Dist.	Dep D. Lat.	Dep	D Lon Dist.	Dep D. Lat.	Dep
Hyp.	Adj.	Opp.	Hyp.	Adj.	Opp.	Hyp.	Adj.	Opp.	Hyp.	Adj.	Opp.	Hyp.	Adj.	Opp.
301	301.0	5.3	361	360.9	6.3	421	420.9	7.3	481	480.9	8.4	541	540.9	9.4
302	302.0	5.3	362	361.9	6.3	422	421.9	7.4	482	481.9	8.4	542	541.9	9.5
303	303.0	5.3	363	362.9	6.3	423	422.9	7.4	483	482.9	8.4	543	542.9	9.5
304	304.0	5.3	364	363.9	6.4	424	423.9	7.4	484	483.9	8.4	544	543.9	9.5
305	305.0	5.3	365	364.9	6.4	425	424.9	7.4	485	484.9	8.5	545	544.9	9.5
306	306.0	5.3	366	365.9	6.4	426	425.9	7.4	486	485.9	8.5	546	545.9	9.5
307	307.0	5.4	367	366.9	6.4	427	426.9	7.5	487	486.9	8.5	547	546.9	9.5
308	308.0	5.4	368	367.9	6.4	428	427.9	7.5	488	487.9	8.5	548	547.9	9.6
309	309.0	5.4	369	368.9	6.4	429	428.9	7.5	489	488.9	8.5	549	548.9	9.6
310	310.0	5.4	370	369.9	6.5	430	429.9	7.5	490	489.9	8.6	550	549.9	9.6
311	311.0	5.4	371	370.9	6.5	431	430.9	7.5	491	490.9	8.6	551	550.9	9.6
312	312.0	5.4	372	371.9	6.5	432	431.9	7.5	492	491.9	8.6	552	551.9	9.6
313	313.0	5.5	373	372.9	6.5	433	432.9	7.6	493	492.9	8.6	553	552.9	9.7
314	314.0	5.5	374	373.9	6.5	434	433.9	7.6	494	493.9	8.6	554	553.9	9.7
315	315.0	5.5	375	374.9	6.5	435	434.9	7.6	495	494.9	8.6	555	554.9	9.7
316	316.0	5.5	376	375.9	6.6	436	435.9	7.6	496	495.9	8.7	556	555.9	9.7
317	317.0	5.5	377	376.9	6.6	437	436.9	7.6	497	496.9	8.7	557	556.9	9.7
318	318.0	5.5	378	377.9	6.6	438	437.9	7.6	498	497.9	8.7	558	557.9	9.7
319	319.0	5.6	379	378.9	6.6	439	438.9	7.7	499	498.9	8.7	559	558.9	9.8
320	320.0	5.6	380	379.9	6.6	440	439.9	7.7	500	499.9	8.7	560	559.9	9.8
321	321.0	5.6	381	380.9	6.6	441	440.9	7.7	501	500.9	8.7	561	560.9	9.8
322	322.0	5.6	382	381.9	6.7	442	441.9	7.7	502	501.9	8.8	562	561.9	9.8
323	323.0	5.6	383	382.9	6.7	443	442.9	7.7	503	502.9	8.8	563	562.9	9.8
324	324.0	5.7	384	383.9	6.7	444	443.9	7.7	504	503.9	8.8	564	563.9	9.8
325	325.0	5.7	385	384.9	6.7	445	444.9	7.8	505	504.9	8.8	565	564.9	9.9
326	326.0	5.7	386	385.9	6.7	446	445.9	7.8	506	505.9	8.8	566	565.9	9.9
327	327.0	5.7	387	386.9	6.8	447	446.9	7.8	507	506.9	8.9	567	566.9	9.9
328	328.0	5.7	388	387.9	6.8	448	447.9	7.8	508	507.9	8.9	568	567.9	9.9
329	328.9	5.7	389	388.9	6.8	449	448.9	7.8	509	508.9	8.9	569	568.9	9.9
330	329.9	5.8	390	389.9	6.8	450	449.9	7.9	510	509.9	8.9	570	569.9	9.9
331	330.9	5.8	391	390.9	6.8	451	450.9	7.9	511	510.9	8.9	571	570.9	10.0
332	331.9	5.8	392	391.9	6.8	452	451.9	7.9	512	511.9	8.9	572	571.9	10.0
333	332.9	5.8	393	392.9	6.9	453	452.9	7.9	513	512.9	9.0	573	572.9	10.0
334	333.9	5.8	394	393.9	6.9	454	453.9	7.9	514	513.9	9.0	574	573.9	10.0
335	334.9	5.8	395	394.9	6.9	455	454.9	7.9	515	514.9	9.0	575	574.9	10.0
336	335.9	5.9	396	395.9	6.9	456	455.9	8.0	516	515.9	9.0	576	575.9	10.1
337	336.9	5.9	397	396.9	6.9	457	456.9	8.0	517	516.9	9.0	577	576.9	10.1
338	337.9	5.9	398	397.9	6.9	458	457.9	8.0	518	517.9	9.0	578	577.9	10.1
339	338.9	5.9	399	398.9	7.0	459	458.9	8.0	519	518.9	9.1	579	578.9	10.1
340	339.9	5.9	400	399.9	7.0	460	459.9	8.0	520	519.9	9.1	580	579.9	10.1
341	340.9	6.0	401	400.9	7.0	461	460.9	8.0	521	520.9	9.1	581	580.9	10.1
342	341.9	6.0	402	401.9	7.0	462	461.9	8.1	522	521.9	9.1	582	581.9	10.2
343	342.9	6.0	403	402.9	7.0	463	462.9	8.1	523	522.9	9.1	583	582.9	10.2
344	343.9	6.0	404	403.9	7.1	464	463.9	8.1	524	523.9	9.1	584	583.9	10.2
345	344.9	6.0	405	404.9	7.1	465	464.9	8.1	525	524.9	9.2	585	584.9	10.2
346	345.9	6.0	406	405.9	7.1	466	465.9	8.1	526	525.9	9.2	586	585.9	10.2
347	346.9	6.1	407	406.9	7.1	467	466.9	8.2	527	526.9	9.2	587	586.9	10.2
348	347.9	6.1	408	407.9	7.1	468	467.9	8.2	528	527.9	9.2	588	587.9	10.3
349	348.9	6.1	409	408.9	7.1	469	468.9	8.2	529	528.9	9.2	589	588.9	10.3
350	349.9	6.1	410	409.9	7.2	470	469.9	8.2	530	529.9	9.2	590	589.9	10.3
351	350.9	6.1	411	410.9	7.2	471	470.9	8.2	531	530.9	9.3	591	590.9	10.3
352	351.9	6.1	412	411.9	7.2	472	471.9	8.2	532	531.9	9.3	592	591.9	10.3
353	352.9	6.2	413	412.9	7.2	473	472.9	8.3	533	532.9	9.3	593	592.9	10.3
354	353.9	6.2	414	413.9	7.2	474	473.9	8.3	534	533.9	9.3	594	593.9	10.4
355	354.9	6.2	415	414.9	7.2	475	474.9	8.3	535	534.9	9.3	595	594.9	10.4
356	355.9	6.2	416	415.9	7.3	476	475.9	8.3	536	535.9	9.4	596	595.9	10.4
357	356.9	6.2	417	416.9	7.3	477	476.9	8.3	537	536.9	9.4	597	596.9	10.4
358	357.9	6.2	418	417.9	7.3	478	477.9	8.3	538	537.9	9.4	598	597.9	10.4
359	358.9	6.3	419	418.9	7.3	479	478.9	8.4	539	538.9	9.4	599	598.9	10.5
360	359.9	6.3	420	419.9	7.3	480	479.9	8.4	540	539.9	9.4	600	599.9	10.5
Hyp.	Opp.	Adj.	Hyp.	Opp.	Adj.	Hyp.	Opp.	Adj.	Hyp.	Opp.	Adj.	Hyp.	Opp.	Adj.

Dist. D Lon	Dep	D. Lat. Dep	Dist. D Lon	Dep	D. Lat. Dep	Dist. D Lon	Dep	D. Lat. Dep	Dist. D Lon	Dep	D. Lat. Dep	Dist. D Lon	Dep	D. Lat. Dep

89°

89°

Table 3

TRAVERSE TABLE

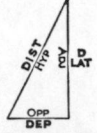

2°   2°

D Lon Dist.	Dep D. Lat.	Dep.	D Lon Dist.	Dep D. Lat.	Dep.	D Lon Dist.	Dep D. Lat.	Dep.	D Lon Dist.	Dep D. Lat.	Dep.	D Lon Dist.	Dep D. Lat.	Dep.
Hyp.	Adj.	Opp.	Hyp.	Adj.	Opp.	Hyp.	Adj.	Opp.	Hyp.	Adj.	Opp.	Hyp.	Adj.	Opp.
1	1.0	0.0	61	61.0	2.1	121	120.9	4.2	181	180.9	6.3	241	240.9	8.4
2	2.0	0.1	62	62.0	2.2	122	121.9	4.3	182	181.9	6.4	242	241.9	8.4
3	3.0	0.1	63	63.0	2.2	123	122.9	4.3	183	182.9	6.4	243	242.9	8.5
4	4.0	0.1	64	64.0	2.2	124	123.9	4.3	184	183.9	6.4	244	243.9	8.5
5	5.0	0.2	65	65.0	2.3	125	124.9	4.4	185	184.9	6.5	245	244.9	8.6
6	6.0	0.2	66	66.0	2.3	126	125.9	4.4	186	185.9	6.5	246	245.9	8.6
7	7.0	0.2	67	67.0	2.3	127	126.9	4.4	187	186.9	6.5	247	246.8	8.6
8	8.0	0.3	68	68.0	2.4	128	127.9	4.5	188	187.9	6.6	248	247.8	8.7
9	9.0	0.3	69	69.0	2.4	129	128.9	4.5	189	188.9	6.6	249	248.8	8.7
10	10.0	0.3	70	70.0	2.4	130	129.9	4.5	190	189.9	6.6	250	249.8	8.7
11	11.0	0.4	71	71.0	2.5	131	130.9	4.6	191	190.9	6.7	251	250.8	8.8
12	12.0	0.4	72	72.0	2.5	132	131.9	4.6	192	191.9	6.7	252	251.8	8.8
13	13.0	0.5	73	73.0	2.5	133	132.9	4.6	193	192.9	6.7	253	252.8	8.8
14	14.0	0.5	74	74.0	2.6	134	133.9	4.7	194	193.9	6.8	254	253.8	8.9
15	15.0	0.5	75	75.0	2.6	135	134.9	4.7	195	194.9	6.8	255	254.8	8.9
16	16.0	0.6	76	76.0	2.7	136	135.9	4.7	196	195.9	6.8	256	255.8	8.9
17	17.0	0.6	77	77.0	2.7	137	136.9	4.8	197	196.9	6.9	257	256.8	9.0
18	18.0	0.6	78	78.0	2.7	138	137.9	4.8	198	197.9	6.9	258	257.8	9.0
19	19.0	0.7	79	79.0	2.8	139	138.9	4.9	199	198.9	6.9	259	258.8	9.0
20	20.0	0.7	80	80.0	2.8	140	139.9	4.9	200	199.9	7.0	260	259.8	9.1
21	21.0	0.7	81	81.0	2.8	141	140.9	4.9	201	200.9	7.0	261	260.8	9.1
22	22.0	0.8	82	82.0	2.9	142	141.9	5.0	202	201.9	7.0	262	261.8	9.1
23	23.0	0.8	83	82.9	2.9	143	142.9	5.0	203	202.9	7.1	263	262.8	9.2
24	24.0	0.8	84	83.9	2.9	144	143.9	5.0	204	203.9	7.1	264	263.8	9.2
25	25.0	0.9	85	84.9	3.0	145	144.9	5.1	205	204.9	7.2	265	264.8	9.2
26	26.0	0.9	86	85.9	3.0	146	145.9	5.1	206	205.9	7.2	266	265.8	9.3
27	27.0	0.9	87	86.9	3.0	147	146.9	5.1	207	206.9	7.2	267	266.8	9.3
28	28.0	1.0	88	87.9	3.1	148	147.9	5.2	208	207.9	7.3	268	267.8	9.4
29	29.0	1.0	89	88.9	3.1	149	148.9	5.2	209	208.9	7.3	269	268.8	9.4
30	30.0	1.0	90	89.9	3.1	150	149.9	5.2	210	209.9	7.3	270	269.8	9.4
31	31.0	1.1	91	90.9	3.2	151	150.9	5.3	211	210.9	7.4	271	270.8	9.5
32	32.0	1.1	92	91.9	3.2	152	151.9	5.3	212	211.9	7.4	272	271.8	9.5
33	33.0	1.2	93	92.9	3.2	153	152.9	5.3	213	212.9	7.4	273	272.8	9.5
34	34.0	1.2	94	93.9	3.3	154	153.9	5.4	214	213.9	7.5	274	273.8	9.6
35	35.0	1.2	95	94.9	3.3	155	154.9	5.4	215	214.9	7.5	275	274.8	9.6
36	36.0	1.3	96	95.9	3.4	156	155.9	5.4	216	215.9	7.5	276	275.8	9.6
37	37.0	1.3	97	96.9	3.4	157	156.9	5.5	217	216.9	7.6	277	276.8	9.7
38	38.0	1.3	98	97.9	3.4	158	157.9	5.5	218	217.9	7.6	278	277.8	9.7
39	39.0	1.4	99	98.9	3.5	159	158.9	5.5	219	218.9	7.6	279	278.8	9.7
40	40.0	1.4	100	99.9	3.5	160	159.9	5.6	220	219.9	7.7	280	279.8	9.8
41	41.0	1.4	101	100.9	3.5	161	160.9	5.6	221	220.9	7.7	281	280.8	9.8
42	42.0	1.5	102	101.9	3.6	162	161.9	5.7	222	221.9	7.7	282	281.8	9.8
43	43.0	1.5	103	102.9	3.6	163	162.9	5.7	223	222.9	7.8	283	282.8	9.9
44	44.0	1.5	104	103.9	3.6	164	163.9	5.7	224	223.9	7.8	284	283.8	9.9
45	45.0	1.6	105	104.9	3.7	165	164.9	5.8	225	224.9	7.9	285	284.8	9.9
46	46.0	1.6	106	105.9	3.7	166	165.9	5.8	226	225.9	7.9	286	285.8	10.0
47	47.0	1.6	107	106.9	3.7	167	166.9	5.8	227	226.9	7.9	287	286.8	10.0
48	48.0	1.7	108	107.9	3.8	168	167.9	5.9	228	227.9	8.0	288	287.8	10.1
49	49.0	1.7	109	108.9	3.8	169	168.9	5.9	229	228.9	8.0	289	288.8	10.1
50	50.0	1.7	110	109.9	3.8	170	169.9	5.9	230	229.9	8.0	290	289.8	10.1
51	51.0	1.8	111	110.9	3.9	171	170.9	6.0	231	230.9	8.1	291	290.8	10.2
52	52.0	1.8	112	111.9	3.9	172	171.9	6.0	232	231.9	8.1	292	291.8	10.2
53	53.0	1.8	113	112.9	3.9	173	172.9	6.0	233	232.9	8.1	293	292.8	10.2
54	54.0	1.9	114	113.9	4.0	174	173.9	6.1	234	233.9	8.2	294	293.8	10.3
55	55.0	1.9	115	114.9	4.0	175	174.9	6.1	235	234.9	8.2	295	294.8	10.3
56	56.0	2.0	116	115.9	4.0	176	175.9	6.1	236	235.9	8.2	296	295.8	10.3
57	57.0	2.0	117	116.9	4.1	177	176.9	6.2	237	236.9	8.3	297	296.8	10.4
58	58.0	2.0	118	117.9	4.1	178	177.9	6.2	238	237.9	8.3	298	297.8	10.4
59	59.0	2.1	119	118.9	4.2	179	178.9	6.2	239	238.9	8.3	299	298.8	10.4
60	60.0	2.1	120	119.9	4.2	180	179.9	6.3	240	239.9	8.4	300	299.8	10.5
Hyp.	Opp.	Adj.	Hyp.	Opp.	Adj.	Hyp.	Opp.	Adj.	Hyp.	Opp.	Adj.	Hyp.	Opp.	Adj.
Dist. D Lon	Dep.	D. Lat. Dep	Dist. D Lon	Dep.	D. Lat. Dep	Dist. D Lon	Dep.	D. Lat. Dep	Dist. D Lon	Dep.	D. Lat. Dep	Dist. D Lon	Dep.	D. Lat Dep

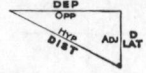

88°   88°

Table 3

TRAVERSE TABLE

2°

$$\frac{358° \mid 002°}{182° \mid 178°}$$

2°

D Lon	Dep		D Lon	Dep		D Lon	Dep		D Lon	Dep		D Lon	Dep	
Dist.	D. Lat.	Dep.	Dist.	D. Lat.	Dep.	Dist.	D. Lat.	Dep.	Dist.	D. Lat.	Dep.	Dist.	D. Lat.	Dep.
Hyp.	Adj.	Opp.	Hyp.	Adj.	Opp.	Hyp.	Adj.	Opp.	Hyp.	Adj.	Opp.	Hyp.	Adj.	Opp.
301	300.8	10.5	361	360.8	12.6	421	420.7	14.7	481	480.7	16.8	541	540.7	18.9
302	301.8	10.5	362	361.8	12.6	422	421.7	14.7	482	481.7	16.8	542	541.7	18.9
303	302.8	10.6	363	362.8	12.7	423	422.7	14.7	483	482.7	16.8	543	542.7	19.0
304	303.8	10.6	364	363.8	12.7	424	423.7	14.8	484	483.7	16.9	544	543.7	19.0
305	304.8	10.6	365	364.8	12.7	425	424.7	14.8	485	484.7	16.9	545	544.7	19.0
306	305.8	10.7	366	365.8	12.8	426	425.7	14.9	486	485.7	16.9	546	545.7	19.1
307	306.8	10.7	367	366.8	12.8	427	426.7	14.9	487	486.7	17.0	547	546.7	19.1
308	307.8	10.7	368	367.8	12.8	428	427.7	14.9	488	487.7	17.0	548	547.7	19.1
309	308.8	10.8	369	368.8	12.9	429	428.7	15.0	489	488.7	17.0	549	548.7	19.2
310	309.8	10.8	370	369.8	12.9	430	429.7	15.0	490	489.7	17.1	550	549.7	19.2
311	310.8	10.8	371	370.8	12.9	431	430.7	15.0	491	490.7	17.1	551	550.7	19.2
312	311.8	10.9	372	371.8	13.0	432	431.7	15.1	492	491.7	17.1	552	551.7	19.3
313	312.8	10.9	373	372.8	13.0	433	432.7	15.1	493	492.7	17.2	553	552.7	19.3
314	313.8	10.9	374	373.8	13.0	434	433.7	15.1	494	493.7	17.2	554	553.7	19.3
315	314.8	11.0	375	374.8	13.1	435	434.7	15.2	495	494.7	17.2	555	554.7	19.4
316	315.8	11.0	376	375.8	13.1	436	435.7	15.2	496	495.7	17.3	556	555.7	19.4
317	316.8	11.0	377	376.8	13.1	437	436.7	15.2	497	496.7	17.3	557	556.7	19.4
318	317.8	11.1	378	377.8	13.2	438	437.7	15.3	498	497.7	17.3	558	557.7	19.5
319	318.8	11.1	379	378.8	13.2	439	438.7	15.3	499	498.7	17.4	559	558.7	19.5
320	319.8	11.2	380	379.8	13.2	440	439.7	15.3	500	499.7	17.4	560	559.7	19.5
321	320.8	11.2	381	380.8	13.3	441	440.7	15.4	501	500.7	17.5	561	560.7	19.6
322	321.8	11.2	382	381.8	13.3	442	441.7	15.4	502	501.7	17.5	562	561.7	19.6
323	322.8	11.3	383	382.8	13.3	443	442.7	15.4	503	502.7	17.5	563	562.7	19.6
324	323.8	11.3	384	383.8	13.4	444	443.7	15.5	504	503.7	17.6	564	563.7	19.7
325	324.8	11.3	385	384.8	13.4	445	444.7	15.5	505	504.7	17.6	565	564.7	19.7
326	325.8	11.4	386	385.8	13.5	446	445.7	15.6	506	505.7	17.6	566	565.7	19.8
327	326.8	11.4	387	386.8	13.5	447	446.7	15.6	507	506.7	17.7	567	566.7	19.8
328	327.8	11.4	388	387.8	13.5	448	447.7	15.6	508	507.7	17.7	568	567.7	19.8
329	328.8	11.5	389	388.8	13.6	449	448.7	15.7	509	508.7	17.7	569	568.7	19.9
330	329.8	11.5	390	389.8	13.6	450	449.7	15.7	510	509.7	17.8	570	569.7	19.9
331	330.8	11.5	391	390.8	13.6	451	450.7	15.7	511	510.7	17.8	571	570.7	19.9
332	331.8	11.6	392	391.8	13.7	452	451.7	15.8	512	511.7	17.9	572	571.7	20.0
333	332.8	11.6	393	392.8	13.7	453	452.7	15.8	513	512.7	17.9	573	572.7	20.0
334	333.8	11.6	394	393.8	13.7	454	453.7	15.8	514	513.7	17.9	574	573.7	20.0
335	334.8	11.7	395	394.8	13.8	455	454.7	15.9	515	514.7	18.0	575	574.6	20.1
336	335.8	11.7	396	395.8	13.8	456	455.7	15.9	516	515.7	18.0	576	575.6	20.1
337	336.8	11.7	397	396.8	13.8	457	456.7	15.9	517	516.7	18.0	577	576.6	20.1
338	337.8	11.8	398	397.8	13.9	458	457.7	16.0	518	517.7	18.1	578	577.6	20.2
339	338.8	11.8	399	398.8	13.9	459	458.7	16.0	519	518.7	18.1	579	578.6	20.2
340	339.8	11.9	400	399.8	13.9	460	459.7	16.0	520	519.7	18.1	580	579.6	20.2
341	340.8	11.9	401	400.8	14.0	461	460.7	16.1	521	520.7	18.2	581	580.6	20.3
342	341.8	11.9	402	401.8	14.0	462	461.7	16.1	522	521.7	18.2	582	581.6	20.3
343	342.8	12.0	403	402.8	14.0	463	462.7	16.1	523	522.7	18.3	583	582.6	20.3
344	343.8	12.0	404	403.8	14.1	464	463.7	16.2	524	523.7	18.3	584	583.6	20.4
345	344.8	12.0	405	404.8	14.1	465	464.7	16.2	525	524.7	18.3	585	584.6	20.4
346	345.8	12.1	406	405.8	14.2	466	465.7	16.2	526	525.7	18.4	586	585.6	20.5
347	346.8	12.1	407	406.8	14.2	467	466.7	16.3	527	526.7	18.4	587	586.6	20.5
348	347.8	12.1	408	407.8	14.2	468	467.7	16.3	528	527.7	18.4	588	587.6	20.5
349	348.8	12.2	409	408.8	14.3	469	468.7	16.4	529	528.7	18.5	589	588.6	20.6
350	349.8	12.2	410	409.8	14.3	470	469.7	16.4	530	529.7	18.5	590	589.6	20.6
351	350.8	12.2	411	410.7	14.3	471	470.7	16.4	531	530.7	18.5	591	590.6	20.6
352	351.8	12.3	412	411.7	14.4	472	471.7	16.5	532	531.7	18.6	592	591.6	20.7
353	352.8	12.3	413	412.7	14.4	473	472.7	16.5	533	532.7	18.6	593	592.6	20.7
354	353.8	12.3	414	413.7	14.4	474	473.7	16.5	534	533.7	18.6	594	593.6	20.7
355	354.8	12.4	415	414.7	14.5	475	474.7	16.6	535	534.7	18.7	595	594.6	20.8
356	355.8	12.4	416	415.7	14.5	476	475.7	16.6	536	535.7	18.7	596	595.6	20.8
357	356.8	12.4	417	416.7	14.5	477	476.7	16.6	537	536.7	18.7	597	596.6	20.8
358	357.8	12.5	418	417.7	14.6	478	477.7	16.7	538	537.7	18.8	598	597.6	20.9
359	358.8	12.5	419	418.7	14.6	479	478.7	16.7	539	538.7	18.8	599	598.6	20.9
360	359.8	12.5	420	419.7	14.6	480	479.7	16.7	540	539.7	18.8	600	599.6	20.9
Hyp.	Opp.	Adj.	Hyp.	Opp.	Adj.	Hyp.	Opp.	Adj.	Hyp.	Opp.	Adj.	Hyp.	Opp.	Adj.
Dist.	Dep.	D. Lat.	Dist.	Dep.	D. Lat.	Dist.	Dep.	D. Lat.	Dist.	Dep.	D. Lat.	Dist.	Dep.	D. Lat.
D Lon		Dep	D Lon		Dep	D Lon		Dep	D Lon		Dep	D Lon		Dep

88°

$$\frac{272° \mid 088°}{268° \mid 092°}$$

88°

Table 3

TRAVERSE TABLE

3°  3°

D Lon Dist.	Dep D. Lat.	Dep.	D Lon Dist.	Dep D. Lat.	Dep.	D Lon Dist.	Dep D. Lat.	Dep.	D Lon Dist.	Dep D. Lat.	Dep.	D Lon Dist.	Dep D. Lat.	Dep.
Hyp.	*Adj.*	*Opp.*	*Hyp.*	*Adj.*	*Opp.*	*Hyp.*	*Adj.*	*Opp.*	*Hyp.*	*Adj.*	*Opp.*	*Hyp.*	*Adj.*	*Opp.*
1	1.0	0.1	61	60.9	3.2	121	120.8	6.3	181	180.8	9.5	241	240.7	12.6
2	2.0	0.1	62	61.9	3.2	122	121.8	6.4	182	181.8	9.5	242	241.7	12.7
3	3.0	0.2	63	62.9	3.3	123	122.8	6.4	183	182.7	9.6	243	242.7	12.7
4	4.0	0.2	64	63.9	3.3	124	123.8	6.5	184	183.7	9.6	244	243.7	12.8
5	5.0	0.3	65	64.9	3.4	125	124.8	6.5	185	184.7	9.7	245	244.7	12.8
6	6.0	0.3	66	65.9	3.5	126	125.8	6.6	186	185.7	9.7	246	245.7	12.9
7	7.0	0.4	67	66.9	3.5	127	126.8	6.6	187	186.7	9.8	247	246.7	12.9
8	8.0	0.4	68	67.9	3.6	128	127.8	6.7	188	187.7	9.8	248	247.7	13.0
9	9.0	0.5	69	68.9	3.6	129	128.8	6.8	189	188.7	9.9	249	248.7	13.0
10	10.0	0.5	70	69.9	3.7	130	129.8	6.8	190	189.7	9.9	250	249.7	13.1
11	11.0	0.6	71	70.9	3.7	131	130.8	6.9	191	190.7	10.0	251	250.7	13.1
12	12.0	0.6	72	71.9	3.8	132	131.8	6.9	192	191.7	10.0	252	251.7	13.2
13	13.0	0.7	73	72.9	3.8	133	132.8	7.0	193	192.7	10.1	253	252.7	13.2
14	14.0	0.7	74	73.9	3.9	134	133.8	7.0	194	193.7	10.2	254	253.7	13.3
15	15.0	0.8	75	74.9	3.9	135	134.8	7.1	195	194.7	10.2	255	254.7	13.3
16	16.0	0.8	76	75.9	4.0	136	135.8	7.1	196	195.7	10.3	256	255.6	13.4
17	17.0	0.9	77	76.9	4.0	137	136.8	7.2	197	196.7	10.3	257	256.6	13.5
18	18.0	0.9	78	77.9	4.1	138	137.8	7.2	198	197.7	10.4	258	257.6	13.5
19	19.0	1.0	79	78.9	4.1	139	138.8	7.3	199	198.7	10.4	259	258.6	13.6
20	20.0	1.0	80	79.9	4.2	140	139.8	7.3	200	199.7	10.5	260	259.6	13.6
21	21.0	1.1	81	80.9	4.2	141	140.8	7.4	201	200.7	10.5	261	260.6	13.7
22	22.0	1.2	82	81.9	4.3	142	141.8	7.4	202	201.7	10.6	262	261.6	13.7
23	23.0	1.2	83	82.9	4.3	143	142.8	7.5	203	202.7	10.6	263	262.6	13.8
24	24.0	1.3	84	83.9	4.4	144	143.8	7.5	204	203.7	10.7	264	263.6	13.8
25	25.0	1.3	85	84.9	4.4	145	144.8	7.6	205	204.7	10.7	265	264.6	13.9
26	26.0	1.4	86	85.9	4.5	146	145.8	7.6	206	205.7	10.8	266	265.6	13.9
27	27.0	1.4	87	86.9	4.6	147	146.8	7.7	207	206.7	10.8	267	266.6	14.0
28	28.0	1.5	88	87.9	4.6	148	147.8	7.7	208	207.7	10.9	268	267.6	14.0
29	29.0	1.5	89	88.9	4.7	149	148.8	7.8	209	208.7	10.9	269	268.6	14.1
30	30.0	1.6	90	89.9	4.7	150	149.8	7.9	210	209.7	11.0	270	269.6	14.1
31	31.0	1.6	91	90.9	4.8	151	150.8	7.9	211	210.7	11.0	271	270.6	14.2
32	32.0	1.7	92	91.9	4.8	152	151.8	8.0	212	211.7	11.1	272	271.6	14.2
33	33.0	1.7	93	92.9	4.9	153	152.8	8.0	213	212.7	11.1	273	272.6	14.3
34	34.0	1.8	94	93.9	4.9	154	153.8	8.1	214	213.7	11.2	274	273.6	14.3
35	35.0	1.8	95	94.9	5.0	155	154.8	8.1	215	214.7	11.3	275	274.6	14.4
36	36.0	1.9	96	95.9	5.0	156	155.8	8.2	216	215.7	11.3	276	275.6	14.4
37	36.9	1.9	97	96.9	5.1	157	156.8	8.2	217	216.7	11.4	277	276.6	14.5
38	37.9	2.0	98	97.9	5.1	158	157.8	8.3	218	217.7	11.4	278	277.6	14.6
39	38.9	2.0	99	98.9	5.2	159	158.8	8.3	219	218.7	11.5	279	278.6	14.6
40	39.9	2.1	100	99.9	5.2	160	159.8	8.4	220	219.7	11.5	280	279.6	14.7
41	40.9	2.1	101	100.9	5.3	161	160.8	8.4	221	220.7	11.6	281	280.6	14.7
42	41.9	2.2	102	101.9	5.3	162	161.8	8.5	222	221.7	11.6	282	281.6	14.8
43	42.9	2.3	103	102.9	5.4	163	162.8	8.5	223	222.7	11.7	283	282.6	14.8
44	43.9	2.3	104	103.9	5.4	164	163.8	8.6	224	223.7	11.7	284	283.6	14.9
45	44.9	2.4	105	104.9	5.5	165	164.8	8.6	225	224.7	11.8	285	284.6	14.9
46	45.9	2.4	106	105.9	5.5	166	165.8	8.7	226	225.7	11.8	286	285.6	15.0
47	46.9	2.5	107	106.9	5.6	167	166.8	8.7	227	226.7	11.9	287	286.6	15.0
48	47.9	2.5	108	107.9	5.7	168	167.8	8.8	228	227.7	11.9	288	287.6	15.1
49	48.9	2.6	109	108.9	5.7	169	168.8	8.8	229	228.7	12.0	289	288.6	15.1
50	49.9	2.6	110	109.8	5.8	170	169.8	8.9	230	229.7	12.0	290	289.6	15.2
51	50.9	2.7	111	110.8	5.8	171	170.8	8.9	231	230.7	12.1	291	290.6	15.2
52	51.9	2.7	112	111.8	5.9	172	171.8	9.0	232	231.7	12.1	292	291.6	15.3
53	52.9	2.8	113	112.8	5.9	173	172.8	9.1	233	232.7	12.2	293	292.6	15.3
54	53.9	2.8	114	113.8	6.0	174	173.8	9.1	234	233.7	12.2	294	293.6	15.4
55	54.9	2.9	115	114.8	6.0	175	174.8	9.2	235	234.7	12.3	295	294.6	15.4
56	55.9	2.9	116	115.8	6.1	176	175.8	9.2	236	235.7	12.4	296	295.6	15.5
57	56.9	3.0	117	116.8	6.1	177	176.8	9.3	237	236.7	12.4	297	296.6	15.5
58	57.9	3.0	118	117.8	6.2	178	177.8	9.3	238	237.7	12.5	298	297.6	15.6
59	58.9	3.1	119	118.8	6.2	179	178.8	9.4	239	238.7	12.5	299	298.6	15.6
60	59.9	3.1	120	119.8	6.3	180	179.8	9.4	240	239.7	12.6	300	299.6	15.7
Hyp.	*Opp.*	*Adj.*	*Hyp.*	*Opp.*	*Adj.*	*Hyp.*	*Opp.*	*Adj.*	*Hyp.*	*Opp.*	*Adj.*	*Hyp.*	*Opp.*	*Adj.*
Dist. D Lon	Dep.	D. Lat. Dep	Dist. D Lon	Dep.	D. Lat. Dep	Dist. D Lon	Dep.	D. Lat. Dep	Dist. D Lon	Dep.	D. Lat. Dep	Dist. D Lon	Dep.	D. Lat. Dep

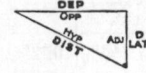

87° 87°

Table 3

TRAVERSE TABLE

3°

	357°	003°
	183°	177°

3°

D Lon	Dep		D Lon	Dep		D Lon	Dep		D Lon	Dep		D Lon	Dep	
Dist.	D. Lat.	Dep.	Dist.	D. Lat.	Dep.	Dist.	D. Lat.	Dep.	Dist.	D. Lat.	Dep.	Dist.	D. Lat.	Dep.
Hyp.	*Adj.*	*Opp.*	*Hyp.*	*Adj.*	*Opp.*	*Hyp.*	*Adj.*	*Opp.*	*Hyp.*	*Adj.*	*Opp.*	*Hyp.*	*Adj.*	*Opp.*
301	300.6	15.8	361	360.5	18.9	421	420.4	22.0	481	480.3	25.2	541	540.3	28.3
302	301.6	15.8	362	361.5	18.9	422	421.4	22.1	482	481.3	25.2	542	541.3	28.4
303	302.6	15.9	363	362.5	19.0	423	422.4	22.1	483	482.3	25.3	543	542.3	28.4
304	303.6	15.9	364	363.5	19.1	424	423.4	22.2	484	483.3	25.3	544	543.3	28.5
305	304.6	16.0	365	364.5	19.1	425	424.4	22.2	485	484.3	25.4	545	544.3	28.5
306	305.6	16.0	366	365.5	19.2	426	425.4	22.3	486	485.3	25.4	546	545.3	28.6
307	306.6	16.1	367	366.5	19.2	427	426.4	22.3	487	486.3	25.5	547	546.3	28.6
308	307.6	16.1	368	367.5	19.3	428	427.4	22.4	488	487.3	25.5	548	547.2	28.7
309	308.6	16.2	369	368.5	19.3	429	428.4	22.5	489	488.3	25.6	549	548.2	28.7
310	309.6	16.2	370	369.5	19.4	430	429.4	22.5	490	489.3	25.6	550	549.2	28.8
311	310.6	16.3	371	370.5	19.4	431	430.4	22.6	491	490.3	25.7	551	550.2	28.8
312	311.6	16.3	372	371.5	19.5	432	431.4	22.6	492	491.3	25.7	552	551.2	28.9
313	312.6	16.4	373	372.5	19.5	433	432.4	22.7	493	492.3	25.8	553	552.2	28.9
314	313.6	16.4	374	373.5	19.6	434	433.4	22.7	494	493.3	25.9	554	553.2	29.0
315	314.6	16.5	375	374.5	19.6	435	434.4	22.8	495	494.3	25.9	555	554.2	29.0
316	315.6	16.5	376	375.5	19.7	436	435.4	22.8	496	495.3	26.0	556	555.2	29.1
317	316.6	16.6	377	376.5	19.7	437	436.4	22.9	497	496.3	26.0	557	556.2	29.2
318	317.6	16.6	378	377.5	19.8	438	437.4	22.9	498	497.3	26.1	558	557.2	29.2
319	318.6	16.7	379	378.5	19.8	439	438.4	23.0	499	498.3	26.1	559	558.2	29.3
320	319.6	16.7	380	379.5	19.9	440	439.4	23.0	500	499.3	26.2	560	559.2	29.3
321	320.6	16.8	381	380.5	19.9	441	440.4	23.1	501	500.3	26.2	561	560.2	29.4
322	321.6	16.9	382	381.5	20.0	442	441.4	23.1	502	501.3	26.3	562	561.2	29.4
323	322.6	16.9	383	382.5	20.0	443	442.4	23.2	503	502.3	26.3	563	562.2	29.5
324	323.6	17.0	384	383.5	20.1	444	443.4	23.2	504	503.3	26.4	564	563.2	29.5
325	324.6	17.0	385	384.5	20.1	445	444.4	23.3	505	504.3	26.4	565	564.2	29.6
326	325.6	17.1	386	385.5	20.2	446	445.4	23.3	506	505.3	26.5	566	565.2	29.6
327	326.6	17.1	387	386.5	20.3	447	446.4	23.4	507	506.3	26.5	567	566.2	29.7
328	327.6	17.2	388	387.5	20.3	448	447.4	23.4	508	507.3	26.6	568	567.2	29.7
329	328.5	17.2	389	388.5	20.4	449	448.4	23.5	509	508.3	26.6	569	568.2	29.8
330	329.5	17.3	390	389.5	20.4	450	449.4	23.6	510	509.3	26.7	570	569.2	29.8
331	330.5	17.3	391	390.5	20.5	451	450.4	23.6	511	510.3	26.7	571	570.2	29.9
332	331.5	17.4	392	391.5	20.5	452	451.4	23.7	512	511.3	26.8	572	571.2	29.9
333	332.5	17.4	393	392.5	20.6	453	452.4	23.7	513	512.3	26.8	573	572.2	30.0
334	333.5	17.5	394	393.5	20.6	454	453.4	23.8	514	513.3	26.9	574	573.2	30.0
335	334.5	17.5	395	394.5	20.7	455	454.4	23.8	515	514.3	27.0	575	574.2	30.1
336	335.5	17.6	396	395.5	20.7	456	455.4	23.9	516	515.3	27.0	576	575.2	30.1
337	336.5	17.6	397	396.5	20.8	457	456.4	23.9	517	516.3	27.1	577	576.2	30.2
338	337.5	17.7	398	397.5	20.8	458	457.4	24.0	518	517.3	27.1	578	577.2	30.3
339	338.5	17.7	399	398.5	20.9	459	458.4	24.0	519	518.3	27.2	579	578.2	30.3
340	339.5	17.8	400	399.5	20.9	460	459.4	24.1	520	519.3	27.2	580	579.2	30.4
341	340.5	17.8	401	400.5	21.0	461	460.4	24.1	521	520.3	27.3	581	580.2	30.4
342	341.5	17.9	402	401.4	21.0	462	461.4	24.2	522	521.3	27.3	582	581.2	30.5
343	342.5	18.0	403	402.4	21.1	463	462.4	24.2	523	522.3	27.4	583	582.2	30.5
344	343.5	18.0	404	403.4	21.1	464	463.4	24.3	524	523.3	27.4	584	583.2	30.6
345	344.5	18.1	405	404.4	21.2	465	464.4	24.3	525	524.3	27.5	585	584.2	30.6
346	345.5	18.1	406	405.4	21.2	466	465.4	24.4	526	525.3	27.5	586	585.2	30.7
347	346.5	18.2	407	406.4	21.3	467	466.4	24.4	527	526.3	27.6	587	586.2	30.7
348	347.5	18.2	408	407.4	21.4	468	467.4	24.5	528	527.3	27.6	588	587.2	30.8
349	348.5	18.3	409	408.4	21.4	469	468.4	24.5	529	528.3	27.7	589	588.2	30.8
350	349.5	18.3	410	409.4	21.5	470	469.4	24.6	530	529.3	27.7	590	589.2	30.9
351	350.5	18.4	411	410.4	21.5	471	470.4	24.7	531	530.3	27.8	591	590.2	30.9
352	351.5	18.4	412	411.4	21.6	472	471.4	24.7	532	531.3	27.8	592	591.2	31.0
353	352.5	18.5	413	412.4	21.6	473	472.4	24.8	533	532.3	27.9	593	592.2	31.0
354	353.5	18.5	414	413.4	21.7	474	473.4	24.8	534	533.3	27.9	594	593.2	31.1
355	354.5	18.6	415	414.4	21.7	475	474.3	24.9	535	534.3	28.0	595	594.2	31.1
356	355.5	18.6	416	415.4	21.8	476	475.3	24.9	536	535.3	28.1	596	595.2	31.2
357	356.5	18.7	417	416.4	21.8	477	476.3	25.0	537	536.3	28.1	597	596.2	31.2
358	357.5	18.7	418	417.4	21.9	478	477.3	25.0	538	537.3	28.2	598	597.2	31.3
359	358.5	18.8	419	418.4	21.9	479	478.3	25.1	539	538.3	28.2	599	598.2	31.3
360	359.5	18.8	420	419.4	22.0	480	479.3	25.1	540	539.3	28.3	600	599.2	31.4
Hyp.	*Opp.*	*Adj.*	*Hyp.*	*Opp.*	*Adj.*	*Hyp.*	*Opp.*	*Adj.*	*Hyp.*	*Opp.*	*Adj.*	*Hyp.*	*Opp.*	*Adj.*
Dist.	Dep.	D. Lat.	Dist.	Dep.	D. Lat.	Dist.	Dep.	D. Lat.	Dist.	Dep.	D. Lat.	Dist.	Dep.	D. Lat.
D Lon		Dep	D Lon		Dep	D Lon		Dep	D Lon		Dep	D Lon		Dep

87°

	273°	087°
	267°	093°

87°

Table 3   **TRAVERSE TABLE**

4°

4°

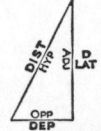

D Lon	Dep		D Lon	Dep		D Lon	Dep		D Lon	Dep		D Lon	Dep	
Dist.	D. Lat.	Dep.	Dist.	D. Lat.	Dep.	Dist.	D. Lat.	Dep.	Dist.	D. Lat.	Dep.	Dist.	D. Lat.	Dep.
Hyp.	Adj.	Opp.	Hyp.	Adj.	Opp.	Hyp.	Adj.	Opp.	Hyp.	Adj.	Opp.	Hyp.	Adj.	Opp.
1	1.0	0.1	61	60.9	4.3	121	120.7	8.4	181	180.6	12.6	241	240.4	16.8
2	2.0	0.1	62	61.8	4.3	122	121.7	8.5	182	181.6	12.7	242	241.4	16.9
3	3.0	0.2	63	62.8	4.4	123	122.7	8.6	183	182.6	12.8	243	242.4	17.0
4	4.0	0.3	64	63.8	4.5	124	123.7	8.6	184	183.6	12.8	244	243.4	17.0
5	5.0	0.3	65	64.8	4.5	125	124.7	8.7	185	184.5	12.9	245	244.4	17.1
6	6.0	0.4	66	65.8	4.6	126	125.7	8.8	186	185.5	13.0	246	245.4	17.2
7	7.0	0.5	67	66.8	4.7	127	126.7	8.9	187	186.5	13.0	247	246.4	17.2
8	8.0	0.6	68	67.8	4.7	128	127.7	8.9	188	187.5	13.1	248	247.4	17.3
9	9.0	0.6	69	68.8	4.8	129	128.7	9.0	189	188.5	13.2	249	248.4	17.4
10	10.0	0.7	70	69.8	4.9	130	129.7	9.1	190	189.5	13.3	250	249.4	17.4
11	11.0	0.8	71	70.8	5.0	131	130.7	9.1	191	190.5	13.3	251	250.4	17.5
12	12.0	0.8	72	71.8	5.0	132	131.7	9.2	192	191.5	13.4	252	251.4	17.6
13	13.0	0.9	73	72.8	5.1	133	132.7	9.3	193	192.5	13.5	253	252.4	17.6
14	14.0	1.0	74	73.8	5.2	134	133.7	9.3	194	193.5	13.5	254	253.4	17.7
15	15.0	1.0	75	74.8	5.2	135	134.7	9.4	195	194.5	13.6	255	254.4	17.8
16	16.0	1.1	76	75.8	5.3	136	135.7	9.5	196	195.5	13.7	256	255.4	17.9
17	17.0	1.2	77	76.8	5.4	137	136.7	9.6	197	196.5	13.7	257	256.4	17.9
18	18.0	1.3	78	77.8	5.4	138	137.7	9.6	198	197.5	13.8	258	257.4	18.0
19	19.0	1.3	79	78.8	5.5	139	138.7	9.7	199	198.5	13.9	259	258.4	18.1
20	20.0	1.4	80	79.8	5.6	140	139.7	9.8	200	199.5	14.0	260	259.4	18.1
21	20.9	1.5	81	80.8	5.7	141	140.7	9.8	201	200.5	14.0	261	260.4	18.2
22	21.9	1.5	82	81.8	5.7	142	141.7	9.9	202	201.5	14.1	262	261.4	18.3
23	22.9	1.6	83	82.8	5.8	143	142.7	10.0	203	202.5	14.2	263	262.4	18.3
24	23.9	1.7	84	83.8	5.9	144	143.6	10.0	204	203.5	14.2	264	263.4	18.4
25	24.9	1.7	85	84.8	5.9	145	144.6	10.1	205	204.5	14.3	265	264.4	18.5
26	25.9	1.8	86	85.8	6.0	146	145.6	10.2	206	205.5	14.4	266	265.4	18.6
27	26.9	1.9	87	86.8	6.1	147	146.6	10.3	207	206.5	14.4	267	266.3	18.6
28	27.9	2.0	88	87.8	6.1	148	147.6	10.3	208	207.5	14.5	268	267.3	18.7
29	28.9	2.0	89	88.8	6.2	149	148.6	10.4	209	208.5	14.6	269	268.3	18.8
30	29.9	2.1	90	89.8	6.3	150	149.6	10.5	210	209.5	14.6	270	269.3	18.8
31	30.9	2.2	91	90.8	6.3	151	150.6	10.5	211	210.5	14.7	271	270.3	18.9
32	31.9	2.2	92	91.8	6.4	152	151.6	10.6	212	211.5	14.8	272	271.3	19.0
33	32.9	2.3	93	92.8	6.5	153	152.6	10.7	213	212.5	14.9	273	272.3	19.0
34	33.9	2.4	94	93.8	6.6	154	153.6	10.7	214	213.5	14.9	274	273.3	19.1
35	34.9	2.4	95	94.8	6.6	155	154.6	10.8	215	214.5	15.0	275	274.3	19.2
36	35.9	2.5	96	95.8	6.7	156	155.6	10.9	216	215.5	15.1	276	275.3	19.3
37	36.9	2.6	97	96.8	6.8	157	156.6	11.0	217	216.5	15.1	277	276.3	19.3
38	37.9	2.7	98	97.8	6.8	158	157.6	11.0	218	217.5	15.2	278	277.3	19.4
39	38.9	2.7	99	98.8	6.9	159	158.6	11.1	219	218.5	15.3	279	278.3	19.5
40	39.9	2.8	100	99.8	7.0	160	159.6	11.2	220	219.5	15.3	280	279.3	19.5
41	40.9	2.9	101	100 8	7.0	161	160.6	11.2	221	220.5	15.4	281	280.3	19.6
42	41.9	2.9	102	101.8	7.1	162	161.6	11.3	222	221.5	15.5	282	281.3	19.7
43	42.9	3.0	103	102.7	7.2	163	162.6	11.4	223	222.5	15.6	283	282.3	19.7
44	43.9	3.1	104	103.7	7.3	164	163.6	11.4	224	223.5	15.6	284	283.3	19.8
45	44.9	3.1	105	104.7	7.3	165	164.6	11.5	225	224.5	15.7	285	284.3	19.9
46	45.9	3.2	106	105.7	7.4	166	165.6	11.6	226	225.4	15.8	286	285.3	20.0
47	46.9	3.3	107	106.7	7.5	167	166.6	11.6	227	226.4	15.8	287	286.3	20.0
48	47.9	3.3	108	107.7	7.5	168	167.6	11.7	228	227.4	15.9	288	287.3	20.1
49	48.9	3.4	109	108.7	7.6	169	168.6	11.8	229	228.4	16.0	289	288.3	20.2
50	49.9	3.5	110	109.7	7.7	170	169.6	11.9	230	229.4	16.0	290	289.3	20.2
51	50.9	3.6	111	110.7	7.7	171	170.6	11.9	231	230.4	16.1	291	290.3	20.3
52	51.9	3.6	112	111.7	7.8	172	171.6	12.0	232	231.4	16.2	292	291.3	20.4
53	52.9	3.7	113	112.7	7.9	173	172.6	12.1	233	232.4	16.3	293	292.3	20.4
54	53.9	3.8	114	113.7	8.0	174	173.6	12.1	234	233.4	16.3	294	293.3	20.5
55	54.9	3.8	115	114.7	8.0	175	174.6	12.2	235	234.4	16.4	295	294.3	20.6
56	55.9	3.9	116	115.7	8.1	176	175.6	12.3	236	235.4	16.5	296	295.3	20.6
57	56.9	4.0	117	116.7	8.2	177	176.6	12.3	237	236.4	16.5	297	296.3	20.7
58	57.9	4.0	118	117.7	8.2	178	177.6	12.4	238	237.4	16.6	298	297.3	20.8
59	58.9	4.1	119	118.7	8.3	179	178.6	12.5	239	238.4	16.7	299	298.3	20.9
60	59.9	4.2	120	119.7	8.4	180	179.6	12.6	240	239.4	16.7	300	299.3	20.9
Hyp.	Opp.	Adj.	Hyp.	Opp.	Adj.	Hyp.	Opp.	Adj.	Hyp.	Opp.	Adj.	Hyp.	Opp.	Adj.
Dist.	Dep.	D. Lat.	Dist.	Dep.	D. Lat.	Dist.	Dep.	D. Lat.	Dist.	Dep.	D. Lat.	Dist.	Dep.	D. Lat.
D Lon		Dep	D Lon		Dep	D Lon		Dep	D Lon		Dep	D Lon		Dep

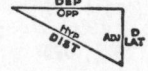

Table 3

TRAVERSE TABLE

4°

356° | 004°

184° | 176°

4°

D Lon Dep Dist. D. Lat. Dep.			D Lon Dep Dist. D. Lat. Dep.			D Lon Dep Dist. D. Lat. Dep.			D Lon Dep Dist. D. Lat. Dep.			D Lon Dep Dist. D. Lat. Dep.		
Hyp.	Adj.	Opp.	Hyp.	Adj.	Opp.	Hyp.	Adj.	Opp.	Hyp.	Adj.	Opp.	Hyp.	Adj.	Opp.
301	300.3	21.0	361	360.1	25.2	421	420.0	29.4	481	479.8	33.6	541	539.7	37.7
302	301.3	21.1	362	361.1	25.3	422	421.0	29.4	482	480.8	33.6	542	540.7	37.8
303	302.3	21.1	363	362.1	25.3	423	422.0	29.5	483	481.8	33.7	543	541.7	37.9
304	303.3	21.2	364	363.1	25.4	424	423.0	29.6	484	482.8	33.7	544	542.7	37.9
305	304.3	21.3	365	364.1	25.5	425	424.0	29.6	485	483.8	33.8	545	543.7	38.0
306	305.3	21.3	366	365.1	25.5	426	425.0	29.7	486	484.8	33.9	546	544.7	38.1
307	306.3	21.4	367	366.1	25.6	427	426.0	29.8	487	485.8	34.0	547	545.7	38.2
308	307.2	21.5	368	367.1	25.7	428	427.0	29.9	488	486.8	34.0	548	546.7	38.2
309	308.2	21.6	369	368.1	25.7	429	428.0	29.9	489	487.8	34.1	549	547.7	38.3
310	309.2	21.6	370	369.1	25.8	430	429.0	30.0	490	488.8	34.2	550	548.7	38.4
311	310.2	21.7	371	370.1	25.9	431	430.0	30.1	491	489.8	34.3	551	549.7	38.4
312	311.2	21.8	372	371.1	25.9	432	430.9	30.1	492	490.8	34.3	552	550.7	38.5
313	312.2	21.8	373	372.1	26.0	433	431.9	30.2	493	491.8	34.4	553	551.7	38.6
314	313.2	21.9	374	373.1	26.1	434	432.9	30.3	494	492.8	34.5	554	552.7	38.6
315	314.2	22.0	375	374.1	26.2	435	433.9	30.3	495	493.8	34.5	555	553.6	38.7
316	315.2	22.0	376	375.1	26.2	436	434.9	30.4	496	494.8	34.6	556	554.6	38.8
317	316.2	22.1	377	376.1	26.3	437	435.9	30.5	497	495.8	34.7	557	555.6	38.9
318	317.2	22.2	378	377.1	26.4	438	436.9	30.6	498	496.8	34.7	558	556.6	38.9
319	318.2	22.3	379	378.1	26.4	439	437.9	30.6	499	497.8	34.8	559	557.6	39.0
320	319.2	22.3	380	379.1	26.5	440	438.9	30.7	500	498.8	34.9	560	558.6	39.1
321	320.2	22.4	381	380.1	26.6	441	439.9	30.8	501	499.8	34.9	561	559.6	39.1
322	321.2	22.5	382	381.1	26.6	442	440.9	30.8	502	500.8	35.0	562	560.6	39.2
323	322.2	22.5	383	382.1	26.7	443	441.9	30.9	503	501.8	35.1	563	561.6	39.3
324	323.2	22.6	384	383.1	26.8	444	442.9	31.0	504	502.8	35.2	564	562.6	39.3
325	324.2	22.7	385	384.1	26.9	445	443.9	31.0	505	503.8	35.2	565	563.6	39.4
326	325.2	22.7	386	385.1	26.9	446	444.9	31.1	506	504.8	35.3	566	564.6	39.5
327	326.2	22.8	387	386.1	27.0	447	445.9	31.2	507	505.8	35.4	567	565.6	39.6
328	327.2	22.9	388	387.1	27.1	448	446.9	31.3	508	506.8	35.4	568	566.6	39.6
329	328.2	22.9	389	388.1	27.1	449	447.9	31.3	509	507.8	35.5	569	567.6	39.7
330	329.2	23.0	390	389.0	27.2	450	448.9	31.4	510	508.8	35.6	570	568.6	39.8
331	330.2	23.1	391	390.0	27.3	451	449.9	31.5	511	509.8	35.6	571	569.6	39.8
332	331.2	23.2	392	391.0	27.3	452	450.9	31.5	512	510.8	35.7	572	570.6	39.9
333	332.2	23.2	393	392.0	27.4	453	451.9	31.6	513	511.8	35.8	573	571.6	40.0
334	333.2	23.3	394	393.0	27.5	454	452.9	31.7	514	512.7	35.9	574	572.6	40.0
335	334.2	23.4	395	394.0	27.6	455	453.9	31.7	515	513.7	35.9	575	573.6	40.1
336	335.2	23.4	396	395.0	27.6	456	454.9	31.8	516	514.7	36.0	576	574.6	40.2
337	336.2	23.5	397	396.0	27.7	457	455.9	31.9	517	515.7	36.1	577	575.6	40.2
338	337.2	23.6	398	397.0	27.8	458	456.9	31.9	518	516.7	36.1	578	576.6	40.3
339	338.2	23.6	399	398.0	27.8	459	457.9	32.0	519	517.7	36.2	579	577.6	40.4
340	339.2	23.7	400	399.0	27.9	460	458.9	32.1	520	518.7	36.3	580	578.6	40.5
341	340.2	23.8	401	400.0	28.0	461	459.9	32.2	521	519.7	36.3	581	579.6	40.5
342	341.2	23.9	402	401.0	28.0	462	460.9	32.2	522	520.7	36.4	582	580.6	40.6
343	342.2	23.9	403	402.0	28.1	463	461.9	32.3	523	521.7	36.5	583	581.6	40.7
344	343.2	24.0	404	403.0	28.2	464	462.9	32.4	524	522.7	36.6	584	582.6	40.7
345	344.2	24.1	405	404.0	28.3	465	463.9	32.4	525	523.7	36.6	585	583.6	40.8
346	345.2	24.1	406	405.0	28.3	466	464.9	32.5	526	524.7	36.7	586	584.6	40.9
347	346.2	24.2	407	406.0	28.4	467	465.9	32.6	527	525.7	36.8	587	585.6	40.9
348	347.2	24.3	408	407.0	28.5	468	466.9	32.6	528	526.7	36.8	588	586.6	41.0
349	348.1	24.3	409	408.0	28.5	469	467.9	32.7	529	527.7	36.9	589	587.6	41.1
350	349.1	24.4	410	409.0	28.6	470	468.9	32.8	530	528.7	37.0	590	588.6	41.2
351	350.1	24.5	411	410.0	28.7	471	469.9	32.9	531	529.7	37.0	591	589.6	41.2
352	351.1	24.6	412	411.0	28.7	472	470.9	32.9	532	530.7	37.1	592	590.6	41.3
353	352.1	24.6	413	412.0	28.8	473	471.8	33.0	533	531.7	37.2	593	591.6	41.4
354	353.1	24.7	414	413.0	28.9	474	472.8	33.1	534	532.7	37.2	594	592.6	41.4
355	354.1	24.8	415	414.0	28.9	475	473.8	33.1	535	533.7	37.3	595	593.6	41.5
356	355.1	24.8	416	415.0	29.0	476	474.8	33.2	536	534.7	37.4	596	594.5	41.6
357	356.1	24.9	417	416.0	29.1	477	475.8	33.3	537	535.7	37.5	597	595.5	41.6
358	357.1	25.0	418	417.0	29.2	478	476.8	33.3	538	536.7	37.5	598	596.5	41.7
359	358.1	25.0	419	418.0	29.2	479	477.8	33.4	539	537.7	37.6	599	597.5	41.8
360	359.1	25.1	420	419.0	29.3	480	478.8	33.5	540	538.7	37.7	600	598.5	41.9
Hyp.	Opp.	Adj.	Hyp.	Opp.	Adj.	Hyp.	Opp.	Adj.	Hyp.	Opp.	Adj.	Hyp.	Opp.	Adj.
Dist.	Dep.	D. Lat.	Dist.	Dep.	D. Lat.	Dist.	Dep.	D. Lat.	Dist.	Dep.	D. Lat.	Dist.	Dep.	D. Lat.
D Lon		Dep	D Lon		Dep	D Lon		Dep	D Lon		Dep	D Lon		Dep

86°

274° | 086°

266° | 094°

86°

Table 3

TRAVERSE TABLE

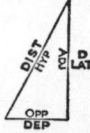

5°   5°

D Lon	Dep		D Lon	Dep		D Lon	Dep		D Lon	Dep		D Lon	Dep	
Dist.	D. Lat.	Dep.	Dist.	D. Lat.	Dep.	Dist.	D. Lat.	Dep.	Dist.	D. Lat.	Dep.	Dist.	D. Lat.	Dep.
Hyp.	Adj.	Opp.	Hyp.	Adj.	Opp.	Hyp.	Adj.	Opp.	Hyp.	Adj.	Opp.	Hyp.	Adj.	Opp.
1	1.0	0.1	61	60.8	5.3	121	120.5	10.5	181	180.3	15.8	241	240.1	21.0
2	2.0	0.2	62	61.8	5.4	122	121.5	10.6	182	181.3	15.9	242	241.1	21.1
3	3.0	0.3	63	62.8	5.5	123	122.5	10.7	183	182.3	15.9	243	242.1	21.2
4	4.0	0.3	64	63.8	5.6	124	123.5	10.8	184	183.3	16.0	244	243.1	21.3
5	5.0	0.4	65	64.8	5.7	125	124.5	10.9	185	184.3	16.1	245	244.1	21.4
6	6.0	0.5	66	65.7	5.8	126	125.5	11.0	186	185.3	16.2	246	245.1	21.4
7	7.0	0.6	67	66.7	5.8	127	126.5	11.1	187	186.3	16.3	247	246.1	21.5
8	8.0	0.7	68	67.7	5.9	128	127.5	11.2	188	187.3	16.4	248	247.1	21.6
9	9.0	0.8	69	68.7	6.0	129	128.5	11.2	189	188.3	16.5	249	248.1	21.7
10	10.0	0.9	70	69.7	6.1	130	129.5	11.3	190	189.3	16.6	250	249.0	21.8
11	11.0	1.0	71	70.7	6.2	131	130.5	11.4	191	190.3	16.6	251	250.0	21.9
12	12.0	1.0	72	71.7	6.3	132	131.5	11.5	192	191.3	16.7	252	251.0	22.0
13	13.0	1.1	73	72.7	6.4	133	132.5	11.6	193	192.3	16.8	253	252.0	22.1
14	13.9	1.2	74	73.7	6.4	134	133.5	11.7	194	193.3	16.9	254	253.0	22.1
15	14.9	1.3	75	74.7	6.5	135	134.5	11.8	195	194.3	17.0	255	254.0	22.2
16	15.9	1.4	76	75.7	6.6	136	135.5	11.9	196	195.3	17.1	256	255.0	22.3
17	16.9	1.5	77	76.7	6.7	137	136.5	11.9	197	196.3	17.2	257	256.0	22.4
18	17.9	1.6	78	77.7	6.8	138	137.5	12.0	198	197.2	17.3	258	257.0	22.5
19	18.9	1.7	79	78.7	6.9	139	138.5	12.1	199	198.2	17.3	259	258.0	22.6
20	19.9	1.7	80	79.7	7.0	140	139.5	12.2	200	199.2	17.4	260	259.0	22.7
21	20.9	1.8	81	80.7	7.1	141	140.5	12.3	201	200.2	17.5	261	260.0	22.7
22	21.9	1.9	82	81.7	7.1	142	141.5	12.4	202	201.2	17.6	262	261.0	22.8
23	22.9	2.0	83	82.7	7.2	143	142.5	12.5	203	202.2	17.7	263	262.0	22.9
24	23.9	2.1	84	83.7	7.3	144	143.5	12.6	204	203.2	17.8	264	263.0	23.0
25	24.9	2.2	85	84.7	7.4	145	144.4	12.6	205	204.2	17.9	265	264.0	23.1
26	25.9	2.3	86	85.7	7.5	146	145.4	12.7	206	205.2	18.0	266	265.0	23.2
27	26.9	2.4	87	86.7	7.6	147	146.4	12.8	207	206.2	18.0	267	266.0	23.3
28	27.9	2.4	88	87.7	7.7	148	147.4	12.9	208	207.2	18.1	268	267.0	23.4
29	28.9	2.5	89	88.7	7.8	149	148.4	13.0	209	208.2	18.2	269	268.0	23.4
30	29.9	2.6	90	89.7	7.8	150	149.4	13.1	210	209.2	18.3	270	269.0	23.5
31	30.9	2.7	91	90.7	7.9	151	150.4	13.2	211	210.2	18.4	271	270.0	23.6
32	31.9	2.8	92	91.6	8.0	152	151.4	13.2	212	211.2	18.5	272	271.0	23.7
33	32.9	2.9	93	92.6	8.1	153	152.4	13.3	213	212.2	18.6	273	272.0	23.8
34	33.9	3.0	94	93.6	8.2	154	153.4	13.4	214	213.2	18.7	274	273.0	23.9
35	34.9	3.1	95	94.6	8.3	155	154.4	13.5	215	214.2	18.7	275	274.0	24.0
36	35.9	3.1	96	95.6	8.4	156	155.4	13.6	216	215.2	18.8	276	274.9	24.1
37	36.9	3.2	97	96.6	8.5	157	156.4	13.7	217	216.2	18.9	277	275.9	24.1
38	37.9	3.3	98	97.6	8.5	158	157.4	13.8	218	217.2	19.0	278	276.9	24.2
39	38.9	3.4	99	98.6	8.6	159	158.4	13.9	219	218.2	19.1	279	277.9	24.3
40	39.8	3.5	100	99.6	8.7	160	159.4	13.9	220	219.2	19.2	280	278.9	24.4
41	40.8	3.6	101	100.6	8.8	161	160.4	14.0	221	220.2	19.3	281	279.9	24.5
42	41.8	3.7	102	101.6	8.9	162	161.4	14.1	222	221.2	19.3	282	280.9	24.6
43	42.8	3.7	103	102.6	9.0	163	162.4	14.2	223	222.2	19.4	283	281.9	24.7
44	43.8	3.8	104	103.6	9.1	164	163.4	14.3	224	223.1	19.5	284	282.9	24.8
45	44.8	3.9	105	104.6	9.2	165	164.4	14.4	225	224.1	19.6	285	283.9	24.8
46	45.8	4.0	106	105.6	9.2	166	165.4	14.5	226	225.1	19.7	286	284.9	24.9
47	46.8	4.1	107	106.6	9.3	167	166.4	14.6	227	226.1	19.8	287	285.9	25.0
48	47.8	4.2	108	107.6	9.4	168	167.4	14.6	228	227.1	19.9	288	286.9	25.1
49	48.8	4.3	109	108.6	9.5	169	168.4	14.7	229	228.1	20.0	289	287.9	25.2
50	49.8	4.4	110	109.6	9.6	170	169.4	14.8	230	229.1	20.0	290	288.9	25.3
51	50.8	4.4	111	110.6	9.7	171	170.3	14.9	231	230.1	20.1	291	289.9	25.4
52	51.8	4.5	112	111.6	9.8	172	171.3	15.0	232	231.1	20.2	292	290.9	25.4
53	52.8	4.6	113	112.6	9.8	173	172.3	15.1	233	232.1	20.3	293	291.9	25.5
54	53.8	4.7	114	113.6	9.9	174	173.3	15.2	234	233.1	20.4	294	292.9	25.6
55	54.8	4.8	115	114.6	10.0	175	174.3	15.3	235	234.1	20.5	295	293.9	25.7
56	55.8	4.9	116	115.6	10.1	176	175.3	15.3	236	235.1	20.6	296	294.9	25.8
57	56.8	5.0	117	116.6	10.2	177	176.3	15.4	237	236.1	20.7	297	295.9	25.9
58	57.8	5.1	118	117.6	10.3	178	177.3	15.5	238	237.1	20.7	298	296.9	26.0
59	58.8	5.1	119	118.5	10.4	179	178.3	15.6	239	238.1	20.8	299	297.9	26.1
60	59.8	5.2	120	119.5	10.5	180	179.3	15.7	240	239.1	20.9	300	298.9	26.1
Hyp.	Opp.	Adj.	Hyp.	Opp.	Adj.	Hyp.	Opp.	Adj.	Hyp.	Opp.	Adj.	Hyp.	Opp.	Adj.
Dist.	Dep.	D. Lat.	Dist.	Dep.	D. Lat.	Dist.	Dep.	D. Lat.	Dist.	Dep.	D. Lat.	Dist.	Dep.	D. Lat.
D Lon		Dep	D Lon		Dep	D Lon		Dep	D Lon		Dep	D Lon		Dep

85°   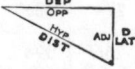   85°

Table 3

TRAVERSE TABLE

D Lon Dist.	Dep D. Lat.	Dep.	D Lon Dist.	Dep D. Lat.	Dep.	D Lon Dist.	Dep D. Lat.	Dep.	D Lon Dist.	Dep D. Lat.	Dep.	D Lon Dist.	Dep D. Lat.	Dep.
Hyp.	Adj.	Opp.	Hyp.	Adj.	Opp.	Hyp.	Adj.	Opp.	Hyp.	Adj.	Opp.	Hyp.	Adj.	Opp.
301	299.9	26.2	361	359.6	31.5	421	419.4	36.7	481	479.2	41.9	541	538.9	47.2
302	300.9	26.3	362	360.6	31.6	422	420.4	36.8	482	480.2	42.0	542	539.9	47.2
303	301.8	26.4	363	361.6	31.6	423	421.4	36.9	483	481.2	42.1	543	540.9	47.3
304	302.8	26.5	364	362.6	31.7	424	422.4	37.0	484	482.2	42.2	544	541.9	47.4
305	303.8	26.6	365	363.6	31.8	425	423.4	37.0	485	483.2	42.3	545	542.9	47.5
306	304.8	26.7	366	364.6	31.9	426	424.4	37.1	486	484.2	42.4	546	543.9	47.6
307	305.8	26.8	367	365.6	32.0	427	425.4	37.2	487	485.1	42.4	547	544.9	47.7
308	306.8	26.8	368	366.6	32.1	428	426.4	37.3	488	486.1	42.5	548	545.9	47.8
309	307.8	26.9	369	367.6	32.2	429	427.4	37.4	489	487.1	42.6	549	546.9	47.8
310	308.8	27.0	370	368.6	32.2	430	428.4	37.5	490	488.1	42.7	550	547.9	47.9
311	309.8	27.1	371	369.6	32.3	431	429.4	37.6	491	489.1	42.8	551	548.9	48.0
312	310.8	27.2	372	370.6	32.4	432	430.4	37.7	492	490.1	42.9	552	549.9	48.1
313	311.8	27.3	373	371.6	32.5	433	431.4	37.7	493	491.1	43.0	553	550.9	48.2
314	312.8	27.4	374	372.6	32.6	434	432.3	37.8	494	492.1	43.1	554	551.9	48.3
315	313.8	27.5	375	373.6	32.7	435	433.3	37.9	495	493.1	43.1	555	552.9	48.4
316	314.8	27.5	376	374.6	32.8	436	434.3	38.0	496	494.1	43.2	556	553.9	48.5
317	315.8	27.6	377	375.6	32.9	437	435.3	38.1	497	495.1	43.3	557	554.9	48.5
318	316.8	27.7	378	376.6	33.0	438	436.3	38.2	498	496.1	43.4	558	555.9	48.6
319	317.8	27.8	379	377.6	33.0	439	437.3	38.3	499	497.1	43.5	559	556.9	48.7
320	318.8	27.9	380	378.6	33.1	440	438.3	38.3	500	498.1	43.6	560	557.9	48.8
321	319.8	28.0	381	379.6	33.2	441	439.3	38.4	501	499.1	43.7	561	558.9	48.9
322	320.8	28.1	382	380.5	33.3	442	440.3	38.5	502	500.1	43.8	562	559.9	49.0
323	321.8	28.2	383	381.5	33.4	443	441.3	38.6	503	501.1	43.8	563	560.9	49.1
324	322.8	28.2	384	382.5	33.5	444	442.3	38.7	504	502.1	43.9	564	561.9	49.2
325	323.8	28.3	385	383.5	33.6	445	443.3	38.8	505	503.1	44.0	565	562.9	49.3
326	324.8	28.4	386	384.5	33.6	446	444.3	38.9	506	504.1	44.1	566	563.8	49.3
327	325.8	28.5	387	385.5	33.7	447	445.3	39.0	507	505.1	44.2	567	564.8	49.4
328	326.8	28.6	388	386.5	33.8	448	446.3	39.0	508	506.1	44.3	568	565.8	49.5
329	327.7	28.7	389	387.5	33.9	449	447.3	39.1	509	507.1	44.4	569	566.8	49.6
330	328.7	28.8	390	388.5	34.0	450	448.3	39.2	510	508.1	44.4	570	567.8	49.7
331	329.7	28.8	391	389.5	34.1	451	449.3	39.3	511	509.1	44.5	571	568.8	49.8
332	330.7	28.9	392	390.5	34.2	452	450.3	39.4	512	510.1	44.6	572	569.8	49.9
333	331.7	29.0	393	391.5	34.3	453	451.3	39.5	513	511.0	44.7	573	570.8	49.9
334	332.7	29.1	394	392.5	34.3	454	452.3	39.6	514	512.0	44.8	574	571.8	50.0
335	333.7	29.2	395	393.5	34.4	455	453.3	39.7	515	513.0	44.9	575	572.8	50.1
336	334.7	29.3	396	394.5	34.5	456	454.3	39.7	516	514.0	45.0	576	573.8	50·2
337	335.7	29.4	397	395.5	34.6	457	455.3	39.8	517	515.0	45.1	577	574.8	50.3
338	336.7	29.5	398	396.5	34.7	458	456.3	39.9	518	516.0	45.1	578	575.8	50.4
339	337.7	29.5	399	397.5	34.8	459	457.3	40.0	519	517.0	45.2	579	576.8	50.5
340	338.7	29.6	400	398.5	34.9	460	458.2	40.1	520	518.0	45.3	580	577.8	50.6
341	339.7	29.7	401	399.5	34.9	461	459.2	40.2	521	519.0	45.4	581	578.8	50.6
342	340.7	29.8	402	400.5	35.0	462	460.2	40.3	522	520.0	45.5	582	579.8	50.7
343	341.7	29.9	403	401.5	35.1	463	461.2	40.4	523	521.0	45.6	583	580.8	50.8
344	342.7	30.0	404	402.5	35.2	464	462.2	40.4	524	522.0	45.7	584	581.8	50.9
345	343.7	30.1	405	403.5	35.3	465	463.2	40.5	525	523.0	45.8	585	582.8	51.0
346	344.7	30.2	406	404.5	35.4	466	464.2	40.6	526	524.0	45.8	586	583.8	51.1
347	345.7	30.2	407	405.5	35.5	467	465.2	40.7	527	525.0	45.9	587	584.8	51.2
348	346.7	30.3	408	406.4	35.6	468	466.2	40.8	528	526.0	46.0	588	585.8	51.2
349	347.7	30.4	409	407.4	35.6	469	467.2	40.9	529	527.0	46.1	589	586.8	51.3
350	348.7	30.5	410	408.4	35.7	470	468.2	41.0	530	528.0	46.2	590	587.8	51.4
351	349.7	30.6	411	409.4	35.8	471	469.2	41.1	531	529.0	46.3	591	588.8	51.5
352	350.7	30.7	412	410.4	35.9	472	470.2	41.1	532	530.0	46.4	592	589.7	51.6
353	351.7	30.8	413	411.4	36.0	473	471.2	41.2	533	531.0	46.5	593	590.7	51.7
354	352.7	30.9	414	412.4	36.1	474	472.2	41.3	534	532.0	46.5	594	591.7	51.8
355	353.6	30.9	415	413.4	36.2	475	473.2	41.4	535	533.0	46.6	595	592.7	51.9
356	354.6	31.0	416	414.4	36.3	476	474.2	41.5	536	534.0	46.7	596	593.7	51.9
357	355.6	31.1	417	415.4	36.3	477	475.2	41.6	537	535.0	46.8	597	594.7	52.0
358	356.6	31.2	418	416.4	36.4	478	476.2	41.7	538	536.0	46.9	598	595.7	52.1
359	357.6	31.3	419	417.4	36.5	479	477.2	41.7	539	536.9	47.0	599	596.7	52.2
360	358.6	31.4	420	418.4	36.6	480	478.2	41.8	540	537.9	47.1	600	597.7	52.3
Hyp.	Opp.	Adj.	Hyp.	Opp.	Adj.	Hyp.	Opp.	Adj.	Hyp.	Opp.	Adj.	Hyp.	Opp.	Adj.
Dist. D Lon	Dep.	D. Lat. Dep	Dist. D Lon	Dep.	D. Lat. Dep	Dist. D Lon	Dep.	D. Lat. Dep	Dist. D Lon	Dep.	D. Lat. Dep	Dist. D Lon	Dep.	D. Lat. Dep

Table 3

TRAVERSE TABLE

6°   6°

D Lon Dist.	Dep D. Lat.	Dep.	D Lon Dist.	Dep D. Lat.	Dep.	D Lon Dist.	Dep D. Lat.	Dep.	D Lon Dist.	Dep D. Lat.	Dep.	D Lon Dist.	Dep D. Lat.	Dep.
Hyp.	Adj.	Opp.	Hyp.	Adj.	Opp.	Hyp.	Adj.	Opp.	Hyp.	Adj.	Opp.	Hyp.	Adj.	Opp.
1	1.0	0.1	61	60.7	6.4	121	120.3	12.6	181	180.0	18.9	241	239.7	25.2
2	2.0	0.2	62	61.7	6.5	122	121.3	12.8	182	181.0	19.0	242	240.7	25.3
3	3.0	0.3	63	62.7	6.6	123	122.3	12.9	183	182.0	19.1	243	241.7	25.4
4	4.0	0.4	64	63.6	6.7	124	123.3	13.0	184	183.0	19.2	244	242.7	25.5
5	5.0	0.5	65	64.6	6.8	125	124.3	13.1	185	184.0	19.3	245	243.7	25.6
6	6.0	0.6	66	65.6	6.9	126	125.3	13.2	186	185.0	19.4	246	244.7	25.7
7	7.0	0.7	67	66.6	7.0	127	126.3	13.3	187	186.0	19.5	247	245.6	25.8
8	8.0	0.8	68	67.6	7.1	128	127.3	13.4	188	187.0	19.7	248	246.6	25.9
9	9.0	0.9	69	68.6	7.2	129	128.3	13.5	189	188.0	19.8	249	247.6	26.0
10	9.9	1.0	70	69.6	7.3	130	129.3	13.6	190	189.0	19.9	250	248.6	26.1
11	10.9	1.1	71	70.6	7.4	131	130.3	13.7	191	190.0	20.0	251	249.6	26.2
12	11.9	1.3	72	71.6	7.5	132	131.3	13.8	192	190.9	20.1	252	250.6	26.3
13	12.9	1.4	73	72.6	7.6	133	132.3	13.9	193	191.9	20.2	253	251.6	26.4
14	13.9	1.5	74	73.6	7.7	134	133.3	14.0	194	192.9	20.3	254	252.6	26.5
15	14.9	1.6	75	74.6	7.8	135	134.3	14.1	195	193.9	20.4	255	253.6	26.7
16	15.9	1.7	76	75.6	7.9	136	135.3	14.2	196	194.9	20.5	256	254.6	26.8
17	16.9	1.8	77	76.6	8.0	137	136.2	14.3	197	195.9	20.6	257	255.6	26.9
18	17.9	1.9	78	77.6	8.2	138	137.2	14.4	198	196.9	20.7	258	256.6	27.0
19	18.9	2.0	79	78.6	8.3	139	138.2	14.5	199	197.9	20.8	259	257.6	27.1
20	19.9	2.1	80	79.6	8.4	140	139.2	14.6	200	198.9	20.9	260	258.6	27.2
21	20.9	2.2	81	80.6	8.5	141	140.2	14.7	201	199.9	21.0	261	259.6	27.3
22	21.9	2.3	82	81.6	8.6	142	141.2	14.8	202	200.9	21.1	262	260.6	27.4
23	22.9	2.4	83	82.5	8.7	143	142.2	14.9	203	201.9	21.2	263	261.6	27.5
24	23.9	2.5	84	83.5	8.8	144	143.2	15.1	204	202.9	21.3	264	262.6	27.6
25	24.9	2.6	85	84.5	8.9	145	144.2	15.2	205	203.9	21.4	265	263.5	27.7
26	25.9	2.7	86	85.5	9.0	146	145.2	15.3	206	204.9	21.5	266	264.5	27.8
27	26.9	2.8	87	86.5	9.1	147	146.2	15.4	207	205.9	21.6	267	265.5	27.9
28	27.8	2.9	88	87.5	9.2	148	147.2	15.5	208	206.9	21.7	268	266.5	28.0
29	28.8	3.0	89	88.5	9.3	149	148.2	15.6	209	207.9	21.8	269	267.5	28.1
30	29.8	3.1	90	89.5	9.4	150	149.2	15.7	210	208.8	22.0	270	268.5	28.2
31	30.8	3.2	91	90.5	9.5	151	150.2	15.8	211	209.8	22.1	271	269.5	28.3
32	31.8	3.3	92	91.5	9.6	152	151.2	15.9	212	210.8	22.2	272	270.5	28.4
33	32.8	3.4	93	92.5	9.7	153	152.2	16.0	213	211.8	22.3	273	271.5	28.5
34	33.8	3.6	94	93.5	9.8	154	153.2	16.1	214	212.8	22.4	274	272.5	28.6
35	34.8	3.7	95	94.5	9.9	155	154.2	16.2	215	213.8	22.5	275	273.5	28.7
36	35.8	3.8	96	95.5	10.0	156	155.1	16.3	216	214.8	22.6	276	274.5	28.8
37	36.8	3.9	97	96.5	10.1	157	156.1	16.4	217	215.8	22.7	277	275.5	29.0
38	37.8	4.0	98	97.5	10.2	158	157.1	16.5	218	216.8	22.8	278	276.5	29.1
39	38.8	4.1	99	98.5	10.3	159	158.1	16.6	219	217.8	22.9	279	277.5	29.2
40	39.8	4.2	100	99.5	10.5	160	159.1	16.7	220	218.8	23.0	280	278.5	29.3
41	40.8	4.3	101	100.4	10.6	161	160.1	16.8	221	219.8	23.1	281	279.5	29.4
42	41.8	4.4	102	101.4	10.7	162	161.1	16.9	222	220.8	23.2	282	280.5	29.5
43	42.8	4.5	103	102.4	10.8	163	162.1	17.0	223	221.8	23.3	283	281.4	29.6
44	43.8	4.6	104	103.4	10.9	164	163.1	17.1	224	222.8	23.4	284	282.4	29.7
45	44.8	4.7	105	104.4	11.0	165	164.1	17.2	225	223.8	23.5	285	283.4	29.8
46	45.7	4.8	106	105.4	11.1	166	165.1	17.4	226	224.8	23.6	286	284.4	29.9
47	46.7	4.9	107	106.4	11.2	167	166.1	17.5	227	225.8	23.7	287	285.4	30.0
48	47.7	5.0	108	107.4	11.3	168	167.1	17.6	228	226.8	23.8	288	286.4	30.1
49	48.7	5.1	109	108.4	11.4	169	168.1	17.7	229	227.7	23.9	289	287.4	30.2
50	49.7	5.2	110	109.4	11.5	170	169.1	17.8	230	228.7	24.0	290	288.4	30.3
51	50.7	5.3	111	110.4	11.6	171	170.1	17.9	231	229.7	24.1	291	289.4	30.4
52	51.7	5.4	112	111.4	11.7	172	171.1	18.0	232	230.7	24.3	292	290.4	30.5
53	52.7	5.5	113	112.4	11.8	173	172.1	18.1	233	231.7	24.4	293	291.4	30.6
54	53.7	5.6	114	113.4	11.9	174	173.0	18.2	234	232.7	24.5	294	292.4	30.7
55	54.7	5.7	115	114.4	12.0	175	174.0	18.3	235	233.7	24.6	295	293.4	30.8
56	55.7	5.9	116	115.4	12.1	176	175.0	18.4	236	234.7	24.7	296	294.4	30.9
57	56.7	6.0	117	116.4	12.2	177	176.0	18.5	237	235.7	24.8	297	295.4	31.0
58	57.7	6.1	118	117.4	12.3	178	177.0	18.6	238	236.7	24.9	298	296.4	31.1
59	58.7	6.2	119	118.3	12.4	179	178.0	18.7	239	237.7	25.0	299	297.4	31.3
60	59.7	6.3	120	119.3	12.5	180	179.0	18.8	240	238.7	25.1	300	298.4	31.4
Hyp.	Opp.	Adj.	Hyp.	Opp.	Adj.	Hyp.	Opp.	Adj.	Hyp.	Opp.	Adj.	Hyp.	Opp.	Adj.

Dist. D Lon	ep D. Lat. Dep		Dist. D Lon	Dep D. Lat. Dep		Dist. D Lon	Dep D. Lat. Dep		Dist. D Lon	Dep D. Lat. Dep		Dist. D Lon	Dep D. Lat. Dep	

84°   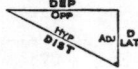   84°

Table 3

TRAVERSE TABLE

D Lon	Dep		D Lon	Dep		D Lon	Dep		D Lon	Dep		D Lon	Dep	
Dist.	D. Lat.	Dep.	Dist.	D. Lat.	Dep.	Dist.	D. Lat.	Dep.	Dist.	D. Lat.	Dep.	Dist.	D. Lat.	Dep.
Hyp.	Adj.	Opp.	Hyp.	Adj.	Opp.	Hyp.	Adj.	Opp.	Hyp.	Adj.	Opp.	Hyp.	Adj.	Opp.
301	299.4	31.5	361	359.0	37.7	421	418.7	44.0	481	478.4	50.3	541	538.0	56.5
302	300.3	31.6	362	360.0	37.8	422	419.7	44.1	482	479.4	50.4	542	539.0	56.7
303	301.3	31.7	363	361.0	37.9	423	420.7	44.2	483	480.4	50.5	543	540.0	56.8
304	302.3	31.8	364	362.0	38.0	424	421.7	44.3	484	481.3	50.6	544	541.0	56.9
305	303.3	31.9	365	363.0	38.2	425	422.7	44.4	485	482.3	50.7	545	542.0	57.0
306	304.3	32.0	366	364.0	38.3	426	423.7	44.5	486	483.3	50.8	546	543.0	57.1
307	305.3	32.1	367	365.0	38.4	427	424.7	44.6	487	484.3	50.9	547	544.0	57.2
308	306.3	32.2	368	366.0	38.5	428	425.7	44.7	488	485.3	51.0	548	545.0	57.3
309	307.3	32.3	369	367.0	38.6	429	426.6	44.8	489	486.3	51.1	549	546.0	57.4
310	308.3	32.4	370	368.0	38.7	430	427.6	44.9	490	487.3	51.2	550	547.0	57.5
311	309.3	32.5	371	369.0	38.8	431	428.6	45.1	491	488.3	51.3	551	548.0	57.6
312	310.3	32.6	372	370.0	38.9	432	429.6	45.2	492	489.3	51.4	552	549.0	57.7
313	311.3	32.7	373	371.0	39.0	433	430.6	45.3	493	490.3	51.5	553	550.0	57.8
314	312.3	32.8	374	372.0	39.1	434	431.6	45.4	494	491.3	51.6	554	551.0	57.9
315	313.3	32.9	375	372.9	39.2	435	432.6	45.5	495	492.3	51.7	555	552.0	58.0
316	314.3	33.0	376	373.9	39.3	436	433.6	45.6	496	493.3	51.8	556	553.0	58.1
317	315.3	33.1	377	374.9	39.4	437	434.6	45.7	497	494.3	52.0	557	553.9	58.2
318	316.3	33.2	378	375.9	39.5	438	435.6	45.8	498	495.3	52.1	558	554.9	58.3
319	317.3	33.3	379	376.9	39.6	439	436.6	45.9	499	496.3	52.2	559	555.9	58.4
320	318.2	33.4	380	377.9	39.7	440	437.6	46.0	500	497.3	52.3	560	556.9	58.5
321	319.2	33.6	381	378.9	39.8	441	438.6	46.1	501	498.3	52.4	561	557.9	58.6
322	320.2	33.7	382	379.9	39.9	442	439.6	46.2	502	499.2	52.5	562	558.9	58.7
323	321.2	33.8	383	380.9	40.0	443	440.6	46.3	503	500.2	52.6	563	559.9	58.8
324	322.2	33.9	384	381.9	40.1	444	441.6	46.4	504	501.2	52.7	564	560.9	59.0
325	323.2	34.0	385	382.9	40.2	445	442.6	46.5	505	502.2	52.8	565	561.9	59.1
326	324.2	34.1	386	383.9	40.3	446	443.6	46.6	506	503.2	52.9	566	562.9	59.2
327	325.2	34.2	387	384.9	40.5	447	444.6	46.7	507	504.2	53.0	567	563.9	59.3
328	326.2	34.3	388	385.9	40.6	448	445.5	46.8	508	505.2	53.1	568	564.9	59.4
329	327.2	34.4	389	386.9	40.7	449	446.5	46.9	509	506.2	53.2	569	565.9	59.5
330	328.2	34.5	390	387.9	40.8	450	447.5	47.0	510	507.2	53.3	570	566.9	59.6
331	329.2	34.6	391	388.9	40.9	451	448.5	47.1	511	508.2	53.4	571	567.9	59.7
332	330.2	34.7	392	389.9	41.0	452	449.5	47.2	512	509.2	53.5	572	568.9	59.8
333	331.2	34.8	393	390.8	41.1	453	450.5	47.4	513	510.2	53.6	573	569.9	59.9
334	332.2	34.9	394	391.8	41.2	454	451.5	47.5	514	511.2	53.7	574	570.9	60.0
335	333.2	35.0	395	392.8	41.3	455	452.5	47.6	515	512.2	53.8	575	571.9	60.1
336	334.2	35.1	396	393.8	41.4	456	453.5	47.7	516	513.2	53.9	576	572.8	60.2
337	335.2	35.2	397	394.8	41.5	457	454.5	47.8	517	514.2	54.0	577	573.8	60.3
338	336.1	35.3	398	395.8	41.6	458	455.5	47.9	518	515.2	54.1	578	574.8	60.4
339	337.1	35.4	399	396.8	41.7	459	456.5	48.0	519	516.2	54.3	579	575.8	60.5
340	338.1	35.5	400	397.8	41.8	460	457.5	48.1	520	517.2	54.4	580	576.8	60.6
341	339.1	35.6	401	398.8	41.9	461	458.5	48.2	521	518.1	54.5	581	577.8	60.7
342	340.1	35.7	402	399.8	42.0	462	459.5	48.3	522	519.1	54.6	582	578.8	60.8
343	341.1	35.9	403	400.8	42.1	463	460.5	48.4	523	520.1	54.7	583	579.8	60.9
344	342.1	36.0	404	401.8	42.2	464	461.5	48.5	524	521.1	54.8	584	580.8	61.0
345	343.1	36.1	405	402.8	42.3	465	462.5	48.6	525	522.1	54.9	585	581.8	61.1
346	344.1	36.2	406	403.8	42.4	466	463.4	48.7	526	523.1	55.0	586	582.8	61.3
347	345.1	36.3	407	404.8	42.5	467	464.4	48.8	527	524.1	55.1	587	583.8	61.4
348	346.1	36.4	408	405.8	42.6	468	465.4	48.9	528	525.1	55.2	588	584.8	61.5
349	347.1	36.5	409	406.8	42.8	469	466.4	49.0	529	526.1	55.3	589	585.8	61.6
350	348.1	36.6	410	407.8	42.9	470	467.4	49.1	530	527.1	55.4	590	586.8	61.7
351	349.1	36.7	411	408.7	43.0	471	468.4	49.2	531	528.1	55.5	591	587.8	61.8
352	350.1	36.8	412	409.7	43.1	472	469.4	49.3	532	529.1	55.6	592	588.8	61.9
353	351.1	36.9	413	410.7	43.2	473	470.4	49.4	533	530.1	55.7	593	589.8	62.0
354	352.1	37.0	414	411.7	43.3	474	471.4	49.5	534	531.1	55.8	594	590.7	62.1
355	353.1	37.1	415	412.7	43.4	475	472.4	49.7	535	532.1	55.9	595	591.7	62.2
356	354.0	37.2	416	413.7	43.5	476	473.4	49.8	536	533.1	56.0	596	592.7	62.3
357	355.0	37.3	417	414.7	43.6	477	474.4	49.9	537	534.1	56.1	597	593.7	62.4
358	356.0	37.4	418	415.7	43.7	478	475.4	50.0	538	535.1	56.2	598	594.7	62.5
359	357.0	37.5	419	416.7	43.8	479	476.4	50.1	539	536.0	56.3	599	595.7	62.6
360	358.0	37.6	420	417.7	43.9	480	477.4	50.2	540	537.0	56.4	600	596.7	62.7
Hyp.	Opp.	Adj.	Hyp.	Opp.	Adj.	Hyp.	Opp.	Adj.	Hyp.	Opp.	Adj.	Hyp.	Opp.	Adj.
Dist.	Dep.	D. Lat.	Dist.	Dep.	D. Lat.	Dist.	Dep.	D. Lat.	Dist.	Dep.	D. Lat.	Dist.	Dep.	D. Lat.
D Lon		Dep	D Lon		Dep	D Lon		Dep	D Lon		Dep	D Lon		Dep

Table 3

TRAVERSE TABLE

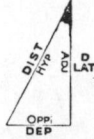

7°   7°

D Lon / Dist.	Dep / D. Lat.	Dep.	D Lon / Dist.	Dep / D. Lat.	Dep.	D Lon / Dist.	Dep / D. Lat.	Dep.	D Lon / Dist.	Dep / D. Lat.	Dep.	D Lon / Dist.	Dep / D. Lat.	Dep.
Hyp.	Adj.	Opp.	Hyp.	Adj.	Opp.	Hyp.	Adj.	Opp.	Hyp.	Adj.	Opp.	Hyp.	Adj.	Opp.
1	1.0	0.1	61	60.5	7.4	121	120.1	14.7	181	179.7	22.1	241	239.2	29.4
2	2.0	0.2	62	61.5	7.6	122	121.1	14.9	182	180.6	22.2	242	240.2	29.5
3	3.0	0.4	63	62.5	7.7	123	122.1	15.0	183	181.6	22.3	243	241.2	29.6
4	4.0	0.5	64	63.5	7.8	124	123.1	15.1	184	182.6	22.4	244	242.2	29.7
5	5.0	0.6	65	64.5	7.9	125	124.1	15.2	185	183.6	22.5	245	243.2	29.9
6	6.0	0.7	66	65.5	8.0	126	125.1	15.4	186	184.6	22.7	246	244.2	30.0
7	6.9	0.9	67	66.5	8.2	127	126.1	15.5	187	185.6	22.8	247	245.2	30.1
8	7.9	1.0	68	67.5	8.3	128	127.0	15.6	188	186.6	22.9	248	246.2	30.2
9	8.9	1.1	69	68.5	8.4	129	128.0	15.7	189	187.6	23.0	249	247.1	30.3
10	9.9	1.2	70	69.5	8.5	130	129.0	15.8	190	188.6	23.2	250	248.1	30.5
11	10.9	1.3	71	70.5	8.7	131	130.0	16.0	191	189.6	23.3	251	249.1	30.6
12	11.9	1.5	72	71.5	8.8	132	131.0	16.1	192	190.6	23.4	252	250.1	30.7
13	12.9	1.6	73	72.5	8.9	133	132.0	16.2	193	191.6	23.5	253	251.1	30.8
14	13.9	1.7	74	73.4	9.0	134	133.0	16.3	194	192.6	23.6	254	252.1	31.0
15	14.9	1.8	75	74.4	9.1	135	134.0	16.5	195	193.5	23.8	255	253.1	31.1
16	15.9	1.9	76	75.4	9.3	136	135.0	16.6	196	194.5	23.9	256	254.1	31.2
17	16.9	2.1	77	76.4	9.4	137	136.0	16.7	197	195.5	24.0	257	255.1	31.3
18	17.9	2.2	78	77.4	9.5	138	137.0	16.8	198	196.5	24.1	258	256.1	31.4
19	18.9	2.3	79	78.4	9.6	139	138.0	16.9	199	197.5	24.3	259	257.1	31.6
20	19.9	2.4	80	79.4	9.7	140	139.0	17.1	200	198.5	24.4	260	258.1	31.7
21	20.8	2.6	81	80.4	9.9	141	139.9	17.2	201	199.5	24.5	261	259.1	31.8
22	21.8	2.7	82	81.4	10.0	142	140.9	17.3	202	200.5	24.6	262	260.0	31.9
23	22.8	2.8	83	82.4	10.1	143	141.9	17.4	203	201.5	24.7	263	261.0	32.1
24	23.8	2.9	84	83.4	10.2	144	142.9	17.5	204	202.5	24.9	264	262.0	32.2
25	24.8	3.0	85	84.4	10.4	145	143.9	17.7	205	203.5	25.0	265	263.0	32.3
26	25.8	3.2	86	85.4	10.5	146	144.9	17.8	206	204.5	25.1	266	264.0	32.4
27	26.8	3.3	87	86.4	10.6	147	145.9	17.9	207	205.5	25.2	267	265.0	32.5
28	27.8	3.4	88	87.3	10.7	148	146.9	18.0	208	206.4	25.3	268	266.0	32.7
29	28.8	3.5	89	88.3	10.8	149	147.9	18.2	209	207.4	25.5	269	267.0	32.8
30	29.8	3.7	90	89.3	11.0	150	148.9	18.3	210	208.4	25.6	270	268.0	32.9
31	30.8	3.8	91	90.3	11.1	151	149.9	18.4	211	209.4	25.7	271	269.0	33.0
32	31.8	3.9	92	91.3	11.2	152	150.9	18.5	212	210.4	25.8	272	270.0	33.1
33	32.8	4.0	93	92.3	11.3	153	151.9	18.6	213	211.4	26.0	273	271.0	33.3
34	33.7	4.1	94	93.3	11.5	154	152.9	18.8	214	212.4	26.1	274	272.0	33.4
35	34.7	4.3	95	94.3	11.6	155	153.8	18.9	215	213.4	26.2	275	273.0	33.5
36	35.7	4.4	96	95.3	11.7	156	154.8	19.0	216	214.4	26.3	276	273.9	33.6
37	36.7	4.5	97	96.3	11.8	157	155.8	19.1	217	215.4	26.4	277	274.9	33.8
38	37.7	4.6	98	97.3	11.9	158	156.8	19.3	218	216.4	26.6	278	275.9	33.9
39	38.7	4.8	99	98.3	12.1	159	157.8	19.4	219	217.4	26.7	279	276.9	34.0
40	39.7	4.9	100	99.3	12.2	160	158.8	19.5	220	218.4	26.8	280	277.9	34.1
41	40.7	5.0	101	100.2	12.3	161	159.8	19.6	221	219.4	26.9	281	278.9	34.2
42	41.7	5.1	102	101.2	12.4	162	160.8	19.7	222	220.3	27.1	282	279.9	34.4
43	42.7	5.2	103	102.2	12.6	163	161.8	19.9	223	221.3	27.2	283	280.9	34.5
44	43.7	5.4	104	103.2	12.7	164	162.8	20.0	224	222.3	27.3	284	281.9	34.6
45	44.7	5.5	105	104.2	12.8	165	163.8	20.1	225	223.3	27.4	285	282.9	34.7
46	45.7	5.6	106	105.2	12.9	166	164.8	20.2	226	224.3	27.5	286	283.9	34.9
47	46.6	5.7	107	106.2	13.0	167	165.8	20.4	227	225.3	27.7	287	284.9	35.0
48	47.6	5.8	108	107.2	13.2	168	166.7	20.5	228	226.3	27.8	288	285.9	35.1
49	48.6	6.0	109	108.2	13.3	169	167.7	20.6	229	227.3	27.9	289	286.8	35.2
50	49.6	6.1	110	109.2	13.4	170	168.7	20.7	230	228.3	28.0	290	287.8	35.3
51	50.6	6.2	111	110.2	13.5	171	169.7	20.8	231	229.3	28.2	291	288.8	35.5
52	51.6	6.3	112	111.2	13.6	172	170.7	21.0	232	230.3	28.3	292	289.8	35.6
53	52.6	6.5	113	112.2	13.8	173	171.7	21.1	233	231.3	28.4	293	290.8	35.7
54	53.6	6.6	114	113.2	13.9	174	172.7	21.2	234	232.3	28.5	294	291.8	35.8
55	54.6	6.7	115	114.1	14.0	175	173.7	21.3	235	233.2	28.6	295	292.8	36.0
56	55.6	6.8	116	115.1	14.1	176	174.7	21.4	236	234.2	28.8	296	293.8	36.1
57	56.6	6.9	117	116.1	14.3	177	175.7	21.6	237	235.2	28.9	297	294.8	36.2
58	57.6	7.1	118	117.1	14.4	178	176.7	21.7	238	236.2	29.0	298	295.8	36.3
59	58.6	7.2	119	118.1	14.5	179	177.7	21.8	239	237.2	29.1	299	296.8	36.4
60	59.6	7.3	120	119.1	14.6	180	178.7	21.9	240	238.2	29.2	300	297.8	36.6
Hyp.	Opp.	Adj.	Hyp.	Opp.	Adj.	Hyp.	Opp.	Adj.	Hyp.	Opp.	Adj.	Hyp.	Opp.	Adj.
Dist. / D Lon	Dep.	D. Lat. / Dep	Dist. / D Lon	Dep.	D. Lat. / Dep	Dist. / D Lon	Dep.	D. Lat. / Dep	Dist. / D Lon	Dep.	D. Lat. / Dep	Dist. / D Lon	Dep.	D. Lat. / Dep

83°   83°

Table 3

TRAVERSE TABLE

D Lon	Dep		D Lon	Dep		D Lon	Dep		D Lon	Dep		D Lon	Dep	
Dist.	D. Lat.	Dep.	Dist.	D. Lat.	Dep.	Dist.	D. Lat.	Dep.	Dist.	D. Lat.	Dep.	Dist.	D. Lat.	Dep.
Hyp.	Adj.	Opp.	Hyp.	Adj.	Opp.	Hyp.	Adj.	Opp.	Hyp.	Adj.	Opp.	Hyp.	Adj.	Opp.
301	298.8	36.7	361	358.3	44.0	421	417.9	51.3	481	477.4	58.6	541	537.0	65.9
302	299.7	36.8	362	359.3	44.1	422	418.9	51.4	482	478.4	58.7	542	538.0	66.1
303	300.7	36.9	363	360.3	44.2	423	419.8	51.6	483	479.4	58.9	543	539.0	66.2
304	301.7	37.0	364	361.3	44.4	424	420.8	51.7	484	480.4	59.0	544	539.9	66.3
305	302.7	37.2	365	362.3	44.5	425	421.8	51.8	485	481.4	59.1	545	540.9	66.4
306	303.7	37.3	366	363.3	44.6	426	422.8	51.9	486	482.4	59.2	546	541.9	66.5
307	304.7	37.4	367	364.3	44.7	427	423.8	52.0	487	483.4	59.4	547	542.9	66.7
308	305.7	37.5	368	365.3	44.8	428	424.8	52.2	488	484.4	59.5	548	543.9	66.8
309	306.7	37.7	369	366.2	45.0	429	425.8	52.3	489	485.4	59.6	549	544.9	66.9
310	307.7	37.8	370	367.2	45.1	430	426.8	52.4	490	486.3	59.7	550	545.9	67.0
311	308.7	37.9	371	368.2	45.2	431	427.8	52.5	491	487.3	59.8	551	546.9	67.1
312	309.7	38.0	372	369.2	45.3	432	428.8	52.6	492	488.3	60.0	552	547.9	67.3
313	310.7	38.1	373	370.2	45.5	433	429.8	52.8	493	489.3	60.1	553	548.9	67.4
314	311.7	38.3	374	371.2	45.6	434	430.8	52.9	494	490.3	60.2	554	549.9	67.5
315	312.7	38.4	375	372.2	45.7	435	431.8	53.0	495	491.3	60.3	555	550.9	67.6
316	313.6	38.5	376	373.2	45.8	436	432.8	53.1	496	492.3	60.4	556	551.9	67.8
317	314.6	38.6	377	374.2	45.9	437	433.7	53.3	497	493.3	60.6	557	552.8	67.9
318	315.6	38.8	378	375.2	46.1	438	434.7	53.4	498	494.3	60.7	558	553.8	68.0
319	316.6	38.9	379	376.2	46.2	439	435.7	53.5	499	495.3	60.8	559	554.8	68.1
320	317.6	39.0	380	377.2	46.3	440	436.7	53.6	500	496.3	60.9	560	555.8	68.2
321	318.6	39.1	381	378.2	46.4	441	437.7	53.7	501	497.3	61.1	561	556.8	68.4
322	319.6	39.2	382	379.2	46.6	442	438.7	53.9	502	498.3	61.2	562	557.8	68.5
323	320.6	39.4	383	380.1	46.7	443	439.7	54.0	503	499.3	61.3	563	558.8	68.6
324	321.6	39.5	384	381.1	46.8	444	440.7	54.1	504	500.2	61.4	564	559.8	68.7
325	322.6	39.6	385	382.1	46.9	445	441.7	54.2	505	501.2	61.5	565	560.8	68.9
326	323.6	39.7	386	383.1	47.0	446	442.7	54.4	506	502.2	61.7	566	561.8	69.0
327	324.6	39.8	387	384.1	47.2	447	443.7	54.5	507	503.2	61.8	567	562.8	69.1
328	325.6	40.0	388	385.1	47.3	448	444.7	54.6	508	504.2	61.9	568	563.8	69.2
329	326.5	40.1	389	386.1	47.4	449	445.7	54.7	509	505.2	62.0	569	564.8	69.3
330	327.5	40.2	390	387.1	47.5	450	446.6	54.8	510	506.2	62.2	570	565.8	69.5
331	328.5	40.3	391	388.1	47.7	451	447.6	55.0	511	507.2	62.3	571	566.7	69.6
332	329.5	40.5	392	389.1	47.8	452	448.6	55.1	512	508.2	62.4	572	567.7	69.7
333	330.5	40.6	393	390.1	47.9	453	449.6	55.2	513	509.2	62.5	573	568.7	69.8
334	331.5	40.7	394	391.1	48.0	454	450.6	55.3	514	510.2	62.6	574	569.7	70.0
335	332.5	40.8	395	392.1	48.1	455	451.6	55.5	515	511.2	62.8	575	570.7	70.1
336	333.5	40.9	396	393.0	48.3	456	452.6	55.6	516	512.2	62.9	576	571.7	70.2
337	334.5	41.1	397	394.0	48.4	457	453.6	55.7	517	513.1	63.0	577	572.7	70.3
338	335.5	41.2	398	395.0	48.5	458	454.6	55.8	518	514.1	63.1	578	573.7	70.4
339	336.5	41.3	399	396.0	48.6	459	455.6	55.9	519	515.1	63.3	579	574.7	70.6
340	337.5	41.4	400	397.0	48.7	460	456.6	56.1	520	516.1	63.4	580	575.7	70.7
341	338.5	41.6	401	398.0	48.9	461	457.6	56.2	521	517.1	63.5	581	576.7	70.8
342	339.5	41.7	402	399.0	49.0	462	458.6	56.3	522	518.1	63.6	582	577.7	70.9
343	340.4	41.8	403	400.0	49.1	463	459.5	56.4	523	519.1	63.7	583	578.7	71.0
344	341.4	41.9	404	401.0	49.2	464	460.5	56.5	524	520.1	63.9	584	579.6	71.2
345	342.4	42.0	405	402.0	49.4	465	461.5	56.7	525	521.1	64.0	585	580.6	71.3
346	343.4	42.2	406	403.0	49.5	466	462.5	56.8	526	522.1	64.1	586	581.6	71.4
347	344.4	42.3	407	404.0	49.6	467	463.5	56.9	527	523.1	64.2	587	582.6	71.5
348	345.4	42.4	408	405.0	49.7	468	464.5	57.0	528	524.1	64.3	588	583.6	71.7
349	346.4	42.5	409	406.0	49.8	469	465.5	57.2	529	525.1	64.5	589	584.6	71.8
350	347.4	42.7	410	406.9	50.0	470	466.5	57.3	530	526.0	64.6	590	585.6	71.9
351	348.4	42.8	411	407.9	50.1	471	467.5	57.4	531	527.0	64.7	591	586.6	72.0
352	349.4	42.9	412	408.9	50.2	472	468.5	57.5	532	528.0	64.8	592	587.6	72.1
353	350.4	43.0	413	409.9	50.3	473	469.5	57.6	533	529.0	65.0	593	588.6	72.3
354	351.4	43.1	414	410.9	50.5	474	470.5	57.7	534	530.0	65.1	594	589.6	72.4
355	352.4	43.3	415	411.9	50.6	475	471.5	57.9	535	531.0	65.2	595	590.6	72.5
356	353.3	43.4	416	412.9	50.7	476	472.5	58.0	536	532.0	65.3	596	591.6	72.6
357	354.3	43.5	417	413.9	50.8	477	473.4	58.1	537	533.0	65.4	597	592.6	72.8
358	355.3	43.6	418	414.9	50.9	478	474.4	58.3	538	534.0	65.6	598	593.5	72.9
359	356.3	43.7	419	415.9	51.1	479	475.4	58.4	539	535.0	65.7	599	594.5	73.0
360	357.3	43.8	420	416.9	51.2	480	476.4	58.5	540	536.0	65.8	600	595.5	73.1
Hyp.	Opp.	Adj.	Hyp.	Opp.	Adj.	Hyp.	Opp.	Adj.	Hyp.	Opp.	Adj.	Hyp.	Opp.	Adj.
Dist.	Dep.	D. Lat.	Dist.	Dep.	D. Lat.	Dist.	Dep.	D. Lat.	Dist.	Dep.	D. Lat.	Dist.	Dep.	D. Lat.
D Lon		Dep	D Lon		Dep	D Lon		Dep	D Lon		Dep	D Lon		Dep

Table 3

TRAVERSE TABLE

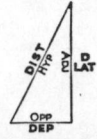

8°   8°

D Lon Dist.	Dep D. Lat.	Dep.	D Lon Dist.	Dep D. Lat.	Dep.	D Lon Dist.	Dep D. Lat.	Dep.	D Lon Dist.	Dep D. Lat.	Dep.	D Lon Dist.	Dep D. Lat.	Dep.
Hyp.	Adj.	Opp.	Hyp.	Adj.	Opp.	Hyp.	Adj.	Opp.	Hyp.	Adj.	Opp.	Hyp.	Adj.	Opp.
1	1.0	0.1	61	60.4	8.5	121	119.8	16.8	181	179.2	25.2	241	238.7	33.5
2	2.0	0.3	62	61.4	8.6	122	120.8	17.0	182	180.2	25.3	242	239.6	33.7
3	3.0	0.4	63	62.4	8.8	123	121.8	17.1	183	181.2	25.5	243	240.6	33.8
4	4.0	0.6	64	63.4	8.9	124	122.8	17.3	184	182.2	25.6	244	241.6	34.0
5	5.0	0.7	65	64.4	9.0	125	123.8	17.4	185	183.2	25.7	245	242.6	34.1
6	5.9	0.8	66	65.4	9.2	126	124.8	17.5	186	184.2	25.9	246	243.6	34.2
7	6.9	1.0	67	66.3	9.3	127	125.8	17.7	187	185.2	26.0	247	244.6	34.4
8	7.9	1.1	68	67.3	9.5	128	126.8	17.8	188	186.2	26.2	248	245.6	34.5
9	8.9	1.3	69	68.3	9.6	129	127.7	18.0	189	187.2	26.3	249	246.6	34.7
10	9.9	1.4	70	69.3	9.7	130	128.7	18.1	190	188.2	26.4	250	247.6	34.8
11	10.9	1.5	71	70.3	9.9	131	129.7	18.2	191	189.1	26.6	251	248.6	34.9
12	11.9	1.7	72	71.3	10.0	132	130.7	18.4	192	190.1	26.7	252	249.5	35.1
13	12.9	1.8	73	72.3	10.2	13ɔ	131.7	18.5	193	191.1	26.9	253	250.5	35.2
14	13.9	1.9	74	73.3	10.3	134	132.7	18.6	194	192.1	27.0	254	251.5	35.3
15	14.9	2.1	75	74.3	10.4	135	133.7	18.8	195	193.1	27.1	255	252.5	35.5
16	15.8	2.2	76	75.3	10.6	136	134.7	18.9	196	194.1	27.3	256	253.5	35.6
17	16.8	2.4	77	76.3	10.7	137	135.7	19.1	197	195.1	27.4	257	254.5	35.8
18	17.8	2.5	78	77.2	10.9	138	136.7	19.2	198	196.1	27.6	258	255.5	35.9
19	18.8	2.6	79	78.2	11.0	139	137.7	19.3	199	197.1	27.7	259	256.5	36.0
20	19.8	2.8	80	79.2	11.1	140	138.6	19.5	200	198.1	27.8	260	257.5	36.2
21	20.8	2.9	81	80.2	11.3	141	139.6	19.6	201	199.0	28.0	261	258.5	36.3
22	21.8	3.1	82	81.2	11.4	142	140.6	19.8	202	200.0	28.1	262	259.5	36.5
23	22.8	3.2	83	82.2	11.6	143	141.6	19.9	203	201.0	28.3	263	260.4	36.6
24	23.8	3.3	84	83.2	11.7	144	142.6	20.0	204	202.0	28.4	264	261.4	36.7
25	24.8	3.5	85	84.2	11.8	145	143.6	20.2	205	203.0	28.5	265	262.4	36.9
26	25.7	3.6	86	85.2	12.0	146	144.6	20.3	206	204.0	28.7	266	263.4	37.0
27	26.7	3.8	87	86.2	12.1	147	145.6	20.5	207	205.0	28.8	267	264.4	37.2
28	27.7	3.9	88	87.1	12.2	148	146.6	20.6	208	206.0	28.9	268	265.4	37.3
29	28.7	4.0	89	88.1	12.4	149	147.5	20.7	209	207.0	29.1	269	266.4	37.4
30	29.7	4.2	90	89.1	12.5	150	148.5	20.9	210	208.0	29.2	270	267.4	37.6
31	30.7	4.3	91	90.1	12.7	151	149.5	21.0	211	208.9	29.4	271	268.4	37.7
32	31.7	4.5	92	91.1	12.8	152	150.5	21.2	212	209.9	29.5	272	269.4	37.9
33	32.7	4.6	93	92.1	12.9	153	151.5	21.3	213	210.9	29.6	273	270.3	38.0
34	33.7	4.7	94	93.1	13.1	154	152.5	21.4	214	211.9	29.8	274	271.3	38.1
35	34.7	4.9	95	94.1	13.2	155	153.5	21.6	215	212.9	29.9	275	272.3	38.3
36	35.6	5.0	96	95.1	13.4	156	154.5	21.7	216	213.9	30.1	276	273.3	38.4
37	36.6	5.1	97	96.1	13.5	157	155.5	21.9	217	214.9	30.2	277	274.3	38.6
38	37.6	5.3	98	97.0	13.6	158	156.5	22.0	218	215.9	30.3	278	275.3	38.7
39	38.6	5.4	99	98.0	13.8	159	157.5	22.1	219	216.9	30.5	279	276.3	38.8
40	39.6	5.6	100	99.0	13.9	160	158.4	22.3	220	217.9	30.6	280	277.3	39.0
41	40.6	5.7	101	100.0	14.1	161	159.4	22.4	221	218.8	30.8	281	278.3	39.1
42	41.6	5.8	102	101.0	14.2	162	160.4	22.5	222	219.8	30.9	282	279.3	39.2
43	42.6	6.0	103	102.0	14.3	163	161.4	22.7	223	220.8	31.0	283	280.2	39.4
44	43.6	6.1	104	103.0	14.5	164	162.4	22.8	224	221.8	31.2	284	281.2	39.5
45	44.6	6.3	105	104.0	14.6	165	163.4	23.0	225	222.8	31.3	285	282.2	39.7
46	45.6	6.4	106	105.0	14.8	166	164.4	23.1	226	223.8	31.5	286	283.2	39.8
47	46.5	6.5	107	106.0	14.9	167	165.4	23.2	227	224.8	31.6	287	284.2	39.9
48	47.5	6.7	108	106.9	15.0	168	166.4	23.4	228	225.8	31.7	288	285.2	40.1
49	48.5	6.8	109	107.9	15.2	169	167.4	23.5	229	226.8	31.9	289	286.2	40.2
50	49.5	7.0	110	108.9	15.3	170	168.3	23.7	230	227.8	32.0	290	287.2	40.4
51	50.5	7.1	111	109.9	15.4	171	169.3	23.8	231	228.8	32.1	291	288.2	40.5
52	51.5	7.2	112	110.9	15.6	172	170.3	23.9	232	229.7	32.3	292	289.2	40.6
53	52.5	7.4	113	111.9	15.7	173	171.3	24.1	233	230.7	32.4	293	290.1	40.8
54	53.5	7.5	114	112.9	15.9	174	172.3	24.2	234	231.7	32.6	294	291.1	40.9
55	54.5	7.7	115	113.9	16.0	175	173.3	24.4	235	232.7	32.7	295	292.1	41.1
56	55.5	7.8	116	114.9	16.1	176	174.3	24.5	236	233.7	32.8	296	293.1	41.2
57	56.4	7.9	117	115.9	16.3	177	175.3	24.6	237	234.7	33.0	297	294.1	41.3
58	57.4	8.1	118	116.9	16.4	178	176.3	24.8	238	235.7	33.1	298	295.1	41.5
59	58.4	8.2	119	117.8	16.6	179	177.3	24.9	239	236.7	33.3	299	296.1	41.6
60	59.4	8.4	120	118.8	16.7	180	178.2	25.1	240	237.7	33.4	300	297.1	41.8
Hyp.	Opp.	Adj.	Hyp.	Opp.	Adj.	Hyp.	Opp.	Adj.	Hyp.	Opp.	Adj.	Hyp.	Opp.	Adj.
Dist. D Lon	Dep.	D. Lat. Dep	Dist. D Lon	Dep.	D. Lat. Dep	Dist. D Lon	Dep.	D. Lat. Dep	Dist. D Lon	Dep.	D. Lat. Dep	Dist. D Lon	Dep.	D. Lat. Dep

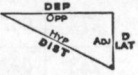

82°   82°

Table 3

TRAVERSE TABLE

8°

352° | 008°
188° | 172°

8°

D Lon Dep Dist. D. Lat. Dep.			D Lon Dep Dist. D. Lat. Dep.			D Lon Dep Dist. D. Lat. Dep.			D Lon Dep Dist. D. Lat. Dep.			D Lon Dep Dist. D. Lat. Dep.		
Hyp.	Adj.	Opp.	Hyp.	Adj.	Opp.	Hyp.	Adj.	Opp.	Hyp.	Adj.	Opp.	Hyp.	Adj.	Opp.
301	298.1	41.9	361	357.5	50.2	421	416.9	58.6	481	476.3	66.9	541	535.7	75.3
302	299.1	42.0	362	358.5	50.4	422	417.9	58.7	482	477.3	67.1	542	536.7	75.4
303	300.1	42.2	363	359.5	50.5	423	418.9	58.9	483	478.3	67.2	543	537.7	75.6
304	301.0	42.3	364	360.5	50.7	424	419.9	59.0	484	479.3	67.4	544	538.7	75.7
305	302.0	42.4	365	361.4	50.8	425	420.9	59.1	485	480.3	67.5	545	539.7	75.8
306	303.0	42.6	366	362.4	50.9	426	421.9	59.3	486	481.3	67.6	546	540.7	76.0
307	304.0	42.7	367	363.4	51.1	427	422.8	59.4	487	482.3	67.8	547	541.7	76.1
308	305.0	42.9	368	364.4	51.2	428	423.8	59.6	488	483.3	67.9	548	542.7	76.3
309	306.0	43.0	369	365.4	51.4	429	424.8	59.7	489	484.2	68.1	549	543.7	76.4
310	307.0	43.1	370	366.4	51.5	430	425.8	59.8	490	485.2	68.2	550	544.6	76.5
311	308.0	43.3	371	367.4	51.6	431	426.8	60.0	491	486.2	68.3	551	545.6	76.7
312	309.0	43.4	372	368.4	51.8	432	427.8	60.1	492	487.2	68.5	552	546.6	76.8
313	310.0	43.6	373	369.4	51.9	433	428.8	60.3	493	488.2	68.6	553	547.6	77.0
314	310.9	43.7	374	370.4	52.1	434	429.8	60.4	494	489.2	68.8	554	548.6	77.1
315	311.9	43.8	375	371.4	52.2	435	430.8	60.5	495	490.2	68.9	555	549.6	77.2
316	312.9	44.0	376	372.3	52.3	436	431.8	60.7	496	491.2	69.0	556	550.6	77.4
317	313.9	44.1	377	373.3	52.5	437	432.7	60.8	497	492.2	69.2	557	551.6	77.5
318	314.9	44.3	378	374.3	52.6	438	433.7	61.0	498	493.2	69.3	558	552.6	77.7
319	315.9	44.4	379	375.3	52.7	439	434.7	61.1	499	494.1	69.4	559	553.6	77.8
320	316.9	44.5	380	376.3	52.9	440	435.7	61.2	500	495.1	69.6	560	554.6	77.9
321	317.9	44.7	381	377.3	53.0	441	436.7	61.4	501	496.1	69.7	561	555.5	78.1
322	318.9	44.8	382	378.3	53.2	442	437.7	61.5	502	497.1	69.9	562	556.5	78.2
323	319.9	45.0	383	379.3	53.3	443	438.7	61.7	503	498.1	70.0	563	557.5	78.4
324	320.8	45.1	384	380.3	53.4	444	439.7	61.8	504	499.1	70.1	564	558.5	78.5
325	321.8	45.2	385	381.3	53.6	445	440.7	61.9	505	500.1	70.3	565	559.5	78.6
326	322.8	45.4	386	382.2	53.7	446	441.7	62.1	506	501.1	70.4	566	560.5	78.8
327	323.8	45.5	387	383.2	53.9	447	442.6	62.2	507	502.1	70.6	567	561.5	78.9
328	324.8	45.6	388	384.2	54.0	448	443.6	62.3	508	503.1	70.7	568	562.5	79.1
329	325.8	45.8	389	385.2	54.1	449	444.6	62.5	509	504.0	70.8	569	563.5	79.2
330	326.8	45.9	390	386.2	54.3	450	445.6	62.6	510	505.0	71.0	570	564.5	79.3
331	327.8	46.1	391	387.2	54.4	451	446.6	62.8	511	506.0	71.1	571	565.4	79.5
332	328.8	46.2	392	388.2	54.6	452	447.6	62.9	512	507.0	71.3	572	566.4	79.6
333	329.8	46.3	393	389.1	54.7	453	448.6	63.0	513	508.0	71.4	573	567.4	79.7
334	330.7	46.5	394	390.1	54.8	454	449.6	63.2	514	509.0	71.5	574	568.4	79.9
335	331.7	46.6	395	391.1	55.0	455	450.6	63.3	515	510.0	71.7	575	569.4	80.0
336	332.7	46.8	396	392.1	55.1	456	451.6	63.5	516	511.0	71.8	576	570.4	80.2
337	333.7	46.9	397	393.1	55.3	457	452.6	63.6	517	512.0	72.0	577	571.4	80.3
338	334.7	47.0	398	394.1	55.4	458	453.5	63.7	518	513.0	72.1	578	572.4	80.4
339	335.7	47.2	399	395.1	55.5	459	454.5	63.9	519	513.9	72.2	579	573.4	80.6
340	336.7	47.3	400	396.1	55.7	460	455.5	64.0	520	514.9	72.4	580	574.4	80.7
341	337.7	47.5	401	397.1	55.8	461	456.5	64.2	521	515.9	72.5	581	575.3	80.9
342	338.7	47.6	402	398.1	55.9	462	457.5	64.3	522	516.9	72.6	582	576.3	81.0
343	339.7	47.7	403	399.1	56.1	463	458.5	64.4	523	517.9	72.8	583	577.3	81.1
344	340.7	47.9	404	400.1	56.2	464	459.5	64.6	524	518.9	72.9	584	578.3	81.3
345	341.6	48.0	405	401.1	56.4	465	460.5	64.7	525	519.9	73.1	585	579.3	81.4
346	342.6	48.2	406	402.0	56.5	466	461.5	64.9	526	520.9	73.2	586	580.3	81.6
347	343.6	48.3	407	403.0	56.6	467	462.5	65.0	527	521.9	73.3	587	581.3	81.7
348	344.6	48.4	408	404.0	56.8	468	463.4	65.1	528	522.9	73.5	588	582.3	81.8
349	345.6	48.6	409	405.0	56.9	469	464.4	65.3	529	523.9	73.6	589	583.3	82.0
350	346.6	48.7	410	406.0	57.1	470	465.4	65.4	530	524.8	73.8	590	584.3	82.1
351	347.6	48.8	411	407.0	57.2	471	466.4	65.6	531	525.8	73.9	591	585.2	82.3
352	348.6	49.0	412	408.0	57.3	472	467.4	65.7	532	526.8	74.0	592	586.2	82.4
353	349.6	49.1	413	409.0	57.5	473	468.4	65.8	533	527.8	74.2	593	587.2	82.5
354	350.6	49.3	414	410.0	57.6	474	469.4	66.0	534	528.8	74.3	594	588.2	82.7
355	351.5	49.4	415	411.0	57.8	475	470.4	66.1	535	529.8	74.5	595	589.2	82.8
356	352.5	49.5	416	412.0	57.9	476	471.4	66.2	536	530.8	74.6	596	590.2	82.9
357	353.5	49.7	417	412.9	58.0	477	472.4	66.4	537	531.8	74.7	597	591.2	83.1
358	354.5	49.8	418	413.9	58.2	478	473.3	66.5	538	532.8	74.9	598	592.2	83.2
359	355.5	50.0	419	414.9	58.3	479	474.3	66.7	539	533.8	75.0	599	593.2	83.4
360	356.5	50.1	420	415.9	58.5	480	475.3	66.8	540	534.7	75.2	600	594.2	83.5
Hyp.	Opp.	Adj.	Hyp.	Opp.	Adj.	Hyp.	Opp.	Adj.	Hyp.	Opp.	Adj.	Hyp.	Opp.	Adj.

Dist. Dep. D. Lat. D Lon Dep			Dist. Dep. D. Lat. D Lon Dep			Dist. Dep. D. Lat. D Lon Dep			Dist. Dep. D. Lat. D Lon Dep			Dist. Dep. D. Lat. D Lon Dep		

82°

278° | 082°
262° | 098°

82°

Table 3

TRAVERSE TABLE

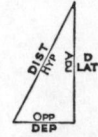

9°   9°

D Lon Dist.	Dep D. Lat.	Dep.	D Lon Dist.	Dep D. Lat.	Dep.	D Lon Dist.	Dep D. Lat.	Dep.	D Lon Dist.	Dep D. Lat.	Dep.	D Lon Dist.	Dep D. Lat.	Dep.
Hyp.	Adj.	Opp.	Hyp.	Adj.	Opp.	Hyp.	Adj.	Opp.	Hyp.	Adj.	Opp.	Hyp.	Adj.	Opp.
1	1.0	0.2	61	60.2	9.5	121	119.5	18.9	181	178.8	28.3	241	238.0	37.7
2	2.0	0.3	62	61.2	9.7	122	120.5	19.1	182	179.8	28.5	242	239.0	37.9
3	3.0	0.5	63	62.2	9.9	123	121.5	19.2	183	180.7	28.6	243	240.0	38.0
4	4.0	0.6	64	63.2	10.0	124	122.5	19.4	184	181.7	28.8	244	241.0	38.2
5	4.9	0.8	65	64.2	10.2	125	123.5	19.6	185	182.7	28.9	245	242.0	38.3
6	5.9	0.9	66	65.2	10.3	126	124.4	19.7	186	183.7	29.1	246	243.0	38.5
7	6.9	1.1	67	66.2	10.5	127	125.4	19.9	187	184.7	29.3	247	244.0	38.6
8	7.9	1.3	68	67.2	10.6	128	126.4	20.0	188	185.7	29.4	248	244.9	38.8
9	8.9	1.4	69	68.2	10.8	129	127.4	20.2	189	186.7	29.6	249	245.9	39.0
10	9.9	1.6	70	69.1	11.0	130	128.4	20.3	190	187.7	29.7	250	246.9	39.1
11	10.9	1.7	71	70.1	11.1	131	129.4	20.5	191	188.6	29.9	251	247.9	39.3
12	11.9	1.9	72	71.1	11.3	132	130.4	20.6	192	189.6	30.0	252	248.9	39.4
13	12.8	2.0	73	72.1	11.4	133	131.4	20.8	193	190.6	30.2	253	249.9	39.6
14	13.8	2.2	74	73.1	11.6	134	132.4	21.0	194	191.6	30.3	254	250.9	39.7
15	14.8	2.3	75	74.1	11.7	135	133.3	21.1	195	192.6	30.5	255	251.9	39.9
16	15.8	2.5	76	75.1	11.9	136	134.3	21.3	196	193.6	30.7	256	252.8	40.0
17	16.8	2.7	77	76.1	12.0	137	135.3	21.4	197	194.6	30.8	257	253.8	40.2
18	17.8	2.8	78	77.0	12.2	138	136.3	21.6	198	195.6	31.0	258	254.8	40.4
19	18.8	3.0	79	78.0	12.4	139	137.3	21.7	199	196.5	31.1	259	255.8	40.5
20	19.8	3.1	80	79.0	12.5	140	138.3	21.9	200	197.5	31.3	260	256.8	40.7
21	20.7	3.3	81	80.0	12.7	141	139.3	22.1	201	198.5	31.4	261	257.8	40.8
22	21.7	3.A	82	81.0	12.8	142	140.3	22.2	202	199.5	31.6	262	258.8	41.0
23	22.7	3.6	83	82.0	13.0	143	141.2	22.4	203	200.5	31.8	263	259.8	41.1
24	23.7	3.8	84	83.0	13.1	144	142.2	22.5	204	201.5	31.9	264	260.7	41.3
25	24.7	3.9	85	84.0	13.3	145	143.2	22.7	205	202.5	32.1	265	261.7	41.5
26	25.7	4.1	86	84.9	13.5	146	144.2	22.8	206	203.5	32.2	266	262.7	41.6
27	26.7	4.2	87	85.9	13.6	147	145.2	23.0	207	204.5	32.4	267	263.7	41.8
28	27.7	4.4	88	86.9	13.8	148	146.2	23.2	208	205.4	32.5	268	264.7	41.9
29	28.6	4.5	89	87.9	13.9	149	147.2	23.3	209	206.4	32.7	269	265.7	42.1
30	29.6	4.7	90	88.9	14.1	150	148.2	23.5	210	207.4	32.9	270	266.7	42.2
31	30.6	4.8	91	89.9	14.2	151	149.1	23.6	211	208.4	33.0	271	267.7	42.4
32	31.6	5.0	92	90.9	14.4	152	150.1	23.8	212	209.4	33.2	272	268.7	42.6
33	32.6	5.2	93	91.9	14.5	153	151.1	23.9	213	210.4	33.3	273	269.6	42.7
34	33.6	5.3	94	92.8	14.7	154	152.1	24.1	214	211.4	33.5	274	270.6	42.9
35	34.6	5.5	95	93.8	14.9	155	153.1	24.2	215	212.4	33.6	275	271.6	43.0
36	35.6	5.6	96	94.8	15.0	156	154.1	24.4	216	213.3	33.8	276	272.6	43.2
37	36.5	5.8	97	95.8	15.2	157	155.1	24.6	217	214.3	33.9	277	273.6	43.3
38	37.5	5.9	98	96.8	15.3	158	156.1	24.7	218	215.3	34.1	278	274.6	43.5
39	38.5	6.1	99	97.8	15.5	159	157.0	24.9	219	216.3	34.3	279	275.6	43.6
40	39.5	6.3	100	98.8	15.6	160	158.0	25.0	220	217.3	34.4	280	276.6	43.8
41	40.5	6.4	101	99.8	15.8	161	159.0	25.2	221	218.3	34.6	281	277.5	44.0
42	41.5	6.6	102	100.7	16.0	162	160.0	25.3	222	219.3	34.7	282	278.5	44.1
43	42.5	6.7	103	101.7	16.1	163	161.0	25.5	223	220.3	34.9	283	279.5	44.3
44	43.5	6.9	104	102.7	16.3	164	162.0	25.7	224	221.2	35.0	284	280.5	44.4
45	44.4	7.0	105	103.7	16.4	165	163.0	25.8	225	222.2	35.2	285	281.5	44.6
46	45.4	7.2	106	104.7	16.6	166	164.0	26.0	226	223.2	35.4	286	282.5	44.7
47	46.4	7.4	107	105.7	16.7	167	164.9	26.1	227	224.2	35.5	287	283.5	44.9
48	47.4	7.5	108	106.7	16.9	168	165.9	26.3	228	225.2	35.7	288	284.5	45.1
49	48.4	7.7	109	107.7	17.1	169	166.9	26.4	229	226.2	35.8	289	285.4	45.2
50	49.4	7.8	110	108.6	17.2	170	167.9	26.6	230	227.2	36.0	290	286.4	45.4
51	50.4	8.0	111	109.6	17.4	171	168.9	26.8	231	228.2	36.1	291	287.4	45.5
52	51.4	8.1	112	110.6	17.5	172	169.9	26.9	232	229.1	36.3	292	288.4	45.7
53	52.3	8.3	113	111.6	17.7	173	170.9	27.1	233	230.1	36.4	293	289.4	45.8
54	53.3	8.4	114	112.6	17.8	174	171.9	27.2	234	231.1	36.6	294	290.4	46.0
55	54.3	8.6	115	113.6	18.0	175	172.8	27.4	235	232.1	36.8	295	291.4	46.1
56	55.3	8.8	116	114.6	18.1	176	173.8	27.5	236	233.1	36.9	296	292.4	46.3
57	56.3	8.9	117	115.6	18.3	177	174.8	27.7	237	234.1	37.1	297	293.3	46.5
58	57.3	9.1	118	116.5	18.5	178	175.8	27.8	238	235.1	37.2	298	294.3	46.6
59	58.3	9.2	119	117.5	18.6	179	176.8	28.0	239	236.1	37.4	299	295.3	46.8
60	59.3	9.4	120	118.5	18.8	180	177.8	28.2	240	237.0	37.5	300	296.3	46.9
Hyp.	Opp.	Adj.	Hyp.	Opp.	Adj.	Hyp.	Opp.	Adj.	Hyp.	Opp.	Adj.	Hyp.	Opp.	Adj.
Dist. D Lon	Dep.	D. Lat. Dep	Dist. D Lon	Dep.	D. Lat. Dep	Dist. D Lon	Dep.	D. Lat. Dep	Dist. D Lon	Dep.	D. Lat. Dep	Dist. D Lon	Dep.	D. Lat. Dep

81°   81°

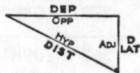

Table 3

TRAVERSE TABLE

9°

9°

D Lon Dep Dist. D. Lat. Dep.			D Lon Dep Dist. D. Lat. Dep.			D Lon Dep Dist. D. Lat. Dep.			D Lon Dep Dist. D. Lat. Dep.			D Lon Dep Dist. D. Lat. Dep.		
Hyp.	Adj.	Opp.	Hyp.	Adj.	Opp.	Hyp.	Adj.	Opp.	Hyp.	Adj.	Opp.	Hyp.	Adj.	Opp.
301	297.3	47.1	361	356.6	56.5	421	415.8	65.9	481	475.1	75.2	541	534.3	84.6
302	298.3	47.2	362	357.5	56.6	422	416.8	66.0	482	476.1	75.4	542	535.3	84.8
303	299.3	47.4	363	358.5	56.8	423	417.8	66.2	483	477.1	75.6	543	536.3	84.9
304	300.3	47.6	364	359.5	56.9	424	418.8	66.3	484	478.0	75.7	544	537.3	85.1
305	301.2	47.7	365	360.5	57.1	425	419.8	66.5	485	479.0	75.9	545	538.3	85.3
306	302.2	47.9	366	361.5	57.3	426	420.8	66.6	486	480.0	76.0	546	539.3	85.4
307	303.2	48.0	367	362.5	57.4	427	421.7	66.8	487	481.0	76.2	547	540.3	85.6
308	304.2	48.2	368	363.5	57.6	428	422.7	67.0	488	482.0	76.3	548	541.3	85.7
309	305.2	48.3	369	364.5	57.7	429	423.7	67.1	489	483.0	76.5	549	542.2	85.9
310	306.2	48.5	370	365.4	57.9	430	424.7	67.3	490	484.0	76.7	550	543.2	86.0
311	307.2	48.7	371	366.4	58.0	431	425.7	67.4	491	485.0	76.8	551	544.2	86.2
312	308.2	48.8	372	367.4	58.2	432	426.7	67.6	492	485.9	77.0	552	545.2	86.4
313	309.1	49.0	373	368.4	58.4	433	427.7	67.7	493	486.9	77.1	553	546.2	86.5
314	310.1	49.1	374	369.4	58.5	434	428.7	67.9	494	487.9	77.3	554	547.2	86.7
315	311.1	49.3	375	370.4	58.7	435	429.6	68.0	495	488.9	77.4	555	548.2	86.8
316	312.1	49.4	376	371.4	58.8	436	430.6	68.2	496	489.9	77.6	556	549.2	87.0
317	313.1	49.6	377	372.4	59.0	437	431.6	68.4	497	490.9	77.7	557	550.1	87.1
318	314.1	49.7	378	373.3	59.1	438	432.6	68.5	498	491.9	77.9	558	551.1	87.3
319	315.1	49.9	379	374.3	59.3	439	433.6	68.7	499	492.9	78.1	559	552.1	87.4
320	316.1	50.1	380	375.3	59.4	440	434.6	68.8	500	493.8	78.2	560	553.1	87.6
321	317.0	50.2	381	376.3	59.6	441	435.6	69.0	501	494.8	78.4	561	554.1	87.8
322	318.0	50.4	382	377.3	59.8	442	436.6	69.1	502	495.8	78.5	562	555.1	87.9
323	319.0	50.5	383	378.3	59.9	443	437.5	69.3	503	496.8	78.7	563	556.1	88.1
324	320.0	50.7	384	379.3	60.1	444	438.5	69.5	504	497.8	78.8	564	557.1	88.2
325	321.0	50.8	385	380.3	60.2	445	439.5	69.6	505	498.8	79.0	565	558.0	88.4
326	322.0	51.0	386	381.2	60.4	446	440.5	69.8	506	499.8	79.2	566	559.0	88.5
327	323.0	51.2	387	382.2	60.5	447	441.5	69.9	507	500.8	79.3	567	560.0	88.7
328	324.0	51.3	388	383.2	60.7	448	442.5	70.1	508	501.7	79.5	568	561.0	88.9
329	324.9	51.5	389	384.2	60.9	449	443.5	70.2	509	502.7	79.6	569	562.0	89.0
330	325.9	51.6	390	385.2	61.0	450	444.5	70.4	510	503.7	79.8	570	563.0	89.2
331	326.9	51.8	391	386.2	61.2	451	445.4	70.6	511	504.7	79.9	571	564.0	89.3
332	327.9	51.9	392	387.2	61.3	452	446.4	70.7	512	505.7	80.1	572	565.0	89.5
333	328.9	52.1	393	388.2	61.5	453	447.4	70.9	513	506.7	80.3	573	565.9	89.6
334	329.9	52.2	394	389.1	61.6	454	448.4	71.0	514	507.7	80.4	574	566.9	89.8
335	330.9	52.4	395	390.1	61.8	455	449.4	71.2	515	508.7	80.6	575	567.9	89.9
336	331.9	52.6	396	391.1	61.9	456	450.4	71.3	516	509.6	80.7	576	568.9	90.1
337	332.9	52.7	397	392.1	62.1	457	451.4	71.5	517	510.6	80.9	577	569.9	90.3
338	333.8	52.9	398	393.1	62.3	458	452.4	71.6	518	511.6	81.0	578	570.9	90.4
339	334.8	53.0	399	394.1	62.4	459	453.3	71.8	519	512.6	81.2	579	571.9	90.6
340	335.8	53.2	400	395.1	62.6	460	454.3	72.0	520	513.6	81.3	580	572.9	90.7
341	336.8	53.3	401	396.1	62.7	461	455.3	72.1	521	514.6	81.5	581	573.8	90.9
342	337.8	53.5	402	397.1	62.9	462	456.3	72.3	522	515.6	81.7	582	574.8	91.0
343	338.8	53.7	403	398.0	63.0	463	457.3	72.4	523	516.6	81.8	583	575.8	91.2
344	339.8	53.8	404	399.0	63.2	464	458.3	72.6	524	517.5	82.0	584	576.8	91.4
345	340.8	54.0	405	400.0	63.4	465	459.3	72.7	525	518.5	82.1	585	577.8	91.5
346	341.7	54.1	406	401.0	63.5	466	460.3	72.9	526	519.5	82.3	586	578.8	91.7
347	342.7	54.3	407	402.0	63.7	467	461.3	73.1	527	520.5	82.4	587	579.8	91.8
348	343.7	54.4	408	403.0	63.8	468	462.2	73.2	528	521.5	82.6	588	580.8	92.0
349	344.7	54.6	409	404.0	64.0	469	463.2	73.4	529	522.5	82.8	589	581.7	92.1
350	345.7	54.8	410	405.0	64.1	470	464.2	73.5	530	523.5	82.9	590	582.7	92.3
351	346.7	54.9	411	405.9	64.3	471	465.2	73.7	531	524.5	83.1	591	583.7	92.5
352	347.7	55.1	412	406.9	64.4	472	466.2	73.8	532	525.5	83.2	592	584.7	92.6
353	348.7	55.2	413	407.9	64.6	473	467.2	74.0	533	526.5	83.4	593	585.7	92.8
354	349.6	55.4	414	408.9	64.8	474	468.2	74.1	534	527.4	83.5	594	586.7	92.9
355	350.6	55.5	415	409.9	64.9	475	469.2	74.3	535	528.4	83.7	595	587.7	93.1
356	351.6	55.7	416	410.9	65.1	476	470.1	74.5	536	529.4	83.8	596	588.7	93.2
357	352.6	55.8	417	411.9	65.2	477	471.1	74.6	537	530.4	84.0	597	589.6	93.4
358	353.6	56.0	418	412.9	65.4	478	472.1	74.8	538	531.4	84.2	598	590.6	93.5
359	354.6	56.2	419	413.8	65.5	479	473.1	74.9	539	532.4	84.3	599	591.6	93.7
360	355.6	56.3	420	414.8	65.7	480	474.1	75.1	540	533.4	84.5	600	592.6	93.9
Hyp.	Opp.	Adj.	Hyp.	Opp.	Adj.	Hyp.	Opp.	Adj.	Hyp.	Opp.	Adj.	Hyp.	Opp.	Adj.

Dist. Dep. D. Lat. D Lon Dep			Dist. Dep. D. Lat. D Lon Dep			Dist. Dep. D. Lat. D Lon Dep			Dist. Dep. D. Lat. D Lon Dep			Dist. Dep. D. Lat. D Lon Dep		

81°

81°

Table 3

TRAVERSE TABLE

10°

10°

D Lon Dist.	Dep D. Lat.	Dep.	D Lon Dist.	Dep D. Lat.	Dep.	D Lon Dist.	Dep D. Lat.	Dep.	D Lon Dist.	Dep D. Lat.	Dep.	D Lon Dist.	Dep D. Lat.	Dep.
Hyp.	Adj.	Opp.	Hyp.	Adj.	Opp.	Hyp.	Adj.	Opp.	Hyp.	Adj.	Opp.	Hyp.	Adj.	Opp.
1	1.0	0.2	61	60.1	10.6	121	119.2	21.0	181	178.3	31.4	241	237.3	41.8
2	2.0	0.3	62	61.1	10.8	122	120.1	21.2	182	179.2	31.6	242	238.3	42.0
3	3.0	0.5	63	62.0	10.9	123	121.1	21.4	183	180.2	31.8	243	239.3	42.2
4	3.9	0.7	64	63.0	11.1	124	122.1	21.5	184	181.2	32.0	244	240.3	42.4
5	4.9	0.9	65	64.0	11.3	125	123.1	21.7	185	182.2	32.1	245	241.3	42.5
6	5.9	1.0	66	65.0	11.5	126	124.1	21.9	186	183.2	32.3	246	242.3	42.7
7	6.9	1.2	67	66.0	11.6	127	125.1	22.1	187	184.2	32.5	247	243.2	42.9
8	7.9	1.4	68	67.0	11.8	128	126.1	22.2	188	185.1	32.6	248	244.2	43.1
9	8.9	1.6	69	68.0	12.0	129	127.0	22.4	189	186.1	32.8	249	245.2	43.2
10	9.8	1.7	70	68.9	12.2	130	128.0	22.6	190	187.1	33.0	250	246.2	43.4
11	10.8	1.9	71	69.9	12.3	131	129.0	22.7	191	188.1	33.2	251	247.2	43.6
12	11.8	2.1	72	70.9	12.5	132	130.0	22.9	192	189.1	33.3	252	248.2	43.8
13	12.8	2.3	73	71.9	12.7	133	131.0	23.1	193	190.1	33.5	253	249.2	43.9
14	13.8	2.4	74	72.9	12.8	134	132.0	23.3	194	191.1	33.7	254	250.1	44.1
15	14.8	2.6	75	73.9	13.0	135	132.9	23.4	195	192.0	33.9	255	251.1	44.3
16	15.8	2.8	76	74.8	13.2	136	133.9	23.6	196	193.0	34.0	256	252.1	44.5
17	16.7	3.0	77	75.8	13.4	137	134.9	23.8	197	194.0	34.2	257	253.1	44.6
18	17.7	3.1	78	76.8	13.5	138	135.9	24.0	198	195.0	34.4	258	254.1	44.8
19	18.7	3.3	79	77.8	13.7	139	136.9	24.1	199	196.0	34.6	259	255.1	45.0
20	19.7	3.5	80	78.8	13.9	140	137.9	24.3	200	197.0	34.7	260	256.1	45.1
21	20.7	3.6	81	79.8	14.1	141	138.9	24.5	201	197.9	34.9	261	257.0	45.3
22	21.7	3.8	82	80.8	14.2	142	139.8	24.7	202	198.9	35.1	262	258.0	45.5
23	22.7	4.0	83	81.7	14.4	143	140.8	24.8	203	199.9	35.3	263	259.0	45.7
24	23.6	4.2	84	82.7	14.6	144	141.8	25.0	204	200.9	35.4	264	260.0	45.8
25	24.6	4.3	85	83.7	14.8	145	142.8	25.2	205	201.9	35.6	265	261.0	46.0
26	25.6	4.5	86	84.7	14.9	146	143.8	25.4	206	202.9	35.8	266	262.0	46.2
27	26.6	4.7	87	85.7	15.1	147	144.8	25.5	207	203.9	35.9	267	262.9	46.4
28	27.6	4.9	88	86.7	15.3	148	145.8	25.7	208	204.8	36.1	268	263.9	46.5
29	28.6	5.0	89	87.6	15.5	149	146.7	25.9	209	205.8	36.3	269	264.9	46.7
30	29.5	5.2	90	88.6	15.6	150	147.7	26.0	210	206.8	36.5	270	265.9	46.9
31	30.5	5.4	91	89.6	15.8	151	148.7	26.2	211	207.8	36.6	271	266.9	47.1
32	31.5	5.6	92	90.6	16.0	152	149.7	26.4	212	208.8	36.8	272	267.9	47.2
33	32.5	5.7	93	91.6	16.1	153	150.7	26.6	213	209.8	37.0	273	268.9	47.4
34	33.5	5.9	94	92.6	16.3	154	151.7	26.7	214	210.7	37.2	274	269.8	47.6
35	34.5	6.1	95	93.6	16.5	155	152.6	26.9	215	211.7	37.3	275	270.8	47.8
36	35.5	6.3	96	94.5	16.7	156	153.6	27.1	216	212.7	37.5	276	271.8	47.9
37	36.4	6.4	97	95.5	16.8	157	154.6	27.3	217	213.7	37.7	277	272.8	48.1
38	37.4	6.6	98	96.5	17.0	158	155.6	27.4	218	214.7	37.9	278	273.8	48.3
39	38.4	6.8	99	97.5	17.2	159	156.6	27.6	219	215.7	38.0	279	274.8	48.4
40	39.4	6.9	100	98.5	17.4	160	157.6	27.8	220	216.7	38.2	280	275.7	48.6
41	40.4	7.1	101	99.5	17.5	161	158.6	28.0	221	217.6	38.4	281	276.7	48.8
42	41.4	7.3	102	100.5	17.7	162	159.5	28.1	222	218.6	38.5	282	277.7	49.0
43	42.3	7.5	103	101.4	17.9	163	160.5	28.3	223	219.6	38.7	283	278.7	49.1
44	43.3	7.6	104	102.4	18.1	164	161.5	28.5	224	220.6	38.9	284	279.7	49.3
45	44.3	7.8	105	103.4	18.2	165	162.5	28.7	225	221.6	39.1	285	280.7	49.5
46	45.3	8.0	106	104.4	18.4	166	163.5	28.8	226	222.6	39.2	286	281.7	49.7
47	46.3	8.2	107	105.4	18.6	167	164.5	29.0	227	223.6	39.4	287	282.6	49.8
48	47.3	8.3	108	106.4	18.8	168	165.4	29.2	228	224.5	39.6	288	283.6	50.0
49	48.3	8.5	109	107.3	18.9	169	166.4	29.3	229	225.5	39.8	289	284.6	50.2
50	49.2	8.7	110	108.3	19.1	170	167.4	29.5	230	226.5	39.9	290	285.6	50.4
51	50.2	8.9	111	109.3	19.3	171	168.4	29.7	231	227.5	40.1	291	286.6	50.5
52	51.2	9.0	112	110.3	19.4	172	169.4	29.9	232	228.5	40.3	292	287.6	50.7
53	52.2	9.2	113	111.3	19.6	173	170.4	30.0	233	229.5	40.5	293	288.5	50.9
54	53.2	9.4	114	112.3	19.8	174	171.4	30.2	234	230.4	40.6	294	289.5	51.1
55	54.2	9.6	115	113.3	20.0	175	172.3	30.4	235	231.4	40.8	295	290.5	51.2
56	55.1	9.7	116	114.2	20.1	176	173.3	30.6	236	232.4	41.0	296	291.5	51.4
57	56.1	9.9	117	115.2	20.3	177	174.3	30.7	237	233.4	41.2	297	292.5	51.6
58	57.1	10.1	118	116.2	20.5	178	175.3	30.9	238	234.4	41.3	298	293.5	51.7
59	58.1	10.2	119	117.2	20.7	179	176.3	31.1	239	235.4	41.5	299	294.5	51.9
60	59.1	10.4	120	118.2	20.8	180	177.3	31.3	240	236.4	41.7	300	295.4	52.1
Hyp.	Opp.	Adj.	Hyp.	Opp.	Adj.	Hyp.	Opp.	Adj.	Hyp.	Opp.	Adj.	Hyp.	Opp.	Adj.

Dist. D Lon	Dep.	D. Lat. Dep	Dist. D Lon	Dep.	D. Lat. Dep	Dist. D Lon	Dep.	D. Lat. Dep	Dist. D Lon	Dep.	D. Lat. Dep	Dist. D Lon	Dep.	D. Lat. Dep

80°

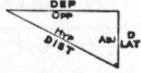

80°

Table 3   **TRAVERSE TABLE**

10°

350° | 010°
190° | 170°

10°

D Lon	Dep		D Lon	Dep		D Lon	Dep		D Lon	Dep		D Lon	Dep	
Dist.	D. Lat.	Dep.	Dist.	D. Lat.	Dep.	Dist.	D. Lat.	Dep.	Dist.	D. Lat.	Dep.	Dist.	D. Lat.	Dep.
Hyp.	*Adj.*	*Opp.*	*Hyp.*	*Adj.*	*Opp.*	*Hyp.*	*Adj.*	*Opp.*	*Hyp.*	*Adj.*	*Opp.*	*Hyp.*	*Adj.*	*Opp.*
301	296.4	52.3	361	355.5	62.7	421	414.6	73.1	481	473.7	83.5	541	532.8	93.9
302	297.4	52.4	362	356.5	62.9	422	415.6	73.3	482	474.7	83.7	542	533.8	94.1
303	298.4	52.6	363	357.5	63.0	423	416.6	73.5	483	475.7	83.9	543	534.8	94.3
304	299.4	52.8	364	358.5	63.2	424	417.6	73.6	484	476.6	84.0	544	535.7	94.5
305	300.4	53.0	365	359.5	63.4	425	418.5	73.8	485	477.6	84.2	545	536.7	94.6
306	301.4	53.1	366	360.4	63.6	426	419.5	74.0	486	478.6	84.4	546	537.7	94.8
307	302.3	53.3	367	361.4	63.7	427	420.5	74.1	487	479.6	84.6	547	538.7	95.0
308	303.3	53.5	368	362.4	63.9	428	421.5	74.3	488	480.6	84.7	548	539.7	95.2
309	304.3	53.7	369	363.4	64.1	429	422.5	74.5	489	481.6	84.9	549	540.7	95.3
310	305.3	53.8	370	364.4	64.2	430	423.5	74.7	490	482.6	85.1	550	541.6	95.5
311	306.3	54.0	371	365.4	64.4	431	424.5	74.8	491	483.5	85.3	551	542.6	95.7
312	307.3	54.2	372	366.4	64.6	432	425.4	75.0	492	484.5	85.4	552	543.6	95.9
313	308.2	54.4	373	367.3	64.8	433	426.4	75.2	493	485.5	85.6	553	544.6	96.0
314	309.2	54.5	374	368.3	64.9	434	427.4	75.4	494	486.5	85.8	554	545.6	96.2
315	310.2	54.7	375	369.3	65.1	435	428.4	75.5	495	487.5	86.0	555	546.6	96.4
316	311.2	54.9	376	370.3	65.3	436	429.4	75.7	496	488.5	86.1	556	547.6	96.5
317	312.2	55.0	377	371.3	65.5	437	430.4	75.9	497	489.4	86.3	557	548.5	96.7
318	313.2	55.2	378	372.3	65.6	438	431.3	76.1	498	490.4	86.5	558	549.5	96.9
319	314.2	55.4	379	373.2	65.8	439	432.3	76.2	499	491.4	86.7	559	550.5	97.1
320	315.1	55.6	380	374.2	66.0	440	433.3	76.4	500	492.4	86.8	560	551.5	97.2
321	316.1	55.7	381	375.2	66.2	441	434.3	76.6	501	493.4	87.0	561	552.5	97.4
322	317.1	55.9	382	376.2	66.3	442	435.3	76.8	502	494.4	87.2	562	553.5	97.6
323	318.1	56.1	383	377.2	66.5	443	436.3	76.9	503	495.4	87.3	563	554.4	97.8
324	319.1	56.3	384	378.2	66.7	444	437.3	77.1	504	496.3	87.5	564	555.4	97.9
325	320.1	56.4	385	379.2	66.9	445	438.2	77.3	505	497.3	87.7	565	556.4	98.1
326	321.0	56.6	386	380.1	67.0	446	439.2	77.4	506	498.3	87.9	566	557.4	98.3
327	322.0	56.8	387	381.1	67.2	447	440.2	77.6	507	499.3	88.0	567	558.4	98.5
328	323.0	57.0	388	382.1	67.4	448	441.2	77.8	508	500.3	88.2	568	559.4	98.6
329	324.0	57.1	389	383.1	67.5	449	442.2	78.0	509	501.3	88.4	569	560.4	98.8
330	325.0	57.3	390	384.1	67.7	450	443.2	78.1	510	502.3	88.6	570	561.3	99.0
331	326.0	57.5	391	385.1	67.9	451	444.1	78.3	511	503.2	88.7	571	562.3	99.2
332	327.0	57.7	392	386.0	68.1	452	445.1	78.5	512	504.2	88.9	572	563.3	99.3
333	327.9	57.8	393	387.0	68.2	453	446.1	78.7	513	505.2	89.1	573	564.3	99.5
334	328.9	58.0	394	388.0	68.4	454	447.1	78.8	514	506.2	89.2	574	565.3	99.7
335	329.9	58.2	395	389.0	68.6	455	448.1	79.0	515	507.2	89.4	575	566.3	99.8
336	330.9	58.3	396	390.0	68.8	456	449.1	79.2	516	508.2	89.6	576	567.2	100.0
337	331.9	58.5	397	391.0	68.9	457	450.1	79.4	517	509.1	89.8	577	568.2	100.2
338	332.9	58.7	398	392.0	69.1	458	451.0	79.5	518	510.1	89.9	578	569.2	100.4
339	333.8	58.9	399	392.9	69.3	459	452.0	79.7	519	511.1	90.1	579	570.2	100.5
340	334.8	59.0	400	393.9	69.5	460	453.0	79.9	520	512.1	90.3	580	571.2	100.7
341	335.8	59.2	401	394.9	69.6	461	454.0	80.1	521	513.1	90.5	581	572.2	100.9
342	336.8	59.4	402	395.9	69.8	462	455.0	80.2	522	514.1	90.6	582	573.2	101.1
343	337.8	59.6	403	396.9	70.0	463	456.0	80.4	523	515.1	90.8	583	574.1	101.2
344	338.8	59.7	404	397.9	70.2	464	457.0	80.6	524	516.0	91.0	584	575.1	101.4
345	339.8	59.9	405	398.9	70.3	465	457.9	80.7	525	517.0	91.2	585	576.1	101.6
346	340.7	60.1	406	399.8	70.5	466	458.9	80.9	526	518.0	91.3	586	577.1	101.8
347	341.7	60.3	407	400.8	70.7	467	459.9	81.1	527	519.0	91.5	587	578.1	101.9
348	342.7	60.4	408	401.8	70.8	468	460.9	81.3	528	520.0	91.7	588	579.1	102.1
349	343.7	60.6	409	402.8	71.0	469	461.9	81.4	529	521.0	91.9	589	580.1	102 3
350	344.7	60.8	410	403.8	71.2	470	462.9	81.6	530	521.9	92.0	590	581.0	102.5
351	345.7	61.0	411	404.8	71.4	471	463.8	81.8	531	522.9	92.2	591	582.0	102.6
352	346.7	61.1	412	405.7	71.5	472	464.8	82.0	532	523.9	92.4	592	583.0	102.8
353	347.6	61.3	413	406.7	71.7	473	465.8	82.1	533	524.9	92.6	593	584.0	103.0
354	348.6	61.5	414	407.7	71.9	474	466.8	82.3	534	525.9	92.7	594	585.0	103.1
355	349.6	61.6	415	408.7	72.1	475	467.8	82.5	535	526.9	92.9	595	586.0	103.3
356	350.6	61.8	416	409.7	72.2	476	468.8	82.7	536	527.9	93.1	596	586.9	103.5
357	351.6	62.0	417	410.7	72.4	477	469.8	82.8	537	528.8	93.2	597	587.9	103.7
358	352.6	62.2	418	411.6	72.6	478	470.7	83.0	538	529.8	93.4	598	588.9	103.8
359	353.5	62.3	419	412.6	72.8	479	471.7	83.2	539	530.8	93.6	599	589.9	104.0
360	354.5	62.5	420	413.6	72.9	480	472.7	83.4	540	531.8	93.8	600	590.9	104.2
Hyp.	*Opp.*	*Adj.*	*Hyp.*	*Opp.*	*Adj.*	*Hyp.*	*Opp.*	*Adj.*	*Hyp.*	*Opp.*	*Adj.*	*Hyp.*	*Opp.*	*Adj.*
Dist.	Dep.	D. Lat.	Dist.	Dep.	D. Lat.	Dist.	Dep.	D. Lat.	Dist.	Dep.	D. Lat.	Dist.	Dep.	D. Lat.
D Lon		Dep	D Lon		Dep	D Lon		Dep	D Lon		Dep	D Lon		Dep

80°

280° | 080°
260° | 100°

80°

Table 3

TRAVERSE TABLE

11°   11°

Hyp.	Adj.	Opp.	Hyp.	Adj.	Opp.	Hyp.	Adj.	Opp.	Hyp.	Adj.	Opp.	Hyp.	Adj.	Opp.
1	1.0	0.2	61	59.9	11.6	121	118.8	23.1	181	177.7	34.5	241	236.6	46.0
2	2.0	0.4	62	60.9	11.8	122	119.8	23.3	182	178.7	34.7	242	237.6	46.2
3	2.9	0.6	63	61.8	12.0	123	120.7	23.5	183	179.6	34.9	243	238.5	46.4
4	3.9	0.8	64	62.8	12.2	124	121.7	23.7	184	180.6	35.1	244	239.5	46.6
5	4.9	1.0	65	63.8	12.4	125	122.7	23.9	185	181.6	35.3	245	240.5	46.7
6	5.9	1.1	66	64.8	12.6	126	123.7	24.0	186	182.6	35.5	246	241.5	46.9
7	6.9	1.3	67	65.8	12.8	127	124.7	24.2	187	183.6	35.7	247	242.5	47.1
8	7.9	1.5	68	66.8	13.0	128	125.6	24.4	188	184.5	35.9	248	243.4	47.3
9	8.8	1.7	69	67.7	13.2	129	126.6	24.6	189	185.5	36.1	249	244.4	47.5
10	9.8	1.9	70	68.7	13.4	130	127.6	24.8	190	186.5	36.3	250	245.4	47.7
11	10.8	2.1	71	69.7	13.5	131	128.6	25.0	191	187.5	36.4	251	246.4	47.9
12	11.8	2.3	72	70.7	13.7	132	129.6	25.2	192	188.5	36.6	252	247.4	48.1
13	12.8	2.5	73	71.7	13.9	133	130.6	25.4	193	189.5	36.8	253	248.4	48.3
14	13.7	2.7	74	72.6	14.1	134	131.5	25.6	194	190.4	37.0	254	249.3	48.5
15	14.7	2.9	75	73.6	14.3	135	132.5	25.8	195	191.4	37.2	255	250.3	48.7
16	15.7	3.1	76	74.6	14.5	136	133.5	26.0	196	192.4	37.4	256	251.3	48.8
17	16.7	3.2	77	75.6	14.7	137	134.5	26.1	197	193.4	37.6	257	252.3	49.0
18	17.7	3.4	78	76.6	14.9	138	135.5	26.3	198	194.4	37.8	258	253.3	49.2
19	18.7	3.6	79	77.5	15.1	139	136.4	26.5	199	195.3	38.0	259	254.2	49.4
20	19.6	3.8	80	78.5	15.3	140	137.4	26.7	200	196.3	38.2	260	255.2	49.6
21	20.6	4.0	81	79.5	15.5	141	138.4	26.9	201	197.3	38.4	261	256.2	49.8
22	21.6	4.2	82	80.5	15.6	142	139.4	27.1	202	198.3	38.5	262	257.2	50.0
23	22.6	4.4	83	81.5	15.8	143	140.4	27.3	203	199.3	38.7	263	258.2	50.2
24	23.6	4.6	84	82.5	16.0	144	141.4	27.5	204	200.3	38.9	264	259.1	50.4
25	24.5	4.8	85	83.4	16.2	145	142.3	27.7	205	201.2	39.1	265	260.1	50.6
26	25.5	5.0	86	84.4	16.4	146	143.3	27.9	206	202.2	39.3	266	261.1	50.8
27	26.5	5.2	87	85.4	16.6	147	144.3	28.0	207	203.2	39.5	267	262.1	50.9
28	27.5	5.3	88	86.4	16.8	148	145.3	28.2	208	204.2	39.7	268	263.1	51.1
29	28.5	5.5	89	87.4	17.0	149	146.3	28.4	209	205.2	39.9	269	264.1	51.3
30	29.4	5.7	90	88.3	17.2	150	147.2	28.6	210	206.1	40.1	270	265.0	51.5
31	30.4	5.9	91	89.3	17.4	151	148.2	28.8	211	207.1	40.3	271	266.0	51.7
32	31.4	6.1	92	90.3	17.6	152	149.2	29.0	212	208.1	40.5	272	267.0	51.9
33	32.4	6.3	93	91.3	17.7	153	150.2	29.2	213	209.1	40.6	273	268.0	52.1
34	33.4	6.5	94	92.3	17.9	154	151.2	29.4	214	210.1	40.8	274	269.0	52.3
35	34.4	6.7	95	93.3	18.1	155	152.2	29.6	215	211.0	41.0	275	269.9	52.5
36	35.3	6.9	96	94.2	18.3	156	153.1	29.8	216	212.0	41.2	276	270.9	52.7
37	36.3	7.1	97	95.2	18.5	157	154.1	30.0	217	213.0	41.4	277	271.9	52.9
38	37.3	7.3	98	96.2	18.7	158	155.1	30.1	218	214.0	41.6	278	272.9	53.0
39	38.3	7.4	99	97.2	18.9	159	156.1	30.3	219	215.0	41.8	279	273.9	53.2
40	39.3	7.6	100	98.2	19.1	160	157.1	30.5	220	216.0	42.0	280	274.9	53.4
41	40.2	7.8	101	99.1	19.3	161	158.0	30.7	221	216.9	42.2	281	275.8	53.6
42	41.2	8.0	102	100.1	19.5	162	159.0	30.9	222	217.9	42.4	282	276.8	53.8
43	42.2	8.2	103	101.1	19.7	163	160.0	31.1	223	218.9	42.6	283	277.8	54.0
44	43.2	8.4	104	102.1	19.8	164	161.0	31.3	224	219.9	42.7	284	278.8	54.2
45	44.2	8.6	105	103.1	20.0	165	162.0	31.5	225	220.9	42.9	285	279.8	54.4
46	45.2	8.8	106	104.1	20.2	166	163.0	31.7	226	221.8	43.1	286	280.7	54.6
47	46.1	9.0	107	105.0	20.4	167	163.9	31.9	227	222.8	43.3	287	281.7	54.8
48	47.1	9.2	108	106.0	20.6	168	164.9	32.1	228	223.8	43.5	288	282.7	55.0
49	48.1	9.3	109	107.0	20.8	169	165.9	32.2	229	224.8	43.7	289	283.7	55.1
50	49.1	9.5	110	108 0	21.0	170	166.9	32.4	230	225.8	43.9	290	284.7	55.3
51	50.1	9.7	111	109.0	21.2	171	167.9	32.6	231	226.8	44.1	291	285.7	55.5
52	51.0	9.9	112	109.9	21.4	172	168.8	32.8	232	227.7	44.3	292	286.6	55.7
53	52.0	10.1	113	110.9	21.6	173	169.8	33.0	233	228.7	44.5	293	287.6	55.9
54	53.0	10.3	114	111.9	21.8	174	170.8	33.2	234	229.7	44.6	294	288.6	56.1
55	54.0	10.5	115	112.9	21.9	175	171.8	33.4	235	230.7	44.8	295	289.6	56.3
56	55.0	10.7	116	113.9	22.1	176	172.8	33.6	236	231.7	45.0	296	290.6	56.5
57	56.0	10.9	117	114.9	22.3	177	173.7	33.8	237	232.6	45.2	297	291.5	56.7
58	56.9	11.1	118	115.8	22.5	178	174.7	34.0	238	233.6	45.4	298	292.5	56.9
59	57.9	11.3	119	116.8	22.7	179	175.7	34.2	239	234.6	45.6	299	293.5	57.1
60	58.9	11.4	120	117.8	22.9	180	176.7	34.3	240	235.6	45.8	300	294.5	57.2
Hyp.	Opp.	Adj.	Hyp.	Opp.	Adj.	Hyp.	Opp.	Adj.	Hyp.	Opp.	Adj.	Hyp.	Opp.	Adj.

Dist.	Dep.	D. Lat.	Dist.	Dep.	D. Lat.	Dist.	Dep.	D. Lat.	Dist.	Dep.	D. Lat.	Dist.	Dep.	D. Lat.
D Lon		Dep	D Lon		Dep	D Lon		Dep	D Lon		Dep	D Lon		Dep

79°   79°

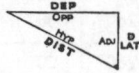

Table 3

TRAVERSE TABLE

11°

	349°	011°
	191°	169°

11°

D Lon Dist. Hyp.	Dep D. Lat. Adj.	 Dep. Opp.	D Lon Dist. Hyp.	Dep D. Lat. Adj.	 Dep. Opp.	D Lon Dist. Hyp.	Dep D. Lat. Adj.	 Dep. Opp.	D Lon Dist. Hyp.	Dep D. Lat. Adj.	 Dep. Opp.	D Lon Dist. Hyp.	Dep D. Lat. Adj.	 Dep. Opp.
301	295.5	57.4	361	354.4	68.9	421	413.3	80.3	481	472.2	91.8	541	531.1	103.2
302	296.5	57.6	362	355.3	69.1	422	414.2	80.5	482	473.1	92.0	542	532.0	103.4
303	297.4	57.8	363	356.3	69.3	423	415.2	80.7	483	474.1	92.2	543	533.0	103.6
304	298.4	58.0	364	357.3	69.5	424	416.2	80.9	484	475.1	92.4	544	534.0	103.8
305	299.4	58.2	365	358.3	69.6	425	417.2	81.1	485	476.1	92.5	545	535.0	104.0
306	300.4	58.4	366	359.3	69.8	426	418.2	81.3	486	477.1	92.7	546	536.0	104.2
307	301.4	58.6	367	360.3	70.0	427	419.2	81.5	487	478.1	92.9	547	537.0	104.4
308	302.3	58.8	368	361.2	70.2	428	420.1	81.7	488	479.0	93.1	548	537.9	104.6
309	303.3	59.0	369	362.2	70.4	429	421.1	81.9	489	480.0	93.3	549	538.9	104.8
310	304.3	59.2	370	363.2	70.6	430	422.1	82.0	490	481.0	93.5	550	539.9	104.9
311	305.3	59.3	371	364.2	70.8	431	423.1	82.2	491	482.0	93.7	551	540.9	105.1
312	306.3	59.5	372	365.2	71.0	432	424.1	82.4	492	483.0	93.9	552	541.9	105.3
313	307.2	59.7	373	366.1	71.2	433	425.0	82.6	493	483.9	94.1	553	542.8	105.5
314	308.2	59.9	374	367.1	71.4	434	426.0	82.8	494	484.9	94.3	554	543.8	105.7
315	309.2	60.1	375	368.1	71.6	435	427.0	83.0	495	485.9	94.5	555	544.8	105.9
316	310.2	60.3	376	369.1	71.7	436	428.0	83.2	496	486.9	94.6	556	545.8	106.1
317	311.2	60.5	377	370.1	71.9	437	429.0	83.4	497	487.9	94.8	557	546.8	106.3
318	312.2	60.7	378	371.1	72.1	438	430.0	83.6	498	488.9	95.0	558	547.7	106.5
319	313.1	60.9	379	372.0	72.3	439	430.9	83.8	499	489.8	95.2	559	548.7	106.7
320	314.1	61.1	380	373.0	72.5	440	431.9	84.0	500	490.8	95.4	560	549.7	106.9
321	315.1	61.2	381	374.0	72.7	441	432.9	84.1	501	491.8	95.6	561	550.7	107.0
322	316.1	61.4	382	375.0	72.9	442	433.9	84.3	502	492.8	95.8	562	551.7	107.2
323	317.1	61.6	383	376.0	73.1	443	434.9	84.5	503	493.8	96.0	563	552.7	107.4
324	318.0	61.8	384	376.9	73.3	444	435.8	84.7	504	494.7	96.2	564	553.6	107.6
325	319.0	62.0	385	377.9	73.5	445	436.8	84.9	505	495.7	96.4	565	554.6	107.8
326	320.0	62.2	386	378.9	73.7	446	437.8	85.1	506	496.7	96.5	566	555.6	108.0
327	321.0	62.4	387	379.9	73.8	447	438.8	85.3	507	497.7	96.7	567	556.6	108.2
328	322.0	62.6	388	380.9	74.0	448	439.8	85.5	508	498.7	96.9	568	557.6	108.4
329	323.0	62.8	389	381.9	74.2	449	440.8	85.7	509	499.6	97.1	569	558.5	108.6
330	323.9	63.0	390	382.8	74.4	450	441.7	85.9	510	500.6	97.3	570	559.5	108.8
331	324.9	63.2	391	383.8	74.6	451	442.7	86.1	511	501.6	97.5	571	560.5	109.0
332	325.9	63.3	392	384.8	74.8	452	443.7	86.2	512	502.6	97.7	572	561.5	109.1
333	326.9	63.5	393	385.8	75.0	453	444.7	86.4	513	503.6	97.9	573	562.5	109.3
334	327.9	63.7	394	386.8	75.2	454	445.7	86.6	514	504.6	98.1	574	563.5	109.5
335	328.8	63.9	395	387.7	75.4	455	446.6	86.8	515	505.5	98.3	575	564.4	109.7
336	329.8	61.1	396	388.7	75.6	456	447.6	87.0	516	506.5	98.5	576	565.4	109.9
337	330.8	64.3	397	389.7	75.8	457	448.6	87.2	517	507.5	98.6	577	566.4	110.1
338	331.8	64.5	398	390.7	75.9	458	449.6	87.4	518	508.5	98.8	578	567.4	110.3
339	332.8	64.7	399	391.7	76.1	459	450.6	87.6	519	509.5	99.0	579	568.4	110.5
340	333.8	64.9	400	392.7	76.3	460	451.5	87.8	520	510.4	99.2	580	569.3	110.7
341	334.7	65.1	401	393.6	76.5	461	452.5	88.0	521	511.4	99.4	581	570.3	110.9
342	335.7	65.3	402	394.6	76.7	462	453.5	88.2	522	512.4	99.6	582	571.3	111.1
343	336.7	65.4	403	395.6	76.9	463	454.5	88.3	523	513.4	99.8	583	572.3	111.2
344	337.7	65.6	404	396.6	77.1	464	455.5	88.5	524	514.4	100.0	584	573.3	111.4
345	338.7	65.8	405	397.6	77.3	465	456.5	88.7	525	515.4	100.2	585	574.3	111.6
346	339.6	66.0	406	398.5	77.5	466	457.4	88.9	526	516.3	100.4	586	575.2	111.8
347	340.6	66.2	407	399.5	77.7	467	458.4	89.1	527	517.3	100.6	587	576.2	112.1
348	341.6	66.4	408	400.5	77.9	468	459.4	89.3	528	518.3	100.7	588	577.2	112.3
349	342.6	66.6	409	401.5	78.0	469	460.4	89.5	529	519.3	100.9	589	578.2	112.4
350	343.6	66.8	410	402.5	78.2	470	461.4	89.7	530	520.3	101.1	590	579.2	112.6
351	344.6	67.0	411	403.4	78.4	471	462.3	89.9	531	521.2	101.3	591	580.1	112.8
352	345.5	67.2	412	404.4	78.6	472	463.3	90.1	532	522.2	101.5	592	581.1	113.0
353	346.5	67.4	413	405.4	78.8	473	464.3	90.3	533	523.2	101.7	593	582.1	113.2
354	347.5	67.5	414	406.4	79.0	474	465.3	90.4	534	524.2	101.9	594	583.1	113.3
355	348.5	67.7	415	407.4	79.2	475	466.3	90.6	535	525.2	102.1	595	584.1	113.5
356	349.5	67.9	416	408.4	79.4	476	467.3	90.8	536	526.2	102.3	596	585.0	113.7
357	350.4	68.1	417	409.3	79.6	477	468.2	91.0	537	527.1	102.5	597	586.0	113.9
358	351.4	68.3	418	410.3	79.8	478	469.2	91.2	538	528.1	102.7	598	587.0	114.1
359	352.4	68.5	419	411.3	79.9	479	470.2	91.4	539	529.1	102.8	599	588.0	114.3
360	353.4	68.7	420	412.3	80.1	480	471.2	91.6	540	530.1	103.0	600	589.0	114.5
Hyp.	Opp.	Adj.	Hyp.	Opp.	Adj.	Hyp.	Opp.	Adj.	Hyp.	Opp.	Adj.	Hyp.	Opp.	Adj.

Dist. D Lon	Dep.	D. Lat. Dep	Dist. D Lon	Dep.	D. Lat. Dep	Dist. D Lon	Dep.	D. Lat. Dep	Dist. D Lon	Dep.	D. Lat. Dep	Dist. D Lon	Dep.	D. Lat. Dep

79°

	281°	079°
	259°	101°

79°

Table 3

TRAVERSE TABLE

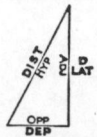

12°   12°

D Lon Dist. Hyp.	Dep D. Lat. Adj.	 Dep. Opp.	D Lon Dist. Hyp.	Dep D. Lat. Adj.	 Dep. Opp.	D Lon Dist. Hyp.	Dep D. Lat. Adj.	 Dep. Opp.	D Lon Dist. Hyp.	Dep D. Lat. Adj.	 Dep. Opp.	D Lon Dist. Hyp.	Dep D. Lat. Adj.	 Dep. Opp.
1	1.0	0.2	61	59.7	12.7	121	118.4	25.2	181	177.0	37.6	241	235.7	50.1
2	2.0	0.4	62	60.6	12.9	122	119.3	25.4	182	178.0	37.8	242	236.7	50.3
3	2.9	0.6	63	61.6	13.1	123	120.3	25.6	183	179.0	38.0	243	237.7	50.5
4	3.9	0.8	64	62.6	13.3	124	121.3	25.8	184	180.0	38.3	244	238.7	50.7
5	4.9	1.0	65	63.6	13.5	125	122.3	26.0	185	181.0	38.5	245	239.6	50.9
6	5.9	1.2	66	64.6	13.7	126	123.2	26.2	186	181.9	38.7	246	240.6	51.1
7	6.8	1.5	67	65.5	13.9	127	124.2	26.4	187	182.9	38.9	247	241.6	51.4
8	7.8	1.7	68	66.5	14.1	128	125.2	26.6	188	183.9	39.1	248	242.6	51.6
9	8.8	1.9	69	67.5	14.3	129	126.2	26.8	189	184.9	39.3	249	243.6	51.8
10	9.8	2.1	70	68.5	14.6	130	127.2	27.0	190	185.8	39.5	250	244.5	52.0
11	10.8	2.3	71	69.4	14.8	131	128.1	27.2	191	186.8	39.7	251	245.5	52.2
12	11.7	2.5	72	70.4	15.0	132	129.1	27.4	192	187.8	39.9	252	246.5	52.4
13	12.7	2.7	73	71.4	15.2	133	130.1	27.7	193	188.8	40.1	253	247.5	52.6
14	13.7	2.9	74	72.4	15.4	134	131.1	27.9	194	189.8	40.3	254	248.4	52.8
15	14.7	3.1	75	73.4	15.6	135	132.0	28.1	195	190.7	40.5	255	249.4	53.0
16	15.7	3.3	76	74.3	15.8	136	133.0	28.3	196	191.7	40.8	256	250.4	53.2
17	16.6	3.5	77	75.3	16.0	137	134.0	28.5	197	192.7	41.0	257	251.4	53.4
18	17.6	3.7	78	76.3	16.2	138	135.0	28.7	198	193.7	41.2	258	252.4	53.6
19	18.6	4.0	79	77.3	16.4	139	136.0	28.9	199	194.7	41.4	259	253.3	53.8
20	19.6	4.2	80	78.3	16.6	140	136.9	29.1	200	195.6	41.6	260	254.3	54.1
21	20.5	4.4	81	79.2	16.8	141	137.9	29.3	201	196.6	41.8	261	255.3	54.3
22	21.5	4.6	82	80.2	17.0	142	138.9	29.5	202	197.6	42.0	262	256.3	54.5
23	22.5	4.8	83	81.2	17.3	143	139.9	29.7	203	198.6	42.2	263	257.3	54.7
24	23.5	5.0	84	82.2	17.5	144	140.9	29.9	204	199.5	42.4	264	258.2	54.9
25	24.5	5.2	85	83.1	17.7	145	141.8	30.1	205	200.5	42.6	265	259.2	55.1
26	25.4	5.4	86	84.1	17.9	146	142.8	30.4	206	201.5	42.8	266	260.2	55.3
27	26.4	5.6	87	85.1	18.1	147	143.8	30.6	207	202.5	43.0	267	261.2	55.5
28	27.4	5.8	88	86.1	18.3	148	144.8	30.8	208	203.5	43.2	268	262.1	55.7
29	28.4	6.0	89	87.1	18.5	149	145.7	31.0	209	204.4	43.5	269	263.1	55.9
30	29.3	6.2	90	88.0	18.7	150	146.7	31.2	210	205.4	43.7	270	264.1	56.1
31	30.3	6.4	91	89.0	18.9	151	147.7	31.4	211	206.4	43.9	271	265.1	56.3
32	31.3	6.7	92	90.0	19.1	152	148.7	31.6	212	207.4	44.1	272	266.1	56.6
33	32.3	6.9	93	91.0	19.3	153	149.7	31.8	213	208.3	44.3	273	267.0	56.8
34	33.3	7.1	94	91.9	19.5	154	150.6	32.0	214	209.3	44.5	274	268.0	57.0
35	34.2	7.3	95	92.9	19.8	155	151.6	32.2	215	210.3	44.7	275	269.0	57.2
36	35.2	7.5	96	93.9	20.0	156	152.6	32.4	216	211.3	44.9	276	270.0	57.4
37	36.2	7.7	97	94.9	20.2	157	153.6	32.6	217	212.3	45.1	277	270.9	57.6
38	37.2	7.9	98	95.9	20.4	158	154.5	32.9	218	213.2	45.3	278	271.9	57.8
39	38.1	8.1	99	96.8	20.6	159	155.5	33.1	219	214.2	45.5	279	272.9	58.0
40	39.1	8.3	100	97.8	20.8	160	156.5	33.3	220	215.2	45.7	280	273.9	58.2
41	40.1	8.5	101	98.8	21.0	161	157.5	33.5	221	216.2	45.9	281	274.9	58.4
42	41.1	8.7	102	99.8	21.2	162	158.5	33.7	222	217.1	46.2	282	275.8	58.6
43	42.1	8.9	103	100.7	21.4	163	159.4	33.9	223	218.1	46.4	283	276.8	58.8
44	43.0	9.1	104	101.7	21.6	164	160.4	34.1	224	219.1	46.6	284	277.8	59.0
45	44.0	9.4	105	102.7	21.8	165	161.4	34.3	225	220.1	46.8	285	278.8	59.3
46	45.0	9.6	106	103.7	22.0	166	162.4	34.5	226	221.1	47.0	286	279.8	59.5
47	46.0	9.8	107	104.7	22.2	167	163.4	34.7	227	222.0	47.2	287	280.7	59.7
48	47.0	10.0	108	105.6	22.5	168	164.3	34.9	228	223.0	47.4	288	281.7	59.9
49	47.9	10.2	109	106.6	22.7	169	165.3	35.1	229	224.0	47.6	289	282.7	60.1
50	48.9	10.4	110	107.6	22.9	170	166.3	35.3	230	225.0	47.8	290	283.7	60.3
51	49.9	10.6	111	108.6	23.1	171	167.3	35.6	231	226.0	48.0	291	284.6	60.5
52	50.9	10.8	112	109.6	23.3	172	168.2	35.8	232	226.9	48.2	292	285.6	60.7
53	51.8	11.0	113	110.5	23.5	173	169.2	36.0	233	227.9	48.4	293	286.6	60.9
54	52.8	11.2	114	111.5	23.7	174	170.2	36.2	234	228.9	48.7	294	287.6	61.1
55	53.8	11.4	115	112.5	23.9	175	171.2	36.4	235	229.9	48.9	295	288.6	61.3
56	54.8	11.6	116	113.5	24.1	176	172.2	36.6	236	230.8	49.1	296	289.5	61.5
57	55.8	11.9	117	114.4	24.3	177	173.1	36.8	237	231.8	49.3	297	290.5	61.7
58	56.7	12.1	118	115.4	24.5	178	174.1	37.0	238	232.8	49.5	298	291.5	62.0
59	57.7	12.3	119	116.4	24.7	179	175.1	37.2	239	233.8	49.7	299	292.5	62.2
60	58.7	12.5	120	117.4	24.9	180	176.1	37.4	240	234.8	49.9	300	293.4	62.4
Hyp.	Opp.	Adj.	Hyp.	Opp.	Adj.	Hyp.	Opp.	Adj.	Hyp.	Opp.	Adj.	Hyp.	Opp.	Adj.

Dist. D Lon	Dep.	D. Lat. Dep	Dist. D Lon	Dep.	D. Lat. Dep	Dist. D Lon	Dep.	D. Lat. Dep	Dist. D Lon	Dep.	D. Lat. Dep	Dist. D Lon	Dep.	D. Lat. Dep

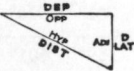

78°   78°

Table 3

TRAVERSE TABLE

12°

12°

D Lon Dep Dist. D. Lat. Dep.			D Lon Dep Dist. D. Lat. Dep.			D Lon Dep Dist. D. Lat. Dep.			D Lon Dep Dist. D. Lat. Dep.			D Lon Dep Dist. D. Lat. Dep.		
Hyp.	Adj.	Opp.	Hyp.	Adj.	Opp.	Hyp.	Adj.	Opp.	Hyp.	Adj.	Opp.	Hyp.	Adj.	Opp.
301	294.4	62.6	361	353.1	75.1	421	411.8	87.5	481	470.5	100.0	541	529.2	112.5
302	295.4	62.8	362	354.1	75.3	422	412.8	87.7	482	471.5	100.2	542	530.2	112.7
303	296.4	63.0	363	355.1	75.5	423	413.8	87.9	483	472.4	100.4	543	531.1	112.9
304	297.4	63.2	364	356.0	75.7	424	414.7	88.2	484	473.4	100.6	544	532.1	113.1
305	298.3	63.4	365	357.0	75.9	425	415.7	88.4	485	474.4	100.8	545	533.1	113.3
306	299.3	63.6	366	358.0	76.1	426	416.7	88.6	486	475.4	101.0	546	534.1	113.5
307	300.3	63.8	367	359.0	76.3	427	417.7	88.8	487	476.4	101.3	547	535.0	113.7
308	301.3	64.0	368	360.0	76.5	428	418.6	89.0	488	477.3	101.5	548	536.0	113.9
309	302.2	64.2	369	360.9	76.7	429	419.6	89.2	489	478.3	101.7	549	537.0	114.1
310	303.2	64.5	370	361.9	76.9	430	420.6	89.4	490	479.3	101.9	550	538.0	114.4
311	304.2	64.7	371	362.9	77.1	431	421.6	89.6	491	480.3	102.1	551	539.0	114.6
312	305.2	64.9	372	363.9	77.3	432	422.6	89.8	492	481.2	102.3	552	539.9	114.8
313	306.2	65.1	373	364.8	77.6	433	423.5	90.0	493	482.2	102.5	553	540.9	115.0
314	307.1	65.3	374	365.8	77.8	434	424.5	90.2	494	483.2	102.7	554	541.9	115.2
315	308.1	65.5	375	366.8	78.0	435	425.5	90.4	495	484.2	102.9	555	542.9	115.4
316	309.1	65.7	376	367.8	78.2	436	426.5	90.6	496	485.2	103.1	556	543.9	115.6
317	310.1	65.9	377	368.8	78.4	437	427.5	90.9	497	486.1	103.3	557	544.8	115.8
318	311.1	66.1	378	369.7	78.6	438	428.4	91.1	498	487.1	103.5	558	545.8	116.0
319	312.0	66.3	379	370.7	78.8	439	429.4	91.3	499	488.1	103.7	559	546.8	116.2
320	313.0	66.5	380	371.7	79.0	440	430.4	91.5	500	489.1	104.0	560	547.8	116.4
321	314.0	66.7	381	372.7	79.2	441	431.4	91.7	501	490.1	104.2	561	548.7	116.6
322	315.0	66.9	382	373.7	79.4	442	432.3	91.9	502	491.0	104.4	562	549.7	116.8
323	315.9	67.2	383	374.6	79.6	443	433.3	92.1	503	492.0	104.6	563	550.7	117.1
324	316.9	67.4	384	375.6	79.8	444	434.3	92.3	504	493.0	104.8	564	551.7	117.3
325	317.9	67.6	385	376.6	80.0	445	435.3	92.5	505	494.0	105.0	565	552.7	117.5
326	318.9	67.8	386	377.6	80.3	446	436.3	92.7	506	494.9	105.2	566	553.6	117.7
327	319.9	68.0	387	378.5	80.5	447	437.2	92.9	507	495.9	105.4	567	554.6	117.9
328	320.8	68.2	388	379.5	80.7	448	438.2	93.1	508	496.9	105.6	568	555.6	118.1
329	321.8	68.4	389	380.5	80.9	449	439.2	93.4	509	497.9	105.8	569	556.6	118.3
330	322.8	68.6	390	381.5	81.1	450	440.2	93.6	510	498.9	106.0	570	557.5	118.5
331	323.8	68.8	391	382.5	81.3	451	441.1	93.8	511	499.8	106.2	571	558.5	118.7
332	324.7	69.0	392	383.4	81.5	452	442.1	94.0	512	500.8	106.5	572	559.5	118.9
333	325.7	69.2	393	384.4	81.7	453	443.1	94.2	513	501.8	106.7	573	560.5	119.1
334	326.7	69.4	394	385.4	81.9	454	444.1	94.4	514	502.8	106.9	574	561.5	119.3
335	327.7	69.7	395	386.4	82.1	455	445.1	94.6	515	503.7	107.1	575	562.4	119.5
336	328.7	69.9	396	387.3	82.3	456	446.0	94.8	516	504.7	107.3	576	563.4	119.8
337	329.6	70.1	397	388.3	82.5	457	447.0	95.0	517	505.7	107.5	577	564.4	120.0
338	330.6	70.3	398	389.3	82.7	458	448.0	95.2	518	506.7	107.7	578	565.4	120.2
339	331.6	70.5	399	390.3	83.0	459	449.0	95.4	519	507.7	107.9	579	566.3	120.4
340	332.6	70.7	400	391.3	83.2	460	449.9	95.6	520	508.6	108.1	580	567.3	120.6
341	333.5	70.9	401	392.2	83.4	461	450.9	95.8	521	509.6	108.3	581	568.3	120.8
342	334.5	71.1	402	393.2	83.6	462	451.9	96.1	522	510.6	108.5	582	569.3	121.0
343	335.5	71.3	403	394.2	83.8	463	452.9	96.3	523	511.6	108.7	583	570.3	121.2
344	336.5	71.5	404	395.2	84.0	464	453.9	96.5	524	512.5	108.9	584	571.2	121.4
345	337.5	71.7	405	396.2	84.2	465	454.8	96.7	525	513.5	109.2	585	572.2	121.6
346	338.4	71.9	406	397.1	84.4	466	455.8	96.9	526	514.5	109.4	586	573.2	121.8
347	339.4	72.1	407	398.1	84.6	467	456.8	97.1	527	515.5	109.6	587	574.2	122.0
348	340.4	72.4	408	399.1	84.8	468	457.8	97.3	528	516.5	109.8	588	575.2	122.3
349	341.4	72.6	409	400.1	85.0	469	458.8	97.5	529	517.4	110.0	589	576.1	122.5
350	342.4	72.8	410	401.0	85.2	470	459.7	97.7	530	518.4	110.2	590	577.1	122.7
351	343.3	73.0	411	402.0	85.5	471	460.7	97.9	531	519.4	110.4	591	578.1	122.9
352	344.3	73.2	412	403.0	85.7	472	461.7	98.1	532	520.4	110.6	592	579.1	123.1
353	345.3	73.4	413	404.0	85.9	473	462.7	98.3	533	521.4	110.8	593	580.0	123.3
354	346.3	73.6	414	405.0	86.1	474	463.6	98.6	534	522.3	111.0	594	581.0	123.5
355	347.2	73.8	415	405.9	86.3	475	464.6	98.8	535	523.3	111.2	595	582.0	123.7
356	348.2	74.0	416	406.9	86.5	476	465.6	99.0	536	524.3	111.4	596	583.0	123.9
357	349.2	74.2	417	407.9	86.7	477	466.6	99.2	537	525.3	111.6	597	584.0	124.1
358	350.2	74.4	418	408.9	86.9	478	467.6	99.4	538	526.2	111.9	598	584.9	124.3
359	351.2	74.6	419	409.8	87.1	479	468.5	99.6	539	527.2	112.1	599	585.9	124.5
360	352.1	74.8	420	410.8	87.3	480	469.5	99.8	540	528.2	112.3	600	586.9	124.7
Hyp.	Opp.	Adj.	Hyp.	Opp.	Adj.	Hyp.	Opp.	Adj.	Hyp.	Opp.	Adj.	Hyp.	Opp.	Adj.

Dist. Dep. D. Lat. D Lon Dep			Dist. Dep. D. Lat. D Lon Dep			Dist. Dep. D. Lat. D Lon Dep			Dist. Dep. D. Lat. D Lon Dep			Dist. Dep. D. Lat. D Lon Dep		

78°

78°

Table 3

TRAVERSE TABLE

13°   13°

D Lon Dist.	Dep D.Lat.	Dep.	D Lon Dist.	Dep D.Lat.	Dep.	D Lon Dist.	Dep D.Lat.	Dep.	D Lon Dist.	Dep D.Lat.	Dep.	D Lon Dist.	Dep D.Lat.	Dep.
Hyp.	Adj.	Opp.	Hyp.	Adj.	Opp.	Hyp.	Adj.	Opp.	Hyp.	Adj.	Opp.	Hyp.	Adj.	Opp.
1	1.0	0.2	61	59.4	13.7	121	117.9	27.2	181	176.4	40.7	241	234.8	54.2
2	1.9	0.4	62	60.4	13.9	122	118.9	27.4	182	177.3	40.9	242	235.8	54.4
3	2.9	0.7	63	61.4	14.2	123	119.8	27.7	183	178.3	41.2	243	236.8	54.7
4	3.9	0.9	64	62.4	14.4	124	120.8	27.9	184	179.3	41.4	244	237.7	54.9
5	4.9	1.1	65	63.3	14.6	125	121.8	28.1	185	180.3	41.6	245	238.7	55.1
6	5.8	1.3	66	64.3	14.8	126	122.8	28.3	186	181.2	41.8	246	239.7	55.3
7	6.8	1.6	67	65.3	15.1	127	123.7	28.6	187	182.2	42.1	247	240.7	55.6
8	7.8	1.8	68	66.3	15.3	128	124.7	28.8	188	183.2	42.3	248	241.6	55.8
9	8.8	2.0	69	67.2	15.5	129	125.7	29.0	189	184.2	42.5	249	242.6	56.0
10	9.7	2.2	70	68.2	15.7	130	126.7	29.2	190	185.1	42.7	250	243.6	56.2
11	10.7	2.5	71	69.2	16.0	131	127.6	29.5	191	186.1	43.0	251	244.6	56.5
12	11.7	2.7	72	70.2	16.2	132	128.6	29.7	192	187.1	43.2	252	245.5	56.7
13	12.7	2.9	73	71.1	16.4	133	129.6	29.9	193	188.1	43.4	253	246.5	56.9
14	13.6	3.1	74	72.1	16.6	134	130.6	30.1	194	189.0	43.6	254	247.5	57.1
15	14.6	3.4	75	73.1	16.9	135	131.5	30.4	195	190.0	43.9	255	248.5	57.4
16	15.6	3.6	76	74.1	17.1	136	132.5	30.6	196	191.0	44.1	256	249.4	57.6
17	16.6	3.8	77	75.0	17.3	137	133.5	30.8	197	192.0	44.3	257	250.4	57.8
18	17.5	4.0	78	76.0	17.5	138	134.5	31.0	198	192.9	44.5	258	251.4	58.0
19	18.5	4.3	79	77.0	17.8	139	135.4	31.3	199	193.9	44.8	259	252.4	58.3
20	19.5	4.5	80	77.9	18.0	140	136.4	31.5	200	194.9	45.0	260	253.3	58.5
21	20.5	4.7	81	78.9	18.2	141	137.4	31.7	201	195.8	45.2	261	254.3	58.7
22	21.4	4.9	82	79.9	18.4	142	138.4	31.9	202	196.8	45.4	262	255.3	58.9
23	22.4	5.2	83	80.9	18.7	143	139.3	32.2	203	197.8	45.7	263	256.3	59.2
24	23.4	5.4	84	81.8	18.9	144	140.3	32.4	204	198.8	45.9	264	257.2	59.4
25	24.4	5.6	85	82.8	19.1	145	141.3	32.6	205	199.7	46.1	265	258.2	59.6
26	25.3	5.8	86	83.8	19.3	146	142.3	32.8	206	200.7	46.3	266	259.2	59.8
27	26.3	6.1	87	84.8	19.6	147	143.2	33.1	207	201.7	46.6	267	260.2	60.1
28	27.3	6.3	88	85.7	19.8	148	144.2	33.3	208	202.7	46.8	268	261.1	60.3
29	28.3	6.5	89	86.7	20.0	149	145.2	33.5	209	203.6	47.0	269	262.1	60.5
30	29.2	6.7	90	87.7	20.2	150	146.2	33.7	210	204.6	47.2	270	263.1	60.7
31	30.2	7.0	91	88.7	20.5	151	147.1	34.0	211	205.6	47.5	271	264.1	61.0
32	31.2	7.2	92	89.6	20.7	152	148.1	34.2	212	206.6	47.7	272	265.0	61.2
33	32.2	7.4	93	90.6	20.9	153	149.1	34.4	213	207.5	47.9	273	266.0	61.4
34	33.1	7.6	94	91.6	21.1	154	150.1	34.6	214	208.5	48.1	274	267.0	61.6
35	34.1	7.9	95	92.6	21.4	155	151.0	34.9	215	209.5	48.4	275	268.0	61.9
36	35.1	8.1	96	93.5	21.6	156	152.0	35.1	216	210.5	48.6	276	268.9	62.1
37	36.1	8.3	97	94.5	21.8	157	153.0	35.3	217	211.4	48.8	277	269.9	62.3
38	37.0	8.5	98	95.5	22.0	158	154.0	35.5	218	212.4	49.0	278	270.9	62.5
39	38.0	8.8	99	96.5	22.3	159	154.9	35.8	219	213.4	49.3	279	271.8	62.8
40	39.0	9.0	100	97.4	22.5	160	155.9	36.0	220	214.4	49.5	280	272.8	63.0
41	39.9	9.2	101	98.4	22.7	161	156.9	36.2	221	215.3	49.7	281	273.8	63.2
42	40.9	9.4	102	99.4	22.9	162	157.8	36.4	222	216.3	49.9	282	274.8	63.4
43	41.9	9.7	103	100.4	23.2	163	158.8	36.7	223	217.3	50.2	283	275.7	63.7
44	42.9	9.9	104	101.3	23.4	164	159.8	36.9	224	218.3	50.4	284	276.7	63.9
45	43.8	10.1	105	102.3	23.6	165	160.8	37.1	225	219.2	50.6	285	277.7	64.1
46	44.8	10.3	106	103.3	23.8	166	161.7	37.3	226	220.2	50.8	286	278.7	64.3
47	45.8	10.6	107	104.3	24.1	167	162.7	37.6	227	221.2	51.1	287	279.6	64.6
48	46.8	10.8	108	105.2	24.3	168	163.7	37.8	228	222.2	51.3	288	280.6	64.8
49	47.7	11.0	109	106.2	24.5	169	164.7	38.0	229	223.1	51.5	289	281.6	65.0
50	48.7	11.2	110	107.2	24.7	170	165.6	38.2	230	224.1	51.7	290	282.6	65.2
51	49.7	11.5	111	108.2	25.0	171	166.6	38.5	231	225.1	52.0	291	283.5	65.5
52	50.7	11.7	112	109.1	25.2	172	167.6	38.7	232	226.1	52.2	292	284.5	65.7
53	51.6	11.9	113	110.1	25.4	173	168.6	38.9	233	227.0	52.4	293	285.5	65.9
54	52.6	12.1	114	111.1	25.6	174	169.5	39.1	234	228.0	52.6	294	286.5	66.1
55	53.6	12.4	115	112.1	25.9	175	170.5	39.4	235	229.0	52.9	295	287.4	66.4
56	54.6	12.6	116	113.0	26.1	176	171.5	39.6	236	230.0	53.1	296	288.4	66.6
57	55.5	12.8	117	114.0	26.3	177	172.5	39.8	237	230.9	53.3	297	289.4	66.8
58	56.5	13.0	118	115.0	26.5	178	173.4	40.0	238	231.9	53.5	298	290.4	67.0
59	57.5	13.3	119	116.0	26.8	179	174.4	40.3	239	232.9	53.8	299	291.3	67.3
60	58.5	13.5	120	116.9	27.0	180	175.4	40.5	240	233.8	54.0	300	292.3	67.5
Hyp.	Opp.	Adj.	Hyp.	Opp.	Adj.	Hyp.	Opp.	Adj.	Hyp.	Opp.	Adj.	Hyp.	Opp.	Adj.
Dist. D Lon	Dep.	D. Lat. Dep	Dist. D Lon	Dep.	D. Lat. Dep	Dist. D Lon	Dep.	D. Lat. Dep	Dist. D Lon	Dep.	D. Lat. Dep	Dist. D Lon	Dep.	D. Lat. Dep

77°   77°

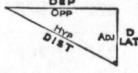

Table 3

TRAVERSE TABLE

347°	013°
193°	167°

D Lon	Dep		D Lon	Dep		D Lon	Dep		D Lon	Dep		D Lon	Dep	
Dist.	D. Lat.	Dep.	Dist.	D. Lat.	Dep.	Dist.	D. Lat.	Dep.	Dist.	D. Lat.	Dep.	Dist.	D. Lat.	Dep.
Hyp.	Adj.	Opp.	Hyp.	Adj.	Opp.	Hyp.	Adj.	Opp.	Hyp.	Adj.	Opp.	Hyp.	Adj.	Opp.
301	293.3	67.7	361	351.7	81.2	421	410.2	94.7	481	468.7	108.2	541	527.1	121.7
302	294.3	67.9	362	352.7	81.4	422	411.2	94.9	482	469.6	108.4	542	528.1	121.9
303	295.2	68.2	363	353.7	81.7	423	412.2	95.2	483	470.6	108.7	543	529.1	122.1
304	296.2	68.4	364	354.7	81.9	424	413.1	95.4	484	471.6	108.9	544	530.1	122.4
305	297.2	68.6	365	355.6	82.1	425	414.1	95.6	485	472.6	109.1	545	531.0	122.6
306	298.2	68.8	366	356.6	82.3	426	415.1	95.8	486	473.5	109.3	546	532.0	122.8
307	299.1	69.1	367	357.6	82.6	427	416.1	96.1	487	474.5	109.6	547	533.0	123.0
308	300.1	69.3	368	358.6	82.8	428	417.0	96.3	488	475.5	109.8	548	534.0	123.3
309	301.1	69.5	369	359.5	83.0	429	418.0	96.5	489	476.5	110.0	549	534.9	123.5
310	302.1	69.7	370	360.5	83.2	430	419.0	96.7	490	477.4	110.2	550	535.9	123.7
311	303.0	70.0	371	361.5	83.5	431	420.0	97.0	491	478.4	110.5	551	536.9	123.9
312	304.0	70.2	372	362.5	83.7	432	420.9	97.2	492	479.4	110.7	552	537.9	124.2
313	305.0	70.4	373	363.4	83.9	433	421.9	97.4	493	480.4	110.9	553	538.8	124.4
314	306.0	70.6	374	364.4	84.1	434	422.9	97.6	494	481.3	111.1	554	539.8	124.6
315	306.9	70.9	375	365.4	84.4	435	423.9	97.9	495	482.3	111.4	555	540.8	124.8
316	307.9	71.1	376	366.4	84.6	436	424.8	98.1	496	483.3	111.6	556	541.7	125.1
317	308.9	71.3	377	367.3	84.8	437	425.8	98.3	497	484.3	111.8	557	542.7	125.3
318	309.8	71.5	378	368.3	85.0	438	426.8	98.5	498	485.2	112.0	558	543.7	125.5
319	310.8	71.8	379	369.3	85.3	439	427.7	98.8	499	486.2	112.3	559	544.7	125.7
320	311.8	72.0	380	370.3	85.5	440	428.7	99.0	500	487.2	112.5	560	545.6	126.0
321	312.8	72.2	381	371.2	85.7	441	429.7	99.2	501	488.2	112.7	561	546.6	126.2
322	313.7	72.4	382	372.2	85.9	442	430.7	99.4	502	489.1	112.9	562	547.6	126.4
323	314.7	72.7	383	373.2	86.2	443	431.6	99.7	503	490.1	113.2	563	548.6	126.6
324	315.7	72.9	384	374.2	86.4	444	432.6	99.9	504	491.1	113.4	564	549.5	126.9
325	316.7	73.1	385	375.1	86.6	445	433.6	100.1	505	492.1	113.6	565	550.5	127.1
326	317.6	73.3	386	376.1	86.8	446	434.6	100.3	506	493.0	113.8	566	551.5	127.3
327	318.6	73.6	387	377.1	87.1	447	435.5	100.6	507	494.0	114.1	567	552.5	127.5
328	319.6	73.8	388	378.1	87.3	448	436.5	100.8	508	495.0	114.3	568	553.4	127.8
329	320.6	74.0	389	379.0	87.5	449	437.5	101.0	509	496.0	114.5	569	554.4	128.0
330	321.5	74.2	390	380.0	87.7	450	438.5	101.2	510	496.9	114.7	570	555.4	128.2
331	322.5	74.5	391	381.0	88.0	451	439.4	101.5	511	497.9	115.0	571	556.4	128.4
332	323.5	74.7	392	382.0	88.2	452	440.4	101.7	512	498.9	115.2	572	557.3	128.7
333	324.5	74.9	393	382.9	88.4	453	441.4	101.9	513	499.9	115.4	573	558.3	128.9
334	325.4	75.1	394	383.9	88.6	454	442.4	102.1	514	500.8	115.6	574	559.3	129.1
335	326.4	75.4	395	384.9	88.9	455	443.3	102.4	515	501.8	115.8	575	560.3	129.3
336	327.4	75.6	396	385.9	89.1	456	444.3	102.6	516	502.8	116.1	576	561.2	129.6
337	328.4	75.8	397	386.8	89.3	457	445.3	102.8	517	503.7	116.3	577	562.2	129.8
338	329.3	76.0	398	387.8	89.5	458	446.3	103.0	518	504.7	116.5	578	563.2	130.0
339	330.3	76.3	399	388.8	89.8	459	447.2	103.3	519	505.7	116.7	579	564.2	130.2
340	331.3	76.5	400	389.7	90.0	460	448.2	103.5	520	506.7	117.0	580	565.1	130.5
341	332.3	76.7	401	390.7	90.2	461	449.2	103.7	521	507.6	117.2	581	566.1	130.7
342	333.2	76.9	402	391.7	90.4	462	450.2	103.9	522	508.6	117.4	582	567.1	130.9
343	334.2	77.2	403	392.7	90.7	463	451.1	104.2	523	509.6	117.6	583	568.1	131.1
344	335.2	77.4	404	393.6	90.9	464	452.1	104.4	524	510.6	117.9	584	569.0	131.4
345	336.2	77.6	405	394.6	91.1	465	453.1	104.6	525	511.5	118.1	585	570.0	131.6
346	337.1	77.8	406	395.6	91.3	466	454.1	104.8	526	512.5	118.3	586	571.0	131.8
347	338.1	78.1	407	396.6	91.6	467	455.0	105.1	527	513.5	118.5	587	572.0	132.0
348	339.1	78.3	408	397.5	91.8	468	456.0	105.3	528	514.5	118.8	588	572.9	132.3
349	340.1	78.5	409	398.5	92.0	469	457.0	105.5	529	515.4	119.0	589	573.9	132.5
350	341.0	78.7	410	399.5	92.2	470	458.0	105.7	530	516.4	119.2	590	574.9	132.7
351	342.0	79.0	411	400.5	92.5	471	458.9	106.0	531	517.4	119.4	591	575.9	132.9
352	343.0	79.2	412	401.4	92.7	472	459.9	106.2	532	518.4	119.7	592	576.8	133.2
353	344.0	79.4	413	402.4	92.9	473	460.9	106.4	533	519.3	119.9	593	577.8	133.4
354	344.9	79.6	414	403.4	93.1	474	461.9	106.6	534	520.3	120.1	594	578.8	133.6
355	345.9	79.9	415	404.4	93.4	475	462.8	106.9	535	521.3	120.3	595	579.8	133.8
356	346.9	80.1	416	405.3	93.6	476	463.8	107.1	536	522.3	120.6	596	580.7	134.1
357	347.9	80.3	417	406.3	93.8	477	464.8	107.3	537	523.2	120.8	597	581.7	134.3
358	348.8	80.5	418	407.3	94.0	478	465.7	107.5	538	524.2	121.0	598	582.7	134.5
359	349.8	80.8	419	408.3	94.3	479	466.7	107.8	539	525.2	121.2	599	583.6	134.7
360	350.8	81.0	420	409.2	94.5	480	467.7	108.0	540	526.2	121.5	600	584.6	135.0
Hyp.	Adj.	Opp.	Hyp.	Adj.	Opp.	Hyp.	Adj.	Opp.	Hyp.	Adj.	Opp.	Hyp.	Adj.	Opp.
Dist.	Dep.	D. Lat.	Dist.	Dep.	D. Lat.	Dist.	Dep.	D. Lat.	Dist.	Dep.	D. Lat.	Dist.	Dep.	D. Lat.
D Lon		Dep	D Lon		Dep	D Lon		Dep	D Lon		Dep	D Lon		Dep

283°	077°
257°	103°

Table 3   **TRAVERSE TABLE**

14°

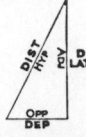

14°

D Lon Dist.	Dep D. Lat.	Dep.	D Lon Dist.	Dep D. Lat.	Dep.	D Lon Dist.	Dep D. Lat.	Dep.	D Lon Dist.	Dep D. Lat.	Dep.	D Lon Dist.	Dep D. Lat.	Dep.
Hyp.	Adj.	Opp.	Hyp.	Adj.	Opp.	Hyp.	Adj.	Opp.	Hyp.	Adj.	Opp.	Hyp.	Adj.	Opp.
1	1.0	0.2	61	59.2	14.8	121	117.4	29.3	181	175.6	43.8	241	233.8	58.3
2	1.9	0.5	62	60.2	15.0	122	118.4	29.5	182	176.6	44.0	242	234.8	58.5
3	2.9	0.7	63	61.1	15.2	123	119.3	29.8	183	177.6	44.3	243	235.8	58.8
4	3.9	1.0	64	62.1	15.5	124	120.3	30.0	184	178.5	44.5	244	236.8	59.0
5	4.9	1.2	65	63.1	15.7	125	121.3	30.2	185	179.5	44.8	245	237.7	59.3
6	5.8	1.5	66	64.0	16.0	126	122.3	30.5	186	180.5	45.0	246	238.7	59.5
7	6.8	1.7	67	65.0	16.2	127	123.2	30.7	187	181.4	45.2	247	239.7	59.8
8	7.8	1.9	68	66.0	16.5	128	124.2	31.0	188	182.4	45.5	248	240.6	60.0
9	8.7	2.2	69	67.0	16.7	129	125.2	31.2	189	183.4	45.7	249	241.6	60.2
10	9.7	2.4	70	67.9	16.9	130	126.1	31.4	190	184.4	46.0	250	242.6	60.5
11	10.7	2.7	71	68.9	17.2	131	127.1	31.7	191	185.3	46.2	251	243.5	60.7
12	11.6	2.9	72	69.9	17.4	132	128.1	31.9	192	186.3	46.4	252	244.5	61.0
13	12.6	3.1	73	70.8	17.7	133	129.0	32.2	193	187.3	46.7	253	245.5	61.2
14	13.6	3.4	74	71.8	17.9	134	130.0	32.4	194	188.2	46.9	254	246.5	61.4
15	14.6	3.6	75	72.8	18.1	135	131.0	32.7	195	189.2	47.2	255	247.4	61.7
16	15.5	3.9	76	73.7	18.4	136	132.0	32.9	196	190.2	47.4	256	248.4	61.9
17	16.5	4.1	77	74.7	18.6	137	132.9	33.1	197	191.1	47.7	257	249.4	62.2
18	17.5	4.4	78	75.7	18.9	138	133.9	33.4	198	192.1	47.9	258	250.3	62.4
19	18.4	4.6	79	76.7	19.1	139	134.9	33.6	199	193.1	48.1	259	251.3	62.7
20	19.4	4.8	80	77.6	19.4	140	135.8	33.9	200	194.1	48.4	260	252.3	62.9
21	20.4	5.1	81	78.6	19.6	141	136.8	34.1	201	195.0	48.6	261	253.2	63.1
22	21.3	5.3	82	79.6	19.8	142	137.8	34.4	202	196.0	48.9	262	254.2	63.4
23	22.3	5.6	83	80.5	20.1	143	138.8	34.6	203	197.0	49.1	263	255.2	63.6
24	23.3	5.8	84	81.5	20.3	144	139.7	34.8	204	197.9	49.4	264	256.2	63.9
25	24.3	6.0	85	82.5	20.6	145	140.7	35.1	205	198.9	49.6	265	257.1	64.1
26	25.2	6.3	86	83.4	20.8	146	141.7	35.3	206	199.9	49.8	266	258.1	64.4
27	26.2	6.5	87	84.4	21.0	147	142.6	35.6	207	200.9	50.1	267	259.1	64.6
28	27.2	6.8	88	85.4	21.3	148	143.6	35.8	208	201.8	50.3	268	260.0	64.8
29	28.1	7.0	89	86.4	21.5	149	144.6	36.0	209	202.8	50.6	269	261.0	65.1
30	29.1	7.3	90	87.3	21.8	150	145.5	36.3	210	203.8	50.8	270	262.0	65.3
31	30.1	7.5	91	88.3	22.0	151	146.5	36.5	211	204.7	51.0	271	263.0	65.6
32	31.0	7.7	92	89.3	22.3	152	147.5	36.8	212	205.7	51.3	272	263.9	65.8
33	32.0	8.0	93	90.2	22.5	153	148.5	37.0	213	206.7	51.5	273	264.9	66.0
34	33.0	8.2	94	91.2	22.7	154	149.4	37.3	214	207.6	51.8	274	265.9	66.3
35	34.0	8.5	95	92.2	23.0	155	150.4	37.5	215	208.6	52.0	275	266.8	66.5
36	34.9	8.7	96	93.1	23.2	156	151.4	37.7	216	209.6	52.3	276	267.8	66.8
37	35.9	9.0	97	94.1	23.5	157	152.3	38.0	217	210.6	52.5	277	268.8	67.0
38	36.9	9.2	98	95.1	23.7	158	153.3	38.2	218	211.5	52.7	278	269.7	67.3
39	37.8	9.4	99	96.1	24.0	159	154.3	38.5	219	212.5	53.0	279	270.7	67.5
40	38.8	9.7	100	97.0	24.2	160	155.2	38.7	220	213.5	53.2	280	271.7	67.7
41	39.8	9.9	101	98.0	24.4	161	156.2	38.9	221	214.4	53.5	281	272.7	68.0
42	40.8	10.2	102	99.0	24.7	162	157.2	39.2	222	215.4	53.7	282	273.6	68.2
43	41.7	10.4	103	99.9	24.9	163	158.2	39.4	223	216.4	53.9	283	274.6	68.5
44	42.7	10.6	104	100.9	25.2	164	159.1	39.7	224	217.3	54.2	284	275.6	68.7
45	43.7	10.9	105	101.9	25.4	165	160.1	39.9	225	218.3	54.4	285	276.5	68.9
46	44.6	11.1	106	102.9	25.6	166	161.1	40.2	226	219.3	54.7	286	277.5	69.2
47	45.6	11.4	107	103.8	25.9	167	162.0	40.4	227	220.3	54.9	287	278.5	69.4
48	46.6	11.6	108	104.8	26.1	168	163.0	40.6	228	221.2	55.2	288	279.4	69.7
49	47.5	11.9	109	105.8	26.4	169	164.0	40.9	229	222.2	55.4	289	280.4	69.9
50	48.5	12.1	110	106.7	26.6	170	165.0	41.1	230	223.2	55.6	290	281.4	70.2
51	49.5	12.3	111	107.7	26.9	171	165.9	41.4	231	224.1	55.9	291	282.4	70.4
52	50.5	12.6	112	108.7	27.1	172	166.9	41.6	232	225.1	56.1	292	283.3	70.6
53	51.4	12.8	113	109.6	27.3	173	167.9	41.9	233	226.1	56.4	293	284.3	70.9
54	52.4	13.1	114	110.6	27.6	174	168.8	42.1	234	227.0	56.6	294	285.3	71.1
55	53.4	13.3	115	111.6	27.8	175	169.8	42.3	235	228.0	56.9	295	286.2	71.4
56	54.3	13.5	116	112.6	28.1	176	170.8	42.6	236	229.0	57.1	296	287.2	71.6
57	55.3	13.8	117	113.5	28.3	177	171.7	42.8	237	230.0	57.3	297	288.2	71.9
58	56.3	14.0	118	114.5	28.5	178	172.7	43.1	238	230.9	57.6	298	289.1	72.1
59	57.2	14.3	119	115.5	28.8	179	173.7	43.3	239	231.9	57.8	299	290.1	72.3
60	58.2	14.5	120	116.4	29.0	180	174.7	43.5	240	232.9	58.1	300	291.1	72.6
Hyp.	Opp.	Adj.	Hyp.	Opp.	Adj.	Hyp.	Opp.	Adj.	Hyp.	Opp.	Adj.	Hyp.	Opp.	Adj.
Dist. D Lon	Dep.	D. Lat. Dep	Dist. D Lon	Dep.	D. Lat. Dep	Dist. D Lon	Dep.	D. Lat. Dep	Dist. D Lon	Dep.	D. Lat. Dep	Dist. D Lon	Dep.	D. Lat. Dep

76°

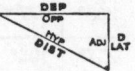

76°

Table 3

TRAVERSE TABLE

	346°	014°	
	194°	166°	

| D Lon | Dep | | D Lon | Dep | | D Lon | Dep | | D Lon | Dep | | D Lon | Dep | |
Dist.	D. Lat.	Dep.	Dist.	D. Lat.	Dep.	Dist.	D. Lat.	Dep.	Dist.	D. Lat.	Dep.	Dist.	D. Lat.	Dep.
Hyp.	Adj.	Opp.	Hyp.	Adj.	Opp.	Hyp.	Adj.	Opp.	Hyp.	Adj.	Opp.	Hyp.	Adj.	Opp.
301	292.1	72.8	361	350.3	87.3	421	408.5	101.8	481	466.7	116.4	541	524.9	130.9
302	293.0	73.1	362	351.2	87.6	422	409.5	102.1	482	467.7	116.6	542	525.9	131.1
303	294.0	73.3	363	352.2	87.8	423	410.4	102.3	483	468.7	116.8	543	526.9	131.4
304	295.0	73.5	364	353.2	88.1	424	411.4	102.6	484	469.6	117.1	544	527.8	131.6
305	295.9	73.8	365	354.2	88.3	425	412.4	102.8	485	470.6	117.3	545	528.8	131.8
306	296.9	74.0	366	355.1	88.5	426	413.3	103.1	486	471.6	117.6	546	529.8	132.1
307	297.9	74.3	367	356.1	88.8	427	414.3	103.3	487	472.5	117.8	547	530.8	132.3
308	298.9	74.5	368	357.1	89.0	428	415.3	103.5	488	473.5	118.1	548	531.7	132.6
309	299.8	74.8	369	358.0	89.3	429	416.3	103.8	489	474.5	118.3	549	532.7	132.8
310	300.8	75.0	370	359.0	89.5	430	417.2	104.0	490	475.4	118.5	550	533.7	133.1
311	301.8	75.2	371	360.0	89.8	431	418.2	104.3	491	476.4	118.8	551	534.6	133.3
312	302.7	75.5	372	361.0	90.0	432	419.2	104.5	492	477.4	119.0	552	535.6	133.5
313	303.7	75.7	373	361.9	90.2	433	420.1	104.8	493	478.4	119.3	553	536.6	133.8
314	304.7	76.0	374	362.9	90.5	434	421.1	105.0	494	479.3	119.5	554	537.5	134.0
315	305.6	76.2	375	363.9	90.7	435	422.1	105.2	495	480.3	119.8	555	538.5	134.3
316	306.6	76.4	376	364.8	91.0	436	423.0	105.5	496	481.3	120.0	556	539.5	134.5
317	307.6	76.7	377	365.8	91.2	437	424.0	105.7	497	482.2	120.2	557	540.5	134.8
318	308.6	76.9	378	366.8	91.4	438	425.0	106.0	498	483.2	120.5	558	541.4	135.0
319	309.5	77.2	379	367.7	91.7	439	426.0	106.2	499	484.2	120.7	559	542.4	135.2
320	310.5	77.4	380	368.7	91.9	440	426.9	106.4	500	485.1	121.0	560	543.4	135.5
321	311.5	77.7	381	359.7	92.2	441	427.9	106.7	501	486.1	121.2	561	544.3	135.7
322	312.4	77.9	382	370.7	92.4	442	428.9	106.9	502	487.1	121.4	562	545.3	136.0
323	313.4	78.1	383	371.6	92.7	443	429.8	107.2	503	488.1	121.7	563	546.3	136.2
324	314.4	78.4	384	372.6	92.9	444	430.8	107.4	504	489.0	121.9	564	547.2	136.4
325	315.3	78.6	385	373.6	93.1	445	431.8	107.7	505	490.0	122.2	565	548.2	136.7
326	316.3	78.9	386	374.5	93.4	446	432.8	107.9	506	491.0	122.4	566	549.2	136.9
327	317.3	79.1	387	375.5	93.6	447	433.7	108.1	507	491.9	122.7	567	550.2	137.2
328	318.3	79.4	388	376.5	93.9	448	434.7	108.4	508	492.9	122.9	568	551.1	137.4
329	319.2	79.6	389	377.4	94.1	449	435.7	108.6	509	493.9	123.1	569	552.1	137.7
330	320.2	79.8	390	378.4	94.3	450	436.6	108.9	510	494.9	123.4	570	553.1	137.9
331	321.2	80.1	391	379.4	94.6	451	437.6	109.1	511	495.8	123.6	571	554.0	138.1
332	322.1	80.3	392	380.4	94.8	452	438.6	109.3	512	496.8	123.9	572	555.0	138.4
333	323.1	80.6	393	381.3	95.1	453	439.5	109.6	513	497.8	124.1	573	556.0	138.6
334	324.1	80.8	394	382.3	95.3	454	440.5	109.8	514	498.7	124.3	574	556.9	138.9
335	325.0	81.0	395	383.3	95.6	455	441.5	110.1	515	499.7	124.6	575	557.9	139.1
336	326.0	81.3	396	384.2	95.8	456	442.5	110.3	516	500.7	124.8	576	558.9	139.3
337	327.0	81.5	397	385.2	96.0	457	443.4	110.6	517	501.6	125.1	577	559.9	139.6
338	328.0	81.8	398	386.2	96.3	458	444.4	110.8	518	502.6	125.3	578	560.8	139.8
339	328.9	82.0	399	387.1	96.5	459	445.4	111.0	519	503.6	125.6	579	561.8	140.1
340	329.9	82.3	400	388.1	96.8	460	446.3	111.3	520	504.6	125.8	580	562.8	140.3
341	330.9	82.5	401	389.1	97.0	461	447.3	111.5	521	505.5	126.0	581	563.7	140.6
342	331.8	82.7	402	390.1	97.3	462	448.3	111.8	522	506.5	126.3	582	564.7	140.8
343	332.8	83.0	403	391.0	97.5	463	449.2	112.0	523	507.5	126.5	583	565.7	141.0
344	333.8	83.2	404	392.0	97.7	464	450.2	112.3	524	508.4	126.8	584	566.7	141.3
345	334.8	83.5	405	393.0	98.0	465	451.2	112.5	525	509.4	127.0	585	567.6	141.5
346	335.7	83.7	406	393.9	98.2	466	452.2	112.7	526	510.4	127.3	586	568.6	141.8
347	336.7	83.9	407	394.9	98.5	467	453.1	113.0	527	511.3	127.5	587	569.6	142.0
348	337.7	84.2	408	395.9	98.7	468	454.1	113.2	528	512.3	127.7	588	570.5	142.3
349	338.6	84.4	409	396.9	98.9	469	455.1	113.5	529	513.3	128.0	589	571.5	142.5
350	339.6	84.7	410	397.8	99.2	470	456.0	113.7	530	514.3	128.2	590	572.5	142.7
351	340.6	84.9	411	398.8	99.4	471	457.0	113.9	531	515.2	128.5	591	573.4	143.0
352	341.5	85.2	412	399.8	99.7	472	458.0	114.2	532	516.2	128.7	592	574.4	143.2
353	342.5	85.4	413	400.7	99.9	473	458.9	114.4	533	517.2	128.9	593	575.4	143.5
354	343.5	85.6	414	401.7	100.2	474	459.9	114.7	534	518.1	129.2	594	576.4	143.7
355	344.5	85.9	415	402.7	100.4	475	460.9	114.9	535	519.1	129.4	595	577.3	143.9
356	345.4	86.1	416	403.6	100.6	476	461.9	115.2	536	520.1	129.7	596	578.3	144.2
357	346.4	86.4	417	404.6	100.9	477	462.8	115.4	537	521.0	129.9	597	579.3	144.4
358	347.4	86.6	418	405.6	101.1	478	463.8	115.6	538	522.0	130.2	598	580.2	144.7
359	348.3	86.8	419	406.6	101.4	479	464.8	115.9	539	523.0	130.4	599	581.2	144.9
360	349.3	87.1	420	407.5	101.6	480	465.7	116.1	540	524.0	130.6	600	582.2	145.2
Hyp.	Opp.	Adj.	Hyp.	Opp.	Adj.	Hyp.	Opp.	Adj.	Hyp.	Opp.	Adj.	Hyp.	Opp.	Adj.
Dist.	Dep.	D. Lat.	Dist.	Dep.	D. Lat.	Dist.	Dep.	D. Lat.	Dist.	Dep.	D. Lat.	Dist.	Dep.	D. Lat.
D Lon		Dep	D Lon		Dep	D Lon		Dep	D Lon		Dep	D Lon		Dep

	284°	076°	
	256°	104°	

Table 3

TRAVERSE TABLE

15° 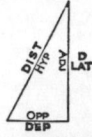 15°

D Lon Dist.	Dep D. Lat.	Dep.	D Lon Dist.	Dep D. Lat.	Dep.	D Lon Dist.	Dep D. Lat.	Dep.	D Lon Dist.	Dep D. Lat.	Dep.	D Lon Dist.	Dep D. Lat.	Dep.
Hyp.	Adj.	Opp.	Hyp.	Adj.	Opp.	Hyp.	Adj.	Opp.	Hyp.	Adj.	Opp.	Hyp.	Adj.	Opp.
1	1.0	0.3	61	58.9	15.8	121	116.9	31.3	181	174.8	46.8	241	232.8	62.4
2	1.9	0.5	62	59.9	16.0	122	117.8	31.6	182	175.8	47.1	242	233.8	62.6
3	2.9	0.8	63	60.9	16.3	123	118.8	31.8	183	176.8	47.4	243	234.7	62.9
4	3.9	1.0	64	61.8	16.6	124	119.8	32.1	184	177.7	47.6	244	235.7	63.2
5	4.8	1.3	65	62.8	16.8	125	120.7	32.4	185	178.7	47.9	245	236.7	63.4
6	5.8	1.6	66	63.8	17.1	126	121.7	32.6	186	179.7	48.1	246	237.6	63.7
7	6.8	1.8	67	64.7	17.3	127	122.7	32.9	187	180.6	48.4	247	238.6	63.9
8	7.7	2.1	68	65.7	17.6	128	123.6	33.1	188	181.6	48.7	248	239.5	64.2
9	8.7	2.3	69	66.6	17.9	129	124.6	33.4	189	182.6	48.9	249	240.5	64.4
10	9.7	2.6	70	67.6	18.1	130	125.6	33.6	190	183.5	49.2	250	241.5	64.7
11	10.6	2.8	71	68.6	18.4	131	126.5	33.9	191	184.5	49.4	251	242.4	65.0
12	11.6	3.1	72	69.5	18.6	132	127.5	34.2	192	185.5	49.7	252	243.4	65.2
13	12.6	3.4	73	70.5	18.9	133	128.5	34.4	193	186.4	50.0	253	244.4	65.5
14	13.5	3.6	74	71.5	19.2	134	129.4	34.7	194	187.4	50.2	254	245.3	65.7
15	14.5	3.9	75	72.4	19.4	135	130.4	34.9	195	188.4	50.5	255	246.3	66.0
16	15.5	4.1	76	73.4	19.7	136	131.4	35.2	196	189.3	50.7	256	247.3	66.3
17	16.4	4.4	77	74.4	19.9	137	132.3	35.5	197	190.3	51.0	257	248.2	66.5
18	17.4	4.7	78	75.3	20.2	138	133.3	35.7	198	191.3	51.2	258	249.2	66.8
19	18.4	4.9	79	76.3	20.4	139	134.3	36.0	199	192.2	51.5	259	250.2	67.0
20	19.3	5.2	80	77.3	20.7	140	135.2	36.2	200	193.2	51.8	260	251.1	67.3
21	20.3	5.4	81	78.2	21.0	141	136.2	36.5	201	194.2	52.0	261	252.1	67.6
22	21.3	5.7	82	79.2	21.2	142	137.2	36.8	202	195.1	52.3	262	253.1	67.8
23	22.2	6.0	83	80.2	21.5	143	138.1	37.0	203	196.1	52.5	263	254.0	68.1
24	23.2	6.2	84	81.1	21.7	144	139.1	37.3	204	197.0	52.8	264	255.0	68.3
25	24.1	6.5	85	82.1	22.0	145	140.1	37.5	205	198.0	53.1	265	256.0	68.6
26	25.1	6.7	86	83.1	22.3	146	141.0	37.8	206	199.0	53.3	266	256.9	68.8
27	26.1	7.0	87	84.0	22.5	147	142.0	38.0	207	199.9	53.6	267	257.9	69.1
28	27.0	7.2	88	85.0	22.8	148	143.0	38.3	208	200.9	53.8	268	258.9	69.4
29	28.0	7.5	89	86.0	23.0	149	143.9	38.6	209	201.9	54.1	269	259.8	69.6
30	29.0	7.8	90	86.9	23.3	150	144.9	38.8	210	202.8	54.4	270	260.8	69.9
31	29.9	8.0	91	87.9	23.6	151	145.9	39.1	211	203.8	54.6	271	261.8	70.1
32	30.9	8.3	92	88.9	23.8	152	146.8	39.3	212	204.8	54.9	272	262.7	70.4
33	31.9	8.5	93	89.8	24.1	153	147.8	39.6	213	205.7	55.1	273	263.7	70.7
34	32.8	8.8	94	90.8	24.3	154	148.8	39.9	214	206.7	55.4	274	264.7	70.9
35	33.8	9.1	95	91.8	24.6	155	149.7	40.1	215	207.7	55.6	275	265.6	71.2
36	34.8	9.3	96	92.7	24.8	156	150.7	40.4	216	208.6	55.9	276	266.6	71.4
37	35.7	9.6	97	93.7	25.1	157	151.7	40.6	217	209.6	56.2	277	267.6	71.7
38	36.7	9.8	98	94.7	25.4	158	152.6	40.9	218	210.6	56.4	278	268.5	72.0
39	37.7	10.1	99	95.6	25.6	159	153.6	41.2	219	211.5	56.7	279	269.5	72.2
40	38.6	10.4	100	96.6	25.9	160	154.5	41.4	220	212.5	56.9	280	270.5	72.5
41	39.6	10.6	101	97.6	26.1	161	155.5	41.7	221	213.5	57.2	281	271.4	72.7
42	40.6	10.9	102	98.5	26.4	162	156.5	41.9	222	214.4	57.5	282	272.4	73.0
43	41.5	11.1	103	99.5	26.7	163	157.4	42.2	223	215.4	57.7	283	273.4	73.2
44	42.5	11.4	104	100.5	26.9	164	158.4	42.4	224	216.4	58.0	284	274.3	73.5
45	43.5	11.6	105	101.4	27.2	165	159.4	42.7	225	217.3	58.2	285	275.3	73.8
46	44.4	11.9	106	102.4	27.4	166	160.3	43.0	226	218.3	58.5	286	276.3	74.0
47	45.4	12.2	107	103.4	27.7	167	161.3	43.2	227	219.3	58.8	287	277.2	74.3
48	46.4	12.4	108	104.3	28.0	168	162.3	43.5	228	220.2	59.0	288	278.2	74.5
49	47.3	12.7	109	105.3	28.2	169	163.2	43.7	229	221.2	59.3	289	279.2	74.8
50	48.3	12.9	110	106.3	28.5	170	164.2	44.0	230	222.2	59.5	290	280.1	75.1
51	49.3	13.2	111	107.2	28.7	171	165.2	44.3	231	223.1	59.8	291	281.1	75.3
52	50.2	13.5	112	108.2	29.0	172	166.1	44.5	232	224.1	60.0	292	282.1	75.6
53	51.2	13.7	113	109.1	29.2	173	167.1	44.8	233	225.1	60.3	293	283.0	75.8
54	52.2	14.0	114	110.1	29.5	174	168.1	45.0	234	226.0	60.6	294	284.0	76.1
55	53.1	14.2	115	111.1	29.8	175	169.0	45.3	235	227.0	60.8	295	284.9	76.4
56	54.1	14.5	116	112.0	30.0	176	170.0	45.6	236	228.0	61.1	296	285.9	76.6
57	55.1	14.8	117	113.0	30.3	177	171.0	45.8	237	228.9	61.3	297	286.9	76.9
58	56.0	15.0	118	114.0	30.5	178	171.9	46.1	238	229.9	61.6	298	287.8	77.1
59	57.0	15.3	119	114.9	30.8	179	172.9	46.3	239	230.9	61.9	299	288.8	77.4
60	58.0	15.5	120	115.9	31.1	180	173.9	46.6	240	231.8	62.1	300	289.8	77.6
Hyp.	Opp.	Adj.	Hyp.	Opp.	Adj.	Hyp.	Opp.	Adj.	Hyp.	Opp.	Adj.	Hyp.	Opp.	Adj.
Dist. D Lon	Dep.	D. Lat. Dep	Dist. D Lon	Dep.	D. Lat. Dep	Dist. D Lon	Dep.	D. Lat. Dep	Dist. D Lon	Dep.	D. Lat. Dep	Dist. D Lon	Dep.	D. Lat. Dep

75° 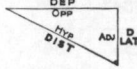 75°

Table 3   **TRAVERSE TABLE**

15°

15°

D Lon / Dist.	Dep / D. Lat.	Dep.	D Lon / Dist.	Dep / D. Lat.	Dep.	D Lon / Dist.	Dep / D. Lat.	Dep.	D Lon / Dist.	Dep / D. Lat.	Dep.	D Lon / Dist.	Dep / D. Lat.	Dep.
Hyp.	Adj.	Opp.	Hyp.	Adj.	Opp.	Hyp.	Adj.	Opp.	Hyp.	Adj.	Opp.	Hyp.	Adj.	Opp.
301	290.7	77.9	361	348.7	93.4	421	406.7	109.0	481	464.6	124.5	541	522.6	140.0
302	291.7	78.2	362	349.7	93.7	422	407.6	109.2	482	465.6	124.8	542	523.5	140.3
303	292.7	78.4	363	350.6	94.0	423	408.6	109.5	483	466.5	125.0	543	524.5	140.5
304	293.6	78.7	364	351.6	94.2	424	409.6	109.7	484	467.5	125.3	544	525.5	140.8
305	294.6	78.9	365	352.6	94.5	425	410.5	110.0	485	468.5	125.5	545	526.4	141.1
306	295.6	79.2	366	353.5	94.7	426	411.5	110.3	486	469.4	125.8	546	527.4	141.3
307	296.5	79.5	367	354.5	95.0	427	412.5	110.5	487	470.4	126.0	547	528.4	141.6
308	297.5	79.7	368	355.5	95.2	428	413.4	110.8	488	471.4	126.3	548	529.3	141.8
309	298.5	80.0	369	356.4	95.5	429	414.4	111.0	489	472.3	126.6	549	530.3	142.1
310	299.4	80.2	370	357.4	95.8	430	415.3	111.3	490	473.3	126.8	550	531.3	142.4
311	300.4	80.5	371	358.4	96.0	431	416.3	111.6	491	474.3	127.1	551	532.2	142.6
312	301.4	80.8	372	359.3	96.3	432	417.3	111.8	492	475.2	127.3	552	533.2	142.9
313	302.3	81.0	373	360.3	96.5	433	418.2	112.1	493	476.2	127.6	553	534.2	143.1
314	303.3	81.3	374	361.3	96.8	434	419.2	112.3	494	477.2	127.9	554	535.1	143.4
315	304.3	81.5	375	362.2	97.1	435	420.2	112.6	495	478.1	128.1	555	536.1	143.6
316	305.2	81.8	376	363.2	97.3	436	421.1	112.8	496	479.1	128.4	556	537.1	143.9
317	306.2	82.0	377	364.2	97.6	437	422.1	113.1	497	480.1	128.6	557	538.0	144.2
318	307.2	82.3	378	365.1	97.8	438	423.1	113.4	498	481.0	128.9	558	539.0	144.4
319	308.1	82.6	379	366.1	98.1	439	424.0	113.6	499	482.0	129.2	559	540.0	144.7
320	309.1	82.8	380	367.1	98.4	440	425.0	113.9	500	483.0	129.4	560	540.9	144.9
321	310.1	83.1	381	368.0	98.6	441	426.0	114.1	501	483.9	129.7	561	541.9	145.2
322	311.0	83.3	382	369.0	98.9	442	426.9	114.4	502	484.9	129.9	562	542.9	145.5
323	312.0	83.6	383	369.9	99.1	443	427.9	114.7	503	485.9	130.2	563	543.8	145.7
324	313.0	83.9	384	370.9	99.4	444	428.9	114.9	504	486.8	130.4	564	544.8	146.0
325	313.9	84.1	385	371.9	99.6	445	429.8	115.2	505	487.8	130.7	565	545.7	146.2
326	314.9	84.4	386	372.8	99.9	446	430.8	115.4	506	488.8	131.0	566	546.7	146.5
327	315.9	84.6	387	373.8	100.2	447	431.8	115.7	507	489.7	131.2	567	547.7	146.8
328	316.8	84.9	388	374.8	100.4	448	432.7	116.0	508	490.7	131.5	568	548.6	147.0
329	317.8	85.2	389	375.7	100.7	449	433.7	116.2	509	491.7	131.7	569	549.6	147.3
330	318.8	85.4	390	376.7	100.9	450	434.7	116.5	510	492.6	132.0	570	550.6	147.5
331	319.7	85.7	391	377.7	101.2	451	435.6	116.7	511	493.6	132.3	571	551.5	147.8
332	320.7	85.9	392	378.6	101.5	452	436.6	117.0	512	494.6	132.5	572	552.5	148.0
333	321.7	86.2	393	379.6	101.7	453	437.6	117.2	513	495.5	132.8	573	553.5	148.3
334	322.6	86.4	394	380.6	102.0	454	438.5	117.5	514	496.5	133.0	574	554.4	148.6
335	323.6	86.7	395	381.5	102.2	455	439.5	117.8	515	497.5	133.3	575	555.4	148.8
336	324.6	87.0	396	382.5	102.5	456	440.5	118.0	516	498.4	133.6	576	556.4	149.1
337	325.5	87.2	397	383.5	102.8	457	441.4	118.3	517	499.4	133.8	577	557.3	149.3
338	326.5	87.5	398	384.4	103.0	458	442.4	118.5	518	500.3	134.1	578	558.3	149.6
339	327.4	87.7	399	385.4	103.3	459	443.4	118.8	519	501.3	134.3	579	559.3	149.8
340	328.4	88.0	400	386.4	103.5	460	444.3	119.1	520	502.3	134.6	580	560.2	150.1
341	329.4	88.3	401	387.3	103.8	461	445.3	119.3	521	503.2	134.8	581	561.2	150.4
342	330.3	88.5	402	388.3	104.0	462	446.3	119.6	522	504.2	135.1	582	562.2	150.6
343	331.3	88.8	403	389.3	104.3	463	447.2	119.8	523	505.2	135.3	583	563.1	150.9
344	332.3	89.0	404	390.2	104.6	464	448.2	120.1	524	506.1	135.6	584	564.1	151.2
345	333.2	89.3	405	391.2	104.8	465	449.2	120.4	525	507.1	135.9	585	565.1	151.4
346	334.2	89.6	406	392.2	105.1	466	450.1	120.6	526	508.1	136.1	586	566.0	151.6
347	335.2	89.8	407	393.1	105.3	467	451.1	120.9	527	509.0	136.4	587	567.0	151.9
348	336.1	90.1	408	394.1	105.6	468	452.1	121.1	528	510.0	136.7	588	568.0	152.2
349	337.1	90.3	409	395.1	105.9	469	453.0	121.4	529	511.0	136.9	589	568.9	152.4
350	338.1	90.6	410	396.0	106.1	470	454.0	121.6	530	511.9	137.2	590	569.9	152.7
351	339.0	90.8	411	397.0	106.4	471	455.0	121.9	531	512.9	137.4	591	570.9	153.0
352	340.0	91.1	412	398.0	106.6	472	455.9	122.2	532	513.9	137.7	592	571.8	153.2
353	341.0	91.4	413	398.9	106.9	473	456.9	122.4	533	514.8	138.0	593	572.8	153.5
354	341.9	91.6	414	399.9	107.2	474	457.8	122.7	534	515.8	138.2	594	573.8	153.7
355	342.9	91.9	415	400.9	107.4	475	458.8	122.9	535	516.8	138.5	595	574.7	154.0
356	343.9	92.1	416	401.8	107.7	476	459.8	123.2	536	517.7	138.7	596	575.7	154.3
357	344.8	92.4	417	402.8	107.9	477	460.7	123.5	537	518.7	139.0	597	576.7	154.5
358	345.8	92.7	418	403.8	108.2	478	461.7	123.7	538	519.7	139.2	598	577.6	154.8
359	346.8	92.9	419	404.7	108.4	479	462.7	124.0	539	520.6	139.5	599	578.6	155.0
360	347.7	93.2	420	405.7	108.7	480	463.6	124.2	540	521.6	139.8	600	579.6	155.3
Hyp.	Opp.	Adj.	Hyp.	Opp.	Adj.	Hyp.	Opp.	Adj.	Hyp.	Opp.	Adj.	Hyp.	Opp.	Adj.
Dist. / D Lon	Dep.	D. Lat. / Dep	Dist. / D Lon	Dep.	D. Lat. / Dep	Dist. / D Lon	Dep.	D. Lat. / Dep	Dist. / D Lon	Dep.	D. Lat. / Dep	Dist. / D Lon	Dep.	D. Lat. / Dep

75°

75°

D

Table 3   **TRAVERSE TABLE**

16°  16°

D Lon	Dep		D Lon	Dep		D Lon	Dep		D Lon	Dep		D Lon	Dep	
Dist.	D. Lat.	Dep.	Dist.	D. Lat.	Dep.	Dist.	D. Lat.	Dep.	Dist.	D. Lat.	Dep.	Dist.	D. Lat.	Dep.
Hyp.	Adj.	Opp.	Hyp.	Adj.	Opp.	Hyp.	Adj.	Opp.	Hyp.	Adj.	Opp.	Hyp.	Adj.	Opp.
1	1.0	0.3	61	58.6	16.8	121	116.3	33.4	181	174.0	49.9	241	231.7	66.4
2	1.9	0.6	62	59.6	17.1	122	117.3	33.6	182	174.9	50.2	242	232.6	66.7
3	2.9	0.8	63	60.6	17.4	123	118.2	33.9	183	175.9	50.4	243	233.6	67.0
4	3.8	1.1	64	61.5	17.6	124	119.2	34.2	184	176.9	50.7	244	234.5	67.3
5	4.8	1.4	65	62.5	17.9	125	120.2	34.5	185	177.8	51.0	245	235.5	67.5
6	5.8	1.7	66	63.4	18.2	126	121.1	34.7	186	178.8	51.3	246	236.5	67.8
7	6.7	1.9	67	64.4	18.5	127	122.1	35.0	187	179.8	51.5	247	237.4	68.1
8	7.7	2.2	68	65.4	18.7	128	123.0	35.3	188	180.7	51.8	248	238.4	68.4
9	8.7	2.5	69	66.3	19.0	129	124.0	35.6	189	181.7	52.1	249	239.4	68.6
10	9.6	2.8	70	67.3	19.3	130	125.0	35.8	190	182.6	52.4	250	240.3	68.9
11	10.6	3.0	71	68.2	19.6	131	125.9	36.1	191	183.6	52.6	251	241.3	69.2
12	11.5	3.3	72	69.2	19.8	132	126.9	36.4	192	184.6	52.9	252	242.2	69.5
13	12.5	3.6	73	70.2	20.1	133	127.8	36.7	193	185.5	53.2	253	243.2	69.7
14	13.5	3.9	74	71.1	20.4	134	128.8	36.9	194	186.5	53.5	254	244.2	70.0
15	14.4	4.1	75	72.1	20.7	135	129.8	37.2	195	187.4	53.7	255	245.1	70.3
16	15.4	4.4	76	73.1	20.9	136	130.7	37.5	196	188.4	54.0	256	246.1	70.6
17	16.3	4.7	77	74.0	21.2	137	131.7	37.8	197	189.4	54.3	257	247.0	70.8
18	17.3	5.0	78	75.0	21.5	138	132.7	38.0	198	190.3	54.6	258	248.0	71.1
19	18.3	5.2	79	75.9	21.8	139	133.6	38.3	199	191.3	54.9	259	249.0	71.4
20	19.2	5.5	80	76.9	22.1	140	134.6	38.6	200	192.3	55.1	260	249.9	71.7
21	20.2	5.8	81	77.9	22.3	141	135.5	38.9	201	193.2	55.4	261	250.9	71.9
22	21.1	6.1	82	78.8	22.6	142	136.5	39.1	202	194.2	55.7	262	251.9	72.2
23	22.1	6.3	83	79.8	22.9	143	137.5	39.4	203	195.1	56.0	263	252.8	72.5
24	23.1	6.6	84	80.7	23.2	144	138.4	39.7	204	196.1	56.2	264	253.8	72.8
25	24.0	6.9	85	81.7	23.4	145	139.4	40.0	205	197.1	56.5	265	254.7	73.0
26	25.0	7.2	86	82.7	23.7	146	140.3	40.2	206	198.0	56.8	266	255.7	73.3
27	26.0	7.4	87	83.6	24.0	147	141.3	40.5	207	199.0	57.1	267	256.7	73.6
28	26.9	7.7	88	84.6	24.3	148	142.3	40.8	208	199.9	57.3	268	257.6	73.9
29	27.9	8.0	89	85.6	24.5	149	143.2	41.1	209	200.9	57.6	269	258.6	74.1
30	28.8	8.3	90	86.5	24.8	150	144.2	41.3	210	201.9	57.9	270	259.5	74.4
31	29.8	8.5	91	87.5	25.1	151	145.2	41.6	211	202.8	58.2	271	260.5	74.7
32	30.8	8.8	92	88.4	25.4	152	146.1	41.9	212	203.8	58.4	272	261.5	75.0
33	31.7	9.1	93	89.4	25.6	153	147.1	42.2	213	204.7	58.7	273	262.4	75.2
34	32.7	9.4	94	90.4	25.9	154	148.0	42.4	214	205.7	59.0	274	263.4	75.5
35	33.6	9.6	95	91.3	26.2	155	149.0	42.7	215	206.7	59.3	275	264.3	75.8
36	34.6	9.9	96	92.3	26.5	156	150.0	43.0	216	207.6	59.5	276	265.3	76.1
37	35.6	10.2	97	93.2	26.7	157	150.9	43.3	217	208.6	59.8	277	266.3	76.4
38	36.5	10.5	98	94.2	27.0	158	151.9	43.6	218	209.6	60.1	278	267.2	76.6
39	37.5	10.7	99	95.2	27.3	159	152.8	43.8	219	210.5	60.4	279	268.2	76.9
40	38.5	11.0	100	96.1	27.6	160	153.8	44.1	220	211.5	60.6	280	269.2	77.2
41	39.4	11.3	101	97.1	27.8	161	154.8	44.4	221	212.4	60.9	281	270.1	77.5
42	40.4	11.6	102	98.0	28.1	162	155.7	44.7	222	213.4	61.2	282	271.1	77.7
43	41.3	11.9	103	99.0	28.4	163	156.7	44.9	223	214.4	61.5	283	272.0	78.0
44	42.3	12.1	104	100.0	28.7	164	157.6	45.2	224	215.3	61.7	284	273.0	78.3
45	43.3	12.4	105	100.9	28.9	165	158.6	45.5	225	216.3	62.0	285	274.0	78.6
46	44.2	12.7	106	101.9	29.2	166	159.6	45.8	226	217.2	62.3	286	274.9	78.8
47	45.2	13.0	107	102.9	29.5	167	160.5	46.0	227	218.2	62.6	287	275.9	79.1
48	46.1	13.2	108	103.8	29.8	168	161.5	46.3	228	219.2	62.8	288	276.8	79.4
49	47.1	13.5	109	104.8	30.0	169	162.5	46.6	229	220.1	63.1	289	277.8	79.7
50	48.1	13.8	110	105.7	30.3	170	163.4	46.9	230	221.1	63.4	290	278.8	79.9
51	49.0	14.1	111	106.7	30.6	171	164.4	47.1	231	222.1	63.7	291	279.7	80.2
52	50.0	14.3	112	107.7	30.9	172	165.3	47.4	232	223.0	63.9	292	280.7	80.5
53	50.9	14.6	113	108.6	31.1	173	166.3	47.7	233	224.0	64.2	293	281.6	80.8
54	51.9	14.9	114	109.6	31.4	174	167.3	48.0	234	224.9	64.5	294	282.6	81.0
55	52.9	15.2	115	110.5	31.7	175	168.2	48.2	235	225.9	64.8	295	283.6	81.3
56	53.8	15.4	116	111.5	32.0	176	169.2	48.5	236	226.9	65.1	296	284.5	81.6
57	54.8	15.7	117	112.5	32.2	177	170.1	48.8	237	227.8	65.3	297	285.5	81.9
58	55.8	16.0	118	113.4	32.5	178	171.1	49.1	238	228.8	65.6	298	286.5	82.1
59	56.7	16.3	119	114.4	32.8	179	172.1	49.3	239	229.7	65.9	299	287.4	82.4
60	57.7	16.5	120	115.4	33.1	180	173.0	49.6	240	230.7	66.2	300	288.4	82.7
Hyp.	Opp.	Adj.	Hyp.	Opp.	Adj.	Hyp.	Opp.	Adj.	Hyp.	Opp.	Adj.	Hyp.	Opp.	Adj.

Dist.	Dep.	D. Lat.	Dist.	Dep.	D. Lat.	Dist.	Dep.	D. Lat.	Dist.	Dep.	D. Lat	Dist.	Dep.	D. Lat.
D Lon		Dep	D Lon		Dep	D Lon		Dep	D Lon		Dep	D Lon		Dep

74° 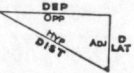 74°

Table 3

TRAVERSE TABLE

16°

	344°	016°
	196°	164°

16°

D Lon	Dep		D Lon	Dep		D Lon	Dep		D Lon	Dep		D Lon	Dep	
Dist.	D. Lat.	Dep.	Dist.	D. Lat.	Dep.	Dist.	D. Lat.	Dep.	Dist.	D. Lat.	Dep.	Dist.	D. Lat.	Dep.
Hyp.	Adj.	Opp.	Hyp.	Adj.	Opp.	Hyp.	Adj.	Opp.	Hyp.	Adj.	Opp.	Hyp.	Adj.	Opp.
301	289.3	83.0	361	347.0	99.5	421	404.7	116.0	481	462.4	132.6	541	520.0	149.1
302	290.3	83.2	362	348.0	99.8	422	405.7	116.3	482	463.3	132.9	542	521.0	149.4
303	291.3	83.5	363	348.9	100.1	423	406.6	116.6	483	464.3	133.1	543	522.0	149.7
304	292.2	83.8	364	349.9	100.3	424	407.6	116.9	484	465.3	133.4	544	522.9	149.9
305	293.2	84.1	365	350.9	100.6	425	408.5	117.1	485	466.2	133.7	545	523.9	150.2
306	294.1	84.3	366	351.8	100.9	426	409.5	117.4	486	467.2	134.0	546	524.8	150.5
307	295.1	84.6	367	352.8	101.2	427	410.5	117.7	487	468.1	134.2	547	525.8	150.8
308	296.1	84.9	368	353.7	101.4	428	411.4	118.0	488	469.1	134.5	548	526.8	151.0
309	297.0	85.2	369	354.7	101.7	429	412.4	118.2	489	470.1	134.8	549	527.7	151.3
310	298.0	85.4	370	355.7	102.0	430	413.3	118.5	490	471.0	135.1	550	528.7	151.6
311	299.0	85.7	371	356.6	102.3	431	414.3	118.8	491	472.0	135.3	551	529.7	151.9
312	299.9	86.0	372	357.6	102.5	432	415.3	119.1	492	472.9	135.6	552	530.6	152.2
313	300.9	86.3	373	358.6	102.8	433	416.2	119.4	493	473.9	135.9	553	531.6	152.4
314	301.8	86.6	374	359.5	103.1	434	417.2	119.6	494	474.9	136.2	554	532.5	152.7
315	302.8	86.8	375	360.5	103.4	435	418.1	119.9	495	475.8	136.4	555	533.5	153.0
316	303.8	87.1	376	361.4	103.6	436	419.1	120.2	496	476.8	136.7	556	534.5	153.3
317	304.7	87.4	377	362.4	103.9	437	420.1	120.5	497	477.7	137.0	557	535.4	153.5
318	305.7	87.7	378	363.4	104.2	438	421.0	120.7	498	478.7	137.3	558	536.4	153.8
319	306.6	87.9	379	364.3	104.5	439	422.0	121.0	499	479.7	137.5	559	537.3	154.1
320	307.6	88.2	380	365.3	104.7	440	423.0	121.3	500	480.6	137.8	560	538.3	154.4
321	308.6	88.5	381	366.2	105.0	441	423.9	121.6	501	481.6	138.1	561	539.3	154.6
322	309.5	88.8	382	367.2	105.3	442	424.9	121.8	502	482.6	138.4	562	540.2	154.9
323	310.5	89.0	383	368.2	105.6	443	425.8	122.1	503	483.5	138.6	563	541.2	155.2
324	311.4	89.3	384	369.1	105.8	444	426.8	122.4	504	484.5	138.9	564	542.2	155.5
325	312.4	89.6	385	370.1	106.1	445	427.8	122.7	505	485.4	139.2	565	543.1	155.7
326	313.4	89.9	386	371.0	106.4	446	428.7	122.9	506	486.4	139.5	566	544.1	156.0
327	314.3	90.1	387	372.0	106.7	447	429.7	123.2	507	487.4	139.7	567	545.0	156.3
328	315.3	90.4	388	373.0	106.9	448	430.6	123.5	508	488.3	140.0	568	546.0	156.6
329	316.3	90.7	389	373.9	107.2	449	431.6	123.8	509	489.3	140.3	569	547.0	156.8
330	317.2	91.0	390	374.9	107.5	450	432.6	124.0	510	490.2	140.6	570	547.9	157.1
331	318.2	91.2	391	375.9	107.8	451	433.5	124.3	511	491.2	140.9	571	548.9	157.4
332	319.1	91.5	392	376.8	108.0	452	434.5	124.6	512	492.2	141.1	572	549.8	157.7
333	320.1	91.8	393	377.8	108.3	453	435.5	124.9	513	493.1	141.4	573	550.8	157.9
334	321.1	92.1	394	378.7	108.6	454	436.4	125.1	514	494.1	141.7	574	551.8	158.2
335	322.0	92.3	395	379.7	108.9	455	437.4	125.4	515	495.0	142.0	575	552.7	158.5
336	323.0	92.6	396	380.7	109.2	456	438.3	125.7	516	496.0	142.2	576	553.7	158.8
337	323.9	92.9	397	381.6	109.4	457	439.3	126.0	517	497.0	142.5	577	554.6	159.0
338	324.9	93.2	398	382.6	109.7	458	440.3	126.2	518	497.9	142.8	578	555.6	159.3
339	325.9	93.4	399	383.5	110.0	459	441.2	126.5	519	498.9	143.1	579	556.6	159.6
340	326.8	93.7	400	384.5	110.3	460	442.2	126.8	520	499.9	143.3	580	557.5	159.9
341	327.8	94.0	401	385.5	110.5	461	443.1	127.1	521	500.8	143.6	581	558.5	160.1
342	328.8	94.3	402	386.4	110.8	462	444.1	127.3	522	501.8	143.9	582	559.5	160.4
343	329.7	94.5	403	387.4	111.1	463	445.1	127.6	523	502.7	144.2	583	560.4	160.7
344	330.7	94.8	404	388.3	111.4	464	446.0	127.9	524	503.7	144.4	584	561.4	161.0
345	331.6	95.1	405	389.3	111.6	465	447.0	128.2	525	504.7	144.7	585	562.3	161.2
346	332.6	95.4	406	390.3	111.9	466	447.9	128.4	526	505.6	145.0	586	563.3	161.5
347	333.6	95.6	407	391.2	112.2	467	448.9	128.7	527	506.6	145.3	587	564.3	161.8
348	334.5	95.9	408	392.2	112.5	468	449.9	129.0	528	507.5	145.5	588	565.2	162.1
349	335.5	96.2	409	393.2	112.7	469	450.8	129.3	529	508.5	145.8	589	566.2	162.4
350	336.4	96.5	410	394.1	113.0	470	451.8	129.5	530	509.5	146.1	590	567.1	162.6
351	337.4	96.7	411	395.1	113.3	471	452.8	129.8	531	510.4	146.4	591	568.1	162.9
352	338.4	97.0	412	396.0	113.6	472	453.7	130.1	532	511.4	146.6	592	569.1	163.2
353	339.3	97.3	413	397.0	113.8	473	454.7	130.4	533	512.4	146.9	593	570.0	163.5
354	340.3	97.6	414	398.0	114.1	474	455.6	130.7	534	513.3	147.2	594	571.0	163.7
355	341.2	97.9	415	398.9	114.4	475	456.6	130.9	535	514.3	147.5	595	572.0	164.0
356	342.2	98.1	416	399.9	114.7	476	457.6	131.2	536	515.2	147.7	596	572.9	164.3
357	343.2	98.4	417	400.8	114.9	477	458.5	131.5	537	516.2	148.0	597	573.9	164.6
358	344.1	98.7	418	401.8	115.2	478	459.5	131.8	538	517.2	148.3	598	574.8	164.8
359	345.1	99.0	419	402.8	115.5	479	460.4	132.0	539	518.1	148.6	599	575.8	165.1
360	346.1	99.2	420	403.7	115.8	480	461.4	132.3	540	519.1	148.8	600	576.8	165.4
Hyp.	Opp.	Adj.	Hyp.	Opp.	Adj.	Hyp.	Opp.	Adj.	Hyp.	Opp.	Adj.	Hyp.	Opp.	Adj.
Dist.	Dep.	D. Lat.	Dist.	Dep.	D. Lat.	Dist.	Dep.	D. Lat.	Dist.	Dep.	D. Lat.	Dist.	Dep.	D. Lat.
D Lon		Dep	D Lon		Dep	D Lon		Dep	D Lon		Dep	D Lon		Dep

74°

	286°	074°
	254°	106°

74°

Table 3

TRAVERSE TABLE

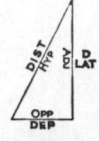

17°   17°

D Lon Dist.	Dep D. Lat.	Dep.	D Lon Dist.	Dep D. Lat.	Dep.	D Lon Dist.	Dep D. Lat.	Dep.	D Lon Dist.	Dep D. Lat.	Dep.	D Lon Dist.	Dep D. Lat.	Dep.
Hyp.	Adj.	Opp.	Hyp.	Adj.	Opp.	Hyp.	Adj.	Opp.	Hyp.	Adj.	Opp.	Hyp.	Adj.	Opp.
1	1.0	0.3	61	58.3	17.8	121	115.7	35.4	181	173.1	52.9	241	230.5	70.5
2	1.9	0.6	62	59.3	18.1	122	116.7	35.7	182	174.0	53.2	242	231.4	70.8
3	2.9	0.9	63	60.2	18.4	123	117.6	36.0	183	175.0	53.5	243	232.4	71.0
4	3.8	1.2	64	61.2	18.7	124	118.6	36.3	184	176.0	53.8	244	233.3	71.3
5	4.8	1.5	65	62.2	19.0	125	119.5	36.5	185	176.9	54.1	245	234.3	71.6
6	5.7	1.8	66	63.1	19.3	126	120.5	36.8	186	177.9	54.4	246	235.3	71.9
7	6.7	2.0	67	64.1	19.6	127	121.5	37.1	187	178.8	54.7	247	236.2	72.2
8	7.7	2.3	68	65.0	19.9	128	122.4	37.4	188	179.8	55.0	248	237.2	72.5
9	8.6	2.6	69	66.0	20.2	129	123.4	37.7	189	180.7	55.3	249	238.1	72.8
10	9.6	2.9	70	66.9	20.5	130	124.3	38.0	190	181.7	55.6	250	239.1	73.1
11	10.5	3.2	71	67.9	20.8	131	125.3	38.3	191	182.7	55.8	251	240.0	73.4
12	11.5	3.5	72	68.9	21.1	132	126.2	38.6	192	183.6	56.1	252	241.0	73.7
13	12.4	3.8	73	69.8	21.3	133	127.2	38.9	193	184.6	56.4	253	241.9	74.0
14	13.4	4.1	74	70.8	21.6	134	128.1	39.2	194	185.5	56.7	254	242.9	74.3
15	14.3	4.4	75	71.7	21.9	135	129.1	39.5	195	186.5	57.0	255	243.9	74.6
16	15.3	4.7	76	72.7	22.2	136	130.1	39.8	196	187.4	57.3	256	244.8	74.8
17	16.3	5.0	77	73.6	22.5	137	131.0	40.1	197	188.4	57.6	257	245.8	75.1
18	17.2	5.3	78	74.6	22.8	138	132.0	40.3	198	189.3	57.9	258	246.7	75.4
19	18.2	5.6	79	75.5	23.1	139	132.9	40.6	199	190.3	58.2	259	247.7	75.7
20	19.1	5.8	80	76.5	23.4	140	133.9	40.9	200	191.3	58.5	260	248.6	76.0
21	20.1	6.1	81	77.5	23.7	141	134.8	41.2	201	192.2	58.8	261	249.6	76.3
22	21.0	6.4	82	78.4	24.0	142	135.8	41.5	202	193.2	59.1	262	250.6	76.6
23	22.0	6.7	83	79.4	24.3	143	136.8	41.8	203	194.1	59.4	263	251.5	76.9
24	23.0	7.0	84	80.3	24.6	144	137.7	42.1	204	195.1	59.6	264	252.5	77.2
25	23.9	7.3	85	81.3	24.9	145	138.7	42.4	205	196.0	59.9	265	253.4	77.5
26	24.9	7.6	86	82.2	25.1	146	139.6	42.7	206	197.0	60.2	266	254.4	77.8
27	25.8	7.9	87	83.2	25.4	147	140.6	43.0	207	198.0	60.5	267	255.3	78.1
28	26.8	8.2	88	84.2	25.7	148	141.5	43.3	208	198.9	60.8	268	256.3	78.4
29	27.7	8.5	89	85.1	26.0	149	142.5	43.6	209	199.9	61.1	269	257.2	78.6
30	28.7	8.8	90	86.1	26.3	150	143.4	43.9	210	200.8	61.4	270	258.2	78.9
31	29.6	9.1	91	87.0	26.6	151	144.4	44.1	211	201.8	61.7	271	259.2	79.2
32	30.6	9.4	92	88.0	26.9	152	145.4	44.4	212	202.7	62.0	272	260.1	79.5
33	31.6	9.6	93	88.9	27.2	153	146.3	44.7	213	203.7	62.3	273	261.1	79.8
34	32.5	9.9	94	89.9	27.5	154	147.3	45.0	214	204.6	62.6	274	262.0	80.1
35	33.5	10.2	95	90.8	27.8	155	148.2	45.3	215	205.6	62.9	275	263.0	80.4
36	34.4	10.5	96	91.8	28.1	156	149.2	45.6	216	206.6	63.2	276	263.9	80.7
37	35.4	10.8	97	92.8	28.4	157	150.1	45.9	217	207.5	63.4	277	264.9	81.0
38	36.3	11.1	98	93.7	28.7	158	151.1	46.2	218	208.5	63.7	278	265.9	81.3
39	37.3	11.4	99	94.7	28.9	159	152.1	46.5	219	209.4	64.0	279	266.8	81.6
40	38.3	11.7	100	95.6	29.2	160	153.0	46.8	220	210.4	64.3	280	267.8	81.9
41	39.2	12.0	101	96.6	29.5	161	154.0	47.1	221	211.3	64.6	281	268.7	82.2
42	40.2	12.3	102	97.5	29.8	162	154.9	47.4	222	212.3	64.9	282	269.7	82.4
43	41.1	12.6	103	98.5	30.1	163	155.9	47.7	223	213.3	65.2	283	270.6	82.7
44	42.1	12.9	104	99.5	30.4	164	156.8	47.9	224	214.2	65.5	284	271.6	83.0
45	43.0	13.2	105	100.4	30.7	165	157.8	48.2	225	215.2	65.8	285	272.5	83.3
46	44.0	13.4	106	101.4	31.0	166	158.7	48.5	226	216.1	66.1	286	273.5	83.6
47	44.9	13.7	107	102.3	31.3	167	159.7	48.8	227	217.1	66.4	287	274.5	83.9
48	45.9	14.0	108	103.3	31.6	168	160.7	49.1	228	218.0	66.7	288	275.4	84.2
49	46.9	14.3	109	104.2	31.9	169	161.6	49.4	229	219.0	67.0	289	276.4	84.5
50	47.8	14.6	110	105.2	32.2	170	162.6	49.7	230	220.0	67.2	290	277.3	84.8
51	48.8	14.9	111	106.1	32.5	171	163.5	50.0	231	220.9	67.5	291	278.3	85.1
52	49.7	15.2	112	107.1	32.7	172	164.5	50.3	232	221.9	67.8	292	279.2	85.4
53	50.7	15.5	113	108.1	33.0	173	165.4	50.6	233	222.8	68.1	293	280.2	85.7
54	51.6	15.8	114	109.0	33.3	174	166.4	50.9	234	223.8	68.4	294	281.2	86.0
55	52.6	16.1	115	110.0	33.6	175	167.4	51.2	235	224.7	68.7	295	282.1	86.2
56	53.5	16.4	116	110.9	33.9	176	168.3	51.5	236	225.7	69.0	296	283.1	86.5
57	54.5	16.7	117	111.9	34.2	177	169.3	51.7	237	226.6	69.3	297	284.0	86.8
58	55.5	17.0	118	112.8	34.5	178	170.2	52.0	238	227.6	69.6	298	285.0	87.1
59	56.4	17.2	119	113.8	34.8	179	171.2	52.3	239	228.6	69.9	299	285.9	87.4
60	57.4	17.5	120	114.8	35.1	180	172.1	52.6	240	229.5	70.2	300	286.9	87.7
Hyp.	Opp.	Adj.	Hyp.	Opp.	Adj.	Hyp.	Opp.	Adj.	Hyp.	Opp.	Adj.	Hyp.	Opp.	Adj.
Dist. D Lon	Dep.	D. Lat. Dep	Dist. D Lon	Dep.	D. Lat. Dep	Dist. D Lon	Dep.	D. Lat. Dep	Dist. D Lon	Dep.	D. Lat. Dep	Dist. D Lon	Dep.	D. Lat. Dep

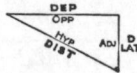

73°   73°

Table 3

TRAVERSE TABLE

17° 343° | 017° / 197° | 163° **17°**

D Lon Dep Dist. D. Lat. Dep.			D Lon Dep Dist. D. Lat. Dep.			D Lon Dep Dist. D. Lat. Dep.			D Lon Dep Dist. D. Lat. Dep.			D Lon Dep Dist. D. Lat. Dep.		
Hyp.	Adj.	Opp.	Hyp.	Adj.	Opp.	Hyp.	Adj.	Opp.	Hyp.	Adj.	Opp.	Hyp.	Adj.	Opp.
301	287.8	88.0	361	345.2	105.5	421	402.6	123.1	481	460.0	140.6	541	517.4	158.2
302	288.8	88.3	362	346.2	105.8	422	403.6	123.4	482	460.9	140.9	542	518.3	158.5
303	289.8	88.6	363	347.1	106.1	423	404.5	123.7	483	461.9	141.2	543	519.3	158.8
304	290.7	88.9	364	348.1	106.4	424	405.5	124.0	484	462.9	141.5	544	520.2	159.1
305	291.7	89.2	365	349.1	106.7	425	406.4	124.3	485	463.8	141.8	545	521.2	159.3
306	292.6	89.5	366	350.0	107.0	426	407.4	124.6	486	464.8	142.1	546	522.1	159.6
307	293.6	89.8	367	351.0	107.3	427	408.3	124.8	487	465.7	142.4	547	523.1	159.9
308	294.5	90.1	368	351.9	107.6	428	409.3	125.1	488	466.7	142.7	548	524.1	160.2
309	295.5	90.3	369	352.9	107.9	429	410.3	125.4	489	467.6	143.0	549	525.0	160.5
310	296.5	90.6	370	353.8	108.2	430	411.2	125.7	490	468.6	143.3	550	526.0	160.8
311	297.4	90.9	371	354.8	108.5	431	412.2	126.0	491	469.5	143.6	551	526.9	161.1
312	298.4	91.2	372	355.7	108.8	432	413.1	126.3	492	470.5	143.8	552	527.9	161.4
313	299.3	91.5	373	356.7	109.1	433	414.1	126.6	493	471.5	144.1	553	528.8	161.7
314	300.3	91.8	374	357.7	109.3	434	415.0	126.9	494	472.4	144.4	554	529.8	162.0
315	301.2	92.1	375	358.6	109.6	435	416.0	127.2	495	473.4	144.7	555	530.7	162.3
316	302.2	92.4	376	359.6	109.9	436	416.9	127.5	496	474.3	145.0	556	531.7	162.6
317	303.1	92.7	377	360.5	110.2	437	417.9	127.8	497	475.3	145.3	557	532.7	162.9
318	304.1	93.0	378	361.5	110.5	438	418.9	128.1	498	476.2	145.6	558	533.6	163.1
319	305.1	93.3	379	362.4	110.8	439	419.8	128.4	499	477.2	145.9	559	534.6	163.4
320	306.0	93.6	380	363.4	111.1	440	420.8	128.6	500	478.2	146.2	560	535.5	163.7
321	307.0	93.9	381	364.4	111.4	441	421.7	128.9	501	479.1	146.5	561	536.5	164.0
322	307.9	94.1	382	365.3	111.7	442	422.7	129.2	502	480.1	146.8	562	537.4	164.3
323	308.9	94.4	383	366.3	112.0	443	423.6	129.5	503	481.0	147.1	563	538.4	164.6
324	309.8	94.7	384	367.2	112.3	444	424.6	129.8	504	482.0	147.4	564	539.4	164.9
325	310.8	95.0	385	368.2	112.6	445	425.6	130.1	505	482.9	147.6	565	540.3	165.2
326	311.8	95.3	386	369.1	112.9	446	426.5	130.4	506	483.9	147.9	566	541.3	165.5
327	312.7	95.6	387	370.1	113.1	447	427.5	130.7	507	484.8	148.2	567	542.2	165.8
328	313.7	95.9	388	371.0	113.4	448	428.4	131.0	508	485.8	148.5	568	543.2	166.1
329	314.6	96.2	389	372.0	113.7	449	429.4	131.3	509	486.8	148.8	569	544.1	166.4
330	315.6	96.5	390	373.0	114.0	450	430.3	131.6	510	487.7	149.1	570	545.1	166.7
331	316.5	96.8	391	373.9	114.3	451	431.3	131.9	511	488.7	149.4	571	546.1	166.9
332	317.5	97.1	392	374.9	114.6	452	432.2	132.2	512	489.6	149.7	572	547.0	167.2
333	318.4	97.4	393	375.8	114.9	453	433.2	132.4	513	490.6	150.0	573	548.0	167.5
334	319.4	97.7	394	376.8	115.2	454	434.2	132.7	514	491.5	150.3	574	548.9	167.8
335	320.4	97.9	395	377.7	115.5	455	435.1	133.0	515	492.5	150.6	575	549.9	168.1
336	321.3	98.2	396	378.7	115.8	456	436.1	133.3	516	493.5	150.9	576	550.8	168.4
337	322.3	98.5	397	379.7	116.1	457	437.0	133.6	517	494.4	151.2	577	551.8	168.7
338	323.2	98.8	398	380.6	116.4	458	438.0	133.9	518	495.4	151.4	578	552.7	169.0
339	324.2	99.1	399	381.6	116.7	459	438.9	134.2	519	496.3	151.7	579	553.7	169.3
340	325.1	99.4	400	382.5	116.9	460	439.9	134.5	520	497.3	152.0	580	554.7	169.6
341	326.1	99.7	401	383.5	117.2	461	440.9	134.8	521	498.3	152.3	581	555.6	169.9
342	327.1	100.0	402	384.4	117.5	462	441.8	135.1	522	499.2	152.6	582	556.6	170.2
343	328.0	100.3	403	385.4	117.8	463	442.8	135.4	523	500.1	152.9	583	557.5	170.5
344	329.0	100.6	404	386.3	118.1	464	443.7	135.7	524	501.1	153.2	584	558.5	170.7
345	329.9	100.9	405	387.3	118.4	465	444.7	136.0	525	502.1	153.5	585	559.4	171.0
346	330.9	101.2	406	388.3	118.7	466	445.6	136.2	526	503.0	153.8	586	560.4	171.3
347	331.8	101.5	407	389.2	119.0	467	446.6	136.5	527	504.0	154.1	587	561.4	171.6
348	332.8	101.7	408	390.2	119.3	468	447.6	136.8	528	504.9	154.4	588	562.3	171.9
349	333.8	102.0	409	391.1	119.6	469	448.5	137.1	529	505.9	154.7	589	563.3	172.2
350	334.7	102.3	410	392.1	119.9	470	449.5	137.4	530	506.8	155.0	590	564.2	172.5
351	335.7	102.6	411	393.0	120.2	471	450.4	137.7	531	507.8	155.2	591	565.2	172.8
352	336.6	102.9	412	394.0	120.5	472	451.4	138.0	532	508.8	155.5	592	566.1	173.1
353	337.6	103.2	413	395.0	120.7	473	452.3	138.3	533	509.7	155.8	593	567.1	173.4
354	338.5	103.5	414	395.9	121.0	474	453.3	138.6	534	510.7	156.1	594	568.0	173.7
355	339.5	103.8	415	396.9	121.3	475	454.2	138.9	535	511.6	156.4	595	569.0	174.0
356	340.4	104.1	416	397.8	121.6	476	455.2	139.2	536	512.6	156.7	596	570.0	174.3
357	341.4	104.4	417	398.8	121.9	477	456.2	139.5	537	513.5	157.0	597	570.9	174.5
358	342.4	104.7	418	399.7	122.2	478	457.1	139.8	538	514.5	157.3	598	571.9	174.8
359	343.3	105.0	419	400.7	122.5	479	458.1	140.0	539	515.4	157.6	599	572.8	175.1
360	344.3	105.3	420	401.6	122.8	480	459.0	140.3	540	516.4	157.9	600	573.8	175.4
Hyp.	Opp.	Adj.	Hyp.	Opp.	Adj.	Hyp.	Opp.	Adj.	Hyp.	Opp.	Adj.	Hyp.	Opp.	Adj.
Dist. D Lon	Dep.	D. Lat. Dep	Dist. D Lon	Dep.	D. Lat. Dep	Dist. D Lon	Dep.	D. Lat. Dep	Dist. D Lon	Dep.	D. Lat. Dep	Dist. D Lon	Dep.	D. Lat. Dep

73° 287° | 073° / 253° | 107° **73°**

Table 3

TRAVERSE TABLE

18°   18°

D Lon Dist.	Dep D. Lat.	Dep.	D Lon Dist.	Dep D. Lat.	Dep.	D Lon Dist.	Dep D. Lat.	Dep.	D Lon Dist.	Dep D. Lat.	Dep.	D Lon Dist.	Dep D. Lat.	Dep.
Hyp.	Adj.	Opp.	Hyp.	Adj.	Opp.	Hyp.	Adj.	Opp.	Hyp.	Adj.	Opp.	Hyp.	Adj.	Opp.
1	1.0	0.3	61	58.0	18.9	121	115.1	37.4	181	172.1	55.9	241	229.2	74.5
2	1.9	0.6	62	59.0	19.2	122	116.0	37.7	182	173.1	56.2	242	230.2	74.8
3	2.9	0.9	63	59.9	19.5	123	117.0	38.0	183	174.0	56.6	243	231.1	75.1
4	3.8	1.2	64	60.9	19.8	124	117.9	38.3	184	175.0	56.9	244	232.1	75.4
5	4.8	1.5	65	61.8	20.1	125	118.9	38.6	185	175.9	57.2	245	233.0	75.7
6	5.7	1.9	66	62.8	20.4	126	119.8	38.9	186	176.9	57.5	246	234.0	76.0
7	6.7	2.2	67	63.7	20.7	127	120.8	39.2	187	177.8	57.8	247	234.9	76.3
8	7.6	2.5	68	64.7	21.0	128	121.7	39.6	188	178.8	58.1	248	235.9	76.6
9	8.6	2.8	69	65.6	21.3	129	122.7	39.9	189	179.7	58.4	249	236.8	76.9
10	9.5	3.1	70	66.6	21.6	130	123.6	40.2	190	180.7	58.7	250	237.8	77.3
11	10.5	3.4	71	67.5	21.9	131	124.6	40.5	191	181.7	59.0	251	238.7	77.6
12	11.4	3.7	72	68.5	22.2	132	125.5	40.8	192	182.6	59.3	252	239.7	77.9
13	12.4	4.0	73	69.4	22.6	133	126.5	41.1	193	183.6	59.6	253	240.6	78.2
14	13.3	4.3	74	70.4	22.9	134	127.4	41.4	194	184.5	59.9	254	241.6	78.5
15	14.3	4.6	75	71.3	23.2	135	128.4	41.7	195	185.5	60.3	255	242.5	78.8
16	15.2	4.9	76	72.3	23.5	136	129.3	42.0	196	186.4	60.6	256	243.5	79.1
17	16.2	5.3	77	73.2	23.8	137	130.3	42.3	197	187.4	60.9	257	244.4	79.4
18	17.1	5.6	78	74.2	24.1	138	131.2	42.6	198	188.3	61.2	258	245.4	79.7
19	18.1	5.9	79	75.1	24.4	139	132.2	43.0	199	189.3	61.5	259	246.3	80.0
20	19.0	6.2	80	76.1	24.7	140	133.1	43.3	200	190.2	61.8	260	247.3	80.3
21	20.0	6.5	81	77.0	25.0	141	134.1	43.6	201	191.2	62.1	261	248.2	80.7
22	20.9	6.8	82	78.0	25.3	142	135.1	43.9	202	192.1	62.4	262	249.2	81.0
23	21.9	7.1	83	78.9	25.6	143	136.0	44.2	203	193.1	62.7	263	250.1	81.3
24	22.8	7.4	84	79.9	26.0	144	137.0	44.5	204	194.0	63.0	264	251.1	81.6
25	23.8	7.7	85	80.8	26.3	145	137.9	44.8	205	195.0	63.3	265	252.0	81.9
26	24.7	8.0	86	81.8	26.6	146	138.9	45.1	206	195.9	63.7	266	253.0	82.2
27	25.7	8.3	87	82.7	26.9	147	139.8	45.4	207	196.9	64.0	267	253.9	82.5
28	26.6	8.7	88	83.7	27.2	148	140.8	45.7	208	197.8	64.3	268	254.9	82.8
29	27.6	9.0	89	84.6	27.5	149	141.7	46.0	209	198.8	64.6	269	255.8	83.1
30	28.5	9.3	90	85.6	27.8	150	142.7	46.4	210	199.7	64.9	270	256.8	83.4
31	29.5	9.6	91	86.5	28.1	151	143.6	46.7	211	200.7	65.2	271	257.7	83.7
32	30.4	9.9	92	87.5	28.4	152	144.6	47.0	212	201.6	65.5	272	258.7	84.1
33	31.4	10.2	93	88.4	28.7	153	145.5	47.3	213	202.6	65.8	273	259.6	84.4
34	32.3	10.5	94	89.4	29.0	154	146.5	47.6	214	203.5	66.1	274	260.6	84.7
35	33.3	10.8	95	90.4	29.4	155	147.4	47.9	215	204.5	66.4	275	261.5	85.0
36	34.2	11.1	96	91.3	29.7	156	148.4	48.2	216	205.4	66.7	276	262.5	85.3
37	35.2	11.4	97	92.3	30.0	157	149.3	48.5	217	206.4	67.1	277	263.4	85.6
38	36.1	11.7	98	93.2	30.3	158	150.3	48.8	218	207.3	67.4	278	264.4	85.9
39	37.1	12.1	99	94.2	30.6	159	151.2	49.1	219	208.3	67.7	279	265.3	86.2
40	38.0	12.4	100	95.1	30.9	160	152.2	49.4	220	209.2	68.0	280	266.3	86.5
41	39.0	12.7	101	96.1	31.2	161	153.1	49.8	221	210.2	68.3	281	267.2	86.8
42	39.9	13.0	102	97.0	31.5	162	154.1	50.1	222	211.1	68.6	282	268.2	87.1
43	40.9	13.3	103	98.0	31.8	163	155.0	50.4	223	212.1	68.9	283	269.1	87.5
44	41.8	13.6	104	98.9	32.1	164	156.0	50.7	224	213.0	69.2	284	270.1	87.8
45	42.8	13.9	105	99.9	32.4	165	156.9	51.0	225	214.0	69.5	285	271.1	88.1
46	43.7	14.2	106	100.8	32.8	166	157.9	51.3	226	214.9	69.8	286	272.0	88.4
47	44.7	14.5	107	101.8	33.1	167	158.8	51.6	227	215.9	70.1	287	273.0	88.7
48	45.7	14.8	108	102.7	33.4	168	159.8	51.9	228	216.8	70.5	288	273.9	89.0
49	46.6	15.1	109	103.7	33.7	169	160.7	52.2	229	217.8	70.8	289	274.9	89.3
50	47.6	15.5	110	104.6	34.0	170	161.7	52.5	230	218.7	71.1	290	275.8	89.6
51	48.5	15.8	111	105.6	34.3	171	162.6	52.8	231	219.7	71.4	291	276.8	89.9
52	49.5	16.1	112	106.5	34.6	172	163.6	53.2	232	220.6	71.7	292	277.7	90.2
53	50.4	16.4	113	107.5	34.9	173	164.5	53.5	233	221.6	72.0	293	278.7	90.5
54	51.4	16.7	114	108.4	35.2	174	165.5	53.8	234	222.5	72.3	294	279.6	90.9
55	52.3	17.0	115	109.4	35.5	175	166.4	54.1	235	223.5	72.6	295	280.6	91.2
56	53.3	17.3	116	110.3	35.8	176	167.4	54.4	236	224.4	72.9	296	281.5	91.5
57	54.2	17.6	117	111.3	36.2	177	168.3	54.7	237	225.4	73.2	297	282.5	91.8
58	55.2	17.9	118	112.2	36.5	178	169.3	55.0	238	226.4	73.5	298	283.4	92.1
59	56.1	18.2	119	113.2	36.8	179	170.2	55.3	239	227.3	73.9	299	284.4	92.4
60	57.1	18.5	120	114.1	37.1	180	171.2	55.6	240	228.3	74.2	300	285.3	92.7
Hyp.	Opp.	Adj.	Hyp.	Opp.	Adj.	Hyp.	Opp.	Adj.	Hyp.	Opp.	Adj.	Hyp.	Opp.	Adj.

Dist. D Lon	Dep.	D. Lat. Dep	Dist. D Lon	Dep.	D. Lat. Dep	Dist. D Lon	Dep.	D. Lat. Dep	Dist. D Lon	Dep.	D. Lat. Dep	Dist. D Lon	Dep.	D. Lat. Dep

72°   72°

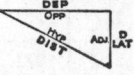

Table 3

TRAVERSE TABLE

18°

342°	018°
198°	162°

18°

D Lon	Dep		D Lon	Dep		D Lon	Dep		D Lon	Dep		D Lon	Dep	
Dist.	D. Lat.	Dep.	Dist.	D. Lat.	Dep.	Dist.	D. Lat.	Dep.	Dist.	D. Lat.	Dep.	Dist.	D. Lat.	Dep.
Hyp.	Adj.	Opp.	Hyp.	Adj.	Opp.	Hyp.	Adj.	Opp.	Hyp.	Adj.	Opp.	Hyp.	Adj.	Opp.
301	286.3	93.0	361	343.3	111.6	421	400.4	130.1	481	457.5	148.6	541	514.5	167.2
302	287.2	93.3	362	344.3	111.9	422	401.3	130.4	482	458.4	148.9	542	515.5	167.5
303	288.2	93.6	363	345.2	112.2	423	402.3	130.7	483	459.4	149.3	543	516.4	167.8
304	289.1	93.9	364	346.2	112.5	424	403.2	131.0	484	460.3	149.6	544	517.4	168.1
305	290.1	94.3	365	347.1	112.8	425	404.2	131.3	485	461.3	149.9	545	518.3	168.4
306	291.0	94.6	366	348.1	113.1	426	405.2	131.6	486	462.2	150.2	546	519.3	168.7
307	292.0	94.9	367	349.0	113.4	427	406.1	132.0	487	463.2	150.5	547	520.2	169.0
308	292.9	95.2	368	350.0	113.7	428	407.1	132.3	488	464.1	150.8	548	521.2	169.3
309	293.9	95.5	369	350.9	114.0	429	408.0	132.6	489	465.1	151.1	549	522.1	169.7
310	294.8	95.8	370	351.9	114.3	430	409.0	132.9	490	466.0	151.4	550	523.1	170.0
311	295.8	96.1	371	352.8	114.6	431	409.9	133.2	491	467.0	151.7	551	524.0	170.3
312	296.7	96.4	372	353.8	115.0	432	410.9	133.5	492	467.9	152.0	552	525.0	170.6
313	297.7	96.7	373	354.7	115.3	433	411.8	133.8	493	468.9	152.3	553	525.9	170.9
314	298.6	97.0	374	355.7	115.6	434	412.8	134.1	494	469.8	152.7	554	526.9	171.2
315	299.6	97.3	375	356.6	115.9	435	413.7	134.4	495	470.8	153.0	555	527.8	171.5
316	300.5	97.6	376	357.6	116.2	436	414.7	134.7	496	471.7	153.3	556	528.8	171.8
317	301.5	98.0	377	358.5	116.5	437	415.6	135.0	497	472.7	153.6	557	529.7	172.1
318	302.4	98.3	378	359.5	116.8	438	416.6	135.3	498	473.6	153.9	558	530.7	172.4
319	303.4	98.6	379	360.5	117.1	439	417.5	135.7	499	474.6	154.2	559	531.6	172.7
320	304.3	98.9	380	361.4	117.4	440	418.5	136.0	500	475.5	154.5	560	532.6	173.0
321	305.3	99.2	381	362.4	117.7	441	419.4	136.3	501	476.5	154.8	561	533.5	173.4
322	306.2	99.5	382	363.3	118.0	442	420.4	136.6	502	477.4	155.1	562	534.5	173.7
323	307.2	99.8	383	364.3	118.4	443	421.3	136.9	503	478.4	155.4	563	535.4	174.0
324	308.2	100.1	384	365.2	118.7	444	422.3	137.2	504	479.3	155.7	564	536.4	174.3
325	309.1	100.4	385	366.2	119.0	445	423.2	137.5	505	480.3	156.1	565	537.3	174.6
326	310.0	100.7	386	367.1	119.3	446	424.2	137.8	506	481.2	156.4	566	538.3	174.9
327	311.0	101.0	387	368.1	119.6	447	425.1	138.1	507	482.2	156.7	567	539.2	175.2
328	311.9	101.4	388	369.0	119.9	448	426.1	138.4	508	483.1	157.0	568	540.2	175.5
329	312.9	101.7	389	370.0	120.2	449	427.0	138.7	509	484.1	157.3	569	541.2	175.8
330	313.8	102.0	390	370.9	120.5	450	428.0	139.1	510	485.0	157.6	570	542.1	176.1
331	314.8	102.3	391	371.9	120.8	451	428.9	139.4	511	486.0	157.9	571	543.1	176.4
332	315.8	102.6	392	372.8	121.1	452	429.9	139.7	512	486.9	158.2	572	544.0	176.8
333	316.7	102.9	393	373.8	121.4	453	430.8	140.0	513	487.9	158.5	573	545.0	177.1
334	317.7	103.2	394	374.7	121.8	454	431.8	140.3	514	488.8	158.8	574	545.9	177.4
335	318.6	103.5	395	375.7	122.1	455	432.7	140.6	515	489.8	159.1	575	546.9	177.7
336	319.6	103.8	396	376.6	122.4	456	433.7	140.9	516	490.7	159.5	576	547.8	178.0
337	320.5	104.1	397	377.6	122.7	457	434.6	141.2	517	491.7	159.8	577	548.8	178.3
338	321.5	104.4	398	378.5	123.0	458	435.6	141.5	518	492.6	160.1	578	549.7	178.6
339	322.4	104.8	399	379.5	123.3	459	436.5	141.8	519	493.6	160.4	579	550.7	178.9
340	323.4	105.1	400	380.4	123.6	460	437.5	142.1	520	494.5	160.7	580	551.6	179.2
341	324.3	105.4	401	381.4	123.9	461	438.4	142.5	521	495.5	161.0	581	552.6	179.5
342	325.3	105.7	402	382.3	124.2	462	439.4	142.8	522	496.5	161.3	582	553.5	179.8
343	326.2	106.0	403	383.3	124.5	463	440.3	143.1	523	497.4	161.6	583	554.5	180.2
344	327.2	106.3	404	384.2	124.8	464	441.3	143.4	524	498.4	161.9	584	555.4	180.5
345	328.1	106.6	405	385.2	125.2	465	442.2	143.7	525	499.3	162.2	585	556.4	180.8
346	329.1	106.9	406	386.1	125.5	466	443.2	144.0	526	500.3	162.5	586	557.3	181.1
347	330.0	107.2	407	387.1	125.8	467	444.1	144.3	527	501.2	162.9	587	558.3	181.4
348	331.0	107.5	408	388.0	126.1	468	445.1	144.6	528	502.2	163.2	588	559.2	181.7
349	331.9	107.8	409	389.0	126.4	469	446.0	144.9	529	503.1	163.5	589	560.2	182.0
350	332.9	108.2	410	389.9	126.7	470	447.0	145.2	530	504.1	163.8	590	561.1	182.3
351	333.8	108.5	411	390.9	127.0	471	447.9	145.5	531	505.0	164.1	591	562.1	182.6
352	334.8	108.8	412	391.8	127.3	472	448.9	145.9	532	506.0	164.4	592	563.0	182.9
353	335.7	109.1	413	392.8	127.6	473	449.8	146.2	533	506.9	164.7	593	564.0	183.2
354	336.7	109.4	414	393.7	127.9	474	450.8	146.5	534	507.9	165.0	594	564.9	183.6
355	337.6	109.7	415	394.7	128.2	475	451.8	146.8	535	508.8	165.3	595	565.9	183.9
356	338.6	110.0	416	395.6	128.6	476	452.7	147.1	536	509.8	165.6	596	566.8	184.2
357	339.5	110.3	417	396.6	128.9	477	453.7	147.4	537	510.7	165.9	597	567.8	184.5
358	340.5	110.6	418	397.5	129.2	478	454.6	147.7	538	511.7	166.3	598	568.7	184.8
359	341.4	110.9	419	398.5	129.5	479	455.6	148.0	539	512.6	166.6	599	569.7	185.1
360	342.4	111.2	420	399.4	129.8	480	456.5	148.3	540	513.6	166.9	600	570.6	185.4
Hyp.	Opp.	Adj.	Hyp.	Opp.	Adj.	Hyp.	Opp.	Adj.	Hyp.	Opp.	Adj.	Hyp.	Opp.	Adj.
Dist.	Dep.	D. Lat.	Dist.	Dep.	D. Lat.	Dist.	Dep.	D. Lat.	Dist.	Dep.	D. Lat.	Dist.	Dep.	D. Lat.
D Lon		Dep	D Lon		Dep	D Lon		Dep	D Lon		Dep	D Lon		Dep

72°

288°	072°
252°	108°

72°

Table 3   TRAVERSE TABLE   19°

19° 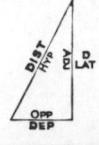 19°

D Lon / Dist.	Dep / D. Lat.	Dep	D Lon / Dist.	Dep / D. Lat.	Dep	D Lon / Dist.	Dep / D. Lat.	Dep	D Lon / Dist.	Dep / D. Lat.	Dep	D Lon / Dist.	Dep / D. Lat.	Dep
Hyp.	Adj.	Opp.	Hyp.	Adj.	Opp.	Hyp.	Adj.	Opp.	Hyp.	Adj.	Opp.	Hyp.	Adj.	Opp.
1	0.9	0.3	61	57.7	19.9	121	114.4	39.4	181	171.1	58.9	241	227.9	78.5
2	1.9	0.7	62	58.6	20.2	122	115.4	39.7	182	172.1	59.3	242	228.8	78.8
3	2.8	1.0	63	59.6	20.5	123	116.3	40.0	183	173.0	59.6	243	229.8	79.1
4	3.8	1.3	64	60.5	20.8	124	117.2	40.4	184	174.0	59.9	244	230.7	79.4
5	4.7	1.6	65	61.5	21.2	125	118.2	40.7	185	174.9	60.2	245	231.7	79.8
6	5.7	2.0	66	62.4	21.5	126	119.1	41.0	186	175.9	60.6	246	232.6	80.1
7	6.6	2.3	67	63.3	21.8	127	120.1	41.3	187	176.8	60.9	247	233.5	80.4
8	7.6	2.6	68	64.3	22.1	128	121.0	41.7	188	177.8	61.2	248	234.5	80.7
9	8.5	2.9	69	65.2	22.5	129	122.0	42.0	189	178.7	61.5	249	235.4	81.1
10	9.5	3.3	70	66.2	22.8	130	122.9	42.3	190	179.6	61.9	250	236.4	81.4
11	10.4	3.6	71	67.1	23.1	131	123.9	42.6	191	180.6	62.2	251	237.3	81.7
12	11.3	3.9	72	68.1	23.4	132	124.8	43.0	192	181.5	62.5	252	238.3	82.0
13	12.3	4.2	73	69.0	23.8	133	125.8	43.3	193	182.5	62.8	253	239.2	82.4
14	13.2	4.6	74	70.0	24.1	134	126.7	43.6	194	183.4	63.2	254	240.2	82.7
15	14.2	4.9	75	70.9	24.4	135	127.6	44.0	195	184.4	63.5	255	241.1	83.0
16	15.1	5.2	76	71.9	24.7	136	128.6	44.3	196	185.3	63.8	256	242.1	83.3
17	16.1	5.5	77	72.8	25.1	137	129.5	44.6	197	186.3	64.1	257	243.0	83.7
18	17.0	5.9	78	73.8	25.4	138	130.5	44.9	198	187.2	64.5	258	243.9	84.0
19	18.0	6.2	79	74.7	25.7	139	131.4	45.3	199	188.2	64.8	259	244.9	84.3
20	18.9	6.5	80	75.6	26.0	140	132.4	45.6	200	189.1	65.1	260	245.8	84.6
21	19.9	6.8	81	76.6	26.4	141	133.3	45.9	201	190.0	65.4	261	246.8	85.0
22	20.8	7.2	82	77.5	26.7	142	134.3	46.2	202	191.0	65.8	262	247.7	85.3
23	21.7	7.5	83	78.5	27.0	143	135.2	46.6	203	191.9	66.1	263	248.7	85.6
24	22.7	7.8	84	79.4	27.3	144	136.2	46.9	204	192.9	66.4	264	249.6	86.0
25	23.6	8.1	85	80.4	27.7	145	137.1	47.2	205	193.8	66.7	265	250.6	86.3
26	24.6	8.5	86	81.3	28.0	146	138.0	47.5	206	194.8	67.1	266	251.5	86.6
27	25.5	8.8	87	82.3	28.3	147	139.0	47.9	207	195.7	67.4	267	252.5	86.9
28	26.5	9.1	88	83.2	28.6	148	139.9	48.2	208	196.7	67.7	268	253.4	87.3
29	27.4	9.4	89	84.2	29.0	149	140.9	48.5	209	197.6	68.0	269	254.3	87.6
30	28.4	9.8	90	85.1	29.3	150	141.8	48.8	210	198.6	68.4	270	255.3	87.9
31	29.3	10.1	91	86.0	29.6	151	142.8	49.2	211	199.5	68.7	271	256.2	88.2
32	30.3	10.4	92	87.0	30.0	152	143.7	49.5	212	200.4	69.0	272	257.2	88.6
33	31.2	10.7	93	87.9	30.3	153	144.7	49.8	213	201.4	69.3	273	258.1	88.9
34	32.1	11.1	94	88.9	30.6	154	145.6	50.1	214	202.3	69.7	274	259.1	89.2
35	33.1	11.4	95	89.8	30.9	155	146.6	50.5	215	203.3	70.0	275	260.0	89.5
36	34.0	11.7	96	90.8	31.3	156	147.5	50.8	216	204.2	70.3	276	261.0	89.9
37	35.0	12.0	97	91.7	31.6	157	148.4	51.1	217	205.2	70.6	277	261.9	90.2
38	35.9	12.4	98	92.7	31.9	158	149.4	51.4	218	206.1	71.0	278	262.9	90.5
39	36.9	12.7	99	93.6	32.2	159	150.3	51.8	219	207.1	71.3	279	263.8	90.8
40	37.8	13.0	100	94.6	32.6	160	151.3	52.1	220	208.0	71.6	280	264.7	91.2
41	38.8	13.3	101	95.5	32.9	161	152.2	52.4	221	209.0	72.0	281	265.7	91.5
42	39.7	13.7	102	96.4	33.2	162	153.2	52.7	222	209.9	72.3	282	266.6	91.8
43	40.7	14.0	103	97.4	33.5	163	154.1	53.1	223	210.9	72.6	283	267.6	92.1
44	41.6	14.3	104	98.3	33.9	164	155.1	53.4	224	211.8	72.9	284	268.5	92.5
45	42.5	14.7	105	99.3	34.2	165	156.0	53.7	225	212.7	73.3	285	269.5	92.8
46	43.5	15.0	106	100.2	34.5	166	157.0	54.0	226	213.7	73.6	286	270.4	93.1
47	44.4	15.3	107	101.2	34.8	167	157.9	54.4	227	214.6	73.9	287	271.4	93.4
48	45.4	15.6	108	102.1	35.2	168	158.8	54.7	228	215.6	74.2	288	272.3	93.8
49	46.3	16.0	109	103.1	35.5	169	159.8	55.0	229	216.5	74.6	289	273.3	94.1
50	47.3	16.3	110	104.0	35.8	170	160.7	55.3	230	217.5	74.9	290	274.2	94.4
51	48.2	16.6	111	105.0	36.1	171	161.7	55.7	231	218.4	75.2	291	275.1	94.7
52	49.2	16.9	112	105.9	36.5	172	162.6	56.0	232	219.4	75.5	292	276.1	95.1
53	50.1	17.3	113	106.8	36.8	173	163.6	56.3	233	220.3	75.9	293	277.0	95.4
54	51.1	17.6	114	107.8	37.1	174	164.5	56.6	234	221.3	76.2	294	278.0	95.7
55	52.0	17.9	115	108.7	37.4	175	165.5	57.0	235	222.2	76.5	295	278.9	96.0
56	52.9	18.2	116	109.7	37.8	176	166.4	57.3	236	223.1	76.8	296	279.9	96.4
57	53.9	18.6	117	110.6	38.1	177	167.4	57.6	237	224.1	77.2	297	280.8	96.7
58	54.8	18.9	118	111.6	38.4	178	168.3	58.0	238	225.0	77.5	298	281.8	97.0
59	55.8	19.2	119	112.5	38.7	179	169.2	58.3	239	226.0	77.8	299	282.7	97.3
60	56.7	19.5	120	113.5	39.1	180	170.2	58.6	240	226.9	78.1	300	283.7	97.7
Hyp.	Opp.	Adj.	Hyp.	Opp.	Adj.	Hyp.	Opp.	Adj.	Hyp.	Opp.	Adj.	Hyp.	Opp.	Adj.
Dist. / D Lon	Dep	D. Lat. / Dep	Dist. / D Lon	Dep	D. Lat. / Dep	Dist. / D Lon	Dep	D. Lat. / Dep	Dist. / D Lon	Dep	D. Lat. / Dep	Dist. / D Lon	Dep	D. Lat. / Dep

71° 71°

Table 3

TRAVERSE TABLE

D Lon	Dep		D Lon	Dep		D Lon	Dep		D Lon	Dep		D Lon	Dep	
Dist.	D. Lat.	Dep.	Dist.	D. Lat.	Dep.	Dist.	D. Lat.	Dep.	Dist.	D. Lat.	Dep.	Dist.	D. Lat.	Dep.
Hyp.	Adj.	Opp.	Hyp.	Adj.	Opp.	Hyp.	Adj.	Opp.	Hyp.	Adj.	Opp.	Hyp.	Adj.	Opp.
301	284.6	98.0	361	341.3	117.5	421	398.1	137.1	481	454.8	156.6	541	511.5	176.1
302	285.5	98.3	362	342.3	117.9	422	399.0	137.4	482	455.7	156.9	542	512.5	176.5
303	286.5	98.6	363	343.2	118.2	423	400.0	137.7	483	456.7	157.2	543	513.4	176.8
304	287.4	99.0	364	344.2	118.5	424	400.9	138.0	484	457.6	157.6	544	514.4	177.1
305	288.4	99.3	365	345.1	118.8	425	401.8	138.4	485	458.6	157.9	545	515.3	177.4
306	289.3	99.6	366	346.1	119.2	426	402.8	138.7	486	459.5	158.2	546	516.3	177.8
307	290.3	99.9	367	347.0	119.5	427	403.7	139.0	487	460.5	158.6	547	517.2	178.1
308	291.2	100.3	368	348.0	119.8	428	404.7	139.3	488	461.4	158.9	548	518.1	178.4
309	292.2	100.6	369	348.9	120.1	429	405.6	139.7	489	462.4	159.2	549	519.1	178.7
310	293.1	100.9	370	349.8	120.5	430	406.6	140.0	490	463.3	159.5	550	520.0	179.1
311	294.1	101.3	371	350.8	120.8	431	407.5	140.3	491	464.2	159.9	551	521.0	179.4
312	295.0	101.6	372	351.7	121.1	432	408.5	140.6	492	465.2	160.2	552	521.9	179.7
313	295.9	101.9	373	352.7	121.4	433	409.4	141.0	493	466.1	160.5	553	522.9	180.0
314	296.9	102.2	374	353.6	121.8	434	410.4	141.3	494	467.1	160.8	554	523.8	180.4
315	297.8	102.6	375	354.6	122.1	435	411.3	141.6	495	468.0	161.2	555	524.8	180.7
316	298.8	102.9	376	355.5	122.4	436	412.2	141.9	496	469.0	161.5	556	525.7	181.0
317	299.7	103.2	377	356.5	122.7	437	413.2	142.3	497	469.9	161.8	557	526.7	181.3
318	300.7	103.5	378	357.4	123.1	438	414.1	142.6	498	470.9	162.1	558	527.6	181.7
319	301.6	103.9	379	358.4	123.4	439	415.1	142.9	499	471.8	162.5	559	528.5	182.0
320	302.6	104.2	380	359.3	123.7	440	416.0	143.3	500	472.8	162.8	560	529.5	182.3
321	303.5	104.5	381	360.2	124.0	441	417.0	143.6	501	473.7	163.1	561	530.4	182.6
322	304.5	104.8	382	361.2	124.4	442	417.9	143.9	502	474.7	163.4	562	531.4	183.0
323	305.4	105.2	383	362.1	124.7	443	418.9	144.2	503	475.6	163.8	563	532.3	183.3
324	306.3	105.5	384	363.1	125.0	444	419.8	144.6	504	476.5	164.1	564	533.3	183.6
325	307.3	105.8	385	364.0	125.3	445	420.8	144.9	505	477.5	164.4	565	534.2	183.9
326	308.2	106.1	386	365.0	125.7	446	421.7	145.2	506	478.4	164.7	566	535.2	184.3
327	309.2	106.5	387	365.9	126.0	447	422.6	145.5	507	479.4	165.1	567	536.1	184.6
328	310.1	106.8	388	366.9	126.3	448	423.6	145.9	508	480.3	165.4	568	537.1	184.9
329	311.1	107.1	389	367.8	126.6	449	424.5	146.2	509	481.3	165.7	569	538.0	185.2
330	312.0	107.4	390	368.8	127.0	450	425.5	146.5	510	482.2	166.0	570	538.9	185.6
331	313.0	107.8	391	369.7	127.3	451	426.4	146.8	511	483.2	166.4	571	539.9	185.9
332	313.9	108.1	392	370.6	127.6	452	427.4	147.2	512	484.1	166.7	572	540.8	186.2
333	314.9	108.4	393	371.6	127.9	453	428.3	147.5	513	485.1	167.0	573	541.8	186.6
334	315.8	108.7	394	372.5	128.3	454	429.3	147.8	514	486.0	167.3	574	542.7	186.9
335	316.7	109.1	395	373.5	128.6	455	430.2	148.1	515	486.9	167.7	575	543.7	187.2
336	317.7	109.4	396	374.4	128.9	456	431.2	148.5	516	487.9	168.0	576	544.6	187.5
337	318.6	109.7	397	375.4	129.3	457	432.1	148.8	517	488.8	168.3	577	545.6	187.9
338	319.6	110.0	398	376.3	129.6	458	433.0	149.1	518	489.8	168.6	578	546.5	188.2
339	320.5	110.4	399	377.3	129.9	459	434.0	149.4	519	490.7	169.0	579	547.5	188.5
340	321.5	110.7	400	378.2	130.2	460	434.9	149.8	520	491.7	169.3	580	548.4	188.8
341	322.4	111.0	401	379.2	130.6	461	435.9	150.1	521	492.6	169.6	581	549.3	189.2
342	323.4	111.3	402	380.1	130.9	462	436.8	150.4	522	493.6	169.9	582	550.3	189.5
343	324.3	111.7	403	381.0	131.2	463	437.8	150.7	523	494.5	170.3	583	551.2	189.8
344	325.3	112.0	404	382.0	131.5	464	438.7	151.1	524	495.5	170.6	584	552.2	190.1
345	326.2	112.3	405	382.9	131.9	465	439.7	151.4	525	496.4	170.9	585	553.1	190.5
346	327.1	112.6	406	383.9	132.2	466	440.6	151.7	526	497.3	171.2	586	554.1	190.8
347	328.1	113.0	407	384.8	132.5	467	441.6	152.0	527	498.3	171.6	587	555.0	191.1
348	329.0	113.3	408	385.8	132.8	468	442.5	152.4	528	499.2	171.9	588	556.0	191.4
349	330.0	113.6	409	386.7	133.2	469	443.4	152.7	529	500.2	172.2	589	556.9	191.8
350	330.9	113.9	410	387.7	133.5	470	444.4	153.0	530	501.1	172.6	590	557.9	192.1
351	331.9	114.3	411	388.6	133.8	471	445.3	153.3	531	502.1	172.9	591	558.8	192.4
352	332.8	114.6	412	389.6	134.1	472	446.3	153.7	532	503.0	173.2	592	559.7	192.7
353	333.8	114.9	413	390.5	134.5	473	447.2	154.0	533	504.0	173.5	593	560.7	193.1
354	334.7	115.3	414	391.4	134.8	474	448.2	154.3	534	504.9	173.9	594	561.6	193.4
355	335.7	115.6	415	392.4	135.1	475	449.1	154.6	535	505.9	174.2	595	562.6	193.7
356	336.6	115.9	416	393.3	135.4	476	450.1	155.0	536	506.8	174.5	596	563.5	194.0
357	337.6	116.2	417	394.3	135.8	477	451.0	155.3	537	507.7	174.8	597	564.5	194.4
358	338.5	116.6	418	395.2	136.1	478	452.0	155.6	538	508.7	175.2	598	565.4	194.7
359	339.4	116.9	419	396.2	136.4	479	452.9	155.9	539	509.6	175.5	599	566.4	195.0
360	340.4	117.2	420	397.1	136.7	480	453.8	156.3	540	510.6	175.8	600	567.3	195.3
Hyp.	Opp.	Adj.	Hyp.	Opp.	Adj.	Hyp.	Opp.	Adj.	Hyp.	Opp.	Adj.	Hyp.	Opp.	Adj.
Dist.	Dep.	D. Lat.	Dist.	Dep.	D. Lat.	Dist.	Dep.	D. Lat.	Dist.	Dep.	D. Lat.	Dist.	Dep.	D. Lat.
D Lon		Dep	D Lon		Dep	D Lon		Dep	D Lon		Dep	D Lon		Dep

Table 3

TRAVERSE TABLE

20° 20°

D Lon	Dep		D Lon	Dep		D Lon	Dep		D Lon	Dep		D Lon	Dep	
Dist.	D. Lat.	Dep.	Dist.	D. Lat.	Dep.	Dist.	D. Lat.	Dep.	Dist.	D. Lat.	Dep.	Dist.	D. Lat.	Dep.
Hyp.	Adj.	Opp.	Hyp.	Adj.	Opp.	Hyp.	Adj.	Opp.	Hyp.	Adj.	Opp.	Hyp.	Adj.	Opp.
1	0.9	0.3	61	57.3	20.9	121	113.7	41.4	181	170.1	61.9	241	226.5	82.4
2	1.9	0.7	62	58.3	21.2	122	114.6	41.7	182	171.0	62.2	242	227.4	82.8
3	2.8	1.0	63	59.2	21.5	123	115.6	42.1	183	172.0	62.6	243	228.3	83.1
4	3.8	1.4	64	60.1	21.9	124	116.5	42.4	184	172.9	62.9	244	229.3	83.5
5	4.7	1.7	65	61.1	22.2	125	117.5	42.8	185	173.8	63.3	245	230.2	83.8
6	5.6	2.1	66	62.0	22.6	126	118.4	43.1	186	174.8	63.6	246	231.2	84.1
7	6.6	2.4	67	63.0	22.9	127	119.3	43.4	187	175.7	64.0	247	232.1	84.5
8	7.5	2.7	68	63.9	23.3	128	120.3	43.8	188	176.7	64.3	248	233.0	84.8
9	8.5	3.1	69	64.8	23.6	129	121.2	44.1	189	177.6	64.6	249	234.0	85.2
10	9.4	3.4	70	65.8	23.9	130	122.2	44.5	190	178.5	65.0	250	234.9	85.5
11	10.3	3.8	71	66.7	24.3	131	123.1	44.8	191	179.5	65.3	251	235.9	85.8
12	11.3	4.1	72	67.7	24.6	132	124.0	45.1	192	180.4	65.7	252	236.8	86.2
13	12.2	4.4	73	68.6	25.0	133	125.0	45.5	193	181.4	66.0	253	237.7	86.5
14	13.2	4.8	74	69.5	25.3	134	125.9	45.8	194	182.3	66.4	254	238.7	86.9
15	14.1	5.1	75	70.5	25.7	135	126.9	46.2	195	183.2	66.7	255	239.6	87.2
16	15.0	5.5	76	71.4	26.0	136	127.8	46.5	196	184.2	67.0	256	240.6	87.6
17	16.0	5.8	77	72.4	26.3	137	128.7	46.9	197	185.1	67.4	257	241.5	87.9
18	16.9	6.2	78	73.3	26.7	138	129.7	47.2	198	186.1	67.7	258	242.4	88.2
19	17.9	6.5	79	74.2	27.0	139	130.6	47.5	199	187.0	68.1	259	243.4	88.6
20	18.8	6.8	80	75.2	27.4	140	131.6	47.9	200	187.9	68.4	260	244.3	88.9
21	19.7	7.2	81	76.1	27.7	141	132.5	48.2	201	188.9	68.7	261	245.3	89.3
22	20.7	7.5	82	77.1	28.0	142	133.4	48.6	202	189.8	69.1	262	246.2	89.6
23	21.6	7.9	83	78.0	28.4	143	134.4	48.9	203	190.8	69.4	263	247.1	90.0
24	22.6	8.2	84	78.9	28.7	144	135.3	49.3	204	191.7	69.8	264	248.1	90.3
25	23.5	8.6	85	79.9	29.1	145	136.3	49.6	205	192.6	70.1	265	249.0	90.6
26	24.4	8.9	86	80.8	29.4	146	137.2	49.9	206	193.6	70.5	266	250.0	91.0
27	25.4	9.2	87	81.8	29.8	147	138.1	50.3	207	194.5	70.8	267	250.9	91.3
28	26.3	9.6	88	82.7	30.1	148	139.1	50.6	208	195.5	71.1	268	251.8	91.7
29	27.3	9.9	89	83.6	30.4	149	140.0	51.0	209	196.4	71.5	269	252.8	92.0
30	28.2	10.3	90	84.6	30.8	150	141.0	51.3	210	197.3	71.8	270	253.7	92.3
31	29.1	10.6	91	85.5	31.1	151	141.9	51.6	211	198.3	72.2	271	254.7	92.7
32	30.1	10.9	92	86.5	31.5	152	142.8	52.0	212	199.2	72.5	272	255.6	93.0
33	31.0	11.3	93	87.4	31.8	153	143.8	52.3	213	200.2	72.9	273	256.5	93.4
34	31.9	11.6	94	88.3	32.1	154	144.7	52.7	214	201.1	73.2	274	257.5	93.7
35	32.9	12.0	95	89.3	32.5	155	145.7	53.0	215	202.0	73.5	275	258.4	94.1
36	33.8	12.3	96	90.2	32.8	156	146.6	53.4	216	203.0	73.9	276	259.4	94.4
37	34.8	12.7	97	91.2	33.2	157	147.5	53.7	217	203.9	74.2	277	260.3	94.7
38	35.7	13.0	98	92.1	33.5	158	148.5	54.0	218	204.9	74.6	278	261.2	95.1
39	36.6	13.3	99	93.0	33.9	159	149.4	54.4	219	205.8	74.9	279	262.2	95.4
40	37.6	13.7	100	94.0	34.2	160	150.4	54.7	220	206.7	75.2	280	263.1	95.8
41	38.5	14.0	101	94.9	34.5	161	151.3	55.1	221	207.7	75.6	281	264.1	96.1
42	39.5	14.4	102	95.8	34.9	162	152.2	55.4	222	208.6	75.9	282	265.0	96.4
43	40.4	14.7	103	96.8	35.2	163	153.2	55.7	223	209.6	76.3	283	265.9	96.8
44	41.3	15.0	104	97.7	35.6	164	154.1	56.1	224	210.5	76.6	284	266.9	97.1
45	42.3	15.4	105	98.7	35.9	165	155.0	56.4	225	211.4	77.0	285	267.8	97.5
46	43.2	15.7	106	99.6	36.3	166	156.0	56.8	226	212.4	77.3	286	268.8	97.8
47	44.2	16.1	107	100.5	36.6	167	156.9	57.1	227	213.3	77.6	287	269.7	98.2
48	45.1	16.4	108	101.5	36.9	168	157.9	57.5	228	214.2	78.0	288	270.6	98.5
49	46.0	16.8	109	102.4	37.3	169	158.8	57.8	229	215.2	78.3	289	271.6	98.8
50	47.0	17.1	110	103.4	37.6	170	159.7	58.1	230	216.1	78.7	290	272.5	99.2
51	47.9	17.4	111	104.3	38.0	171	160.7	58.5	231	217.1	79.0	291	273.5	99.5
52	48.9	17.8	112	105.2	38.3	172	161.6	58.8	232	218.0	79.3	292	274.4	99.9
53	49.8	18.1	113	106.2	38.6	173	162.6	59.2	233	218.9	79.7	293	275.3	100.2
54	50.7	18.5	114	107.1	39.0	174	163.5	59.5	234	219.9	80.0	294	276.3	100.6
55	51.7	18.8	115	108.1	39.3	175	164.4	59.9	235	220.8	80.4	295	277.2	100.9
56	52.6	19.2	116	109.0	39.7	176	165.4	60.2	236	221.8	80.7	296	278.1	101.2
57	53.6	19.5	117	109.9	40.0	177	166.3	60.5	237	222.7	81.1	297	279.1	101.6
58	54.5	19.8	118	110.9	40.4	178	167.3	60.9	238	223.6	81.4	298	280.0	101.9
59	55.4	20.2	119	111.8	40.7	179	168.2	61.2	239	224.6	81.7	299	281.0	102.3
60	56.4	20.5	120	112.8	41.0	180	169.1	61.6	240	225.5	82.1	300	281.9	102.6
Hyp.	Opp.	Adj.	Hyp.	Opp.	Adj.	Hyp.	Opp.	Adj.	Hyp.	Opp.	Adj.	Hyp.	Opp	Adj.
Dist. D Lon	Dep.	D. Lat. Dep	Dist. D Lon	Dep.	D. Lat. Dep	Dist. D Lon	Dep.	D. Lat. Dep	Dist. D Lon	Dep.	D. Lat. Dep	Dist. D Lon	Dep.	D. Lat. Dep

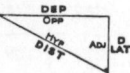

70° 70°

Table 3 TRAVERSE TABLE

20°

20°

D Lon Dist.	Dep D. Lat.	Dep.	D Lon Dist.	Dep D. Lat.	Dep.	D Lon Dist.	Dep D. Lat.	Dep.	D Lon Dist.	Dep D. Lat.	Dep.	D Lon Dist.	Dep D. Lat.	Dep.
Hyp.	Adj.	Opp.	Hyp.	Adj.	Opp.	Hyp.	Adj.	Opp.	Hyp.	Adj.	Opp.	Hyp.	Adj.	Opp.
301	282.8	102.9	361	339.2	123.5	421	395.6	144.0	481	452.0	164.5	541	508.4	185.0
302	283.8	103.3	362	340.2	123.8	422	396.6	144.3	482	452.9	164.9	542	509.3	185.4
303	284.7	103.6	363	341.1	124.2	423	397.5	144.7	483	453.9	165.2	543	510.3	185.7
304	285.7	104.0	364	342.0	124.5	424	398.4	145.0	484	454.8	165.5	544	511.2	186.1
305	286.6	104.3	365	343.0	124.8	425	399.4	145.4	485	455.8	165.9	545	512.1	186.4
306	287.5	104.7	366	343.9	125.2	426	400.3	145.7	486	456.7	166.2	546	513.1	186.7
307	288.5	105.0	367	344.9	125.5	427	401.2	146.0	487	457.6	166.6	547	514.0	187.1
308	289.4	105.3	368	345.8	125.9	428	402.2	146.4	488	458.6	166.9	548	515.0	187.4
309	290.4	105.7	369	346.7	126.2	429	403.1	146.7	489	459.5	167.2	549	515.9	187.8
310	291.3	106.0	370	347.7	126.5	430	404.1	147.1	490	460.4	167.6	550	516.8	188.1
311	292.2	106.4	371	348.6	126.9	431	405.0	147.4	491	461.4	167.9	551	517.8	188.5
312	293.2	106.7	372	349.6	127.2	432	405.9	147.8	492	462.3	168.3	552	518.7	188.8
313	294.1	107.1	373	350.5	127.6	433	406.9	148.1	493	463.3	168.6	553	519.7	189.1
314	295.1	107.4	374	351.4	127.9	434	407.8	148.4	494	464.2	169.0	554	520.6	189.5
315	296.0	107.7	375	352.4	128.3	435	408.8	148.8	495	465.1	169.3	555	521.5	189.8
316	296.9	108.1	376	353.3	128.6	436	409.7	149.1	496	466.1	169.6	556	522.5	190.2
317	297.9	108.4	377	354.3	128.9	437	410.6	149.5	497	467.0	170.0	557	523.4	190.5
318	298.8	108.8	378	355.2	129.3	438	411.6	149.8	498	468.0	170.3	558	524.3	190.8
319	299.8	109.1	379	356.1	129.6	439	412.5	150.1	499	468.9	170.7	559	525.3	191.2
320	300.7	109.4	380	357.1	130.0	440	413.5	150.5	500	469.8	171.0	560	526.2	191.5
321	301.6	109.8	381	358.0	130.3	441	414.4	150.8	501	470.8	171.4	561	527.2	191.9
322	302.6	110.1	382	359.0	130.7	442	415.3	151.2	502	471.7	171.7	562	528.1	192.2
323	303.5	110.5	383	359.9	131.0	443	416.3	151.5	503	472.7	172.0	563	529.0	192.6
324	304.5	110.8	384	360.8	131.3	444	417.2	151.9	504	473.6	172.4	564	530.0	192.9
325	305.4	111.2	385	361.8	131.7	445	418.2	152.2	505	474.5	172.7	565	530.9	193.2
326	306.3	111.5	386	362.7	132.0	446	419.1	152.5	506	475.5	173.1	566	531.9	193.6
327	307.3	111.8	387	363.7	132.4	447	420.0	152.9	507	476.4	173.4	567	532.8	193.9
328	308.2	112.2	388	364.6	132.7	448	421.0	153.2	508	477.4	173.7	568	533.7	194.3
329	309.2	112.5	389	365.5	133.0	449	421.9	153.6	509	478.3	174.1	569	534.7	194.6
330	310.1	112.9	390	366.5	133.4	450	422.9	153.9	510	479.2	174.4	570	535.6	195.0
331	311.0	113.2	391	367.4	133.7	451	423.8	154.3	511	480.2	174.8	571	536.6	195.3
332	312.0	113.6	392	368.4	134.1	452	424.7	154.6	512	481.1	175.1	572	537.5	195.6
333	312.9	113.9	393	369.3	134.4	453	425.7	154.9	513	482.1	175.5	573	538.4	196.0
334	313.9	114.2	394	370.2	134.8	454	426.6	155.3	514	483.0	175.8	574	539.4	196.3
335	314.8	114.6	395	371.2	135.1	455	427.6	155.6	515	483.9	176.1	575	540.3	196.7
336	315.7	114.9	396	372.1	135.4	456	428.5	156.0	516	484.9	176.5	576	541.3	197.0
337	316.7	115.3	397	373.1	135.8	457	429.4	156.3	517	485.8	176.8	577	542.2	197.3
338	317.6	115.6	398	374.0	136.1	458	430.4	156.6	518	486.8	177.2	578	543.1	197.7
339	318.6	115.9	399	374.9	136.5	459	431.3	157.0	519	487.7	177.5	579	544.1	198.0
340	319.5	116.3	400	375.9	136.8	460	432.3	157.3	520	488.6	177.9	580	545.0	198.4
341	320.4	116.6	401	376.8	137.2	461	433.2	157.7	521	489.6	178.2	581	546.0	198.7
342	321.4	117.0	402	377.8	137.5	462	434.1	158.0	522	490.5	178.5	582	546.9	199.1
343	322.3	117.3	403	378.7	137.8	463	435.1	158.4	523	491.5	178.9	583	547.8	199.4
344	323.3	117.7	404	379.6	138.2	464	436.0	158.7	524	492.4	179.2	584	548.8	199.7
345	324.2	118.0	405	380.6	138.5	465	437.0	159.0	525	493.3	179.6	585	549.7	200.1
346	325.1	118.3	406	381.5	138.9	466	437.9	159.4	526	494.3	179.9	586	550.7	200.4
347	326.1	118.7	407	382.5	139.2	467	438.8	159.7	527	495.2	180.2	587	551.6	200.8
348	327.0	119.0	408	383.4	139.5	468	439.8	160.1	528	496.2	180.6	588	552.5	201.1
349	328.0	119.4	409	384.3	139.9	469	440.7	160.4	529	497.1	180.9	589	553.5	201.4
350	328.9	119.7	410	385.3	140.2	470	441.7	160.7	530	498.0	181.3	590	554.4	201.8
351	329.8	120.0	411	386.2	140.6	471	442.6	161.1	531	499.0	181.6	591	555.4	202.1
352	330.8	120.4	412	387.2	140.9	472	443.5	161.4	532	499.9	182.0	592	556.3	202.5
353	331.7	120.7	413	388.1	141.3	473	444.5	161.8	533	500.9	182.3	593	557.2	202.8
354	332.7	121.1	414	389.0	141.6	474	445.4	162.1	534	501.8	182.6	594	558.2	203.2
355	333.6	121.4	415	390.0	141.9	475	446.4	162.5	535	502.7	183.0	595	559.1	203.5
356	334.5	121.8	416	390.9	142.3	476	447.3	162.8	536	503.7	183.3	596	560.1	203.8
357	335.5	122.1	417	391.9	142.6	477	448.2	163.1	537	504.6	183.7	597	561.0	204.2
358	336.4	122.4	418	392.8	143.0	478	449.2	163.5	538	505.6	184.0	598	561.9	204.5
359	337.4	122.8	419	393.7	143.3	479	450.1	163.8	539	506.5	184.3	599	562.9	204.9
360	338.3	123.1	420	394.7	143.6	480	451.1	164.2	540	507.4	184.7	600	563.8	205.2
Hyp.	Opp.	Adj.	Hyp.	Opp.	Adj.	Hyp.	Opp.	Adj.	Hyp.	Opp.	Adj.	Hyp.	Opp.	Adj.
Dist. D Lon	Dep.	D. Lat. Dep	Dist. D Lon	Dep.	D. Lat. Dep	Dist. D Lon	Dep.	D. Lat. Dep	Dist. D Lon	Dep.	D. Lat. Dep	Dist. D Lon	Dep.	D. Lat. Dep

70°

70°

Table 3

TRAVERSE TABLE

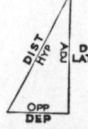

21°   21°

D Lon Dist.	Dep D. Lat.	Dep.	D Lon Dist.	Dep D. Lat	Dep.	D Lon Dist.	Dep D. Lat.	Dep.	D Lon Dist.	Dep D. Lat.	Dep.	D Lon Dist.	Dep D. Lat.	Dep.
Hyp.	Adj.	Opp.	Hyp.	Adj.	Opp.	Hyp.	Adj.	Opp.	Hyp.	Adj.	Opp.	Hyp.	Adj.	Opp.
1	0.9	0.4	61	56.9	21.9	121	113.0	43.4	181	169.0	64.9	241	225.0	86.4
2	1.9	0.7	62	57.9	22.2	122	113.9	43.7	182	169.9	65.2	242	225.9	86.7
3	2.8	1.1	63	58.8	22.6	123	114.8	44.1	183	170.8	65.6	243	226.9	87.1
4	3.7	1.4	64	59.7	22.9	124	115.8	44.4	184	171.8	65.9	244	227.8	87.4
5	4.7	1.8	65	60.7	23.3	125	116.7	44.8	185	172.7	66.3	245	228.7	87.8
6	5.6	2.2	66	61.6	23.7	126	117.6	45.2	186	173.6	66.7	246	229.7	88.2
7	6.5	2.5	67	62.5	24.0	127	118.6	45.5	187	174.6	67.0	247	230.6	88.5
8	7.5	2.9	68	63.5	24.4	128	119.5	45.9	188	175.5	67.4	248	231.5	88.9
9	8.4	3.2	69	64.4	24.7	129	120.4	46.2	189	176.4	67.7	249	232.5	89.2
10	9.3	3.6	70	65.4	25.1	130	121.4	46.6	190	177.4	68.1	250	233.4	89.6
11	10.3	3.9	71	66.3	25.4	131	122.3	46.9	191	178.3	68.4	251	234.3	90.0
12	11.2	4.3	72	67.2	25.8	132	123.2	47.3	192	179.2	68.8	252	235.3	90.3
13	12.1	4.7	73	68.2	26.2	133	124.2	47.7	193	180.2	69.2	253	236.2	90.7
14	13.1	5.0	74	69.1	26.5	134	125.1	48.0	194	181.1	69.5	254	237.1	91.0
15	14.0	5.4	75	70.0	26.9	135	126.0	48.4	195	182.0	69.9	255	238.1	91.4
16	14.9	5.7	76	71.0	27.2	136	127.0	48.7	196	183.0	70.2	256	239.0	91.7
17	15.9	6.1	77	71.9	27.6	137	127.9	49.1	197	183.9	70.6	257	239.9	92.1
18	16.8	6.5	78	72.8	28.0	138	128.8	49.5	198	184.8	71.0	258	240.9	92.5
19	17.7	6.8	79	73.8	28.3	139	129.8	49.8	199	185.8	71.3	259	241.8	92.8
20	18.7	7.2	80	74.7	28.7	140	130.7	50.2	200	186.7	71.7	260	242.7	93.2
21	19.6	7.5	81	75.6	29.0	141	131.6	50.5	201	187.6	72.0	261	243.7	93.5
22	20.5	7.9	82	76.6	29.4	142	132.6	50.9	202	188.6	72.4	262	244.6	93.9
23	21.5	8.2	83	77.5	29.7	143	133.5	51.2	203	189.5	72.7	263	245.5	94.3
24	22.4	8.6	84	78.4	30.1	144	134.4	51.6	204	190.5	73.1	264	246.5	94.6
25	23.3	9.0	85	79.4	30.5	145	135.4	52.0	205	191.4	73.5	265	247.4	95.0
26	24.3	9.3	86	80.3	30.8	146	136.3	52.3	206	192.3	73.8	266	248.3	95.3
27	25.2	9.7	87	81.2	31.2	147	137.2	52.7	207	193.3	74.2	267	249.3	95.7
28	26.1	10.0	88	82.2	31.5	148	138.2	53.0	208	194.2	74.5	268	250.2	96.0
29	27.1	10.4	89	83.1	31.9	149	139.1	53.4	209	195.1	74.9	269	251.1	96.4
30	28.0	10.8	90	84.0	32.3	150	140.0	53.8	210	196.1	75.3	270	252.1	96.8
31	28.9	11.1	91	85.0	32.6	151	141.0	54.1	211	197.0	75.6	271	253.0	97.1
32	29.9	11.5	92	85.9	33.0	152	141.9	54.5	212	197.9	76.0	272	253.9	97.5
33	30.8	11.8	93	86.8	33.3	153	142.8	54.8	213	198.9	76.3	273	254.9	97.8
34	31.7	12.2	94	87.8	33.7	154	143.8	55.2	214	199.8	76.7	274	255.8	98.2
35	32.7	12.5	95	88.7	34.0	155	144.7	55.5	215	200.7	77.0	275	256.7	98.6
36	33.6	12.9	96	89.6	34.4	156	145.6	55.9	216	201.7	77.4	276	257.7	98.9
37	34.5	13.3	97	90.6	34.8	157	146.6	56.3	217	202.6	77.8	277	258.6	99.3
38	35.5	13.6	98	91.5	35.1	158	147.5	56.6	218	203.5	78.1	278	259.5	99.6
39	36.4	14.0	99	92.4	35.5	159	148.4	57.0	219	204.5	78.5	279	260.5	100.0
40	37.3	14.3	100	93.4	35.8	160	149.4	57.3	220	205.4	78.8	280	261.4	100.3
41	38.3	14.7	101	94.3	36.2	161	150.3	57.7	221	206.3	79.2	281	262.3	100.7
42	39.2	15.1	102	95.2	36.6	162	151.2	58.1	222	207.3	79.6	282	263.3	101.1
43	40.1	15.4	103	96.2	36.9	163	152.2	58.4	223	208.2	79.9	283	264.2	101.4
44	41.1	15.8	104	97.1	37.3	164	153.1	58.8	224	209.1	80.3	284	265.1	101.8
45	42.0	16.1	105	98.0	37.6	165	154.0	59.1	225	210.1	80.6	285	266.1	102.1
46	42.9	16.5	106	99.0	38.0	166	155.0	59.5	226	211.0	81.0	286	267.0	102.5
47	43.9	16.8	107	99.9	38.3	167	155.9	59.8	227	211.9	81.3	287	267.9	102.9
48	44.8	17.2	108	100.8	38.7	168	156.8	60.2	228	212.9	81.7	288	268.9	103.2
49	45.7	17.6	109	101.8	39.1	169	157.8	60.6	229	213.8	82.1	289	269.8	103.6
50	46.7	17.9	110	102.7	39.4	170	158.7	60.9	230	214.7	82.4	290	270.7	103.9
51	47.6	18.3	111	103.6	39.8	171	159.6	61.3	231	215.7	82.8	291	271.7	104.3
52	48.5	18.6	112	104.6	40.1	172	160.6	61.6	232	216.6	83.1	292	272.6	104.6
53	49.5	19.0	113	105.5	40.5	173	161.5	62.0	233	217.5	83.5	293	273.5	105.0
54	50.4	19.4	114	106.4	40.9	174	162.4	62.4	234	218.5	83.9	294	274.5	105.4
55	51.3	19.7	115	107.4	41.2	175	163.4	62.7	235	219.4	84.2	295	275.4	105.7
56	52.3	20.1	116	108.3	41.6	176	164.3	63.1	236	220.3	84.6	296	276.3	106.1
57	53.2	20.4	117	109.2	41.9	177	165.2	63.4	237	221.3	84.9	297	277.3	106.4
58	54.1	20.8	118	110.2	42.3	178	166.2	63.8	238	222.2	85.3	298	278.2	106.8
59	55.1	21.1	119	111.1	42.6	179	167.1	64.1	239	223.1	85.6	299	279.1	107.2
60	56.0	21.5	120	112.0	43.0	180	168.0	64.5	240	224.1	86.0	300	280.1	107.5
Hyp.	Opp.	Adj.	Hyp.	Opp.	Adj.	Hyp.	Opp.	Adj.	Hyp.	Opp.	Adj.	Hyp.	Opp.	Adj.
Dist. D Lon	Dep.	D. Lat. Dep	Dist. D Lon	Dep.	D. Lat. Dep	Dist. D Lon	Dep.	D. Lat. Dep	Dist. D Lon	Dep.	D. Lat. Dep	Dist. D Lon	Dep.	D. Lat. Dep

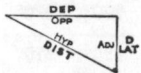

69°   69°

Table 3

TRAVERSE TABLE

D Lon Dep Dist. D. Lat. Dep.			D Lon Dep Dist. D. Lat. Dep.			D Lon Dep Dist. D. Lat. Dep.			D Lon Dep Dist. D. Lat. Dep.			D Lon Dep Dist. D. Lat. Dep.		
Hyp.	Adj.	Opp.	Hyp.	Adj.	Opp.	Hyp.	Adj.	Opp.	Hyp.	Adj.	Opp.	Hyp.	Adj.	Opp.
301	281.0	107.9	361	337.0	129.4	421	393.0	150.9	481	449.1	172.4	541	505.1	193.9
302	281.9	108.2	362	338.0	129.7	422	394.0	151.2	482	450.0	172.7	542	506.0	194.2
303	282.9	108.6	363	338.9	130.1	423	394.9	151.6	483	450.9	173.1	543	506.9	194.6
304	283.8	108.9	364	339.8	130.4	424	395.8	151.9	484	451.9	173.5	544	507.9	195.0
305	284.7	109.3	365	340.8	130.8	425	396.8	152.3	485	452.8	173.8	545	508.8	195.3
306	285.7	109.7	366	341.7	131.2	426	397.7	152.7	486	453.7	174.2	546	509.7	195.7
307	286.6	110.0	367	342.6	131.5	427	398.6	153.0	487	454.7	174.5	547	510.7	196.0
308	287.5	110.4	368	343.6	131.9	428	399.6	153.4	488	455.6	174.9	548	511.6	196.4
309	288.5	110.7	369	344.5	132.2	429	400.5	153.7	489	456.5	175.2	549	512.5	196.7
310	289.4	111.1	370	345.4	132.6	430	401.4	154.1	490	457.5	175.6	550	513.5	197.1
311	290.3	111.5	371	346.4	133.0	431	402.4	154.5	491	458.4	176.0	551	514.4	197.5
312	291.3	111.8	372	347.3	133.3	432	403.3	154.8	492	459.3	176.3	552	515.3	197.8
313	292.2	112.2	373	348.2	133.7	433	404.2	155.2	493	460.3	176.7	553	516.3	198.2
314	293.1	112.5	374	349.1	134.0	434	405.2	155.5	494	461.2	177.0	554	517.2	198.5
315	294.1	112.9	375	350.1	134.4	435	406.1	155.9	495	462.1	177.4	555	518.1	198.9
316	295.0	113.2	376	351.0	134.7	436	407.0	156.2	496	463.1	177.8	556	519.1	199.3
317	295.9	113.6	377	352.0	135.1	437	408.0	156.6	497	464.0	178.1	557	520.0	199.6
318	296.9	114.0	378	352.9	135.5	438	408.9	157.0	498	464.9	178.5	558	520.9	200.0
319	297.8	114.3	379	353.8	135.8	439	409.8	157.3	499	465.9	178.8	559	521.9	200.3
320	298.7	114.7	380	354.8	136.2	440	410.8	157.7	500	466.8	179.2	560	522.8	200.7
321	299.7	115.0	381	355.7	136.5	441	411.7	158.0	501	467.7	179.5	561	523.7	201.0
322	300.6	115.4	382	356.6	136.9	442	412.6	158.4	502	468.7	179.9	562	524.7	201.4
323	301.5	115.8	383	357.6	137.3	443	413.6	158.8	503	469.6	180.3	563	525.6	201.8
324	302.5	116.1	384	358.5	137.6	444	414.5	159.1	504	470.5	180.6	564	526.5	202.1
325	303.4	116.5	385	359.4	138.0	445	415.4	159.5	505	471.5	181.0	565	527.5	202.5
326	304.3	116.8	386	360.4	138.3	446	416.4	159.8	506	472.4	181.3	566	528.4	202.8
327	305.3	117.2	387	361.3	138.7	447	417.3	160.2	507	473.3	181.7	567	529.3	203.2
328	306.2	117.5	388	362.2	139.0	448	418.2	160.5	508	474.3	182.1	568	530.3	203.6
329	307.1	117.9	389	363.2	139.4	449	419.2	160.9	509	475.2	182.4	569	531.2	203.9
330	308.1	118.3	390	364.1	139.8	450	420.1	161.3	510	476.1	182.8	570	532.1	204.3
331	309.0	118.6	391	365.0	140.1	451	421.0	161.6	511	477.1	183.1	571	533.1	204.6
332	309.9	119.0	392	365.9	140.5	452	422.0	162.0	512	478.0	183.5	572	534.0	205.0
333	310.9	119.3	393	366.9	140.8	453	422.9	162.3	513	478.9	183.8	573	534.9	205.3
334	311.8	119.7	394	367.8	141.2	454	423.8	162.7	514	479.9	184.2	574	535.9	205.7
335	312.7	120.1	395	368.8	141.6	455	424.8	163.1	515	480.8	184.6	575	536.8	206.1
336	313.7	120.4	396	369.7	141.9	456	425.7	163.4	516	481.7	184.9	576	537.7	206.4
337	314.6	120.8	397	370.6	142.3	457	426.6	163.8	517	482.7	185.3	577	538.7	206.8
338	315.6	121.1	398	371.6	142.6	458	427.6	164.1	518	483.6	185.6	578	539.6	207.1
339	316.5	121.5	399	372.5	143.0	459	428.5	164.5	519	484.5	186.0	579	540.5	207.5
340	317.4	121.8	400	373.4	143.3	460	429.4	164.8	520	485.5	186.4	580	541.5	207.9
341	318.4	122.2	401	374.4	143.7	461	430.4	165.2	521	486.4	186.7	581	542.4	208.2
342	319.3	122.6	402	375.3	144.1	462	431.3	165.6	522	487.3	187.1	582	543.3	208.6
343	320.2	122.9	403	376.2	144.4	463	432.2	165.9	523	488.3	187.4	583	544.3	208.9
344	321.2	123.3	404	377.2	144.8	464	433.2	166.3	524	489.2	187.8	584	545.2	209.3
345	322.1	123.6	405	378.1	145.1	465	434.1	166.6	525	490.1	188.1	585	546.1	209.6
346	323.0	124.0	406	379.0	145.5	466	435.0	167.0	526	491.1	188.5	586	547.1	210.0
347	324.0	124.4	407	380.0	145.9	467	436.0	167.4	527	492.0	188.9	587	548.0	210.4
348	324.9	124.7	408	380.9	146.2	468	436.9	167.7	528	492.9	189.2	588	548.9	210.7
349	325.8	125.1	409	381.8	146.6	469	437.8	168.1	529	493.9	189.6	589	549.9	211.1
350	326.8	125.4	410	382.8	146.9	470	438.8	168.4	530	494.8	189.9	590	550.8	211.4
351	327.7	125.8	411	383.7	147.3	471	439.7	168.8	531	495.7	190.3	591	551.7	211.8
352	328.6	126.1	412	384.6	147.6	472	440.6	169.1	532	496.7	190.7	592	552.7	212.2
353	329.6	126.5	413	385.6	148.0	473	441.6	169.5	533	497.6	191.0	593	553.6	212.5
354	330.5	126.9	414	386.5	148.4	474	442.5	169.9	534	498.5	191.4	594	554.5	212.9
355	331.4	127.2	415	387.4	148.7	475	443.5	170.2	535	499.5	191.7	595	555.5	213.2
356	332.4	127.6	416	388.4	149.1	476	444.4	170.6	536	500.4	192.1	596	556.4	213.6
357	333.3	127.9	417	389.3	149.4	477	445.3	170.9	537	501.3	192.4	597	557.3	213.9
358	334.2	128.3	418	390.2	149.8	478	446.3	171.3	538	502.3	192.8	598	558.2	214.3
359	335.2	128.7	419	391.2	150.2	479	447.2	171.7	539	503.2	193.2	599	559.2	214.7
360	336.1	129.0	420	392.1	150.5	480	448.1	172.0	540	504.1	193.5	600	560.1	215.0
Hyp.	Opp.	Adj.	Hyp.	Opp.	Adj.	Hyp.	Opp.	Adj.	Hyp.	Opp.	Adj.	Hyp.	Opp.	Adj.

Dist. D Lon	Dep.	D. Lat. Dep	Dist. D Lon	Dep.	D. Lat. Dep	Dist. D Lon	Dep.	D. Lat. Dep	Dist. D Lon	Dep.	D. Lat. Dep	Dist. D Lon	Dep.	D. Lat. Dep

Table 3

TRAVERSE TABLE

22°   22°

D Lon Dist.	Dep D. Lat.	Dep.	D Lon Dist.	Dep D. Lat.	Dep.	D Lon Dist.	Dep D. Lat.	Dep.	D Lon Dist.	Dep D. Lat.	Dep.	D Lon Dist.	Dep D. Lat.	Dep.
Hyp.	Adj.	Opp.	Hyp.	Adj.	Opp.	Hyp.	Adj.	Opp.	Hyp.	Adj.	Opp.	Hyp.	Adj.	Opp.
1	0.9	0.4	61	56.6	22.9	121	112.2	45.3	181	167.8	67.8	241	223.5	90.3
2	1.9	0.7	62	57.5	23.2	122	113.1	45.7	182	168.7	68.2	242	224.4	90.7
3	2.8	1.1	63	58.4	23.6	123	114.0	46.1	183	169.7	68.6	243	225.3	91.0
4	3.7	1.5	64	59.3	24.0	124	115.0	46.5	184	170.6	68.9	244	226.2	91.4
5	4.6	1.9	65	60.3	24.3	125	115.9	46.8	185	171.5	69.3	245	227.2	91.8
6	5.6	2.2	66	61.2	24.7	126	116.8	47.2	186	172.5	69.7	246	228.1	92.2
7	6.5	2.6	67	62.1	25.1	127	117.8	47.6	187	173.4	70.1	247	229.0	92.5
8	7.4	3.0	68	63.0	25.5	128	118.7	47.9	188	174.3	70.4	248	229.9	92.9
9	8.3	3.4	69	64.0	25.8	129	119.6	48.3	189	175.2	70.8	249	230.9	93.3
10	9.3	3.7	70	64.9	26.2	130	120.5	48.7	190	176.2	71.2	250	231.8	93.7
11	10.2	4.1	71	65.8	26.6	131	121.5	49.1	191	177.1	71.5	251	232.7	94.0
12	11.1	4.5	72	66.8	27.0	132	122.4	49.4	192	178.0	71.9	252	233.7	94.4
13	12.1	4.9	73	67.7	27.3	133	123.3	49.8	193	178.9	72.3	253	234.6	94.8
14	13.0	5.2	74	68.6	27.7	134	124.2	50.2	194	179.9	72.7	254	235.5	95.2
15	13.9	5.6	75	69.5	28.1	135	125.2	50.6	195	180.8	73.0	255	236.4	95.5
16	14.8	6.0	76	70.5	28.5	136	126.1	50.9	196	181.7	73.4	256	237.4	95.9
17	15.8	6.4	77	71.4	28.8	137	127.0	51.3	197	182.7	73.8	257	238.3	96.3
18	16.7	6.7	78	72.3	29.2	138	128.0	51.7	198	183.6	74.2	258	239.2	96.6
19	17.6	7.1	79	73.2	29.6	139	128.9	52.1	199	184.5	74.5	259	240.1	97.0
20	18.5	7.5	80	74.2	30.0	140	129.8	52.4	200	185.4	74.9	260	241.1	97.4
21	19.5	7.9	81	75.1	30.3	141	130.7	52.8	201	186.4	75.3	261	242.0	97.8
22	20.4	8.2	82	76.0	30.7	142	131.7	53.2	202	187.3	75.7	262	242.9	98.1
23	21.3	8.6	83	77.0	31.1	143	132.6	53.6	203	188.2	76.0	263	243.8	98.5
24	22.3	9.0	84	77.9	31.5	144	133.5	53.9	204	189.1	76.4	264	244.8	98.9
25	23.2	9.4	85	78.8	31.8	145	134.4	54.3	205	190.1	76.8	265	245.7	99.3
26	24.1	9.7	86	79.7	32.2	146	135.4	54.7	206	191.0	77.2	266	246.6	99.6
27	25.0	10.1	87	80.7	32.6	147	136.3	55.1	207	191.9	77.5	267	247.6	100.0
28	26.0	10.5	88	81.6	33.0	148	137.2	55.4	208	192.9	77.9	268	248.5	100.4
29	26.9	10.9	89	82.5	33.3	149	138.2	55.8	209	193.8	78.3	269	249.4	100.8
30	27.8	11.2	90	83.4	33.7	150	139.1	56.2	210	194.7	78.7	270	250.3	101.1
31	28.7	11.6	91	84.4	34.1	151	140.0	56.6	211	195.6	79.0	271	251.3	101.5
32	29.7	12.0	92	85.3	34.5	152	140.9	56.9	212	196.6	79.4	272	252.2	101.9
33	30.6	12.4	93	86.2	34.8	153	141.9	57.3	213	197.5	79.8	273	253.1	102.3
34	31.5	12.7	94	87.2	35.2	154	142.8	57.7	214	198.4	80.2	274	254.0	102.6
35	32.5	13.1	95	88.1	35.6	155	143.7	58.1	215	199.3	80.5	275	255.0	103.0
36	33.4	13.5	96	89.0	36.0	156	144.6	58.4	216	200.3	80.9	276	255.9	103.4
37	34.3	13.9	97	89.9	36.3	157	145.6	58.8	217	201.2	81.3	277	256.8	103.8
38	35.2	14.2	98	90.9	36.7	158	146.5	59.2	218	202.1	81.7	278	257.8	104.1
39	36.2	14.6	99	91.8	37.1	159	147.4	59.6	219	203.1	82.0	279	258.7	104.5
40	37.1	15.0	100	92.7	37.5	160	148.3	59.9	220	204.0	82.4	280	259.6	104.9
41	38.0	15.4	101	93.6	37.8	161	149.3	60.3	221	204.9	82.8	281	260.5	105.3
42	38.9	15.7	102	94.6	38.2	162	150.2	60.7	222	205.8	83.2	282	261.5	105.6
43	39.9	16.1	103	95.5	38.6	163	151.1	61.1	223	206.8	83.5	283	262.4	106.0
44	40.8	16.5	104	96.4	39.0	164	152.1	61.4	224	207.7	83.9	284	263.3	106.4
45	41.7	16.9	105	97.4	39.3	165	153.0	61.8	225	208.6	84.3	285	264.2	106.8
46	42.7	17.2	106	98.3	39.7	166	153.9	62.2	226	209.5	84.7	286	265.2	107.1
47	43.6	17.6	107	99.2	40.1	167	154.8	62.6	227	210.5	85.0	287	266.1	107.5
48	44.5	18.0	108	100.1	40.5	168	155.8	62.9	228	211.4	85.4	288	267.0	107.9
49	45.4	18.4	109	101.1	40.8	169	156.7	63.3	229	212.3	85.8	289	268.0	108.3
50	46.4	18.7	110	102.0	41.2	170	157.6	63.7	230	213.3	86.2	290	268.9	108.6
51	47.3	19.1	111	102.9	41.6	171	158.5	64.1	231	214.2	86.5	291	269.8	109.0
52	48.2	19.5	112	103.8	42.0	172	159.5	64.4	232	215.1	86.9	292	270.7	109.4
53	49.1	19.9	113	104.8	42.3	173	160.4	64.8	233	216.0	87.3	293	271.7	109.8
54	50.1	20.2	114	105.7	42.7	174	161.3	65.2	234	217.0	87.7	294	272.6	110.1
55	51.0	20.6	115	106.6	43.1	175	162.3	65.6	235	217.9	88.0	295	273.5	110.5
56	51.9	21.0	116	107.6	43.5	176	163.2	65.9	236	218.8	88.4	296	274.4	110.9
57	52.8	21.4	117	108.5	43.8	177	164.1	66.3	237	219.7	88.8	297	275.4	111.3
58	53.8	21.7	118	109 4	44.2	178	165.0	66.7	238	220.7	89.2	298	276.3	111.6
59	54.7	22.1	119	110.3	44.6	179	166.0	67.1	239	221.6	89.5	299	277.2	112.0
60	55.6	22.5	120	111.3	45.0	180	166.9	67.4	240	222.5	89.9	300	278.2	112.4
Hyp.	Opp.	Adj.	Hyp.	Opp.	Adj.	Hyp.	Opp.	Adj.	Hyp.	Opp.	Adj.	Hyp.	Opp.	Adj.

Dist. Dep. D. Lat. D Lon Dep	Dist. Dep. D. Lat. D Lon Dep	Dist. Dep. D. Lat. D Lon Dep	Dist. Dep. D. Lat. D Lon Dep	Dist. Dep. D. Lat. D Lon Dep

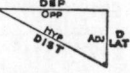

68°   68°

Table 3 **TRAVERSE TABLE** **22°**

338° | 022°
202° | 158°

22°

Dist. D Lon	D. Lat. Dep	Dep.	Dist. D Lon	D. Lat. Dep	Dep.	Dist. D Lon	D. Lat. Dep	Dep.	Dist. D Lon	D. Lat. Dep	Dep.	Dist. D Lon	D. Lat. Dep	Dep.
Hyp.	Adj.	Opp.	Hyp.	Adj.	Opp.	Hyp.	Adj.	Opp.	Hyp.	Adj.	Opp.	Hyp.	Adj.	Opp.
301	279.1	112.8	361	334.7	135.2	421	390.3	157.7	481	446.0	180.2	541	501.6	202.7
302	280.0	113.1	362	335.6	135.6	422	391.3	158.1	482	446.9	180.6	542	502.5	203.0
303	280.9	113.5	363	336.6	136.0	423	392.2	158.5	483	447.8	180.9	543	503.5	203.4
304	281.9	113.9	364	337.5	136.4	424	393.1	158.8	484	448.8	181.3	544	504.4	203.8
305	282.8	114.3	365	338.4	136.7	425	394.1	159.2	485	449.7	181.7	545	505.3	204.2
306	283.7	114.6	366	339.3	137.1	426	395.0	159.6	486	450.6	182.1	546	506.2	204.5
307	284.6	115.0	367	340.3	137.5	427	395.9	160.0	487	451.5	182.4	547	507.2	204.9
308	285.6	115.4	368	341.2	137.9	428	396.8	160.3	488	452.5	182.8	548	508.1	205.3
309	286.5	115.8	369	342.1	138.2	429	397.8	160.7	489	453.4	183.2	549	509.0	205.7
310	287.4	116.1	370	343.1	138.6	430	398.7	161.1	490	454.3	183.6	550	510.0	206.0
311	288.4	116.5	371	344.0	139.0	431	399.6	161.5	491	455.2	183.9	551	510.9	206.4
312	289.3	116.9	372	344.9	139.4	432	400.5	161.8	492	456.2	184.3	552	511.8	206.8
313	290.2	117.3	373	345.8	139.7	433	401.5	162.2	493	457.1	184.7	553	512.7	207.2
314	291.1	117.6	374	346.8	140.1	434	402.4	162.6	494	458.0	185.1	554	513.7	207.5
315	292.1	118.0	375	347.7	140.5	435	403.3	163.0	495	459.0	185.4	555	514.6	207.9
316	293.0	118.4	376	348.6	140.9	436	404.3	163.3	496	459.9	185.8	556	515.5	208.3
317	293.9	118.8	377	349.5	141.2	437	405.2	163.7	497	460.8	186.2	557	516.4	208.7
318	294.8	119.1	378	350.5	141.6	438	406.1	164.1	498	461.7	186.6	558	517.4	209.0
319	295.8	119.5	379	351.4	142.0	439	407.0	164.5	499	462.7	186.9	559	518.3	209.4
320	296.7	119.9	380	352.3	142.4	440	408.0	164.8	500	463.6	187.3	560	519.2	209.8
321	297.6	120.2	381	353.3	142.7	441	408.9	165.2	501	464.5	187.7	561	520.2	210.2
322	298.6	120.6	382	354.2	143.1	442	409.8	165.6	502	465.4	188.1	562	521.1	210.5
323	299.5	121.0	383	355.1	143.5	443	410.7	166.0	503	466.4	188.4	563	522.0	210.9
324	300.4	121.4	384	356.0	143.8	444	411.7	166.3	504	467.3	188.8	564	522.9	211.3
325	301.3	121.7	385	357.0	144.2	445	412.6	166.7	505	468.2	189.2	565	523.9	211.7
326	302.3	122.1	386	357.9	144.6	446	413.5	167.1	506	469.2	189.6	566	524.8	212.0
327	303.2	122.5	387	358.8	145.0	447	414.5	167.4	507	470.1	189.9	567	525.7	212.4
328	304.1	122.9	388	359.7	145.3	448	415.4	167.8	508	471.0	190.3	568	526.6	212.8
329	305.0	123.2	389	360.7	145.7	449	416.3	168.2	509	471.9	190.7	569	527.6	213.2
330	306.0	123.6	390	361.6	146.1	450	417.2	168.6	510	472.9	191.0	570	528.5	213.5
331	306.9	124.0	391	362.5	146.5	451	418.2	168.9	511	473.8	191.4	571	529.4	213.9
332	307.8	124.4	392	363.5	146.8	452	419.1	169.3	512	474.7	191.8	572	530.3	214.3
333	308.8	124.7	393	364.4	147.2	453	420.0	169.7	513	475.6	192.2	573	531.3	214.6
334	309.7	125.1	394	365.3	147.6	454	420.9	170.1	514	476.6	192.5	574	532.2	215.0
335	310.6	125.5	395	366.2	148.0	455	421.9	170.4	515	477.5	192.9	575	533.1	215.4
336	311.5	125.9	396	367.2	148.3	456	422.8	170.8	516	478.4	193.3	576	534.1	215.8
337	312.5	126.2	397	368.1	148.7	457	423.7	171.2	517	479.4	193.7	577	535.0	216.1
338	313.4	126.6	398	369.0	149.1	458	424.7	171.6	518	480.3	194.0	578	535.9	216.5
339	314.3	127.0	399	369.9	149.5	459	425.6	171.9	519	481.2	194.4	579	536.8	216.9
340	315.2	127.4	400	370.9	149.8	460	426.5	172.3	520	482.1	194.8	580	537.8	217.3
341	316.2	127.7	401	371.8	150.2	461	427.4	172.7	521	483.1	195.2	581	538.7	217.6
342	317.1	128.1	402	372.7	150.6	462	428.4	173.1	522	484.0	195.5	582	539.6	218.0
343	318.0	128.5	403	373.7	151.0	463	429.3	173.4	523	484.9	195.9	583	540.5	218.4
344	319.0	128.9	404	374.6	151.3	464	430.2	173.8	524	485.8	196.3	584	541.5	218.8
345	319.9	129.2	405	375.5	151.7	465	431.1	174.2	525	486.8	196.7	585	542.4	219.1
346	320.8	129.6	406	376.4	152.1	466	432.1	174.6	526	487.7	197.0	586	543.3	219.5
347	321.7	130.0	407	377.4	152.5	467	433.0	174.9	527	488.6	197.4	587	544.3	219.9
348	322.7	130.4	408	378.3	152.8	468	433.9	175.3	528	489.6	197.8	588	545.2	220.3
349	323.6	130.7	409	379.2	153.2	469	434.8	175.7	529	490.5	198.2	589	546.1	220.6
350	324.5	131.1	410	380.1	153.6	470	435.8	176.1	530	491.4	198.5	590	547.0	221.0
351	325.4	131.5	411	381.1	154.0	471	436.7	176.4	531	492.3	198.9	591	548.0	221.4
352	326.4	131.9	412	382.0	154.3	472	437.6	176.8	532	493.3	199.3	592	548.9	221.8
353	327.3	132.2	413	382.9	154.7	473	438.6	177.2	533	494.2	199.7	593	549.8	222.1
354	328.2	132.6	414	383.9	155.1	474	439.5	177.6	534	495.1	200.0	594	550.7	222.5
355	329.2	133.0	415	384.8	155.5	475	440.4	177.9	535	496.0	200.4	595	551.7	222.9
356	330.1	133.4	416	385.7	155.8	476	441.3	178.3	536	497.0	200.8	596	552.6	223.3
357	331.0	133.7	417	386.6	156.2	477	442.3	178.7	537	497.9	201.2	597	553.5	223.6
358	332.0	134.1	418	387.6	156.6	478	443.2	179.1	538	498.8	201.5	598	554.5	224.0
359	332.9	134.5	419	388.5	157.0	479	444.1	179.4	539	499.8	201.9	599	555.4	224.4
360	333.8	134.9	420	389.4	157.3	480	445.0	179.8	540	500.7	202.3	600	556.3	224.8
Hyp.	Opp.	Adj.	Hyp.	Opp.	Adj.	Hyp.	Opp.	Adj.	Hyp.	Opp.	Adj.	Hyp.	Opp.	Adj.

Dist. D Lon	Dep.	D. Lat. Dep	Dist. D Lon	Dep.	D. Lat. Dep	Dist. D Lon	Dep.	D. Lat. Dep	Dist. D Lon	Dep.	D. Lat. Dep	Dist. D Lon	Dep.	D. Lat. Dep

Table 3   **TRAVERSE TABLE**

23°   23°

D Lon / Dist.	Dep D. Lat.	Dep.	D Lon / Dist.	Dep D. Lat.	Dep.	D Lon / Dist.	Dep D. Lat.	Dep.	D Lon / Dist.	Dep D. Lat.	Dep.	D Lon / Dist.	Dep D. Lat.	Dep.
Hyp.	Adj.	Opp.	Hyp.	Adj.	Opp.	Hyp.	Adj.	Opp.	Hyp.	Adj.	Opp.	Hyp.	Adj.	Opp.
1	0.9	0.4	61	56.2	23.8	121	111.4	47.3	181	166.6	70.7	241	221.8	94.2
2	1.8	0.8	62	57.1	24.2	122	112.3	47.7	182	167.5	71.1	242	222.8	94.6
3	2.8	1.2	63	58.0	24.6	123	113.2	48.1	183	168.5	71.5	243	223.7	94.9
4	3.7	1.6	64	58.9	25.0	124	114.1	48.5	184	169.4	71.9	244	224.6	95.3
5	4.6	2.0	65	59.8	25.4	125	115.1	48.8	185	170.3	72.3	245	225.5	95.7
6	5.5	2.3	66	60.8	25.8	126	116.0	49.2	186	171.2	72.7	246	226.4	96.1
7	6.4	2.7	67	61.7	26.2	127	116.9	49.6	187	172.1	73.1	247	227.4	96.5
8	7.4	3.1	68	62.6	26.6	128	117.8	50.0	188	173.1	73.5	248	228.3	96.9
9	8.3	3.5	69	63.5	27.0	129	118.7	50.4	189	174.0	73.8	249	229.2	97.3
10	9.2	3.9	70	64.4	27.4	130	119.7	50.8	190	174.9	74.2	250	230.1	97.7
11	10.1	4.3	71	65.4	27.7	131	120.6	51.2	191	175.8	74.6	251	231.0	98.1
12	11.0	4.7	72	66.3	28.1	132	121.5	51.6	192	176.7	75.0	252	232.0	98.5
13	12.0	5.1	73	67.2	28.5	133	122.4	52.0	193	177.7	75.4	253	232.9	98.9
14	12.9	5.5	74	68.1	28.9	134	123.3	52.4	194	178.6	75.8	254	233.8	99.2
15	13.8	5.9	75	69.0	29.3	135	124.3	52.7	195	179.5	76.2	255	234.7	99.6
16	14.7	6.3	76	70.0	29.7	136	125.2	53.1	196	180.4	76.6	256	235.6	100.0
17	15.6	6.6	77	70.9	30.1	137	126.1	53.5	197	181.3	77.0	257	236.6	100.4
18	16.6	7.0	78	71.8	30.5	138	127.0	53.9	198	182.3	77.4	258	237.5	100.8
19	17.5	7.4	79	72.7	30.9	139	128.0	54.3	199	183.2	77.8	259	238.4	101.2
20	18.4	7.8	80	73.6	31.3	140	128.9	54.7	200	184.1	78.1	260	239.3	101.6
21	19.3	8.2	81	74.6	31.6	141	129.8	55.1	201	185.0	78.5	261	240.3	102.0
22	20.3	8.6	82	75.5	32.0	142	130.7	55.5	202	185.9	78.9	262	241.2	102.4
23	21.2	9.0	83	76.4	32.4	143	131.6	55.9	203	186.9	79.3	263	242.1	102.8
24	22.1	9.4	84	77.3	32.8	144	132.6	56.3	204	187.8	79.7	264	243.0	103.2
25	23.0	9.8	85	78.2	33.2	145	133.5	56.7	205	188.7	80.1	265	243.9	103.5
26	23.9	10.2	86	79.2	33.6	146	134.4	57.0	206	189.6	80.5	266	244.9	103.9
27	24.9	10.5	87	80.1	34.0	147	135.3	57.4	207	190.5	80.9	267	245.8	104.3
28	25.8	10.9	88	81.0	34.4	148	136.2	57.8	208	191.5	81.3	268	246.7	104.7
29	26.7	11.3	89	81.9	34.8	149	137.2	58.2	209	192.4	81.7	269	247.6	105.1
30	27.6	11.7	90	82.8	35.2	150	138.1	58.6	210	193.3	82.1	270	248.5	105.5
31	28.5	12.1	91	83.8	35.6	151	139.0	59.0	211	194.2	82.4	271	249.5	105.9
32	29.5	12.5	92	84.7	35.9	152	139.9	59.4	212	195.1	82.8	272	250.4	106.3
33	30.4	12.9	93	85.6	36.3	153	140.8	59.8	213	196.1	83.2	273	251.3	106.7
34	31.3	13.3	94	86.5	36.7	154	141.8	60.2	214	197.0	83.6	274	252.2	107.1
35	32.2	13.7	95	87.4	37.1	155	142.7	60.6	215	197.9	84.0	275	253.1	107.5
36	33.1	14.1	96	88.4	37.5	156	143.6	61.0	216	198.8	84.4	276	254.1	107.8
37	34.1	14.5	97	89.3	37.9	157	144.5	61.3	217	199.7	84.8	277	255.0	108.2
38	35.0	14.8	98	90.2	38.3	158	145.4	61.7	218	200.7	85.2	278	255.9	108.6
39	35.9	15.2	99	91.1	38.7	159	146.4	62.1	219	201.6	85.6	279	256.8	109.0
40	36.8	15.6	100	92.1	39.1	160	147.3	62.5	220	202.5	86.0	280	257.7	109.4
41	37.7	16.0	101	93.0	39.5	161	148.2	62.9	221	203.4	86.4	281	258.7	109.8
42	38.7	16.4	102	93.9	39.9	162	149.1	63.3	222	204.4	86.7	282	259.6	110.2
43	39.6	16.8	103	94.8	40.2	163	150.0	63.7	223	205.3	87.1	283	260.5	110.6
44	40.5	17.2	104	95.7	40.6	164	151.0	64.1	224	206.2	87.5	284	261.4	111.0
45	41.4	17.6	105	96.7	41.0	165	151.9	64.5	225	207.1	87.9	285	262.3	111.4
46	42.3	18.0	106	97.6	41.4	166	152.8	64.9	226	208.0	88.3	286	263.3	111.7
47	43.3	18.4	107	98.5	41.8	167	153.7	65.3	227	209.0	88.7	287	264.2	112.1
48	44.2	18.8	108	99.4	42.2	168	154.6	65.6	228	209.9	89.1	288	265.1	112.5
49	45.1	19.1	109	100.3	42.6	169	155.6	66.0	229	210.8	89.5	289	266.0	112.9
50	46.0	19.5	110	101.3	43.0	170	156.5	66.4	230	211.7	89.9	290	266.9	113.3
51	46.9	19.9	111	102.2	43.4	171	157.4	66.8	231	212.6	90.3	291	267.9	113.7
52	47.9	20.3	112	103.1	43.8	172	158.3	67.2	232	213.6	90.6	292	268.8	114.1
53	48.8	20.7	113	104.0	44.2	173	159.2	67.6	233	214.5	91.0	293	269.7	114.5
54	49.7	21.1	114	104.9	44.5	174	160.2	68.0	234	215.4	91.4	294	270.6	114.9
55	50.6	21.5	115	105.9	44.9	175	161.1	68.4	235	216.3	91.8	295	271.5	115.3
56	51.5	21.9	116	106.8	45.3	176	162.0	68.8	236	217.2	92.2	296	272.5	115.7
57	52.5	22.3	117	107.7	45.7	177	162.9	69.2	237	218.2	92.6	297	273.4	116.0
58	53.4	22.7	118	108.6	46.1	178	163.8	69.6	238	219.1	93.0	298	274.3	116.4
59	54.3	23.1	119	109.5	46.5	179	164.8	69.9	239	220.0	93.4	299	275.2	116.8
60	55.2	23.4	120	110.5	46.9	180	165.7	70.3	240	220.9	93.8	300	276.2	117.2
Hyp.	Opp.	Adj.	Hyp.	Opp.	Adj.	Hyp.	Opp.	Adj.	Hyp.	Opp.	Adj.	Hyp.	Opp.	Adj.
Dist. / D Lon	Dep.	D. Lat. Dep	Dist. / D Lon	Dep.	D. Lat. Dep	Dist. / D Lon	Dep.	D. Lat. Dep	Dist. / D Lon	Dep.	D. Lat. Dep	Dist. / D Lon	Dep.	D. Lat. Dep

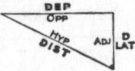

67°   67°

Table 3

TRAVERSE TABLE

D Lon	Dep		D Lon	Dep		D Lon	Dep		D Lon	Dep		D Lon	Dep	
Dist.	D. Lat.	Dep.	Dist.	D. Lat.	Dep.	Dist.	D. Lat.	Dep.	Dist.	D. Lat.	Dep.	Dist.	D. Lat.	Dep.
Hyp.	Adj.	Opp.	Hyp.	Adj.	Opp.	Hyp.	Adj.	Opp.	Hyp.	Adj.	Opp.	Hyp.	Adj.	Opp.
301	277.1	117.6	361	332.3	141.1	421	387.5	164.5	481	442.8	187.9	541	498.0	211.4
302	278.0	118.0	362	333.2	141.4	422	388.5	164.9	482	443.7	188.3	542	498.9	211.8
303	278.9	118.4	363	334.1	141.8	423	389.4	165.3	483	444.6	188.7	543	499.8	212.2
304	279.8	118.8	364	335.1	142.2	424	390.3	165.7	484	445.5	189.1	544	500.8	212.6
305	280.8	119.2	365	336.0	142.6	425	391.2	166.1	485	446.4	189.5	545	501.7	212.9
306	281.7	119.6	366	336.9	143.0	426	392.1	166.5	486	447.4	189.9	546	502.6	213.3
307	282.6	120.0	367	337.8	143.4	427	393.1	166.8	487	448.3	190.3	547	503.5	213.7
308	283.5	120.3	368	338.7	143.8	428	394.0	167.2	488	449.2	190.7	548	504.4	214.1
309	284.4	120.7	369	339.7	144.2	429	394.9	167.6	489	450.1	191.1	549	505.4	214.5
310	285.4	121.1	370	340.6	144.6	430	395.8	168.0	490	451.0	191.5	550	506.3	214.9
311	286.3	121.5	371	341.5	145.0	431	396.7	168.4	491	452.0	191.8	551	507.2	215.3
312	287.2	121.9	372	342.4	145.4	432	397.7	168.8	492	452.9	192.2	552	508.1	215.7
313	288.1	122.3	373	343.3	145.7	433	398.6	169.2	493	453.8	192.6	553	509.0	216.1
314	289.0	122.7	374	344.3	146.1	434	399.5	169.6	494	454.7	193.0	554	510.0	216.5
315	290.0	123.1	375	345.2	146.5	435	400.4	170.0	495	455.6	193.4	555	510.9	216.9
316	290.9	123.5	376	346.1	146.9	436	401.3	170.4	496	456.6	193.8	556	511.8	217.2
317	291.8	123.9	377	347.0	147.3	437	402.3	170.7	497	457.5	194.2	557	512.7	217.6
318	292.7	124.3	378	348.0	147.7	438	403.2	171.1	498	458.4	194.6	558	513.6	218.0
319	293.6	124.6	379	348.9	148.1	439	404.1	171.5	499	459.3	195.0	559	514.6	218.4
320	294.6	125.0	380	349.8	148.5	440	405.0	171.9	500	460.3	195.4	560	515.5	218.8
321	295.5	125.4	381	350.7	148.9	441	405.9	172.3	501	461.2	195.8	561	516.4	219.2
322	296.4	125.8	382	351.6	149.3	442	406.9	172.7	502	462.1	196.1	562	517.3	219.6
323	297.3	126.2	383	352.6	149.7	443	407.8	173.1	503	463.0	196.5	563	518.2	220.0
324	298.2	126.6	384	353.5	150.0	444	408.7	173.5	504	463.9	196.9	564	519.2	220.4
325	299.2	127.0	385	354.4	150.4	445	409.6	173.9	505	464.9	197.3	565	520.1	220.8
326	300.1	127.4	386	355.3	150.8	446	410.5	174.3	506	465.8	197.7	566	521.0	221.2
327	301.0	127.8	387	356.2	151.2	447	411.5	174.7	507	466.7	198.1	567	521.9	221.5
328	301.9	128.2	388	357.2	151.6	448	412.4	175.0	508	467.6	198.5	568	522.8	221.9
329	302.8	128.6	389	358.1	152.0	449	413.3	175.4	509	468.5	198.9	569	523.8	222.3
330	303.8	128.9	390	359.0	152.4	450	414.2	175.8	510	469.5	199.3	570	524.7	222.7
331	304.7	129.3	391	359.9	152.8	451	415.1	176.2	511	470.4	199.7	571	525.6	223.1
332	305.6	129.7	392	360.8	153.2	452	416.1	176.6	512	471.3	200.1	572	526.5	223.5
333	306.5	130.1	393	361.8	153.6	453	417.0	177.0	513	472.2	200.4	573	527.4	223.9
334	307.4	130.5	394	362.7	153.9	454	417.9	177.4	514	473.1	200.8	574	528.4	224.3
335	308.4	130.9	395	363.6	154.3	455	418.8	177.8	515	474.1	201.2	575	529.3	224.7
336	309.3	131.3	396	364.5	154.7	456	419.8	178.2	516	475.0	201.6	576	530.2	225.1
337	310.2	131.7	397	365.4	155.1	457	420.7	178.6	517	475.9	202.0	577	531.1	225.5
338	311.1	132.1	398	366.4	155.5	458	421.6	179.0	518	476.8	202.4	578	532.1	225.8
339	312.1	132.5	399	367.3	155.9	459	422.5	179.3	519	477.7	202.8	579	533.0	226.2
340	313.0	132.8	400	368.2	156.3	460	423.4	179.7	520	478.7	203.2	580	533.9	226.6
341	313.9	133.2	401	369.1	156.7	461	424.4	180.1	521	479.6	203.6	581	534.8	227.0
342	314.8	133.6	402	370.0	157.1	462	425.3	180.5	522	480.5	204.0	582	535.7	227.4
343	315.7	134.0	403	371.0	157.5	463	426.2	180.9	523	481.4	204.4	583	536.7	227.8
344	316.7	134.4	404	371.9	157.9	464	427.1	181.3	524	482.3	204.7	584	537.6	228.2
345	317.6	135.2	405	372.8	158.2	465	428.0	181.7	525	483.3	205.1	585	538.5	228.6
346	318.5	135.2	406	373.7	158.6	466	429.0	182.1	526	484.2	205.5	586	539.4	229.0
347	319.4	135.6	407	374.6	159.0	467	429.9	182.5	527	485.1	205.9	587	540.3	229.4
348	320.3	136.0	408	375.6	159.4	468	430.8	182.9	528	486.0	206.3	588	541.3	229.7
349	321.3	136.4	409	376.5	159.8	469	431.7	183.3	529	486.9	206.7	589	542.2	230.1
350	322.2	136.8	410	377.4	160.2	470	432.6	183.6	530	487.9	207.1	590	543.1	230.5
351	323.1	137.1	411	378.3	160.6	471	433.6	184.0	531	488.8	207.5	591	544.0	230.9
352	324.0	137.5	412	379.2	161.0	472	434.5	184.4	532	489.7	207.9	592	544.9	231.3
353	324.9	137.9	413	380.2	161.4	473	435.4	184.8	533	490.6	208.3	593	545.9	231.7
354	325.9	138.3	414	381.1	161.8	474	436.3	185.2	534	491.5	208.7	594	546.8	232.1
355	326.8	138.7	415	382.0	162.2	475	437.2	185.6	535	492.5	209.0	595	547.7	232.5
356	327.7	139.1	416	382.9	162.5	476	438.2	186.0	536	493.4	209.4	596	548.6	232.9
357	328.6	139.5	417	383.9	162.9	477	439.1	186.4	537	494.3	209.8	597	549.5	233.3
358	329.5	139.9	418	384.8	163.3	478	440.0	186.8	538	495.2	210.2	598	550.5	233.7
359	330.5	140.3	419	385.7	163.7	479	440.9	187.2	539	496.2	210.6	599	551.4	234.0
360	331.4	140.7	420	386.6	164.1	480	441.8	187.6	540	497.1	211.0	600	552.3	234.4
Hyp.	Opp.	Adj.	Hyp.	Opp.	Adj.	Hyp.	Opp.	Adj.	Hyp.	Opp.	Adj.	Hyp.	Opp.	Adj.
Dist.	Dep.	D. Lat.	Dist.	Dep.	D. Lat.	Dist.	Dep.	D. Lat.	Dist.	Dep.	D. Lat.	Dist.	Dep.	D. Lat.
D Lon		Dep	D Lon		Dep	D Lon		Dep	D Lon		Dep	D Lon		Dep

Table 3

TRAVERSE TABLE

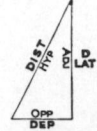

24°   24°

D Lon Dist.	Dep D. Lat.	Dep.	D Lon Dist.	Dep D. Lat.	Dep.	D Lon Dist.	Dep D. Lat.	Dep.	D Lon Dist.	Dep D. Lat.	Dep.	D Lon Dist.	Dep D. Lat.	Dep.
Hyp.	Adj.	Opp.	Hyp.	Adj.	Opp.	Hyp.	Adj.	Opp.	Hyp.	Adj.	Opp.	Hyp.	Adj.	Opp
1	0.9	0.4	61	55.7	24.8	121	110.5	49.2	181	165.4	73.6	241	220.2	98.0
2	1.8	0.8	62	56.6	25.2	122	111.5	49.6	182	166.3	74.0	242	221.1	98.4
3	2.7	1.2	63	57.6	25.6	123	112.4	50.0	183	167.2	74.4	243	222.0	98.8
4	3.7	1.6	64	58.5	26.0	124	113.3	50.4	184	168.1	74.8	244	222.9	99.2
5	4.6	2.0	65	59.4	26.4	125	114.2	50.8	185	169.0	75.2	245	223.8	99.7
6	5.5	2.4	66	60.3	26.8	126	115.1	51.2	186	169.9	75.7	246	224.7	100.1
7	6.4	2.8	67	61.2	27.3	127	116.0	51.7	187	170.8	76.1	247	225.6	100.5
8	7.3	3.3	68	62.1	27.7	128	116.9	52.1	188	171.7	76.5	248	226.6	100.9
9	8.2	3.7	69	63.0	28.1	129	117.8	52.5	189	172.7	76.9	249	227.5	101.3
10	9.1	4.1	70	63.9	28.5	130	118.8	52.9	190	173.6	77.3	250	228.4	101.7
11	10.0	4.5	71	64.9	28.9	131	119.7	53.3	191	174.5	77.7	251	229.3	102.1
12	11.0	4.9	72	65.8	29.3	132	120.6	53.7	192	175.4	78.1	252	230.2	102.5
13	11.9	5.3	73	66.7	29.7	133	121.5	54.1	193	176.3	78.5	253	231.1	102.9
14	12.8	5.7	74	67.6	30.1	134	122.4	54.5	194	177.2	78.9	254	232.0	103.3
15	13.7	6.1	75	68.5	30.5	135	123.3	54.9	195	178.1	79.3	255	233.0	103.7
16	14.6	6.5	76	69.4	30.9	136	124.2	55.3	196	179.1	79.7	256	233.9	104.1
17	15.5	6.9	77	70.3	31.3	137	125.2	55.7	197	180.0	80.1	257	234.8	104.5
18	16.4	7.3	78	71.3	31.7	138	126.1	56.1	198	180.9	80.5	258	235.7	104.9
19	17.4	7.7	79	72.2	32.1	139	127.0	56.5	199	181.8	80.9	259	236.6	105.3
20	18.3	8.1	80	73.1	32.5	140	127.9	56.9	200	182.7	81.3	260	237.5	105.8
21	19.2	8.5	81	74.0	32.9	141	128.8	57.3	201	183.6	81.8	261	238.4	106.2
22	20.1	8.9	82	74.9	33.4	142	129.7	57.8	202	184.5	82.2	262	239.3	106.6
23	21.0	9.4	83	75.8	33.8	143	130.6	58.2	203	185.4	82.6	263	240.3	107.0
24	21.9	9.8	84	76.7	34.2	144	131.6	58.6	204	186.4	83.0	264	241.2	107.4
25	22.8	10.2	85	77.7	34.6	145	132.5	59.0	205	187.3	83.4	265	242.1	107.8
26	23.8	10.6	86	78.6	35.0	146	133.4	59.4	206	188.2	83.8	266	243.0	108.2
27	24.7	11.0	87	79.5	35.4	147	134.3	59.8	207	189.1	84.2	267	243.9	108.6
28	25.6	11.4	88	80.4	35.8	148	135.2	60.2	208	190.0	84.6	268	244.8	109.0
29	26.5	11.8	89	81.3	36.2	149	136.1	60.6	209	190.9	85.0	269	245.7	109.4
30	27.4	12.2	90	82.2	36.6	150	137.0	61.0	210	191.8	85.4	270	246.7	109.8
31	28.3	12.6	91	83.1	37.0	151	137.9	61.4	211	192.8	85.8	271	247.6	110.2
32	29.2	13.0	92	84.0	37.4	152	138.9	61.8	212	193.7	86.2	272	248.5	110.6
33	30.1	13.4	93	85.0	37.8	153	139.8	62.2	213	194.6	86.6	273	249.4	111.0
34	31.1	13.8	94	85.9	38.2	154	140.7	62.6	214	195.5	87.0	274	250.3	111.4
35	32.0	14.2	95	86.8	38.6	155	141.6	63.0	215	196.4	87.4	275	251.2	111.9
36	32.9	14.6	96	87.7	39.0	156	142.5	63.5	216	197.3	87.9	276	252.1	112.3
37	33.8	15.0	97	88.6	39.5	157	143.4	63.9	217	198.2	88.3	277	253.1	112.7
38	34.7	15.5	98	89.5	39.9	158	144.3	64.3	218	199.2	88.7	278	254.0	113.1
39	35.6	15.9	99	90.4	40.3	159	145.3	64.7	219	200.1	89.1	279	254.9	113.5
40	36.5	16.3	100	91.4	40.7	160	146.2	65.1	220	201.0	89.5	280	255.8	113.9
41	37.5	16.7	101	92.3	41.1	161	147.1	65.5	221	201.9	89.9	281	256.7	114.3
42	38.4	17.1	102	93.2	41.5	162	148.0	65.9	222	202.8	90.3	282	257.6	114.7
43	39.3	17.5	103	94.1	41.9	163	148.9	66.3	223	203.7	90.7	283	258.5	115.1
44	40.2	17.9	104	95.0	42.3	164	149.8	66.7	224	204.6	91.1	284	259.4	115.5
45	41.1	18.3	105	95.9	42.7	165	150.7	67.1	225	205.5	91.5	285	260.4	115.9
46	42.0	18.7	106	96.8	43.1	166	151.6	67.5	226	206.5	91.9	286	261.3	116.3
47	42.9	19.1	107	97.7	43.5	167	152.6	67.9	227	207.4	92.3	287	262.2	116.7
48	43.9	19.5	108	98.7	43.9	168	153.5	68.3	228	208.3	92.7	288	263.1	117.1
49	44.8	19.9	109	99.6	44.3	169	154.4	68.7	229	209.2	93.1	289	264.0	117.5
50	45.7	20.3	110	100.5	44.7	170	155.3	69.1	230	210.1	93.5	290	264.9	118.0
51	46.6	20.7	111	101.4	45.1	171	156.2	69.6	231	211.0	94.0	291	265.8	118.4
52	47.5	21.2	112	102.3	45.6	172	157.1	70.0	232	211.9	94.4	292	266.8	118.8
53	48.4	21.6	113	103.2	46.0	173	158.0	70.4	233	212.9	94.8	293	267.7	119.2
54	49.3	22.0	114	104.1	46.4	174	159.0	70.8	234	213.8	95.2	294	268.6	119.6
55	50.2	22.4	115	105.1	46.8	175	159.9	71.2	235	214.7	95.6	295	269.5	120.0
56	51.2	22.8	116	106.0	47.2	176	160.8	71.6	236	215.6	96.0	296	270.4	120.4
57	52.1	23.2	117	106.9	47.6	177	161.7	72.0	237	216.5	96.4	297	271.3	120.8
58	53.0	23.6	118	107.8	48.0	178	162.6	72.4	238	217.4	96.8	298	272.2	121.2
59	53.9	24.0	119	108.7	48.4	179	163.5	72.8	239	218.3	97.2	299	273.2	121.6
60	54.8	24.4	120	109.6	48.8	180	164.4	73.2	240	219.3	97.6	300	274.1	122.0
Hyp.	Opp.	Adj.	Hyp.	Opp.	Adj.	Hyp.	Opp.	Adj.	Hyp.	Opp.	Adj.	Hyp.	Opp.	Adj.

Dist. D Lon	Dep.	D. Lat. Dep	Dist. D Lon	Dep.	D. Lat. Dep	Dist. D Lon	Dep.	D. Lat. Dep	Dist. D Lon	Dep.	D. Lat. Dep	Dist. D Lon	Dep.	D. Lat. Dep

66°   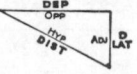   66°

Table 3   **TRAVERSE TABLE**

24°

24°

D Lon Dist.	Dep D. Lat.	Dep.	D Lon Dist.	Dep D. Lat.	Dep.	D Lon Dist.	Dep D. Lat.	Dep.	D Lon Dist.	Dep D. Lat.	Dep.	D Lon Dist.	Dep D. Lat.	Dep.
Hyp.	*Adj.*	*Opp.*	*Hyp.*	*Adj.*	*Opp.*	*Hyp.*	*Adj.*	*Opp.*	*Hyp.*	*Adj.*	*Opp.*	*Hyp.*	*Adj.*	*Opp.*
301	275.0	122.4	361	329.8	146.8	421	384.6	171.2	481	439.4	195.6	541	494.2	220.0
302	275.9	122.8	362	330.7	147.2	422	385.5	171.6	482	440.3	196.0	542	495.1	220.5
303	276.8	123.2	363	331.6	147.6	423	386.4	172.0	483	441.2	196.5	543	496.1	220.9
304	277.7	123.6	364	332.5	148.1	424	387.3	172.5	484	442.2	196.9	544	497.0	221.3
305	278.6	124.1	365	333.4	148.5	425	388.3	172.9	485	443.1	197.3	545	497.9	221.7
306	279.5	124.5	366	334.4	148.9	426	389.2	173.3	486	444.0	197.7	546	498.8	222.1
307	280.5	124.9	367	335.3	149.3	427	390.1	173.7	487	444.9	198.1	547	499.7	222.5
308	281.4	125.3	368	336.2	149.7	428	391.0	174.1	488	445.8	198.5	548	500.6	222.9
309	282.3	125.7	369	337.1	150.1	429	391.9	174.5	489	446.7	198.9	549	501.5	223.3
310	283.2	126.1	370	338.0	150.5	430	392.8	174.9	490	447.6	199.3	550	502.5	223.7
311	284.1	126.5	371	338.9	150.9	431	393.7	175.3	491	448.6	199.7	551	503.4	224.1
312	285.0	126.9	372	339.8	151.3	432	394.7	175.7	492	449.5	200.1	552	504.3	224.5
313	285.9	127.3	373	340.7	151.7	433	395.6	176.1	493	450.4	200.5	553	505.2	224.9
314	286.9	127.7	374	341.7	152.1	434	396.5	176.5	494	451.3	200.9	554	506.1	225.3
315	287.8	128.1	375	342.6	152.5	435	397.4	176.9	495	452.2	201.3	555	507.0	225.7
316	288.7	128.5	376	343.5	152.9	436	398.3	177.3	496	453.1	201.7	556	507.9	226.1
317	289.6	128.9	377	344.4	153.3	437	399.2	177.7	497	454.0	202.1	557	508.8	226.6
318	290.5	129.3	378	345.3	153.7	438	400.1	178.2	498	454.9	202.6	558	509.8	227.0
319	291.4	129.7	379	346.2	154.2	439	401.0	178.6	499	455.9	203.0	559	510.7	227.4
320	292.3	130.2	380	347.1	154.6	440	402.0	179.0	500	456.8	203.4	560	511.6	227.8
321	293.2	130.6	381	348.1	155.0	441	402.9	179.4	501	457.7	203.8	561	512.5	228.2
322	294.2	131.0	382	349.0	155.4	442	403.8	179.8	502	458.6	204.2	562	513.4	228.6
323	295.1	131.4	383	349.9	155.8	443	404.7	180.2	503	459.5	204.6	563	514.3	229.0
324	296.0	131.8	384	350.8	156.2	444	405.6	180.6	504	460.4	205.0	564	515.2	229.4
325	296.9	132.2	385	351.7	156.6	445	406.5	181.0	505	461.3	205.4	565	516.2	229.8
326	297.8	132.6	386	352.6	157.0	446	407.4	181.4	506	462.3	205.8	566	517.1	230.2
327	298.7	133.0	387	353.5	157.4	447	408.4	181.8	507	463.2	206.2	567	518.0	230.6
328	299.6	133.4	388	354.5	157.8	448	409.3	182.2	508	464.1	206.6	568	518.9	231.0
329	300.6	133.8	389	355.4	158.2	449	410.2	182.6	509	465.0	207.0	569	519.8	231.4
330	301.5	134.2	390	356.3	158.6	450	411.1	183.0	510	465.9	207.4	570	520.7	231.8
331	302.4	134.6	391	357.2	159.0	451	412.0	183.4	511	466.8	207.8	571	521.6	232.2
332	303.3	135.0	392	358.1	159.4	452	412.9	183.8	512	467.7	208.2	572	522.5	232.7
333	304.2	135.4	393	359.0	159.8	453	413.8	184.3	513	468.6	208.7	573	523.5	233.1
334	305.1	135.9	394	359.9	160.3	454	414.7	184.7	514	469.6	209.1	574	524.4	233.5
335	306.0	136.3	395	360.9	160.7	455	415.7	185.1	515	470.5	209.5	575	525.3	233.9
336	307.0	136.7	396	361.8	161.1	456	416.6	185.5	516	471.4	209.9	576	526.2	234.3
337	307.9	137.1	397	362.7	161.5	457	417.5	185.9	517	472.3	210.3	577	527.1	234.7
338	308.8	137.5	398	363.6	161.9	458	418.4	186.3	518	473.2	210.7	578	528.0	235.1
339	309.7	137.9	399	364.5	162.3	459	419.3	186.7	519	474.1	211.1	579	528.9	235.5
340	310.6	138.3	400	365.4	162.7	460	420.2	187.1	520	475.0	211.5	580	529.9	235.9
341	311.5	138.7	401	366.3	163.1	461	421.1	187.5	521	476.0	211.9	581	530.8	236.3
342	312.4	139.1	402	367.2	163.5	462	422.1	187.9	522	476.9	212.3	582	531.7	236.7
343	313.3	139.5	403	368.2	163.9	463	423.0	188.3	523	477.8	212.7	583	532.6	237.1
344	314.3	139.9	404	369.1	164.3	464	423.9	188.7	524	478.7	213.1	584	533.5	237.5
345	315.2	140.3	405	370.0	164.7	465	424.8	189.1	525	479.6	213.5	585	534.4	237.9
346	316.1	140.7	406	370.9	165.1	466	425.7	189.5	526	480.5	213.9	586	535.3	238.3
347	317.0	141.1	407	371.8	165.5	467	426.6	189.9	527	481.4	214.4	587	536.3	238.8
348	317.9	141.5	408	372.7	165.9	468	427.5	190.4	528	482.4	214.8	588	537.2	239.2
349	318.8	142.0	409	373.6	166.4	469	428.5	190.8	529	483.3	215.2	589	538.1	239.6
350	319.7	142.4	410	374.6	166.8	470	429.4	191.2	530	484.2	215.6	590	539.0	240.0
351	320.7	142.8	411	375.5	167.2	471	430.3	191.6	531	485.1	216.0	591	539.9	240.4
352	321.6	143.2	412	376.4	167.6	472	431.2	192.0	532	486.0	216.4	592	540.8	240.8
353	322.5	143.6	413	377.3	168.0	473	432.1	192.4	533	486.9	216.8	593	541.7	241.2
354	323.4	144.0	414	378.2	168.4	474	433.0	192.8	534	487.8	217.2	594	542.6	241.6
355	324.3	144.4	415	379.1	168.8	475	433.9	193.2	535	488.7	217.6	595	543.6	242.0
356	325.2	144.8	416	380.0	169.2	476	434.8	193.6	536	489.7	218.0	596	544.5	242.4
357	326.1	145.2	417	380.9	169.6	477	435.8	194.0	537	490.6	218.4	597	545.4	242.8
358	327.0	145.6	418	381.9	170.0	478	436.7	194.4	538	491.5	218.8	598	546.3	243.2
359	328.0	146.0	419	382.8	170.4	479	437.6	194.8	539	492.4	219.2	599	547.2	243.6
360	328.9	146.4	420	383.7	170.8	480	438.5	195.2	540	493.3	219.6	600	548.1	244.0
Hyp.	*Cpp.*	*Adj.*	*Hyp.*	*Opp.*	*Adj.*	*Hyp.*	*Opp.*	*Adj.*	*Hyp.*	*Opp.*	*Adj.*	*Hyp.*	*Opp.*	*Adj.*
Dist. D Lon	Dep.	D. Lat. Dep	**Dist.** D Lon	Dep.	D. Lat. Dep	**Dist.** D Lon	Dep.	D. Lat. Dep	**Dist.** D Lon	Dep.	D. Lat. Dep	**Dist.** D Lon	Dep.	D. Lat. Dep

66°

66°

Table 3 — TRAVERSE TABLE

25°   25°

D Lon Dist.	Dep D. Lat.	Dep.	D Lon Dist.	Dep D. Lat.	Dep.	D Lon Dist.	Dep D. Lat.	Opp.	D Lon Dist.	Dep D. Lat.	Dep.	D Lon Dist.	Dep D. Lat.	Dep.
Hyp.	Adj.	Opp.	Hyp.	Adj.	Opp.	Hyp.	Adj.	Opp.	Hyp.	Adj.	Opp.	Hyp.	Adj.	Opp.
1	0.9	0.4	61	55.3	25.8	121	109.7	51.1	181	164.0	76.5	241	218.4	101.9
2	1.8	0.8	62	56.2	26.2	122	110.6	51.6	182	164.9	76.9	242	219.3	102.3
3	2.7	1.3	63	57.1	26.6	123	111.5	52.0	183	165.9	77.3	243	220.2	102.7
4	3.6	1.7	64	58.0	27.0	124	112.4	52.4	184	166.8	77.8	244	221.1	103.1
5	4.5	2.1	65	58.9	27.5	125	113.3	52.8	185	167.7	78.2	245	222.0	103.5
6	5.4	2.5	66	59.8	27.9	126	114.2	53.2	186	168.6	78 6	246	223.0	104.0
7	6.3	3.0	67	60.7	28.3	127	115.1	53.7	187	169.5	79.0	247	223.9	104.4
8	7.3	3.4	68	61.6	28.7	128	116.0	54.1	188	170.4	79.5	248	224.8	104.8
9	8.2	3.8	69	62.5	29.2	129	116.9	54.5	189	171.3	79.9	249	225.7	105.2
10	9.1	4.2	70	63.4	29.6	130	117.8	54.9	190	172.2	80.3	250	226.6	105.7
11	10.0	4.6	71	64.3	30.0	131	118.7	55.4	191	173.1	80.7	251	227.5	106.1
12	10.9	5.1	72	65.3	30.4	132	119.6	55.8	192	174.0	81.1	252	228.4	106.5
13	11.8	5.5	73	66.2	30.9	133	120.5	56.2	193	174.9	81.6	253	229.3	106.9
14	12.7	5.9	74	67.1	31.3	134	121.4	56.6	194	175.8	82.0	254	230.2	107.3
15	13.6	6.3	75	68.0	31.7	135	122.4	57.1	195	176.7	82.4	255	231.1	107.8
16	14.5	6.8	76	68.9	32.1	136	123.3	57.5	196	177.6	82.8	256	232.0	108.2
17	15.4	7.2	77	69.8	32.5	137	124.2	57.9	197	178.5	83.3	257	232.9	108.6
18	16.3	7.6	78	70.7	33.0	138	125.1	58.3	198	179.4	83.7	258	233.8	109.0
19	17.2	8.0	79	71.6	33.4	139	126.0	58.7	199	180.4	84.1	259	234.7	109.5
20	18.1	8.5	80	72.5	33.8	140	126.9	59.2	200	181.3	84.5	260	235.6	109.9
21	19.0	8.9	81	73.4	34.2	141	127.8	59.6	201	182.2	84.9	261	236.5	110.3
22	19.9	9.3	82	74.3	34.7	142	128.7	60.0	202	183.1	85.4	262	237.5	110.7
23	20.8	9.7	83	75.2	35.1	143	129.6	60.4	203	184.0	85.8	263	238.4	111.1
24	21.8	10.1	84	76.1	35.5	144	130.5	60.9	204	184.9	86.2	264	239.3	111.6
25	22.7	10.6	85	77.0	35.9	145	131.4	61.3	205	185.8	86.6	265	240.2	112.0
26	23.6	11.0	86	77.9	36.3	146	132.3	61.7	206	186.7	87.1	266	241.1	112.4
27	24.5	11.4	87	78.8	36.8	147	133.2	62.1	207	187.6	87.5	267	242.0	112.8
28	25.4	11.8	88	79.8	37.2	148	134.1	62.5	208	188.5	87.9	268	242.9	113.3
29	26.3	12.3	89	80.7	37.6	149	135.0	63.0	209	189.4	88.3	269	243.8	113.7
30	27.2	12.7	90	81.6	38.0	150	135.9	63.4	210	190.3	88.7	270	244.7	114.1
31	28.1	13.1	91	82.5	38.5	151	136.9	63.8	211	191.2	89.2	271	245.6	114.5
32	29.0	13.5	92	83.4	38.9	152	137.8	64.2	212	192.1	89.6	272	246.5	115.0
33	29.9	13.9	93	84.3	39.3	153	138.7	64.7	213	193.0	90.0	273	247.4	115.4
34	30.8	14.4	94	85.2	39.7	154	139.6	65.1	214	193.9	90.4	274	248.3	115.8
35	31.7	14.8	95	86.1	40.1	155	140.5	65.5	215	194.9	90.9	275	249.2	116.2
36	32.6	15.2	96	87.0	40.6	156	141.4	65.9	216	195.8	91.3	276	250.1	116.6
37	33.5	15.6	97	87.9	41.0	157	142.3	66.4	217	196.7	91.7	277	251.0	117.1
38	34.4	16.1	98	88.8	41.4	158	143.2	66.8	218	197.6	92.1	278	252.0	117.5
39	35.3	16.5	99	89.7	41.8	159	144.1	67.2	219	198.5	92.6	279	252.9	117.9
40	36.3	16.9	100	90.6	42.3	160	145.0	67.6	220	199.4	93.0	280	253.8	118.3
41	37.2	17.3	101	91.5	42.7	161	145.9	68.0	221	200.3	93.4	281	254.7	118.8
42	38.1	17.7	102	92.4	43.1	162	146.8	68.5	222	201.2	93.8	282	255.6	119.2
43	39.0	18.2	103	93.3	43.5	163	147.7	68.9	223	202.1	94.2	283	256.5	119.6
44	39.9	18.6	104	94.3	44.0	164	148.6	69.3	224	203.0	94.7	284	257.4	120.0
45	40.8	19.0	105	95.2	44.4	165	149.5	69.7	225	203.9	95.1	285	258.3	120.4
46	41.7	19.4	106	96.1	44.8	166	150.4	70.2	226	204.8	95.5	286	259.2	120.9
47	42.6	19.9	107	97.0	45.2	167	151.4	70.6	227	205.7	95.9	287	260.1	121.3
48	43.5	20.3	108	97.9	45.6	168	152.3	71.0	228	206.6	96.4	288	261.0	121.7
49	44.4	20.7	109	98.8	46.1	169	153.2	71.4	229	207.5	96.8	289	261.9	122.1
50	45.3	21.1	110	99.7	46.5	170	154.1	71.8	230	208.5	97.2	290	262.8	122.6
51	46.2	21.6	111	100.6	46.9	171	155.0	72.3	231	209.4	97.6	291	263.7	123.0
52	47.1	22.0	112	101.5	47.3	172	155.9	72.7	232	210.3	98.0	292	264.6	123.4
53	48.0	22.4	113	102.4	47.8	173	156.8	73.1	233	211.2	98.5	293	265.5	123.8
54	48.9	22.8	114	103.3	48.2	174	157.7	73.5	234	212.1	98.9	294	266.5	124.2
55	49.8	23.2	115	104.2	48.6	175	158.6	74.0	235	213.0	99.3	295	267.4	124.7
56	50.8	23.7	116	105.1	49.0	176	159.5	74.4	236	213.9	99.7	296	268.3	125.1
57	51.7	24.1	117	106.0	49.4	177	160.4	74.8	237	214.8	100.2	297	269.2	125.5
58	52.6	24.5	118	106.9	49.9	178	161.3	75.2	238	215.7	100.6	298	270.1	125.9
59	53.5	24.9	119	107.9	50.3	179	162.2	75.6	239	216.6	101.0	299	271.0	126.4
60	54.4	25.4	120	108.8	50.7	180	163.1	76.1	240	217.5	101.4	300	271.9	126.8
Hyp.	Opp.	Adj.	Hyp.	Opp.	Adj.	Hyp.	Opp.	Adj.	Hyp.	Opp.	Adj.	Hyp.	Opp.	Adj.
Dist. D Lon	Dep.	D. Lat. Dep	Dist. D Lon	Dep.	D. Lat. Dep	Dist. D Lon	Dep.	D. Lat. Dep	Dist. D Lon	Dep.	D. Lat. Dep	Dist. D Lon	Dep.	D. Lat. Dep

65°   65°

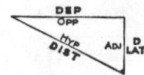

Table 3 TRAVERSE TABLE

25° 335° | 025° / 205° | 155° **25°**

D Lon Dep Dist. D. Lat. Dep. Hyp. Adj. Opp.			D Lon Dep Dist. D. Lat. Dep. Hyp. Adj. Opp.			D Lon Dep Dist. D. Lat. Dep. Hyp. Adj. Opp.			D Lon Dep Dist. D. Lat. Dep. Hyp. Adj. Opp.			D Lon Dep Dist. D. Lat. Dep. Hyp. Adj. Opp.		
301	272.8	127.2	361	327.2	152.6	421	381.6	177.9	481	435.9	203.3	541	490.3	228.6
302	273.7	127.6	362	328.1	153.0	422	382.5	178.3	482	436.8	203.7	542	491.2	229.1
303	274.6	128.1	363	329.0	153.4	423	383.4	178.8	483	437.7	204.1	543	492.1	229.5
304	275.5	128.5	364	329.9	153.8	424	384.3	179.2	484	438.7	204.5	544	493.0	229.9
305	276.4	128.9	365	330.8	154.3	425	385.2	179.6	485	439.6	205.0	545	493.9	230.3
306	277.3	129.3	366	331.7	154.7	426	386.1	180.0	486	440.5	205.4	546	494.8	230.7
307	278.2	129.7	367	332.6	155.1	427	387.0	180.5	487	441.4	205.8	547	495.8	231.2
308	279.1	130.2	368	333.5	155.5	428	387.9	180.9	488	442.3	206.2	548	496.7	231.6
309	280.0	130.6	369	334.4	155.9	429	388.8	181.3	489	443.2	206.7	549	497.6	232.0
310	281.0	131.0	370	335.3	156.4	430	389.7	181.7	490	444.1	207.1	550	498.5	232.4
311	281.9	131.4	371	336.2	156.8	431	390.6	182.1	491	445.0	207.5	551	499.4	232.9
312	282.8	131.9	372	337.1	157.2	432	391.5	182.6	492	445.9	207.9	552	500.3	233.3
313	283.7	132.3	373	338.1	157.6	433	392.4	183.0	493	446.8	208.4	553	501.2	233.7
314	284.6	132.7	374	339.0	158.1	434	393.3	183.4	494	447.7	208.8	554	502.1	234.1
315	285.5	133.1	375	339.9	158.5	435	394.2	183.8	495	448.6	209.2	555	503.0	234.6
316	286.4	133.5	376	340.8	158.9	436	395.2	184.3	496	449.5	209.6	556	503.9	235.0
317	287.3	134.0	377	341.7	159.3	437	396.1	184.7	497	450.4	210.0	557	504.8	235.4
318	288.2	134.4	378	342.6	159.7	438	397.0	185.1	498	451.3	210.5	558	505.7	235.8
319	289.1	134.8	379	343.5	160.2	439	397.9	185.5	499	452.2	210.9	559	506.6	236.2
320	290.0	135.2	380	344.4	160.6	440	398.8	186.0	500	453.2	211.3	560	507.5	236.7
321	290.9	135.7	381	345.3	161.0	441	399.7	186.4	501	454.1	211.7	561	508.4	237.1
322	291.8	136.1	382	346.2	161.4	442	400.6	186.8	502	455.0	212.2	562	509.3	237.5
323	292.7	136.5	383	347.1	161.9	443	401.5	187.2	503	455.9	212.6	563	510.3	237.9
324	293.6	136.9	384	348.0	162.3	444	402.4	187.6	504	456.8	213.0	564	511.2	238.4
325	294.6	137.4	385	348.9	162.7	445	403.3	188.1	505	457.7	213.4	565	512.1	238.8
326	295.5	137.8	386	349.8	163.1	446	404.2	188.5	506	458.6	213.8	566	513.0	239.2
327	296.4	138.2	387	350.7	163.6	447	405.1	188.9	507	459.5	214.3	567	513.9	239.6
328	297.3	138.6	388	351.6	164.0	448	406.0	189.3	508	460.4	214.7	568	514.8	240.0
329	298.2	139.0	389	352.6	164.4	449	406.9	189.8	509	461.3	215.1	569	515.7	240.5
330	299.1	139.5	390	353.5	164.8	450	407.8	190.2	510	462.2	215.5	570	516.6	240.9
331	300.0	139.9	391	354.4	165.2	451	408.7	190.6	511	463.1	216.0	571	517.5	241.3
332	300.9	140.3	392	355.3	165.7	452	409.7	191.0	512	464.0	216.4	572	518.4	241.7
333	301.8	140.7	393	356.2	166.1	453	410.6	191.4	513	464.9	216.8	573	519.3	242.2
334	302.7	141.2	394	357.1	166.5	454	411.5	191.9	514	465.8	217.2	574	520.2	242.6
335	303.6	141.6	395	358.0	166.9	455	412.4	192.3	515	466.7	217.6	575	521.1	243.0
336	304.5	142.0	396	358.9	167.4	456	413.3	192.7	516	467.7	218.1	576	522.0	243.4
337	305.4	142.4	397	359.8	167.8	457	414.2	193.1	517	468.6	218.5	577	522.9	243.9
338	306.3	142.8	398	360.7	168.2	458	415.1	193.6	518	469.5	218.9	578	523.8	244.3
339	307.2	143.3	399	361.6	168.6	459	416.0	194.0	519	470.4	219.3	579	524.8	244.7
340	308.1	143.7	400	362.5	169.0	460	416.9	194.4	520	471.3	219.8	580	525.7	245.1
341	309.1	144.1	401	363.4	169.5	461	417.8	194.8	521	472.2	220.2	581	526.6	245.5
342	310.0	144.5	402	364.3	169.9	462	418.7	195.2	522	473.1	220.6	582	527.5	246.0
343	310.9	145.0	403	365.2	170.3	463	419.6	195.7	523	474.0	221.0	583	528.4	246.4
344	311.8	145.4	404	366.1	170.7	464	420.5	196.1	524	474.9	221.5	584	529.3	246.8
345	312.7	145.8	405	367.1	171.2	465	421.4	196.5	525	475.8	221.9	585	530.2	247.2
346	313.6	146.2	406	368.0	171.6	466	422.3	196.9	526	476.7	222.3	586	531.1	247.7
347	314.5	146.6	407	368.9	172.0	467	423.2	197.4	527	477.6	222.7	587	532.0	248.1
348	315.4	147.1	408	369.8	172.4	468	424.2	197.8	528	478.5	223.1	588	532.9	248.5
349	316.3	147.5	409	370.7	172.9	469	425.1	198.2	529	479.4	223.6	589	533.8	248.9
350	317.2	147.9	410	371.6	173.3	470	426.0	198.6	530	480.3	224.0	590	534.7	249.3
351	318.1	148.3	411	372.5	173.7	471	426.9	199.1	531	481.2	224.4	591	535.6	249.8
352	319.0	148.8	412	373.4	174.1	472	427.8	199.5	532	482.2	224.8	592	536.5	250.2
353	319.9	149.2	413	374.3	174.5	473	428.7	199.9	533	483.1	225.3	593	537.4	250.6
354	320.8	149.6	414	375.2	175.0	474	429.6	200.3	534	484.0	225.7	594	538.3	251.0
355	321.7	150.0	415	376.1	175.4	475	430.5	200.7	535	484.9	226.1	595	539.3	251.5
356	322.6	150.5	416	377.0	175.8	476	431.4	201.2	536	485.8	226.5	596	540.2	251.9
357	323.6	150.9	417	377.9	176.2	477	432.3	201.6	537	486.7	226.9	597	541.1	252.3
358	324.5	151.3	418	378.8	176.7	478	433.2	202.0	538	487.6	227.4	598	542.0	252.7
359	325.4	151.7	419	379.7	177.1	479	434.1	202.4	539	488.5	227.8	599	542.9	253.1
360	326.3	152.1	420	380.6	177.5	480	435.0	202.9	540	489.4	228.2	600	543.8	253.6
Hyp. Opp. Adj.			Hyp. Opp. Adj.			Hyp. Opp. Adj.			Hyp. Opp. Adj.			Hyp. Opp. Adj.		

Dist. Dep. D. Lat. / D Lon Dep   Dist. Dep. D. Lat. / D Lon Dep   Dist. Dep. D. Lat. / D Lon Dep   Dist. Dep. D. Lat. / D Lon Dep   Dist. Dep. D. Lat. / D Lon Dep

65° 295° | 065° / 245° | 115° **65°**

Table 3

TRAVERSE TABLE

26° 26°

D Lon Dist.	Dep D. Lat.	Dep.	D Lon Dist.	Dep D. Lat.	Dep.	D Lon Dist.	Dep D. Lat.	Dep.	D Lon Dist.	Dep D. Lat.	Dep.	D Lon Dist.	Dep D. Lat.	Dep.
Hyp.	Adj.	Opp.	Hyp.	Adj.	Opp.	Hyp.	Adj.	Cpp.	Hyp.	Adj.	Opp.	Hyp.	Adj.	Opp.
1	0.9	0.4	61	54.8	26.7	121	108.8	53.0	181	162.7	79.3	241	216.6	105.6
2	1.8	0.9	62	55.7	27.2	122	109.7	53.5	182	163.6	79.8	242	217.5	106.1
3	2.7	1.3	63	56.6	27.6	123	110.6	53.9	183	164.5	80.2	243	218.4	106.5
4	3.6	1.8	64	57.5	28.1	124	111.5	54.4	184	165.4	80.7	244	219.3	107.0
5	4.5	2.2	65	58.4	28.5	125	112.3	54.8	185	166.3	81.1	245	220.2	107.4
6	5.4	2.6	66	59.3	28.9	126	113.2	55.2	186	167.2	81.5	246	221.1	107.8
7	6.3	3.1	67	60.2	29.4	127	114.1	55.7	187	168.1	82.0	247	222.0	108.3
8	7.2	3.5	68	61.1	29.8	128	115.0	56.1	188	169.0	82.4	248	222.9	108.7
9	8.1	3.9	69	62.0	30.2	129	115.9	56.5	189	169.9	82.9	249	223.8	109.2
10	9.0	4.4	70	62.9	30.7	130	116.8	57.0	190	170.8	83.3	250	224.7	109.6
11	9.9	4.8	71	63.8	31.1	131	117.7	57.4	191	171.7	83.7	251	225.6	110.0
12	10.8	5.3	72	64.7	31.6	132	118.6	57.9	192	172.6	84.2	252	226.5	110.5
13	11.7	5.7	73	65.6	32.0	133	119.5	58.3	193	173.5	84.6	253	227.4	110.9
14	12.6	6.1	74	66.5	32.4	134	120.4	58.7	194	174.4	85.0	254	228.3	111.3
15	13.5	6.6	75	67.4	32.9	135	121.3	59.2	195	175.3	85.5	255	229.2	111.8
16	14.4	7.0	76	68.3	33.3	136	122.2	59.6	196	176.2	85.9	256	230.1	112.2
17	15.3	7.5	77	69.2	33.8	137	123.1	60.1	197	177.1	86.4	257	231.0	112.7
18	16.2	7.9	78	70.1	34.2	138	124.0	60.5	198	178.0	86.8	258	231.9	113.1
19	17.1	8.3	79	71.0	34.6	139	124.9	60.9	199	178.9	87.2	259	232.8	113.5
20	18.0	8.8	80	71.9	35.1	140	125.8	61.4	200	179.8	87.7	260	233.7	114.0
21	18.9	9.2	81	72.8	35.5	141	126.7	61.8	201	180.7	88.1	261	234.6	114.4
22	19.8	9.6	82	73.7	35.9	142	127.6	62.2	202	181.6	88.6	262	235.5	114.9
23	20.7	10.1	83	74.6	36.4	143	128.5	62.7	203	182.5	89.0	263	236.4	115.3
24	21.6	10.5	84	75.5	36.8	144	129.4	63.1	204	183.4	89.4	264	237.3	115.7
25	22.5	11.0	85	76.4	37.3	145	130.3	63.6	205	184.3	89.9	265	238.2	116.2
26	23.4	11.4	86	77.3	37.7	146	131.2	64.0	206	185.2	90.3	266	239.1	116.6
27	24.3	11.8	87	78.2	38.1	147	132.1	64.4	207	186.1	90.7	267	240.0	117.0
28	25.2	12.3	88	79.1	38.6	148	133.0	64.9	208	186.9	91.2	268	240.9	117.5
29	26.1	12.7	89	80.0	39.0	149	133.9	65.3	209	187.8	91.6	269	241.8	117.9
30	27.0	13.2	90	80.9	39.5	150	134.8	65.8	210	188.7	92.1	270	242.7	118.4
31	27.9	13.6	91	81.8	39.9	151	135.7	66.2	211	189.6	92.5	271	243.6	118.8
32	28.8	14.0	92	82.7	40.3	152	136.6	66.6	212	190.5	92.9	272	244.5	119.2
33	29.7	14.5	93	83.6	40.8	153	137.5	67.1	213	191.4	93.4	273	245.4	119.7
34	30.6	14.9	94	84.5	41.2	154	138.4	67.5	214	192.3	93.8	274	246.3	120.1
35	31.5	15.3	95	85.4	41.6	155	139.3	67.9	215	193.2	94.2	275	247.2	120.6
36	32.4	15.8	96	86.3	42.1	156	140.2	68.4	216	194.1	94.7	276	248.1	121.0
37	33.3	16.2	97	87.2	42.5	157	141.1	68.8	217	195.0	95.1	277	249.0	121.4
38	34.2	16.7	98	88.1	43.0	158	142.0	69.3	218	195.9	95.6	278	249.9	121.9
39	35.1	17.1	99	89.0	43.4	159	142.9	69.7	219	196.8	96.0	279	250.8	122.3
40	36.0	17.5	100	89.9	43.8	160	143.8	70.1	220	197.7	96.4	280	251.7	122.7
41	36.9	18.0	101	90.8	44.3	161	144.7	70.6	221	198.6	96.9	281	252.6	123.2
42	37.7	18.4	102	91.7	44.7	162	145.6	71.0	222	199.5	97.3	282	253.5	123.6
43	38.6	18.8	103	92.6	45.2	163	146.5	71.5	223	200.4	97.8	283	254.4	124.1
44	39.5	19.3	104	93.5	45.6	164	147.4	71.9	224	201.3	98.2	284	255.3	124.5
45	40.4	19.7	105	94.4	46.0	165	148.3	72.3	225	202.2	98.6	285	256.2	124.9
46	41.3	20.2	106	95.3	46.5	166	149.2	72.8	226	203.1	99.1	286	257.1	125.4
47	42.2	20.6	107	96.2	46.9	167	150.1	73.2	227	204.0	99.5	287	258.0	125.8
48	43.1	21.0	108	97.1	47.3	168	151.0	73.6	228	204.9	99.9	288	258.9	126.3
49	44.0	21.5	109	98.0	47.8	169	151.9	74.1	229	205.8	100.4	289	259.8	126.7
50	44.9	21.9	110	98.9	48.2	170	152.8	74.5	230	206.7	100.8	290	260.7	127.1
51	45.8	22.4	111	99.8	48.7	171	153.7	75.0	231	207.6	101.3	291	261.5	127.6
52	46.7	22.8	112	100.7	49.1	172	154.6	75.4	232	208.5	101.7	292	262.4	128.0
53	47.6	23.2	113	101.6	49.5	173	155.5	75.8	233	209.4	102.1	293	263.3	128.4
54	48.5	23.7	114	102.5	50.0	174	156.4	76.3	234	210.3	102.6	294	264.2	128.9
55	49.4	24.1	115	103.4	50.4	175	157.3	76.7	235	211.2	103.0	295	265.1	129.3
56	50.3	24.5	116	104.3	50.9	176	158.2	77.2	236	212.1	103.5	296	266.0	129.8
57	51.2	25.0	117	105.2	51.3	177	159.1	77.6	237	213.0	103.9	297	266.9	130.2
58	52.1	25.4	118	106.1	51.7	178	160.0	78.0	238	213.9	104.3	298	267.8	130.6
59	53.0	25.9	119	107.0	52.2	179	160.9	78.5	239	214.8	104.8	299	268.7	131.1
60	53.9	26.3	120	107.9	52.6	180	161.8	78.9	240	215.7	105.2	300	269.6	131.5
Hyp.	Opp.	Adj.	Hyp.	Opp.	Adj.	Hyp.	Opp.	Adj.	Hyp.	Opp.	Adj.	Hyp.	Opp.	Adj.

Dist. D Lon	Dep.	D. Lat. Dep	Dist. D Lon	Dep.	D. Lat. Dep	Dist. D Lon	Dep.	D. Lat. Dep	Dist. D Lon	Dep.	D. Lat. Dep	Dist. D Lon	Dep.	D. Lat. Dep

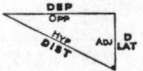

64° 64°

Table 3 **TRAVERSE TABLE**

26°

26°

D Lon	Dep		D Lon	Dep		D Lon	Dep		D Lon	Dep		D Lon	Dep	
Dist.	D. Lat.	Dep.	Dist.	D. Lat.	Dep.	Dist.	D. Lat.	Dep.	Dist.	D. Lat.	Dep.	Dist.	D. Lat.	Dep.
Hyp.	*Adj.*	*Opp.*	*Hyp.*	*Adj.*	*Opp.*	*Hyp.*	*Adj.*	*Opp.*	*Hyp.*	*Adj.*	*Opp.*	*Hyp.*	*Adj.*	*Opp.*
301	270.5	131.9	361	324.5	158.3	421	378.4	184.6	481	432.3	210.9	541	486.2	237.2
302	271.4	132.4	362	325.4	158.7	422	379.3	185.0	482	433.2	211.3	542	487.1	237.6
303	272.3	132.8	363	326.3	159.1	423	380.2	185.4	483	434.1	211.7	543	488.0	238.0
304	273.2	133.3	364	327.2	159.6	424	381.1	185.9	484	435.0	212.2	544	488.9	238.5
305	274.1	133.7	365	328.1	160.0	425	382.0	186.3	485	435.9	212.6	545	489.8	238.9
306	275.0	134.1	366	329.0	160.4	426	382.9	186.7	486	436.8	213.0	546	490.7	239.4
307	275.9	134.6	367	329.9	160.9	427	383.8	187.2	487	437.7	213.5	547	491.6	239.8
308	276.8	135.0	368	330.8	161.3	428	384.7	187.6	488	438.6	213.9	548	492.5	240.2
309	277.7	135.5	369	331.7	161.8	429	385.6	188.1	489	439.5	214.4	549	493.4	240.7
310	278.5	135.9	370	332.6	162.2	430	386.5	188.5	490	440.4	214.8	550	494.3	241.1
311	279.5	136.3	371	333.5	162.6	431	387.4	188.9	491	441.3	215.2	551	495.2	241.5
312	280.4	136.8	372	334.4	163.1	432	388.3	189.4	492	442.2	215.7	552	496.1	242.0
313	281.3	137.2	373	335.3	163.5	433	389.2	189.8	493	443.1	216.1	553	497.0	242.4
314	282.2	137.6	374	336.1	164.0	434	390.1	190.3	494	444.0	216.6	554	497.9	242.9
315	283.1	138.1	375	337.0	164.4	435	391.0	190.7	495	444.9	217.0	555	498.8	243.3
316	284.0	138.5	376	337.9	164.8	436	391.9	191.1	496	445.8	217.4	556	499.7	243.7
317	284.9	139.0	377	338.8	165.3	437	392.8	191.6	497	446.7	217.9	557	500.6	244.2
318	285.8	139.4	378	339.7	165.7	438	393.7	192.0	498	447.6	218.3	558	501.5	244.6
319	286.7	139.8	379	340.6	166.1	439	394.6	192.4	499	448.5	218.7	559	502.4	245.0
320	287.6	140.3	380	341.5	166.6	440	395.5	192.9	500	449.4	219.2	560	503.3	245.5
321	288.5	140.7	381	342.4	167.0	441	396.4	193.3	501	450.3	219.6	561	504.2	245.9
322	289.4	141.2	382	343.3	167.5	442	397.3	193.8	502	451.2	220.1	562	505.1	246.4
323	290.3	141.6	383	344.2	167.9	443	398.2	194.2	503	452.1	220.5	563	506.0	246.8
324	291.2	142.0	384	345.1	168.3	444	399.1	194.6	504	453.0	220.9	564	506.9	247.2
325	292.1	142.5	385	346.0	168.8	445	400.0	195.1	505	453.9	221.4	565	507.8	247.7
326	293.0	142.9	386	346.9	169.2	446	400.9	195.5	506	454.8	221.8	566	508.7	248.1
327	293.9	143.3	387	347.8	169.6	447	401.8	196.0	507	455.7	222.3	567	509.6	248.6
328	294.8	143.8	388	348.7	170.1	448	402.7	196.4	508	456.6	222.7	568	510.5	249.0
329	295.7	144.2	389	349.6	170.5	449	403.6	196.8	509	457.5	223.1	569	511.4	249.4
330	296.6	144.7	390	350.5	171.0	450	404.5	197.3	510	458.4	223.6	570	512.3	249.9
331	297.5	145.1	391	351.4	171.4	451	405.4	197.7	511	459.3	224.0	571	513.2	250.3
332	298.4	145.5	392	352.3	171.8	452	406.3	198.1	512	460.2	224.4	572	514.1	250.7
333	299.3	146.0	393	353.2	172.3	453	407.2	198.6	513	461.1	224.9	573	515.0	251.2
334	300.2	146.4	394	354.1	172.7	454	408.1	199.0	514	462.0	225.3	574	515.9	251.6
335	301.1	146.9	395	355.0	173.2	455	409.0	199.5	515	462.9	225.8	575	516.8	252.1
336	302.0	147.3	396	355.9	173.6	456	409.9	199.9	516	463.8	226.2	576	517.7	252.5
337	302.9	147.7	397	356.8	174.0	457	410.7	200.3	517	464.7	226.6	577	518.6	252.9
338	303.8	148.2	398	357.7	174.5	458	411.6	200.8	518	465.6	227.1	578	519.5	253.4
339	304.7	148.6	399	358.6	174.9	459	412.5	201.2	519	466.5	227.5	579	520.4	253.8
340	305.6	149.0	400	359.5	175.3	460	413.4	201.7	520	467.4	228.0	580	521.3	254.3
341	306.5	149.5	401	360.4	175.8	461	414.3	202.1	521	468.3	228.4	581	522.2	254.7
342	307.4	149.9	402	361.3	176.2	462	415.2	202.5	522	469.2	228.8	582	523.1	255.1
343	308.3	150.4	403	362.2	176.7	463	416.1	203.0	523	470.1	229.3	583	524.0	255.6
344	309.2	150.8	404	363.1	177.1	464	417.0	203.4	524	471.0	229.7	584	524.9	256.0
345	310.1	151.2	405	364.0	177.5	465	417.9	203.8	525	471.9	230.1	585	525.8	256.4
346	311.0	151.7	406	364.9	178.0	466	418.8	204.3	526	472.8	230.6	586	526.7	256.9
347	311.9	152.1	407	365.8	178.4	467	419.7	204.7	527	473.7	231.0	587	527.6	257.3
348	312.8	152.6	408	366.7	178.9	468	420.6	205.2	528	474.6	231.5	588	528.5	257.8
349	313.7	153.0	409	367.6	179.3	469	421.5	205.6	529	475.5	231.9	589	529.4	258.2
350	314.6	153.4	410	368.5	179.7	470	422.4	206.0	530	476.4	232.3	590	530.3	258.6
351	315.5	153.9	411	369.4	180.2	471	423.3	206.5	531	477.3	232.8	591	531.2	259.1
352	316.4	154.3	412	370.3	180.6	472	424.2	206.9	532	478.2	233.2	592	532.1	259.5
353	317.3	154.7	413	371.2	181.0	473	425.1	207.3	533	479.1	233.7	593	533.0	260.0
354	318.2	155.2	414	372.1	181.5	474	426.0	207.8	534	480.0	234.1	594	533.9	260.4
355	319.1	155.6	415	373.0	181.9	475	426.9	208.2	535	480.9	234.5	595	534.8	260.8
356	320.0	156.1	416	373.9	182.4	476	427.8	208.7	536	481.8	235.0	596	535.7	261.3
357	320.9	156.5	417	374.8	182.8	477	428.7	209.1	537	482.7	235.4	597	536.6	261.7
358	321.8	156.9	418	375.7	183.2	478	429.6	209.5	538	483.6	235.8	598	537.5	262.1
359	322.7	157.4	419	376.6	183.7	479	430.5	210.0	539	484.4	236.3	599	538.4	262.6
360	323.6	157.8	420	377.5	184.1	480	431.4	210.4	540	485.3	236.7	600	539.3	263.0
Hyp.	*Opp.*	*Adj.*	*Hyp.*	*Opp.*	*Adj.*	*Hyp.*	*Opp.*	*Adj.*	*Hyp.*	*Opp.*	*Adj.*	*Hyp.*	*Opp.*	*Adj.*
Dist.	Dep.	D. Lat.	Dist.	Dep.	D. Lat.	Dist.	Dep.	D. Lat.	Dist.	Dep.	D. Lat.	Dist.	Dep.	D. Lat.
D Lon		Dep	D Lon		Dep	D Lon		Dep	D Lon		Dep	D Lon		Dep

64°

64°

Table 3

TRAVERSE TABLE

27°   27°

D Lon	Dep		D Lon	Dep		D Lon	Dep		D Lon	Dep		D Lon	Dep	
Dist.	**D. Lat.**	**Dep.**	**Dist.**	**D. Lat.**	**Dep.**	**Dist.**	**D. Lat.**	**Dep.**	**Dist.**	**D. Lat.**	**Dep.**	**Dist.**	**D. Lat.**	**Dep.**
Hyp.	*Adj.*	*Opp.*	*Hyp.*	*Adj.*	*Opp.*	*Hyp.*	*Adj.*	*Opp.*	*Hyp.*	*Adj.*	*Opp.*	*Hyp.*	*Adj.*	*Opp.*
1	0.9	0.5	61	54.4	27.7	121	107.8	54.9	181	161.3	82.2	241	214.7	109.4
2	1.8	0.9	62	55.2	28.1	122	108.7	55.4	182	162.2	82.6	242	215.6	109.9
3	2.7	1.4	63	56.1	28.6	123	109.6	55.8	183	163.1	83.1	243	216.5	110.3
4	3.6	1.8	64	57.0	29.1	124	110.5	56.3	184	163.9	83.5	244	217.4	110.8
5	4.5	2.3	65	57.9	29.5	125	111.4	56.7	185	164.8	84.0	245	218.3	111.2
6	5.3	2.7	66	58.8	30.0	126	112.3	57.2	186	165.7	84.4	246	219.2	111.7
7	6.2	3.2	67	59.7	30.4	127	113.2	57.7	187	166.6	84.9	247	220.1	112.1
8	7.1	3.6	68	60.6	30.9	128	114.0	58.1	188	167.5	85.4	248	221.0	112.6
9	8.0	4.1	69	61.5	31.3	129	114.9	58.6	189	168.4	85.8	249	221.9	113.0
10	8.9	4.5	70	62.4	31.8	130	115.8	59.0	190	169.3	86.3	250	222.8	113.5
11	9.8	5.0	71	63.3	32.2	131	116.7	59.5	191	170.2	86.7	251	223.6	114.0
12	10.7	5.4	72	64.2	32.7	132	117.6	59.9	192	171.1	87.2	252	224.5	114.4
13	11.6	5.9	73	65.0	33.1	133	118.5	60.4	193	172.0	87.6	253	225.4	114.9
14	12.5	6.4	74	65.9	33.6	134	119.4	60.8	194	172.9	88.1	254	226.3	115.3
15	13.4	6.8	75	66.8	34.0	135	120.3	61.3	195	173.7	88.5	255	227.2	115.8
16	14.3	7.3	76	67.7	34.5	136	121.2	61.7	196	174.6	89.0	256	228.1	116.2
17	15.1	7.7	77	68.6	35.0	137	122.1	62.2	197	175.5	89.4	257	229.0	116.7
18	16.0	8.2	78	69.5	35.4	138	123.0	62.7	198	176.4	89.9	258	229.9	117.1
19	16.9	8.6	79	70.4	35.9	139	123.8	63.1	199	177.3	90.3	259	230.8	117.6
20	17.8	9.1	80	71.3	36.3	140	124.7	63.6	200	178.2	90.8	260	231.7	118.0
21	18.7	9.5	81	72.2	36.8	141	125.6	64.0	201	179.1	91.3	261	232.6	118.5
22	19.6	10.0	82	73.1	37.2	142	126.5	64.5	202	180.0	91.7	262	233.4	118.9
23	20.5	10.4	83	74.0	37.7	143	127.4	64.9	203	180.9	92.2	263	234.3	119.4
24	21.4	10.9	84	74.8	38.1	144	128.3	65.4	204	181.8	92.6	264	235.2	119.9
25	22.3	11.3	85	75.7	38.6	145	129.2	65.8	205	182.7	93.1	265	236.1	120.3
26	23.2	11.8	86	76.6	39.0	146	130.1	66.3	206	183.5	93.5	266	237.0	120.8
27	24.1	12.3	87	77.5	39.5	147	131.0	66.7	207	184.4	94.0	267	237.9	121.2
28	24.9	12.7	88	78.4	40.0	148	131.9	67.2	208	185.3	94.4	268	238.8	121.7
29	25.8	13.2	89	79.3	40.4	149	132.8	67.6	209	186.2	94.9	269	239.7	122.1
30	26.7	13.6	90	80.2	40.9	150	133.7	68.1	210	187.1	95.3	270	240.6	122.6
31	27.6	14.1	91	81.1	41.3	151	134.5	68.6	211	188.0	95.8	271	241.5	123.0
32	28.5	14.5	92	82.0	41.8	152	135.4	69.0	212	188.9	96.2	272	242.4	123.5
33	29.4	15.0	93	82.9	42.2	153	136.3	69.5	213	189.8	96.7	273	243.2	123.9
34	30.3	15.4	94	83.8	42.7	154	137.2	69.9	214	190.7	97.2	274	244.1	124.4
35	31.2	15.9	95	84.6	43.1	155	138.1	70.4	215	191.6	97.6	275	245.0	124.8
36	32.1	16.3	96	85.5	43.6	156	139.0	70.8	216	192.5	98.1	276	245.9	125.3
37	33.0	16.8	97	86.4	44.0	157	139.9	71.3	217	193.3	98.5	277	246.8	125.8
38	33.9	17.3	98	87.3	44.5	158	140.8	71.7	218	194.2	99.0	278	247.7	126.2
39	34.7	17.7	99	88.2	44.9	159	141.7	72.2	219	195.1	99.4	279	248.6	126.7
40	35.6	18.2	100	89.1	45.4	160	142.6	72.6	220	196.0	99.9	280	249.5	127.1
41	36.5	18.6	101	90.0	45.9	161	143.5	73.1	221	196.9	100.3	281	250.4	127.6
42	37.4	19.1	102	90.9	46.3	162	144.3	73.5	222	197.8	100.8	282	251.3	128.0
43	38.3	19.5	103	91.8	46.8	163	145.2	74.0	223	198.7	101.2	283	252.2	128.5
44	39.2	20.0	104	92.7	47.2	164	146.1	74.5	224	199.6	101.7	284	253.0	128.9
45	40.1	20.4	105	93.6	47.7	165	147.0	74.9	225	200.5	102.1	285	253.9	129.4
46	41.0	20.9	106	94.4	48.1	166	147.9	75.4	226	201.4	102.6	286	254.8	129.8
47	41.9	21.3	107	95.3	48.6	167	148.8	75.8	227	202.3	103.1	287	255.7	130.3
48	42.8	21.8	108	96.2	49.0	168	149.7	76.3	228	203.1	103.5	288	256.6	130.7
49	43.7	22.2	109	97.1	49.5	169	150.6	76.7	229	204.0	104.0	289	257.5	131.2
50	44.6	22.7	110	98.0	49.9	170	151.5	77.2	230	204.9	104.4	290	258.4	131.7
51	45.4	23.2	111	98.9	50.4	171	152.4	77.6	231	205.8	104.9	291	259.3	132.1
52	46.3	23.6	112	99.8	50.8	172	153.3	78.1	232	206.7	105.3	292	260.2	132.6
53	47.2	24.1	113	100.7	51.3	173	154.1	78.5	233	207.6	105.8	293	261.1	133.0
54	48.1	24.5	114	101.6	51.8	174	155.0	79.0	234	208.5	106.2	294	262.0	133.5
55	49.0	25.0	115	102.5	52.2	175	155.9	79.4	235	209.4	106.7	295	262.8	133.9
56	49.9	25.4	116	103.4	52.7	176	156.8	79.9	236	210.3	107.1	296	263.7	134.4
57	50.8	25.9	117	104.2	53.1	177	157.7	80.4	237	211.2	107.6	297	264.6	134.8
58	51.7	26.3	118	105.1	53.6	178	158.6	80.8	238	212.1	108.0	298	265.5	135.3
59	52.6	26.8	119	106.0	54.0	179	159.5	81.3	239	213.0	108.5	299	266.4	135.7
60	53.5	27.2	120	106.9	54.5	180	160.4	81.7	240	213.8	109.0	300	267.3	136.2
Hyp.	*Opp.*	*Adj.*	*Hyp.*	*Opp.*	*Adj.*	*Hyp.*	*Opp.*	*Adj.*	*Hyp.*	*Opp.*	*Adj.*	*Hyp.*	*Opp.*	*Adj.*
Dist.	**Dep.**	**D. Lat.**	**Dist.**	**Dep.**	**D. Lat.**	**Dist.**	**Dep.**	**D. Lat.**	**Dist.**	**Dep.**	**D. Lat.**	**Dist.**	**Dep.**	**D. Lat.**
D Lon		Dep	D Lon		Dep	D Lon		Dep	D Lon		Dep	D Lon		Dep

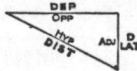

63°   63°

Table 3

27°

333° | 027°
207° | 153°

27°

D Lon	Dep		D Lon	Dep		D Lon	Dep		D Lon	Dep		D Lon	Dep	
Dist.	D. Lat.	Dep.	Dist.	D. Lat.	Dep.	Dist.	D. Lat.	Dep.	Dist.	D. Lat.	Dep.	Dist.	D. Lat.	Dep.
Hyp.	Adj.	Opp.	Hyp.	Adj.	Opp.	Hyp.	Adj.	Opp.	Hyp.	Adj.	Opp.	Hyp.	Adj.	Opp.
301	268.2	136.7	361	321.7	163.9	421	375.1	191.1	481	428.6	218.4	541	482.0	245.6
302	269.1	137.1	362	322.5	164.3	422	376.0	191.6	482	429.5	218.8	542	482.9	246.1
303	270.0	137.6	363	323.4	164.8	423	376.9	192.0	483	430.4	219.3	543	483.8	246.5
304	270.9	138.0	364	324.3	165.3	424	377.8	192.5	484	431.2	219.7	544	484.7	247.0
305	271.8	138.5	365	325.2	165.7	425	378.7	192.9	485	432.1	220.2	545	485.6	247.4
306	272.6	138.9	366	326.1	166.2	426	379.6	193.4	486	433.0	220.6	546	486.5	247.9
307	273.5	139.4	367	327.0	166.6	427	380.5	193.9	487	433.9	221.1	547	487.4	248.3
308	274.4	139.8	368	327.9	167.1	428	381.4	194.3	488	434.8	221.5	548	488.3	248.8
309	275.3	140.3	369	328.8	167.5	429	382.2	194.8	489	435.7	222.0	549	489.2	249.2
310	276.2	140.7	370	329.7	168.0	430	383.1	195.2	490	436.6	222.5	550	490.1	249.7
311	277.1	141.2	371	330.6	168.4	431	384.0	195.7	491	437.5	222.9	551	490.9	250.1
312	278.0	141.6	372	331.5	168.9	432	384.9	196.1	492	438.4	223.4	552	491.8	250.6
313	278.9	142.1	373	332.3	169.3	433	385.8	196.6	493	439.3	223.8	553	492.7	251.1
314	279.8	142.6	374	333.2	169.8	434	386.7	197.0	494	440.2	224.3	554	493.6	251.5
315	280.7	143.0	375	334.1	170.2	435	387.6	197.5	495	441.0	224.7	555	494.5	252.0
316	281.6	143.5	376	335.0	170.7	436	388.5	197.9	496	441.9	225.2	556	495.4	252.4
317	282.4	143.9	377	335.9	171.2	437	389.4	198.4	497	442.8	225.6	557	496.3	252.9
318	283.3	144.4	378	336.8	171.6	438	390.3	198.8	498	443.7	226.1	558	497.2	253.3
319	284.2	144.8	379	337.7	172.1	439	391.2	199.3	499	444.6	226.5	559	498.1	253.8
320	285.1	145.3	380	338.6	172.5	440	392.0	199.8	500	445.5	227.0	560	499.0	254.2
321	286.0	145.7	381	339.5	173.0	441	392.9	200.2	501	446.4	227.4	561	499.9	254.7
322	286.9	146.2	382	340.4	173.4	442	393.8	200.7	502	447.3	227.9	562	500.7	255.1
323	287.8	146.6	383	341.3	173.9	443	394.7	201.1	503	448.2	228.4	563	501.6	255.6
324	288.7	147.1	384	342.1	174.3	444	395.6	201.6	504	449.1	228.8	564	502.5	256.1
325	289.6	147.5	385	343.0	174.8	445	396.5	202.0	505	450.0	229.3	565	503.4	256.5
326	290.5	148.0	386	343.9	175.2	446	397.4	202.5	506	450.8	229.7	566	504.3	257.0
327	291.4	148.5	387	344.8	175.7	447	398.3	202.9	507	451.7	230.2	567	505.2	257.4
328	292.3	148.9	388	345.7	176.1	448	399.2	203.4	508	452.6	230.6	568	506.1	257.9
329	293.1	149.4	389	346.6	176.6	449	400.1	203.8	509	453.5	231.1	569	507.0	258.3
330	294.0	149.8	390	347.5	177.1	450	401.0	204.3	510	454.4	231.5	570	507.9	258.8
331	294.9	150.3	391	348.4	177.5	451	401.8	204.7	511	455.3	232.0	571	508.8	259.2
332	295.8	150.7	392	349.3	178.0	452	402.7	205.2	512	456.2	232.4	572	509.7	259.7
333	296.7	151.2	393	350.2	178.4	453	403.6	205.7	513	457.1	232.9	573	510.5	260.1
334	297.6	151.6	394	351.1	178.9	454	404.5	206.1	514	458.0	233.4	574	511.4	260.6
335	298.5	152.1	395	351.9	179.3	455	405.4	206.6	515	458.9	233.8	575	512.3	261.0
336	299.4	152.5	396	352.8	179.8	456	406.3	207.0	516	459.8	234.3	576	513.2	261.5
337	300.3	153.0	397	353.7	180.2	457	407.2	207.5	517	460.7	234.7	577	514.1	262.0
338	301.2	153.4	398	354.6	180.7	458	408.1	207.9	518	461.5	235.2	578	515.0	262.4
339	302.1	153.9	399	355.5	181.1	459	409.0	208.4	519	462.4	235.6	579	515.9	262.9
340	302.9	154.4	400	356.4	181.6	460	409.9	208.8	520	463.3	236.1	580	516.8	263.3
341	303.8	154.8	401	357.3	182.1	461	410.8	209.3	521	464.2	236.5	581	517.7	263.8
342	304.7	155.3	402	358.2	182.5	462	411.6	209.7	522	465.1	237.0	582	518.6	264.2
343	305.6	155.7	403	359.1	183.0	463	412.5	210.2	523	466.0	237.4	583	519.5	264.7
344	306.5	156.2	404	360.0	183.4	464	413.4	210.7	524	466.9	237.9	584	520.3	265.1
345	307.4	156.6	405	360.9	183.9	465	414.3	211.1	525	467.8	238.3	585	521.2	265.6
346	308.3	157.1	406	361.8	184.3	466	415.2	211.6	526	468.7	238.8	586	522.1	266.0
347	309.2	157.5	407	362.6	184.8	467	416.1	212.0	527	469.6	239.3	587	523.0	266.5
348	310.1	158.0	408	363.5	185.2	468	417.0	212.5	528	470.5	239.7	588	523.9	266.9
349	311.0	158.4	409	364.4	185.7	469	417.9	212.9	529	471.3	240.2	589	524.8	267.4
350	311.9	158.9	410	365.3	186.1	470	418.8	213.4	530	472.2	240.6	590	525.7	267.9
351	312.7	159.4	411	366.2	186.6	471	419.7	213.8	531	473.1	241.1	591	526.6	268.3
352	313.6	159.8	412	367.1	187.0	472	420.6	214.3	532	474.0	241.5	592	527.5	268.8
353	314.5	160.3	413	368.0	187.5	473	421.4	214.7	533	474.9	242.0	593	528.4	269.2
354	315.4	160.7	414	368.9	188.0	474	422.3	215.2	534	475.8	242.4	594	529.3	269.7
355	316.3	161.2	415	369.8	188.4	475	423.2	215.6	535	476.7	242.9	595	530.1	270.1
356	317.2	161.6	416	370.7	188.9	476	424.1	216.1	536	477.6	243.3	596	531.0	270.6
357	318.1	162.1	417	371.5	189.3	477	425.0	216.6	537	478.5	243.8	597	531.9	271.0
358	319.0	162.5	418	372.4	189.8	478	425.9	217.0	538	479.4	244.2	598	532.8	271.5
359	319.9	163.0	419	373.3	190.2	479	426.8	217.5	539	480.3	244.7	599	533.7	271.9
360	320.8	163.4	420	374.2	190.7	480	427.7	217.9	540	481.1	245.2	600	534.6	272.4
Hyp.	Opp.	Adj.	Hyp.	Opp.	Adj.	Hyp.	Opp.	Adj.	Hyp.	Opp.	Adj.	Hyp.	Opp.	Adj.
Dist.	Dep.	D. Lat.	Dist.	Dep.	D. Lat.	Dist.	Dep.	D. Lat.	Dist.	Dep.	D. Lat.	Dist.	Dep.	D. Lat.
D Lon		Dep	D Lon		Dep	D Lon		Dep	D Lon		Dep	D Lon		Dep

Table 3

TRAVERSE TABLE

28°   28°

D Lon Dist.	Dep D. Lat.	Dep.	D Lon Dist.	Dep D. Lat.	Dep.	D Lon Dist.	Dep D. Lat.	Dep.	D Lon Dist.	Dep D. Lat.	Dep.	D Lon Dist.	Dep D. Lat.	Dep.
Hyp.	Adj.	Opp.	Hyp.	Adj.	Opp.	Hyp.	Adj.	Opp.	Hyp.	Adj.	Opp.	Hyp.	Adj.	Opp.
1	0.9	0.5	61	53.9	28.6	121	106.8	56.8	181	159.8	85.0	241	212.8	113.1
2	1.8	0.9	62	54.7	29.1	122	107.7	57.3	182	160.7	85.4	242	213.7	113.6
3	2.6	1.4	63	55.6	29.6	123	108.6	57.7	183	161.6	85.9	243	214.6	114.1
4	3.5	1.9	64	56.5	30.0	124	109.5	58.2	184	162.5	86.4	244	215.4	114.6
5	4.4	2.3	65	57.4	30.5	125	110.4	58.7	185	163.3	86.9	245	216.3	115.0
6	5.3	2.8	66	58.3	31.0	126	111.3	59.2	186	164.2	87.3	246	217.2	115.5
7	6.2	3.3	67	59.2	31.5	127	112.1	59.6	187	165.1	87.8	247	218.1	116.0
8	7.1	3.8	68	60.0	31.9	128	113.0	60.1	188	166.0	88.3	248	219.0	116.4
9	7.9	4.2	69	60.9	32.4	129	113.9	60.6	189	166.9	88.7	249	219.9	116.9
10	8.8	4.7	70	61.8	32.9	130	114.8	61.0	190	167.8	89.2	250	220.7	117.4
11	9.7	5.2	71	62.7	33.3	131	115.7	61.5	191	168.6	89.7	251	221.6	117.8
12	10.6	5.6	72	63.6	33.8	132	116.5	62.0	192	169.5	90.1	252	222.5	118.3
13	11.5	6.1	73	64.5	34.3	133	117.4	62.4	193	170.4	90.6	253	223.4	118.8
14	12.4	6.6	74	65.3	34.7	134	118.3	62.9	194	171.3	91.1	254	224.3	119.2
15	13.2	7.0	75	66.2	35.2	135	119.2	63.4	195	172.2	91.5	255	225.2	119.7
16	14.1	7.5	76	67.1	35.7	136	120.1	63.8	196	173.1	92.0	256	226.0	120.2
17	15.0	8.0	77	68.0	36.1	137	121.0	64.3	197	173.9	92.5	257	226.9	120.7
18	15.9	8.5	78	68.9	36.6	138	121.8	64.8	198	174.8	93.0	258	227.8	121.1
19	16.8	8.9	79	69.8	37.1	139	122.7	65.3	199	175.7	93.4	259	228.7	121.6
20	17.7	9.4	80	70.6	37.6	140	123.6	65.7	200	176.6	93.9	260	229.6	122.1
21	18.5	9.9	81	71.5	38.0	141	124.5	66.2	201	177.5	94.4	261	230.4	122.5
22	19.4	10.3	82	72.4	38.5	142	125.4	66.7	202	178.4	94.8	262	231.3	123.0
23	20.3	10.8	83	73.3	39.0	143	126.3	67.1	203	179.2	95.3	263	232.2	123.5
24	21.2	11.3	84	74.2	39.4	144	127.1	67.6	204	180.1	95.8	264	233.1	123.9
25	22.1	11.7	85	75.1	39.9	145	128.0	68.1	205	181.0	96.2	265	234.0	124.4
26	23.0	12.2	86	75.9	40.4	146	128.9	68.5	206	181.9	96.7	266	234.9	124.9
27	23.8	12.7	87	76.8	40.8	147	129.8	69.0	207	182.8	97.2	267	235.7	125.3
28	24.7	13.1	88	77.7	41.3	148	130.7	69.5	208	183.7	97.7	268	236.6	125.8
29	25.6	13.6	89	78.6	41.8	149	131.6	70.0	209	184.5	98.1	269	237.5	126.3
30	26.5	14.1	90	79.5	42.3	150	132.4	70.4	210	185.4	98.6	270	238.4	126.8
31	27.4	14.6	91	80.3	42.7	151	133.3	70.9	211	186.3	99.1	271	239.3	127.2
32	28.3	15.0	92	81.2	43.2	152	134.2	71.4	212	187.2	99.5	272	240.2	127.7
33	29.1	15.5	93	82.1	43.7	153	135.1	71.8	213	188.1	100.0	273	241.0	128.2
34	30.0	16.0	94	83.0	44.1	154	136.0	72.3	214	189.0	100.5	274	241.9	128.6
35	30.9	16.4	95	83.9	44.6	155	136.9	72.8	215	189.8	100.9	275	242.8	129.1
36	31.8	16.9	96	84.8	45.1	156	137.7	73.2	216	190.7	101.4	276	243.7	129.6
37	32.7	17.4	97	85.6	45.5	157	138.6	73.7	217	191.6	101.9	277	244.6	130.0
38	33.6	17.8	98	86.5	46.0	158	139.5	74.2	218	192.5	102.3	278	245.5	130.5
39	34.4	18.3	99	87.4	46.5	159	140.4	74.6	219	193.4	102.8	279	246.3	131.0
40	35.3	18.8	100	88.3	46.9	160	141.3	75.1	220	194.2	103.3	280	247.2	131.5
41	36.2	19.2	101	89.2	47.4	161	142.2	75.6	221	195.1	103.8	281	248.1	131.9
42	37.1	19.7	102	90.1	47.9	162	143.0	76.1	222	196.0	104.2	282	249.0	132.4
43	38.0	20.2	103	90.9	48.4	163	143.9	76.5	223	196.9	104.7	283	249.9	132.9
44	38.8	20.7	104	91.8	48.8	164	144.8	77.0	224	197.8	105.2	284	250.8	133.3
45	39.7	21.1	105	92.7	49.3	165	145.7	77.5	225	198.7	105.6	285	251.6	133.8
46	40.6	21.6	106	93.6	49.8	166	146.6	77.9	226	199.5	106.1	286	252.5	134.3
47	41.5	22.1	107	94.5	50.2	167	147.5	78.4	227	200.4	106.6	287	253.4	134.7
48	42.4	22.5	108	95.4	50.7	168	148.3	78.9	228	201.3	107.0	288	254.3	135.2
49	43.3	23.0	109	96.2	51.2	169	149.2	79.3	229	202.2	107.5	289	255.2	135.7
50	44.1	23.5	110	97.1	51.6	170	150.1	79.8	230	203.1	108.0	290	256.1	136.1
51	45.0	23.9	111	98.0	52.1	171	151.0	80.3	231	204.0	108.4	291	256.9	136.6
52	45.9	24.4	112	98.9	52.6	172	151.9	80.7	232	204.8	108.9	292	257.8	137.1
53	46.8	24.9	113	99.8	53.1	173	152.7	81.2	233	205.7	109.4	293	258.7	137.6
54	47.7	25.4	114	100.7	53.5	174	153.6	81.7	234	206.6	109.9	294	259.6	138.0
55	48.6	25.8	115	101.5	54.0	175	154.5	82.2	235	207.5	110.3	295	260.5	138.5
56	49.4	26.3	116	102.4	54.5	176	155.4	82.6	236	208.4	110.8	296	261.3	139.0
57	50.3	26.8	117	103.3	54.9	177	156.3	83.1	237	209.3	111.3	297	262.2	139.4
58	51.2	27.2	118	104.2	55.4	178	157.2	83.6	238	210.1	111.7	298	263.1	139.9
59	52.1	27.7	119	105.1	55.9	179	158.0	84.0	239	211.0	112.2	299	264.0	140.4
60	53.0	28.2	120	106.0	56.3	180	158.9	84.5	240	211.9	112.7	300	264.9	140.8
Hyp.	Opp.	Adj.	Hyp.	Opp.	Adj.	Hyp.	Opp.	Adj.	Hyp.	Opp.	Adj.	Hyp.	Opp.	Adj.
Dist. D Lon	Dep.	D. Lat. Dep	Dist. D Lon	Dep.	D. Lat. Dep	Dist. D Lon	Dep.	D. Lat. Dep	Dist. D Lon	Dep.	D. Lat. Dep	Dist. D Lon	Dep.	D. Lat. Dep

62° 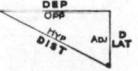 62°

Table 3

TRAVERSE TABLE

28°   28°

D Lon Dep / Dist. D. Lat. Dep.			D Lon Dep / Dist. D. Lat. Dep.			D Lon Dep / Dist. D. Lat. Dep.			D Lon Dep / Dist. D. Lat. Dep.			D Lon Dep / Dist. D. Lat. Dep.		
Hyp.	Adj.	Opp.	Hyp.	Adj.	Opp.	Hyp.	Adj.	Opp.	Hyp.	Adj.	Opp.	Hyp.	Adj.	Opp.
301	265.8	141.3	361	318.7	169.5	421	371.7	197.6	481	424.7	225.8	541	477.7	254.0
302	266.7	141.8	362	319.6	169.9	422	372.6	198.1	482	425.6	226.3	542	478.6	254.5
303	267.5	142.2	363	320.5	170.4	423	373.5	198.6	483	426.5	226.8	543	479.4	254.9
304	268.4	142.7	364	321.4	170.9	424	374.4	199.1	484	427.3	227.2	544	480.3	255.4
305	269.3	143.2	365	322.3	171.4	425	375.3	199.5	485	428.2	227.7	545	481.2	255.9
306	270.2	143.7	366	323.2	171.8	426	376.1	200.0	486	429.1	228.2	546	482.1	256.3
307	271.1	144.1	367	324.0	172.3	427	377.0	200.5	487	430.0	228.6	547	483.0	256.8
308	271.9	144.6	368	324.9	172.8	428	377.9	200.9	488	430.9	229.1	548	483.9	257.3
309	272.8	145.1	369	325.8	173.2	429	378.8	201.4	489	431.8	229.6	549	484.7	257.7
310	273.7	145.5	370	326.7	173.7	430	379.7	201.9	490	432.6	230.0	550	485.6	258.2
311	274.6	146.0	371	327.6	174.2	431	380.6	202.3	491	433.5	230.5	551	486.5	258.7
312	275.5	146.5	372	328.5	174.6	432	381.4	202.8	492	434.4	231.0	552	487.4	259.1
313	276.4	146.9	373	329.3	175.1	433	382.3	203.3	493	435.3	231.4	553	488.3	259.6
314	277.2	147.4	374	330.2	175.6	434	383.2	203.8	494	436.2	231.9	554	489.2	260.1
315	278.1	147.9	375	331.1	176.1	435	384.1	204.2	495	437.1	232.4	555	490.0	260.6
316	279.0	148.4	376	332.0	176.5	436	385.0	204.7	496	437.9	232.9	556	490.9	261.0
317	279.9	148.8	377	332.9	177.0	437	385.8	205.2	497	438.8	233.3	557	491.8	261.5
318	280.8	149.3	378	333.8	177.5	438	386.7	205.6	498	439.7	233.8	558	492.7	262.0
319	281.7	149.8	379	334.6	177.9	439	387.6	206.1	499	440.6	234.3	559	493.6	262.4
320	282.5	150.2	380	335.5	178.4	440	388.5	206.6	500	441.5	234.7	560	494.5	262.9
321	283.4	150.7	381	336.4	178.9	441	389.4	207.0	501	442.4	235.2	561	495.3	263.4
322	284.3	151.2	382	337.3	179.3	442	390.3	207.5	502	443.2	235.7	562	496.2	263.8
323	285.2	151.6	383	338.2	179.8	443	391.1	208.0	503	444.1	236.1	563	497.1	264.3
324	286.1	152.1	384	339.1	180.3	444	392.0	208.4	504	445.0	236.6	564	498.0	264.8
325	287.0	152.6	385	339.9	180.7	445	392.9	208.9	505	445.9	237.1	565	498.9	265.3
326	287.8	153.0	386	340.8	181.2	446	393.8	209.4	506	446.8	237.6	566	499.7	265.8
327	288.7	153.5	387	341.7	181.7	447	394.7	209.9	507	447.7	238.0	567	500.6	266.2
328	289.6	154.0	388	342.6	182.2	448	395.6	210.3	508	448.5	238.5	568	501.5	266.7
329	290.5	154.5	389	343.5	182.6	449	396.4	210.8	509	449.4	239.0	569	502.4	267.1
330	291.4	154.9	390	344.3	183.1	450	397.3	211.3	510	450.3	239.4	570	503.3	267.6
331	292.3	155.4	391	345.2	183.6	451	398.2	211.7	511	451.2	239.9	571	504.2	268.1
332	293.1	155.9	392	346.1	184.0	452	399.1	212.2	512	452.1	240.4	572	505.0	268.5
333	294.0	156.3	393	347.0	184.5	453	400.0	212.7	513	453.0	240.8	573	505.9	269.0
334	294.9	156.8	394	347.9	185.0	454	400.9	213.1	514	453.8	241.3	574	506.8	269.5
335	295.8	157.3	395	348.8	185.4	455	401.7	213.6	515	454.7	241.8	575	507.7	269.9
336	296.7	157.7	396	349.6	185.9	456	402.6	214.1	516	455.6	242.2	576	508.6	270.4
337	297.6	158.2	397	350.5	186.4	457	403.5	214.5	517	456.5	242.7	577	509.5	270.9
338	298.4	158.7	398	351.4	186.8	458	404.4	215.0	518	457.4	243.2	578	510.3	271.4
339	299.3	159.2	399	352.3	187.3	459	405.3	215.5	519	458.2	243.7	579	511.2	271.8
340	300.2	159.6	400	353.2	187.8	460	406.2	216.0	520	459.1	244.1	580	512.1	272.3
341	301.1	160.1	401	354.1	188.3	461	407.0	216.4	521	460.0	244.6	581	513.0	272.8
342	302.0	160.6	402	354.9	188.7	462	407.9	216.9	522	460.9	245.1	582	513.9	273.2
343	302.9	161.0	403	355.8	189.2	463	408.8	217.4	523	461.8	245.5	583	514.8	273.7
344	303.7	161.5	404	356.7	189.7	464	409.7	217.8	524	462.7	246.0	584	515.6	274.2
345	304.6	162.0	405	357.6	190.1	465	410.6	218.3	525	463.5	246.5	585	516.5	274.6
346	305.5	162.4	406	358.5	190.6	466	411.5	218.8	526	464.4	246.9	586	517.4	275.1
347	306.4	162.9	407	359.4	191.1	467	412.3	219.2	527	465.3	247.4	587	518.3	275.6
348	307.3	163.4	408	360.2	191.5	468	413.2	219.7	528	466.2	247.9	588	519.2	276.0
349	308.1	163.8	409	361.1	192.0	469	414.1	220.2	529	467.1	248.4	589	520.1	276.5
350	309.0	164.3	410	362.0	192.5	470	415.0	220.7	530	468.0	248.8	590	520.9	277.0
351	309.9	164.8	411	362.9	193.0	471	415.9	221.1	531	468.8	249.3	591	521.8	277.5
352	310.8	165.3	412	363.8	193.4	472	416.8	221.6	532	469.7	249.8	592	522.7	277.9
353	311.7	165.7	413	364.7	193.9	473	417.6	222.1	533	470.6	250.2	593	523.6	278.4
354	312.6	166.2	414	365.5	194.4	474	418.5	222.5	534	471.5	250.7	594	524.5	278.9
355	313.4	166.7	415	366.4	194.8	475	419.4	223.0	535	472.4	251.2	595	525.4	279.3
356	314.3	167.1	416	367.3	195.3	476	420.3	223.5	536	473.3	251.6	596	526.2	279.8
357	315.2	167.6	417	368.2	195.8	477	421.2	223.9	537	474.1	252.1	597	527.1	280.3
358	316.1	168.1	418	369.1	196.2	478	422.0	224.4	538	475.0	252.6	598	528.0	280.7
359	317.0	168.5	419	370.0	196.7	479	422.9	224.9	539	475.9	253.0	599	528.9	281.2
360	317.9	169.0	420	370.8	197.2	480	423.8	225.3	540	476.8	253.5	600	529.8	281.7
Hyp.	Opp.	Adj.	Hyp.	Opp.	Adj.	Hyp.	Opp.	Adj.	Hyp.	Opp.	Adj.	Hyp.	Opp.	Adj.
Dist.	Dep.	D. Lat.	Dist.	Dep.	D. Lat.	Dist.	Dep.	D. Lat.	Dist.	Dep.	D. Lat.	Dist.	Dep.	D. Lat.
D Lon		Dep	D Lon		Dep	D Lon		Dep	D Lon		Dep	D Lon		Dep

62°   62°

Table 3

TRAVERSE TABLE

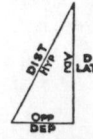

29° 29°

D Lon Dist.	Dep D. Lat.	Dep.	D Lon Dist.	Dep D. Lat.	Dep.	D Lon Dist.	Dep D. Lat.	Dep.	D Lon Dist.	Dep D. Lat.	Dep.	D Lon Dist.	Dep D. Lat.	Dep.
Hyp.	Adj.	Opp.	Hyp.	Adj.	Opp.	Hyp.	Adj.	Opp.	Hyp.	Adj.	Opp.	Hyp.	Adj.	Opp.
1	0.9	0.5	61	53.4	29.6	121	105.8	58.7	181	158.3	87.8	241	210.8	116.8
2	1.7	1.0	62	54.2	30.1	122	106.7	59.1	182	159.2	88.2	242	211.7	117.3
3	2.6	1.5	63	55.1	30.5	123	107.6	59.6	183	160.1	88.7	243	212.5	117.8
4	3.5	1.9	64	56.0	31.0	124	108.5	60.1	184	160.9	89.2	244	213.4	118.3
5	4.4	2.4	65	56.9	31.5	125	109.3	60.6	185	161.8	89.7	245	214.3	118.8
6	5.2	2.9	66	57.7	32.0	126	110.2	61.1	186	162.7	90.2	246	215.2	119.3
7	6.1	3.4	67	58.6	32.5	127	111.1	61.6	187	163.6	90.7	247	216.0	119.7
8	7.0	3.9	68	59.5	33.0	128	112.0	62.1	188	164.4	91.1	248	216.9	120.2
9	7.9	4.4	69	60.3	33.5	129	112.8	62.5	189	165.3	91.6	249	217.8	120.7
10	8.7	4.8	70	61.2	33.9	130	113.7	63.0	190	166.2	92.1	250	218.7	121.2
11	9.6	5.3	71	62.1	34.4	131	114.6	63.5	191	167.1	92.6	251	219.5	121.7
12	10.5	5.8	72	63.0	34.9	132	115.4	64.0	192	167.9	93.1	252	220.4	122.2
13	11.4	6.3	73	63.8	35.4	133	116.3	64.5	193	168.8	93.6	253	221.3	122.7
14	12.2	6.8	74	64.7	35.9	134	117.2	65.0	194	169.7	94.1	254	222.2	123.1
15	13.1	7.3	75	65.6	36.4	135	118.1	65.4	195	170.6	94.5	255	223.0	123.6
16	14.0	7.8	76	66.5	36.8	136	118.9	65.9	196	171.4	95.0	256	223.9	124.1
17	14.9	8.2	77	67.3	37.3	137	119.8	66.4	197	172.3	95.5	257	224.8	124.6
18	15.7	8.7	78	68.2	37.8	138	120.7	66.9	198	173.2	96.0	258	225.7	125.1
19	16.6	9.2	79	69.1	38.3	139	121.6	67.4	199	174.0	96.5	259	226.5	125.6
20	17.5	9.7	80	70.0	38.8	140	122.4	67.9	200	174.9	97.0	260	227.4	126.1
21	18.4	10.2	81	70.8	39.3	141	123.3	68.4	201	175.8	97.4	261	228.3	126.5
22	19.2	10.7	82	71.7	39.8	142	124.2	68.8	202	176.7	97.9	262	229.2	127.0
23	20.1	11.2	83	72.6	40.2	143	125.1	69.3	203	177.5	98.4	263	230.0	127.5
24	21.0	11.6	84	73.5	40.7	144	125.9	69.8	204	178.4	98.9	264	230.9	128.0
25	21.9	12.1	85	74.3	41.2	145	126.8	70.3	205	179.3	99.4	265	231.8	128.5
26	22.7	12.6	86	75.2	41.7	146	127.7	70.8	206	180.2	99.9	266	232.6	129.0
27	23.6	13.1	87	76.1	42.2	147	128.6	71.3	207	181.0	100.4	267	233.5	129.4
28	24.5	13.6	88	77.0	42.7	148	129.4	71.8	208	181.9	100.8	268	234.4	129.9
29	25.4	14.1	89	77.8	43.1	149	130.3	72.2	209	182.8	101.3	269	235.3	130.4
30	26.2	14.5	90	78.7	43.6	150	131.2	72.7	210	183.7	101.8	270	236.1	130.9
31	27.1	15.0	91	79.6	44.1	151	132.1	73.2	211	184.5	102.3	271	237.0	131.4
32	28.0	15.5	92	80.5	44.6	152	132.9	73.7	212	185.4	102.8	272	237.9	131.9
33	28.9	16.0	93	81.3	45.1	153	133.8	74.2	213	186.3	103.3	273	238.8	132.4
34	29.7	16.5	94	82.2	45.6	154	134.7	74.7	214	187.2	103.7	274	239.6	132.8
35	30.6	17.0	95	83.1	46.1	155	135.6	75.1	215	188.0	104.2	275	240.5	133.3
36	31.5	17.5	96	84.0	46.5	156	136.4	75.6	216	188.9	104.7	276	241.4	133.8
37	32.4	17.9	97	84.8	47.0	157	137.3	76.1	217	189.8	105.2	277	242.3	134.3
38	33.2	18.4	98	85.7	47.5	158	138.2	76.6	218	190.7	105.7	278	243.1	134.8
39	34.1	18.9	99	86.6	48.0	159	139.1	77.1	219	191.5	106.2	279	244.0	135.3
40	35.0	19.4	100	87.5	48.5	160	139.9	77.6	220	192.4	106.7	280	244.9	135.7
41	35.9	19.9	101	88.3	49.0	161	140.8	78.1	221	193.3	107.1	281	245.8	136.2
42	36.7	20.4	102	89.2	49.5	162	141.7	78.5	222	194.2	107.6	282	246.6	136.7
43	37.6	20.8	103	90.1	49.9	163	142.6	79.0	223	195.0	108.1	283	247.5	137.2
44	38.5	21.3	104	91.0	50.4	164	143.4	79.5	224	195.9	108.6	284	248.4	137.7
45	39.4	21.8	105	91.8	50.9	165	144.3	80.0	225	196.8	109.1	285	249.3	138.2
46	40.2	22.3	106	92.7	51.4	166	145.2	80.5	226	197.7	109.6	286	250.1	138.7
47	41.1	22.8	107	93.6	51.9	167	146.1	81.0	227	198.5	110.1	287	251.0	139.1
48	42.0	23.3	108	94.5	52.4	168	146.9	81.4	228	199.4	110.5	288	251.9	139.6
49	42.9	23.8	109	95.3	52.8	169	147.8	81.9	229	200.3	111.0	289	252.8	140.1
50	43.7	24.2	110	96.2	53.3	170	148.7	82.4	230	201.2	111.5	290	253.6	140.6
51	44.6	24.7	111	97.1	53.8	171	149.6	82.9	231	202.0	112.0	291	254.5	141.1
52	45.5	25.2	112	98.0	54.3	172	150.4	83.4	232	202.9	112.5	292	255.4	141.6
53	46.4	25.7	113	98.8	54.8	173	151.3	83.9	233	203.8	113.0	293	256.3	142.0
54	47.2	26.2	114	99.7	55.3	174	152.2	84.4	234	204.7	113.4	294	257.1	142.5
55	48.1	26.7	115	100.6	55.8	175	153.1	84.8	235	205.5	113.9	295	258.0	143.0
56	49.0	27.1	116	101.5	56.2	176	153.9	85.3	236	206.4	114.4	296	258.9	143.5
57	49.9	27.6	117	102.3	56.7	177	154.8	85.8	237	207.3	114.9	297	259.8	144.0
58	50.7	28.1	118	103.2	57.2	178	155.7	86.3	238	208.2	115.4	298	260.6	144.5
59	51.6	28.6	119	104.1	57.7	179	156.6	86.8	239	209.0	115.9	299	261.5	145.0
60	52.5	29.1	120	105.0	58.2	180	157.4	87.3	240	209.9	116.4	300	262.4	145.4
Hyp.	Opp.	Adj.	Hyp.	Opp.	Adj.	Hyp.	Opp.	Adj.	Hyp.	Opp.	Adj.	Hyp.	Opp.	Adj.
Dist. D Lon	Dep.	D. Lat. Dep	Dist. D Lon	Dep.	D. Lat. Dep	Dist. D Lon	Dep.	D. Lat. Dep	Dist. D Lon	Dep.	D. Lat. Dep	Dist. D Lon	Dep.	D. Lat. Dep

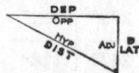

61° 61°

Table 3

TRAVERSE TABLE

D Lon Dep Dist. D. Lat. Dep.			D Lon Dep Dist. D. Lat. Dep.			D Lon Dep Dist. D. Lat. Dep.			D Lon Dep Dist. D. Lat. Dep.			D Lon Dep Dist. D. Lat. Dep.		
Hyp.	Adj.	Opp.	Hyp.	Adj.	Opp.	Hyp.	Adj.	Opp.	Hyp.	Adj.	Opp.	Hyp.	Adj.	Opp.
301	263.3	145.9	361	315.7	175.0	421	368.2	204.1	481	420.7	233.2	541	473.2	262.3
302	264.1	146.4	362	316.6	175.5	422	369.1	204.6	482	421.6	233.7	542	474.0	262.8
303	265.0	146.9	363	317.5	176.0	423	370.0	205.1	483	422.4	234.2	543	474.9	263.3
304	265.9	147.4	364	318.4	176.5	424	370.8	205.6	484	423.3	234.6	544	475.8	263.7
305	266.8	147.9	365	319.2	177.0	425	371.7	206.0	485	424.2	235.1	545	476.7	264.2
306	267.6	148.4	366	320.1	177.4	426	372.6	206.5	486	425.1	235.6	546	477.5	264.7
307	268.5	148.8	367	321.0	177.9	427	373.5	207.0	487	425.9	236.1	547	478.4	265.2
308	269.4	149.3	368	321.9	178.4	428	374.3	207.5	488	426.8	236.6	548	479.3	265.7
309	270.3	149.8	369	322.7	178.9	429	375.2	208.0	489	427.7	237.1	549	480.2	266.2
310	271.1	150.3	370	323.6	179.4	430	376.1	208.5	490	428.6	237.6	550	481.0	266.6
311	272.0	150.8	371	324.5	179.9	431	377.0	209.0	491	429.4	238.0	551	481.9	267.1
312	272.9	151.3	372	325.4	180.3	432	377.8	209.4	492	430.3	238.5	552	482.8	267.6
313	273.8	151.7	373	326.2	180.8	433	378.7	209.9	493	431.2	239.0	553	483.7	268.1
314	274.6	152.2	374	327.1	181.3	434	379.6	210.4	494	432.1	239.5	554	484.5	268.6
315	275.5	152.7	375	328.0	181.8	435	380.5	210.9	495	432.9	240.0	555	485.4	269.1
316	276.4	153.2	376	328.9	182.3	436	381.3	211.4	496	433.8	240.5	556	486.3	269.6
317	277.3	153.7	377	329.7	182.8	437	382.2	211.9	497	434.7	241.0	557	487.2	270.0
318	278.1	154.2	378	330.6	183.3	438	383.1	212.3	498	435.6	241.4	558	488.0	270.5
319	279.0	154.7	379	331.5	183.7	439	384.0	212.8	499	436.4	241.9	559	488.9	271.0
320	279.9	155.1	380	332.4	184.2	440	384.8	213.3	500	437.3	242.4	560	489.8	271.5
321	280.8	155.6	381	333.2	184.7	441	385.7	213.8	501	438.2	242.9	561	490.7	272.0
322	281.6	156.1	382	334.1	185.2	442	386.6	214.3	502	439.1	243.4	562	491.5	272.5
323	282.5	156.6	383	335.0	185.7	443	387.5	214.8	503	439.9	243.9	563	492.4	273.0
324	283.4	157.1	384	335.9	186.2	444	388.3	215.3	504	440.8	244.3	564	493.3	273.4
325	284.3	157.6	385	336.7	186.7	445	389.2	215.7	505	441.7	244.8	565	494.2	273.9
326	285.1	158.0	386	337.6	187.1	446	390.1	216.2	506	442.6	245.3	566	495.0	274.4
327	286.0	158.5	387	338.5	187.6	447	391.0	216.7	507	443.4	245.8	567	495.9	274.9
328	286.9	159.0	388	339.4	188.1	448	391.8	217.2	508	444.3	246.3	568	496.8	275.4
329	287.7	159.5	389	340.2	188.6	449	392.7	217.7	509	445.2	246.8	569	497.7	275.9
330	288.6	160.0	390	341.1	189.1	450	393.6	218.2	510	446.1	247.3	570	498.5	276.3
331	289.5	160.5	391	342.0	189.6	451	394.5	218.6	511	446.9	247.7	571	499.4	276.8
332	290.4	161.0	392	342.9	190.0	452	395.3	219.1	512	447.8	248.2	572	500.3	277.3
333	291.2	161.4	393	343.7	190.5	453	396.2	219.6	513	448.7	248.7	573	501.2	277.8
334	292.1	161.9	394	344.6	191.0	454	397.1	220.1	514	449.6	249.2	574	502.0	278.3
335	293.0	162.4	395	345.5	191.5	455	398.0	220.6	515	450.4	249.7	575	502.9	278.8
336	293.9	162.9	396	346.3	192.0	456	398.8	221.1	516	451.3	250.2	576	503.8	279.3
337	294.7	163.4	397	347.2	192.5	457	399.7	221.6	517	452.2	250.6	577	504.7	279.7
338	295.6	163.9	398	348.1	193.0	458	400.6	222.0	518	453.1	251.1	578	505.5	280.2
339	296.5	164.4	399	349.0	193.4	459	401.5	222.5	519	453.9	251.6	579	506.4	280.7
340	297.4	164.8	400	349.8	193.9	460	402.3	223.0	520	454.8	252.1	580	507.3	281.2
341	298.2	165.3	401	350.7	194.4	461	403.2	223.5	521	455.7	252.6	581	508.2	281.7
342	299.1	165.8	402	351.6	194.9	462	404.1	224.0	522	456.6	253.1	582	509.0	282.2
343	300.0	166.3	403	352.5	195.4	463	404.9	224.5	523	457.4	253.6	583	509.9	282.6
344	300.9	166.8	404	353.3	195.9	464	405.8	225.0	524	458.3	254.0	584	510.8	283.1
345	301.7	167.3	405	354.2	196.3	465	406.7	225.4	525	459.2	254.5	585	511.7	283.6
346	302.6	167.7	406	355.1	196.8	466	407.6	225.9	526	460.0	255.0	586	512.5	284.1
347	303.5	168.2	407	356.0	197.3	467	408.4	226.4	527	460.9	255.5	587	513.4	284.6
348	304.4	168.7	408	356.8	197.8	468	409.3	226.9	528	461.8	256.0	588	514.3	285.1
349	305.2	169.2	409	357.7	198.3	469	410.2	227.4	529	462.7	256.5	589	515.2	285.6
350	306.1	169.7	410	358.6	198.8	470	411.1	227.9	530	463.5	256.9	590	516.0	286.0
351	307.0	170.2	411	359.5	199.3	471	411.9	228.3	531	464.4	257.4	591	516.9	286.5
352	307.9	170.7	412	360.3	199.7	472	412.8	228.8	532	465.3	257.9	592	517.8	287.0
353	308.7	171.1	413	361.2	200.2	473	413.7	229.3	533	466.2	258.4	593	518.6	287.5
354	309.6	171.6	414	362.1	200.7	474	414.6	229.8	534	467.0	258.9	594	519.5	288.0
355	310.5	172.1	415	363.0	201.2	475	415.4	230.3	535	467.9	259.4	595	520.4	288.5
356	311.4	172.6	416	363.8	201.7	476	416.3	230.8	536	468.8	259.9	596	521.3	288.9
357	312.2	173.1	417	364.7	202.2	477	417.2	231.3	537	469.7	260.3	597	522.1	289.4
358	313.1	173.6	418	365.6	202.7	478	418.1	231.7	538	470.5	260.8	598	523.0	289.9
359	314.0	174.0	419	366.5	203.1	479	418.9	232.2	539	471.4	261.3	599	523.9	290.4
360	314.9	174.5	420	367.3	203.6	480	419.8	232.7	540	472.3	261.8	600	524.8	290.9
Hyp.	Opp.	Adj.	Hyp.	Opp.	Adj.	Hyp.	Opp.	Adj.	Hyp.	Opp.	Adj.	Hyp.	Opp.	Adj.
Dist. D Lon	Dep.	D. Lat. Dep	Dist. D Lon	Dep.	D. Lat. Dep	Dist. D Lon	Dep.	D. Lat. Dep	Dist. D Lon	Dep.	D. Lat. Dep	Dist. D Lon	Dep.	D. Lat. Dep

Table 3

TRAVERSE TABLE

30°  30°

D Lon Dist.	Dep D. Lat.	Dep.	D Lon Dist.	Dep D. Lat.	Dep.	D Lon Dist.	Dep D. Lat.	Dep.	D Lon Dist.	Dep D. Lat.	Dep.	D Lon Dist.	Dep D. Lat.	Dep.
Hyp.	Adj.	Opp.	Hyp.	Adj.	Opp.	Hyp.	Adj.	Opp.	Hyp.	Adj.	Opp.	Hyp.	Adj.	Opp.
1	0.9	0.5	61	52.8	30.5	121	104.8	60.5	181	156.8	90.5	241	208.7	120.5
2	1.7	1.0	62	53.7	31.0	122	105.7	61.0	182	157.6	91.0	242	209.6	121.0
3	2.6	1.5	63	54.6	31.5	123	106.5	61.5	183	158.5	91.5	243	210.4	121.5
4	3.5	2.0	64	55.4	32.0	124	107.4	62.0	184	159.3	92.0	244	211.3	122.0
5	4.3	2.5	65	56.3	32.5	125	108.3	62.5	185	160.2	92.5	245	212.2	122.5
6	5.2	3.0	66	57.2	33.0	126	109.1	63.0	186	161.1	93.0	246	213.0	123.0
7	6.1	3.5	67	58.0	33.5	127	110.0	63.5	187	161.9	93.5	247	213.9	123.5
8	6.9	4.0	68	58.9	34.0	128	110.9	64.0	188	162.8	94.0	248	214.8	124.0
9	7.8	4.5	69	59.8	34.5	129	111.7	64.5	189	163.7	94.5	249	215.6	124.5
10	8.7	5.0	70	60.6	35.0	130	112.6	65.0	190	164.5	95.0	250	216.5	125.0
11	9.5	5.5	71	61.5	35.5	131	113.4	65.5	191	165.4	95.5	251	217.4	125.5
12	10.4	6.0	72	62.4	36.0	132	114.3	66.0	192	166.3	96.0	252	218.2	126.0
13	11.3	6.5	73	63.2	36.5	133	115.2	66.5	193	167.1	96.5	253	219.1	126.5
14	12.1	7.0	74	64.1	37.0	134	116.0	67.0	194	168.0	97.0	254	220.0	127.0
15	13.0	7.5	75	65.0	37.5	135	116.9	67.5	195	168.9	97.5	255	220.8	127.5
16	13.9	8.0	76	65.8	38.0	136	117.8	68.0	196	169.7	98.0	256	221.7	128.0
17	14.7	8.5	77	66.7	38.5	137	118.6	68.5	197	170.6	98.5	257	222.6	128.5
18	15.6	9.0	78	67.5	39.0	138	119.5	69.0	198	171.5	99.0	258	223.4	129.0
19	16.5	9.5	79	68.4	39.5	139	120.4	69.5	199	172.3	99.5	259	224.3	129.5
20	17.3	10.0	80	69.3	40.0	140	121.2	70.0	200	173.2	100.0	260	225.2	130.0
21	18.2	10.5	81	70.1	40.5	141	122.1	70.5	201	174.1	100.5	261	226.0	130.5
22	19.1	11.0	82	71.0	41.0	142	123.0	71.0	202	174.9	101.0	262	226.9	131.0
23	19.9	11.5	83	71.9	41.5	143	123.8	71.5	203	175.8	101.5	263	227.8	131.5
24	20.8	12.0	84	72.7	42.0	144	124.7	72.0	204	176.7	102.0	264	228.6	132.0
25	21.7	12.5	85	73.6	42.5	145	125.6	72.5	205	177.5	102.5	265	229.5	132.5
26	22.5	13.0	86	74.5	43.0	146	126.4	73.0	206	178.4	103.0	266	230.4	133.0
27	23.4	13.5	87	75.3	43.5	147	127.3	73.5	207	179.3	103.5	267	231.2	133.5
28	24.2	14.0	88	76.2	44.0	148	128.2	74.0	208	180.1	104.0	268	232.1	134.0
29	25.1	14.5	89	77.1	44.5	149	129.0	74.5	209	181.0	104.5	269	233.0	134.5
30	26.0	15.0	90	77.9	45.0	150	129.9	75.0	210	181.9	105.0	270	233.8	135.0
31	26.8	15.5	91	78.8	45.5	151	130.8	75.5	211	182.7	105.5	271	234.7	135.5
32	27.7	16.0	92	79.7	46.0	152	131.6	76.0	212	183.6	106.0	272	235.6	136.0
33	28.6	16.5	93	80.5	46.5	153	132.5	76.5	213	184.5	106.5	273	236.4	136.5
34	29.4	17.0	94	81.4	47.0	154	133.4	77.0	214	185.3	107.0	274	237.3	137.0
35	30.3	17.5	95	82.3	47.5	155	134.2	77.5	215	186.2	107.5	275	238.2	137.5
36	31.2	18.0	96	83.1	48.0	156	135.1	78.0	216	187.1	108.0	276	239.0	138.0
37	32.0	18.5	97	84.0	48.5	157	136.0	78.5	217	187.9	108.5	277	239.9	138.5
38	32.9	19.0	98	84.9	49.0	158	136.8	79.0	218	188.8	109.0	278	240.8	139.0
39	33.8	19.5	99	85.7	49.5	159	137.7	79.5	219	189.7	109.5	279	241.6	139.5
40	34.6	20.0	100	86.6	50.0	160	138.6	80.0	220	190.5	110.0	280	242.5	140.0
41	35.5	20.5	101	87.5	50.5	161	139.4	80.5	221	191.4	110.5	281	243.4	140.5
42	36.4	21.0	102	88.3	51.0	162	140.3	81.0	222	192.3	111.0	282	244.2	141.0
43	37.2	21.5	103	89.2	51.5	163	141.2	81.5	223	193.1	111.5	283	245.1	141.5
44	38.1	22.0	104	90.1	52.0	164	142.0	82.0	224	194.0	112.0	284	246.0	142.0
45	39.0	22.5	105	90.9	52.5	165	142.9	82.5	225	194.9	112.5	285	246.8	142.5
46	39.8	23.0	106	91.8	53.0	166	143.8	83.0	226	195.7	113.0	286	247.7	143.0
47	40.7	23.5	107	92.7	53.5	167	144.6	83.5	227	196.6	113.5	287	248.5	143.5
48	41.6	24.0	108	93.5	54.0	168	145.5	84.0	228	197.5	114.0	288	249.4	144.0
49	42.4	24.5	109	94.4	54.5	169	146.4	84.5	229	198.3	114.5	289	250.3	144.5
50	43.3	25.0	110	95.3	55.0	170	147.2	85.0	230	199.2	115.0	290	251.1	145.0
51	44.2	25.5	111	96.1	55.5	171	148.1	85.5	231	200.1	115.5	291	252.0	145.5
52	45.0	26.0	112	97.0	56.0	172	149.0	86.0	232	200.9	116.0	292	252.9	146.0
53	45.9	26.5	113	97.9	56.5	173	149.8	86.5	233	201.8	116.5	293	253.7	146.5
54	46.8	27.0	114	98.7	57.0	174	150.7	87.0	234	202.6	117.0	294	254.6	147.0
55	47.6	27.5	115	99.6	57.5	175	151.6	87.5	235	203.5	117.5	295	255.5	147.5
56	48.5	28.0	116	100.5	58.0	176	152.4	88.0	236	204.4	118.0	296	256.3	148.0
57	49.4	28.5	117	101.3	58.5	177	153.3	88.5	237	205.2	118.5	297	257.2	148.5
58	50.2	29.0	118	102.2	59.0	178	154.2	89.0	238	206.1	119.0	298	258.1	149.0
59	51.1	29.5	119	103.1	59.5	179	155.0	89.5	239	207.0	119.5	299	258.9	149.5
60	52.0	30.0	120	103.9	60.0	180	155.9	90.0	240	207.8	120.0	300	259.8	150.0
Hyp.	Opp.	Adj.	Hyp.	Opp.	Adj.	Hyp.	Opp.	Adj.	Hyp.	Opp.	Adj.	Hyp.	Opp.	Adj.
Dist. D Lon	Dep.	D. Lat. Dep	Dist. D Lon	Dep.	D. Lat. Dep	Dist. D Lon	Dep.	D. Lat. Dep	Dist. D Lon	Dep.	D. Lat. Dep	Dist. D Lon	Dep.	D. Lat. Dep

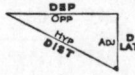

60° 60°

Table 3 TRAVERSE TABLE

30°

	330°	030°
	210°	150°

30°

D Lon Dist.	Dep D. Lat.	Dep.	D Lon Dist.	Dep D. Lat.	Dep.	D Lon Dist.	Dep D. Lat.	Dep.	D Lon Dist.	Dep D. Lat.	Dep.	D Lon Dist.	Dep D. Lat.	Dep.
Hyp.	*Adj.*	*Opp.*	*Hyp.*	*Adj.*	*Opp.*	*Hyp.*	*Adj.*	*Opp.*	*Hyp.*	*Adj.*	*Opp.*	*Hyp.*	*Adj.*	*Opp.*
301	260.7	150.5	361	312.6	180.5	421	364.6	210.5	481	416.6	240.5	541	468.5	270.5
302	261.5	151.0	362	313.5	181.0	422	365.5	211.0	482	417.4	241.0	542	469.4	271.0
303	262.4	151.5	363	314.4	181.5	423	366.3	211.5	483	418.3	241.5	543	470.3	271.5
304	263.3	152.0	364	315.2	182.0	424	367.2	212.0	484	419.2	242.0	544	471.1	272.0
305	264.1	152.5	365	316.1	182.5	425	368.1	212.5	485	420.0	242.5	545	472.0	272.5
306	265.0	153.0	366	317.0	183.0	426	368.9	213.0	486	420.9	243.0	546	472.8	273.0
307	265.9	153.5	367	317.8	183.5	427	369.8	213.5	487	421.8	243.5	547	473.7	273.5
308	266.7	154.0	368	318.7	184.0	428	370.7	214.0	488	422.6	244.0	548	474.6	274.0
309	267.6	154.5	369	319.6	184.5	429	371.5	214.5	489	423.5	244.5	549	475.4	274.5
310	268.5	155.0	370	320.4	185.0	430	372.4	215.0	490	424.4	245.0	550	476.3	275.0
311	269.3	155.5	371	321.3	185.5	431	373.3	215.5	491	425.2	245.5	551	477.2	275.5
312	270.2	156.0	372	322.2	186.0	432	374.1	216.0	492	426.1	246.0	552	478.0	276.0
313	271.1	156.5	373	323.0	186.5	433	375.0	216.5	493	427.0	246.5	553	478.9	276.5
314	271.9	157.0	374	323.9	187.0	434	375.9	217.0	494	427.8	247.0	554	479.8	277.0
315	272.8	157.5	375	324.8	187.5	435	376.7	217.5	495	428.7	247.5	555	480.6	277.5
316	273.7	158.0	376	325.6	188.0	436	377.6	218.0	496	429.5	248.0	556	481.5	278.0
317	274.5	158.5	377	326.5	188.5	437	378.5	218.5	497	430.4	248.5	557	482.4	278.5
318	275.4	159.0	378	327.4	189.0	438	379.3	219.0	498	431.3	249.0	558	483.2	279.0
319	276.3	159.5	379	328.2	189.5	439	380.2	219.5	499	432.1	249.5	559	484.1	279.5
320	277.1	160.0	380	329.1	190.0	440	381.1	220.0	500	433.0	250.0	560	485.0	280.0
321	278.0	160.5	381	330.0	190.5	441	381.9	220.5	501	433.9	250.5	561	485.8	280.5
322	278.9	161.0	382	330.8	191.0	442	382.8	221.0	502	434.7	251.0	562	486.7	281.0
323	279.7	161.5	383	331.7	191.5	443	383.6	221.5	503	435.6	251.5	563	487.6	281.5
324	280.6	162.0	384	332.6	192.0	444	384.5	222.0	504	436.5	252.0	564	488.4	282.0
325	281.5	162.5	385	333.4	192.5	445	385.4	222.5	505	437.3	252.5	565	489.3	282.5
326	282.3	163.0	386	334.3	193.0	446	386.3	223.0	506	438.2	253.0	566	490.2	283.0
327	283.2	163.5	387	335.2	193.5	447	387.1	223.5	507	439.1	253.5	567	491.0	283.5
328	284.1	164.0	388	336.0	194.0	448	388.0	224.0	508	439.9	254.0	568	491.9	284.0
329	284.9	164.5	389	336.9	194.5	449	388.8	224.5	509	440.8	254.5	569	492.8	284.5
330	285.8	165.0	390	337.7	195.0	450	389.7	225.0	510	441.7	255.0	570	493.6	285.0
331	286.7	165.5	391	338.6	195.5	451	390.6	225.5	511	442.5	255.5	571	494.5	285.5
332	287.5	166.0	392	339.5	196.0	452	391.4	226.0	512	443.4	256.0	572	495.4	286.0
333	288.4	166.5	393	340.3	196.5	453	392.3	226.5	513	444.3	256.5	573	496.2	286.5
334	289.3	167.0	394	341.2	197.0	454	393.2	227.0	514	445.1	257.0	574	497.1	287.0
335	290.1	167.5	395	342.1	197.5	455	394.0	227.5	515	446.0	257.5	575	498.0	287.5
336	291.0	168.0	396	342.9	198.0	456	394.9	228.0	516	446.9	258.0	576	498.8	288.0
337	291.9	168.5	397	343.8	198.5	457	395.8	228.5	517	447.7	258.5	577	499.7	288.5
338	292.7	169.0	398	344.7	199.0	458	396.6	229.0	518	448.6	259.0	578	500.6	289.0
339	293.6	169.5	399	345.5	199.5	459	397.5	229.5	519	449.5	259.5	579	501.4	289.5
340	294.5	170.0	400	346.4	200.0	460	398.4	230.0	520	450.3	260.0	580	502.3	290.0
341	295.3	170.5	401	347.3	200.5	461	399.2	230.5	521	451.2	260.5	581	503.2	290.5
342	296.2	171.0	402	348.1	201.0	462	400.1	231.0	522	452.1	261.0	582	504.0	291.0
343	297.0	171.5	403	349.0	201.5	463	401.0	231.5	523	452.9	261.5	583	504.9	291.5
344	297.9	172.0	404	349.9	202.0	464	401.8	232.0	524	453.8	262.0	584	505.8	292.0
345	298.8	172.5	405	350.7	202.5	465	402.7	232.5	525	454.7	262.5	585	506.6	292.5
346	299.6	173.0	406	351.6	203.0	466	403.6	233.0	526	455.5	263.0	586	507.5	293.0
347	300.5	173.5	407	352.5	203.5	467	404.4	233.5	527	456.4	263.5	587	508.4	293.5
348	301.4	174.0	408	353.3	204.0	468	405.3	234.0	528	457.3	264.0	588	509.2	294.0
349	302.2	174.5	409	354.2	204.5	469	406.2	234.5	529	458.1	264.5	589	510.1	294.5
350	303.1	175.0	410	355.1	205.0	470	407.0	235.0	530	459.0	265.0	590	511.0	295.0
351	304.0	175.5	411	355.9	205.5	471	407.9	235.5	531	459.9	265.5	591	511.8	295.5
352	304.8	176.0	412	356.8	206.0	472	408.8	236.0	532	460.7	266.0	592	512.7	296.0
353	305.7	176.5	413	357.7	206.5	473	409.6	236.5	533	461.6	266.5	593	513.6	296.5
354	306.6	177.0	414	358.5	207.0	474	410.5	237.0	534	462.5	267.0	594	514.4	297.0
355	307.4	177.5	415	359.4	207.5	475	411.4	237.5	535	463.3	267.5	595	515.3	297.5
356	308.3	178.0	416	360.3	208.0	476	412.2	238.0	536	464.2	268.0	596	516.2	298.0
357	309.2	178.5	417	361.1	208.5	477	413.1	238.5	537	465.1	268.5	597	517.0	298.5
358	310.0	179.0	418	362.0	209.0	478	414.0	239.0	538	465.9	269.0	598	517.9	299.0
359	310.9	179.5	419	362.9	209.5	479	414.8	239.5	539	466.8	269.5	599	518.7	299.5
360	311.8	180.0	420	363.7	210.0	480	415.7	240.0	540	467.7	270.0	600	519.6	300.0
Hyp.	*Opp.*	*Adj.*	*Hyp.*	*Opp.*	*Adj.*	*Hyp.*	*Opp.*	*Adj.*	*Hyp.*	*Opp.*	*Adj.*	*Hyp.*	*Opp.*	*Adj.*

Dist. D Lon	Dep.	D. Lat. Dep	Dist. D Lon	Dep.	D. Lat. Dep	Dist. D Lon	Dep.	D. Lat. Dep	Dist. D Lon	Dep.	D. Lat. Dep	Dist. D Lon	Dep.	D. Lat. Dep

60°

	300°	060°
	240°	120°

60°

Table 3

TRAVERSE TABLE

31°  31°

D Lon Dist.	Dep D. Lat.	Dep.	D Lon Dist.	Dep D. Lat.	Dep.	D Lon Dist.	Dep D. Lat.	Dep.	D Lon Dist.	Dep D. Lat.	Dep.	D Lon Dist.	Dep D. Lat.	Dep.
Hyp.	Adj.	Opp.	Hyp.	Adj.	Opp.	Hyp.	Adj.	Opp.	Hyp.	Adj.	Opp.	Hyp.	Adj.	Opp.
1	0.9	0.5	61	52.3	31.4	121	103.7	62.3	181	155.1	93.2	241	206.6	124.1
2	1.7	1.0	62	53.1	31.9	122	104.6	62.8	182	156.0	93.7	242	207.4	124.6
3	2.6	1.5	63	54.0	32.4	123	105.4	63.3	183	156.9	94.3	243	208.3	125.2
4	3.4	2.1	64	54.9	33.0	124	106.3	63.9	184	157.7	94.8	244	209.1	125.7
5	4.3	2.6	65	55.7	33.5	125	107.1	64.4	185	158.6	95.3	245	210.0	126.2
6	5.1	3.1	66	56.6	34.0	126	108.0	64.9	186	159.4	95.8	246	210.9	126.7
7	6.0	3.6	67	57.4	34.5	127	108.9	65.4	187	160.3	96.3	247	211.7	127.2
8	6.9	4.1	68	58.3	35.0	128	109.7	65.9	188	161.1	96.8	248	212.6	127.7
9	7.7	4.6	69	59.1	35.5	129	110.6	66.4	189	162.0	97.3	249	213.4	128.2
10	8.6	5.2	70	60.0	36.1	130	111.4	67.0	190	162.9	97.9	250	214.3	128.8
11	9.4	5.7	71	60.9	36.6	131	112.3	67.5	191	163.7	98.4	251	215.1	129.3
12	10.3	6.2	72	61.7	37.1	132	113.1	68.0	192	164.6	98.9	252	216.0	129.8
13	11.1	6.7	73	62.6	37.6	133	114.0	68.5	193	165.4	99.4	253	216.9	130.3
14	12.0	7.2	74	63.4	38.1	134	114.9	69.0	194	166.3	99.9	254	217.7	130.8
15	12.9	7.7	75	64.3	38.6	135	115.7	69.5	195	167.1	100.4	255	218.6	131.3
16	13.7	8.2	76	65.1	39.1	136	116.6	70.0	196	168.0	100.9	256	219.4	131.8
17	14.6	8.8	77	66.0	39.7	137	117.4	70.6	197	168.9	101.5	257	220.3	132.4
18	15.4	9.3	78	66.9	40.2	138	118.3	71.1	198	169.7	102.0	258	221.1	132.9
19	16.3	9.8	79	67.7	40.7	139	119.1	71.6	199	170.6	102.5	259	222.0	133.4
20	17.1	10.3	80	68.6	41.2	140	120.0	72.1	200	171.4	103.0	260	222.9	133.9
21	18.0	10.8	81	69.4	41.7	141	120.9	72.6	201	172.3	103.5	261	223.7	134.4
22	18.9	11.3	82	70.3	42.2	142	121.7	73.1	202	173.1	104.0	262	224.6	134.9
23	19.7	11.8	83	71.1	42.7	143	122.6	73.7	203	174.0	104.6	263	225.4	135.5
24	20.6	12.4	84	72.0	43.3	144	123.4	74.2	204	174.9	105.1	264	226.3	136.0
25	21.4	12.9	85	72.9	43.8	145	124.3	74.7	205	175.7	105.6	265	227.1	136.5
26	22.3	13.4	86	73.7	44.3	146	125.1	75.2	206	176.6	106.1	266	228.0	137.0
27	23.1	13.9	87	74.6	44.8	147	126.0	75.7	207	177.4	106.6	267	228.9	137.5
28	24.0	14.4	88	75.4	45.3	148	126.9	76.2	208	178.3	107.1	268	229.7	138.0
29	24.9	14.9	89	76.3	45.8	149	127.7	76.7	209	179.1	107.6	269	230.6	138.5
30	25.7	15.5	90	77.1	46.4	150	128.6	77.3	210	180.0	108.2	270	231.4	139.1
31	26.6	16.0	91	78.0	46.9	151	129.4	77.8	211	180.9	108.7	271	232.3	139.6
32	27.4	16.5	92	78.9	47.4	152	130.3	78.3	212	181.7	109.2	272	233.1	140.1
33	28.3	17.0	93	79.7	47.9	153	131.1	78.8	213	182.6	109.7	273	234.0	140.6
34	29.1	17.5	94	80.6	48.4	154	132.0	79.3	214	183.4	110.2	274	234.9	141.1
35	30.0	18.0	95	81.4	48.9	155	132.9	79.8	215	184.3	110.7	275	235.7	141.6
36	30.9	18.5	96	82.3	49.4	156	133.7	80.3	216	185.1	111.2	276	236.6	142.2
37	31.7	19.1	97	83.1	50.0	157	134.6	80.9	217	186.0	111.8	277	237.4	142.7
38	32.6	19.6	98	84.0	50.5	158	135.4	81.4	218	186.9	112.3	278	238.3	143.2
39	33.4	20.1	99	84.9	51.0	159	136.3	81.9	219	187.7	112.8	279	239.1	143.7
40	34.3	20.6	100	85.7	51.5	160	137.1	82.4	220	188.6	113.3	280	240.0	144.2
41	35.1	21.1	101	86.6	52.0	161	138.0	82.9	221	189.4	113.8	281	240.9	144.7
42	36.0	21.6	102	87.4	52.5	162	138.9	83.4	222	190.3	114.3	282	241.7	145.2
43	36.9	22.1	103	88.3	53.0	163	139.7	84.0	223	191.1	114.9	283	242.6	145.8
44	37.7	22.7	104	89.1	53.6	164	140.6	84.5	224	192.0	115.4	284	243.4	146.3
45	38.6	23.2	105	90.0	54.1	165	141.4	85.0	225	192.9	115.9	285	244.3	146.8
46	39.4	23.7	106	90.9	54.6	166	142.3	85.5	226	193.7	116.4	286	245.1	147.3
47	40.3	24.2	107	91.7	55.1	167	143.1	86.0	227	194.6	116.9	287	246.0	147.8
48	41.1	24.7	108	92.6	55.6	168	144.0	86.5	228	195.4	117.4	288	246.9	148.3
49	42.0	25.2	109	93.4	56.1	169	144.9	87.0	229	196.3	117.9	289	247.7	148.8
50	42.9	25.8	110	94.3	56.7	170	145.7	87.6	230	197.1	118.5	290	248.6	149.4
51	43.7	26.3	111	95.1	57.2	171	146.6	88.1	231	198.0	119.0	291	249.4	149.9
52	44.6	26.8	112	96.0	57.7	172	147.4	88.6	232	198.9	119.5	292	250.3	150.4
53	45.4	27.3	113	96.9	58.2	173	148.3	89.1	233	199.7	120.0	293	251.2	150.9
54	46.3	27.8	114	97.7	58.7	174	149.1	89.6	234	200.6	120.5	294	252.0	151.4
55	47.1	28.3	115	98.6	59.2	175	150.0	90.1	235	201.4	121.0	295	252.9	151.9
56	48.0	28.8	116	99.4	59.7	176	150.9	90.6	236	202.3	121.5	296	253.7	152.5
57	48.9	29.4	117	100.3	60.3	177	151.7	91.2	237	203.1	122.1	297	254.6	153.0
58	49.7	29.9	118	101.1	60.8	178	152.6	91.7	238	204.0	122.6	298	255.4	153.5
59	50.6	30.4	119	102.0	61.3	179	153.4	92.2	239	204.9	123.1	299	256.3	154.0
60	51.4	30.9	120	102.9	61.8	180	154.3	92.7	240	205.7	123.6	300	257.2	154.5
Hyp.	Opp.	Adj.	Hyp.	Opp.	Adj.	Hyp.	Opp.	Adj.	Hyp.	Opp.	Adj.	Hyp.	Opp.	Adj.
Dist. D Lon	Dep.	D. Lat. Dep	Dist. D Lon	Dep.	D. Lat. Dep	Dist. D Lon	Dep.	D. Lat. Dep	Dist. D Lon	Dep.	D. Lat. Dep	Dist. D Lon	Dep.	D. Lat. Dep

59°  59°

Table 3 — TRAVERSE TABLE

31°

329° | 031°
211° | 149°

31°

D Lon / Dist.	Dep D.Lat.	Dep.	D Lon / Dist.	Dep D.Lat.	Dep.	D Lon / Dist.	Dep D.Lat.	Dep.	D Lon / Dist.	Dep D.Lat.	Dep.	D Lon / Dist.	Dep D.Lat.	Dep.
Hyp.	Adj.	Opp.	Hyp.	Adj.	Opp.	Hyp.	Adj.	Opp.	Hyp.	Adj.	Opp.	Hyp.	Adj.	Opp.
301	258.0	155.0	361	309.4	185.9	421	360.9	216.8	481	412.3	247.7	541	463.7	278.6
302	258.9	155.5	362	310.3	186.4	422	361.7	217.3	482	413.2	248.2	542	464.6	279.2
303	259.7	156.1	363	311.2	187.0	423	362.6	217.9	483	414.0	248.8	543	465.4	279.7
304	260.6	156.6	364	312.0	187.5	424	363.4	218.4	484	414.9	249.3	544	466.3	280.2
305	261.4	157.1	365	312.9	188.0	425	364.3	218.9	485	415.7	249.8	545	467.2	280.7
306	262.3	157.6	366	313.7	188.5	426	365.2	219.4	486	416.6	250.3	546	468.0	281.2
307	263.2	158.1	367	314.6	189.0	427	366.0	219.9	487	417.4	250.8	547	468.9	281.7
308	264.0	158.6	368	315.4	189.5	428	366.9	220.4	488	418.3	251.3	548	469.7	282.2
309	264.9	159.1	369	316.3	190.0	429	367.7	221.0	489	419.2	251.9	549	470.6	282.8
310	265.7	159.7	370	317.2	190.6	430	368.6	221.5	490	420.0	252.4	550	471.4	283.3
311	266.6	160.2	371	318.0	191.1	431	369.4	222.0	491	420.9	252.9	551	472.3	283.8
312	267.4	160.7	372	318.9	191.6	432	370.3	222.5	492	421.7	253.4	552	473.2	284.3
313	268.3	161.2	373	319.7	192.1	433	371.2	223.0	493	422.6	253.9	553	474.0	284.8
314	269.2	161.7	374	320.6	192.6	434	372.0	223.5	494	423.4	254.4	554	474.9	285.3
315	270.0	162.2	375	321.4	193.1	435	372.9	224.0	495	424.3	254.9	555	475.7	285.8
316	270.9	162.8	376	322.3	193.7	436	373.7	224.6	496	425.2	255.5	556	476.6	286.4
317	271.7	163.3	377	323.2	194.2	437	374.6	225.1	497	426.0	256.0	557	477.4	286.9
318	272.6	163.8	378	324.0	194.7	438	375.4	225.6	498	426.9	256.5	558	478.3	287.4
319	273.4	164.3	379	324.9	195.2	439	376.3	226.1	499	427.7	257.0	559	479.2	287.9
320	274.3	164.8	380	325.7	195.7	440	377.2	226.6	500	428.6	257.5	560	480.0	288.4
321	275.2	165.3	381	326.6	196.2	441	378.0	227.1	501	429.4	258.0	561	480.9	288.9
322	276.0	165.8	382	327.4	196.7	442	378.9	227.6	502	430.3	258.5	562	481.7	289.5
323	276.9	166.4	383	328.3	197.3	443	379.7	228.2	503	431.2	259.1	563	482.6	290.0
324	277.7	166.9	384	329.2	197.8	444	380.6	228.7	504	432.0	259.6	564	483.4	290.5
325	278.6	167.4	385	330.0	198.3	445	381.4	229.2	505	432.9	260.1	565	484.3	291.0
326	279.4	167.9	386	330.9	198.8	446	382.3	229.7	506	433.7	260.6	566	485.2	291.5
327	280.3	168.4	387	331.7	199.3	447	383.2	230.2	507	434.6	261.1	567	486.0	292.0
328	281.2	168.9	388	332.6	199.8	448	384.0	230.7	508	435.4	261.6	568	486.9	292.5
329	282.0	169.4	389	333.4	200.3	449	384.9	231.3	509	436.3	262.2	569	487.7	293.1
330	282.9	170.0	390	334.3	200.9	450	385.7	231.8	510	437.2	262.7	570	488.6	293.6
331	283.7	170.5	391	335.2	201.4	451	386.6	232.3	511	438.0	263.2	571	489.4	294.1
332	284.6	171.0	392	336.0	201.9	452	387.4	232.8	512	438.9	263.7	572	490.3	294.6
333	285.4	171.5	393	336.9	202.4	453	388.3	233.3	513	439.7	264.2	573	491.2	295.1
334	286.3	172.0	394	337.7	202.9	454	389.2	233.8	514	440.6	264.7	574	492.0	295.6
335	287.2	172.5	395	338.6	203.4	455	390.0	234.3	515	441.4	265.2	575	492.9	296.1
336	288.0	173.1	396	339.4	204.0	456	390.9	234.9	516	442.3	265.8	576	493.7	296.7
337	288.9	173.6	397	340.3	204.5	457	391.7	235.4	517	443.2	266.3	577	494.6	297.2
338	289.7	174.1	398	341.2	205.0	458	392.6	235.9	518	444.0	266.8	578	495.4	297.7
339	290.6	174.6	399	342.0	205.5	459	393.4	236.4	519	444.9	267.3	579	496.3	298.2
340	291.4	175.1	400	342.9	206.0	460	394.3	236.9	520	445.7	267.8	580	497.2	298.7
341	292.3	175.6	401	343.7	206.5	461	395.2	237.4	521	446.6	268.3	581	498.0	299.2
342	293.2	176.1	402	344.6	207.0	462	396.0	237.9	522	447.4	268.8	582	498.9	299.8
343	294.0	176.7	403	345.4	207.6	463	396.9	238.5	523	448.3	269.4	583	499.7	300.3
344	294.9	177.2	404	346.3	208.1	464	397.7	239.0	524	449.2	269.9	584	500.6	300.8
345	295.7	177.7	405	347.2	208.6	465	398.6	239.5	525	450.0	270.4	585	501.4	301.3
346	296.6	178.2	406	348.0	209.1	466	399.4	240.0	526	450.9	270.9	586	502.3	301.8
347	297.4	178.7	407	348.9	209.6	467	400.3	240.5	527	451.7	271.4	587	503.2	302.3
348	298.3	179.2	408	349.7	210.1	468	401.2	241.0	528	452.6	271.9	588	504.0	302.8
349	299.2	179.7	409	350.6	210.7	469	402.0	241.6	529	453.4	272.5	589	504.9	303.4
350	300.0	180.3	410	351.4	211.2	470	402.9	242.1	530	454.3	273.0	590	505.7	303.9
351	300.9	180.8	411	352.3	211.7	471	403.7	242.6	531	455.2	273.5	591	506.6	304.4
352	301.7	181.3	412	353.2	212.2	472	404.6	243.1	532	456.0	274.0	592	507.4	304.9
353	302.6	181.8	413	354.0	212.7	473	405.4	243.6	533	456.9	274.5	593	508.3	305.4
354	303.4	182.3	414	354.9	213.2	474	406.3	244.1	534	457.7	275.0	594	509.2	305.9
355	304.3	182.8	415	355.7	213.7	475	407.2	244.6	535	458.6	275.5	595	510.0	306.4
356	305.2	183.4	416	356.6	214.3	476	408.0	245.2	536	459.4	276.1	596	510.9	307.0
357	306.0	183.9	417	357.4	214.8	477	408.9	245.7	537	460.3	276.6	597	511.7	307.5
358	306.9	184.4	418	358.3	215.3	478	409.7	246.2	538	461.2	277.1	598	512.6	308.0
359	307.7	184.9	419	359.2	215.8	479	410.6	246.7	539	462.0	277.6	599	513.4	308.5
360	308.6	185.4	420	360.0	216.3	480	411.4	247.2	540	462.9	278.1	600	514.3	309.0
Hyp.	Opp.	Adj.	Hyp.	Opp.	Adj.	Hyp.	Opp.	Adj.	Hyp.	Opp.	Adj.	Hyp.	Opp.	Adj.
Dist. / D Lon	Dep.	D. Lat. Dep	Dist. / D Lon	Dep.	D. Lat. Dep	Dist. / D Lon	Dep.	D. Lat. Dep	Dist. / D Lon	Dep.	D. Lat. Dep	Dist. / D Lon	Dep.	D. Lat. Dep

59°

301° | 059°
239° | 121°

59°

Table 3 — TRAVERSE TABLE

32°  32°

D Lon Dist.	Dep D. Lat. (Hyp. Adj.)	Dep. (Opp.)	D Lon Dist.	Dep D. Lat. (Hyp. Adj.)	Dep. (Opp.)	D Lon Dist.	Dep D. Lat. (Hyp. Adj.)	Dep. (Opp.)	D Lon Dist.	Dep D. Lat. (Hyp. Adj.)	Dep. (Opp.)	D Lon Dist.	Dep D. Lat. (Hyp. Adj.)	Dep. (Opp.)
1	0.8	0.5	61	51.7	32.3	121	102.6	64.1	181	153.5	95.9	241	204.4	127.7
2	1.7	1.1	62	52.6	32.9	122	103.5	64.7	182	154.3	96.4	242	205.2	128.2
3	2.5	1.6	63	53.4	33.4	123	104.3	65.2	183	155.2	97.0	243	206.1	128.8
4	3.4	2.1	64	54.3	33.9	124	105.2	65.7	184	156.0	97.5	244	206.9	129.3
5	4.2	2.6	65	55.1	34.4	125	106.0	66.2	185	156.9	98.0	245	207.8	129.8
6	5.1	3.2	66	56.0	35.0	126	106.9	66.8	186	157.7	98.6	246	208.6	130.4
7	5.9	3.7	67	56.8	35.5	127	107.7	67.3	187	158.6	99.1	247	209.5	130.9
8	6.8	4.2	68	57.7	36.0	128	108.6	67.8	188	159.4	99.6	248	210.3	131.4
9	7.6	4.8	69	58.5	36.6	129	109.4	68.4	189	160.3	100.2	249	211.2	131.9
10	8.5	5.3	70	59.4	37.1	130	110.2	68.9	190	161.1	100.7	250	212.0	132.5
11	9.3	5.8	71	60.2	37.6	131	111.1	69.4	191	162.0	101.2	251	212.9	133.0
12	10.2	6.4	72	61.1	38.2	132	111.9	69.9	192	162.8	101.7	252	213.7	133.5
13	11.0	6.9	73	61.9	38.7	133	112.8	70.5	193	163.7	102.3	253	214.6	134.1
14	11.9	7.4	74	62.8	39.2	134	113.6	71.0	194	164.5	102.8	254	215.4	134.6
15	12.7	7.9	75	63.6	39.7	135	114.5	71.5	195	165.4	103.3	255	216.3	135.1
16	13.6	8.5	76	64.5	40.3	136	115.3	72.1	196	166.2	103.9	256	217.1	135.7
17	14.4	9.0	77	65.3	40.8	137	116.2	72.6	197	167.1	104.4	257	217.9	136.2
18	15.3	9.5	78	66.1	41.3	138	117.0	73.1	198	167.9	104.9	258	218.8	136.7
19	16.1	10.1	79	67.0	41.9	139	117.9	73.7	199	168.8	105.5	259	219.6	137.2
20	17.0	10.6	80	67.8	42.4	140	118.7	74.2	200	169.6	106.0	260	220.5	137.8
21	17.8	11.1	81	68.7	42.9	141	119.6	74.7	201	170.5	106.5	261	221.3	138.3
22	18.7	11.7	82	69.5	43.5	142	120.4	75.2	202	171.3	107.0	262	222.2	138.8
23	19.5	12.2	83	70.4	44.0	143	121.3	75.8	203	172.2	107.6	263	223.0	139.4
24	20.4	12.7	84	71.2	44.5	144	122.1	76.3	204	173.0	108.1	264	223.9	139.9
25	21.2	13.2	85	72.1	45.0	145	123.0	76.8	205	173.8	108.6	265	224.7	140.4
26	22.0	13.8	86	72.9	45.6	146	123.8	77.4	206	174.7	109.2	266	225.6	141.0
27	22.9	14.3	87	73.8	46.1	147	124.7	77.9	207	175.5	109.7	267	226.4	141.5
28	23.7	14.8	88	74.6	46.6	148	125.5	78.4	208	176.4	110.2	268	227.3	142.0
29	24.6	15.4	89	75.5	47.2	149	126.4	79.0	209	177.2	110.8	269	228.1	142.5
30	25.4	15.9	90	76.3	47.7	150	127.2	79.5	210	178.1	111.3	270	229.0	143.1
31	26.3	16.4	91	77.2	48.2	151	128.1	80.0	211	178.9	111.8	271	229.8	143.6
32	27.1	17.0	92	78.0	48.8	152	128.9	80.5	212	179.8	112.3	272	230.7	144.1
33	28.0	17 5	93	78.9	49.3	153	129.8	81.1	213	180.6	112.9	273	231.5	144.7
34	28.8	18.0	94	79.7	49.8	154	130.6	81.6	214	181.5	113.4	274	232.4	145.2
35	29.7	18.5	95	80.6	50.3	155	131.4	82.1	215	182.3	113.9	275	233.2	145.7
36	30.5	19.1	96	81.4	50.9	156	132.3	82.7	216	183.2	114.5	276	234.1	146.3
37	31.4	19.6	97	82.3	51.4	157	133.1	83.2	217	184.0	115.0	277	234.9	146.8
38	32.2	20.1	98	83.1	51.9	158	134.0	83.7	218	184.9	115.5	278	235.8	147.3
39	33.1	20.7	99	84.0	52.5	159	134.8	84.3	219	185.7	116.1	279	236.6	147.8
40	33.9	21.2	100	84.8	53.0	160	135.7	84.8	220	186.6	116.6	280	237.5	148.4
41	34.8	21.7	101	85.7	53.5	161	136.5	85.3	221	187.4	117.1	281	238.3	148.9
42	35.6	22.3	102	86.5	54.1	162	137.4	85.8	222	188.3	117.6	282	239.1	149.4
43	36.5	22.8	103	87.3	54.6	163	138.2	86.4	223	189.1	118.2	283	240.0	150.0
44	37.3	23.3	104	88.2	55.1	164	139.1	86.9	224	190.0	118.7	284	240.8	150.5
45	38.2	23.8	105	89.0	55.6	165	139.9	87.4	225	190.8	119.2	285	241.7	151.0
46	39.0	24.4	106	89.9	56.2	166	140.8	88.0	226	191.7	119.8	286	242.5	151.6
47	39.9	24.9	107	90.7	56.7	167	141.6	88.5	227	192.5	120.3	287	243.4	152.1
48	40.7	25.4	108	91.6	57.2	168	142.5	89.0	228	193.4	120.8	288	244.2	152.6
49	41.6	26.0	109	92.4	57.8	169	143.3	89.6	229	194.2	121.4	289	245.1	153.1
50	42.4	26.5	110	93.3	58.3	170	144.2	90.1	230	195.1	121.9	290	245.9	153.7
51	43.3	27.0	111	94.1	58.8	171	145.0	90.6	231	195.9	122.4	291	246.8	154.2
52	44.1	27.6	112	95.0	59.4	172	145.9	91.1	232	196.7	122.9	292	247.6	154.7
53	44.9	28.1	113	95.8	59.9	173	146.7	91.7	233	197.6	123.5	293	248.5	155.3
54	45.8	28.6	114	96.7	60.4	174	147.6	92.2	234	198.4	124.0	294	249.3	155.8
55	46.6	29.1	115	97.5	60.9	175	148.4	92.7	235	199.3	124.5	295	250.2	156.3
56	47.5	29.7	116	98.4	61.5	176	149.3	93.3	236	200.1	125.1	296	251.0	156.9
57	48.3	30.2	117	99.2	62.0	177	150.1	93.8	237	201.0	125.6	297	251.9	157.4
58	49.2	30.7	118	100.1	62.5	178	151.0	94.3	238	201.8	126.1	298	252.7	157.9
59	50.0	31.3	119	100.9	63.1	179	151.8	94.9	239	202.7	126.7	299	253.6	158.4
60	50.9	31.8	120	101.8	63.6	180	152.6	95.4	240	203.5	127.2	300	254.4	159.0
Hyp.	Opp.	Adj.	Hyp.	Opp.	Adj.	Hyp.	Opp.	Adj.	Hyp.	Opp.	Adj.	Hyp.	Opp.	Adj.
Dist. D Lon	Dep.	D. Lat. Dep	Dist. D Lon	Dep.	D. Lat. Dep	Dist. D Lon	Dep.	D. Lat. Dep	Dist. D Lon	Dep.	D. Lat. Dep	Dist. D Lon	Dep.	D. Lat. Dep

58° 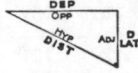 58°

Table 3

TRAVERSE TABLE

32° 328° | 032° / 212° | 148° **32°**

D Lon Dist.	Dep D. Lat.	Dep.	D Lon Dist.	Dep D. Lat.	Dep.	D Lon Dist.	Dep D. Lat.	Dep.	D Lon Dist.	Dep D. Lat.	Dep.	D Lon Dist.	Dep D. Lat.	Dep.
Hyp.	Adj.	Opp.	Hyp.	Adj.	Opp.	Hyp.	Adj.	Opp.	Hyp.	Adj.	Opp.	Hyp.	Adj.	Opp.
301	255.3	159.5	361	306.1	191.3	421	357.0	223.1	481	407.9	254.9	541	458.8	286.7
302	256.1	160.0	362	307.0	191.8	422	357.9	223.6	482	408.8	255.4	542	459.6	287.2
303	257.0	160.6	363	307.8	192.4	423	358.7	224.2	483	409.6	256.0	543	460.5	287.7
304	257.8	161.1	364	308.7	192.9	424	359.6	224.7	484	410.5	256.5	544	461.3	288.3
305	258.7	161.6	365	309.5	193.4	425	360.4	225.2	485	411.3	257.0	545	462.2	288.8
306	259.5	162.2	366	310.4	194.0	426	361.3	225.7	486	412.2	257.5	546	463.0	289.3
307	260.4	162.7	367	311.2	194.5	427	362.1	226.3	487	413.0	258.1	547	463.9	289.9
308	261.2	163.2	368	312.1	195.0	428	363.0	226.8	488	413.8	258.6	548	464.7	290.4
309	262.0	163.7	369	312.9	195.5	429	363.8	227.3	489	414.7	259.1	549	465.6	290.9
310	262.9	164.3	370	313.8	196.1	430	364.7	227.9	490	415.5	259.7	550	466.4	291.5
311	263.7	164.8	371	314.6	196.6	431	365.5	228.4	491	416.4	260.2	551	467.3	292.0
312	264.6	165.3	372	315.5	197.1	432	366.4	228.9	492	417.2	260.7	552	468.1	292.5
313	265.4	165.9	373	316.3	197.7	433	367.2	229.5	493	418.1	261.3	553	469.0	293.0
314	266.3	166.4	374	317.2	198.2	434	368.1	230.0	494	418.9	261.8	554	469.8	293.6
315	267.1	166.9	375	318.0	198.7	435	368.9	230.5	495	419.8	262.3	555	470.7	294.1
316	268.0	167.5	376	318.9	199.2	436	369.7	231.0	496	420.6	262.8	556	471.5	294.6
317	268.8	168.0	377	319.7	199.8	437	370.6	231.6	497	421.5	263.4	557	472.4	295.2
318	269.7	168.5	378	320.6	200.3	438	371.4	232.1	498	422.3	263.9	558	473.2	295.7
319	270.5	169.0	379	321.4	200.8	439	372.3	232.6	499	423.2	264.4	559	474.1	296.2
320	271.4	169.6	380	322.3	201.4	440	373.1	233.2	500	424.0	265.0	560	474.9	296.8
321	272.2	170.1	381	323.1	201.9	441	374.0	233.7	501	424.9	265.5	561	475.8	297.3
322	273.1	170.6	382	324.0	202.4	442	374.8	234.2	502	425.7	266.0	562	476.6	297.8
323	273.9	171.2	383	324.8	203.0	443	375.7	234.8	503	426.6	266.5	563	477.5	298.3
324	274.8	171.7	384	325.7	203.5	444	376.5	235.3	504	427.4	267.1	564	478.3	298.9
325	275.6	172.2	385	326.5	204.0	445	377.4	235.8	505	428.3	267.6	565	479.1	299.4
326	276.5	172.8	386	327.3	204.5	446	378.2	236.3	506	429.1	268.1	566	480.0	299.9
327	277.3	173.3	387	328.2	205.1	447	379.1	236.9	507	430.0	268.7	567	480.8	300.5
328	278.2	173.8	388	329.0	205.6	448	379.9	237.4	508	430.8	269.2	568	481.7	301.0
329	279.0	174.3	389	329.9	206.1	449	380.8	237.9	509	431.7	269.7	569	482.5	301.5
330	279.9	174.9	390	330.7	206.7	450	381.6	238.5	510	432.5	270.3	570	483.4	302.1
331	280.7	175.4	391	331.6	207.2	451	382.5	239.0	511	433.4	270.8	571	484.2	302.6
332	281.6	175.9	392	332.4	207.7	452	383.3	239.5	512	434.2	271.3	572	485.1	303.1
333	282.4	176.5	393	333.3	208.3	453	384.2	240.1	513	435.0	271.9	573	485.9	303.6
334	283.2	177.0	394	334.1	208.8	454	385.0	240.6	514	435.9	272.4	574	486.8	304.2
335	284.1	177.5	395	335.0	209.3	455	385.9	241.1	515	436.7	272.9	575	487.6	304.7
336	284.9	178.1	396	335.8	209.8	456	386.7	241.6	516	437.6	273.4	576	488.5	305.2
337	285.8	178.6	397	336.7	210.4	457	387.6	242.2	517	438.4	274.0	577	489.3	305.8
338	286.6	179.1	398	337.5	210.9	458	388.4	242.7	518	439.3	274.5	578	490.2	306.3
339	287.5	179.6	399	338.4	211.4	459	389.3	243.2	519	440.1	275.0	579	491.0	306.8
340	288.3	180.2	400	339.2	212.0	460	390.1	243.8	520	441.0	275.6	580	491.9	307.4
341	289.2	180.7	401	340.1	212.5	461	391.0	244.3	521	441.8	276.1	581	492.7	307.9
342	290.0	181.2	402	340.9	213.0	462	391.8	244.8	522	442.7	276.6	582	493.6	308.4
343	290.9	181.8	403	341.8	213.6	463	392.6	245.4	523	443.5	277.1	583	494.4	308.9
344	291.7	182.3	404	342.6	214.1	464	393.5	245.9	524	444.4	277.7	584	495.3	309.5
345	292.6	182.8	405	343.5	214.6	465	394.3	246.4	525	445.2	278.2	585	496.1	310.0
346	293.4	183.4	406	344.3	215.1	466	395.2	246.9	526	446.1	278.7	586	497.0	310.5
347	294.3	183.9	407	345.2	215.7	467	396.0	247.5	527	446.9	279.3	587	497.8	311.1
348	295.1	184.4	408	346.0	216.2	468	396.9	248.0	528	447.8	279.8	588	498.7	311.6
349	296.0	184.9	409	346.9	216.7	469	397.7	248.5	529	448.6	280.3	589	499.5	312.1
350	296.8	185.5	410	347.7	217.3	470	398.6	249.1	530	449.5	280.9	590	500.3	312.7
351	297.7	186.0	411	348.5	217.8	471	399.4	249.6	531	450.3	281.4	591	501.2	313.2
352	298.5	186.5	412	349.4	218.3	472	400.3	250.1	532	451.2	281.9	592	502.0	313.7
353	299.4	187.1	413	350.2	218.9	473	401.1	250.7	533	452.0	282.4	593	502.9	314.2
354	300.2	187.6	414	351.1	219.4	474	402.0	251.2	534	452.9	283.0	594	503.7	314.8
355	301.1	188.1	415	351.9	219.9	475	402.8	251.7	535	453.7	283.5	595	504.6	315.3
356	301.9	188.7	416	352.8	220.4	476	403.7	252.2	536	454.6	284.0	596	505.4	315.8
357	302.8	189.2	417	353.6	221.0	477	404.5	252.8	537	455.4	284.6	597	506.3	316.4
358	303.6	189.7	418	354.5	221.5	478	405.4	253.3	538	456.2	285.1	598	507.1	316.9
359	304.4	190.2	419	355.3	222.0	479	406.2	253.8	539	457.1	285.6	599	508.0	317.4
360	305.3	190.8	420	356.2	222.6	480	407.1	254.4	540	457.9	286.2	600	508.8	318.0
Hyp.	Opp.	Adj.	Hyp.	Opp.	Adj.	Hyp.	Opp.	Adj.	Hyp.	Opp.	Adj.	Hyp.	Opp.	Adj.

Dist. D Lon	Dep.	D. Lat. Dep	Dist. D Lon	Dep.	D. Lat. Dep	Dist. D Lon	Dep.	D. Lat. Dep	Dist. D Lon	Dep.	D. Lat. Dep	Dist. D Lon	Dep.	D. Lat. Dep

58° 302° | 058° / 238° | 122° **58°**

TRAVERSE TABLE

Table 3

33°  33°

D Lon / Dist.	Dep / D. Lat.	Dep.	D Lon / Dist.	Dep / D. Lat.	Dep.	D Lon / Dist.	Dep / D. Lat.	Dep.	D Lon / Dist.	Dep / D. Lat.	Dep.	D Lon / Dist.	Dep / D. Lat.	Dep.
Hyp.	*Adj.*	*Opp.*	*Hyp.*	*Adj.*	*Opp.*	*Hyp.*	*Adj.*	*Opp.*	*Hyp.*	*Adj.*	*Opp.*	*Hyp.*	*Adj.*	*Opp.*
1	0.8	0.5	61	51.2	33.2	121	101.5	65.9	181	151.8	98.6	241	202.1	131.3
2	1.7	1.1	62	52.0	33.8	122	102.3	66.4	182	152.6	99.1	242	203.0	131.8
3	2.5	1.6	63	52.8	34.3	123	103.2	67.0	183	153.5	99.7	243	203.8	132.3
4	3.4	2.2	64	53.7	34.9	124	104.0	67.5	184	154.3	100.2	244	204.6	132.9
5	4.2	2.7	65	54.5	35.4	125	104.8	68.1	185	155.2	100.8	245	205.5	133.4
6	5.0	3.3	66	55.4	35.9	126	105.7	68.6	186	156.0	101.3	246	206.3	134.0
7	5.9	3.8	67	56.2	36.5	127	106.5	69.2	187	156.8	101.8	247	207.2	134.5
8	6.7	4.4	68	57.0	37.0	128	107.3	69.7	188	157.7	102.4	248	208.0	135.1
9	7.5	4.9	69	57.9	37.6	129	108.2	70.3	189	158.5	102.9	249	208.8	135.6
10	8.4	5.4	70	58.7	38.1	130	109.0	70.8	190	159.3	103.5	250	209.7	136.2
11	9.2	6.0	71	59.5	38.7	131	109.9	71.3	191	160.2	104.0	251	210.5	136.7
12	10.1	6.5	72	60.4	39.2	132	110.7	71.9	192	161.0	104.6	252	211.3	137.2
13	10.9	7.1	73	61.2	39.8	133	111.5	72.4	193	161.9	105.1	253	212.2	137.8
14	11.7	7.6	74	62.1	40.3	134	112.4	73.0	194	162.7	105.7	254	213.0	138.3
15	12.6	8.2	75	62.9	40.8	135	113.2	73.5	195	163.5	106.2	255	213.9	138.8
16	13.4	8.7	76	63.7	41.4	136	114.1	74.1	196	164.4	106.7	256	214.7	139.4
17	14.3	9.3	77	64.6	41.9	137	114.9	74.6	197	165.2	107.3	257	215.5	140.0
18	15.1	9.8	78	65.4	42.5	138	115.7	75.2	198	166.1	107.8	258	216.4	140.5
19	15.9	10.3	79	66.3	43.0	139	116.6	75.7	199	166.9	108.4	259	217.2	141.1
20	16.8	10.9	80	67.1	43.6	140	117.4	76.2	200	167.7	108.9	260	218.1	141.6
21	17.6	11.4	81	67.9	44.1	141	118.3	76.8	201	168.6	109.5	261	218.9	142.2
22	18.5	12.0	82	68.8	44.7	142	119.1	77.3	202	169.4	110.0	262	219.7	142.7
23	19.3	12.5	83	69.6	45.2	143	119.9	77.9	203	170.3	110.6	263	220.6	143.2
24	20.1	13.1	84	70.4	45.7	144	120.8	78.4	204	171.1	111.1	264	221.4	143.8
25	21.0	13.6	85	71.3	46.3	145	121.6	79.0	205	171.9	111.7	265	222.2	144.3
26	21.8	14.2	86	72.1	46.8	146	122.4	79.5	206	172.8	112.2	266	223.1	144.9
27	22.6	14.7	87	73.0	47.4	147	123.3	80.1	207	173.6	112.7	267	223.9	145.4
28	23.5	15.2	88	73.8	47.9	148	124.1	80.6	208	174.4	113.3	268	224.8	146.0
29	24.3	15.8	89	74.6	48.5	149	125.0	81.2	209	175.3	113.8	269	225.6	146.5
30	25.2	16.3	90	75.5	49.0	150	125.8	81.7	210	176.1	114.4	270	226.4	147.1
31	26.0	16.9	91	76.3	49.6	151	126.6	82.2	211	177.0	114.9	271	227.3	147.6
32	26.8	17.4	92	77.2	50.1	152	127.5	82.8	212	177.8	115.5	272	228.1	148.1
33	27.7	18.0	93	78.0	50.7	153	128.3	83.3	213	178.6	116.0	273	229.0	148.7
34	28.5	18.5	94	78.8	51.2	154	129.2	83.9	214	179.5	116.6	274	229.8	149.2
35	29.4	19.1	95	79.7	51.7	155	130.0	84.4	215	180.3	117.1	275	230.6	149.8
36	30.2	19.6	96	80.5	52.3	156	130.8	85.0	216	181.2	117.6	276	231.5	150.3
37	31.0	20.2	97	81.4	52.8	157	131.7	85.5	217	182.0	118.2	277	232.3	150.9
38	31.9	20.7	98	82.2	53.4	158	132.5	86.1	218	182.8	118.7	278	233.2	151.4
39	32.7	21.2	99	83.0	53.9	159	133.3	86.6	219	183.7	119.3	279	234.0	152.0
40	33.5	21.8	100	83.9	54.5	160	134.2	87.1	220	184.5	119.8	280	234.8	152.5
41	34.4	22.3	101	84.7	55.0	161	135.0	87.7	221	185.3	120.4	281	235.7	153.0
42	35.2	22.9	102	85.5	55.6	162	135.9	88.2	222	186.2	120.9	282	236.5	153.6
43	36.1	23.4	103	86.4	56.1	163	136.7	88.8	223	187.0	121.5	283	237.3	154.1
44	36.9	24.0	104	87.2	56.6	164	137.5	89.3	224	187.9	122.0	284	238.2	154.7
45	37.7	24.5	105	88.1	57.2	165	138.4	89.9	225	188.7	122.5	285	239.0	155.2
46	38.6	25.1	106	88.9	57.7	166	139.2	90.4	226	189.5	123.1	286	239.9	155.8
47	39.4	25.6	107	89.7	58.3	167	140.1	91.0	227	190.4	123.6	287	240.7	156.3
48	40.3	26.1	108	90.6	58.8	168	140.9	91.5	228	191.2	124.2	288	241.5	156.9
49	41.1	26.7	109	91.4	59.4	169	141.7	92.0	229	192.1	124.7	289	242.4	157.4
50	41.9	27.2	110	92.3	59.9	170	142.6	92.6	230	192.9	125.3	290	243.2	157.9
51	42.8	27.8	111	93.1	60.5	171	143.4	93.1	231	193.7	125.8	291	244.1	158.5
52	43.6	28.3	112	93.9	61.0	172	144.3	93.7	232	194.6	126.4	292	244.9	159.0
53	44.4	28.9	113	94.8	61.5	173	145.1	94.2	233	195.4	126.9	293	245.7	159.6
54	45.3	29.4	114	95.6	62.1	174	145.9	94.8	234	196.2	127.4	294	246.6	160.1
55	46.1	30.0	115	96.4	62.6	175	146.8	95.3	235	197.1	128.0	295	247.4	160.7
56	47.0	30.5	116	97.3	63.2	176	147.6	95.9	236	197.9	128.5	296	248.2	161.2
57	47.8	31.0	117	98.1	63.7	177	148.4	96.4	237	198.8	129.1	297	249.1	161.8
58	48.6	31.6	118	99.0	64.3	178	149.3	96.9	238	199.6	129.6	298	249.9	162.3
59	49.5	32.1	119	99.8	64.8	179	150.1	97.5	239	200.4	130.2	299	250.8	162.8
60	50.3	32.7	120	100.6	65.4	180	151.0	98.0	240	201.3	130.7	300	251.6	163.4
Hyp.	*Opp.*	*Adj.*	*Hyp.*	*Opp.*	*Adj.*	*Hyp.*	*Opp.*	*Adj.*	*Hyp.*	*Opp.*	*Adj.*	*Hyp.*	*Opp.*	*Adj.*
Dist. D Lon	**Dep.**	**D. Lat.** Dep	**Dist.** D Lon	**Dep.**	**D. Lat.** Dep	**Dist.** D Lon	**Dep.**	**D. Lat.** Dep	**Dist.** D Lon	**Dep.**	**D. Lat.** Dep	**Dist.** D Lon	**Dep.**	**D. Lat.** Dep

57° 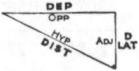 57°

Table 3

TRAVERSE TABLE

33°

33°

Dist. (Hyp.)	D. Lat. (Adj.)	Dep. (Opp.)	Dist. (Hyp.)	D. Lat. (Adj.)	Dep. (Opp.)	Dist. (Hyp.)	D. Lat. (Adj.)	Dep. (Opp.)	Dist. (Hyp.)	D. Lat. (Adj.)	Dep. (Opp.)	Dist. (Hyp.)	D. Lat. (Adj.)	Dep. (Opp.)
301	252.4	163.9	361	302.8	196.6	421	353.1	229.3	481	403.4	262.0	541	453.7	294.6
302	253.3	164.5	362	303.6	197.2	422	353.9	229.8	482	404.2	262.5	542	454.6	295.2
303	254.1	165.0	363	304.4	197.7	423	354.8	230.4	483	405.1	263.1	543	455.4	295.7
304	255.0	165.6	364	305.3	198.2	424	355.6	230.9	484	405.9	263.6	544	456.2	296.3
305	255.8	166.1	365	306.1	198.8	425	356.4	231.5	485	406.8	264.1	545	457.1	296.8
306	256.6	166.7	366	307.0	199.3	426	357.3	232.0	486	407.6	264.7	546	457.9	297.4
307	257.5	167.2	367	307.8	199.9	427	358.1	232.6	487	408.4	265.2	547	458.8	297.9
308	258.3	167.7	368	308.6	200.4	428	359.0	233.1	488	409.3	265.8	548	459.6	298.5
309	259.1	168.3	369	309.5	201.0	429	359.8	233.7	489	410.1	266.3	549	460.4	299.0
310	260.0	168.8	370	310.3	201.5	430	360.6	234.2	490	410.9	266.9	550	461.3	299.6
311	260.8	169.4	371	311.1	202.1	431	361.5	234.7	491	411.8	267.4	551	462.1	300.1
312	261.7	169.9	372	312.0	202.6	432	362.3	235.3	492	412.6	268.0	552	462.9	300.6
313	262.5	170.5	373	312.8	203.2	433	363.1	235.8	493	413.5	268.5	553	463.8	301.2
314	263.3	171.0	374	313.7	203.7	434	364.0	236.4	494	414.3	269.0	554	464.6	301.7
315	264.2	171.6	375	314.5	204.2	435	364.8	236.9	495	415.1	269.6	555	465.5	302.3
316	265.0	172.1	376	315.3	204.8	436	365.7	237.5	496	416.0	270.1	556	466.3	302.8
317	265.9	172.7	377	316.2	205.3	437	366.5	238.0	497	416.8	270.7	557	467.1	303.4
318	266.7	173.2	378	317.0	205.9	438	367.3	238.6	498	417.7	271.2	558	468.0	303.9
319	267.5	173.7	379	317.9	206.4	439	368.2	239.1	499	418.5	271.8	559	468.8	304.5
320	268.4	174.3	380	318.7	207.0	440	369.0	239.6	500	419.3	272.3	560	469.7	305.0
321	269.2	174.8	381	319.5	207.5	441	369.9	240.2	501	420.2	272.9	561	470.5	305.5
322	270.1	175.4	382	320.4	208.1	442	370.7	240.7	502	421.0	273.4	562	471.3	306.1
323	270.9	175.9	383	321.2	208.6	443	371.5	241.3	503	421.9	274.0	563	472.2	306.6
324	271.7	176.5	384	322.0	209.1	444	372.4	241.8	504	422.7	274.5	564	473.0	307.2
325	272.6	177.0	385	322.9	209.7	445	373.2	242.4	505	423.5	275.0	565	473.8	307.7
326	273.4	177.6	386	323.7	210.2	446	374.0	242.9	506	424.4	275.6	566	474.7	308.3
327	274.2	178.1	387	324.6	210.8	447	374.9	243.5	507	425.2	276.1	567	475.5	308.8
328	275.1	178.6	388	325.4	211.3	448	375.7	244.0	508	426.0	276.7	568	476.4	309.4
329	275.9	179.2	389	326.2	211.9	449	376.6	244.5	509	426.9	277.2	569	477.2	309.9
330	276.8	179.7	390	327.1	212.4	450	377.4	245.1	510	427.7	277.8	570	478.0	310.4
331	277.6	180.3	391	327.9	213.0	451	378.2	245.6	511	428.6	278.3	571	478.9	311.0
332	278.4	180.8	392	328.8	213.5	452	379.1	246.2	512	429.4	278.9	572	479.7	311.5
333	279.3	181.4	393	329.6	214.0	453	379.9	246.7	513	430.2	279.4	573	480.6	312.1
334	280.1	181.9	394	330.4	214.6	454	380.8	247.3	514	431.1	279.9	574	481.4	312.6
335	281.0	182.5	395	331.3	215.1	455	381.6	247.8	515	431.9	280.5	575	482.2	313.2
336	281.8	183.0	396	332.1	215.7	456	382.4	248.4	516	432.8	281.0	576	483.1	313.7
337	282.6	183.5	397	333.0	216.2	457	383.3	248.9	517	433.6	281.6	577	483.9	314.3
338	283.5	184.1	398	333.8	216.8	458	384.1	249.4	518	434.4	282.1	578	484.8	314.8
339	284.3	184.6	399	334.6	217.3	459	384.9	250.0	519	435.3	282.7	579	485.6	315.3
340	285.1	185.2	400	335.5	217.9	460	385.8	250.5	520	436.1	283.2	580	486.4	315.9
341	286.0	185.7	401	336.3	218.4	461	386.6	251.1	521	436.9	283.8	581	487.3	316.4
342	286.8	186.3	402	337.1	218.9	462	387.5	251.6	522	437.8	284.3	582	488.1	317.0
343	287.7	186.8	403	338.0	219.5	463	388.3	252.2	523	438.6	284.8	583	488.9	317.5
344	288.5	187.4	404	338.8	220.0	464	389.1	252.7	524	439.5	285.4	584	489.8	318.1
345	289.3	187.9	405	339.7	220.6	465	390.0	253.3	525	440.3	285.9	585	490.6	318.6
346	290.2	188.4	406	340.5	221.1	466	390.8	253.8	526	441.1	286.5	586	491.5	319.2
347	291.0	189.0	407	341.3	221.7	467	391.7	254.3	527	442.0	287.0	587	492.3	319.7
348	291.9	189.5	408	342.2	222.2	468	392.5	254.9	528	442.8	287.6	588	493.1	320.2
349	292.7	190.1	409	343.0	222.8	469	393.3	255.4	529	443.7	288.1	589	494.0	320.8
350	293.5	190.6	410	343.9	223.3	470	394.2	256.0	530	444.5	288.7	590	494.8	321.3
351	294.4	191.2	411	344.7	223.8	471	395.0	256.5	531	445.3	289.2	591	495.7	321.9
352	295.2	191.7	412	345.5	224.4	472	395.9	257.1	532	446.2	289.7	592	496.5	322.4
353	296.1	192.3	413	346.4	224.9	473	396.7	257.6	533	447.0	290.3	593	497.3	323.0
354	296.9	192.8	414	347.2	225.5	474	397.5	258.2	534	447.9	290.8	594	498.2	323.5
355	297.7	193.3	415	348.0	226.0	475	398.4	258.7	535	448.7	291.4	595	499.0	324.1
356	298.6	193.9	416	348.9	226.6	476	399.2	259.2	536	449.5	291.9	596	499.8	324.6
357	299.4	194.4	417	349.7	227.1	477	400.0	259.8	537	450.4	292.5	597	500.7	325.1
358	300.2	195.0	418	350.6	227.7	478	400.9	260.3	538	451.2	293.0	598	501.5	325.7
359	301.1	195.5	419	351.4	228.2	479	401.7	260.9	539	452.0	293.6	599	502.4	326.2
360	301.9	196.1	420	352.2	228.7	480	402.6	261.4	540	452.9	294.1	600	503.2	326.8
Hyp.	Opp.	Adj.	Hyp.	Opp.	Adj.	Hyp.	Opp.	Adj.	Hyp.	Opp.	Adj.	Hyp.	Opp.	Adj.

Dist. / D Lon	Dep.	D. Lat. Dep	Dist. / D Lon	Dep.	D. Lat. Dep	Dist. / D Lon	Dep.	D. Lat. Dep	Dist. / D Lon	Dep.	D. Lat. Dep	Dist. / D Lon	Dep.	D. Lat. Dep

57°

57°

Table 3

TRAVERSE TABLE

34°   34°

D Lon Dist.	Dep D. Lat.	Dep.	D Lon Dist.	Dep D. Lat.	Dep.	D Lon Dist.	Dep D. Lat.	Dep.	D Lon Dist.	Dep D. Lat.	Dep.	D Lon Dist.	Dep D. Lat.	Dep.
Hyp.	Adj.	Opp.	Hyp.	Adj.	Opp.	Hyp.	Adj.	Opp.	Hyp.	Adj.	Opp.	Hyp.	Adj.	Opp.
1	0.8	0.6	61	50.6	34.1	121	100.3	67.7	181	150.1	101.2	241	199.8	134.8
2	1.7	1.1	62	51.4	34.7	122	101.1	68.2	182	150.9	101.8	242	200.6	135.3
3	2.5	1.7	63	52.2	35.2	123	102.0	68.8	183	151.7	102.3	243	201.5	135.9
4	3.3	2.2	64	53.1	35.8	124	102.8	69.3	184	152.5	102.9	244	202.3	136.4
5	4.1	2.8	65	53.9	36.3	125	103.6	69.9	185	153.4	103.5	245	203.1	137.0
6	5.0	3.4	66	54.7	36.9	126	104.5	70.5	186	154.2	104.0	246	203.9	137.6
7	5.8	3.9	67	55.5	37.5	127	105.3	71.0	187	155.0	104.6	247	204.8	138.1
8	6.6	4.5	68	56.4	38.0	128	106.1	71.6	188	155.9	105.1	248	205.6	138.7
9	7.5	5.0	69	57.2	38.6	129	106.9	72.1	189	156.7	105.7	249	206.4	139.2
10	8.3	5.6	70	58.0	39.1	130	107.8	72.7	190	157.5	106.2	250	207.3	139.8
11	9.1	6.2	71	58.9	39.7	131	108.6	73.3	191	158.3	106.8	251	208.1	140.4
12	9.9	6.7	72	59.7	40.3	132	109.4	73.8	192	159.2	107.4	252	208.9	140.9
13	10.8	7.3	73	60.5	40.8	133	110.3	74.4	193	160.0	107.9	253	209.7	141.5
14	11.6	7.8	74	61.3	41.4	134	111.1	74.9	194	160.8	108.5	254	210.6	142.0
15	12.4	8.4	75	62.2	41.9	135	111.9	75.5	195	161.7	109.0	255	211.4	142.6
16	13.3	8.9	76	63.0	42.5	136	112.7	76.1	196	162.5	109.6	256	212.2	143.2
17	14.1	9.5	77	63.8	43.1	137	113.6	76.6	197	163.3	110.2	257	213.1	143.7
18	14.9	10.1	78	64.7	43.6	138	114.4	77.2	198	164.1	110.7	258	213.9	144.3
19	15.8	10.6	79	65.5	44.2	139	115.2	77.7	199	165.0	111.3	259	214.7	144.8
20	16.6	11.2	80	66.3	44.7	140	116.1	78.3	200	165.8	111.8	260	215.5	145.4
21	17.4	11.7	81	67.2	45.3	141	116.9	78.8	201	166.6	112.4	261	216.4	145.9
22	18.2	12.3	82	68.0	45.9	142	117.7	79.4	202	167.5	113.0	262	217.2	146.5
23	19.1	12.9	83	68.8	46.4	143	118.6	80.0	203	168.3	113.5	263	218.0	147.1
24	19.9	13.4	84	69.6	47.0	144	119.4	80.5	204	169.1	114.1	264	218.9	147.6
25	20.7	14.0	85	70.5	47.5	145	120.2	81.1	205	170.0	114.6	265	219.7	148.2
26	21.6	14.5	86	71.3	48.1	146	121.0	81.6	206	170.8	115.2	266	220.5	148.7
27	22.4	15.1	87	72.1	48.6	147	121.9	82.2	207	171.6	115.8	267	221.4	149.3
28	23.2	15.7	88	73.0	49.2	148	122.7	82.8	208	172.4	116.3	268	222.2	149.9
29	24.0	16.2	89	73.8	49.8	149	123.5	83.3	209	173.3	116.9	269	223.0	150.4
30	24.9	16.8	90	74.6	50.3	150	124.4	83.9	210	174.1	117.4	270	223.8	151.0
31	25.7	17.3	91	75.4	50.9	151	125.2	84.4	211	174.9	118.0	271	224.7	151.5
32	26.5	17.9	92	76.3	51.4	152	126.0	85.0	212	175.8	118.5	272	225.5	152.1
33	27.4	18.5	93	77.1	52.0	153	126.8	85.6	213	176.6	119.1	273	226.3	152.7
34	28.2	19.0	94	77.9	52.6	154	127.7	86.1	214	177.4	119.7	274	227.2	153.2
35	29.0	19.6	95	78.8	53.1	155	128.5	86.7	215	178.2	120.2	275	228.0	153.8
36	29.8	20.1	96	79.6	53.7	156	129.3	87.2	216	179.1	120.8	276	228.8	154.3
37	30.7	20.7	97	80.4	54.2	157	130.2	87.8	217	179.9	121.3	277	229.6	154.9
38	31.5	21.2	98	81.2	54.8	158	131.0	88.4	218	180.7	121.9	278	230.5	155.5
39	32.3	21.8	99	82.1	55.4	159	131.8	88.9	219	181.6	122.5	279	231.3	156.0
40	33.2	22.4	100	82.9	55.9	160	132.6	89.5	220	182.4	123.0	280	232.1	156.6
41	34.0	22.9	101	83.7	56.5	161	133.5	90.0	221	183.2	123.6	281	233.0	157.1
42	34.8	23.5	102	84.6	57.0	162	134.3	90.6	222	184.0	124.1	282	233.8	157.7
43	35.6	24.0	103	85.4	57.6	163	135.1	91.1	223	184.9	124.7	283	234.6	158.3
44	36.5	24.6	104	86.2	58.2	164	136.0	91.7	224	185.7	125.3	284	235.4	158.8
45	37.3	25.2	105	87.0	58.7	165	136.8	92.3	225	186.5	125.8	285	236.3	159.4
46	38.1	25.7	106	87.9	59.3	166	137.6	92.8	226	187.4	126.4	286	237.1	159.9
47	39.0	26.3	107	88.7	59.8	167	138.4	93.4	227	188.2	126.9	287	237.9	160.5
48	39.8	26.8	108	89.5	60.4	168	139.3	93.9	228	189.0	127.5	288	238.8	161.0
49	40.6	27.4	109	90.4	61.0	169	140.1	94.5	229	189.8	128.1	289	239.6	161.6
50	41.5	28.0	110	91.2	61.5	170	140.9	95.1	230	190.7	128.6	290	240.4	162.2
51	42.3	28.5	111	92.0	62.1	171	141.8	95.6	231	191.5	129.2	291	241.2	162.7
52	43.1	29.1	112	92.9	62.6	172	142.6	96.2	232	192.3	129.7	292	242.1	163.3
53	43.9	29.6	113	93.7	63.2	173	143.4	96.7	233	193.2	130.3	293	242.9	163.8
54	44.8	30.2	114	94.5	63.7	174	144.3	97.3	234	194.0	130.9	294	243.7	164.4
55	45.6	30.8	115	95.3	64.3	175	145.1	97.9	235	194.8	131.4	295	244.6	165.0
56	46.4	31.3	116	96.2	64.9	176	145.9	98.4	236	195.7	132.0	296	245.4	165.5
57	47.3	31.9	117	97.0	65.4	177	146.7	99.0	237	196.5	132.5	297	246.2	166.1
58	48.1	32.4	118	97.8	66.0	178	147.6	99.5	238	197.3	133.1	298	247.1	166.6
59	48.9	33.0	119	98.7	66.5	179	148.4	100.1	239	198.1	133.6	299	247.9	167.2
60	49.7	33.6	120	99.5	67.1	180	149.2	100.7	240	199.0	134.2	300	248.7	167.8
Hyp.	Opp.	Adj.	Hyp.	Opp.	Adj.	Hyp.	Opp.	Adj.	Hyp.	Opp.	Adj.	Hyp.	Opp.	Adj.
Dist. D Lon	Dep.	D. Lat. Dep	Dist. D Lon	Dep.	D. Lat. Dep	Dist. D Lon	Dep.	D. Lat. Dep	Dist. D Lon	Dep.	D. Lat. Dep	Dist. D Lon	Dep.	D. Lat. Dep

56°   56°

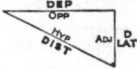

Table 3

34°

TRAVERSE TABLE

D Lon Dep Dist. D. Lat. Dep.			D Lon Dep Dist. D. Lat. Dep.			D Lon Dep Dist. D. Lat. Dep.			D Lon Dep Dist. D. Lat. Dep.			D Lon Dep Dist. D. Lat. Dep.		
Hyp.	Adj.	Opp.	Hyp.	Adj.	Opp.	Hyp.	Adj.	Opp.	Hyp.	Adj.	Opp.	Hyp.	Adj.	Opp.
301	249.5	168.3	361	299.3	201.9	421	349.0	235.4	481	398.8	269.0	541	448.5	302.5
302	250.4	168.9	362	300.1	202.4	422	349.9	236.0	482	399.6	269.5	542	449.3	303.1
303	251.2	169.4	363	300.9	203.0	423	350.7	236.5	483	400.4	270.1	543	450.2	303.6
304	252.0	170.0	364	301.8	203.5	424	351.5	237.1	484	401.3	270.6	544	451.0	304.2
305	252.9	170.6	365	302.6	204.1	425	352.3	237.7	485	402.1	271.2	545	451.8	304.8
306	253.7	171.1	366	303.4	204.7	426	353.2	238.2	486	402.9	271.8	546	452.7	305.3
307	254.5	171.7	367	304.3	205.2	427	354.0	238.8	487	403.7	272.3	547	453.5	305.9
308	255.3	172.2	368	305.1	205.8	428	354.8	239.3	488	404.6	272.9	548	454.3	306.4
309	256.2	172.8	369	305.9	206.3	429	355.7	239.9	489	405.4	273.4	549	455.1	307.0
310	257.0	173.3	370	306.7	206.9	430	356.5	240.5	490	406.2	274.0	550	456.0	307.6
311	257.8	173.9	371	307.6	207.5	431	357.3	241.0	491	407.1	274.6	551	456.8	308.1
312	258.7	174.5	372	308.4	208.0	432	358.1	241.6	492	407.9	275.1	552	457.6	308.7
313	259.5	175.0	373	309.2	208.6	433	359.0	242.1	493	408.7	275.7	553	458.5	309.2
314	260.3	175.6	374	310.1	209.1	434	359.8	242.7	494	409.5	276.2	554	459.3	309.8
315	261.1	176.1	375	310.9	209.7	435	360.6	243.2	495	410.4	276.8	555	460.1	310.4
316	262.0	176.7	376	311.7	210.3	436	361.5	243.8	496	411.2	277.4	556	460.9	310.9
317	262.8	177.3	377	312.5	210.8	437	362.3	244.4	497	412.0	277.9	557	461.8	311.5
318	263.6	177.8	378	313.4	211.4	438	363.1	244.9	498	412.9	278.5	558	462.6	312.0
319	264.5	178.4	379	314.2	211.9	439	363.9	245.5	499	413.7	279.0	559	463.4	312.6
320	265.3	178.9	380	315.0	212.5	440	364.8	246.0	500	414.5	279.6	560	464.3	313.1
321	266.1	179.5	381	315.9	213.1	441	365.6	246.6	501	415.3	280.2	561	465.1	313.7
322	267.0	180.1	382	316.7	213.6	442	366.4	247.2	502	416.2	280.7	562	465.9	314.3
323	267.8	180.6	383	317.5	214.2	443	367.3	247.7	503	417.0	281.3	563	466.7	314.8
324	268.6	181.2	384	318.4	214.7	444	368.1	248.3	504	417.8	281.8	564	467.6	315.4
325	269.4	181.7	385	319.2	215.3	445	368.9	248.8	505	418.7	282.4	565	468.4	315.9
326	270.3	182.3	386	320.0	215.8	446	369.8	249.4	506	419.5	283.0	566	469.2	316.5
327	271.1	182.9	387	320.8	216.4	447	370.6	250.0	507	420.3	283.5	567	470.1	317.1
328	271.9	183.4	388	321.7	217.0	448	371.4	250.5	508	421.2	284.1	568	470.9	317.6
329	272.8	184.0	389	322.5	217.5	449	372.2	251.1	509	422.0	284.6	569	471.7	318.2
330	273.6	184.5	390	323.3	218.1	450	373.1	251.6	510	422.8	285.2	570	472.6	318.7
331	274.4	185.1	391	324.2	218.6	451	373.9	252.2	511	423.6	285.7	571	473.4	319.3
332	275.2	185.7	392	325.0	219.2	452	374.7	252.8	512	424.5	286.3	572	474.2	319.9
333	276.1	186.2	393	325.8	219.8	453	375.6	253.3	513	425.3	286.9	573	475.0	320.4
334	276.9	186.8	394	326.6	220.3	454	376.4	253.9	514	426.1	287.4	574	475.9	321.0
335	277.7	187.3	395	327.5	220.9	455	377.2	254.4	515	427.0	288.0	575	476.7	321.5
336	278.6	187.9	396	328.3	221.4	456	378.0	255.0	516	427.8	288.5	576	477.5	322.1
337	279.4	188.4	397	329.1	222.0	457	378.9	255.6	517	428.6	289.1	577	478.4	322.7
338	280.2	189.0	398	330.0	222.6	458	379.7	256.1	518	429.4	289.7	578	479.2	323.2
339	281.0	189.6	399	330.8	223.1	459	380.5	256.7	519	430.3	290.2	579	480.0	323.8
340	281.9	190.1	400	331.6	223.7	460	381.4	257.2	520	431.1	290.8	580	480.8	324.3
341	282.7	190.7	401	332.4	224.2	461	382.2	257.8	521	431.9	291.3	581	481.7	324.9
342	283.5	191.2	402	333.3	224.8	462	383.0	258.3	522	432.8	291.9	582	482.5	325.4
343	284.4	191.8	403	334.1	225.4	463	383.8	258.9	523	433.6	292.5	583	483.3	326.0
344	285.2	192.4	404	334.9	225.9	464	384.7	259.5	524	434.4	293.0	584	484.2	326.6
345	286.0	192.9	405	335.8	226.5	465	385.5	260.0	525	435.2	293.6	585	485.0	327.1
346	286.8	193.5	406	336.6	227.0	466	386.3	260.6	526	436.1	294.1	586	485.8	327.7
347	287.7	194.0	407	337.4	227.6	467	387.2	261.1	527	436.9	294.7	587	486.6	328.2
348	288.5	194.6	408	338.2	228.2	468	388.0	261.7	528	437.7	295.3	588	487.5	328.8
349	289.3	195.2	409	339.1	228.7	469	388.8	262.3	529	438.6	295.8	589	488.3	329.4
350	290.2	195.7	410	339.9	229.3	470	389.6	262.8	530	439.4	296.4	590	489.1	329.9
351	291.0	196.3	411	340.7	229.8	471	390.5	263.4	531	440.2	296.9	591	490.0	330.5
352	291.8	196.8	412	341.6	230.4	472	391.3	263.9	532	441.0	297.5	592	490.8	331.0
353	292.7	197.4	413	342.4	230.9	473	392.1	264.5	533	441.9	298.0	593	491.6	331.6
354	293.5	198.0	414	343.2	231.5	474	393.0	265.1	534	442.7	298.6	594	492.4	332.2
355	294.3	198.5	415	344.1	232.1	475	393.8	265.6	535	443.5	299.2	595	493.3	332.7
356	295.1	199.1	416	344.9	232.6	476	394.6	266.2	536	444.4	299.7	596	494.1	333.3
357	296.0	199.6	417	345.7	233.2	477	395.5	266.7	537	445.2	300.3	597	494.9	333.8
358	296.8	200.2	418	346.5	233.7	478	396.3	267.3	538	446.0	300.8	598	495.8	334.4
359	297.6	200.8	419	347.4	234.3	479	397.1	267.9	539	446.9	301.4	599	496.6	335.0
360	298.5	201.3	420	348.2	234.9	480	397.9	268.4	540	447.7	302.0	600	497.4	335.5
Hyp.	Opp.	Adj.	Hyp.	Opp.	Adj.	Hyp.	Opp.	Adj.	Hyp.	Opp.	Adj.	Hyp.	Opp.	Adj.
Dist. Dep. D. Lat. D Lon Dep			Dist. Dep. D. Lat. D Lon Dep			Dist. Dep. D. Lat. D Lon Dep			Dist. Dep. D. Lat. D Lon Dep			Dist. Dep. D. Lat. D Lon Dep		

Table 3

35°

TRAVERSE TABLE

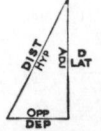

35°

D Lon Dist.	Dep D. Lat.	Dep.	D Lon Dist.	Dep D. Lat.	Dep.	D Lon Dist.	Dep D. Lat.	Dep.	D Lon Dist.	Dep D. Lat.	Dep.	D Lon Dist.	Dep D. Lat.	Dep.
Hyp.	*Adj.*	*Opp.*	*Hyp.*	*Adj.*	*Opp.*	*Hyp.*	*Adj.*	*Opp.*	*Hyp.*	*Adj.*	*Opp.*	*Hyp.*	*Adj.*	*Opp.*
1	0.8	0.6	61	50.0	35.0	121	99.1	69.4	181	148.3	103.8	241	197.4	138.2
2	1.6	1.1	62	50.8	35.6	122	99.9	70.0	182	149.1	104.4	242	198.2	138.8
3	2.5	1.7	63	51.6	36.1	123	100.8	70.5	183	149.9	105.0	243	199.1	139.4
4	3.3	2.3	64	52.4	36.7	124	101.6	71.1	184	150.7	105.5	244	199.9	140.0
5	4.1	2.9	65	53.2	37.3	125	102.4	71.7	185	151.5	106.1	245	200.7	140.5
6	4.9	3.4	66	54.1	37.9	126	103.2	72.3	186	152.4	106.7	246	201.5	141.1
7	5.7	4.0	67	54.9	38.4	127	104.0	72.8	187	153.2	107.3	247	202.3	141.7
8	6.6	4.6	68	55.7	39.0	128	104.9	73.4	188	154.0	107.8	248	203.1	142.2
9	7.4	5.2	69	56.5	39.6	129	105.7	74.0	189	154.8	108.4	249	204.0	142.8
10	8.2	5.7	70	57.3	40.2	130	106.5	74.6	190	155.6	109.0	250	204.8	143.4
11	9.0	6.3	71	58.2	40.7	131	107.3	75.1	191	156.5	109.6	251	205.6	144.0
12	9.8	6.9	72	59.0	41.3	132	108.1	75.7	192	157.3	110.1	252	206.4	144.5
13	10.6	7.5	73	59.8	41.9	133	108.9	76.3	193	158.1	110.7	253	207.2	145.1
14	11.5	8.0	74	60.6	42.4	134	109.8	76.9	194	158.9	111.3	254	208.1	145.7
15	12.3	8.6	75	61.4	43.0	135	110.6	77.4	195	159.7	111.8	255	208.9	146.3
16	13.1	9.2	76	62.3	43.6	136	111.4	78.0	196	160.6	112.4	256	209.7	146.8
17	13.9	9.8	77	63.1	44.2	137	112.2	78.6	197	161.4	113.0	257	210.5	147.4
18	14.7	10.3	78	63.9	44.7	138	113.0	79.2	198	162.2	113.6	258	211.3	148.0
19	15.6	10.9	79	64.7	45.3	139	113.9	79.7	199	163.0	114.1	259	212.2	148.6
20	16.4	11.5	80	65.5	45.9	140	114.7	80.3	200	163.8	114.7	260	213.0	149.1
21	17.2	12.0	81	66.4	46.5	141	115.5	80.9	201	164.6	115.3	261	213.8	149.7
22	18.0	12.6	82	67.2	47.0	142	116.3	81.4	202	165.5	115.9	262	214.6	150.3
23	18.8	13.2	83	68.0	47.6	143	117.1	82.0	203	166.3	116.4	263	215.4	150.9
24	19.7	13.8	84	68.8	48.2	144	118.0	82.6	204	167.1	117.0	264	216.3	151.4
25	20.5	14.3	85	69.6	48.8	145	118.8	83.2	205	167.9	117.6	265	217.1	152.0
26	21.3	14.9	86	70.4	49.3	146	119.6	83.7	206	168.7	118.2	266	217.9	152.6
27	22.1	15.5	87	71.3	49.9	147	120.4	84.3	207	169.6	118.7	267	218.7	153.1
28	22.9	16.1	88	72.1	50.5	148	121.2	84.9	208	170.4	119.3	268	219.5	153.7
29	23.8	16.6	89	72.9	51.0	149	122.1	85.5	209	171.2	119.9	269	220.4	154.3
30	24.6	17.2	90	73.7	51.6	150	122.9	86.0	210	172.0	120.5	270	221.2	154.9
31	25.4	17.8	91	74.5	52.2	151	123.7	86.6	211	172.8	121.0	271	222.0	155.4
32	26.2	18.4	92	75.4	52.8	152	124.5	87.2	212	173.7	121.6	272	222.8	156.0
33	27.0	18.9	93	76.2	53.3	153	125.3	87.8	213	174.5	122.2	273	223.6	156.6
34	27.9	19.5	94	77.0	53.9	154	126.1	88.3	214	175.3	122.7	274	224.4	157.2
35	28.7	20.1	95	77.8	54.5	155	127.0	88.9	215	176.1	123.3	275	225.3	157.7
36	29.5	20.6	96	78.6	55.1	156	127.8	89.5	216	176.9	123.9	276	226.1	158.3
37	30.3	21.2	97	79.5	55.6	157	128.6	90.1	217	177.8	124.5	277	226.9	158.9
38	31.1	21.8	98	80.3	56.2	158	129.4	90.6	218	178.6	125.0	278	227.7	159.5
39	31.9	22.4	99	81.1	56.8	159	130.2	91.2	219	179.4	125.6	279	228.5	160.0
40	32.8	22.9	100	81.9	57.4	160	131.1	91.8	220	180.2	126.2	280	229.4	160.6
41	33.6	23.5	101	82.7	57.9	161	131.9	92.3	221	181.0	126.8	281	230.2	161.2
42	34.4	24.1	102	83.6	58.5	162	132.7	92.9	222	181.9	127.3	282	231.0	161.7
43	35.2	24.7	103	84.4	59.1	163	133.5	93.5	223	182.7	127.9	283	231.8	162.3
44	36.0	25.2	104	85.2	59.7	164	134.3	94.1	224	183.5	128.5	284	232.6	162.9
45	36.9	25.8	105	86.0	60.2	165	135.2	94.6	225	184.3	129.1	285	233.5	163.5
46	37.7	26.4	106	86.8	60.8	166	136.0	95.2	226	185.1	129.6	286	234.3	164.0
47	38.5	27.0	107	87.6	61.4	167	136.8	95.8	227	185.9	130.2	287	235.1	164.6
48	39.3	27.5	108	88.5	61.9	168	137.6	96.4	228	186.8	130.8	288	235.9	165.2
49	40.1	28.1	109	89.3	62.5	169	138.4	96.9	229	187.6	131.3	289	236.7	165.8
50	41.0	28.7	110	90.1	63.1	170	139.3	97.5	230	188.4	131.9	290	237.6	166.3
51	41.8	29.3	111	90.9	63.7	171	140.1	98.1	231	189.2	132.5	291	238.4	166.9
52	42.6	29.8	112	91.7	64.2	172	140.9	98.7	232	190.0	133.1	292	239.2	167.5
53	43.4	30.4	113	92.6	64.8	173	141.7	99.2	233	190.9	133.6	293	240.0	168.1
54	44.2	31.0	114	93.4	65.4	174	142.5	99.8	234	191.7	134.2	294	240.8	168.6
55	45.1	31.5	115	94.2	66.0	175	143.4	100.4	235	192.5	134.8	295	241.6	169.2
56	45.9	32.1	116	95.0	66.5	176	144.2	100.9	236	193.3	135.4	296	242.5	169.8
57	46.7	32.7	117	95.8	67.1	177	145.0	101.5	237	194.1	135.9	297	243.3	170.4
58	47.5	33.3	118	96.7	67.7	178	145.8	102.1	238	195.0	136.5	298	244.1	170.9
59	48.3	33.8	119	97.5	68.3	179	146.6	102.7	239	195.8	137.1	299	244.9	171.5
60	49.1	34.4	120	98.3	68.8	180	147.4	103.2	240	196.6	137.7	300	245.7	172.1
Hyp.	*Opp.*	*Adj.*	*Hyp.*	*Opp.*	*Adj.*	*Hyp.*	*Opp.*	*Adj.*	*Hyp.*	*Opp.*	*Adj.*	*Hyp.*	*Opp.*	*Adj.*
Dist. D Lon	Dep.	D. Lat. Dep	Dist. D Lon	Dep.	D. Lat. Dep	Dist. D Lon	Dep.	D. Lat. Dep	Dist. D Lon	Dep.	D. Lat. Dep	Dist D Lon	Dep.	D. Lat. Dep

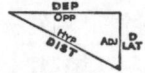

55°

55°

Table 3   71

TRAVERSE TABLE

35°

	325° | 035°
	215° | 145°

D Lon — Dist.	Dep — D. Lat.	Dep.	D Lon — Dist.	Dep — D. Lat.	Dep.	D Lon — Dist.	Dep — D. Lat.	Dep.	D Lon — Dist.	Dep — D. Lat.	Dep.	D Lon — Dist.	Dep — D. Lat.	Dep.
Hyp.	Adj.	Opp.	Hyp.	Adj.	Opp.	Hyp.	Adj.	Opp.	Hyp.	Adj.	Opp.	Hyp.	Adj.	Opp.
301	246.6	172.6	361	295.7	207.1	421	344.9	241.5	481	394.0	275.9	541	443.2	310.3
302	247.4	173.2	362	296.5	207.6	422	345.7	242.0	482	394.8	276.5	542	444.0	310.9
303	248.2	173.8	363	297.4	208.2	423	346.5	242.6	483	395.7	277.0	543	444.8	311.5
304	249.0	174.4	364	298.2	208.8	424	347.3	243.2	484	396.5	277.6	544	445.6	312.0
305	249.8	174.9	365	299.0	209.4	425	348.1	243.8	485	397.3	278.2	545	446.4	312.6
306	250.7	175.5	366	299.8	209.9	426	349.0	244.3	486	398.1	278.8	546	447.3	313.2
307	251.5	176.1	367	300.6	210.5	427	349.8	244.9	487	398.9	279.3	547	448.1	313.7
308	252.3	176.7	368	301.4	211.1	428	350.6	245.5	488	399.7	279.9	548	448.9	314.3
309	253.1	177.2	369	302.3	211.6	429	351.4	246.1	489	400.6	280.5	549	449.7	314.9
310	253.9	177.8	370	303.1	212.2	430	352.2	246.6	490	401.4	281.1	550	450.5	315.5
311	254.8	178.4	371	303.9	212.8	431	353.1	247.2	491	402.2	281.6	551	451.4	316.0
312	255.6	179.0	372	304.7	213.4	432	353.9	247.8	492	403.0	282.2	552	452.2	316.6
313	256.4	179.5	373	305.5	213.9	433	354.7	248.4	493	403.8	282.8	553	453.0	317.2
314	257.2	180.1	374	306.4	214.5	434	355.5	248.9	494	404.7	283.3	554	453.8	317.8
315	258.0	180.7	375	307.2	215.1	435	356.3	249.5	495	405.5	283.9	555	454.6	318.3
316	258.9	181.3	376	308.0	215.7	436	357.2	250.1	496	406.3	284.5	556	455.4	318.9
317	259.7	181.8	377	308.8	216.2	437	358.0	250.7	497	407.1	285.1	557	456.3	319.5
318	260.5	182.4	378	309.6	216.8	438	358.8	251.2	498	407.9	285.6	558	457.1	320.1
319	261.3	183.0	379	310.5	217.4	439	359.6	251.8	499	408.8	286.2	559	457.9	320.6
320	262.1	183.5	380	311.3	218.0	440	360.4	252.4	500	409.6	286.8	560	458.7	321.2
321	262.9	184.1	381	312.1	218.5	441	361.2	252.9	501	410.4	287.4	561	459.5	321.8
322	263.8	184.7	382	312.9	219.1	442	362.1	253.5	502	411.2	287.9	562	460.4	322.3
323	264.6	185.3	383	313.7	219.7	443	362.9	254.1	503	412.0	288.5	563	461.2	322.9
324	265.4	185.8	384	314.6	220.3	444	363.7	254.7	504	412.9	289.1	564	462.0	323.5
325	266.2	186.4	385	315.4	220.8	445	364.5	255.2	505	413.7	289.7	565	462.8	324.1
326	267.0	187.0	386	316.2	221.4	446	365.3	255.8	506	414.5	290.2	566	463.6	324.6
327	267.9	187.6	387	317.0	222.0	447	366.2	256.4	507	415.3	290.8	567	464.5	325.2
328	268.7	188.1	388	317.8	222.5	448	367.0	257.0	508	416.1	291.4	568	465.3	325.8
329	269.5	188.7	389	318.7	223.1	449	367.8	257.5	509	416.9	292.0	569	466.1	326.4
330	270.3	189.3	390	319.5	223.7	450	368.6	258.1	510	417.8	292.5	570	466.9	326.9
331	271.1	189.9	391	320.3	224.3	451	369.4	258.7	511	418.6	293.1	571	467.7	327.5
332	272.0	190.4	392	321.1	224.8	452	370.3	259.3	512	419.4	293.7	572	468.6	328.1
333	272.8	191.0	393	321.9	225.4	453	371.1	259.8	513	420.2	294.2	573	469.4	328.7
334	273.6	191.6	394	322.7	226.0	454	371.9	260.4	514	421.0	294.8	574	470.2	329.2
335	274.4	192.1	395	323.6	226.6	455	372.7	261.0	515	421.9	295.4	575	471.0	329.8
336	275.2	192.7	396	324.4	227.1	456	373.5	261.6	516	422.7	296.0	576	471.8	330.4
337	276.1	193.3	397	325.2	227.7	457	374.4	262.1	517	423.5	296.5	577	472.7	331.0
338	276.9	193.9	398	326.0	228.3	458	375.2	262.7	518	424.3	297.1	578	473.5	331.5
339	277.7	194.4	399	326.8	228.9	459	376.0	263.3	519	425.1	297.7	579	474.3	332.1
340	278.5	195.0	400	327.7	229.4	460	376.8	263.8	520	426.0	298.3	580	475.1	332.7
341	279.3	195.6	401	328.5	230.0	461	377.6	264.4	521	426.8	298.8	581	475.9	333.2
342	280.1	196.2	402	329.3	230.6	462	378.4	265.0	522	427.6	299.4	582	476.7	333.8
343	281.0	196.7	403	330.1	231.2	463	379.3	265.6	523	428.4	300.0	583	477.6	334.4
344	281.8	197.3	404	330.9	231.7	464	380.1	266.1	524	429.2	300.6	584	478.4	335.0
345	282.6	197.9	405	331.8	232.3	465	380.9	266.7	525	430.1	301.1	585	479.2	335.5
346	283.4	198.5	406	332.6	232.9	466	381.7	267.3	526	430.9	301.7	586	480.0	336.1
347	284.2	199.0	407	333.4	233.4	467	382.5	267.9	527	431.7	302.3	587	480.8	336.7
348	285.1	199.6	408	334.2	234.0	468	383.4	268.4	528	432.5	302.8	588	481.7	337.3
349	285.9	200.2	409	335.0	234.6	469	384.2	269.0	529	433.3	303.4	589	482.5	337.8
350	286.7	200.8	410	335.9	235.2	470	385.0	269.6	530	434.2	304.0	590	483.3	338.4
351	287.5	201.3	411	336.7	235.7	471	385.8	270.2	531	435.0	304.6	591	484.1	339.0
352	288.3	201.9	412	337.5	236.3	472	386.6	270.7	532	435.8	305.1	592	484.9	339.6
353	289.2	202.5	413	338.3	236.9	473	387.5	271.3	533	436.6	305.7	593	485.8	340.1
354	290.0	203.0	414	339.1	237.5	474	388.3	271.9	534	437.4	306.3	594	486.6	340.7
355	290.8	203.6	415	339.9	238.0	475	389.1	272.4	535	438.2	306.9	595	487.4	341.3
356	291.6	204.2	416	340.8	238.6	476	389.9	273.0	536	439.1	307.4	596	488.2	341.9
357	292.4	204.8	417	341.6	239.2	477	390.7	273.6	537	439.9	308.0	597	489.0	342.4
358	293.3	205.3	418	342.4	239.8	478	391.6	274.2	538	440.7	308.6	598	489.7	343.0
359	294.1	205.9	419	343.2	240.3	479	392.4	274.7	539	441.5	309.2	599	490.7	343.6
360	294.9	206.5	420	344.0	240.9	480	393.2	275.3	540	442.3	309.7	600	491.5	344.1
Hyp.	Opp.	Adj.	Hyp.	Opp.	Adj.	Hyp.	Opp.	Adj.	Hyp.	Opp.	Adj.	Hyp.	Opp.	Adj.

Dist. — D Lon	Dep.	D. Lat. — Dep	Dist. — D Lon	Dep.	D. Lat. — Dep	Dist. — D Lon	Dep.	D. Lat. — Dep	Dist. — D Lon	Dep.	D. Lat. — Dep	Dist. — D Lon	Dep.	D. Lat. — Dep

55°

	305° | 055°
	235° | 125°

Table 3   **TRAVERSE TABLE**

36° 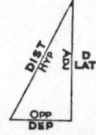 36°

D Lon Dist.	Dep D. Lat.	Dep.	D Lon Dist.	Dep D. Lat.	Dep.	D Lon Dist.	Dep D. Lat.	Dep.	D Lon Dist.	Dep D. Lat.	Dep.	D Lon Dist.	Dep D. Lat.	Dep.
Hyp.	Adj.	Opp.	Hyp.	Adj.	Opp.	Hyp.	Adj.	Opp.	Hyp.	Adj.	Opp.	Hyp.	Adj.	Opp.
1	0.8	0.6	61	49.4	35.9	121	97.9	71.1	181	146.4	106.4	241	195.0	141.7
2	1.6	1.2	62	50.2	36.4	122	98.7	71.7	182	147.2	107.0	242	195.8	142.2
3	2.4	1.8	63	51.0	37.0	123	99.5	72.3	183	148.1	107.6	243	196.6	142.8
4	3.2	2.4	64	51.8	37.6	124	100.3	72.9	184	148.9	108.2	244	197.4	143.4
5	4.0	2.9	65	52.6	38.2	125	101.1	73.5	185	149.7	108.7	245	198.2	144.0
6	4.9	3.5	66	53.4	38.8	126	101.9	74.1	186	150.5	109.3	246	199.0	144.6
7	5.7	4.1	67	54.2	39.4	127	102.7	74.6	187	151.3	109.9	247	199.8	145.2
8	6.5	4.7	68	55.0	40.0	128	103.6	75.2	188	152.1	110.5	248	200.6	145.8
9	7.3	5.3	69	55.8	40.6	129	104.4	75.8	189	152.9	111.1	249	201.4	146.4
10	8.1	5.9	70	56.6	41.1	130	105.2	76.4	190	153.7	111.7	250	202.3	146.9
11	8.9	6.5	71	57.4	41.7	131	106.0	77.0	191	154.5	112.3	251	203.1	147.5
12	9.7	7.1	72	58.2	42.3	132	106.8	77.6	192	155.3	112.9	252	203.9	148.1
13	10.5	7.6	73	59.1	42.9	133	107.6	78.2	193	156.1	113.4	253	204.7	148.7
14	11.3	8.2	74	59.9	43.5	134	108.4	78.8	194	156.9	114.0	254	205.5	149.3
15	12.1	8.8	75	60.7	44.1	135	109.2	79.4	195	157.8	114.6	255	206.3	149.9
16	12.9	9.4	76	61.5	44.7	136	110.0	79.9	196	158.6	115.2	256	207.1	150.5
17	13.8	10.0	77	62.3	45.3	137	110.8	80.5	197	159.4	115.8	257	207.9	151.1
18	14.6	10.6	78	63.1	45.8	138	111.6	81.1	198	160.2	116.4	258	208.7	151.6
19	15.4	11.2	79	63.9	46.4	139	112.5	81.7	199	161.0	117.0	259	209.5	152.2
20	16.2	11.8	80	64.7	47.0	140	113.3	82.3	200	161.8	117.6	260	210.3	152.8
21	17.0	12.3	81	65.5	47.6	141	114.1	82.9	201	162.6	118.1	261	211.2	153.4
22	17.8	12.9	82	66.3	48.2	142	114.9	83.5	202	163.4	118.7	262	212.0	154.0
23	18.6	13.5	83	67.1	48.8	143	115.7	84.1	203	164.2	119.3	263	212.8	154.6
24	19.4	14.1	84	68.0	49.4	144	116.5	84.6	204	165.0	119.9	264	213.6	155.2
25	20.2	14.7	85	68.8	50.0	145	117.3	85.2	205	165.8	120.5	265	214.4	155.8
26	21.0	15.3	86	69.6	50.5	146	118.1	85.8	206	166.7	121.1	266	215.2	156.4
27	21.8	15.9	87	70.4	51.1	147	118.9	86.4	207	167.5	121.7	267	216.0	156.9
28	22.7	16.5	88	71.2	51.7	148	119.7	87.0	208	168.3	122.3	268	216.8	157.5
29	23.5	17.0	89	72.0	52.3	149	120.5	87.6	209	169.1	122.8	269	217.6	158.1
30	24.3	17.6	90	72.8	52.9	150	121.4	88.2	210	169.9	123.4	270	218.4	158.7
31	25.1	18.2	91	73.6	53.5	151	122.2	88.8	211	170.7	124.0	271	219.2	159.3
32	25.9	18.8	92	74.4	54.1	152	123.0	89.3	212	171.5	124.6	272	220.1	159.9
33	26.7	19.4	93	75.2	54.7	153	123.8	89.9	213	172.3	125.2	273	220.9	160.5
34	27.5	20.0	94	76.0	55.3	154	124.6	90.5	214	173.1	125.8	274	221.7	161.1
35	28.3	20.6	95	76.9	55.8	155	125.4	91.1	215	173.9	126.4	275	222.5	161.6
36	29.1	21.2	96	77.7	56.4	156	126.2	91.7	216	174.7	127.0	276	223.3	162.2
37	29.9	21.7	97	78.5	57.0	157	127.0	92.3	217	175.6	127.5	277	224.1	162.8
38	30.7	22.3	98	79.3	57.6	158	127.8	92.9	218	176.4	128.1	278	224.9	163.4
39	31.6	22.9	99	80.1	58.2	159	128.6	93.5	219	177.2	128.7	279	225.7	164.0
40	32.4	23.5	100	80.9	58.8	160	129.4	94.0	220	178.0	129.3	280	226.5	164.6
41	33.2	24.1	101	81.7	59.4	161	130.3	94.6	221	178.8	129.9	281	227.3	165.2
42	34.0	24.7	102	82.5	60.0	162	131.1	95.2	222	179.6	130.5	282	228.1	165.8
43	34.8	25.3	103	83.3	60.5	163	131.9	95.8	223	180.4	131.1	283	229.0	166.3
44	35.6	25.9	104	84.1	61.1	164	132.7	96.4	224	181.2	131.7	284	229.8	166.9
45	36.4	26.5	105	84.9	61.7	165	133.5	97.0	225	182.0	132.3	285	230.6	167.5
46	37.2	27.0	106	85.8	62.3	166	134.3	97.6	226	182.8	132.8	286	231.4	168.1
47	38.0	27.6	107	86.6	62.9	167	135.1	98.2	227	183.6	133.4	287	232.2	168.7
48	38.8	28.2	108	87.4	63.5	168	135.9	98.7	228	184.5	134.0	288	233.0	169.3
49	39.6	28.8	109	88.2	64.1	169	136.7	99.3	229	185.3	134.6	289	233.8	169.9
50	40.5	29.4	110	89.0	64.7	170	137.5	99.9	230	186.1	135.2	290	234.6	170.5
51	41.3	30.0	111	89.8	65.2	171	138.3	100.5	231	186.9	135.8	291	235.4	171.0
52	42.1	30.6	112	90.6	65.8	172	139.2	101.1	232	187.7	136.4	292	236.2	171.6
53	42.9	31.2	113	91.4	66.4	173	140.0	101.7	233	188.5	137.0	293	237.0	172.2
54	43.7	31.7	114	92.2	67.0	174	140.8	102.3	234	189.3	137.5	294	237.9	172.8
55	44.5	32.3	115	93.0	67.6	175	141.6	102.9	235	190.1	138.1	295	238.7	173.4
56	45.3	32.9	116	93.8	68.2	176	142.4	103.5	236	190.9	138.7	296	239.5	174.0
57	46.1	33.5	117	94.7	68.8	177	143.2	104.0	237	191.7	139.3	297	240.3	174.6
58	46.9	34.1	118	95.5	69.4	178	144.0	104.6	238	192.5	139.9	298	241.1	175.2
59	47.7	34.7	119	96.3	69.9	179	144.8	105.2	239	193.4	140.5	299	241.9	175.7
60	48.5	35.3	120	97.1	70.5	180	145.6	105.8	240	194.2	141.1	300	242.7	176.3
Hyp.	Opp.	Adj.	Hyp.	Opp.	Adj.	Hyp.	Opp.	Adj.	Hyp.	Opp.	Adj.	Hyp.	Opp.	Adj.
Dist. D Lon	Dep.	D. Lat. Dep	Dist. D Lon	Dep.	D. Lat. Dep	Dist. D Lon	Dep.	D. Lat. Dep	Dist. D Lon	Dep.	D. Lat. Dep	Dist. D Lon	Dep.	D. Lat. Dep

54° 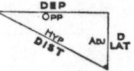 54°

Table 3

TRAVERSE TABLE

36°   324° | 036° / 216° | 144°   **36°**

D Lon Dist.	Dep D. Lat.	Dep.	D Lon Dist.	Dep D. Lat.	Dep.	D Lon Dist.	Dep D. Lat.	Dep.	D Lon Dist.	Dep D. Lat.	Dep.	D Lon Dist.	Dep D. Lat.	Dep.
Hyp.	Adj.	Opp.	Hyp.	Adj.	Opp.	Hyp.	Adj.	Opp.	Hyp.	Adj.	Opp.	Hyp.	Adj.	Opp.
301	243.5	176.9	361	292.1	212.2	421	340.6	247.5	481	389.1	282.7	541	437.7	318.0
302	244.3	177.5	362	292.9	212.8	422	341.4	248.0	482	389.9	283.3	542	438.5	318.6
303	245.1	178.1	363	293.7	213.4	423	342.2	248.6	483	390.8	283.9	543	439.3	319.2
304	245.9	178.7	364	294.5	214.0	424	343.0	249.2	484	391.6	284.5	544	440.1	319.8
305	246.8	179.3	365	295.3	214.5	425	343.8	249.8	485	392.4	285.1	545	440.9	320.3
306	247.6	179.9	366	296.1	215.1	426	344.6	250.4	486	393.2	285.7	546	441.7	320.9
307	248.4	180.5	367	296.9	215.7	427	345.5	251.0	487	394.0	286.3	547	442.5	321.5
308	249.2	181.0	368	297.7	216.3	428	346.3	251.6	488	394.8	286.8	548	443.3	322.1
309	250.0	181.6	369	298.5	216.9	429	347.1	252.2	489	395.6	287.4	549	444.2	322.7
310	250.8	182.2	370	299.3	217.5	430	347.9	252.7	490	396.4	288.0	550	445.0	323.3
311	251.6	182.8	371	300.1	218.1	431	348.7	253.3	491	397.2	288.6	551	445.8	323.9
312	252.4	183.4	372	301.0	218.7	432	349.5	253.9	492	398.0	289.2	552	446.6	324.5
313	253.2	184.0	373	301.8	219.2	433	350.3	254.5	493	398.8	289.8	553	447.4	325.0
314	254.0	184.6	374	302.6	219.8	434	351.1	255.1	494	399.7	290.4	554	448.2	325.6
315	254.8	185.2	375	303.4	220.4	435	351.9	255.7	495	400.5	291.0	555	449.0	326.2
316	255.6	185.7	376	304.2	221.0	436	352.7	256.3	496	401.3	291.5	556	449.8	326.8
317	256.5	186.3	377	305.0	221.6	437	353.5	256.9	497	402.1	292.1	557	450.6	327.4
318	257.3	186.9	378	305.8	222.2	438	354.3	257.4	498	402.9	292.7	558	451.4	328.0
319	258.1	187.5	379	306.6	222.8	439	355.2	258.0	499	403.7	293.3	559	452.2	328.6
320	258.9	188.1	380	307.4	223.4	440	356.0	258.6	500	404.5	293.9	560	453.0	329.2
321	259.7	188.7	381	308.2	223.9	441	356.8	259.2	501	405.3	294.5	561	453.9	329.7
322	260.5	189.3	382	309.0	224.5	442	357.6	259.8	502	406.1	295.1	562	454.7	330.3
323	261.3	189.9	383	309.9	225.1	443	358.4	260.4	503	406.9	295.7	563	455.5	330.9
324	262.1	190.4	384	310.7	225.7	444	359.2	261.0	504	407.7	296.2	564	456.3	331.5
325	262.9	191.0	385	311.5	226.3	445	360.0	261.6	505	408.6	296.8	565	457.1	332.1
326	263.7	191.6	386	312.3	226.9	446	360.8	262.2	506	409.4	297.4	566	457.9	332.7
327	264.5	192.2	387	313.1	227.5	447	361.6	262.7	507	410.2	298.0	567	458.7	333.3
328	265.4	192.8	388	313.9	228.1	448	362.4	263.3	508	411.0	298.6	568	459.5	333.9
329	266.2	193.4	389	314.7	228.6	449	363.2	263.9	509	411.8	299.2	569	460.3	334.4
330	267.0	194.0	390	315.5	229.2	450	364.1	264.5	510	412.6	299.8	570	461.1	335.0
331	267.8	194.6	391	316.3	229.8	451	364.9	265.1	511	413.4	300.4	571	461.9	335.6
332	268.6	195.1	392	317.1	230.4	452	365.7	265.7	512	414.2	300.9	572	462.8	336.2
333	269.4	195.7	393	317.9	231.0	453	366.5	266.3	513	415.0	301.5	573	463.6	336.8
334	270.2	196.3	394	318.8	231.6	454	367.3	266.9	514	415.8	302.1	574	464.4	337.4
335	271.0	196.9	395	319.6	232.2	455	368.1	267.4	515	416.6	302.7	575	465.2	338.0
336	271.8	197.5	396	320.4	232.8	456	368.9	268.0	516	417.5	303.3	576	466.0	338.6
337	272.6	198.1	397	321.2	233.4	457	369.7	268.6	517	418.3	303.9	577	466.8	339.2
338	273.4	198.7	398	322.0	233.9	458	370.5	269.2	518	419.1	304.5	578	467.6	339.7
339	274.3	199.3	399	322.8	234.5	459	371.3	269.8	519	419.9	305.1	579	468.4	340.3
340	275.1	199.8	400	323.6	235.1	460	372.1	270.4	520	420.7	305.6	580	469.2	340.9
341	275.9	200.4	401	324.4	235.7	461	373.0	271.0	521	421.5	306.2	581	470.0	341.5
342	276.7	201.0	402	325.2	236.3	462	373.8	271.6	522	422.3	306.8	582	470.8	342.1
343	277.5	201.6	403	326.0	236.9	463	374.6	272.1	523	423.1	307.4	583	471.7	342.7
344	278.3	202.2	404	326.8	237.5	464	375.4	272.7	524	423.9	308.0	584	472.5	343.3
345	279.1	202.8	405	327.7	238.1	465	376.2	273.3	525	424.7	308.6	585	473.3	343.9
346	279.9	203.4	406	328.5	238.7	466	377.0	273.9	526	425.5	309.2	586	474.1	344.4
347	280.7	204.0	407	329.3	239.2	467	377.8	274.5	527	426.4	309.8	587	474.9	345.0
348	281.5	204.5	408	330.1	239.8	468	378.6	275.1	528	427.2	310.4	588	475.7	345.6
349	282.3	205.1	409	330.9	240.4	469	379.4	275.7	529	428.0	310.9	589	476.5	346.2
350	283.2	205.7	410	331.7	241.0	470	380.2	276.3	530	428.8	311.5	590	477.3	346.8
351	284.0	206.3	411	332.5	241.6	471	381.1	276.8	531	429.6	312.1	591	478.1	347.4
352	284.8	206.9	412	333.3	242.2	472	381.9	277.4	532	430.4	312.7	592	478.9	348.0
353	285.6	207.5	413	334.1	242.8	473	382.7	278.0	533	431.2	313.3	593	479.7	348.6
354	286.4	208.1	414	334.9	243.3	474	383.5	278.6	534	432.0	313.9	594	480.6	349.1
355	287.2	208.7	415	335.7	243.9	475	384.3	279.2	535	432.8	314.5	595	481.4	349.7
356	288.0	209.3	416	336.6	244.5	476	385.1	279.8	536	433.6	315.1	596	482.2	350.3
357	288.8	209.8	417	337.4	245.1	477	385.9	280.4	537	434.4	315.6	597	483.0	350.9
358	289.6	210.4	418	338.2	245.7	478	386.7	281.0	538	435.3	316.2	598	483.8	351.5
359	290.4	211.0	419	339.0	246.3	479	387.5	281.5	539	436.1	316.8	599	484.6	352.1
360	291.2	211.6	420	339.8	246.9	480	388.3	282.1	540	436.9	317.4	600	485.4	352.7
Hyp.	Opp.	Adj.	Hyp.	Opp.	Adj.	Hyp.	Opp.	Adj.	Hyp.	Opp.	Adj.	Hyp.	Opp.	Adj.
Dist. D Lon	Dep.	D. Lat. Dep	Dist. D Lon	Dep.	D. Lat. Dep	Dist. D Lon	Dep.	D. Lat. Dep	Dist. D Lon	Dep.	D. Lat. Dep	Dist. D Lon	Dep.	D. Lat. Dep

54°   306° | 054° / 234° | 126°   **54°**

Table 3 · TRAVERSE TABLE · 37° · 37°

TRAVERSE TABLE

Table 3

37°   37°

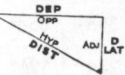

D Lon / Dist.	Dep / D. Lat.	Dep.	D Lon / Dist.	Dep / D. Lat.	Dep.	D Lon / Dist.	Dep / D. Lat.	Dep.	D Lon / Dist.	Dep / D. Lat.	Dep.	D Lon / Dist.	Dep / D. Lat.	Dep.
Hyp.	Adj.	Opp.	Hyp.	Adj.	Opp.	Hyp.	Adj.	Opp.	Hyp.	Adj.	Opp.	Hyp.	Adj.	Opp.
1	0.8	0.6	61	48.7	36.7	121	96.6	72.8	181	144.6	108.9	241	192.5	145.0
2	1.6	1.2	62	49.5	37.3	122	97.4	73.4	182	145.4	109.5	242	193.3	145.6
3	2.4	1.8	63	50.3	37.9	123	98.2	74.0	183	146.2	110.1	243	194.1	146.2
4	3.2	2.4	64	51.1	38.5	124	99.0	74.6	184	146.9	110.7	244	194.9	146.8
5	4.0	3.0	65	51.9	39.1	125	99.8	75.2	185	147.7	111.3	245	195.7	147.4
6	4.8	3.6	66	52.7	39.7	126	100.6	75.8	186	148.5	111.9	246	196.5	148.0
7	5.6	4.2	67	53.5	40.3	127	101.4	76.4	187	149.3	112.5	247	197.3	148.6
8	6.4	4.8	68	54.3	40.9	128	102.2	77.0	188	150.1	113.1	248	198.1	149.3
9	7.2	5.4	69	55.1	41.5	129	103.0	77.6	189	150.9	113.7	249	198.9	149.9
10	8.0	6.0	70	55.9	42.1	130	103.8	78.2	190	151.7	114.3	250	199.7	150.5
11	8.8	6.6	71	56.7	42.7	131	104.6	78.8	191	152.5	114.9	251	200.5	151.1
12	9.6	7.2	72	57.5	43.3	132	105.4	79.4	192	153.3	115.5	252	201.3	151.7
13	10.4	7.8	73	58.3	43.9	133	106.2	80.0	193	154.1	116.2	253	202.1	152.3
14	11.2	8.4	74	59.1	44.5	134	107.0	80.6	194	154.9	116.8	254	202.9	152.9
15	12.0	9.0	75	59.9	45.1	135	107.8	81.2	195	155.7	117.4	255	203.7	153.5
16	12.8	9.6	76	60.7	45.7	136	108.6	81.8	196	156.5	118.0	256	204.5	154.1
17	13.6	10.2	77	61.5	46.3	137	109.4	82.4	197	157.3	118.6	257	205.3	154.7
18	14.4	10.8	78	62.3	46.9	138	110.2	83.1	198	158.1	119.2	258	206.0	155.3
19	15.2	11.4	79	63.1	47.5	139	111.0	83.7	199	158.9	119.8	259	206.8	155.9
20	16.0	12.0	80	63.9	48.1	140	111.8	84.3	200	159.7	120.4	260	207.6	156.5
21	16.8	12.6	81	64.7	48.7	141	112.6	84.9	201	160.5	121.0	261	208.4	157.1
22	17.6	13.2	82	65.5	49.3	142	113.4	85.5	202	161.3	121.6	262	209.2	157.7
23	18.4	13.8	83	66.3	50.0	143	114.2	86.1	203	162.1	122.2	263	210.0	158.3
24	19.2	14.4	84	67.1	50.6	144	115.0	86.7	204	162.9	122.8	264	210.8	158.9
25	20.0	15.0	85	67.9	51.2	145	115.8	87.3	205	163.7	123.4	265	211.6	159.5
26	20.8	15.6	86	68.7	51.8	146	116.6	87.9	206	164.5	124.0	266	212.4	160.1
27	21.6	16.2	87	69.5	52.4	147	117.4	88.5	207	165.3	124.6	267	213.2	160.7
28	22.4	16.9	88	70.3	53.0	148	118.2	89.1	208	166.1	125.2	268	214.0	161.3
29	23.2	17.5	89	71.1	53.6	149	119.0	89.7	209	166.9	125.8	269	214.8	161.9
30	24.0	18.1	90	71.9	54.2	150	119.8	90.3	210	167.7	126.4	270	215.6	162.5
31	24.8	18.7	91	72.7	54.8	151	120.6	90.9	211	168.5	127.0	271	216.4	163.1
32	25.6	19.3	92	73.5	55.4	152	121.4	91.5	212	169.3	127.6	272	217.2	163.7
33	26.4	19.9	93	74.3	56.0	153	122.2	92.1	213	170.1	128.2	273	218.0	164.3
34	27.2	20.5	94	75.1	56.6	154	123.0	92.7	214	170.9	128.8	274	218.8	164.9
35	28.0	21.1	95	75.9	57.2	155	123.8	93.3	215	171.7	129.4	275	219.6	165.5
36	28.8	21.7	96	76.7	57.8	156	124.6	93.9	216	172.5	130.0	276	220.4	166.1
37	29.5	22.3	97	77.5	58.4	157	125.4	94.5	217	173.3	130.6	277	221.2	166.7
38	30.3	22.9	98	78.3	59.0	158	126.2	95.1	218	174.1	131.2	278	222.0	167.3
39	31.1	23.5	99	79.1	59.6	159	127.0	95.7	219	174.9	131.8	279	222.8	167.9
40	31.9	24.1	100	79.9	60.2	160	127.8	96.3	220	175.7	132.4	280	223.6	168.5
41	32.7	24.7	101	80.7	60.8	161	128.6	96.9	221	176.5	133.0	281	224.4	169.1
42	33.5	25.3	102	81.5	61.4	162	129.4	97.5	222	177.3	133.6	282	225.2	169.7
43	34.3	25.9	103	82.3	62.0	163	130.2	98.1	223	178.1	134.2	283	226.0	170.3
44	35.1	26.5	104	83.1	62.6	164	131.0	98.7	224	178.9	134.8	284	226.8	170.9
45	35.9	27.1	105	83.9	63.2	165	131.8	99.3	225	179.7	135.4	285	227.6	171.5
46	36.7	27.7	106	84.7	63.8	166	132.6	99.9	226	180.5	136.0	286	228.4	172.1
47	37.5	28.3	107	85.5	64.4	167	133.4	100.5	227	181.3	136.6	287	229.2	172.7
48	38.3	28.9	108	86.3	65.0	168	134.2	101.1	228	182.1	137.2	288	230.0	173.3
49	39.1	29.5	109	87.1	65.6	169	135.0	101.7	229	182.9	137.8	289	230.8	173.9
50	39.9	30.1	110	87.8	66.2	170	135.8	102.3	230	183.7	138.4	290	231.6	174.5
51	40.7	30.7	111	88.6	66.8	171	136.6	102.9	231	184.5	139.0	291	232.4	175.1
52	41.5	31.3	112	89.4	67.4	172	137.4	103.5	232	185.3	139.6	292	233.2	175.7
53	42.3	31.9	113	90.2	68.0	173	138.2	104.1	233	186.1	140.2	293	234.0	176.3
54	43.1	32.5	114	91.0	68.6	174	139.0	104.7	234	186.9	140.8	294	234.8	176.9
55	43.9	33.1	115	91.8	69.2	175	139.8	105.3	235	187.7	141.4	295	235.6	177.5
56	44.7	33.7	116	92.6	69.8	176	140.6	105.9	236	188.5	142.0	296	236.4	178.1
57	45.5	34.3	117	93.4	70.4	177	141.4	106.5	237	189.3	142.6	297	237.2	178.7
58	46.3	34.9	118	94.2	71.0	178	142.2	107.1	238	190.1	143.2	298	238.0	179.3
59	47.1	35.5	119	95.0	71.6	179	143.0	107.7	239	190.9	143.8	299	238.8	179.9
60	47.9	36.1	120	95.8	72.2	180	143.8	108.3	240	191.7	144.4	300	239.6	180.5
Hyp.	Opp.	Adj.	Hyp.	Opp.	Adj.	Hyp.	Opp.	Adj.	Hyp.	Opp.	Adj.	Hyp.	Opp.	Adj.
Dist. / D Lon	Dep.	D. Lat. / Dep	Dist. / D Lon	Dep.	D. Lat. / Dep	Dist. / D Lon	Dep.	D. Lat. / Dep	Dist. / D Lon	Dep.	D. Lat. / Dep	Dist. / D Lon	Dep.	D. Lat. / Dep

53°   53°

Table 3

37°

TRAVERSE TABLE

D Lon	Dep		D Lon	Dep		D Lon	Dep		D Lon	Dep		D Lon	Dep	
Dist.	D. Lat.	Dep.	Dist.	D. Lat.	Dep.	Dist.	D. Lat.	Dep.	Dist.	D. Lat.	Dep.	Dist.	D. Lat.	Dep.
Hyp.	Adj.	Opp.	Hyp.	Adj.	Opp.	Hyp.	Adj.	Opp.	Hyp.	Adj.	Opp.	Hyp.	Adj.	Opp.
301	240.4	181.1	361	288.3	217.3	421	336.2	253.4	481	384.1	289.5	541	432.1	325.6
302	241.2	181.7	362	289.1	217.9	422	337.0	254.0	482	384.9	290.1	542	432.9	326.2
303	242.0	182.3	363	289.9	218.5	423	337.8	254.6	483	385.7	290.7	543	433.7	326.8
304	242.8	183.0	364	290.7	219.1	424	338.6	255.2	484	386.5	291.3	544	434.5	327.4
305	243.6	183.6	365	291.5	219.7	425	339.4	255.8	485	387.3	291.9	545	435.3	328.0
306	244.4	184.2	366	292.3	220.3	426	340.2	256.4	486	388.1	292.5	546	436.1	328.6
307	245.2	184.8	367	293.1	220.9	427	341.0	257.0	487	388.9	293.1	547	436.9	329.2
308	246.0	185.4	368	293.9	221.5	428	341.8	257.6	488	389.7	293.7	548	437.7	329.8
309	246.8	186.0	369	294.7	222.1	429	342.6	258.2	489	390.5	294.3	549	438.5	330.4
310	247.6	186.6	370	295.5	222.7	430	343.4	258.8	490	391.3	294.9	550	439.2	331.0
311	248.4	187.2	371	296.3	223.3	431	344.2	259.4	491	392.1	295.5	551	440.0	331.6
312	249.2	187.8	372	297.1	223.9	432	345.0	260.0	492	392.9	296.1	552	440.8	332.2
313	250.0	188.4	373	297.9	224.5	433	345.8	260.6	493	393.7	296.7	553	441.6	332.8
314	250.8	189.0	374	298.7	225.1	434	346.6	261.2	494	394.5	297.3	554	442.4	333.4
315	251.6	189.6	375	299.5	225.7	435	347.4	261.8	495	395.3	297.9	555	443.2	334.0
316	252.4	190.2	376	300.3	226.3	436	348.2	262.4	496	396.1	298.5	556	444.0	334.6
317	253.2	190.8	377	301.1	226.9	437	349.0	263.0	497	396.9	299.1	557	444.8	335.2
318	254.0	191.4	378	301.9	227.5	438	349.8	263.6	498	397.7	299.7	558	445.6	335.8
319	254.8	192.0	379	302.7	228.1	439	350.6	264.2	499	398.5	300.3	559	446.4	336.4
320	255.6	192.6	380	303.5	228.7	440	351.4	264.8	500	399.3	300.9	560	447.2	337.0
321	256.4	193.2	381	304.3	229.3	441	352.2	265.4	501	400.1	301.5	561	448.0	337.6
322	257.2	193.8	382	305.1	229.9	442	353.0	266.0	502	400.9	302.1	562	448.8	338.2
323	258.0	194.4	383	305.9	230.5	443	353.8	266.6	503	401.7	302.7	563	449.6	338.8
324	258.8	195.0	384	306.7	231.1	444	354.6	267.2	504	402.5	303.3	564	450.4	339.4
325	259.6	195.6	385	307.5	231.7	445	355.4	267.8	505	403.3	303.9	565	451.2	340.0
326	260.4	196.2	386	308.3	232.3	446	356.2	268.4	506	404.1	304.5	566	452.0	340.6
327	261.2	196.8	387	309.1	232.9	447	357.0	269.0	507	404.9	305.1	567	452.8	341.2
328	262.0	197.4	388	309.9	233.5	448	357.8	269.6	508	405.7	305.7	568	453.6	341.8
329	262.8	198.0	389	310.7	234.1	449	358.6	270.2	509	406.5	306.3	569	454.4	342.4
330	263.5	198.6	390	311.5	234.7	450	359.4	270.8	510	407.3	306.9	570	455.2	343.0
331	264.3	199.2	391	312.3	235.3	451	360.2	271.4	511	408.1	307.5	571	456.0	343.6
332	265.1	199.8	392	313.1	235.9	452	361.0	272.0	512	408.9	308.1	572	456.8	344.2
333	265.9	200.4	393	313.9	236.5	453	361.8	272.6	513	409.7	308.7	573	457.6	344.8
334	266.7	201.0	394	314.7	237.1	454	362.6	273.2	514	410.5	309.3	574	458.4	345.4
335	267.5	201.6	395	315.5	237.7	455	363.4	273.8	515	411.3	309.9	575	459.2	346.0
336	268.3	202.2	396	316.3	238.3	456	364.2	274.4	516	412.1	310.5	576	460.0	346.6
337	269.1	202.8	397	317.1	238.9	457	365.0	275.0	517	412.9	311.1	577	460.8	347.2
338	269.9	203.4	398	317.9	239.5	458	365.8	275.6	518	413.7	311.7	578	461.6	347.8
339	270.7	204.0	399	318.7	240.1	459	366.6	276.2	519	414.5	312.3	579	462.4	348.5
340	271.5	204.6	400	319.5	240.7	460	367.4	276.8	520	415.3	312.9	580	463.2	349.1
341	272.3	205.2	401	320.3	241.3	461	368.2	277.4	521	416.1	313.5	581	464.0	349.7
342	273.1	205.8	402	321.1	241.9	462	369.0	278.0	522	416.9	314.1	582	464.8	350.3
343	273.9	206.4	403	321.9	242.5	463	369.8	278.6	523	417.7	314.7	583	465.6	350.9
344	274.7	207.0	404	322.6	243.1	464	370.6	279.2	524	418.5	315.4	584	466.4	351.5
345	275.5	207.6	405	323.4	243.7	465	371.4	279.8	525	419.3	316.0	585	467.2	352.1
346	276.3	208.2	406	324.2	244.3	466	372.2	280.4	526	420.1	316.6	586	468.0	352.7
347	277.1	208.8	407	325.0	244.9	467	373.0	281.0	527	420.9	317.2	587	468.8	353.3
348	277.9	209.4	408	325.8	245.5	468	373.8	281.6	528	421.7	317.8	588	469.6	353.9
349	278.7	210.0	409	326.6	246.1	469	374.6	282.3	529	422.5	318.4	589	470.4	354.5
350	279.5	210.6	410	327.4	246.7	470	375.4	282.9	530	423.3	319.0	590	471.2	355.1
351	280.3	211.2	411	328.2	247.3	471	376.2	283.5	531	424.1	319.6	591	472.0	355.7
352	281.1	211.8	412	329.0	247.9	472	377.0	284.1	532	424.9	320.2	592	472.8	356.3
353	281.9	212.4	413	329.8	248.5	473	377.8	284.7	533	425.7	320.8	593	473.6	356.9
354	282.7	213.0	414	330.6	249.2	474	378.6	285.3	534	426.5	321.4	594	474.4	357.5
355	283.5	213.6	415	331.4	249.8	475	379.4	285.9	535	427.3	322.0	595	475.2	358.1
356	284.3	214.2	416	332.2	250.4	476	380.2	286.5	536	428.1	322.6	596	476.0	358.7
357	285.1	214.8	417	333.0	251.0	477	380.9	287.1	537	428.9	323.2	597	476.8	359.3
358	285.9	215.4	418	333.8	251.6	478	381.7	287.7	538	429.7	323.8	598	477.6	359.9
359	286.7	216.1	419	334.6	252.2	479	382.5	288.3	539	430.5	324.4	599	478.4	360.5
360	287.5	216.7	420	335.4	252.8	480	383.3	288.9	540	431.3	325.0	600	479.2	361.1
Hyp.	Opp.	Adj.	Hyp.	Opp.	Adj.	Hyp.	Opp.	Adj.	Hyp.	Opp.	Adj.	Hyp.	Opp.	Adj.
Dist.	Dep.	D. Lat.	Dist.	Dep.	D. Lat.	Dist.	Dep.	D. Lat.	Dist.	Dep.	D. Lat.	Dist.	Dep.	D. Lat.
D Lon		Dep	D Lon		Dep	D Lon		Dep	D Lon		Dep	D Lon		Dep

Table 3 TRAVERSE TABLE

38° 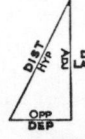 38°

D Lon Dist.	Dep D. Lat.	Dep.	D Lon Dist.	Dep D. Lat.	Dep.	D Lon Dist.	Dep D. Lat.	Dep.	D Lon Dist.	Dep D. Lat.	Dep.	D Lon Dist.	Dep D. Lat.	Dep.
Hyp.	Adj.	Opp.	Hyp.	Adj.	Opp.	Hyp.	Adj.	Opp.	Hyp.	Adj.	Opp.	Hyp.	Adj.	Opp.
1	0.8	0.6	61	48.1	37.6	121	95.3	74.5	181	142.6	111.4	241	189.9	148.4
2	1.6	1.2	62	48.9	38.2	122	96.1	75.1	182	143.4	112.1	242	190.7	149.0
3	2.4	1.8	63	49.6	38.8	123	96.9	75.7	183	144.2	112.7	243	191.5	149.6
4	3.2	2.5	64	50.4	39.4	124	97.7	76.3	184	145.0	113.3	244	192.3	150.2
5	3.9	3.1	65	51.2	40.0	125	98.5	77.0	185	145.8	113.9	245	193.1	150.8
6	4.7	3.7	66	52.0	40.6	126	99.3	77.6	186	146.6	114.5	246	193.9	151.5
7	5.5	4.3	67	52.8	41.2	127	100.1	78.2	187	147.4	115.1	247	194.6	152.1
8	6.3	4.9	68	53.6	41.9	128	100.9	78.8	188	148.1	115.7	248	195.4	152.7
9	7.1	5.5	69	54.4	42.5	129	101.7	79.4	189	148.9	116.4	249	196.2	153.3
10	7.9	6.2	70	55.2	43.1	130	102.4	80.0	190	149.7	117.0	250	197.0	153.9
11	8.7	6.8	71	55.9	43.7	131	103.2	80.7	191	150.5	117.6	251	197.8	154.5
12	9.5	7.4	72	56.7	44.3	132	104.0	81.3	192	151.3	118.2	252	198.6	155.1
13	10.2	8.0	73	57.5	44.9	133	104.8	81.9	193	152.1	118.8	253	199.4	155.8
14	11.0	8.6	74	58.3	45.6	134	105.6	82.5	194	152.9	119.4	254	200.2	156.4
15	11.8	9.2	75	59.1	46.2	135	106.4	83.1	195	153.7	120.1	255	200.9	157.0
16	12.6	9.9	76	59.9	46.8	136	107.2	83.7	196	154.5	120.7	256	201.7	157.6
17	13.4	10.5	77	60.7	47.4	137	108.0	84.3	197	155.2	121.3	257	202.5	158.2
18	14.2	11.1	78	61.5	48.0	138	108.7	85.0	198	156.0	121.9	258	203.3	158.8
19	15.0	11.7	79	62.3	48.6	139	109.5	85.6	199	156.8	122.5	259	204.1	159.5
20	15.8	12.3	80	63.0	49.3	140	110.3	86.2	200	157.6	123.1	260	204.9	160.1
21	16.5	12.9	81	63.8	49.9	141	111.1	86.8	201	158.4	123.7	261	205.7	160.7
22	17.3	13.5	82	64.6	50.5	142	111.9	87.4	202	159.2	124.4	262	206.5	161.3
23	18.1	14.2	83	65.4	51.1	143	112.7	88.0	203	160.0	125.0	263	207.2	161.9
24	18.9	14.8	84	66.2	51.7	144	113.5	88.7	204	160.8	125.6	264	208.0	162.5
25	19.7	15.4	85	67.0	52.3	145	114.3	89.3	205	161.5	126.2	265	208.8	163.2
26	20.5	16.0	86	67.8	52.9	146	115.0	89.9	206	162.3	126.8	266	209.6	163.8
27	21.3	16.6	87	68.6	53.6	147	115.8	90.5	207	163.1	127.4	267	210.4	164.4
28	22.1	17.2	88	69.3	54.2	148	116.6	91.1	208	163.9	128.1	268	211.2	165.0
29	22.9	17.9	89	70.1	54.8	149	117.4	91.7	209	164.7	128.7	269	212.0	165.6
30	23.6	18.5	90	70.9	55.4	150	118.2	92.3	210	165.5	129.3	270	212.8	166.2
31	24.4	19.1	91	71.7	56.0	151	119.0	93.0	211	166.3	129.9	271	213.6	166.8
32	25.2	19.7	92	72.5	56.6	152	119.8	93.6	212	167.1	130.5	272	214.3	167.5
33	26.0	20.3	93	73.3	57.3	153	120.6	94.2	213	167.8	131.1	273	215.1	168.1
34	26.8	20.9	94	74.1	57.9	154	121.4	94.8	214	168.6	131.8	274	215.9	168.7
35	27.6	21.5	95	74.9	58.5	155	122.1	95.4	215	169.4	132.4	275	216.7	169.3
36	28.4	22.2	96	75.6	59.1	156	122.9	96.0	216	170.2	133.0	276	217.5	169.9
37	29.2	22.8	97	76.4	59.7	157	123.7	96.7	217	171.0	133.6	277	218.3	170.5
38	29.9	23.4	98	77.2	60.3	158	124.5	97.3	218	171.8	134.2	278	219.1	171.2
39	30.7	24.0	99	78.0	61.0	159	125.3	97.9	219	172.6	134.8	279	219.9	171.8
40	31.5	24.6	100	78.8	61.6	160	126.1	98.5	220	173.4	135.4	280	220.6	172.4
41	32.3	25.2	101	79.6	62.2	161	126.9	99.1	221	174.2	136.1	281	221.4	173.0
42	33.1	25.9	102	80.4	62.8	162	127.7	99.7	222	174.9	136.7	282	222.2	173.6
43	33.9	26.5	103	81.2	63.4	163	128.4	100.4	223	175.7	137.3	283	223.0	174.2
44	34.7	27.1	104	82.0	64.0	164	129.2	101.0	224	176.5	137.9	284	223.8	174.8
45	35.5	27.7	105	82.7	64.6	165	130.0	101.6	225	177.3	138.5	285	224.6	175.5
46	36.2	28.3	106	83.5	65.3	166	130.8	102.2	226	178.1	139.1	286	225.4	176.1
47	37.0	28.9	107	84.3	65.9	167	131.6	102.8	227	178.9	139.8	287	226.2	176.7
48	37.8	29.6	108	85.1	66.5	168	132.4	103.4	228	179.7	140.4	288	226.9	177.3
49	38.6	30.2	109	85.9	67.1	169	133.2	104.0	229	180.5	141.0	289	227.7	177.9
50	39.4	30.8	110	86.7	67.7	170	134.0	104.7	230	181.2	141.6	290	228.5	178.5
51	40.2	31.4	111	87.5	68.3	171	134.7	105.3	231	182.0	142.2	291	229.3	179.2
52	41.0	32.0	112	88.3	69.0	172	135.5	105.9	232	182.8	142.8	292	230.1	179.8
53	41.8	32.6	113	89.0	69.6	173	136.3	106.5	233	183.6	143.4	293	230.9	180.4
54	42.6	33.2	114	89.8	70.2	174	137.1	107.1	234	184.4	144.1	294	231.7	181.0
55	43.3	33.9	115	90.6	70.8	175	137.9	107.7	235	185.2	144.7	295	232.5	181.6
56	44.1	34.5	116	91.4	71.4	176	138.7	108.4	236	186.0	145.3	296	233.3	182.2
57	44.9	35.1	117	92.2	72.0	177	139.5	109.0	237	186.8	145.9	297	234.0	182.9
58	45.7	35.7	118	93.0	72.6	178	140.3	109.6	238	187.5	146.5	298	234.8	183.5
59	46.5	36.3	119	93.8	73.3	179	141.1	110.2	239	188.3	147.1	299	235.6	184.1
60	47.3	36.9	120	94.6	73.9	180	141.8	110.8	240	189.1	147.8	300	236.4	184.7
Hyp.	Opp.	Adj.	Hyp.	Opp.	Adj.	Hyp.	Opp.	Adj.	Hyp.	Opp.	Adj.	Hyp.	Opp.	Adj.
Dist. D Lon	Dep.	D. Lat. Dep	Dist. D Lon	Dep.	D. Lat. Dep	Dist. D Lon	Dep.	D. Lat. Dep	Dist. D Lon	Dep.	D. Lat. Dep	Dist. D Lon	Dep.	D. Lat. Dep

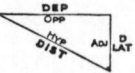

52° 52°

Table 3

TRAVERSE TABLE

38°

	322°	038°	
	218°	142°	

38°

D Lon	Dep		D Lon	Dep		D Lon	Dep		D Lon	Dep		D Lon	Dep	
Dist.	**D. Lat.**	**Dep.**	**Dist.**	**D. Lat.**	**Dep.**	**Dist.**	**D. Lat.**	**Dep.**	**Dist.**	**D. Lat.**	**Dep.**	**Dist.**	**D. Lat.**	**Dep.**
Hyp.	*Adj.*	*Opp.*	*Hyp.*	*Adj.*	*Opp.*	*Hyp.*	*Adj.*	*Orp.*	*Hyp.*	*Adj.*	*Opp.*	*Hyp.*	*Adj.*	*Opp.*
301	237.2	185.3	361	284.5	222.3	421	331.8	259.2	481	379.0	296.1	541	426.3	333.1
302	238.0	185.9	362	285.3	222.9	422	332.5	259.8	482	379.8	296.7	542	427.1	333.7
303	238.8	186.5	363	286.0	223.5	423	333.3	260.4	483	380.6	297.4	543	427.9	334.3
304	239.6	187.2	364	286.8	224.1	424	334.1	261.0	484	381.4	298.0	544	428.7	334.9
305	240.3	187.8	365	287.6	224.7	425	334.9	261.7	485	382.2	298.6	545	429.5	335.5
306	241.1	188.4	366	288.4	225.3	426	335.7	262.3	486	383.0	299.2	546	430.3	336.2
307	241.9	189.0	367	289.2	225.9	427	336.5	262.9	487	383.8	299.8	547	431.0	336.8
308	242.7	189.6	368	290.0	226.6	428	337.3	263.5	488	384.5	300.4	548	431.8	337.4
309	243.5	190.2	369	290.8	227.2	429	338.1	264.1	489	385.3	301.1	549	432.6	338.0
310	244.3	190.9	370	291.6	227.8	430	338.8	264.7	490	386.1	301.7	550	433.4	338.6
311	245.1	191.5	371	292.4	228.4	431	339.6	265.4	491	386.9	302.3	551	434.2	339.2
312	245.9	192.1	372	293.1	229.0	432	340.4	266.0	492	387.7	302.9	552	435.0	339.8
313	246.6	192.7	373	293.9	229.6	433	341.2	266.6	493	388.5	303.5	553	435.8	340.5
314	247.4	193.3	374	294.7	230.3	434	342.0	267.2	494	389.3	304.1	554	436.6	341.1
315	248.2	193.9	375	295.5	230.9	435	342.8	267.8	495	390.1	304.8	555	437.3	341.7
316	249.0	194.5	376	296.3	231.5	436	343.6	268.4	496	390.9	305.4	556	438.1	342.3
317	249.8	195.2	377	297.1	232.1	437	344.4	269.0	497	391.6	306.0	557	438.9	342.9
318	250.6	195.8	378	297.9	232.7	438	345.1	269.7	498	392.4	306.6	558	439.7	343.5
319	251.4	196.4	379	298.7	233.3	439	345.9	270.3	499	393.2	307.2	559	440.5	344.2
320	252.2	197.0	380	299.4	234.0	440	346.7	270.9	500	394.0	307.8	560	441.3	344.8
321	253.0	197.6	381	300.2	234.6	441	347.5	271.5	501	394.8	308.4	561	442.1	345.4
322	253.7	198.2	382	301.0	235.2	442	348.3	272.1	502	395.6	309.1	562	442.9	346.0
323	254.5	198.9	383	301.8	235.8	443	349.1	272.7	503	396.4	309.7	563	443.7	346.6
324	255.3	199.5	384	302.6	236.4	444	349.9	273.4	504	397.2	310.3	564	444.4	347.2
325	256.1	200.1	385	303.4	237.0	445	350.7	274.0	505	397.9	310.9	565	445.2	347.8
326	256.9	200.7	386	304.2	237.6	446	351.5	274.6	506	398.7	311.5	566	446.0	348.5
327	257.7	201.3	387	305.0	238.3	447	352.2	275.2	507	399.5	312.1	567	446.8	349.1
328	258.5	201.9	388	305.7	238.9	448	353.0	275.8	508	400.3	312.8	568	447.6	349.7
329	259.3	202.6	389	306.5	239.5	449	353.8	276.4	509	401.1	313.4	569	448.4	350.3
330	260.0	203.2	390	307.3	240.1	450	354.6	277.0	510	401.9	314.0	570	449.2	350.9
331	260.8	203.8	391	308.1	240.7	451	355.4	277.7	511	402.7	314.6	571	450.0	351.5
332	261.6	204.4	392	308.9	241.3	452	356.2	278.3	512	403.5	315.2	572	450.7	352.2
333	262.4	205.0	393	309.7	242.0	453	357.0	278.9	513	404.2	315.8	573	451.5	352.8
334	263.2	205.6	394	310.5	242.6	454	357.8	279.5	514	405.0	316.5	574	452.3	353.4
335	264.0	206.2	395	311.3	243.2	455	358.5	280.1	515	405.8	317.1	575	453.1	354.0
336	264.8	206.9	396	312.1	243.8	456	359.3	280.7	516	406.6	317.7	576	453.9	354.6
337	265.6	207.5	397	312.8	244.4	457	360.1	281.4	517	407.4	318.3	577	454.7	355.2
338	266.3	208.1	398	313.6	245.0	458	360.9	282.0	518	408.2	318.9	578	455.5	355.9
339	267.1	208.7	399	314.4	245.6	459	361.7	282.6	519	409.0	319.5	579	456.3	356.5
340	267.9	209.3	400	315.2	246.3	460	362.5	283.2	520	409.8	320.1	580	457.0	357.1
341	268.7	209.9	401	316.0	246.9	461	363.3	283.8	521	410.6	320.8	581	457.8	357.7
342	269.5	210.6	402	316.8	247.5	462	364.1	284.4	522	411.3	321.4	582	458.6	358.3
343	270.3	211.2	403	317.6	248.1	463	364.8	285.1	523	412.1	322.0	583	459.4	358.9
344	271.1	211.8	404	318.4	248.7	464	365.6	285.7	524	412.9	322.6	584	460.2	359.5
345	271.9	212.4	405	319.1	249.3	465	366.4	286.3	525	413.7	323.2	585	461.0	360.2
346	272.7	213.0	406	319.9	250.0	466	367.2	286.9	526	414.5	323.8	586	461.8	360.8
347	273.4	213.6	407	320.7	250.6	467	368.0	287.5	527	415.3	324.5	587	462.6	361.4
348	274.2	214.3	408	321.5	251.2	468	368.8	288.1	528	416.1	325.1	588	463.4	362.0
349	275.0	214.9	409	322.3	251.8	469	369.6	288.7	529	416.9	325.7	589	464.1	362.6
350	275.8	215.5	410	323.1	252.4	470	370.4	289.4	530	417.6	326.3	590	464.9	363.2
351	276.6	216.1	411	323.9	253.0	471	371.2	290.0	531	418.4	326.9	591	465.7	363.9
352	277.4	216.7	412	324.7	253.7	472	371.9	290.6	532	419.2	327.5	592	466.5	364.5
353	278.2	217.3	413	325.4	254.3	473	372.7	291.2	533	420.0	328.1	593	467.3	365.1
354	279.0	217.9	414	326.2	254.9	474	373.5	291.8	534	420.8	328.8	594	468.1	365.7
355	279.7	218.6	415	327.0	255.5	475	374.3	292.4	535	421.6	329.4	595	468.9	366.3
356	280.5	219.2	416	327.8	256.1	476	375.1	293.1	536	422.4	330.0	596	469.7	366.9
357	281.3	219.8	417	328.6	256.7	477	375.9	293.7	537	423.2	330.6	597	470.4	367.5
358	282.1	220.4	418	329.4	257.3	478	376.7	294.3	538	423.9	331.2	598	471.2	368.2
359	282.9	221.0	419	330.2	258.0	479	377.5	294.9	539	424.7	331.8	599	472.0	368.8
360	283.7	221.6	420	331.0	258.6	480	378.2	295.5	540	425.5	332.5	600	472.8	369.4
Hyp.	*Opp.*	*Adj.*	*Hyp.*	*Opp.*	*Adj.*	*Hyp.*	*Opp.*	*Adj.*	*Hyp.*	*Opp.*	*Adj.*	*Hyp.*	*Opp.*	*Adj.*
Dist.	**Dep.**	**D. Lat.**	**Dist.**	**Dep.**	**D. Lat.**	**Dist.**	**Dep.**	**D. Lat.**	**Dist.**	**Dep.**	**D. Lat.**	**Dist.**	**Dep.**	**D. Lat.**
D Lon		Dep	D Lon		Dep	D Lon		Dep	D Lon		Dep	D Lon		Dep

52°

	308°	052°	
	232°	128°	

52°

Table 3

TRAVERSE TABLE

39°

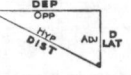

39°

D Lon Dist.	Dep D. Lat.	Dep.	D Lon Dist.	Dep D. Lat.	Dep.	D Lon Dist.	Dep D. Lat.	Dep.	D Lon Dist.	Dep D. Lat.	Dep.	D Lon Dist.	Dep D. Lat.	Dep.
Hyp.	Adj.	Opp.	Hyp.	Adj.	Opp.	Hyp.	Adj.	Opp.	Hyp.	Adj.	Opp.	Hyp.	Adj.	Opp.
1	0.8	0.6	61	47.4	38.4	121	94.0	76.1	181	140.7	113.9	241	187.3	151.7
2	1.6	1.3	62	48.2	39.0	122	94.8	76.8	182	141.4	114.5	242	188.1	152.3
3	2.3	1.9	63	49.0	39.6	123	95.6	77.4	183	142.2	115.2	243	188.8	152.9
4	3.1	2.5	64	49.7	40.3	124	96.4	78.0	184	143.0	115.8	244	189.6	153.6
5	3.9	3.1	65	50.5	40.9	125	97.1	78.7	185	143.8	116.4	245	190.4	154.2
6	4.7	3.8	66	51.3	41.5	126	97.9	79.3	186	144.5	117.1	246	191.2	154.8
7	5.4	4.4	67	52.1	42.2	127	98.7	79.9	187	145.3	117.7	247	192.0	155.4
8	6.2	5.0	68	52.8	42.8	128	99.5	80.6	188	146.1	118.3	248	192.7	156.1
9	7.0	5.7	69	53.6	43.4	129	100.3	81.2	189	146.9	118.9	249	193.5	156.7
10	7.8	6.3	70	54.4	44.1	130	101.0	81.8	190	147.7	119.6	250	194.3	157.3
11	8.5	6.9	71	55.2	44.7	131	101.8	82.4	191	148.4	120.2	251	195.1	158.0
12	9.3	7.6	72	56.0	45.3	132	102.6	83.1	192	149.2	120.8	252	195.8	158.6
13	10.1	8.2	73	56.7	45.9	133	103.4	83.7	193	150.0	121.5	253	196.6	159.2
14	10.9	8.8	74	57.5	46.6	134	104.1	84.3	194	150.8	122.1	254	197.4	159.8
15	11.7	9.4	75	58.3	47.2	135	104.9	85.0	195	151.5	122.7	255	198.2	160.5
16	12.4	10.1	76	59.1	47.8	136	105.7	85.6	196	152.3	123.3	256	198.9	161.1
17	13.2	10.7	77	59.8	48.5	137	106.5	86.2	197	153.1	124.0	257	199.7	161.7
18	14.0	11.3	78	60.6	49.1	138	107.2	86.8	198	153.9	124.6	258	200.5	162.4
19	14.8	12.0	79	61.4	49.7	139	108.0	87.5	199	154.7	125.2	259	201.3	163.0
20	15.5	12.6	80	62.2	50.3	140	108.8	88.1	200	155.4	125.9	260	202.1	163.6
21	16.3	13.2	81	62.9	51.0	141	109.6	88.7	201	156.2	126.5	261	202.8	164.3
22	17.1	13.8	82	63.7	51.6	142	110.4	89.4	202	157.0	127.1	262	203.6	164.9
23	17.9	14.5	83	64.5	52.2	143	111.1	90.0	203	157.8	127.8	263	204.4	165.5
24	18.7	15.1	84	65.3	52.9	144	111.9	90.6	204	158.5	128.4	264	205.2	166.1
25	19.4	15.7	85	66.1	53.5	145	112.7	91.3	205	159.3	129.0	265	205.9	166.8
26	20.2	16.4	86	66.8	54.1	146	113.5	91.9	206	160.1	129.6	266	206.7	167.4
27	21.0	17.0	87	67.6	54.8	147	114.2	92.5	207	160.9	130.3	267	207.5	168.0
28	21.8	17.6	88	68.4	55.4	148	115.0	93.1	208	161.6	130.9	268	208.3	168.7
29	22.5	18.3	89	69.2	56.0	149	115.8	93.8	209	162.4	131.5	269	209.1	169.3
30	23.3	18.9	90	69.9	56.6	150	116.6	94.4	210	163.2	132.2	270	209.8	169.9
31	24.1	19.5	91	70.7	57.3	151	117.3	95.0	211	164.0	132.8	271	210.6	170.5
32	24.9	20.1	92	71.5	57.9	152	118.1	95.7	212	164.8	133.4	272	211.4	171.2
33	25.6	20.8	93	72.3	58.5	153	118.9	96.3	213	165.5	134.0	273	212.2	171.8
34	26.4	21.4	94	73.1	59.2	154	119.7	96.9	214	166.3	134.7	274	212.9	172.4
35	27.2	22.0	95	73.8	59.8	155	120.5	97.5	215	167.1	135.3	275	213.7	173.1
36	28.0	22.7	96	74.6	60.4	156	121.2	98.2	216	167.9	135.9	276	214.5	173.7
37	28.8	23.3	97	75.4	61.0	157	122.0	98.8	217	168.6	136.6	277	215.3	174.3
38	29.5	23.9	98	76.2	61.7	158	122.8	99.4	218	169.4	137.2	278	216.0	175.0
39	30.3	24.5	99	76.9	62.3	159	123.6	100.1	219	170.2	137.8	279	216.8	175.6
40	31.1	25.2	100	77.7	62.9	160	124.3	100.7	220	171.0	138.5	280	217.6	176.2
41	31.9	25.8	101	78.5	63.6	161	125.1	101.3	221	171.7	139.1	281	218.4	176.8
42	32.6	26.4	102	79.3	64.2	162	125.9	101.9	222	172.5	139.7	282	219.2	177.5
43	33.4	27.1	103	80.0	64.8	163	126.7	102.6	223	173.3	140.3	283	219.9	178.1
44	34.2	27.7	104	80.8	65.4	164	127.5	103.2	224	174.1	141.0	284	220.7	178.7
45	35.0	28.3	105	81.6	66.1	165	128.2	103.8	225	174.9	141.6	285	221.5	179.4
46	35.7	28.9	106	82.4	66.7	166	129.0	104.5	226	175.6	142.2	286	222.3	180.0
47	36.5	29.6	107	83.2	67.3	167	129.8	105.1	227	176.4	142.9	287	223.0	180.6
48	37.3	30.2	108	83.9	68.0	168	130.6	105.7	228	177.2	143.5	288	223.8	181.2
49	38.1	30.8	109	84.7	68.6	169	131.3	106.4	229	178.0	144.1	289	224.6	181.9
50	38.9	31.5	110	85.5	69.2	170	132.1	107.0	230	178.7	144.7	290	225.4	182.5
51	39.6	32.1	111	86.3	69.9	171	132.9	107.6	231	179.5	145.4	291	226.1	183.1
52	40.4	32.7	112	87.0	70.5	172	133.7	108.2	232	180.3	146.0	292	226.9	183.8
53	41.2	33.4	113	87.8	71.1	173	134.4	108.9	233	181.1	146.6	293	227.7	184.4
54	42.0	34.0	114	88.6	71.7	174	135.2	109.5	234	181.9	147.3	294	228.5	185.0
55	42.7	34.6	115	89.4	72.4	175	136.0	110.1	235	182.6	147.9	295	229.3	185.6
56	43.5	35.2	116	90.1	73.0	176	136.8	110.8	236	183.4	148.5	296	230.0	186.3
57	44.3	35.9	117	90.9	73.6	177	137.6	111.4	237	184.2	149.1	297	230.8	186.9
58	45.1	36.5	118	91.7	74.3	178	138.3	112.0	238	185.0	149.8	298	231.6	187.5
59	45.9	37.1	119	92.5	74.9	179	139.1	112.6	239	185.7	150.4	299	232.4	188.2
60	46.6	37.8	120	93.3	75.5	180	139.9	113.3	240	186.5	151.0	300	233.1	188.8
Hyp.	Opp.	Adj.	Hyp.	Opp.	Adj.	Hyp.	Opp.	Adj.	Hyp.	Opp.	Adj.	Hyp.	Opp.	Adj.
Dist. D Lon	Dep.	D. Lat. Dep	Dist. D Lon	Dep.	D. Lat. Dep	Dist. D Lon	Dep.	D. Lat. Dep	Dist. D Lon	Dep.	D. Lat. Dep	Dist. D Lon	Dep.	D. Lat. Dep

51°

51°

Table 3

TRAVERSE TABLE

39° — 39°

D Lon	Dep		D Lon	Dep		D Lon	Dep		D Lon	Dep		D Lon	Dep	
Dist.	D. Lat.	Dep.	Dist.	D. Lat.	Dep.	Dist.	D. Lat.	Dep.	Dist.	D. Lat.	Dep.	Dist.	D. Lat.	Dep.
Hyp.	*Adj.*	*Opp*	*Hyp.*	*Adj.*	*Opp.*	*Hyp.*	*Adj.*	*Opp.*	*Hyp.*	*Adj.*	*Opp.*	*Hyp.*	*Adj.*	*Opp.*
301	233.9	189.4	361	280.5	227.2	421	327.2	264.9	481	373.8	302.7	541	420.4	340.5
302	234.7	190.1	362	281.3	227.8	422	328.0	265.6	482	374.6	303.3	542	421.2	341.1
303	235.5	190.7	363	282.1	228.4	423	328.7	266.2	483	375.4	304.0	543	422.0	341.7
304	236.3	191.3	364	282.9	229.1	424	329.5	266.8	484	376.1	304.6	544	422.8	342.2
305	237.0	191.9	365	283.7	229.7	425	330.3	267.5	485	376.9	305.2	545	423.5	343.0
306	237.8	192.6	366	284.4	230.3	426	331.1	268.1	486	377.7	305.8	546	424.3	343.6
307	238.6	193.2	367	285.2	231.0	427	331.8	268.7	487	378.5	306.5	547	425.1	344.2
308	239.4	193.8	368	286.0	231.5	428	332.6	269.3	488	379.2	307.1	548	425.9	344.9
309	240.1	194.5	369	286.8	232.2	429	333.4	270.0	489	380.0	307.7	549	426.7	345.5
310	240.9	195.1	370	287.5	232.8	430	334.2	270.6	490	380.8	308.4	550	427.4	346.1
311	241.7	195.7	371	288.3	233.5	431	334.9	271.2	491	381.6	309.0	551	428.2	346.8
312	242.5	196.3	372	289.1	234.1	432	335.7	271.9	492	382.4	309.6	552	429.0	347.4
313	243.2	197.0	373	289.9	234.7	433	336.5	272.5	493	383.1	310.3	553	429.8	348.0
314	244.0	197.6	374	290.7	235.4	434	337.3	273.1	494	383.9	310.9	554	430.5	348.6
315	244.8	198.2	375	291.4	236.0	435	338.1	273.8	495	384.7	311.5	555	431.3	349.3
316	245.6	198.9	376	292.2	236.6	436	338.8	274.4	496	385.5	312.1	556	432.1	349.9
317	246.4	199.5	377	293.0	237.3	437	339.6	275.0	497	386.2	312.8	557	432.9	350.5
318	247.1	200.1	378	293.8	237.9	438	340.4	275.6	498	387.0	313.4	558	433.6	351.2
319	247.9	200.8	379	294.5	238.5	439	341.2	276.3	499	387.8	314.0	559	434.4	351.8
320	248.7	201.4	380	295.3	239.1	440	341.9	276.9	500	388.6	314.7	560	435.2	352.4
321	249.5	202.0	381	296.1	239.8	441	342.7	277.5	501	389.4	315.3	561	436.0	353.0
322	250.2	202.6	382	296.9	240.4	442	343.5	278.2	502	390.1	315.9	562	436.8	353.7
323	251.0	203.3	383	297.6	241.0	443	344.3	278.8	503	390.9	316.5	563	437.5	354.3
324	251.8	203.9	384	298.4	241.7	444	345.1	279.4	504	391.7	317.2	564	438.3	354.9
325	252.6	204.5	385	299.2	242.3	445	345.8	280.0	505	392.5	317.8	565	439.1	355.6
326	253.3	205.2	386	300.0	242.9	446	346.6	280.7	506	393.2	318.4	566	439.9	356.2
327	254.1	205.8	387	300.8	243.5	447	347.4	281.3	507	394.0	319.1	567	440.6	356.8
328	254.9	206.4	388	301.5	244.2	448	348.2	281.9	508	394.8	319.7	568	441.4	357.5
329	255.7	207.0	389	302.3	244.8	449	348.9	282.6	509	395.6	320.3	569	442.2	358.1
330	256.5	207.7	390	303.1	245.4	450	349.7	283.2	510	396.3	321.0	570	443.0	358.7
331	257.2	208.3	391	303.9	246.1	451	350.5	283.8	511	397.1	321.6	571	443.8	359.3
332	258.0	208.9	392	304.6	246.7	452	351.3	284.5	512	397.9	322.2	572	444.5	360.0
333	258.8	209.6	393	305.4	247.3	453	352.0	285.1	513	398.7	322.8	573	445.3	360.6
334	259.6	210.2	394	306.2	248.0	454	352.8	285.7	514	399.5	323.5	574	446.1	361.2
335	260.3	210.8	395	307.0	248.6	455	353.6	286.3	515	400.2	324.1	575	446.9	361.9
336	261.1	211.5	396	307.7	249.2	456	354.4	287.0	516	401.0	324.7	576	447.6	362.5
337	261.9	212.1	397	308.5	249.8	457	355.2	287.6	517	401.8	325.4	577	448.4	363.1
338	262.7	212.7	398	309.3	250.5	458	355.9	288.2	518	402.6	326.0	578	449.2	363.7
339	263.5	213.3	399	310.1	251.1	459	356.7	288.9	519	403.3	326.6	579	450.0	364.4
340	264.2	214.0	400	310.9	251.7	460	357.5	289.5	520	404.1	327.2	580	450.7	365.0
341	265.0	214.6	401	311.6	252.4	461	358.3	290.1	521	404.9	327.9	581	451.5	365.6
342	265.8	215.2	402	312.4	253.0	462	359.0	290.7	522	405.7	328.5	582	452.3	366.3
343	266.6	215.9	403	313.2	253.6	463	359.8	291.4	523	406.4	329.1	583	453.1	366.9
344	267.3	216.5	404	314.0	254.2	464	360.6	292.0	524	407.2	329.8	584	453.9	367.5
345	268.1	217.1	405	314.7	254.9	465	361.4	292.6	525	408.0	330.4	585	454.6	368.2
346	268.9	217.7	406	315.5	255.5	466	362.2	293.3	526	408.8	331.0	586	455.4	368.8
347	269.7	218.4	407	316.3	256.1	467	362.9	293.9	527	409.6	331.7	587	456.2	369.4
348	270.4	219.0	408	317.1	256.8	468	363.7	294.5	528	410.3	332.3	588	457.0	370.0
349	271.2	219.6	409	317.9	257.4	469	364.5	295.2	529	411.1	332.9	589	457.7	370.7
350	272.0	220.3	410	318.6	258.0	470	365.3	295.8	530	411.9	333.5	590	458.5	371.3
351	272.8	220.9	411	319.4	258.7	471	366.0	296.4	531	412.7	334.2	591	459.3	371.9
352	273.6	221.5	412	320.2	259.3	472	366.8	297.0	532	413.4	334.8	592	460.1	372.6
353	274.3	222.2	413	321.0	259.9	473	367.6	297.7	533	414.2	335.4	593	460.8	373.2
354	275.1	222.7	414	321.7	260.5	474	368.4	298.3	534	415.0	336.1	594	461.6	373.8
355	275.9	223.4	415	322.5	261.2	475	369.1	298.9	535	415.8	336.7	595	462.4	374.4
356	276.7	224.0	416	323.3	261.8	476	369.9	299.6	536	416.6	337.3	596	463.2	375.1
357	277.4	224.7	417	324.1	262.4	477	370.7	300.2	537	417.3	337.9	597	464.0	375.7
358	278.2	225.3	418	324.8	263.1	478	371.5	300.8	538	418.1	338.6	598	464.7	376.3
359	279.0	225.9	419	325.6	263.7	479	372.3	301.4	539	418.9	339.2	599	465.5	377.0
360	279.8	226.6	420	326.4	264.3	480	373.0	302.1	540	419.7	339.8	600	466.3	377.6
Hyp.	*Opp.*	*Adj.*	*Hyp.*	*Opp.*	*Adj.*	*Hyp.*	*Opp.*	*Adj.*	*Hyp.*	*Opp.*	*Adj.*	*Hyp.*	*Opp.*	*Adj.*
Dist.	Dep.	D. Lat.	Dist.	Dep.	D. Lat.	Dist.	Dep.	D. Lat.	Dist.	Dep.	D. Lat.	Dist.	Dep.	D. Lat.
D Lon		Dep	D Lon		Dep	D Lon		Dep	D Lon		Dep	D Lon		Dep

51° — 51°

Table 3

TRAVERSE TABLE

40°  40°

D Lon Dist.	Dep D. Lat.	Dep.	D Lon Dist.	Dep D. Lat.	Dep.	D Lon Dist.	Dep D. Lat.	Dep.	D Lon Dist.	Dep D. Lat.	Dep.	D Lon Dist.	Dep D. Lat.	Dep.
Hyp.	Adj.	Opp.	Hyp.	Adj.	Opp.	Hyp.	Adj.	Opp.	Hyp.	Adj.	Opp.	Hyp.	Adj.	Opp.
1	0.8	0.6	61	46.7	39.2	121	92.7	77.8	181	138.7	116.3	241	184.6	154.9
2	1.5	1.3	62	47.5	39.9	122	93.5	78.4	182	139.4	117.0	242	185.4	155.6
3	2.3	1.9	63	48.3	40.5	123	94.2	79.1	183	140.2	117.6	243	186.1	156.2
4	3.1	2.6	64	49.0	41.1	124	95.0	79.7	184	141.0	118.3	244	186.9	156.8
5	3.8	3.2	65	49.8	41.8	125	95.8	80.3	185	141.7	118.9	245	187.7	157.5
6	4.6	3.9	66	50.6	42.4	126	96.5	81.0	186	142.5	119.6	246	188.4	158.1
7	5.4	4.5	67	51.3	43.1	127	97.3	81.6	187	143.3	120.2	247	189.2	158.8
8	6.1	5.1	68	52.1	43.7	128	98.1	82.3	188	144.0	120.8	248	190.0	159.4
9	6.9	5.8	69	52.9	44.4	129	98.8	82.9	189	144.8	121.5	249	190.7	160.1
10	7.7	6.4	70	53.6	45.0	130	99.6	83.6	190	145.5	122.1	250	191.5	160.7
11	8.4	7.1	71	54.4	45.6	131	100.4	84.2	191	146.3	122.8	251	192.3	161.3
12	9.2	7.7	72	55.2	46.3	132	101.1	84.8	192	147.1	123.4	252	193.0	162.0
13	10.0	8.4	73	55.9	46.9	133	101.9	85.5	193	147.8	124.1	253	193.8	162.6
14	10.7	9.0	74	56.7	47.6	134	102.6	86.1	194	148.6	124.7	254	194.6	163.3
15	11.5	9.6	75	57.5	48.2	135	103.4	86.8	195	149.4	125.3	255	195.3	163.9
16	12.3	10.3	76	58.2	48.9	136	104.2	87.4	196	150.1	126.0	256	196.1	164.6
17	13.0	10.9	77	59.0	49.5	137	104.9	88.1	197	150.9	126.6	257	196.9	165.2
18	13.8	11.6	78	59.8	50.1	138	105.7	88.7	198	151.7	127.3	258	197.6	165.8
19	14.6	12.2	79	60.5	50.8	139	106.5	89.3	199	152.4	127.9	259	198.4	166.5
20	15.3	12.9	80	61.3	51.4	140	107.2	90.0	200	153.2	128.6	260	199.2	167.1
21	16.1	13.5	81	62.0	52.1	141	108.0	90.6	201	154.0	129.2	261	199.9	167.8
22	16.9	14.1	82	62.8	52.7	142	108.8	91.3	202	154.7	129.8	262	200.7	168.4
23	17.6	14.8	83	63.6	53.4	143	109.5	91.9	203	155.5	130.5	263	201.5	169.1
24	18.4	15.4	84	64.3	54.0	144	110.3	92.6	204	156.3	131.1	264	202.2	169.7
25	19.2	16.1	85	65.1	54.6	145	111.1	93.2	205	157.0	131.8	265	203.0	170.3
26	19.9	16.7	86	65.9	55.3	146	111.8	93.8	206	157.8	132.4	266	203.8	171.0
27	20.7	17.4	87	66.6	55.9	147	112.6	94.5	207	158.6	133.1	267	204.5	171.6
28	21.4	18.0	88	67.4	56.6	148	113.4	95.1	208	159.3	133.7	268	205.3	172.3
29	22.2	18.6	89	68.2	57.2	149	114.1	95.8	209	160.1	134.3	269	206.1	172.9
30	23.0	19.3	90	68.9	57.9	150	114.9	96.4	210	160.9	135.0	270	206.8	173.6
31	23.7	19.9	91	69.7	58.5	151	115.7	97.1	211	161.6	135.6	271	207.6	174.2
32	24.5	20.6	92	70.5	59.1	152	116.4	97.7	212	162.4	136.3	272	208.4	174.8
33	25.3	21.2	93	71.2	59.8	153	117.2	98.3	213	163.2	136.9	273	209.1	175.5
34	26.0	21.9	94	72.0	60.4	154	118.0	99.0	214	163.9	137.6	274	209.9	176.1
35	26.8	22.5	95	72.8	61.1	155	118.7	99.6	215	164.7	138.2	275	210.7	176.8
36	27.6	23.1	96	73.5	61.7	156	119.5	100.3	216	165.5	138.8	276	211.4	177.4
37	28.3	23.8	97	74.3	62.4	157	120.3	100.9	217	166.2	139.5	277	212.2	178.1
38	29.1	24.4	98	75.1	63.0	158	121.0	101.6	218	167.0	140.1	278	213.0	178.7
39	29.9	25.1	99	75.8	63.6	159	121.8	102.2	219	167.8	140.8	279	213.7	179.3
40	30.6	25.7	100	76.6	64.3	160	122.6	102.8	220	168.5	141.4	280	214.5	180.0
41	31.4	26.4	101	77.4	64.9	161	123.3	103.5	221	169.3	142.1	281	215.3	180.6
42	32.2	27.0	102	78.1	65.6	162	124.1	104.1	222	170.1	142.7	282	216.0	181.3
43	32.9	27.6	103	78.9	66.2	163	124.9	104.8	223	170.8	143.3	283	216.8	181.9
44	33.7	28.3	104	79.7	66.8	164	125.6	105.4	224	171.6	144.0	284	217.6	182.6
45	34.5	28.9	105	80.4	67.5	165	126.4	106.1	225	172.4	144.6	285	218.3	183.2
46	35.2	29.6	106	81.2	68.1	166	127.2	106.7	226	173.1	145.3	286	219.1	183.8
47	36.0	30.2	107	82.0	68.8	167	127.9	107.3	227	173.9	145.9	287	219.9	184.5
48	36.8	30.9	108	82.7	69.4	168	128.7	108.0	228	174.7	146.6	288	220.6	185.1
49	37.5	31.5	109	83.5	70.1	169	129.5	108.6	229	175.4	147.2	289	221.4	185.8
50	38.3	32.1	110	84.3	70.7	170	130.2	109.3	230	176.2	147.8	290	222.2	186.4
51	39.1	32.8	111	85.0	71.3	171	131.0	109.9	231	177.0	148.5	291	222.9	187.1
52	39.8	33.4	112	85.8	72.0	172	131.8	110.6	232	177.7	149.1	292	223.7	187.7
53	40.6	34.1	113	86.6	72.6	173	132.5	111.2	233	178.5	149.8	293	224.5	188.3
54	41.4	34.7	114	87.3	73.3	174	133.3	111.8	234	179.3	150.4	294	225.2	189.0
55	42.1	35.4	115	88.1	73.9	175	134.1	112.5	235	180.0	151.1	295	226.0	189.6
56	42.9	36.0	116	88.9	74.6	176	134.8	113.1	236	180.8	151.7	296	226.7	190.3
57	43.7	36.6	117	89.6	75.2	177	135.6	113.8	237	181.6	152.3	297	227.5	190.9
58	44.4	37.3	118	90.4	75.8	178	136.4	114.4	238	182.3	153.0	298	228.3	191.6
59	45.2	37.9	119	91.2	76.5	179	137.1	115.1	239	183.1	153.6	299	229.0	192.2
60	46.0	38.6	120	91.9	77.1	180	137.9	115.7	240	183.9	154.3	300	229.8	192.8
Hyp.	Opp.	Adj.	Hyp.	Opp.	Adj.	Hyp.	Opp.	Adj.	Hyp.	Opp.	Adj.	Hyp.	Opp.	Adj.
Dist. D Lon	Dep.	D. Lat. Dep	Dist. D Lon	Dep.	D. Lat. Dep	Dist. D Lon	Dep.	D. Lat. Dep	Dist. D Lon	Dep.	D. Lat. Dep	Dist. D Lon	Dep.	D. Lat. Dep

50° 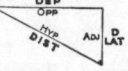 50°

Table 3

TRAVERSE TABLE

40°

320°	040°
220°	140°

40°

D Lon Dist.	Dep D. Lat.	Dep.	D Lon Dist.	Dep D. Lat.	Dep.	D Lon Dist.	Dep D. Lat.	Dep.	D Lon Dist.	Dep D. Lat.	Dep.	D Lon Dist.	Dep D. Lat.	Dep.
Hyp.	*Adj.*	*Opp.*	*Hyp.*	*Adj.*	*Opp.*	*Hyp.*	*Adj.*	*Opp.*	*Hyp.*	*Adj.*	*Opp.*	*Hyp.*	*Adj.*	*Opp.*
301	230.6	193.5	361	276.5	232.0	421	322.5	270.6	481	368.5	309.2	541	414.4	347.7
302	231.3	194.1	362	277.3	232.7	422	323.3	271.3	482	369.2	309.8	542	415.2	348.4
303	232.1	194.8	363	278.1	233.3	423	324.0	271.9	483	370.0	310.5	543	416.0	349.0
304	232.9	195.4	364	278.8	234.0	424	324.8	272.5	484	370.8	311.1	544	416.7	349.7
305	233.6	196.1	365	279.6	234.6	425	325.6	273.2	485	371.5	311.8	545	417.5	350.3
306	234.4	196.7	366	280.4	235.3	426	326.3	273.8	486	372.3	312.4	546	418.3	351.0
307	235.2	197.3	367	281.1	235.9	427	327.1	274.5	487	373.1	313.0	547	419.0	351.6
308	235.9	198.0	368	281.9	236.5	428	327.9	275.1	488	373.8	313.7	548	419.8	352.2
309	236.7	198.6	369	282.7	237.2	429	328.6	275.8	489	374.6	314.3	549	420.6	352.9
310	237.5	199.3	370	283.4	237.8	430	329.4	276.4	490	375.4	315.0	550	421.3	353.5
311	238.2	199.9	371	284.2	238.5	431	330.2	277.0	491	376.1	315.6	551	422.1	354.2
312	239.0	200.5	372	285.0	239.1	432	330.9	277.7	492	376.9	316.3	552	422.9	354.8
313	239.8	201.2	373	285.7	239.8	433	331.7	278.3	493	377.7	316.9	553	423.6	355.5
314	240.5	201.8	374	286.5	240.4	434	332.5	279.0	494	378.4	317.5	554	424.4	356.1
315	241.3	202.5	375	287.3	241.0	435	333.2	279.6	495	379.2	318.2	555	425.2	356.7
316	242.1	203.1	376	288.0	241.7	436	334.0	280.3	496	380.0	318.8	556	425.9	357.4
317	242.8	203.8	377	288.8	242.3	437	334.8	280.9	497	380.7	319.5	557	426.7	358.0
318	243.6	204.4	378	289.6	243.0	438	335.5	281.5	498	381.5	320.1	558	427.5	358.7
319	244.4	205.0	379	290.3	243.6	439	336.3	282.2	499	382.3	320.8	559	428.2	359.3
320	245.1	205.7	380	291.1	244.3	440	337.1	282.8	500	383.0	321.4	560	429.0	360.0
321	245.9	206.3	381	291.9	244.9	441	337.8	283.5	501	383.8	322.0	561	429.8	360.6
322	246.7	207.0	382	292.6	245.5	442	338.6	284.1	502	384.6	322.7	562	430.5	361.2
323	247.4	207.6	383	293.4	246.2	443	339.4	284.8	503	385.3	323.3	563	431.3	361.9
324	248.2	208.3	384	294.2	246.8	444	340.1	285.4	504	386.1	324.0	564	432.0	362.5
325	249.0	208.9	385	294.9	247.5	445	340.9	286.0	505	386.9	324.6	565	432.8	363.2
326	249.7	209.5	386	295.7	248.1	446	341.7	286.7	506	387.6	325.3	566	433.6	363.8
327	250.5	210.2	387	296.5	248.8	447	342.4	287.3	507	388.4	325.9	567	434.3	364.5
328	251.3	210.8	388	297.2	249.4	448	343.2	288.0	508	389.2	326.5	568	435.1	365.1
329	252.0	211.5	389	298.0	250.0	449	344.0	288.6	509	389.9	327.2	569	435.9	365.7
330	252.8	212.1	390	298.8	250.7	450	344.7	289.3	510	390.7	327.8	570	436.6	366.4
331	253.6	212.8	391	299.5	251.3	451	345.5	289.9	511	391.4	328.5	571	437.4	367.0
332	254.3	213.4	392	300.3	252.0	452	346.3	290.5	512	392.2	329.1	572	438.2	367.7
333	255.1	214.0	393	301.1	252.6	453	347.0	291.2	513	393.0	329.8	573	438.9	368.3
334	255.9	214.7	394	301.8	253.3	454	347.8	291.8	514	393.7	330.4	574	439.7	369.0
335	256.6	215.3	395	302.6	253.9	455	348.6	292.5	515	394.5	331.0	575	440.5	369.6
336	257.4	216.0	396	303.4	254.5	456	349.3	293.1	516	395.3	331.7	576	441.2	370.2
337	258.2	216.6	397	304.1	255.2	457	350.1	293.8	517	396.0	332.3	577	442.0	370.9
338	258.9	217.3	398	304.9	255.8	458	350.8	294.4	518	396.8	333.0	578	442.8	371.5
339	259.7	217.9	399	305.7	256.5	459	351.6	295.0	519	397.6	333.6	579	443.5	372.2
340	260.5	218.5	400	306.4	257.1	460	352.4	295.7	520	398.3	334.2	580	444.3	372.8
341	261.2	219.2	401	307.2	257.8	461	353.1	296.3	521	399.1	334.9	581	445.1	373.5
342	262.0	219.8	402	307.9	258.4	462	353.9	297.0	522	399.9	335.5	582	445.8	374.1
343	262.8	220.5	403	308.7	259.0	463	354.7	297.6	523	400.6	336.2	583	446.6	374.7
344	263.5	221.1	404	309.5	259.7	464	355.4	298.3	524	401.4	336.8	584	447.4	375.4
345	264.3	221.8	405	310.2	260.3	465	356.2	298.9	525	402.2	337.5	585	448.1	376.0
346	265.1	222.4	406	311.0	261.0	466	357.0	299.5	526	402.9	338.1	586	448.9	376.7
347	265.8	223.0	407	311.8	261.6	467	357.7	300.2	527	403.7	338.7	587	449.7	377.3
348	266.6	223.7	408	312.5	262.3	468	358.5	300.8	528	404.5	339.4	588	450.4	378.0
349	267.3	224.3	409	313.3	262.9	469	359.3	301.5	529	405.2	340.0	589	451.2	378.6
350	268.1	225.0	410	314.1	263.5	470	360.0	302.1	530	406.0	340.7	590	452.0	379.2
351	268.9	225.6	411	314.8	264.2	471	360.8	302.8	531	406.8	341.3	591	452.7	379.9
352	269.6	226.3	412	315.6	264.8	472	361.6	303.4	532	407.5	342.0	592	453.5	380.5
353	270.4	226.9	413	316.4	265.5	473	362.3	304.0	533	408.3	342.6	593	454.3	381.2
354	271.2	227.5	414	317.1	266.1	474	363.1	304.7	534	409.1	343.2	594	455.0	381.8
355	271.9	228.2	415	317.9	266.8	475	363.9	305.3	535	409.8	343.9	595	455.8	382.5
356	272.7	228.8	416	318.7	267.4	476	364.6	306.0	536	410.6	344.5	596	456.6	383.1
357	273.5	229.5	417	319.4	268.0	477	365.4	306.6	537	411.4	345.2	597	457.3	383.7
358	274.2	230.1	418	320.2	268.7	478	366.2	307.3	538	412.1	345.8	598	458.1	384.4
359	275.0	230.8	419	321.0	269.3	479	366.9	307.9	539	412.9	346.5	599	458.9	385.0
360	275.8	231.4	420	321.7	270.0	480	367.7	308.5	540	413.7	347.1	600	459.6	385.7
Hyp.	*Opp.*	*Adj.*	*Hyp.*	*Opp.*	*Adj.*	*Hyp.*	*Opp.*	*Adj.*	*Hyp.*	*Opp.*	*Adj.*	*Hyp.*	*Opp.*	*Adj.*
Dist. D Lon	Dep.	D. Lat. Dep	**Dist.** D Lon	Dep.	D. Lat. Dep	**Dist.** D Lon	Dep.	D. Lat. Dep	**Dist.** D Lon	Dep.	D. Lat. Dep	**Dist.** D Lon	Dep.	D. Lat. Dep

50°

310°	050°
230°	130°

50°

Table 3   **TRAVERSE TABLE**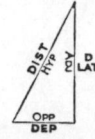

41°   41°

D Lon / Dist.	Dep / D. Lat.	Dep.	D Lon / Dist.	Dep / D. Lat.	Dep.	D Lon / Dist.	Dep / D. Lat.	Dep.	D Lon / Dist.	Dep / D. Lat.	Dep.	D Lon / Dist.	Dep / D. Lat.	Dep.
Hyp.	Adj.	Opp.	Hyp.	Adj.	Opp.	Hyp.	Adj.	Opp.	Hyp.	Adj.	Opp.	Hyp.	Adj.	Opp.
1	0.8	0.7	61	46.0	40.0	121	91.3	79.4	181	136.6	118.7	241	181.9	158.1
2	1.5	1.3	62	46.8	40.7	122	92.1	80.0	182	137.4	119.4	242	182.6	158.8
3	2.3	2.0	63	47.5	41.3	123	92.8	80.7	183	138.1	120.1	243	183.4	159.4
4	3.0	2.6	64	48.3	42.0	124	93.6	81.4	184	138.9	120.7	244	184.1	160.1
5	3.8	3.3	65	49.1	42.6	125	94.3	82.0	185	139.6	121.4	245	184.9	160.7
6	4.5	3.9	66	49.8	43.3	126	95.1	82.7	186	140.4	122.0	246	185.7	161.4
7	5.3	4.6	67	50.6	44.0	127	95.8	83.3	187	141.1	122.7	247	186.4	162.0
8	6.0	5.2	68	51.3	44.6	128	96.6	84.0	188	141.9	123.3	248	187.2	162.7
9	6.8	5.9	69	52.1	45.3	129	97.4	84.6	189	142.6	124.0	249	187.9	163.4
10	7.5	6.6	70	52.8	45.9	130	98.1	85.3	190	143.4	124.7	250	188.7	164.0
11	8.3	7.2	71	53.6	46.6	131	98.9	85.9	191	144.1	125.3	251	189.4	164.7
12	9.1	7.9	72	54.3	47.2	132	99.6	86.6	192	144.9	126.0	252	190.2	165.3
13	9.8	8.5	73	55.1	47.9	133	100.4	87.3	193	145.7	126.6	253	190.9	166.0
14	10.6	9.2	74	55.8	48.5	134	101.1	87.9	194	146.4	127.3	254	191.7	166.6
15	11.3	9.8	75	56.6	49.2	135	101.9	88.6	195	147.2	127.9	255	192.5	167.3
16	12.1	10.5	76	57.4	49.9	136	102.6	89.2	196	147.9	128.6	256	193.2	168.0
17	12.8	11.2	77	58.1	50.5	137	103.4	89.9	197	148.7	129.2	257	194.0	168.6
18	13.6	11.8	78	58.9	51.2	138	104.1	90.5	198	149.4	129.9	258	194.7	169.3
19	14.3	12.5	79	59.6	51.8	139	104.9	91.2	199	150.2	130.6	259	195.5	169.9
20	15.1	13.1	80	60.4	52.5	140	105.7	91.8	200	150.9	131.2	260	196.2	170.6
21	15.8	13.8	81	61.1	53.1	141	106.4	92.5	201	151.7	131.9	261	197.0	171.2
22	16.6	14.4	82	61.9	53.8	142	107.2	93.2	202	152.5	132.5	262	197.7	171.9
23	17.4	15.1	83	62.6	54.5	143	107.9	93.8	203	153.2	133.2	263	198.5	172.5
24	18.1	15.7	84	63.4	55.1	144	108.7	94.5	204	154.0	133.8	264	199.2	173.2
25	18.9	16.4	85	64.2	55.8	145	109.4	95.1	205	154.7	134.5	265	200.0	173.9
26	19.6	17.1	86	64.9	56.4	146	110.2	95.8	206	155.5	135.1	266	200.8	174.5
27	20.4	17.7	87	65.7	57.1	147	110.9	96.4	207	156.2	135.8	267	201.5	175.2
28	21.1	18.4	88	66.4	57.7	148	111.7	97.1	208	157.0	136.5	268	202.3	175.8
29	21.9	19.0	89	67.2	58.4	149	112.5	97.8	209	157.7	137.1	269	203.0	176.5
30	22.6	19.7	90	67.9	59.0	150	113.2	98.4	210	158.5	137.8	270	203.8	177.1
31	23.4	20.3	91	68.7	59.7	151	114.0	99.1	211	159.2	138.4	271	204.5	177.8
32	24.2	21.0	92	69.4	60.4	152	114.7	99.7	212	160.0	139.1	272	205.3	178.4
33	24.9	21.6	93	70.2	61.0	153	115.5	100.4	213	160.8	139.7	273	206.0	179.1
34	25.7	22.3	94	70.9	61.7	154	116.2	101.0	214	161.5	140.4	274	206.8	179.8
35	26.4	23.0	95	71.7	62.3	155	117.0	101.7	215	162.3	141.1	275	207.5	180.4
36	27.2	23.6	96	72.5	63.0	156	117.7	102.3	216	163.0	141.7	276	208.3	181.1
37	27.9	24.3	97	73.2	63.6	157	118.5	103.0	217	163.8	142.4	277	209.1	181.7
38	28.7	24.9	98	74.0	64.3	158	119.2	103.7	218	164.5	143.0	278	209.8	182.4
39	29.4	25.6	99	74.7	64.9	159	120.0	104.3	219	165.3	143.7	279	210.6	183.0
40	30.2	26.2	100	75.5	65.6	160	120.8	105.0	220	166.0	144.3	280	211.3	183.7
41	30.9	26.9	101	76.2	66.3	161	121.5	105.6	221	166.8	145.0	281	212.1	184.4
42	31.7	27.6	102	77.0	66.9	162	122.3	106.3	222	167.5	145.6	282	212.8	185.0
43	32.5	28.2	103	77.7	67.6	163	123.0	106.9	223	168.3	146.3	283	213.6	185.7
44	33.2	28.9	104	78.5	68.2	164	123.8	107.6	224	169.1	147.0	284	214.3	186.3
45	34.0	29.5	105	79.2	68.9	165	124.5	108.2	225	169.8	147.6	285	215.1	187.0
46	34.7	30.2	106	80.0	69.5	166	125.3	108.9	226	170.6	148.3	286	215.8	187.6
47	35.5	30.8	107	80.8	70.2	167	126.0	109.6	227	171.3	148.9	287	216.6	188.3
48	36.2	31.5	108	81.5	70.9	168	126.8	110.2	228	172.1	149.6	288	217.4	188.9
49	37.0	32.1	109	82.3	71.5	169	127.5	110.9	229	172.8	150.2	289	218.1	189.6
50	37.7	32.8	110	83.0	72.2	170	128.3	111.5	230	173.6	150.9	290	218.9	190.3
51	38.5	33.5	111	83.8	72.8	171	129.1	112.2	231	174.3	151.5	291	219.6	190.9
52	39.2	34.1	112	84.5	73.5	172	129.8	112.8	232	175.1	152.2	292	220.4	191.6
53	40.0	34.8	113	85.3	74.1	173	130.6	113.5	233	175.8	152.9	293	221.1	192.2
54	40.8	35.4	114	86.0	74.8	174	131.3	114.2	234	176.6	153.5	294	221.9	192.9
55	41.5	36.1	115	86.8	75.4	175	132.1	114.8	235	177.4	154.2	295	222.6	193.5
56	42.3	36.7	116	87.5	76.1	176	132.8	115.5	236	178.1	154.8	296	223.4	194.2
57	43.0	37.4	117	88.3	76.8	177	133.6	116.1	237	178.9	155.5	297	224.1	194.8
58	43.8	38.1	118	89.1	77.4	178	134.3	116.8	238	179.6	156.1	298	224.9	195.5
59	44.5	38.7	119	89.8	78.1	179	135.1	117.4	239	180.4	156.8	299	225.7	196.2
60	45.3	39.4	120	90.6	78.7	180	135.8	118.1	240	181.1	157.5	300	226.4	196.8
Hyp.	Opp.	Adj.	Hyp.	Opp.	Adj.	Hyp.	Opp.	Adj.	Hyp.	Opp.	Adj.	Hyp.	Opp.	Adj.
Dist. / D Lon	Dep.	D. Lat. / Dep	Dist. / D Lon	Dep.	D. Lat. / Dep	Dist. / D Lon	Dep.	D. Lat. / Dep	Dist. / D Lon	Dep.	D. Lat. / Dep	Dist. / D Lon	Dep.	D. Lat. / Dep

49°   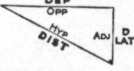   49°

Table 3

TRAVERSE TABLE

41°

319°	041°
221°	139°

41°

D Lon Dep Dist. D. Lat. Dep.			D Lon Dep Dist. D. Lat. Dep.			D Lon Dep Dist. D. Lat. Dep.			D Lon Dep Dist. D. Lat. Dep.			D Lon Dep Dist. D. Lat. Dep.		
Hyp.	Adj.	Opp.	Hyp.	Adj.	Opp.	Hyp.	Adj.	Opp.	Hyp.	Adj.	Opp.	Hyp.	Adj.	Opp.
301	227.2	197.5	361	272.5	236.8	421	317.7	276.2	481	363.0	315.6	541	408.3	354.9
302	227.9	198.1	362	273.2	237.5	422	318.5	276.9	482	363.8	316.2	542	409.1	355.6
303	228.7	198.8	363	274.0	238.1	423	319.2	277.5	483	364.5	316.9	543	409.8	356.2
304	229.4	199.4	364	274.7	238.8	424	320.0	278.2	484	365.3	317.5	544	410.6	356.9
305	230.2	200.1	365	275.5	239.5	425	320.8	278.8	485	366.0	318.2	545	411.3	357.6
306	230.9	200.8	366	276.2	240.1	426	321.5	279.5	486	366.8	318.8	546	412.1	358.2
307	231.7	201.4	367	277.0	240.8	427	322.3	280.1	487	367.5	319.5	547	412.8	358.9
308	232.5	202.1	368	277.7	241.4	428	323.0	280.8	488	368.3	320.2	548	413.6	359.5
309	233.2	202.7	369	278.5	242.1	429	323.8	281.4	489	369.1	320.8	549	414.3	360.2
310	234.0	203.4	370	279.2	242.7	430	324.5	282.1	490	369.8	321.5	550	415.1	360.8
311	234.7	204.0	371	280.0	243.4	431	325.3	282.8	491	370.6	322.1	551	415.8	361.5
312	235.5	204.7	372	280.8	244.1	432	326.0	283.4	492	371.3	322.8	552	416.6	362.1
313	236.2	205.3	373	281.5	244.7	433	326.8	284.1	493	372.1	323.4	553	417.4	362.8
314	237.0	206.0	374	282.3	245.4	434	327.5	284.7	494	372.8	324.1	554	418.1	363.5
315	237.7	206.7	375	283.0	246.0	435	328.3	285.4	495	373.6	324.7	555	418.9	364.1
316	238.5	207.3	376	283.8	246.7	436	329.1	286.0	496	374.3	325.4	556	419.6	364.8
317	239.2	208.0	377	284.5	247.3	437	329.8	286.7	497	375.1	326.1	557	420.4	365.4
318	240.0	208.6	378	285.3	248.0	438	330.6	287.4	498	375.8	326.7	558	421.1	366.1
319	240.8	209.3	379	286.0	248.6	439	331.3	288.0	499	376.6	327.4	559	421.9	366.7
320	241.5	209.9	380	286.8	249.3	440	332.1	288.7	500	377.4	328.0	560	422.6	367.4
321	242.3	210.6	381	287.5	250.0	441	332.8	289.3	501	378.1	328.7	561	423.4	368.0
322	243.0	211.3	382	288.3	250.6	442	333.6	290.0	502	378.9	329.3	562	424.1	368.7
323	243.8	211.9	383	289.1	251.3	443	334.3	290.6	503	379.6	330.0	563	424.9	369.4
324	244.5	212.6	384	289.8	251.9	444	335.1	291.3	504	380.4	330.7	564	425.7	370.0
325	245.3	213.2	385	290.6	252.6	445	335.8	291.9	505	381.1	331.3	565	426.4	370.7
326	246.0	213.9	386	291.3	253.2	446	336.6	292.6	506	381.9	332.0	566	427.2	371.3
327	246.8	214.5	387	292.1	253.9	447	337.4	293.3	507	382.6	332.6	567	427.9	372.0
328	247.5	215.2	388	292.8	254.6	448	338.1	293.9	508	383.4	333.3	568	428.7	372.6
329	248.3	215.8	389	293.6	255.2	449	338.9	294.6	509	384.1	333.9	569	429.4	373.3
330	249.1	216.5	390	294.3	255.9	450	339.6	295.2	510	384.9	334.6	570	430.2	374.0
331	249.8	217.2	391	295.1	256.5	451	340.4	295.9	511	385.7	335.2	571	430.9	374.6
332	250.6	217.8	392	295.8	257.2	452	341.1	296.5	512	386.4	335.9	572	431.7	375.3
333	251.3	218.5	393	296.6	257.8	453	341.9	297.2	513	387.2	336.6	573	432.4	375.9
334	252.1	219.1	394	297.4	258.5	454	342.6	297.9	514	387.9	337.2	574	433.2	376.6
335	252.8	219.8	395	298.1	259.1	455	343.4	298.5	515	388.7	337.9	575	434.0	377.2
336	253.6	220.4	396	298.9	259.8	456	344.1	299.2	516	389.4	338.5	576	434.7	377.9
337	254.3	221.1	397	299.6	260.5	457	344.9	299.8	517	390.2	339.2	577	435.5	378.5
338	255.1	221.7	398	300.4	261.1	458	345.7	300.5	518	390.9	339.8	578	436.2	379.2
339	255.8	222.4	399	301.1	261.8	459	346.4	301.1	519	391.7	340.5	579	437.0	379.9
340	256.6	223.1	400	301.9	262.4	460	347.2	301.8	520	392.4	341.2	580	437.7	380.5
341	257.4	223.7	401	302.6	263.1	461	347.9	302.4	521	393.2	341.8	581	438.5	381.2
342	258.1	224.4	402	303.4	263.7	462	348.7	303.1	522	394.0	342.5	582	439.2	381.8
343	258.9	225.0	403	304.1	264.4	463	349.4	303.8	523	394.7	343.1	583	440.0	382.5
344	259.6	225.7	404	304.9	265.0	464	350.2	304.4	524	395.5	343.8	584	440.8	383.1
345	260.4	226.3	405	305.7	265.7	465	350.9	305.1	525	396.2	344.4	585	441.5	383.8
346	261.1	227.0	406	306.4	266.4	466	351.7	305.7	526	397.0	345.1	586	442.3	384.5
347	261.9	227.7	407	307.2	267.0	467	352.4	306.4	527	397.7	345.7	587	443.0	385.1
348	262.6	228.3	408	307.9	267.7	468	353.2	307.0	528	398.5	346.4	588	443.8	385.8
349	263.4	229.0	409	308.7	268.3	469	354.0	307.7	529	399.2	347.1	589	444.5	386.4
350	264.1	229.6	410	309.4	269.0	470	354.7	308.3	530	400.0	347.7	590	445.3	387.1
351	264.9	230.3	411	310.2	269.6	471	355.5	309.0	531	400.8	348.4	591	446.0	387.7
352	265.7	230.9	412	310.9	270.3	472	356.2	309.7	532	401.5	349.0	592	446.8	388.4
353	266.4	231.6	413	311.7	271.0	473	357.0	310.3	533	402.3	349.7	593	447.5	389.0
354	267.2	232.2	414	312.4	271.6	474	357.7	311.0	534	403.0	350.3	594	448.3	389.7
355	267.9	232.9	415	313.2	272.3	475	358.5	311.6	535	403.8	351.0	595	449.1	390.4
356	268.7	233.6	416	314.0	272.9	476	359.2	312.3	536	404.5	351.6	596	449.8	391.0
357	269.4	234.2	417	314.7	273.6	477	360.0	312.9	537	405.3	352.3	597	450.6	391.7
358	270.2	234.9	418	315.5	274.2	478	360.8	313.6	538	406.0	353.0	598	451.3	392.3
359	270.9	235.5	419	316.2	274.9	479	361.5	314.3	539	406.8	353.6	599	452.1	393.0
360	271.7	236.2	420	317.0	275.5	480	362.3	314.9	540	407.5	354.3	600	452.8	393.6
Hyp.	Opp.	Adj.	Hyp.	Opp.	Adj.	Hyp.	Opp.	Adj.	Hyp.	Opp.	Adj.	Hyp.	Opp.	Adj.

Dist. Dep. D. Lat. D Lon Dep			Dist. Dep. D. Lat. D Lon Dep			Dist. Dep. D. Lat. D Lon Dep			Dist. Dep. D. Lat. D Lon Dep			Dist. Dep. D. Lat. D Lon Dep		

49°

311°	049°
229°	131°

49°

Table 3 — TRAVERSE TABLE — 42°　42°

TRAVERSE TABLE

Table 3

42°　　　**42°**

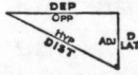

D Lon Dist. (Hyp.)	Dep D. Lat. (Adj.)	Dep. (Opp.)
1	0.7	0.7
2	1.5	1.3
3	2.2	2.0
4	3.0	2.7
5	3.7	3.3
6	4.5	4.0
7	5.2	4.7
8	5.9	5.4
9	6.7	6.0
10	7.4	6.7
11	8.2	7.4
12	8.9	8.0
13	9.7	8.7
14	10.4	9.4
15	11.1	10.0
16	11.9	10.7
17	12.6	11.4
18	13.4	12.0
19	14.1	12.7
20	14.9	13.4
21	15.6	14.1
22	16.3	14.7
23	17.1	15.4
24	17.8	16.1
25	18.6	16.7
26	19.3	17.4
27	20.1	18.1
28	20.8	18.7
29	21.6	19.4
30	22.3	20.1
31	23.0	20.7
32	23.8	21.4
33	24.5	22.1
34	25.3	22.8
35	26.0	23.4
36	26.8	24.1
37	27.5	24.8
38	28.2	25.4
39	29.0	26.1
40	29.7	26.8
41	30.5	27.4
42	31.2	28.1
43	32.0	28.8
44	32.7	29.4
45	33.4	30.1
46	34.2	30.8
47	34.9	31.4
48	35.7	32.1
49	36.4	32.8
50	37.2	33.5
51	37.9	34.1
52	38.6	34.8
53	39.4	35.5
54	40.1	36.1
55	40.9	36.8
56	41.6	37.5
57	42.4	38.1
58	43.1	38.8
59	43.8	39.5
60	44.6	40.1

D Lon Dist. (Hyp.)	Dep D. Lat. (Adj.)	Dep. (Opp.)
61	45.3	40.8
62	46.1	41.5
63	46.8	42.2
64	47.6	42.8
65	48.3	43.5
66	49.0	44.2
67	49.8	44.8
68	50.5	45.5
69	51.3	46.2
70	52.0	46.8
71	52.8	47.5
72	53.5	48.2
73	54.2	48.8
74	55.0	49.5
75	55.7	50.2
76	56.5	50.9
77	57.2	51.5
78	58.0	52.2
79	58.7	52.9
80	59.5	53.5
81	60.2	54.2
82	60.9	54.9
83	61.7	55.5
84	62.4	56.2
85	63.2	56.9
86	63.9	57.5
87	64.7	58.2
88	65.4	58.9
89	66.1	59.6
90	66.9	60.2
91	67.6	60.9
92	68.4	61.6
93	69.1	62.2
94	69.9	62.9
95	70.6	63.6
96	71.3	64.2
97	72.1	64.9
98	72.8	65.6
99	73.6	66.2
100	74.3	66.9
101	75.1	67.6
102	75.8	68.3
103	76.5	68.9
104	77.3	69.6
105	78.0	70.3
106	78.8	70.9
107	79.5	71.6
108	80.3	72.3
109	81.0	72.9
110	81.7	73.6
111	82.5	74.3
112	83.2	74.9
113	84.0	75.6
114	84.7	76.3
115	85.5	77.0
116	86.2	77.6
117	86.9	78.3
118	87.7	79.0
119	88.4	79.6
120	89.2	80.3

D Lon Dist. (Hyp.)	Dep D. Lat. (Adj.)	Dep. (Opp.)
121	89.9	81.0
122	90.7	81.6
123	91.4	82.3
124	92.1	83.0
125	92.9	83.6
126	93.6	84.3
127	94.4	85.0
128	95.1	85.6
129	95.9	86.3
130	96.6	87.0
131	97.4	87.7
132	98.1	88.3
133	98.8	89.0
134	99.6	89.7
135	100.3	90.3
136	101.1	91.0
137	101.8	91.7
138	102.6	92.3
139	103.3	93.0
140	104.0	93.7
141	104.8	94.3
142	105.5	95.0
143	106.3	95.7
144	107.0	96.4
145	107.8	97.0
146	108.5	97.7
147	109.2	98.4
148	110.0	99.0
149	110.7	99.7
150	111.5	100.4
151	112.2	101.0
152	113.0	101.7
153	113.7	102.4
154	114.4	103.0
155	115.2	103.7
156	115.9	104.4
157	116.7	105.1
158	117.4	105.7
159	118.2	106.4
160	118.9	107.1
161	119.6	107.7
162	120.4	108.4
163	121.1	109.1
164	121.9	109.7
165	122.6	110.4
166	123.4	111.1
167	124.1	111.7
168	124.8	112.4
169	125.6	113.1
170	126.3	113.8
171	127.1	114.4
172	127.8	115.1
173	128.6	115.8
174	129.3	116.4
175	130.1	117.1
176	130.8	117.8
177	131.5	118.4
178	132.3	119.1
179	133.0	119.8
180	133.8	120.4

D Lon Dist. (Hyp.)	Dep D. Lat. (Adj.)	Dep. (Opp.)
181	134.5	121.1
182	135.3	121.8
183	136.0	122.5
184	136.7	123.1
185	137.5	123.8
186	138.2	124.5
187	139.0	125.1
188	139.7	125.8
189	140.5	126.5
190	141.2	127.1
191	141.9	127.8
192	142.7	128.5
193	143.4	129.1
194	144.2	129.8
195	144.9	130.5
196	145.7	131.1
197	146.4	131.8
198	147.1	132.5
199	147.9	133.2
200	148.6	133.8
201	149.4	134.5
202	150.1	135.2
203	150.9	135.8
204	151.6	136.5
205	152.3	137.2
206	153.1	137.8
207	153.8	138.5
208	154.6	139.2
209	155.3	139.8
210	156.1	140.5
211	156.8	141.2
212	157.5	141.9
213	158.3	142.5
214	159.0	143.2
215	159.8	143.9
216	160.5	144.5
217	161.3	145.2
218	162.0	145.9
219	162.7	146.5
220	163.5	147.2
221	164.2	147.9
222	165.0	148.5
223	165.7	149.2
224	166.5	149.9
225	167.2	150.6
226	168.0	151.2
227	168.7	151.9
228	169.4	152.6
229	170.2	153.2
230	170.9	153.9
231	171.7	154.6
232	172.4	155.2
233	173.2	155.9
234	173.9	156.6
235	174.6	157.2
236	175.4	157.9
237	176.1	158.6
238	176.9	159.3
239	177.6	159.9
240	178.4	160.6

D Lon Dist. (Hyp.)	Dep D. Lat. (Adj.)	Dep. (Opp.)
241	179.1	161.3
242	179.8	161.9
243	180.6	162.6
244	181.3	163.3
245	182.1	163.9
246	182.8	164.6
247	183.6	165.3
248	184.3	165.9
249	185.0	166.6
250	185.8	167.3
251	186.5	168.0
252	187.3	168.6
253	188.0	169.3
254	188.8	170.0
255	189.5	170.6
256	190.2	171.3
257	191.0	172.0
258	191.7	172.6
259	192.5	173.3
260	193.2	174.0
261	194.0	174.6
262	194.7	175.3
263	195.4	176.0
264	196.2	176.7
265	196.9	177.3
266	197.7	178.0
267	198.4	178.7
268	199.2	179.3
269	199.9	180.0
270	200.6	180.7
271	201.4	181.3
272	202.1	182.0
273	202.9	182.7
274	203.6	183.3
275	204.4	184.0
276	205.1	184.7
277	205.9	185.3
278	206.6	186.0
279	207.3	186.7
280	208.1	187.4
281	208.8	188.0
282	209.6	188.7
283	210.3	189.4
284	211.1	190.0
285	211.8	190.7
286	212.5	191.4
287	213.3	192.0
288	214.0	192.7
289	214.8	193.4
290	215.5	194.0
291	216.3	194.7
292	217.0	195.4
293	217.7	196.1
294	218.5	196.7
295	219.2	197.4
296	220.0	198.1
297	220.7	198.7
298	221.5	199.4
299	222.2	200.1
300	222.9	200.7

Hyp.	Opp.	Adj.
Dist. / D Lon	Dep.	D. Lat. / Dep

48°　　　**48°**

LAUNCHED IN 1832

AND STILL WELL AHEAD

WRITTEN by men who know the ropes and read all round the globe between Greenland and the Antarctic, the *Nautical Magazine* needs no introduction to seafarers, shipping people and marine enthusiasts of any nationality. Its subscribers, some of whom were avid readers long before many modern countries were on the map, are found under every flag, afloat and ashore. If you are not yet one of them, now is the time to sign on. The first issue came out over 140 years ago, and there is still no better bargain anywhere for only 20p a month or £3·00 a year, mailed free to any address on earth, even to the South Pole.

Right from the windjammer reign of Britain's sailor-king William IV, through the succeeding steam age of Queen Victoria, and into our own era of atomic ships, the *Nautical Magazine* has been the voice of the experienced navigator. It still is, more than ever. And not only of masters, mates, apprentices and pilots, but engineers, radio officers, pursers, stewards, the deck crowd and the black gang. The independent voice of all those whose life is the sea and whose know-how is the key to the world's commerce. So you are welcome to write letters to the Editor—who will print them gladly—on any apt subject under the sun, moon and stars, provided you keep your temper. Your views will be read by owners, builders, marine superintendents, examiners and navigation teachers, for they are all among our subscribers, as well as old-timers who have swallowed the anchor but keep abreast in our correspondence columns. Regular letter-writers and readers prefer the three-year subscription for only £8·60, which saves money and time. Many much-needed reforms in the Merchant Service stem from the pages of the *Nautical Magazine*, which was founded by Rear-Admiral A. B. Becher, the foremost hydrographer of his day, and who was also its first editor for 39 years until he retired in 1871. And the Admiralty got so much information out of the *Nautical Magazine* for its own early survey records that it used to grant the editor £100 a year, that is, £50 from Naval Funds and £50 from the Mercantile Marine Fund. Today our sheet-anchor is the subscription at £3·00 a year from men—and women, too—who know a good thing when they see it.

So the *Nautical Magazine* started serving the Merchant Marine eight years before the very first Cunard liner *Britannia* left Liverpool on her maiden voyage to Halifax and Boston. And since that time it has had only five editors before the present one, who is the son of the fourth editor and also edits *Brown's Nautical Almanac*, 'the seamen's bible'.

It was in the editorial epoch of the founder, Rear-Admiral Becher, that the *Nautical Magazine* brought new ideas to the shipyards and was active in exposing a lot of dirty work, not least in marine insurance, thanks to its alert readers and writers. Among these we find James Ballingall, a Scottish shipping surveyor who ended in Australia and who was the first witness called upon to give evidence before the House of Commons Shipwreck Committee' of 1836, which made life at sea last longer. As a source of maritime history, the *Nautical Magazine* has no equal. Indeed, it is not only the second-oldest monthly in the world, but also the oldest reviewer of books in the English language. The Editor is always ready to obtain for *Nautical* readers any British books that are in print, on any subject, upon receipt of the published price, plus postage.

Expert book reviews; salty letters to the Editor; shipping news from all over the world; examination results for named Extra Masters, Masters, Mates and Engineers; the new ships ordered, launched and tried for British owners; monthly list of recent casualties from the Liverpool Underwriters' Association; the movements of Merchant Navy men, a personnel section where one often finds old shipmates mentioned; a dozen feature articles by well-known and unknown writers—scientific, technical, professional, dead serious or dead-pan funny. These are only a few of the items you get for 20p a month. The *Nautical Magazine* is loaded down to the marks with worth-while reading material. Yarns to while away a watch below; problems to ponder over a whole voyage. Do you collect stamps? Want to start an argument around the globe? It's all yours, for only 20p a month, £3·00 a year, or £8·60 for three years. Just sign the subscription order form and send it with your remittance for £3·00 or £8·60 to Brown, Son & Ferguson, Ltd., 52 Darnley Street, Glasgow, G41 2SG, Scotland.

And remember, the *Nautical Magazine* is absolutely independent, so you are at liberty to express your opinion freely on anything and everything of interest to men of the Merchant Service.

Subscription Order Form

The Nautical Magazine

20p MONTHLY (per post: 25p)

The Subscription for 12 Months posted free to any address is £3·00, for 3 years £8·60.

Please supply the "NAUTICAL MAGAZINE" each month from

....19........*to*..19...........

for which I enclose Remittance..*for*............*year(s).*

Name...
(BLOCK LETTERS)

(*Address in full*)..

To   (BLOCK LETTERS)

The "Nautical Magazine"   ....

BROWN, SON & FERGUSON, LTD.

52 Darnley St., GLASGOW, G41 2SG   ....

SCOTLAND

Cheques, Postal and Money Orders should be made payable to Brown, Son & Ferguson, Ltd.   1/73

Table 3 — TRAVERSE TABLE

42° 318° | 042° / 222° | 138° **42°**

Dist. (Hyp.)	D. Lat. (Adj.)	Dep. (Opp.)	Dist. (Hyp.)	D. Lat. (Adj.)	Dep. (Opp.)	Dist. (Hyp.)	D. Lat. (Adj.)	Dep. (Opp.)	Dist. (Hyp.)	D. Lat. (Adj.)	Dep. (Opp.)	Dist. (Hyp.)	D. Lat. (Adj.)	Dep. (Opp.)
301	223.7	201.4	361	268.3	241.6	421	312.9	281.7	481	357.5	321.9	541	402.0	362.0
302	224.4	202.1	362	269.0	242.2	422	313.6	282.4	482	358.2	322.5	542	402.8	362.7
303	225.2	202.7	363	269.8	242.9	423	314.4	283.0	483	358.9	323.2	543	403.5	363.3
304	225.9	203.4	364	270.5	243.6	424	315.1	283.7	484	359.7	323.9	544	404.3	364.0
305	226.7	204.1	365	271.2	244.2	425	315.8	284.4	485	360.4	324.5	545	405.0	364.7
306	227.4	204.8	366	272.0	244.9	426	316.6	285.0	486	361.2	325.2	546	405.8	365.3
307	228.1	205.4	367	272.7	245.6	427	317.3	285.7	487	361.9	325.9	547	406.5	366.0
308	228.9	206.1	368	273.5	246.2	428	318.1	286.4	488	362.7	326.5	548	407.2	366.7
309	229.6	206.8	369	274.2	246.9	429	318.8	287.1	489	363.4	327.2	549	408.0	367.4
310	230.4	207.4	370	275.0	247.6	430	319.6	287.7	490	364.1	327.9	550	408.7	368.0
311	231.1	208.1	371	275.7	248.2	431	320.3	288.4	491	364.9	328.5	551	409.5	368.7
312	231.9	208.8	372	276.4	248.9	432	321.0	289.1	492	365.6	329.2	552	410.2	369.4
313	232.6	209.4	373	277.2	249.6	433	321.8	289.7	493	366.4	329.9	553	411.0	370.0
314	233.3	210.1	374	277.9	250.3	434	322.5	290.4	494	367.1	330.6	554	411.7	370.7
315	234.1	210.8	375	278.7	250.9	435	323.3	291.1	495	367.9	331.2	555	412.4	371.4
316	234.8	211.4	376	279.4	251.6	436	324.0	291.7	496	368.6	331.9	556	413.2	372.0
317	235.6	212.1	377	280.2	252.3	437	324.8	292.4	497	369.3	332.6	557	413.9	372.7
318	236.3	212.8	378	280.9	252.9	438	325.5	293.1	498	370.1	333.2	558	414.7	373.4
319	237.1	213.5	379	281.7	253.6	439	326.2	293.7	499	370.8	333.9	559	415.4	374.0
320	237.8	214.1	380	282.4	254.3	440	327.0	294.4	500	371.6	334.6	560	416.2	374.7
321	238.5	214.8	381	283.1	254.9	441	327.7	295.1	501	372.3	335.2	561	416.9	375.4
322	239.3	215.5	382	283.9	255.6	442	328.5	295.8	502	373.1	335.9	562	417.6	376.1
323	240.0	216.1	383	284.6	256.3	443	329.2	296.4	503	373.8	336.6	563	418.4	376.7
324	240.8	216.8	384	285.4	256.9	444	330.0	297.1	504	374.5	337.2	564	419.1	377.4
325	241.5	217.5	385	286.1	257.6	445	330.7	297.8	505	375.3	337.9	565	419.9	378.1
326	242.3	218.1	386	286.9	258.3	446	331.4	298.4	506	376.0	338.6	566	420.6	378.7
327	243.0	218.8	387	287.6	259.0	447	332.2	299.1	507	376.8	339.2	567	421.4	379.4
328	243.8	219.5	388	288.3	259.6	448	332.9	299.8	508	377.5	339.9	568	422.1	380.1
329	244.5	220.1	389	289.1	260.3	449	333.7	300.4	509	378.3	340.6	569	422.8	380.7
330	245.2	220.8	390	289.8	261.0	450	334.4	301.1	510	379.0	341.3	570	423.6	381.4
331	246.0	221.5	391	290.6	261.6	451	335.2	301.8	511	379.7	341.9	571	424.3	382.1
332	246.7	222.2	392	291.3	262.3	452	335.9	302.4	512	380.5	342.6	572	425.1	382.7
333	247.5	222.8	393	292.1	263.0	453	336.6	303.1	513	381.2	343.3	573	425.8	383.4
334	248.2	223.5	394	292.8	263.6	454	337.4	303.8	514	382.0	343.9	574	426.6	384.1
335	249.0	224.2	395	293.5	264.3	455	338.1	304.5	515	382.7	344.6	575	427.3	384.8
336	249.7	224.8	396	294.3	265.0	456	338.9	305.1	516	383.5	345.3	576	428.1	385.4
337	250.4	225.5	397	295.0	265.6	457	339.6	305.8	517	384.2	345.9	577	428.8	386.1
338	251.2	226.2	398	295.8	266.3	458	340.4	306.5	518	384.9	346.6	578	429.5	386.8
339	251.9	226.8	399	296.5	267.0	459	341.1	307.1	519	385.7	347.3	579	430.3	387.4
340	252.7	227.5	400	297.3	267.7	460	341.8	307.8	520	386.4	347.9	580	431.0	388.1
341	253.4	228.2	401	298.0	268.3	461	342.6	308.5	521	387.2	348.6	581	431.8	388.8
342	254.2	228.8	402	298.7	269.0	462	343.3	309.1	522	387.9	349.3	582	432.5	389.4
343	254.9	229.5	403	299.5	269.7	463	344.1	309.8	523	388.7	350.0	583	433.3	390.1
344	255.6	230.2	404	300.2	270.3	464	344.8	310.5	524	389.4	350.6	584	434.0	390.8
345	256.4	230.9	405	301.0	271.0	465	345.6	311.1	525	390.2	351.3	585	434.7	391.4
346	257.1	231.5	406	301.7	271.7	466	346.3	311.8	526	390.9	352.0	586	435.5	392.1
347	257.9	232.2	407	302.5	272.3	467	347.0	312.5	527	391.6	352.6	587	436.2	392.8
348	258.6	232.9	408	303.2	273.0	468	347.8	313.2	528	392.4	353.3	588	437.0	393.4
349	259.4	233.5	409	303.9	273.7	469	348.5	313.8	529	393.1	354.0	589	437.7	394.1
350	260.1	234.2	410	304.7	274.3	470	349.3	314.5	530	393.9	354.6	590	438.5	394.8
351	260.8	234.9	411	305.4	275.0	471	350.0	315.2	531	394.6	355.3	591	439.2	395.5
352	261.6	235.5	412	306.2	275.7	472	350.8	315.8	532	395.4	356.0	592	439.9	396.1
353	262.3	236.2	413	306.9	276.4	473	351.5	316.5	533	396.1	356.6	593	440.7	396.8
354	263.1	236.9	414	307.7	277.0	474	352.3	317.2	534	396.8	357.3	594	441.4	397.5
355	263.8	237.5	415	308.4	277.7	475	353.0	317.8	535	397.6	358.0	595	442.2	398.1
356	264.6	238.2	416	309.1	278.4	476	353.7	318.5	536	398.3	358.7	596	442.9	398.8
357	265.3	238.9	417	309.9	279.0	477	354.5	319.2	537	399.1	359.3	597	443.7	399.5
358	266.0	239.5	418	310.6	279.7	478	355.2	319.8	538	399.8	360.0	598	444.4	400.1
359	266.8	240.2	419	311.4	280.4	479	356.0	320.5	539	400.6	360.7	599	445.1	400.8
360	267.5	240.9	420	312.1	281.0	480	356.7	321.2	540	401.3	361.3	600	445.9	401.5
Hyp.	Opp.	Adj.	Hyp.	Opp.	Adj.	Hyp.	Opp.	Adj.	Hyp.	Opp.	Adj.	Hyp.	Opp.	Adj.

Dist. Dep. D. Lat. / D Lon ... Dep

Table 3

TRAVERSE TABLE

43°

D Lon / Dist. (Hyp.)	Dep / D. Lat. (Adj.)	Dep (Opp.)	D Lon / Dist. (Hyp.)	Dep / D. Lat. (Adj.)	Dep (Opp.)	D Lon / Dist. (Hyp.)	Dep / D. Lat. (Adj.)	Dep (Opp.)	D Lon / Dist. (Hyp.)	Dep / D. Lat. (Adj.)	Dep (Opp.)	D Lon / Dist. (Hyp.)	Dep / D. Lat. (Adj.)	Dep (Opp.)
1	0.7	0.7	61	44.6	41.6	121	88.5	82.5	181	132.4	123.4	241	176.3	164.4
2	1.5	1.4	62	45.3	42.3	122	89.2	83.2	182	133.1	124.1	242	177.0	165.0
3	2.2	2.0	63	46.1	43.0	123	90.0	83.9	183	133.8	124.8	243	177.7	165.7
4	2.9	2.7	64	46.8	43.6	124	90.7	84.6	184	134.6	125.5	244	178.5	166.4
5	3.7	3.4	65	47.5	44.3	125	91.4	85.2	185	135.3	126.2	245	179.2	167.1
6	4.4	4.1	66	48.3	45.0	126	92.2	85.9	186	136.0	126.9	246	179.9	167.8
7	5.1	4.8	67	49.0	45.7	127	92.9	86.6	187	136.8	127.5	247	180.6	168.5
8	5.9	5.5	68	49.7	46.4	128	93.6	87.3	188	137.5	128.2	248	181.4	169.1
9	6.6	6.1	69	50.5	47.1	129	94.3	88.0	189	138.2	128.9	249	182.1	169.8
10	7.3	6.8	70	51.2	47.7	130	95.1	88.7	190	139.0	129.6	250	182.8	170.5
11	8.0	7.5	71	51.9	48.4	131	95.8	89.3	191	139.7	130.3	251	183.6	171.2
12	8.8	8.2	72	52.7	49.1	132	96.5	90.0	192	140.4	130.9	252	184.3	171.9
13	9.5	8.9	73	53.4	49.8	133	97.3	90.7	193	141.2	131.6	253	185.0	172.5
14	10.2	9.5	74	54.1	50.5	134	98.0	91.4	194	141.9	132.3	254	185.8	173.2
15	11.0	10.2	75	54.9	51.1	135	98.7	92.1	195	142.6	133.0	255	186.5	173.9
16	11.7	10.9	76	55.6	51.8	136	99.5	92.8	196	143.3	133.7	256	187.2	174.6
17	12.4	11.6	77	56.3	52.5	137	100.2	93.4	197	144.1	134.4	257	188.0	175.3
18	13.2	12.3	78	57.0	53.2	138	100.9	94.1	198	144.8	135.0	258	188.7	176.0
19	13.9	13.0	79	57.8	53.9	139	101.7	94.8	199	145.5	135.7	259	189.4	176.6
20	14.6	13.6	80	58.5	54.6	140	102.4	95.5	200	146.3	136.4	260	190.2	177.3
21	15.4	14.3	81	59.2	55.2	141	103.1	96.2	201	147.0	137.1	261	190.9	178.0
22	16.1	15.0	82	60.0	55.9	142	103.9	96.8	202	147.7	137.8	262	191.6	178.7
23	16.8	15.7	83	60.7	56.6	143	104.6	97.5	203	148.5	138.4	263	192.3	179.4
24	17.6	16.4	84	61.4	57.3	144	105.3	98.2	204	149.2	139.1	264	193.1	180.0
25	18.3	17.0	85	62.2	58.0	145	106.0	98.9	205	149.9	139.8	265	193.8	180.7
26	19.0	17.7	86	62.9	58.7	146	106.8	99.6	206	150.7	140.5	266	194.5	181.4
27	19.7	18.4	87	63.6	59.3	147	107.5	100.3	207	151.4	141.2	267	195.3	182.1
28	20.5	19.1	88	64.4	60.0	148	108.2	100.9	208	152.1	141.9	268	196.0	182.8
29	21.2	19.8	89	65.1	60.7	149	109.0	101.6	209	152.9	142.5	269	196.7	183.5
30	21.9	20.5	90	65.8	61.4	150	109.7	102.3	210	153.6	143.2	270	197.5	184.1
31	22.7	21.1	91	66.6	62.1	151	110.4	103.0	211	154.3	143.9	271	198.2	184.8
32	23.4	21.8	92	67.3	62.7	152	111.2	103.7	212	155.0	144.6	272	198.9	185.5
33	24.1	22.5	93	68.0	63.4	153	111.9	104.3	213	155.8	145.3	273	199.7	186.2
34	24.9	23.2	94	68.7	64.1	154	112.6	105.0	214	156.5	145.9	274	200.4	186.9
35	25.6	23.9	95	69.5	64.8	155	113.4	105.7	215	157.2	146.6	275	201.1	187.5
36	26.3	24.6	96	70.2	65.5	156	114.1	106.4	216	158.0	147.3	276	201.9	188.2
37	27.1	25.2	97	70.9	66.2	157	114.8	107.1	217	158.7	148.0	277	202.6	188.9
38	27.8	25.9	98	71.7	66.8	158	115.6	107.8	218	159.4	148.7	278	203.3	189.6
39	28.5	26.6	99	72.4	67.5	159	116.3	108.4	219	160.2	149.4	279	204.0	190.3
40	29.3	27.3	100	73.1	68.2	160	117.0	109.1	220	160.9	150.0	280	204.8	191.0
41	30.0	28.0	101	73.9	68.9	161	117.7	109.8	221	161.6	150.7	281	205.5	191.6
42	30.7	28.6	102	74.6	69.6	162	118.5	110.5	222	162.4	151.4	282	206.2	192.3
43	31.4	29.3	103	75.3	70.2	163	119.2	111.2	223	163.1	152.1	283	207.0	193.0
44	32.2	30.0	104	76.1	70.9	164	119.9	111.8	224	163.8	152.8	284	207.7	193.7
45	32.9	30.7	105	76.8	71.6	165	120.7	112.5	225	164.6	153.4	285	208.4	194.4
46	33.6	31.4	106	77.5	72.3	166	121.4	113.2	226	165.3	154.1	286	209.2	195.1
47	34.4	32.1	107	78.3	73.0	167	122.1	113.9	227	166.0	154.8	287	209.9	195.7
48	35.1	32.7	108	79.0	73.7	168	122.9	114.6	228	166.7	155.5	288	210.6	196.4
49	35.8	33.4	109	79.7	74.3	169	123.6	115.3	229	167.5	156.2	289	211.4	197.1
50	36.6	34.1	110	80.4	75.0	170	124.3	115.9	230	168.2	156.9	290	212.1	197.8
51	37.3	34.8	111	81.2	75.7	171	125.1	116.6	231	168.9	157.5	291	212.8	198.5
52	38.0	35.5	112	81.9	76.4	172	125.8	117.3	232	169.7	158.2	292	213.6	199.1
53	38.8	36.1	113	82.6	77.1	173	126.5	118.0	233	170.4	158.9	293	214.3	199.8
54	39.5	36.8	114	83.4	77.7	174	127.3	118.7	234	171.1	159.6	294	215.0	200.5
55	40.2	37.5	115	84.1	78.4	175	128.0	119.3	235	171.9	160.3	295	215.7	201.2
56	41.0	38.2	116	84.8	79.1	176	128.7	120.0	236	172.6	161.0	296	216.5	201.9
57	41.7	38.9	117	85.6	79.8	177	129.4	120.7	237	173.3	161.7	297	217.2	202.6
58	42.4	39.6	118	86.3	80.5	178	130.2	121.4	238	174.1	162.3	298	217.9	203.2
59	43.1	40.2	119	87.0	81.2	179	130.9	122.1	239	174.8	163.0	299	218.7	203.9
60	43.9	40.9	120	87.8	81.8	180	131.6	122.8	240	175.5	163.7	300	219.4	204.6
Hyp.	Opp.	Adj.	Hyp.	Opp.	Adj.	Hyp.	Opp.	Adj.	Hyp.	Opp.	Adj.	Hyp.	Opp.	Adj.

Dist. / D Lon	Dep	D. Lat. / Dep	Dist. / D Lon	Dep	D. Lat. / Dep	Dist. / D Lon	Dep	D. Lat. / Dep	Dist. / D Lon	Dep	D. Lat. / Dep	Dist. / D Lon	Dep	D. Lat. / Dep

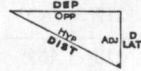

Table 3   TRAVERSE TABLE

43°

43°

D Lon	Dep		D Lon	Dep		D Lon	Dep		D Lon	Dep		D Lon	Dep	
Dist.	D. Lat.	Dep.	Dist.	D. Lat.	Dep.	Dist.	D. Lat.	Dep.	Dist.	D. Lat.	Dep.	Dist.	D. Lat.	Dep.
Hyp.	Adj.	Opp.	Hyp.	Adj.	Opp.	Hyp.	Adj.	Opp.	Hyp.	Adj.	Opp.	Hyp.	Adj.	Opp.
301	220.1	205.3	361	264.0	246.2	421	307.9	287.1	481	351.8	328.0	541	395.7	369.0
302	220.9	206.0	362	264.8	246.9	422	308.6	287.8	482	352.5	328.7	542	396.4	369.6
303	221.6	206.6	363	265.5	247.6	423	309.4	288.5	483	353.2	329.4	543	397.1	370.3
304	222.3	207.3	364	266.2	248.2	424	310.1	289.2	484	354.0	330.1	544	397.9	371.0
305	223.1	208.0	365	266.9	248.9	425	310.8	289.8	485	354.7	330.8	545	398.6	371.7
306	223.8	208.7	366	267.7	249.6	426	311.6	290.5	486	355.4	331.5	546	399.3	372.4
307	224.5	209.4	367	268.4	250.3	427	312.3	291.2	487	356.2	332.1	547	400.1	373.1
308	225.3	210.1	368	269.1	251.0	428	313.0	291.9	488	356.9	332.8	548	400.8	373.7
309	226.0	210.7	369	269.9	251.7	429	313.8	292.6	489	357.6	333.5	549	401.5	374.4
310	226.7	211.4	370	270.6	252.3	430	314.5	293.3	490	358.4	334.2	550	402.2	375.1
311	227.5	212.1	371	271.3	253.0	431	315.2	293.9	491	359.1	334.9	551	403.0	375.8
312	228.2	212.8	372	272.1	253.7	432	315.9	294.6	492	359.8	335.5	552	403.7	376.5
313	228.9	213.5	373	272.8	254.4	433	316.7	295.3	493	360.6	336.2	553	404.4	377.1
314	229.6	214.1	374	273.5	255.1	434	317.4	296.0	494	361.3	336.9	554	405.2	377.8
315	230.4	214.8	375	274.3	255.7	435	318.1	296.7	495	362.0	337.6	555	405.9	378.5
316	231.1	215.5	376	275.0	256.4	436	318.9	297.4	496	362.8	338.3	556	406.6	379.2
317	231.8	216.2	377	275.7	257.1	437	319.6	298.0	497	363.5	339.0	557	407.4	379.9
318	232.6	216.9	378	276.5	257.8	438	320.3	298.7	498	364.2	339.6	558	408.1	380.6
319	233.3	217.6	379	277.2	258.5	439	321.1	299.4	499	364.9	340.3	559	408.8	381.2
320	234.0	218.2	380	277.9	259.2	440	321.8	300.1	500	365.7	341.0	560	409.6	381.9
321	234.8	218.9	381	278.6	259.8	441	322.5	300.8	501	366.4	341.7	561	410.3	382.6
322	235.5	219.6	382	279.4	260.5	442	323.3	301.4	502	367.1	342.4	562	411.0	383.3
323	236.2	220.3	383	280.1	261.2	443	324.0	302.1	503	367.9	343.0	563	411.8	384.0
324	237.0	221.0	384	280.8	261.9	444	324.7	302.8	504	368.6	343.7	564	412.5	384.6
325	237.7	221.6	385	281.6	262.6	445	325.5	303.5	505	369.3	344.4	565	413.2	385.3
326	238.4	222.3	386	282.3	263.3	446	326.2	304.2	506	370.1	345.1	566	413.9	386.0
327	239.2	223.0	387	283.0	263.9	447	326.9	304.9	507	370.8	345.8	567	414.7	386.7
328	239.9	223.7	388	283.8	264.6	448	327.6	305.5	508	371.5	346.5	568	415.4	387.4
329	240.6	224.4	389	284.5	265.3	449	328.4	306.2	509	372.3	347.1	569	416.1	388.1
330	241.3	225.1	390	285.2	266.0	450	329.1	306.9	510	373.0	347.8	570	416.9	388.7
331	242.1	225.7	391	286.0	266.7	451	329.8	307.6	511	373.7	348.5	571	417.6	389.4
332	242.8	226.4	392	286.7	267.3	452	330.6	308.3	512	374.5	349.2	572	418.3	390.1
333	243.5	227.1	393	287.4	268.0	453	331.3	308.9	513	375.2	349.9	573	419.1	390.8
334	244.3	227.8	394	288.2	268.7	454	332.0	309.6	514	375.9	350.5	574	419.8	391.5
335	245.0	228.5	395	288.9	269.4	455	332.8	310.3	515	376.6	351.2	575	420.5	392.1
336	245.7	229.2	396	289.6	270.1	456	333.5	311.0	516	377.4	351.9	576	421.3	392.8
337	246.5	229.8	397	290.3	270.8	457	334.2	311.7	517	378.1	352.6	577	422.0	393.5
338	247.2	230.5	398	291.1	271.4	458	335.0	312.4	518	378.8	353.3	578	422.7	394.2
339	247.9	231.2	399	291.8	272.1	459	335.7	313.0	519	379.6	354.0	579	423.5	394.9
340	248.7	231.9	400	292.5	272.8	460	336.4	313.7	520	380.3	354.6	580	424.2	395.6
341	249.4	232.6	401	293.3	273.5	461	337.2	314.4	521	381.0	355.3	581	424.9	396.2
342	250.1	233.2	402	294.0	274.2	462	337.9	315.1	522	381.8	356.0	582	425.6	396.9
343	250.9	233.9	403	294.7	274.8	463	338.6	315.8	523	382.5	356.7	583	426.4	397.6
344	251.6	234.6	404	295.5	275.5	464	339.3	316.4	524	383.2	357.4	584	427.1	398.3
345	252.3	235.3	405	296.2	276.2	465	340.1	317.1	525	384.0	358.0	585	427.8	399.0
346	253.0	236.0	406	296.9	276.9	466	340.8	317.8	526	384.7	358.7	586	428.6	399.7
347	253.8	236.7	407	297.7	277.6	467	341.5	318.5	527	385.4	359.4	587	429.3	400.3
348	254.5	237.3	408	298.4	278.3	468	342.3	319.2	528	386.2	360.1	588	430.0	401.0
349	255.2	238.0	409	299.1	278.9	469	343.0	319.9	529	386.9	360.8	589	430.8	401.7
350	256.0	238.7	410	299.9	279.6	470	343.7	320.5	530	387.6	361.5	590	431.5	402.4
351	256.7	239.4	411	300.6	280.3	471	344.5	321.2	531	388.3	362.1	591	432.2	403.1
352	257.4	240.1	412	301.3	281.0	472	345.2	321.9	532	389.1	362.8	592	433.0	403.7
353	258.2	240.7	413	302.0	281.7	473	345.9	322.6	533	389.8	363.5	593	433.7	404.4
354	258.9	241.4	414	302.8	282.3	474	346.7	323.3	534	390.5	364.2	594	434.4	405.1
355	259.6	242.1	415	303.5	283.0	475	347.4	323.9	535	391.3	364.9	595	435.2	405.8
356	260.4	242.8	416	304.2	283.7	476	348.1	324.6	536	392.0	365.6	596	435.9	406.5
357	261.1	243.5	417	305.0	284.4	477	348.9	325.3	537	392.7	366.2	597	436.6	407.2
358	261.8	244.2	418	305.7	285.1	478	349.6	326.0	538	393.5	366.9	598	437.3	407.8
359	262.6	244.8	419	306.4	285.8	479	350.3	326.7	539	394.2	367.6	599	438.1	408.5
360	263.3	245.5	420	307.2	286.4	480	351.0	327.4	540	394.9	368.3	600	438.8	409.2
Hyp.	Opp.	Adj.	Hyp.	Opp.	Adj.	Hyp.	Opp.	Adj.	Hyp.	Opp.	Adj.	Hyp.	Opp.	Adj.
Dist.	Dep.	D. Lat.	Dist.	Dep.	D. Lat.	Dist.	Dep.	D. Lat.	Dist.	Dep.	D. Lat.	Dist.	Dep.	D. Lat.
D Lon		Dep	D Lon		Dep	D Lon		Dep	D Lon		Dep	D Lon		Dep

47°

47°

Table 3

TRAVERSE TABLE

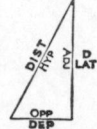

44°   44°

D Lon Dist.	Dep D. Lat.	Dep.	D Lon Dist.	Dep D. Lat.	Dep.	D Lon Dist.	Dep D. Lat.	Dep.	D Lon Dist.	Dep D. Lat.	Dep.	D Lon Dist.	Dep D. Lat.	Dep.
Hyp.	Adj.	Opp.	Hyp.	Adj.	Opp.	Hyp.	Adj.	Opp.	Hyp.	Adj.	Opp.	Hyp.	Adj.	Opp.
1	0.7	0.7	61	43.9	42.4	121	87.0	84.1	181	130.2	125.7	241	173.4	167.4
2	1.4	1.4	62	44.6	43.1	122	87.8	84.7	182	130.9	126.4	242	174.1	168.1
3	2.2	2.1	63	45.3	43.8	123	88.5	85.4	183	131.6	127.1	243	174.8	168.8
4	2.9	2.8	64	46.0	44.5	124	89.2	86.1	184	132.4	127.8	244	175.5	169.5
5	3.6	3.5	65	46.8	45.2	125	89.9	86.8	185	133.1	128.5	245	176.2	170.2
6	4.3	4.2	66	47.5	45.8	126	90.6	87.5	186	133.8	129.2	246	177.0	170.9
7	5.0	4.9	67	48.2	46.5	127	91.4	88.2	187	134.5	129.9	247	177.7	171.6
8	5.8	5.6	68	48.9	47.2	128	92.1	88.9	188	135.2	130.6	248	178.4	172.3
9	6.5	6.3	69	49.6	47.9	129	92.8	89.6	189	136.0	131.3	249	179.1	173.0
10	7.2	6.9	70	50.4	48.6	130	93.5	90.3	190	136.7	132.0	250	179.8	173.7
11	7.9	7.6	71	51.1	49.3	131	94.2	91.0	191	137.4	132.7	251	180.6	174.4
12	8.6	8.3	72	51.8	50.0	132	95.0	91.7	192	138.1	133.4	252	181.3	175.1
13	9.4	9.0	73	52.5	50.7	133	95.7	92.4	193	138.8	134.1	253	182.0	175.7
14	10.1	9.7	74	53.2	51.4	134	96.4	93.1	194	139.6	134.8	254	182.7	176.4
15	10.8	10.4	75	54.0	52.1	135	97.1	93.8	195	140.3	135.5	255	183.4	177.1
16	11.5	11.1	76	54.7	52.8	136	97.8	94.5	196	141.0	136.2	256	184.2	177.8
17	12.2	11.8	77	55.4	53.5	137	98.5	95.2	197	141.7	136.8	257	184.9	178.5
18	12.9	12.5	78	56.1	54.2	138	99.3	95.9	198	142.4	137.5	258	185.6	179.2
19	13.7	13.2	79	56.8	54.9	139	100.0	96.6	199	143.1	138.2	259	186.3	179.9
20	14.4	13.9	80	57.5	55.6	140	100.7	97.3	200	143.9	138.9	260	187.0	180.6
21	15.1	14.6	81	58.3	56.3	141	101.4	97.9	201	144.6	139.6	261	187.7	181.3
22	15.8	15.3	82	59.0	57.0	142	102.1	98.6	202	145.3	140.3	262	188.5	182.0
23	16.5	16.0	83	59.7	57.7	143	102.9	99.3	203	146.0	141.0	263	189.2	182.7
24	17.3	16.7	84	60.4	58.4	144	103.6	100.0	204	146.7	141.7	264	189.9	183.4
25	18.0	17.4	85	61.1	59.0	145	104.3	100.7	205	147.5	142.4	265	190.6	184.1
26	18.7	18.1	86	61.9	59.7	146	105.0	101.4	206	148.2	143.1	266	191.3	184.8
27	19.4	18.8	87	62.6	60.4	147	105.7	102.1	207	148.9	143.8	267	192.1	185.5
28	20.1	19.5	88	63.3	61.1	148	106.5	102.8	208	149.6	144.5	268	192.8	186.2
29	20.9	20.1	89	64.0	61.8	149	107.2	103.5	209	150.3	145.2	269	193.5	186.9
30	21.6	20.8	90	64.7	62.5	150	107.9	104.2	210	151.1	145.9	270	194.2	187.6
31	22.3	21.5	91	65.5	63.2	151	108.6	104.9	211	151.8	146.6	271	194.9	188.3
32	23.0	22.2	92	66.2	63.9	152	109.3	105.6	212	152.5	147.3	272	195.7	188.9
33	23.7	22.9	93	66.9	64.6	153	110.1	106.3	213	153.2	148.0	273	196.4	189.6
34	24.5	23.6	94	67.6	65.3	154	110.8	107.0	214	153.9	148.7	274	197.1	190.3
35	25.2	24.3	95	68.3	66.0	155	111.5	107.7	215	154.7	149.4	275	197.8	191.0
36	25.9	25.0	96	69.1	66.7	156	112.2	108.4	216	155.4	150.0	276	198.5	191.7
37	26.6	25.7	97	69.8	67.4	157	112.9	109.1	217	156.1	150.7	277	199.3	192.4
38	27.3	26.4	98	70.5	68.1	158	113.7	109.8	218	156.8	151.4	278	200.0	193.1
39	28.1	27.1	99	71.2	68.8	159	114.4	110.5	219	157.5	152.1	279	200.7	193.8
40	28.8	27.8	100	71.9	69.5	160	115.1	111.1	220	158.3	152.8	280	201.4	194.5
41	29.5	28.5	101	72.7	70.2	161	115.8	111.8	221	159.0	153.5	281	202.1	195.2
42	30.2	29.2	102	73.4	70.9	162	116.5	112.5	222	159.7	154.2	282	202.9	195.9
43	30.9	29.9	103	74.1	71.5	163	117.3	113.2	223	160.4	154.9	283	203.6	196.6
44	31.7	30.6	104	74.8	72.2	164	118.0	113.9	224	161.1	155.6	284	204.3	197.3
45	32.4	31.3	105	75.5	72.9	165	118.7	114.6	225	161.9	156.3	285	205.0	198.0
46	33.1	32.0	106	76.3	73.6	166	119.4	115.3	226	162.6	157.0	286	205.7	198.7
47	33.8	32.6	107	77.0	74.3	167	120.1	116.0	227	163.3	157.7	287	206.5	199.4
48	34.5	33.3	108	77.7	75.0	168	120.8	116.7	228	164.0	158.4	288	207.2	200.1
49	35.2	34.0	109	78.4	75.7	169	121.6	117.4	229	164.7	159.1	289	207.9	200.8
50	36.0	34.7	110	79.1	76.4	170	122.3	118.1	230	165.4	159.8	290	208.6	201.5
51	36.7	35.4	111	79.8	77.1	171	123.0	118.8	231	166.2	160.5	291	209.3	202.1
52	37.4	36.1	112	80.6	77.8	172	123.7	119.5	232	166.9	161.2	292	210.0	202.8
53	38.1	36.8	113	81.3	78.5	173	124.4	120.2	233	167.6	161.9	293	210.8	203.5
54	38.8	37.5	114	82.0	79.2	174	125.2	120.9	234	168.3	162.6	294	211.5	204.2
55	39.6	38.2	115	82.7	79.9	175	125.9	121.6	235	169.0	163.2	295	212.2	204.9
56	40.3	38.9	116	83.4	80.6	176	126.6	122.3	236	169.8	163.9	296	212.9	205.6
57	41.0	39.6	117	84.2	81.3	177	127.3	123.0	237	170.5	164.6	297	213.6	206.3
58	41.7	40.3	118	84.9	82.0	178	128.0	123.6	238	171.2	165.3	298	214.4	207.0
59	42.4	41.0	119	85.6	82.7	179	128.8	124.3	239	171.9	166.0	299	215.1	207.7
60	43.2	41.7	120	86.3	83.4	180	129.5	125.0	240	172.6	166.7	300	215.8	208.4
Hyp.	Opp.	Adj.	Hyp.	Opp.	Adj.	Hyp.	Opp.	Adj.	Hyp.	Opp.	Adj.	Hyp.	Opp.	Adj.
Dist. D Lon	Dep.	D. Lat. Dep	Dist. D Lon	Dep.	D. Lat. Dep	Dist. D Lon	Dep.	D. Lat. Dep	Dist. D Lon	Dep.	D. Lat. Dep	Dist. D Lon	Dep.	D. Lat. Dep

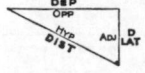

46°   46°

Table 3

TRAVERSE TABLE

316°	044°
224°	136°

D Lon Dist.	Dep D. Lat.	Dep	D Lon Dist.	Dep D. Lat.	Dep	D Lon Dist.	Dep D. Lat.	Dep	D Lon Dist.	Dep D. Lat.	Dep	D Lon Dist.	Dep D. Lat.	Dep
Hyp.	Adj.	Opp.	Hyp.	Adj.	Opp.	Hyp.	Adj.	Opp.	Hyp.	Adj.	Opp.	Hyp.	Adj.	Opp.
301	216.5	209.1	361	259.7	250.8	421	302.8	292.5	481	346.0	334.1	541	389.2	375.8
302	217.2	209.8	362	260.4	251.5	422	303.6	293.1	482	346.7	334.8	542	389.9	376.5
303	218.0	210.5	363	261.1	252.2	423	304.3	293.8	483	347.4	335.5	543	390.6	377.2
304	218.7	211.2	364	261.8	252.9	424	305.0	294.5	484	348.2	336.2	544	391.3	377.9
305	219.4	211.9	365	262.6	253.6	425	305.7	295.2	485	348.9	336.9	545	392.0	378.6
306	220.1	212.6	366	263.3	254.2	426	306.4	295.9	486	349.6	337.6	546	392.8	379.3
307	220.8	213.3	367	264.0	254.9	427	307.2	296.6	487	350.3	338.3	547	393.5	380.0
308	221.6	214.0	368	264.7	255.6	428	307.9	297.3	488	351.0	339.0	548	394.2	380.7
309	222.3	214.6	369	265.4	256.3	429	308.6	298.0	489	351.8	339.7	549	394.9	381.4
310	223.0	215.3	370	266.2	257.0	430	309.3	298.7	490	352.5	340.4	550	395.6	382.1
311	223.7	216.0	371	266.9	257.7	431	310.0	299.4	491	353.2	341.1	551	396.4	382.8
312	224.4	216.7	372	267.6	258.4	432	310.8	300.1	492	353.9	341.8	552	397.1	383.5
313	225.2	217.4	373	268.3	259.1	433	311.5	300.8	493	354.6	342.5	553	397.8	384.1
314	225.9	218.1	374	269.0	259.8	434	312.2	301.5	494	355.4	343.2	554	398.5	384.8
315	226.6	218.8	375	269.8	260.5	435	312.9	302.2	495	356.1	343.9	555	399.2	385.5
316	227.3	219.5	376	270.5	261.2	436	313.6	302.9	496	356.8	344.6	556	400.0	386.2
317	228.0	220.2	377	271.2	261.9	437	314.4	303.6	497	357.5	345.2	557	400.7	386.9
318	228.8	220.9	378	271.9	262.6	438	315.1	304.3	498	358.2	345.9	558	401.4	387.6
319	229.5	221.6	379	272.6	263.3	439	315.8	305.0	499	359.0	346.6	559	402.1	388.3
320	230.2	222.3	380	273.3	264.0	440	316.5	305.6	500	359.7	347.3	560	402.8	389.0
321	230.9	223.0	381	274.1	264.7	441	317.2	306.3	501	360.4	348.0	561	403.5	389.7
322	231.6	223.7	382	274.8	265.4	442	317.9	307.0	502	361.1	348.7	562	404.3	390.4
323	232.3	224.4	383	275.5	266.1	443	318.7	307.7	503	361.8	349.4	563	405.0	391.1
324	233.1	225.1	384	276.2	266.7	444	319.4	308.4	504	362.5	350.1	564	405.7	391.8
325	233.8	225.8	385	276.9	267.4	445	320.1	309.1	505	363.3	350.8	565	406.4	392.5
326	234.5	226.5	386	277.7	268.1	446	320.8	309.8	506	364.0	351.5	566	407.1	393.2
327	235.2	227.2	387	278.4	268.8	447	321.5	310.5	507	364.7	352.2	567	407.9	393.9
328	235.9	227.8	388	279.1	269.5	448	322.3	311.2	508	365.4	352.9	568	408.6	394.6
329	236.7	228.5	389	279.8	270.2	449	323.0	311.9	509	366.1	353.6	569	409.3	395.3
330	237.4	229.2	390	280.5	270.9	450	323.7	312.6	510	366.9	354.3	570	410.0	396.0
331	238.1	229.9	391	281.3	271.6	451	324.4	313.3	511	367.6	355.0	571	410.7	396.6
332	238.8	230.6	392	282.0	272.3	452	325.1	314.0	512	368.3	355.7	572	411.5	397.3
333	239.5	231.3	393	282.7	273.0	453	325.9	314.7	513	369.0	356.4	573	412.2	398.0
334	240.3	232.0	394	283.4	273.7	454	326.6	315.4	514	369.7	357.1	574	412.9	398.7
335	241.0	232.7	395	284.1	274.4	455	327.3	316.1	515	370.5	357.7	575	413.6	399.4
336	241.7	233.4	396	284.9	275.1	456	328.0	316.8	516	371.2	358.4	576	414.3	400.1
337	242.4	234.1	397	285.6	275.8	457	328.7	317.5	517	371.9	359.1	577	415.1	400.8
338	243.1	234.8	398	286.3	276.5	458	329.5	318.2	518	372.6	359.8	578	415.8	401.5
339	243.9	235.5	399	287.0	277.2	459	330.2	318.8	519	373.3	360.5	579	416.5	402.2
340	244.6	236.2	400	287.7	277.9	460	330.9	319.5	520	374.1	361.2	580	417.2	402.9
341	245.3	236.9	401	288.5	278.6	461	331.6	320.2	521	374.8	361.9	581	417.9	403.6
342	246.0	237.6	402	289.2	279.3	462	332.3	320.9	522	375.5	362.6	582	418.7	404.3
343	246.7	238.3	403	289.9	279.9	463	333.1	321.6	523	376.2	363.3	583	419.4	405.0
344	247.5	239.0	404	290.6	280.6	464	333.8	322.3	524	376.9	364.0	584	420.1	405.7
345	248.2	239.7	405	291.3	281.3	465	334.5	323.0	525	377.7	364.7	585	420.8	406.4
346	248.9	240.4	406	292.1	282.0	466	335.2	323.7	526	378.4	365.4	586	421.5	407.1
347	249.6	241.0	407	292.8	282.7	467	335.9	324.4	527	379.1	366.1	587	422.3	407.8
348	250.3	241.7	408	293.5	283.4	468	336.7	325.1	528	379.8	366.8	588	423.0	408.5
349	251.0	242.4	409	294.2	284.1	469	337.4	325.8	529	380.5	367.5	589	423.7	409.2
350	251.8	243.1	410	294.9	284.8	470	338.1	326.5	530	381.3	368.2	590	424.4	409.8
351	252.5	243.8	411	295.6	285.5	471	338.8	327.2	531	382.0	368.9	591	425.1	410.5
352	253.2	244.5	412	296.4	286.2	472	339.5	327.9	532	382.7	369.6	592	425.8	411.2
353	253.9	245.2	413	297.1	286.9	473	340.2	328.6	533	383.4	370.3	593	426.6	411.9
354	254.6	245.9	414	297.8	287.6	474	341.0	329.3	534	384.1	370.9	594	427.3	412.6
355	255.4	246.6	415	298.5	288.3	475	341.7	330.0	535	384.8	371.6	595	428.0	413.3
356	256.1	247.3	416	299.2	289.0	476	342.4	330.7	536	385.6	372.3	596	428.7	414.0
357	256.8	248.0	417	300.0	289.7	477	343.1	331.4	537	386.3	373.0	597	429.4	414.7
358	257.5	248.7	418	300.7	290.4	478	343.8	332.0	538	387.0	373.7	598	430.2	415.4
359	258.2	249.4	419	301.4	291.1	479	344.6	332.7	539	387.7	374.4	599	430.9	416.1
360	259.0	250.1	420	302.1	291.8	480	345.3	333.4	540	388.4	375.1	600	431.6	416.8
Hyp.	Opp.	Adj.	Hyp.	Opp.	Adj.	Hyp.	Opp.	Adj.	Hyp.	Opp.	Adj.	Hyp.	Opp.	Adj.
Dist. D Lon	Dep.	D. Lat. Dep	Dist. D Lon	Dep.	D. Lat. Dep	Dist. D Lon	Dep.	D. Lat. Dep	Dist. D Lon	Dep.	D. Lat. Dep	Dist. D Lon	Dep.	D. Lat. Dep

314°	046°
226°	134°

Table 3

TRAVERSE TABLE

45°

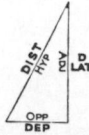

45°

D Lon Dist.	Dep D. Lat.	Dep.	D Lon Dist.	Dep D. Lat.	Dep.	D Lon Dist.	Dep D. Lat.	Dep.	D Lon Dist.	Dep D. Lat.	Dep.	D Lon Dist.	Dep D. Lat.	Dep.
Hyp.	Adj.	Opp.	Hyp.	Adj.	Opp.	Hyp.	Adj.	Opp.	Hyp.	Adj.	Opp.	Hyp.	Adj.	Opp.
1	0.7	0.7	61	43.1	43.1	121	85.6	85.6	181	128.0	128.0	241	170.4	170.4
2	1.4	1.4	62	43.8	43.8	122	86.3	86.3	182	128.7	128.7	242	171.1	171.1
3	2.1	2.1	63	44.5	44.5	123	87.0	87.0	183	129.4	129.4	243	171.8	171.8
4	2.8	2.8	64	45.3	45.3	124	87.7	87.7	184	130.1	130.1	244	172.5	172.5
5	3.5	3.5	65	46.0	46.0	125	88.4	88.4	185	130.8	130.8	245	173.2	173.2
6	4.2	4.2	66	46.7	46.7	126	89.1	89.1	186	131.5	131.5	246	173.9	173.9
7	4.9	4.9	67	47.4	47.4	127	89.8	89.8	187	132.2	132.2	247	174.7	174.7
8	5.7	5.7	68	48.1	48.1	128	90.5	90.5	188	132.9	132.9	248	175.4	175.4
9	6.4	6.4	69	48.8	48.8	129	91.2	91.2	189	133.6	133.6	249	176.1	176.1
10	7.1	7.1	70	49.5	49.5	130	91.9	91.9	190	134.4	134.4	250	176.8	176.8
11	7.8	7.8	71	50.2	50.2	131	92.6	92.6	191	135.1	135.1	251	177.5	177.5
12	8.5	8.5	72	50.9	50.9	132	93.3	93.3	192	135.8	135.8	252	178.2	178.2
13	9.2	9.2	73	51.6	51.6	133	94.0	94.0	193	136.5	136.5	253	178.9	178.9
14	9.9	9.9	74	52.3	52.3	134	94.8	94.8	194	137.2	137.2	254	179.6	179.6
15	10.6	10.6	75	53.0	53.0	135	95.5	95.5	195	137.9	137.9	255	180.3	180.3
16	11.3	11.3	76	53.7	53.7	136	96.2	96.2	196	138.6	138.6	256	181.0	181.0
17	12.0	12.0	77	54.4	54.4	137	96.9	96.9	197	139.3	139.3	257	181.7	181.7
18	12.7	12.7	78	55.2	55.2	138	97.6	97.6	198	140.0	140.0	258	182.4	182.4
19	13.4	13.4	79	55.9	55.9	139	98.3	98.3	199	140.7	140.7	259	183.1	183.1
20	14.1	14.1	80	56.6	56.6	140	99.0	99.0	200	141.4	141.4	260	183.8	183.8
21	14.8	14.8	81	57.3	57.3	141	99.7	99.7	201	142.1	142.1	261	184.6	184.6
22	15.6	15.6	82	58.0	58.0	142	100.4	100.4	202	142.8	142.8	262	185.3	185.3
23	16.3	16.3	83	58.7	58.7	143	101.1	101.1	203	143.5	143.5	263	186.0	186.0
24	17.0	17.0	84	59.4	59.4	144	101.8	101.8	204	144.2	144.2	264	186.7	186.7
25	17.7	17.7	85	60.1	60.1	145	102.5	102.5	205	145.0	145.0	265	187.4	187.4
26	18.4	18.4	86	60.8	60.8	146	103.2	103.2	206	145.7	145.7	266	188.1	188.1
27	19.1	19.1	87	61.5	61.5	147	103.9	103.9	207	146.4	146.4	267	188.8	188.8
28	19.8	19.8	88	62.2	62.2	148	104.7	104.7	208	147.1	147.1	268	189.5	189.5
29	20.5	20.5	89	62.9	62.9	149	105.4	105.4	209	147.8	147.8	269	190.2	190.2
30	21.2	21.2	90	63.6	63.6	150	106.1	106.1	210	148.5	148.5	270	190.9	190.9
31	21.9	21.9	91	64.3	64.3	151	106.8	106.8	211	149.2	149.2	271	191.6	191.6
32	22.6	22.6	92	65.1	65.1	152	107.5	107.5	212	149.9	149.9	272	192.3	192.3
33	23.3	23.3	93	65.8	65.8	153	108.2	108.2	213	150.6	150.6	273	193.0	193.0
34	24.0	24.0	94	66.5	66.5	154	108.9	108.9	214	151.3	151.3	274	193.7	193.7
35	24.7	24.7	95	67.2	67.2	155	109.6	109.6	215	152.0	152.0	275	194.5	194.5
36	25.5	25.5	96	67.9	67.9	156	110.3	110.3	216	152.7	152.7	276	195.2	195.2
37	26.2	26.2	97	68.6	68.6	157	111.0	111.0	217	153.4	153.4	277	195.9	195.9
38	26.9	26.9	98	69.3	69.3	158	111.7	111.7	218	154.1	154.1	278	196.6	196.6
39	27.6	27.6	99	70.0	70.0	159	112.4	112.4	219	154.9	154.9	279	197.3	197.3
40	28.3	28.3	100	70.7	70.7	160	113.1	113.1	220	155.6	155.6	280	198.0	198.0
41	29.0	29.0	101	71.4	71.4	161	113.8	113.8	221	156.3	156.3	281	198.7	198.7
42	29.7	29.7	102	72.1	72.1	162	114.6	114.6	222	157.0	157.0	282	199.4	199.4
43	30.4	30.4	103	72.8	72.8	163	115.3	115.3	223	157.7	157.7	283	200.1	200.1
44	31.1	31.1	104	73.5	73.5	164	116.0	116.0	224	158.4	158.4	284	200.8	200.8
45	31.8	31.8	105	74.2	74.2	165	116.7	116.7	225	159.1	159.1	285	201.5	201.5
46	32.5	32.5	106	75.0	75.0	166	117.4	117.4	226	159.8	159.8	286	202.2	202.2
47	33.2	33.2	107	75.7	75.7	167	118.1	118.1	227	160.5	160.5	287	202.9	202.9
48	33.9	33.9	108	76.4	76.4	168	118.8	118.8	228	161.2	161.2	288	203.6	203.6
49	34.6	34.6	109	77.1	77.1	169	119.5	119.5	229	161.9	161.9	289	204.4	204.4
50	35.4	35.4	110	77.8	77.8	170	120.2	120.2	230	162.6	162.6	290	205.1	205.1
51	36.1	36.1	111	78.5	78.5	171	120.9	120.9	231	163.3	163.3	291	205.8	205.8
52	36.8	36.8	112	79.2	79.2	172	121.6	121.6	232	164.0	164.0	292	206.5	206.5
53	37.5	37.5	113	79.9	79.9	173	122.3	122.3	233	164.8	164.8	293	207.2	207.2
54	38.2	38.2	114	80.6	80.6	174	123.0	123.0	234	165.5	165.5	294	207.9	207.9
55	38.9	38.9	115	81.3	81.3	175	123.7	123.7	235	166.2	166.2	295	208.6	208.6
56	39.6	39.6	116	82.0	82.0	176	124.5	124.5	236	166.9	166.9	296	209.3	209.3
57	40.3	40.3	117	82.7	82.7	177	125.2	125.2	237	167.6	167.6	297	210.0	210.0
58	41.0	41.0	118	83.4	83.4	178	125.9	125.9	238	168.3	168.3	298	210.7	210.7
59	41.7	41.7	119	84.1	84.1	179	126.6	126.6	239	169.0	169.0	299	211.4	211.4
60	42.4	42.4	120	84.9	84.9	180	127.3	127.3	240	169.7	169.7	300	212.1	212.1
Hyp.	Opp.	Adj.	Hyp.	Opp.	Adj.	Hyp.	Opp.	Adj.	Hyp.	Opp.	Adj.	Hyp.	Opp.	Adj.
Dist. D Lon	Dep.	D. Lat. Dep	Dist. D Lon	Dep.	D. Lat. Dep	Dist. D Lon	Dep.	D. Lat. Dep	Dist. D Lon	Dep.	D. Lat. Dep	Dist. D Lon	Dep.	D. Lat. Dep

45°

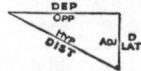

45°

Table 3   **TRAVERSE TABLE**

45°

45°

D Lon Dist.	Dep D. Lat.	Dep.	D Lon Dist.	Dep D. Lat.	Dep.	D Lon Dist.	Dep D. Lat.	Dep.	D Lon Dist.	Dep D. Lat.	Dep.	D Lon Dist.	Dep D. Lat.	Dep.
Hyp.	Adj.	Opp.	Hyp.	Adj.	Opp.	Hyp.	Adj.	Opp.	Hyp.	Adj.	Opp.	Hyp.	Adj.	Opp.
301	212.8	212.8	361	255.3	255.3	421	297.7	297.7	481	340.1	340.1	541	382.5	382.5
302	213.5	213.5	362	256.0	256.0	422	298.4	298.4	482	340.8	340.8	542	383.3	383.3
303	214.3	214.3	363	256.7	256.7	423	299.1	299.1	483	341.5	341.5	543	384.0	384.0
304	215.0	215.0	364	257.4	257.4	424	299.8	299.8	484	342.2	342.2	544	384.7	384.7
305	215.7	215.7	365	258.1	258.1	425	300.5	300.5	485	342.9	342.9	545	385.4	385.4
306	216.4	216.4	366	258.8	258.8	426	301.2	301.2	486	343.7	343.7	546	386.1	386.1
307	217.1	217.1	367	259.5	259.5	427	301.9	301.9	487	344.4	344.4	547	386.8	386.8
308	217.8	217.8	368	260.2	260.2	428	302.6	302.6	488	345.1	345.1	548	387.5	387.5
309	218.5	218.5	369	260.9	260.9	429	303.3	303.3	489	345.8	345.8	549	388.2	388.2
310	219.2	219.2	370	261.6	261.6	430	304.1	304.1	490	346.5	346.5	550	388.9	388.9
311	219.9	219.9	371	262.3	262.3	431	304.8	304.8	491	347.2	347.2	551	389.6	389.6
312	220.6	220.6	372	263.0	263.0	432	305.5	305.5	492	347.9	347.9	552	390.3	390.3
313	221.3	221.3	373	263.8	263.8	433	306.2	306.2	493	348.6	348.6	553	391.0	391.0
314	222.0	222.0	374	264.5	264.5	434	306.9	306.9	494	349.3	349.3	554	391.7	391.7
315	222.7	222.7	375	265.2	265.2	435	307.6	307.6	495	350.0	350.0	555	392.4	392.4
316	223.4	223.4	376	265.9	265.9	436	308.3	308.3	496	350.7	350.7	556	393.2	393.2
317	224.2	224.2	377	266.6	266.6	437	309.0	309.0	497	351.4	351.4	557	393.9	393.9
318	224.9	224.9	378	267.3	267.3	438	309.7	309.7	498	352.1	352.1	558	394.6	394.6
319	225.6	225.6	379	268.0	268.0	439	310.4	310.4	499	352.8	352.8	559	395.3	395.3
320	226.3	226.3	380	268.7	268.7	440	311.1	311.1	500	353.6	353.6	560	396.0	396.0
321	227.0	227.0	381	269.4	269.4	441	311.8	311.8	501	354.3	354.3	561	396.7	396.7
322	227.7	227.7	382	270.1	270.1	442	312.5	312.5	502	355.0	355.0	562	397.4	397.4
323	228.4	228.4	383	270.8	270.8	443	313.2	313.2	503	355.7	355.7	563	398.1	398.1
324	229.1	229.1	384	271.5	271.5	444	314.0	314.0	504	356.4	356.4	564	398.8	398.8
325	229.8	229.8	385	272.2	272.2	445	314.7	314.7	505	357.1	357.1	565	399.5	399.5
326	230.5	230.5	386	272.9	272.9	446	315.4	315.4	506	357.8	357.8	566	400.2	400.2
327	231.2	231.2	387	273.7	273.7	447	316.1	316.1	507	358.5	358.5	567	400.9	400.9
328	231.9	231.9	388	274.4	274.4	448	316.8	316.8	508	359.2	359.2	568	401.6	401.6
329	232.6	232.6	389	275.1	275.1	449	317.5	317.5	509	359.9	359.9	569	402.3	402.3
330	233.3	233.3	390	275.8	275.8	450	318.2	318.2	510	360.6	360.6	570	403.1	403.1
331	234.1	234.1	391	276.5	276.5	451	318.9	318.9	511	361.3	361.3	571	403.8	403.8
332	234.8	234.8	392	277.2	277.2	452	319.6	319.6	512	362.0	362.0	572	404.5	404.5
333	235.5	235.5	393	277.9	277.9	453	320.3	320.3	513	362.7	362.7	573	405.2	405.2
334	236.2	236.2	394	278.6	278.6	454	321.0	321.0	514	363.5	363.5	574	405.9	405.9
335	236.9	236.9	395	279.3	279.3	455	321.7	321.7	515	364.2	364.2	575	406.6	406.6
336	237.6	237.6	396	280.0	280.0	456	322.4	322.4	516	364.9	364.9	576	407.3	407.3
337	238.3	238.3	397	280.7	280.7	457	323.1	323.1	517	365.6	365.6	577	408.0	408.0
338	239.0	239.0	398	281.4	281.4	458	323.9	323.9	518	366.3	366.3	578	408.7	408.7
339	239.7	239.7	399	282.1	282.1	459	324.6	324.6	519	367.0	367.0	579	409.4	409.4
340	240.4	240.4	400	282.8	282.8	460	325.3	325.3	520	367.7	367.7	580	410.1	410.1
341	241.1	241.1	401	283.5	283.5	461	326.0	326.0	521	368.4	368.4	581	410.8	410.8
342	241.8	241.8	402	284.3	284.3	462	326.7	326.7	522	369.1	369.1	582	411.5	411.5
343	242.5	242.5	403	285.0	285.0	463	327.4	327.4	523	369.8	369.8	583	412.2	412.2
344	243.2	243.2	404	285.7	285.7	464	328.1	328.1	524	370.5	370.5	584	413.0	413.0
345	244.0	244.0	405	286.4	286.4	465	328.8	328.8	525	371.2	371.2	585	413.7	413.7
346	244.7	244.7	406	287.1	287.1	466	329.5	329.5	526	371.9	371.9	586	414.4	414.4
347	245.4	245.4	407	287.8	287.8	467	330.2	330.2	527	372.6	372.6	587	415.1	415.1
348	246.1	246.1	408	288.5	288.5	468	330.9	330.9	528	373.4	373.4	588	415.8	415.8
349	246.8	246.8	409	289.2	289.2	469	331.6	331.6	529	374.1	374.1	589	416.5	416.5
350	247.5	247.5	410	289.9	289.9	470	332.3	332.3	530	374.8	374.8	590	417.2	417.2
351	248.2	248.2	411	290.6	290.6	471	333.0	333.0	531	375.5	375.5	591	417.9	417.9
352	248.9	248.9	412	291.3	291.3	472	333.8	333.8	532	376.2	376.2	592	418.6	418.6
353	249.6	249.6	413	292.0	292.0	473	334.5	334.5	533	376.9	376.9	593	419.3	419.3
354	250.3	250.3	414	292.7	292.7	474	335.2	335.2	534	377.6	377.6	594	420.0	420.0
355	251.0	251.0	415	293.4	293.4	475	335.9	335.9	535	378.3	378.3	595	420.7	420.7
356	251.7	251.7	416	294.2	294.2	476	336.6	336.6	536	379.0	379.0	596	421.4	421.4
357	252.4	252.4	417	294.9	294.9	477	337.3	337.3	537	379.7	379.7	597	422.1	422.1
358	253.1	253.1	418	295.6	295.6	478	338.0	338.0	538	380.4	380.4	598	422.8	422.8
359	253.9	253.9	419	296.3	296.3	479	338.7	338.7	539	381.1	381.1	599	423.6	423.6
360	254.6	254.6	420	297.0	297.0	480	339.4	339.4	540	381.8	381.8	600	424.3	424.3
Hyp.	Opp.	Adj.	Hyp.	Opp.	Adj.	Hyp.	Opp.	Adj.	Hyp.	Opp.	Adj.	Hyp.	Opp.	Adj.

Dist. D Lon	Dep	D. Lat. Dep	Dist. D Lon	Dep	D. Lat. Dep	Dist. D Lon	Dep	D. Lat. Dep	Dist. D Lon	Dep	D. Lat. Dep	Dist. D Lon	Dep	D. Lat. Dep

45°

45°

Table 4

MERIDIONAL PARTS

For the Terrestrial Spheroid

LATITUDE

'	0°	1°	2°	3°	4°	5°	6°	7°	8°	9°	10°	'
0	0.0	59.6	119.2	178.9	238.6	298.3	358.2	418.2	478.3	538.6	599.0	0
1	1.0	60.6	120.2	179.9	239.6	299.3	359.2	419.2	479.3	539.6	600.0	1
2	2.0	61.6	121.2	180.8	240.6	300.3	360.2	420.2	480.3	540.6	601.0	2
3	3.0	62.6	122.2	181.8	241.5	301.3	361.2	421.2	481.3	541.6	602.0	3
4	4.0	63.6	123.2	182.8	242.5	302.3	362.2	422.2	482.3	542.6	603.0	4
5	5.0	64.6	124.2	183.8	243.5	303.3	363.2	423.2	483.3	543.6	604.1	5
6	6.0	65.6	125.2	184.8	244.5	304.3	364.2	424.2	484.3	544.6	605.1	6
7	7.0	66.5	126.2	185.8	245.5	305.3	365.2	425.2	485.3	545.6	606.1	7
8	7.9	67.5	127.2	186.8	246.5	306.3	366.2	426.2	486.3	546.6	607.1	8
9	8.9	68.5	128.2	187.8	247.5	307.3	367.2	427.2	487.3	547.6	608.1	9
10	9.9	69.5	129.1	188.8	248.5	308.3	368.2	428.2	488.3	548.6	609.1	10
11	10.9	70.5	130.1	189.8	249.5	309.3	369.2	429.2	489.3	549.6	610.1	11
12	11.9	71.5	131.1	190.8	250.5	310.3	370.2	430.2	490.4	550.6	611.1	12
13	12.9	72.5	132.1	191.8	251.5	311.3	371.2	431.2	491.4	551.7	612.1	13
14	13.9	73.5	133.1	192.8	252.5	312.3	372.2	432.2	492.4	552.7	613.1	14
15	14.9	74.5	134.1	193.8	253.5	313.3	373.2	433.2	493.4	553.7	614.1	15
16	15.9	75.5	135.1	194.8	254.5	314.3	374.2	434.2	494.4	554.7	615.2	16
17	16.9	76.5	136.1	195.8	255.5	315.3	375.2	435.2	495.4	555.7	616.2	17
18	17.9	77.5	137.1	196.8	256.5	316.3	376.2	436.2	496.4	556.7	617.2	18
19	18.9	78.5	138.1	197.8	257.5	317.3	377.2	437.2	497.4	557.7	618.2	19
20	19.9	79.5	139.1	198.8	258.5	318.3	378.2	438.2	498.4	558.7	619.2	20
21	20.9	80.5	140.1	199.7	259.5	319.3	379.2	439.2	499.4	559.7	620.2	21
22	21.9	81.5	141.1	200.7	260.5	320.3	380.2	440.2	500.4	560.7	621.2	22
23	22.8	82.4	142.1	201.7	261.5	321.3	381.2	441.2	501.4	561.7	622.2	23
24	23.8	83.4	143.1	202.7	262.5	322.3	382.2	442.2	502.4	562.7	623.2	24
25	24.8	84.4	144.1	203.7	263.5	323.3	383.2	443.2	503.4	563.7	624.2	25
26	25.8	85.4	145.1	204.7	264.5	324.3	384.2	444.2	504.4	564.7	625.3	26
27	26.8	86.4	146.0	205.7	265.5	325.3	385.2	445.2	505.4	565.7	626.3	27
28	27.8	87.4	147.0	206.7	266.5	326.3	386.2	446.2	506.4	566.8	627.3	28
29	28.8	88.4	148.0	207.7	267.4	327.3	387.2	447.2	507.4	567.8	628.3	29
30	29.8	89.4	149.0	208.7	268.4	328.3	388.2	448.2	508.4	568.8	629.3	30
31	30.8	90.4	150.0	209.7	269.4	329.3	389.2	449.2	509.4	569.8	630.3	31
32	31.8	91.4	151.0	210.7	270.4	330.3	390.2	450.2	510.4	570.8	631.3	32
33	32.8	92.4	152.0	211.7	271.4	331.3	391.2	451.2	511.4	571.8	632.3	33
34	33.8	93.4	153.0	212.7	272.4	332.3	392.2	452.2	512.4	572.8	633.3	34
35	34.8	94.4	154.0	213.7	273.4	333.3	393.2	453.2	513.4	573.8	634.3	35
36	35.8	95.4	155.0	214.7	274.4	334.3	394.2	454.3	514.5	574.8	635.4	36
37	36.8	96.4	156.0	215.7	275.4	335.3	395.2	455.3	515.5	575.8	636.4	37
38	37.7	97.3	157.0	216.7	276.4	336.2	396.2	456.3	516.5	576.8	637.4	38
39	38.7	98.3	158.0	217.7	277.4	337.2	397.2	457.3	517.5	577.8	638.4	39
40	39.7	99.3	159.0	218.7	278.4	338.2	398.2	458.3	518.5	578.8	639.4	40
41	40.7	100.3	160.0	219.7	279.4	339.2	399.2	459.3	519.5	579.9	640.4	41
42	41.7	101.3	161.0	220.6	280.4	340.2	400.2	460.3	520.5	580.9	641.4	42
43	42.7	102.3	162.0	221.6	281.4	341.2	401.2	461.3	521.5	581.9	642.4	43
44	43.7	103.3	162.9	222.6	282.4	342.2	402.2	462.3	522.5	582.9	643.4	44
45	44.7	104.3	163.9	223.6	283.4	343.2	403.2	463.3	523.5	583.9	644.5	45
46	45.7	105.3	164.9	224.6	284.4	344.2	404.2	464.3	524.5	584.9	645.5	46
47	46.7	106.3	165.9	225.6	285.4	345.2	405.2	465.3	525.5	585.9	646.5	47
48	47.7	107.3	166.9	226.6	286.4	346.2	406.2	466.3	526.5	586.9	647.5	48
49	48.7	108.3	167.9	227.6	287.4	347.2	407.2	467.3	527.5	587.9	648.5	49
50	49.7	109.3	168.9	228.6	288.4	348.2	408.2	468.3	528.5	588.9	649.5	50
51	50.7	110.3	169.9	229.6	289.4	349.2	409.2	469.3	529.5	589.9	650.5	51
52	51.6	111.3	170.9	230.6	290.4	350.2	410.2	470.3	530.5	590.9	651.5	52
53	52.6	112.3	171.9	231.6	291.4	351.2	411.2	471.3	531.5	591.9	652.5	53
54	53.6	113.2	172.9	232.6	292.4	352.2	412.2	472.3	532.5	593.0	653.6	54
55	54.6	114.2	173.9	233.6	293.4	353.2	413.2	473.3	533.5	594.0	654.6	55
56	55.6	115.2	174.9	234.6	294.4	354.2	414.2	474.3	534.6	595.0	655.6	56
57	56.6	116.2	175.9	235.6	295.4	355.2	415.2	475.3	535.6	596.0	656.6	57
58	57.6	117.2	176.9	236.6	296.3	356.2	416.2	476.3	536.6	597.0	657.6	58
59	58.6	118.2	177.9	237.6	297.3	357.2	417.2	477.3	537.6	598.0	658.6	59
	0°	1°	2°	3°	4°	5°	6°	7°	8°	9°	10°	

Table 4

MERIDIONAL PARTS

For the Terrestrial Spheroid

LATITUDE

′	11°	12°	13°	14°	15°	16°	17°	18°	19°	20°	′
0	659.6	720.5	781.5	842.8	904.4	966.3	1028.5	1091.0	1153.9	1217.1	0
1	660.6	721.5	782.5	843.9	905.4	967.3	1029.5	1092.0	1154.9	1218.2	1
2	661.7	722.5	783.6	844.9	906.5	968.3	1030.5	1093.1	1156.0	1219.3	2
3	662.7	723.5	784.6	845.9	907.5	969.4	1031.6	1094.1	1157.0	1220.3	3
4	663.7	724.5	785.6	846.9	908.5	970.4	1032.6	1095.2	1158.1	1221.4	4
5	664.7	725.5	786.6	847.9	909.6	971.4	1033.7	1096.2	1159.1	1222.4	5
6	665.7	726.6	787.6	849.0	910.6	972.5	1034.7	1097.3	1160.2	1223.5	6
7	666.7	727.6	788.7	850.0	911.6	973.5	1035.7	1098.3	1161.2	1224.5	7
8	667.7	728.6	789.7	851.0	912.6	974.6	1036.8	1099.4	1162.3	1225.6	8
9	668.7	729.6	790.7	852.0	913.7	975.6	1037.8	1100.4	1163.3	1226.7	9
10	669.8	730.6	791.7	853.1	914.7	976.6	1038.9	1101.4	1164.4	1227.7	10
11	670.8	731.6	792.7	854.1	915.7	977.7	1039.9	1102.5	1165.4	1228.8	11
12	671.8	732.7	793.8	855.1	916.8	978.7	1040.9	1103.5	1166.5	1229.8	12
13	672.8	733.7	794.8	856.1	917.8	979.7	1042.0	1104.6	1167.5	1230.9	13
14	673.8	734.7	795.8	857.2	918.8	980.8	1043.0	1105.6	1168.6	1232.0	14
15	674.8	735.7	796.8	858.2	919.8	981.8	1044.1	1106.7	1169.7	1233.0	15
16	675.8	736.7	797.8	859.2	920.9	982.8	1045.1	1107.7	1170.7	1234.1	16
17	676.8	737.7	798.9	860.2	921.9	983.9	1046.1	1108.8	1171.8	1235.1	17
18	677.9	738.8	799.9	861.3	922.9	984.9	1047.2	1109.8	1172.8	1236.2	18
19	678.9	739.8	800.9	862.3	924.0	985.9	1048.2	1110.9	1173.9	1237.3	19
20	679.9	740.8	801.9	863.3	925.0	987.0	1049.3	1111.9	1174.9	1238.3	20
21	680.9	741.8	802.9	864.3	926.0	988.0	1050.3	1113.0	1176.0	1239.4	21
22	681.9	742.8	804.0	865.4	927.1	989.0	1051.3	1114.0	1177.0	1240.4	22
23	682.9	743.8	805.0	866.4	928.1	990.1	1052.4	1115.1	1178.1	1241.5	23
24	683.9	744.9	806.0	867.4	929.1	991.1	1053.4	1116.1	1179.1	1242.6	24
25	684.9	745.9	807.0	868.5	930.2	992.1	1054.5	1117.1	1180.2	1243.6	25
26	686.0	746.9	808.1	869.5	931.2	993.2	1055.5	1118.2	1181.2	1244.7	26
27	687.0	747.9	809.1	870.5	932.2	994.2	1056.6	1119.2	1182.3	1245.7	27
28	688.0	748.9	810.1	871.5	933.2	995.3	1057.6	1120.3	1183.3	1246.8	28
29	689.0	749.9	811.1	872.6	934.3	996.3	1058.6	1121.3	1184.4	1247.9	29
30	690.0	751.0	812.1	873.6	935.3	997.3	1059.7	1122.4	1185.5	1248.9	30
31	691.0	752.0	813.2	874.6	936.3	998.4	1060.7	1123.4	1186.5	1250.0	31
32	692.0	753.0	814.2	875.6	937.4	999.4	1061.8	1124.5	1187.6	1251.0	32
33	693.1	754.0	815.2	876.7	938.4	1000.4	1062.8	1125.5	1188.6	1252.1	33
34	694.1	755.0	816.2	877.7	939.4	1001.5	1063.9	1126.6	1189.7	1253.2	34
35	695.1	756.0	817.3	878.7	940.5	1002.5	1064.9	1127.6	1190.7	1254.2	35
36	696.1	757.1	818.3	879.7	941.5	1003.6	1065.9	1128.7	1191.8	1255.3	36
37	697.1	758.1	819.3	880.8	942.5	1004.6	1067.0	1129.7	1192.8	1256.4	37
38	698.1	759.1	820.3	881.8	943.6	1005.6	1068.0	1130.8	1193.9	1257.4	38
39	699.1	760.1	821.3	882.8	944.6	1006.7	1069.1	1131.8	1194.9	1258.5	39
40	700.2	761.1	822.4	883.8	945.6	1007.7	1070.1	1132.9	1196.0	1259.5	40
41	701.2	762.2	823.4	884.9	946.7	1008.7	1071.2	1133.9	1197.1	1260.6	41
42	702.2	763.2	824.4	885.9	947.7	1009.8	1072.2	1135.0	1198.1	1261.7	42
43	703.2	764.2	825.4	886.9	948.7	1010.8	1073.2	1136.0	1199.2	1262.7	43
44	704.2	765.2	826.5	888.0	949.7	1011.8	1074.3	1137.1	1200.2	1263.8	44
45	705.2	766.2	827.5	889.0	950.8	1012.9	1075.3	1138.1	1201.3	1264.9	45
46	706.2	767.2	828.5	890.0	951.8	1013.9	1076.4	1139.2	1202.3	1265.9	46
47	707.3	768.3	829.5	891.0	952.8	1015.0	1077.4	1140.2	1203.4	1267.0	47
48	708.3	769.3	830.5	892.1	953.9	1016.0	1078.5	1141.3	1204.5	1268.0	48
49	709.3	770.3	831.6	893.1	954.9	1017.0	1079.5	1142.3	1205.5	1269.1	49
50	710.3	771.3	832.6	894.1	955.9	1018.1	1080.5	1143.4	1206.6	1270.2	50
51	711.3	772.3	833.6	895.2	957.0	1019.1	1081.6	1144.4	1207.6	1271.2	51
52	712.3	773.4	834.6	896.2	958.0	1020.2	1082.6	1145.5	1208.7	1272.3	52
53	713.4	774.4	835.7	897.2	959.0	1021.2	1083.7	1146.5	1209.7	1273.4	53
54	714.4	775.4	836.7	898.2	960.1	1022.2	1084.7	1147.6	1210.8	1274.4	54
55	715.4	776.4	837.7	899.3	961.1	1023.3	1085.8	1148.6	1211.8	1275.5	55
56	716.4	777.4	838.7	900.3	962.1	1024.3	1086.8	1149.7	1212.9	1276.6	56
57	717.4	778.5	839.8	901.3	963.2	1025.3	1087.9	1150.7	1214.0	1277.6	57
58	718.4	779.5	840.8	902.3	964.2	1026.4	1088.9	1151.8	1215.0	1278.7	58
59	719.4	780.5	841.8	903.4	965.2	1027.4	1089.9	1152.8	1216.1	1279.7	59
	11°	12°	13°	14°	15°	16°	17°	18°	19°	20°	

Table 4

MERIDIONAL PARTS

For the Terrestrial Spheroid

LATITUDE

′	21°	22°	23°	24°	25°	26°	27°	28°	29°	30°	′
0	1280.8	1344.9	1409.5	1474.5	1540.1	1606.2	1672.9	1740.2	1808.1	1876.7	0
1	1281.9	1346.0	1410.6	1475.6	1541.2	1607.3	1674.0	1741.3	1809.2	1877.8	1
2	1282.9	1347.1	1411.6	1476.7	1542.3	1608.4	1675.1	1742.4	1810.4	1879.0	2
3	1284.0	1348.1	1412.7	1477.8	1543.4	1609.5	1676.2	1743.6	1811.5	1880.1	3
4	1285.1	1349.2	1413.8	1478.9	1544.5	1610.6	1677.4	1744.7	1812.6	1881.3	4
5	1286.1	1350.3	1414.9	1480.0	1545.6	1611.7	1678.5	1745.8	1813.8	1882.4	5
6	1287.2	1351.4	1416.0	1481.1	1546.7	1612.9	1679.6	1746.9	1814.9	1883.6	6
7	1288.3	1352.4	1417.1	1482.2	1547.8	1614.0	1680.7	1748.1	1816.1	1884.7	7
8	1289.3	1353.5	1418.1	1483.3	1548.9	1615.1	1681.8	1749.2	1817.2	1885.9	8
9	1290.4	1354.6	1419.2	1484.3	1550.0	1616.2	1682.9	1750.3	1818.3	1887.0	9
10	1291.5	1355.7	1420.3	1485.4	1551.1	1617.3	1684.1	1751.5	1819.5	1888.2	10
11	1292.5	1356.7	1421.4	1486.5	1552.2	1618.4	1685.2	1752.6	1820.6	1889.3	11
12	1293.6	1357.8	1422.5	1487.6	1553.3	1619.5	1686.3	1753.7	1821.8	1890.5	12
13	1294.7	1358.9	1423.5	1488.7	1554.4	1620.6	1687.4	1754.8	1822.9	1891.6	13
14	1295.7	1359.9	1424.6	1489.8	1555.5	1621.7	1688.5	1756.0	1824.0	1892.8	14
15	1296.8	1361.0	1425.7	1490.9	1556.6	1622.8	1689.7	1757.1	1825.2	1893.9	15
16	1297.9	1362.1	1426.8	1492.0	1557.7	1623.9	1690.8	1758.2	1826.3	1895.1	16
17	1298.9	1363.2	1427.9	1493.1	1558.8	1625.0	1691.9	1759.4	1827.5	1896.2	17
18	1300.0	1364.2	1429.0	1494.2	1559.9	1626.2	1693.0	1760.5	1828.6	1897.4	18
19	1301.1	1365.3	1430.0	1495.2	1561.0	1627.3	1694.1	1761.6	1829.7	1898.5	19
20	1302.1	1366.4	1431.1	1496.3	1562.1	1628.4	1695.3	1762.7	1830.9	1899.7	20
21	1303.2	1367.5	1432.2	1497.4	1563.2	1629.5	1696.4	1763.9	1832.0	1900.8	21
22	1304.3	1368.5	1433.3	1498.5	1564.3	1630.6	1697.5	1765.0	1833.2	1902.0	22
23	1305.3	1369.6	1434.4	1499.6	1565.4	1631.7	1698.6	1766.1	1834.3	1903.1	23
24	1306.4	1370.7	1435.4	1500.7	1566.5	1632.8	1699.7	1767.3	1835.4	1904.3	24
25	1307.5	1371.8	1436.5	1501.8	1567.6	1633.9	1700.9	1768.4	1836.6	1905.5	25
26	1308.5	1372.8	1437.6	1502.9	1568.7	1635.0	1702.0	1769.5	1837.7	1906.6	26
27	1309.6	1373.9	1438.7	1504.0	1569.8	1636.1	1703.1	1770.7	1838.9	1907.8	27
28	1310.7	1375.0	1439.8	1505.1	1570.9	1637.3	1704.2	1771.8	1840.0	1908.9	28
29	1311.7	1376.0	1440.9	1506.2	1572.0	1638.4	1705.3	1772.9	1841.2	1910.1	29
30	1312.8	1377.1	1442.0	1507.3	1573.1	1639.5	1706.5	1774.1	1842.3	1911.2	30
31	1313.9	1378.2	1443.0	1508.4	1574.2	1640.6	1707.6	1775.2	1843.4	1912.4	31
32	1314.9	1379.3	1444.1	1509.4	1575.3	1641.7	1708.7	1776.3	1844.6	1913.5	32
33	1316.0	1380.4	1445.2	1510.5	1576.4	1642.8	1709.8	1777.4	1845.7	1914.7	33
34	1317.1	1381.5	1446.3	1511.6	1577.5	1643.9	1710.9	1778.6	1846.9	1915.8	34
35	1318.2	1382.5	1447.4	1512.7	1578.6	1645.0	1712.1	1779.7	1848.0	1917.0	35
36	1319.2	1383.6	1448.5	1513.8	1579.7	1646.2	1713.2	1780.8	1849.2	1918.2	36
37	1320.3	1384.7	1449.5	1514.9	1580.8	1647.3	1714.3	1782.0	1850.3	1919.3	37
38	1321.4	1385.8	1450.6	1516.0	1581.9	1648.4	1715.4	1783.1	1851.4	1920.5	38
39	1322.4	1386.8	1451.7	1517.1	1583.0	1649.5	1716.6	1784.2	1852.6	1921.6	39
40	1323.5	1387.9	1452.8	1518.2	1584.1	1650.6	1717.7	1785.4	1853.7	1922.8	40
41	1324.6	1389.0	1453.9	1519.3	1585.2	1651.7	1718.8	1786.5	1854.9	1923.9	41
42	1325.6	1390.1	1455.0	1520.4	1586.3	1652.8	1719.9	1787.6	1856.0	1925.1	42
43	1326.7	1391.1	1456.1	1521.5	1587.4	1653.9	1721.1	1788.8	1857.2	1926.3	43
44	1327.8	1392.2	1457.1	1522.6	1588.5	1655.1	1722.2	1789.9	1858.3	1927.4	44
45	1328.8	1393.3	1458.2	1523.7	1589.6	1656.2	1723.3	1791.1	1859.5	1928.6	45
46	1329.9	1394.4	1459.3	1524.8	1590.7	1657.3	1724.4	1792.2	1860.6	1929.7	46
47	1331.0	1395.5	1460.4	1525.9	1591.8	1658.4	1725.5	1793.3	1861.8	1930.9	47
48	1332.1	1396.5	1461.5	1527.0	1592.9	1659.5	1726.7	1794.5	1862.9	1932.0	48
49	1333.1	1397.6	1462.6	1528.0	1594.1	1660.6	1727.8	1795.6	1864.0	1933.2	49
50	1334.2	1398.7	1463.7	1529.1	1595.2	1661.7	1728.9	1796.7	1865.2	1934.4	50
51	1335.3	1399.8	1464.8	1530.2	1596.3	1662.9	1730.0	1797.9	1866.3	1935.5	51
52	1336.3	1400.9	1465.8	1531.3	1597.4	1664.0	1731.2	1799.0	1867.5	1936.7	52
53	1337.4	1401.9	1466.9	1532.4	1598.5	1665.1	1732.3	1800.1	1868.6	1937.8	53
54	1338.5	1403.0	1468.0	1533.5	1599.6	1666.2	1733.4	1801.3	1869.8	1939.0	54
55	1339.6	1404.1	1469.1	1534.6	1600.7	1667.3	1734.5	1802.4	1870.9	1940.2	55
56	1340.6	1405.2	1470.2	1535.7	1601.8	1668.4	1735.7	1803.5	1872.1	1941.3	56
57	1341.7	1406.2	1471.3	1536.8	1602.9	1669.5	1736.8	1804.7	1873.2	1942.5	57
58	1342.8	1407.3	1472.4	1537.9	1604.0	1670.7	1737.9	1805.8	1874.4	1943.6	58
59	1343.8	1408.4	1473.5	1539.0	1605.1	1671.8	1739.0	1807.0	1875.5	1944.8	59
	21°	22°	23°	24°	25°	26°	27°	28°	29°	30°	

Table 4

MERIDIONAL PARTS

For the Terrestrial Spheroid

LATITUDE

′	31°	32°	33°	34°	35°	36°	37°	38°	39°	40°	′
0	1946.0	2016.0	2086.8	2158.4	2230.9	2304.2	2378.5	2453.8	2530.2	2607.6	0
1	1947.1	2017.2	2088.0	2159.6	2232.1	2305.5	2379.8	2455.1	2531.5	2608.9	1
2	1948.3	2018.3	2089.2	2160.8	2233.3	2306.7	2381.0	2456.4	2532.8	2610.2	2
3	1949.4	2019.5	2090.3	2162.0	2234.5	2307.9	2382.3	2457.6	2534.0	2611.5	3
4	1950.6	2020.7	2091.5	2163.2	2235.7	2309.1	2383.5	2458.9	2535.3	2612.8	4
5	1951.8	2021.9	2092.7	2164.4	2236.9	2310.4	2384.8	2460.2	2536.6	2614.1	5
6	1952.9	2023.0	2093.9	2165.6	2238.2	2311.6	2386.0	2461.4	2537.9	2615.4	6
7	1954.1	2024.2	2095.1	2166.8	2239.4	2312.9	2387.3	2462.7	2539.2	2616.8	7
8	1955.3	2025.4	2096.3	2168.0	2240.6	2314.1	2388.5	2464.0	2540.5	2618.1	8
9	1956.4	2026.6	2097.5	2169.2	2241.8	2315.3	2389.8	2465.2	2541.7	2619.4	9
10	1957.6	2027.7	2098.7	2170.4	2243.0	2316.5	2391.0	2466.5	2543.0	2620.7	10
11	1958.7	2028.9	2099.9	2171.6	2244.2	2317.8	2392.3	2467.8	2544.3	2622.0	11
12	1959.9	2030.1	2101.0	2172.8	2245.5	2319.0	2393.5	2469.0	2545.6	2623.3	12
13	1961.1	2031.3	2102.2	2174.0	2246.7	2320.3	2394.8	2470.3	2546.9	2624.6	13
14	1962.2	2032.4	2103.4	2175.2	2247.9	2321.5	2396.0	2471.6	2548.2	2625.9	14
15	1963.4	2033.6	2104.6	2176.4	2249.1	2322.7	2397.3	2472.8	2549.5	2627.2	15
16	1964.6	2034.8	2105.8	2177.6	2250.3	2324.0	2398.5	2474.1	2550.7	2628.5	16
17	1965.7	2036.0	2107.0	2178.8	2251.6	2325.2	2399.8	2475.4	2552.0	2629.8	17
18	1966.9	2037.1	2108.2	2180.0	2252.8	2326.4	2401.0	2476.6	2553.3	2631.1	18
19	1968.1	2038.3	2109.4	2181.2	2254.0	2327.7	2402.3	2477.9	2554.6	2632.4	19
20	1969.2	2039.5	2110.6	2182.5	2255.2	2328.9	2403.5	2479.2	2555.9	2633.7	20
21	1970.4	2040.7	2111.8	2183.7	2256.4	2330.1	2404.8	2480.4	2557.2	2635.0	21
22	1971.5	2041.8	2112.9	2184.9	2257.7	2331.4	2406.0	2481.7	2558.5	2636.3	22
23	1972.7	2043.0	2114.1	2186.1	2258.9	2332.6	2407.3	2483.0	2559.8	2637.6	23
24	1973.9	2044.2	2115.3	2187.3	2260.1	2333.8	2408.5	2484.3	2561.0	2638.9	24
25	1975.0	2045.4	2116.5	2188.5	2261.3	2335.1	2409.8	2485.5	2562.3	2640.2	25
26	1976.2	2046.6	2117.7	2189.7	2262.5	2336.3	2411.1	2486.8	2563.6	2641.6	26
27	1977.4	2047.7	2118.9	2190.9	2263.8	2337.6	2412.3	2488.1	2564.9	2642.9	27
28	1978.5	2048.9	2120.1	2192.1	2265.0	2338.8	2413.6	2489.3	2566.2	2644.2	28
29	1979.7	2050.1	2121.3	2193.3	2266.2	2340.0	2414.8	2490.6	2567.5	2645.5	29
30	1980.9	2051.3	2122.5	2194.5	2267.4	2341.3	2416.1	2491.9	2568.8	2646.8	30
31	1982.0	2052.5	2123.7	2195.7	2268.7	2342.5	2417.3	2493.2	2570.1	2648.1	31
32	1983.2	2053.6	2124.9	2196.9	2269.9	2343.7	2418.6	2494.4	2571.4	2649.4	32
33	1984.4	2054.8	2126.1	2198.1	2271.1	2345.0	2419.8	2495.7	2572.7	2650.7	33
34	1985.5	2056.0	2127.3	2199.4	2272.3	2346.2	2421.1	2497.0	2573.9	2652.0	34
35	1986.7	2057.2	2128.5	2200.6	2273.5	2347.5	2422.3	2498.3	2575.2	2653.3	35
36	1987.9	2058.4	2129.6	2201.8	2274.8	2348.7	2423.6	2499.5	2576.5	2654.7	36
37	1989.1	2059.5	2130.8	2203.0	2276.0	2349.9	2424.9	2500.8	2577.8	2656.0	37
38	1990.2	2060.7	2132.0	2204.2	2277.2	2351.2	2426.1	2502.1	2579.1	2657.3	38
39	1991.4	2061.9	2133.2	2205.4	2278.4	2352.4	2427.4	2503.4	2580.4	2658.6	39
40	1992.6	2063.1	2134.4	2206.6	2279.7	2353.7	2428.6	2504.6	2581.7	2659.9	40
41	1993.7	2064.3	2135.6	2207.8	2280.9	2354.9	2429.9	2505.9	2583.0	2661.2	41
42	1994.9	2065.5	2136.8	2209.0	2282.1	2356.1	2431.2	2507.2	2584.3	2662.5	42
43	1996.1	2066.6	2138.0	2210.2	2283.3	2357.4	2432.4	2508.5	2585.6	2663.9	43
44	1997.2	2067.8	2139.2	2211.5	2284.6	2358.6	2433.7	2509.7	2586.9	2665.2	44
45	1998.4	2069.0	2140.4	2212.7	2285.8	2359.9	2434.9	2511.0	2588.2	2666.5	45
46	1999.6	2070.2	2141.6	2213.9	2287.0	2361.1	2436.2	2512.3	2589.5	2667.8	46
47	2000.7	2071.4	2142.8	2215.1	2288.3	2362.4	2437.4	2513.6	2590.8	2669.1	47
48	2001.9	2072.6	2144.0	2216.3	2289.5	2363.6	2438.7	2514.8	2592.1	2670.4	48
49	2003.1	2073.7	2145.2	2217.5	2290.7	2364.8	2440.0	2516.1	2593.4	2671.7	49
50	2004.3	2074.9	2146.4	2218.7	2291.9	2366.1	2441.2	2517.4	2594.7	2673.1	50
51	2005.4	2076.1	2147.6	2219.9	2293.2	2367.3	2442.5	2518.7	2596.0	2674.4	51
52	2006.6	2077.3	2148.8	2221.1	2294.4	2368.6	2443.7	2520.0	2597.3	2675.7	52
53	2007.8	2078.5	2150.0	2222.4	2295.6	2369.8	2445.0	2521.2	2598.5	2677.0	53
54	2008.9	2079.7	2151.2	2223.6	2296.8	2371.1	2446.3	2522.5	2599.8	2678.3	54
55	2010.1	2080.8	2152.4	2224.8	2298.1	2372.3	2447.5	2523.8	2601.1	2679.6	55
56	2011.3	2082.0	2153.6	2226.0	2299.3	2373.6	2448.8	2525.1	2602.4	2681.0	56
57	2012.5	2083.2	2154.8	2227.2	2300.5	2374.8	2450.1	2526.4	2603.7	2682.3	57
58	2013.6	2084.4	2156.0	2228.4	2301.8	2376.1	2451.3	2527.6	2605.0	2683.6	58
59	2014.8	2085.6	2157.2	2229.6	2303.0	2377.3	2452.6	2528.9	2606.3	2684.9	59
	31°	32°	33°	34°	35°	36°	37°	38°	39°	40°	

Table 4

MERIDIONAL PARTS

For the Terrestrial Spheroid

LATITUDE

/	41°	42°	43°	44°	45°	46°	47°	48°	49°	50°	/
0	2686.2	2766.1	2847.1	2929.5	3013.4	3098.7	3185.6	3274.1	3364.4	3456.5	0
1	2687.6	2767.4	2848.5	2930.9	3014.8	3100.1	3187.1	3275.6	3365.9	3458.1	1
2	2688.9	2768.7	2849.9	2932.3	3016.2	3101.6	3188.5	3277.1	3367.4	3459.6	2
3	2690.2	2770.1	2851.2	2933.7	3017.6	3103.0	3190.0	3278.6	3369.0	3461.2	3
4	2691.5	2771.4	2852.6	2935.1	3019.0	3104.4	3191.4	3280.1	3370.5	3462.7	4
5	2692.8	2772.8	2853.9	2936.5	3020.4	3105.9	3192.9	3281.6	3372.0	3464.3	5
6	2694.2	2774.1	2855.3	2937.9	3021.8	3107.3	3194.4	3283.1	3373.5	3465.9	6
7	2695.5	2775.4	2856.7	2939.3	3023.3	3108.8	3195.8	3284.6	3375.1	3467.4	7
8	2696.8	2776.8	2858.0	2940.6	3024.7	3110.2	3197.3	3286.1	3376.6	3469.0	8
9	2698.1	2778.1	2859.4	2942.0	3026.1	3111.6	3198.8	3287.6	3378.1	3470.5	9
10	2699.5	2779.5	2860.8	2943.4	3027.5	3113.1	3200.2	3289.0	3379.6	3472.1	10
11	2700.8	2780.8	2862.1	2944.8	3028.9	3114.5	3201.7	3290.5	3381.2	3473.6	11
12	2702.1	2782.2	2863.5	2946.2	3030.3	3116.0	3203.2	3292.0	3382.7	3475.2	12
13	2703.4	2783.5	2864.9	2947.6	3031.7	3117.4	3204.6	3293.5	3384.2	3476.7	13
14	2704.7	2784.8	2866.2	2949.0	3033.2	3118.8	3206.1	3295.0	3385.7	3478.3	14
15	2706.1	2786.2	2867.6	2950.4	3034.6	3120.3	3207.6	3296.5	3387.3	3479.9	15
16	2707.4	2787.5	2869.0	2951.8	3036.0	3121.7	3209.0	3298.0	3388.8	3481.4	16
17	2708.7	2788.9	2870.3	2953.2	3037.4	3123.2	3210.5	3299.5	3390.3	3483.0	17
18	2710.1	2790.2	2871.7	2954.5	3038.8	3124.6	3212.0	3301.0	3391.8	3484.5	18
19	2711.4	2791.6	2873.1	2955.9	3040.2	3126.0	3213.4	3302.5	3393.4	3486.1	19
20	2712.7	2792.9	2874.4	2957.3	3041.7	3127.5	3214.9	3304.0	3394.9	3487.7	20
21	2714.0	2794.3	2875.8	2958.7	3043.1	3128.9	3216.4	3305.5	3396.4	3489.2	21
22	2715.4	2795.6	2877.2	2960.1	3044.5	3130.4	3217.9	3307.0	3398.0	3490.8	22
23	2716.7	2797.0	2878.6	2961.5	3045.9	3131.8	3219.3	3308.5	3399.5	3492.4	23
24	2718.0	2798.3	2879.9	2962.9	3047.3	3133.3	3220.8	3310.0	3401.0	3493.9	24
25	2719.3	2799.7	2881.3	2964.3	3048.7	3134.7	3222.3	3311.5	3402.6	3495.5	25
26	2720.7	2801.0	2882.7	2965.7	3050.2	3136.2	3223.7	3313.0	3404.1	3497.1	26
27	2722.0	2802.4	2884.0	2967.1	3051.6	3137.6	3225.2	3314.5	3405.6	3498.6	27
28	2723.3	2803.7	2885.4	2968.5	3053.0	3139.0	3226.7	3316.0	3407.2	3500.2	28
29	2724.7	2805.1	2886.8	2969.9	3054.4	3140.5	3228.2	3317.5	3408.7	3501.8	29
30	2726.0	2806.4	2888.2	2971.3	3055.9	3141.9	3229.6	3319.0	3410.2	3503.3	30
31	2727.3	2807.8	2889.5	2972.7	3057.3	3143.4	3231.1	3320.5	3411.8	3504.9	31
32	2728.6	2809.1	2890.9	2974.1	3058.7	3144.8	3232.6	3322.1	3413.3	3506.5	32
33	2730.0	2810.5	2892.3	2975.5	3060.1	3146.3	3234.1	3323.6	3414.8	3508.0	33
34	2731.3	2811.8	2893.7	2976.9	3061.5	3147.7	3235.6	3325.1	3416.4	3509.6	34
35	2732.6	2813.2	2895.0	2978.3	3063.0	3149.2	3237.0	3326.6	3417.9	3511.2	35
36	2734.0	2814.5	2896.4	2979.7	3064.4	3150.6	3238.5	3328.1	3419.5	3512.7	36
37	2735.3	2815.9	2897.8	2981.1	3065.8	3152.1	3240.0	3329.6	3421.0	3514.3	37
38	2736.6	2817.2	2899.2	2982.5	3067.2	3153.5	3241.5	3331.1	3422.5	3515.9	38
39	2738.0	2818.6	2900.5	2983.9	3068.7	3155.0	3242.9	3332.6	3424.1	3517.5	39
40	2739.3	2820.0	2901.9	2985.3	3070.1	3156.4	3244.4	3334.1	3425.6	3519.0	40
41	2740.6	2821.3	2903.3	2986.7	3071.5	3157.9	3245.9	3335.6	3427.2	3520.6	41
42	2742.0	2822.7	2904.7	2988.1	3072.9	3159.4	3247.4	3337.1	3428.7	3522.2	42
43	2743.3	2824.0	2906.1	2989.5	3074.4	3160.8	3248.9	3338.6	3430.2	3523.7	43
44	2744.6	2825.4	2907.4	2990.9	3075.8	3162.3	3250.3	3340.2	3431.8	3525.3	44
45	2746.0	2826.7	2908.8	2992.3	3077.2	3163.7	3251.8	3341.7	3433.3	3526.9	45
46	2747.3	2828.1	2910.2	2993.7	3078.7	3165.2	3253.3	3343.2	3434.9	3528.5	46
47	2748.6	2829.4	2911.6	2995.1	3080.1	3166.6	3254.8	3344.7	3436.4	3530.1	47
48	2750.0	2830.8	2913.0	2996.5	3081.5	3168.1	3256.3	3346.2	3438.0	3531.6	48
49	2751.3	2832.2	2914.3	2997.9	3082.9	3169.5	3257.8	3347.7	3439.5	3533.2	49
50	2752.7	2833.5	2915.7	2999.3	3084.4	3171.0	3259.3	3349.2	3441.0	3534.8	50
51	2754.0	2834.9	2917.1	3000.7	3085.8	3172.5	3260.7	3350.8	3442.6	3536.4	51
52	2755.3	2836.2	2918.5	3002.1	3087.2	3173.9	3262.2	3352.3	3444.1	3537.9	52
53	2756.7	2837.6	2919.9	3003.5	3088.7	3175.4	3263.7	3353.8	3445.7	3539.5	53
54	2758.0	2839.0	2921.2	3004.9	3090.1	3176.8	3265.2	3355.3	3447.2	3541.1	54
55	2759.3	2840.3	2922.6	3006.3	3091.5	3178.3	3266.7	3356.8	3448.8	3542.7	55
56	2760.7	2841.7	2924.0	3007.7	3093.0	3179.7	3268.2	3358.3	3450.3	3544.3	56
57	2762.0	2843.0	2925.4	3009.2	3094.4	3181.2	3269.7	3359.9	3451.9	3545.9	57
58	2763.4	2844.4	2926.8	3010.6	3095.8	3182.7	3271.1	3361.4	3453.4	3547.4	58
59	2764.7	2845.8	2928.2	3012.0	3097.3	3184.1	3272.6	3362.9	3455.0	3549.0	59
	41°	42°	43°	44°	45°	46°	47°	48°	49°	50°	

Table 4 — MERIDIONAL PARTS

For the Terrestrial Spheroid

LATITUDE

/	51°	52°	53°	54°	55°	56°	57°	58°	59°	60°	/
0	3550.6	3646.7	3745.1	3845.7	3948.8	4054.5	4163.0	4274.4	4389.1	4507.1	0
1	3552.2	3648.4	3746.7	3847.4	3950.5	4056.3	4164.8	4276.3	4391.0	4509.1	1
2	3553.8	3650.0	3748.4	3849.1	3952.3	4058.1	4166.6	4278.2	4392.9	4511.1	2
3	3555.4	3651.6	3750.0	3850.8	3954.0	4059.8	4168.5	4280.1	4394.9	4513.1	3
4	3556.9	3653.2	3751.7	3852.5	3955.7	4061.6	4170.3	4282.0	4396.8	4515.1	4
5	3558.5	3654.8	3753.4	3854.2	3957.5	4063.4	4172.1	4283.9	4398.8	4517.1	5
6	3560.1	3656.5	3755.0	3855.9	3959.2	4065.2	4174.0	4285.7	4400.7	4519.1	6
7	3561.7	3658.1	3756.7	3857.6	3961.0	4067.0	4175.8	4287.6	4402.6	4521.1	7
8	3563.3	3659.7	3758.3	3859.3	3962.7	4068.8	4177.7	4289.5	4404.6	4523.1	8
9	3564.9	3661.3	3760.0	3861.0	3964.5	4070.6	4179.5	4291.4	4406.5	4525.1	9
10	3566.5	3663.0	3761.7	3862.7	3966.2	4072.4	4181.3	4293.3	4408.5	4527.1	10
11	3568.1	3664.6	3763.3	3864.4	3968.0	4074.2	4183.2	4295.2	4410.4	4529.1	11
12	3569.7	3666.2	3765.0	3866.1	3969.7	4076.0	4185.0	4297.1	4412.4	4531.1	12
13	3571.3	3667.9	3766.7	3867.8	3971.5	4077.7	4186.9	4299.0	4414.3	4533.1	13
14	3572.8	3669.5	3768.3	3869.5	3973.2	4079.5	4188.7	4300.9	4416.3	4535.1	14
15	3574.4	3671.1	3770.0	3871.2	3975.0	4081.3	4190.6	4302.8	4418.2	4537.1	15
16	3576.0	3672.7	3771.7	3872.9	3976.7	4083.1	4192.4	4304.7	4420.2	4539.2	16
17	3577.6	3674.4	3773.3	3874.6	3978.5	4084.9	4194.2	4306.6	4422.1	4541.2	17
18	3579.2	3676.0	3775.0	3876.3	3980.2	4086.7	4196.1	4308.5	4424.1	4543.2	18
19	3580.8	3677.6	3776.7	3878.1	3982.0	4088.5	4197.9	4310.4	4426.1	4545.2	19
20	3582.4	3679.3	3778.3	3879.8	3983.7	4090.3	4199.8	4312.3	4428.0	4547.2	20
21	3584.0	3680.9	3780.0	3881.5	3985.5	4092.1	4201.6	4314.2	4430.0	4549.2	21
22	3585.6	3682.5	3781.7	3883.2	3987.2	4093.9	4203.5	4316.1	4431.9	4551.3	22
23	3587.2	3684.2	3783.3	3884.9	3989.0	4095.7	4205.3	4318.0	4433.9	4553.3	23
24	3588.8	3685.8	3785.0	3886.6	3990.7	4097.5	4207.2	4319.9	4435.9	4555.3	24
25	3590.4	3687.4	3786.7	3888.3	3992.5	4099.3	4209.0	4321.8	4437.8	4557.3	25
26	3592.0	3689.1	3788.4	3890.0	3994.3	4101.1	4210.9	4323.7	4439.8	4559.3	26
27	3593.6	3690.7	3790.0	3891.8	3996.0	4102.9	4212.8	4325.6	4441.7	4561.4	27
28	3595.2	3692.3	3791.7	3893.5	3997.8	4104.8	4214.6	4327.5	4443.7	4563.4	28
29	3596.8	3694.0	3793.4	3895.2	3999.5	4106.6	4216.5	4329.4	4445.7	4565.4	29
30	3598.4	3695.6	3795.1	3896.9	4001.3	4108.4	4218.3	4331.3	4447.6	4567.4	30
31	3600.0	3697.3	3796.8	3898.6	4003.1	4110.2	4220.2	4333.2	4449.6	4569.5	31
32	3601.6	3698.9	3798.4	3900.4	4004.8	4112.0	4222.0	4335.2	4451.6	4571.5	32
33	3603.2	3700.5	3800.1	3902.1	4006.6	4113.8	4223.9	4337.1	4453.5	4573.5	33
34	3604.8	3702.2	3801.8	3903.8	4008.3	4115.6	4225.8	4339.0	4455.5	4575.6	34
35	3606.4	3703.8	3803.5	3905.5	4010.1	4117.4	4227.6	4340.9	4457.5	4577.6	35
36	3608.0	3705.5	3805.1	3907.2	4011.9	4119.2	4229.5	4342.8	4459.4	4579.6	36
37	3609.6	3707.1	3806.8	3909.0	4013.6	4121.0	4231.3	4344.7	4461.4	4581.7	37
38	3611.2	3708.7	3808.5	3910.7	4015.4	4122.9	4233.2	4346.6	4463.4	4583.7	38
39	3612.8	3710.4	3810.2	3912.4	4017.2	4124.7	4235.1	4348.6	4465.4	4585.7	39
40	3614.5	3712.0	3811.9	3914.1	4018.9	4126.5	4236.9	4350.5	4467.3	4587.8	40
41	3616.1	3713.7	3813.6	3915.9	4020.7	4128.3	4238.8	4352.4	4469.3	4589.8	41
42	3617.7	3715.3	3815.2	3917.6	4022.5	4130.1	4240.7	4354.3	4471.3	4591.8	42
43	3619.3	3717.0	3816.9	3919.3	4024.3	4131.9	4242.5	4356.2	4473.3	4593.9	43
44	3620.9	3718.6	3818.6	3921.0	4026.0	4133.8	4244.4	4358.2	4475.3	4595.9	44
45	3622.5	3720.3	3820.3	3922.8	4027.8	4135.6	4246.3	4360.1	4477.2	4598.0	45
46	3624.1	3721.9	3822.0	3924.5	4029.6	4137.4	4248.1	4362.0	4479.2	4600.0	46
47	3625.7	3723.6	3823.7	3926.2	4031.4	4139.2	4250.0	4363.9	4481.2	4602.1	47
48	3627.3	3725.2	3825.4	3928.0	4033.1	4141.0	4251.9	4365.9	4483.2	4604.1	48
49	3629.0	3726.9	3827.1	3929.7	4034.9	4142.9	4253.8	4367.8	4485.2	4606.1	49
50	3630.6	3728.5	3828.7	3931.4	4036.7	4144.7	4255.6	4369.7	4487.2	4608.2	50
51	3632.2	3730.2	3830.4	3933.2	4038.5	4146.5	4257.5	4371.7	4489.1	4610.2	51
52	3633.8	3731.8	3832.1	3934.9	4040.2	4148.3	4259.4	4373.6	4491.1	4612.3	52
53	3635.4	3733.5	3833.8	3936.6	4042.0	4150.2	4261.3	4375.5	4493.1	4614.3	53
54	3637.0	3735.1	3835.5	3938.4	4043.8	4152.0	4263.1	4377.4	4495.1	4616.4	54
55	3638.6	3736.8	3837.2	3940.1	4045.6	4153.8	4265.0	4379.4	4497.1	4618.5	55
56	3640.3	3738.4	3838.9	3941.8	4047.4	4155.7	4266.9	4381.3	4499.1	4620.5	56
57	3641.9	3740.1	3840.6	3943.6	4049.1	4157.5	4268.8	4383.2	4501.1	4622.6	57
58	3643.5	3741.7	3842.3	3945.3	4050.9	4159.3	4270.7	4385.2	4503.1	4624.6	58
59	3645.1	3743.4	3844.0	3947.0	4052.7	4161.1	4272.5	4387.1	4505.1	4626.7	59
	51°	52°	53°	54°	55°	56°	57°	58°	59°	60°	

Table 4

MERIDIONAL PARTS

For the Terrestrial Spheroid

LATITUDE

′	61°	62°	63°	64°	65°	66°	67°	68°	69°	70°	71°	′
0	4628.7	4754.3	4884.1	5018.4	5157.6	5302.1	5452.4	5609.1	5772.7	5943.9	6123.5	0
1	4630.8	4756.4	4886.3	5020.6	5159.9	5304.6	5455.0	5611.8	5775.5	5946.8	6126.6	1
2	4632.9	4758.6	4888.5	5022.9	5162.3	5307.0	5457.6	5614.4	5778.3	5949.7	6129.7	2
3	4634.9	4760.7	4890.7	5025.2	5164.7	5309.5	5460.1	5617.1	5781.1	5952.7	6132.8	3
4	4637.0	4762.8	4892.9	5027.5	5167.0	5311.9	5462.7	5619.8	5783.8	5955.6	6135.8	4
5	4639.0	4764.9	4895.1	5029.8	5169.4	5314.4	5465.2	5622.4	5786.6	5958.5	6138.9	5
6	4641.1	4767.1	4897.3	5032.1	5171.8	5316.9	5467.8	5625.1	5789.4	5961.5	6142.0	6
7	4643.2	4769.2	4899.5	5034.3	5174.2	5319.3	5470.4	5627.8	5792.2	5964.4	6145.1	7
8	4645.2	4771.3	4901.7	5036.6	5176.5	5321.8	5472.9	5630.5	5795.1	5967.3	6148.2	8
9	4647.3	4773.4	4903.9	5038.9	5178.9	5324.3	5475.5	5633.2	5797.9	5970.3	6151.3	9
10	4649.4	4775.6	4906.1	5041.2	5181.3	5326.7	5478.1	5635.8	5800.7	5973.2	6154.4	10
11	4651.5	4777.8	4908.3	5043.5	5183.7	5329.2	5480.7	5638.5	5803.5	5976.2	6157.5	11
12	4653.5	4779.9	4910.5	5045.8	5186.0	5331.7	5483.2	5641.2	5806.3	5979.1	6160.6	12
13	4655.6	4782.0	4912.8	5048.1	5188.4	5334.2	5485.8	5643.9	5809.1	5982.1	6163.7	13
14	4657.7	4784.2	4915.0	5050.4	5190.8	5336.6	5488.4	5646.6	5811.9	5985.0	6166.8	14
15	4659.7	4786.3	4917.2	5052.7	5193.2	5339.1	5491.0	5649.3	5814.7	5988.0	6169.9	15
16	4661.8	4788.5	4919.4	5055.0	5195.6	5341.6	5493.6	5652.0	5817.6	5990.9	6173.0	16
17	4663.9	4790.6	4921.6	5057.3	5198.0	5344.1	5496.2	5654.7	5820.4	5993.9	6176.1	17
18	4666.0	4792.8	4923.9	5059.6	5200.4	5346.6	5498.7	5657.4	5823.2	5996.9	6179.2	18
19	4668.1	4794.9	4926.1	5061.9	5202.7	5349.1	5501.3	5660.1	5826.0	5999.8	6182.3	19
20	4670.1	4797.1	4928.3	5064.2	5205.1	5351.5	5503.9	5662.8	5828.9	6002.8	6185.5	20
21	4672.2	4799.2	4930.5	5066.5	5207.5	5354.0	5506.5	5665.5	5831.7	6005.8	6188.6	21
22	4674.3	4801.4	4932.8	5068.8	5209.9	5356.5	5509.1	5668.2	5834.5	6008.7	6191.7	22
23	4676.4	4803.5	4935.0	5071.1	5212.3	5359.0	5511.7	5670.9	5837.4	6011.7	6194.8	23
24	4678.5	4805.7	4937.2	5073.4	5214.7	5361.5	5514.3	5673.7	5840.2	6014.7	6198.0	24
25	4680.6	4807.8	4939.4	5075.7	5217.1	5364.0	5516.9	5676.4	5843.0	6017.7	6201.1	25
26	4682.6	4810.0	4941.7	5078.1	5219.6	5366.5	5519.5	5679.1	5845.9	6020.7	6204.2	26
27	4684.7	4812.1	4943.9	5080.4	5221.9	5369.0	5522.1	5681.8	5848.7	6023.6	6207.4	27
28	4686.8	4814.3	4946.1	5082.7	5224.3	5371.5	5524.7	5684.5	5851.6	6026.6	6210.5	28
29	4688.9	4816.5	4948.4	5085.0	5226.7	5374.0	5527.3	5687.3	5854.4	6029.6	6213.7	29
30	4691.0	4818.6	4950.6	5087.3	5229.1	5376.5	5529.9	5690.0	5857.3	6032.6	6216.8	30
31	4693.1	4820.8	4952.9	5089.6	5231.6	5379.0	5532.5	5692.7	5860.1	6035.6	6220.0	31
32	4695.2	4823.0	4955.1	5092.0	5234.0	5381.5	5535.2	5695.4	5863.0	6038.6	6223.1	32
33	4697.3	4825.1	4957.3	5094.3	5236.4	5384.0	5537.8	5698.2	5865.9	6041.6	6226.3	33
34	4699.4	4827.3	4959.6	5096.6	5238.8	5386.5	5540.4	5700.9	5868.7	6044.6	6229.4	34
35	4701.5	4829.5	4961.8	5098.9	5241.2	5389.1	5543.0	5703.6	5871.6	6047.6	6232.6	35
36	4703.6	4831.6	4964.1	5101.3	5243.6	5391.6	5545.6	5706.4	5874.4	6050.6	6235.8	36
37	4705.7	4833.8	4966.3	5103.6	5246.0	5394.1	5548.3	5709.1	5877.3	6053.6	6238.9	37
38	4707.8	4836.0	4968.6	5105.9	5248.5	5396.6	5550.9	5711.9	5880.2	6056.6	6242.1	38
39	4709.9	4838.1	4970.8	5108.3	5250.9	5399.1	5553.5	5714.6	5883.1	6059.7	6245.3	39
40	4712.0	4840.3	4973.1	5110.6	5253.3	5401.6	5556.1	5717.3	5885.9	6062.7	6248.4	40
41	4714.1	4842.5	4975.3	5112.9	5255.7	5404.2	5558.8	5720.1	5888.8	6065.7	6251.6	41
42	4716.2	4844.7	4977.6	5115.3	5258.2	5406.7	5561.4	5722.8	5891.7	6068.7	6254.8	42
43	4718.3	4846.8	4979.8	5117.6	5260.6	5409.2	5564.0	5725.6	5894.6	6071.7	6258.0	43
44	4720.4	4849.0	4982.1	5119.9	5263.0	5411.8	5566.7	5728.3	5897.4	6074.8	6261.2	44
45	4722.5	4851.2	4984.3	5122.3	5265.4	5414.3	5569.3	5731.1	5900.3	6077.8	6264.4	45
46	4724.6	4853.4	4986.6	5124.6	5267.9	5416.8	5571.9	5733.9	5903.2	6080.8	6267.6	46
47	4726.7	4855.6	4988.9	5127.0	5270.3	5419.3	5574.6	5736.6	5906.1	6083.9	6270.8	47
48	4728.9	4857.8	4991.1	5129.3	5272.8	5421.9	5577.2	5739.4	5909.0	6086.9	6274.0	48
49	4731.0	4859.9	4993.4	5131.7	5275.2	5424.4	5579.9	5742.1	5911.9	6089.9	6277.2	49
50	4733.1	4862.1	4995.6	5134.0	5277.6	5427.0	5582.5	5744.9	5914.8	6093.0	6280.4	50
51	4735.2	4864.3	4997.9	5136.4	5280.1	5429.5	5585.2	5747.7	5917.7	6096.0	6283.6	51
52	4737.3	4866.5	5000.2	5138.7	5282.5	5432.0	5587.8	5750.4	5920.6	6099.1	6286.8	52
53	4739.4	4868.7	5002.4	5141.1	5285.0	5434.6	5590.5	5753.2	5923.5	6102.1	6290.0	53
54	4741.6	4870.9	5004.7	5143.4	5287.4	5437.1	5593.1	5756.0	5926.4	6105.2	6293.2	54
55	4743.7	4873.1	5007.0	5145.8	5289.8	5439.7	5595.8	5758.8	5929.3	6108.2	6296.4	55
56	4745.8	4875.3	5009.3	5148.1	5292.3	5442.2	5598.4	5761.5	5932.2	6111.3	6299.6	56
57	4747.9	4877.5	5011.5	5150.5	5294.7	5444.8	5601.1	5764.3	5935.1	6114.3	6302.9	57
58	4750.0	4879.7	5013.8	5152.8	5297.2	5447.3	5603.8	5767.1	5938.1	6117.4	6306.1	58
59	4752.2	4881.9	5016.1	5155.2	5299.7	5449.9	5606.4	5769.9	5941.0	6120.5	6309.3	59
	61°	62°	63°	64°	65°	66°	67°	68°	69°	70°	71°	

Table 4

MERIDIONAL PARTS
For the Terrestrial Spheroid

LATITUDE

/	72°	73°	74°	75°	76°	77°	78°	79°	80°	81°	82°	/
0	6312.5	6512.0	6723.2	6947.7	7187.3	7444.4	7721.6	8022.7	8352.1	8715.9	9122.2	0
1	6315.8	6515.4	6726.8	6951.6	7191.5	7448.8	7726.4	8027.9	8357.9	8722.3	9129.4	1
2	6319.0	6518.8	6730.5	6955.4	7195.6	7453.3	7731.3	8033.2	8363.6	8728.7	9136.6	2
3	6322.3	6522.3	6734.1	6959.3	7199.7	7457.7	7736.1	8038.4	8369.4	8735.1	9143.9	3
4	6325.5	6525.7	6737.7	6963.2	7203.9	7462.2	7740.9	8043.7	8375.2	8741.6	9151.1	4
5	6328.7	6529.1	6741.4	6967.1	7208.0	7466.7	7745.8	8049.0	8381.0	8748.0	9158.3	5
6	6332.0	6532.6	6745.0	6970.9	7212.2	7471.1	7750.6	8054.3	8386.8	8754.5	9165.6	6
7	6335.3	6536.0	6748.7	6974.8	7216.4	7475.6	7755.5	8059.6	8392.6	8760.9	9172.9	7
8	6338.5	6539.5	6752.3	6978.7	7220.5	7480.1	7760.3	8064.9	8398.5	8767.4	9180.2	8
9	6341.8	6542.9	6756.0	6982.6	7224.7	7484.6	7765.2	8070.2	8404.3	8773.9	9187.5	9
10	6345.0	6546.4	6759.7	6986.5	7228.9	7489.1	7770.0	8075.5	8410.2	8780.4	9194.8	10
11	6348.3	6549.8	6763.3	6990.4	7233.1	7493.6	7774.9	8080.8	8416.0	8786.9	9202.2	11
12	6351.6	6553.3	6767.0	6994.3	7237.3	7498.1	7779.8	8086.1	8421.9	8793.5	9209.5	12
13	6354.8	6556.7	6770.7	6998.3	7241.4	7502.6	7784.7	8091.5	8427.8	8800.0	9216.9	13
14	6358.1	6560.2	6774.3	7002.2	7245.6	7507.1	7789.6	8096.8	8433.7	8806.6	9224.3	14
15	6361.4	6563.6	6778.0	7006.1	7249.8	7511.7	7794.5	8102.2	8439.6	8813.1	9231.7	15
16	6364.7	6567.1	6781.7	7010.0	7254.1	7516.2	7799.4	8107.5	8445.5	8819.7	9239.1	16
17	6367.9	6570.6	6785.4	7014.0	7258.3	7520.7	7804.3	8112.9	8451.4	8826.3	9246.6	17
18	6371.2	6574.1	6789.1	7017.9	7262.5	7525.3	7809.3	8118.3	8457.3	8832.9	9254.0	18
19	6374.5	6577.5	6792.8	7021.8	7266.7	7529.8	7814.2	8123.7	8463.3	8839.5	9261.5	19
20	6377.8	6581.0	6796.5	7025.8	7270.9	7534.4	7819.1	8129.1	8469.2	8846.1	9269.0	20
21	6381.1	6584.5	6800.2	7029.7	7275.2	7538.9	7824.1	8134.5	8475.2	8852.8	9276.5	21
22	6384.4	6588.0	6803.9	7033.7	7279.4	7543.5	7829.0	8139.9	8481.1	8859.4	9284.0	22
23	6387.7	6591.5	6807.6	7037.6	7283.7	7548.1	7834.0	8145.3	8487.1	8866.1	9291.5	23
24	6391.0	6595.0	6811.3	7041.6	7287.9	7552.7	7839.0	8150.8	8493.1	8872.8	9299.1	24
25	6394.3	6598.5	6815.0	7045.6	7292.2	7557.2	7843.9	8156.2	8499.1	8879.5	9306.7	25
26	6397.6	6602.0	6818.8	7049.6	7296.4	7561.8	7848.9	8161.6	8505.1	8886.2	9314.3	26
27	6400.9	6605.5	6822.5	7053.5	7300.7	7566.4	7853.9	8167.1	8511.1	8892.9	9321.9	27
28	6404.3	6609.0	6826.2	7057.5	7304.9	7571.0	7858.9	8172.6	8517.2	8899.6	9329.5	28
29	6407.6	6612.5	6829.9	7061.5	7309.2	7575.7	7863.9	8178.0	8523.2	8906.4	9337.1	29
30	6410.9	6616.0	6833.7	7065.5	7313.5	7580.3	7868.9	8183.5	8529.3	8913.1	9344.8	30
31	6414.2	6619.6	6837.4	7069.5	7317.8	7584.9	7873.9	8189.0	8535.3	8919.9	9352.4	31
32	6417.5	6623.1	6841.2	7073.5	7322.1	7589.5	7879.0	8194.5	8541.4	8926.7	9360.1	32
33	6420.9	6626.6	6844.9	7077.5	7326.4	7594.1	7884.0	8200.0	8547.5	8933.5	9367.8	33
34	6424.2	6630.2	6848.7	7081.5	7330.7	7598.8	7889.0	8205.5	8553.6	8940.3	9375.5	34
35	6427.5	6633.7	6852.4	7085.5	7335.0	7603.4	7894.1	8211.1	8559.7	8947.1	9383.3	35
36	6430.9	6637.2	6856.2	7089.5	7339.3	7608.1	7899.1	8216.6	8565.8	8954.0	9391.0	36
37	6434.2	6640.8	6860.0	7093.5	7343.6	7612.7	7904.2	8222.1	8571.9	8960.8	9398.8	37
38	6437.6	6644.3	6863.7	7097.6	7347.9	7617.4	7909.3	8227.7	8578.1	8967.7	9406.6	38
39	6440.9	6647.9	6867.5	7101.6	7352.3	7622.1	7914.4	8233.2	8584.2	8974.6	9414.4	39
40	6444.3	6651.4	6871.3	7105.6	7356.6	7626.8	7919.4	8238.8	8590.4	8981.4	9422.2	40
41	6447.6	6655.0	6875.1	7109.7	7360.9	7631.4	7924.5	8244.4	8596.5	8988.4	9430.1	41
42	6451.0	6658.5	6878.9	7113.7	7365.3	7636.1	7929.6	8250.0	8602.7	8995.3	9437.9	42
43	6454.4	6662.1	6882.6	7117.8	7369.6	7640.8	7934.7	8255.6	8608.9	9002.2	9445.8	43
44	6457.7	6665.7	6886.4	7121.8	7374.0	7645.5	7939.8	8261.2	8615.1	9009.2	9453.7	44
45	6461.1	6669.2	6890.2	7125.9	7378.3	7650.2	7945.0	8266.8	8621.3	9016.1	9461.6	45
46	6464.5	6672.8	6894.0	7129.9	7382.7	7655.0	7950.1	8272.4	8627.6	9023.1	9469.5	46
47	6467.8	6676.4	6897.8	7134.0	7387.1	7659.7	7955.2	8278.0	8633.8	9030.1	9477.5	47
48	6471.2	6680.0	6901.7	7138.1	7391.4	7664.4	7960.4	8283.7	8640.0	9037.1	9485.5	48
49	6474.6	6683.5	6905.5	7142.2	7395.8	7669.1	7965.5	8289.3	8646.3	9044.1	9493.5	49
50	6478.0	6687.1	6909.3	7146.2	7400.2	7673.9	7970.7	8295.0	8652.6	9051.1	9501.5	50
51	6481.4	6690.7	6913.1	7150.3	7404.6	7678.6	7975.8	8300.7	8658.9	9058.2	9509.5	51
52	6484.8	6694.3	6916.9	7154.4	7409.0	7683.4	7981.0	8306.3	8665.1	9065.2	9517.5	52
53	6488.2	6697.9	6920.8	7158.5	7413.4	7688.1	7986.2	8312.0	8671.5	9072.3	9525.6	53
54	6491.6	6701.5	6924.6	7162.6	7417.8	7692.9	7991.4	8317.7	8677.8	9079.4	9533.7	54
55	6495.0	6705.1	6928.4	7166.7	7422.2	7697.7	7996.6	8323.4	8684.1	9086.5	9541.8	55
56	6498.4	6708.7	6932.3	7170.8	7426.6	7702.5	8001.8	8329.2	8690.4	9093.6	9549.9	56
57	6501.8	6712.3	6936.1	7174.9	7431.1	7707.2	8007.0	8334.9	8696.8	9100.8	9558.0	57
58	6505.2	6716.0	6940.0	7179.1	7435.5	7712.0	8012.2	8340.6	8703.1	9107.9	9566.2	58
59	6508.6	6719.6	6943.8	7183.2	7439.9	7716.8	8017.5	8346.4	8709.5	9115.1	9574.4	59
	72°	73°	74°	75°	76°	77°	78°	79°	80°	81°	82°	

Table 4a

Correction to apply to **MEAN LAT.** to obtain **MID. LAT.**

Mean Lat.	DIFF. LAT.																Mean Lat.
°	2°	4°	6°	8°	10°	11°	12°	13°	14°	15°	16°	17°	18°	19°	20°	21°	°
11	129	125	118	110	100	93	87	80	72	64	57	48	38	29	18	8	11
12	114	111	105	98	89	83	77	71	64	57	49	42	33	23	15	5	12
13	102	100	95	88	79	75	69	63	57	51	43	36	27	20	12	3	13
14	93	90	86	80	72	67	62	57	51	45	38	31	24	16	9	0	14
15	85	83	79	73	65	61	56	51	46	40	34	27	21	13	6	1	15
16	79	76	72	66	60	56	51	46	41	36	30	24	17	10	4	4	16
17	72	70	66	61	55	51	47	42	37	32	27	21	15	8	2	6	17
18	67	65	61	56	50	46	43	38	34	29	24	18	12	6	1	8	18
19	62	60	57	52	46	43	39	35	30	25	21	15	9	3	3	10	19
20	58	56	53	48	42	39	35	31	27	22	18	13	7	1	5	13	20
22	50	48	45	41	36	33	29	25	22	17	13	8	3	3	9	15	22
24	44	42	40	36	31	28	24	21	17	13	8	4	1	6	12	17	24
26	39	37	35	31	26	23	20	16	13	9	5	0	5	10	15	21	26
28	34	32	30	26	22	19	16	12	9	5	1	3	8	13	18	23	28
30	30	29	26	22	18	15	12	9	6	2	2	6	11	16	21	26	30
35	22	21	18	15	10	7	5	1	2	6	10	14	18	23	28	33	35
40	16	14	12	8	4	1	2	5	8	12	16	20	25	29	34	40	40
45	11	10	7	3	1	4	7	11	14	18	22	27	31	36	41	47	45
50	8	6	3	1	6	9	12	16	20	24	28	33	38	44	49	55	50
55	5	3	0	5	10	14	17	21	25	30	35	40	46	52	58	65	55
60	3	1	3	8	14	18	22	27	32	37	43	49	55	62	69	77	60

ADD

Mean Lat.	DIFF. LAT.																Mean Lat.
°	22°	23°	24°	25°	26°	27°	28°	29°	30°	31°	32°	33°	34°	35°	36°	37°	°
11	3	—															11
12	5	14	25	—	—												12
13	7	16	26	36	47												13
14	8	18	27	36	46	56	67	—	—								14
15	10	19	27	36	46	55	65	76	86	—	—						15
16	12	20	28	36	46	55	65	74	84	95	105	—	—				16
17	14	21	29	38	46	55	64	73	83	93	103	113	124	—	—		17
18	15	22	30	38	46	55	64	73	82	91	101	111	122	132	143	—	18
19	17	23	31	39	47	55	63	72	81	90	100	110	119	130	140	151	19
20	18	25	32	39	47	55	63	72	80	90	99	108	118	128	138	149	20
22	20	27	34	41	48	56	64	72	80	89	97	106	116	125	135	145	22
24	23	30	36	43	50	57	64	72	80	89	97	106	115	124	133	143	24
26	26	32	38	45	52	59	66	74	81	89	97	106	114	124	133	142	26
28	29	34	41	47	54	60	68	75	83	90	99	107	115	124	133	143	28
30	32	37	43	49	56	63	70	77	85	92	100	108	117	125	134	143	30
35	38	44	50	56	62	69	76	83	90	98	106	114	122	131	140	149	35
40	45	51	57	63	70	77	84	91	99	106	115	123	132	141	150	159	40
45	53	59	65	72	79	86	93	101	109	116	126	135	144	154	164	174	45
50	61	68	75	82	90	97	105	114	123	132	141	151	161	172	183	194	50
55	72	79	87	95	103	112	121	131	141	151	162	173	185	197	210	223	55
60	85	94	103	112	122	132	143	155	166	179	192	205	219	234	250	266	60

Table 5

Total Correction to apply to Obs. Alt. ☉ to obtain True Alt. ADDITIVE

Seasonal Correction	Jan. +0'.3	Feb. +0'.2	Mar. +0'.1	April 0'.0	May −0'.2	June −0'.2	July −0'.2	Aug. −0'.2	Sept. −0'.1	Oct. +0'.1	Nov. +0'.2	Dec. +0'.3

Height of Eye in Feet

☉	14	16	18	20	22	24	26	28	30	32	35	40	45	50	55	60	65	70	☉
6° '	4.0	3.7	3.5	3.3	3.1	2.9	2.7	2.5	2.3	2.1	1.8	1.4	1.1	.7	.3	.0	—	—	**6**° '
15	4.3	4.0	3.8	3.6	3.4	3.2	3.0	2.8	2.6	2.4	2.2	1.8	1.3	1.0	.6	.2	.0	—	15
30	4.6	4.3	4.1	3.9	3.6	3.4	3.2	3.0	2.9	2.7	2.4	2.0	1.6	1.3	.9	.6	.3	.0	30
45	4.8	4.6	4.4	4.1	3.9	3.7	3.5	3.3	3.1	2.9	2.7	2.3	1.9	1.5	1.2	.9	.5	.2	45
7	5.1	4.8	4.6	4.4	4.1	3.9	3.7	3.5	3.4	3.2	2.9	2.5	2.1	1.8	1.4	1.1	.8	.5	**7**
15	5.3	5.1	4.8	4.6	4.4	4.2	4.0	3.8	3.6	3.4	3.2	2.8	2.4	2.0	1.7	1.4	1.0	.7	15
30	5.5	5.3	5.0	4.8	4.6	4.4	4.2	4.0	3.8	3.6	3.4	3.0	2.6	2.2	1.9	1.6	1.2	.9	30
45	5.7	5.5	5.2	5.0	4.8	4.6	4.4	4.2	4.0	3.8	3.6	3.2	2.8	2.4	2.1	1.8	1.5	1.2	45
8	5.9	5.7	5.4	5.2	5.0	4.8	4.6	4.4	4.2	4.0	3.8	3.4	3.0	2.6	2.3	2.0	1.6	1.3	**8**
20	6.2	5.9	5.7	5.5	5.2	5.0	4.8	4.6	4.5	4.3	4.0	3.6	3.2	2.9	2.5	2.2	1.9	1.6	20
40	6.4	6.1	5.9	5.7	5.5	5.3	5.1	4.9	4.7	4.5	4.2	3.8	3.5	3.1	2.8	2.4	2.1	1.8	40
9	6.6	6.4	6.1	5.9	5.7	5.5	5.3	5.1	4.9	4.7	4.5	4.1	3.7	3.3	3.0	2.6	2.3	2.0	**9**
20	6.8	6.6	6.3	6.1	5.9	5.7	5.5	5.3	5.1	4.9	4.7	4.3	3.9	3.5	3.2	2.9	2.6	2.3	20
40	7.0	6.8	6.6	6.3	6.1	5.9	5.7	5.5	5.3	5.1	4.9	4.5	4.1	3.7	3.4	3.1	2.8	2.5	40
10	7.2	7.0	6.7	6.5	6.3	6.1	5.9	5.7	5.5	5.3	5.0	4.6	4.2	3.9	3.6	3.3	3.0	2.6	**10**
20	7.3	7.1	6.8	6.6	6.4	6.2	6.0	5.8	5.7	5.5	5.2	4.8	4.4	4.1	3.7	3.4	3.1	2.8	20
40	7.5	7.2	7.0	6.8	6.5	6.3	6.1	6.0	5.8	5.6	5.3	5.0	4.6	4.2	3.9	3.6	3.3	3.0	40
11	7.6	7.4	7.2	7.0	6.7	6.5	6.3	6.2	6.0	5.8	5.5	5.1	4.7	4.4	4.1	3.7	3.4	3.1	**11**
30	7.8	7.6	7.4	7.1	6.9	6.7	6.5	6.4	6.2	6.0	5.7	5.3	4.9	4.6	4.3	3.9	3.6	3.3	30
12	8.0	7.8	7.6	7.3	7.1	6.9	6.7	6.6	6.4	6.2	5.9	5.5	5.2	4.8	4.5	4.1	3.8	3.5	**12**
30	8.2	8.0	7.8	7.5	7.3	7.1	6.9	6.7	6.5	6.4	6.1	5.7	5.3	5.0	4.6	4.3	4.0	3.7	30
13	8.4	8.1	7.9	7.7	7.4	7.2	7.0	6.8	6.7	6.5	6.2	5.9	5.5	5.1	4.8	4.5	4.2	3.9	**13**
30	8.5	8.3	8.0	7.8	7.6	7.4	7.2	7.0	6.8	6.7	6.4	6.0	5.6	5.3	5.0	4.7	4.3	4.0	30
14	8.7	8.4	8.2	8.0	7.7	7.5	7.3	7.1	7.0	6.8	6.5	6.2	5.8	5.4	5.1	4.8	4.5	4.2	**14**
30	8.8	8.5	8.3	8.1	7.9	7.7	7.5	7.3	7.1	6.9	6.7	6.3	5.9	5.5	5.2	4.9	4.6	4.3	30
15	8.9	8.7	8.4	8.2	8.0	7.8	7.6	7.4	7.2	7.0	6.8	6.4	6.1	5.7	5.3	5.0	4.7	4.4	**15**
30	9.0	8.8	8.5	8.3	8.1	7.9	7.7	7.5	7.3	7.1	6.9	6.5	6.2	5.8	5.4	5.1	4.8	4.5	30
16	9.1	8.9	8.6	8.4	8.2	8.0	7.8	7.6	7.5	7.3	7.0	6.7	6.3	5.9	5.6	5.3	4.9	4.6	**16**
17	9.3	9.1	8.8	8.6	8.4	8.2	8.0	7.8	7.7	7.5	7.2	6.9	6.5	6.1	5.8	5.5	5.1	4.8	**17**
18	9.5	9.3	9.0	8.8	8.6	8.4	8.2	8.0	7.9	7.7	7.4	7.0	6.7	6.3	6.0	5.7	5.3	5.0	**18**
19	9.7	9.4	9.2	9.0	8.7	8.5	8.3	8.1	8.0	7.9	7.5	7.2	6.8	6.5	6.1	5.8	5.5	5.2	**19**
20	9.8	9.6	9.3	9.1	8.9	8.7	8.5	8.3	8.2	8.0	7.7	7.4	7.0	6.6	6.3	6.0	5.6	5.3	**20**
21	10.0	9.7	9.5	9.3	9.0	8.8	8.6	8.4	8.3	8.1	7.8	7.4	7.1	6.7	6.4	6.0	5.7	5.4	**21**
22	10.1	9.8	9.6	9.4	9.2	9.0	8.8	8.6	8.4	8.2	8.0	7.6	7.2	6.8	6.5	6.2	5.9	5.6	**22**
24	10.3	10.0	9.8	9.6	9.4	9.2	9.0	8.8	8.6	8.4	8.2	7.8	7.4	7.0	6.7	6.4	6.1	5.8	**24**
26	10.5	10.2	10.0	9.8	9.6	9.4	9.2	9.0	8.8	8.6	8.4	8.0	7.6	7.2	6.9	6.6	6.3	6.0	**26**
28	10.6	10.4	10.2	9.9	9.7	9.5	9.3	9.1	8.9	8.8	8.5	8.1	7.7	7.4	7.0	6.7	6.4	6.1	**28**
30	10.8	10.5	10.3	10.1	9.9	9.7	9.5	9.3	9.1	8.9	8.6	8.3	7.9	7.6	7.2	6.9	6.6	6.3	**30**
32	10.9	10.7	10.4	10.2	10.0	9.8	9.6	9.4	9.2	9.0	8.8	8.4	8.0	7.7	7.3	7.0	6.7	6.4	**32**
35	11.1	10.8	10.6	10.4	10.1	9.9	9.7	9.6	9.4	9.2	9.0	8.6	8.2	7.9	7.5	7.2	6.9	6.6	**35**
40	11.3	11.0	10.8	10.6	10.4	10.2	10.0	9.8	9.6	9.4	9.2	8.8	8.4	8.1	7.7	7.4	7.1	6.8	**40**
45	11.5	11.2	11.0	10.8	10.5	10.3	10.1	9.9	9.8	9.6	9.3	9.0	8.6	8.2	7.9	7.6	7.3	7.0	**45**
50	11.6	11.4	11.2	10.9	10.7	10.5	10.3	10.1	9.9	9.7	9.5	9.1	8.7	8.4	8.0	7.7	7.4	7.1	**50**
60	11.8	11.6	11.4	11.1	10.9	10.7	10.5	10.3	10.1	10.0	9.7	9.3	9.0	8.6	8.3	8.0	7.6	7.3	**60**
70	12.0	11.8	11.6	11.3	11.1	10.9	10.7	10.5	10.3	10.2	9.9	9.5	9.2	8.8	8.5	8.1	7.8	7.5	**70**
80	12.2	11.9	11.7	11.5	11.2	11.0	10.8	10.7	10.5	10.3	10.0	9.7	9.3	8.9	8.6	8.3	8.0	7.7	**80**
90	12.3	12.1	11.8	11.6	11.4	11.2	11.0	10.8	10.6	10.5	10.2	9.8	9.4	9.1	8.7	8.4	8.1	7.8	**90**

Table 6

Total Correction to apply to Obs. Alt. ★ to obtain True Alt. **SUBTRACTIVE**

✳	Height of Eye in Feet																		✳
	14	16	18	20	22	24	26	28	30	32	35	40	45	50	55	60	65	70	
° ′	′	′	′	′	′	′	′	′	′	′	′	′	′	′	′	′	′	′	° ′
6	12.1	12.4	12.6	12.9	13.1	13.3	13.5	13.7	13.9	14.0	14.3	14.7	15.1	15.5	15.8	16.1	16.4	16.8	6
15	11.8	12.1	12.3	12.6	12.8	13.0	13.2	13.4	13.6	13.7	14.0	14.4	14.8	15.2	15.5	15.8	16.2	16.5	15
30	11.6	11.8	12.1	12.3	12.5	12.7	12.9	13.1	13.3	13.5	13.7	14.1	14.5	14.9	15.2	15.6	15.9	16.2	30
45	11.3	11.6	11.8	12.0	12.3	12.5	12.7	12.8	13.0	13.2	13.5	13.9	14.2	14.6	15.0	15.3	15.6	15.9	45
7	11.1	11.3	11.5	11.8	12.0	12.2	12.4	12.6	12.8	13.0	13.2	13.6	14.0	14.4	14.7	15.0	15.4	15.7	7
15	10.8	11.1	11.3	11.5	11.8	12.0	12.2	12.4	12.6	12.8	13.0	13.4	13.8	14.2	14.5	14.8	15.1	15.4	15
30	10.6	10.9	11.1	11.3	11.6	11.8	12.0	12.2	12.3	12.5	12.8	13.2	13.6	13.9	14.3	14.6	14.9	15.2	30
45	10.4	10.7	10.9	11.1	11.4	11.6	11.8	12.0	12.1	12.3	12.6	13.0	13.4	13.7	14.1	14.4	14.7	15.0	45
8	10.2	10.5	10.7	10.9	11.2	11.4	11.6	11.8	11.9	12.1	12.4	12.8	13.2	13.5	13.9	14.2	14.5	14.8	8
20	10.0	10.2	10.4	10.7	10.9	11.1	11.3	11.5	11.7	11.9	12.1	12.5	12.9	13.3	13.6	13.9	14.2	14.5	20
40	9.7	10.0	10.2	10.5	10.7	10.9	11.1	11.3	11.4	11.6	11.9	12.3	12.7	13.0	13.4	13.7	14.0	14.3	40
9	9.5	9.8	10.0	10.3	10.5	10.7	10.9	11.1	11.2	11.4	11.7	12.1	12.4	12.8	13.2	13.5	13.8	14.1	9
20	9.3	9.6	9.8	10.1	10.3	10.5	10.7	10.9	11.0	11.2	11.5	11.9	12.3	12.6	13.0	13.3	13.6	13.9	20
40	9.2	9.4	9.6	9.9	10.1	10.3	10.5	10.7	10.8	11.0	11.3	11.7	12.1	12.4	12.8	13.1	13.4	13.7	40
10	9.0	9.2	9.4	9.7	9.9	10.1	10.3	10.5	10.7	10.9	11.1	11.5	11.9	12.2	12.6	12.9	13.2	13.5	10
20	8.8	9.0	9.3	9.5	9.7	9.9	10.1	10.3	10.5	10.7	10.9	11.3	11.7	12.1	12.4	12.8	13.1	13.4	20
40	8.7	8.9	9.1	9.4	9.6	9.8	10.0	10.2	10.4	10.5	10.8	11.2	11.6	11.9	12.3	12.6	12.9	13.2	40
11	8.5	8.7	9.0	9.2	9.4	9.6	9.8	10.0	10.2	10.4	10.6	11.0	11.4	11.7	12.1	12.4	12.7	13.0	11
30	8.3	8.5	8.8	9.0	9.2	9.4	9.6	9.8	10.0	10.2	10.4	10.8	11.2	11.6	11.9	12.2	12.5	12.8	30
12	8.1	8.3	8.6	8.8	9.0	9.2	9.4	9.6	9.8	10.0	10.2	10.6	11.0	11.4	11.7	12.0	12.3	12.6	12
30	7.9	8.1	8.4	8.7	8.8	9.0	9.2	9.4	9.6	9.8	10.0	10.4	10.8	11.2	11.5	11.8	12.1	12.5	30
13	7.8	8.0	8.2	8.5	8.7	8.9	9.1	9.3	9.4	9.7	9.9	10.3	10.7	11.0	11.4	11.7	12.0	12.3	13
30	7.6	7.8	8.1	8.3	8.5	8.7	8.9	9.1	9.3	9.5	9.7	10.1	10.5	10.9	11.2	11.5	11.8	12.1	30
14	7.5	7.7	7.9	8.2	8.4	8.6	8.8	9.0	9.2	9.4	9.6	10.0	10.4	10.7	11.1	11.4	11.7	12.0	14
30	7.3	7.6	7.8	8.1	8.3	8.5	8.7	8.9	9.0	9.2	9.5	9.9	10.3	10.6	11.0	11.3	11.6	11.9	30
15	7.2	7.5	7.7	7.9	8.1	8.3	8.5	8.7	8.9	9.1	9.3	9.7	10.1	10.5	10.8	11.1	11.4	11.7	15
30	7.1	7.4	7.6	7.8	8.0	8.2	8.4	8.6	8.8	9.0	9.2	9.6	10.0	10.4	10.7	11.0	11.3	11.6	30
16	7.0	7.3	7.5	7.7	7.9	8.1	8.3	8.5	8.7	8.9	9.1	9.5	9.9	10.2	10.6	10.9	11.2	11.5	16
17	6.8	7.1	7.3	7.5	7.7	7.9	8.1	8.3	8.5	8.7	8.9	9.3	9.7	10.0	10.4	10.7	11.0	11.3	17
18	6.6	6.9	7.1	7.3	7.5	7.7	7.9	8.1	8.3	8.5	8.7	9.1	9.5	9.8	10.2	10.5	10.8	11.1	18
19	6.5	6.7	6.9	7.1	7.3	7.5	7.7	7.9	8.1	8.3	8.6	9.0	9.3	9.7	10.0	10.3	10.7	11.0	19
20	6.3	6.6	6.8	7.0	7.2	7.4	7.6	7.8	8.0	8.2	8.4	8.8	9.2	9.6	9.9	10.2	10.5	10.8	20
21	6.2	6.4	6.7	6.9	7.1	7.3	7.5	7.7	7.9	8.0	8.3	8.6	9.0	9.4	9.7	10.1	10.4	10.7	21
22	6.1	6.3	6.5	6.7	6.9	7.1	7.3	7.5	7.7	7.9	8.1	8.5	8.9	9.2	9.6	9.9	10.2	10.5	22
24	5.8	6.1	6.3	6.5	6.8	7.0	7.2	7.4	7.5	7.7	7.9	8.3	8.7	9.1	9.4	9.7	10.0	10.3	24
26	5.6	5.9	6.1	6.3	6.6	6.8	7.0	7.2	7.3	7.5	7.7	8.1	8.5	8.9	9.2	9.5	9.8	10.1	26
28	5.5	5.7	6.0	6.2	6.4	6.6	6.8	7.0	7.2	7.4	7.6	8.0	8.4	8.7	9.1	9.4	9.7	10.0	28
30	5.3	5.6	5.8	6.0	6.2	6.4	6.6	6.8	7.0	7.2	7.4	7.8	8.2	8.6	8.9	9.2	9.5	9.8	30
32	5.2	5.5	5.7	5.9	6.1	6.3	6.5	6.7	6.9	7.1	7.3	7.7	8.1	8.5	8.8	9.1	9.4	9.7	32
35	5.1	5.3	5.5	5.7	6.0	6.2	6.4	6.6	6.7	6.9	7.1	7.5	7.9	8.3	8.6	8.9	9.2	9.5	35
40	4.8	5.1	5.3	5.5	5.8	6.0	6.2	6.4	6.5	6.7	6.9	7.3	7.7	8.1	8.4	8.7	9.0	9.3	40
45	4.6	4.9	5.1	5.3	5.6	5.8	6.0	6.2	6.3	6.5	6.7	7.1	7.5	7.9	8.2	8.5	8.8	9.1	45
50	4.5	4.7	5.0	5.2	5.4	5.6	5.8	6.0	6.2	6.4	6.6	7.0	7.4	7.7	8.1	8.4	8.7	9.0	50
60	4.2	4.5	4.7	4.9	5.2	5.4	5.6	5.8	5.9	6.1	6.4	6.8	7.1	7.5	7.8	8.1	8.5	8.8	60
70	4.0	4.3	4.5	4.7	5.0	5.2	5.4	5.5	5.7	5.9	6.2	6.6	6.9	7.3	7.6	7.9	8.3	8.6	70
80	3.8	4.1	4.3	4.6	4.8	5.0	5.2	5.4	5.5	5.7	6.0	6.4	6.7	7.1	7.4	7.7	8.1	8.4	80
90	3.7	3.9	4.2	4.4	4.6	4.8	5.0	5.2	5.4	5.6	5.8	6.2	6.6	6.9	7.3	7.6	7.9	8.2	90

102

Table 7
SUN'S

Semi-Diameter on first day of each Month		Parallax-in-Altitude	
Month	S.D.	App. Alt.	Pax.
	′	°	′
January	16.28	0	.15
February	16.25	10	.14
March	16.15	20	.13
April	16.02	30	.12
May	15.88	40	.11
June	15.78	50	.09
July	15.75	60	.07
August	15.78	70	.05
September	15.88	75	.04
October	16.02	80	.02
November	16.15	85	.01
December	16.25	90	.00

Table 7a
PLANET'S PAX.-IN-ALT.

Alt.	Planet's Hor. Pax.					
	5″	10″	15″	20″	25″	30″
°	′	′	′	′	′	′
20	.08	.16	.24	.31	.39	.47
40	.06	.13	.19	.26	.32	.38
50	.05	.11	.16	.22	.27	.32
60	.04	.08	.13	.17	.21	.25
70	.03	.06	.09	.11	.14	.17
80	.02	.03	.04	.06	.07	.09
90	.00	.00	.00	.00	.00	.00

Table 8
EQUATION OF TIME
As applied to Apparent Time

Date	m.	Date	m.	Date	m.	Date	m.
Jan. 1		Mar. 27		Aug. 9		Oct. 18	
	+3		+5		+5		−15
2		Mar. 31		16		Oct. 23	
	+4		+4		+4		−16
4		April 3		21		Nov. 15	
	+5		+3		+3		−15
6		7		24		20	
	+6		+2		+2		−14
8		10		Aug. 28		24	
	+7		+1		+1		−13
11		14		Sept. 1		28	
	+8		0		0		−12
14		18		4		Nov. 30	
	+9		−1		−1		−11
16		22		7		Dec. 3	
	+10		−2		−2		−10
19		April 28		10		6	
	+11		−3		−3		−9
23		May 7		13		8	
	+12		−4		−4		−8
Jan. 26		22		15		10	
	+13		−3		−5		−7
Feb. 1		May 31		18		13	
	+14		−2		−6		−6
Feb. 24		June 7		21		15	
	+13		−1		−7		−5
Mar. 2		12		24		17	
	+12		0		−8		−4
6		17		27		19	
	+11		+1		−9		−3
10		21		Sept. 30		20	
	+10		+2		−10		−2
14		26		Oct. 3		23	
	+9		+3		−11		−1
17		June 30		6		25	
	+8		+4		−12		0
21		July 6		9		27	
	+7		+5		−13		+1
24		July 13		13		29	
	+6		+6		−14		+2
Mar. 27		Aug. 9		Oct. 18		Dec. 31	
							+3

Table 9
A

Correction to be applied to Obs. Alt. (to obtain True Alt. **ADDITIVE**

HORIZONTAL PARALLAX

(	54′	.2	.4	.6	.8	55′	.2	.4	.6	.8	56′	.2	.4	.6	.8	57′	.2	.4	(
6°	20.6	20.8	20.9	21.1	21.2	21.4	21.5	21.6	21.8	21.9	22.1	22.2	22.4	22.5	22.7	22.8	23.0	23.1	6°
7	21.6	21.8	21.9	22.1	22.2	22.3	22.5	22.6	22.8	22.9	23.1	23.2	23.3	23.5	23.6	23.8	23.9	24.1	7
8	22.4	22.5	22.6	22.8	22.9	23.0	23.2	23.3	23.5	23.6	23.7	23.9	24.0	24.2	24.3	24.4	24.6	24.8	8
9	22.8	23.0	23.2	23.3	23.5	23.6	23.7	23.9	24.0	24.2	24.3	24.5	24.6	24.8	24.9	25.1	25.2	25.3	9
10	23.3	23.4	23.5	23.7	23.9	24.0	24.2	24.3	24.5	24.6	24.7	24.9	25.0	25.1	25.3	25.5	25.6	25.7	10
11	23.6	23.8	23.9	24.0	24.2	24.3	24.5	24.6	24.7	24.9	25.0	25.2	25.3	25.4	25.6	25.7	25.9	26.0	11
12	23.8	24.0	24.1	24.3	24.4	24.5	24.7	24.8	25.0	25.1	25.2	25.4	25.5	25.7	25.8	25.9	26.1	26.2	12
13	23.9	24.1	24.3	24.4	24.6	24.7	24.8	25.0	25.1	25.2	25.3	25.5	25.7	25.8	25.9	26.0	26.2	26.4	13
14	24.0	24.2	24.3	24.5	24.6	24.7	24.9	25.0	25.2	25.3	25.4	25.6	25.7	25.9	26.0	26.1	26.3	26.4	14
15	24.0	24.2	24.4	24.5	24.6	24.7	24.9	25.0	25.2	25.3	25.4	25.6	25.7	25.9	26.0	26.1	26.3	26.4	15
16	24.0	24.2	24.3	24.5	24.6	24.7	24.9	25.0	25.2	25.3	25.4	25.6	25.7	25.9	26.0	26.1	26.3	26.4	16
17	24.0	24.1	24.3	24.4	24.5	24.6	24.8	25.0	25.1	25.2	25.3	25.5	25.6	25.8	25.9	26.0	26.2	26.3	17
18	23.9	24.0	24.2	24.3	24.4	24.5	24.7	24.8	25.0	25.1	25.2	25.4	25.5	25.7	25.8	25.9	26.1	26.2	18
19	23.7	23.9	24.0	24.2	24.3	24.4	24.6	24.7	24.8	25.0	25.1	25.2	25.4	25.5	25.7	25.8	25.9	26.1	19
20	23.5	23.7	23.9	24.0	24.1	24.2	24.4	24.5	24.7	24.8	24.9	25.1	25.2	25.3	25.5	25.6	25.7	25.9	20
21	23.4	23.5	23.7	23.8	23.9	24.0	24.2	24.3	24.5	24.6	24.7	24.9	25.0	25.1	25.3	25.4	25.5	25.7	21
22	23.2	23.3	23.5	23.6	23.7	23.8	24.0	24.1	24.2	24.4	24.5	24.6	24.8	24.9	25.0	25.1	25.3	25.4	22
23	22.9	23.1	23.2	23.3	23.5	23.6	23.7	23.8	24.0	24.1	24.2	24.4	24.5	24.6	24.8	24.9	25.0	25.2	23
24	22.6	22.8	22.9	23.1	23.2	23.3	23.4	23.6	23.7	23.8	23.9	24.1	24.2	24.3	24.5	24.6	24.7	24.9	24
25	22.3	22.5	22.7	22.8	22.9	23.0	23.2	23.3	23.4	23.5	23.6	23.8	23.9	24.0	24.2	24.3	24.4	24.6	25
26	22.0	22.2	22.3	22.5	22.6	22.7	22.8	22.9	23.1	23.2	23.3	23.5	23.6	23.7	23.8	23.9	24.1	24.2	26
27	21.7	21.9	22.0	22.1	22.3	22.4	22.5	22.6	22.7	22.9	23.0	23.1	23.2	23.4	23.5	23.6	23.7	23.9	27
28	21.3	21.5	21.6	21.8	21.9	22.0	22.1	22.2	22.4	22.5	22.6	22.7	22.9	23.0	23.1	23.2	23.3	23.5	28
29	21.0	21.1	21.3	21.4	21.5	21.6	21.7	21.8	22.0	22.1	22.2	22.3	22.5	22.6	22.7	22.8	22.9	23.1	29
30	20.6	20.7	20.9	21.0	21.1	21.2	21.3	21.4	21.6	21.7	21.8	21.9	22.1	22.2	22.3	22.4	22.5	22.7	30
31	20.2	20.3	20.5	20.6	20.7	20.8	20.9	21.0	21.2	21.3	21.4	21.5	21.6	21.7	21.9	22.0	22.1	22.2	31
32	19.7	19.9	20.0	20.1	20.3	20.4	20.5	20.6	20.7	20.8	20.9	21.1	21.2	21.3	21.4	21.5	21.6	21.8	32
33	19.3	19.5	19.6	19.7	19.8	19.9	20.0	20.1	20.3	20.4	20.5	20.6	20.7	20.8	20.9	21.0	21.2	21.3	33
34	18.9	19.0	19.1	19.2	19.3	19.4	19.6	19.7	19.8	19.9	20.0	20.1	20.2	20.3	20.5	20.6	20.7	20.8	34
35	18.4	18.5	18.6	18.7	18.8	18.9	19.0	19.1	19.3	19.4	19.5	19.6	19.7	19.8	19.9	20.0	20.1	20.3	35
36	17.9	18.0	18.1	18.2	18.3	18.4	18.5	18.6	18.8	18.9	19.0	19.1	19.2	19.3	19.4	19.5	19.6	19.7	36
37	17.3	17.5	17.6	17.7	17.8	17.9	18.0	18.1	18.2	18.3	18.4	18.6	18.7	18.8	18.9	19.0	19.1	19.2	37
38	16.8	17.0	17.1	17.2	17.3	17.4	17.5	17.6	17.7	17.8	17.9	18.0	18.1	18.2	18.3	18.4	18.5	18.6	38
39	16.3	16.4	16.5	16.6	16.7	16.8	16.9	17.0	17.1	17.2	17.3	17.4	17.6	17.7	17.8	17.9	18.0	18.1	39
40	15.8	15.9	16.0	16.1	16.2	16.3	16.4	16.5	16.6	16.7	16.8	16.9	17.0	17.1	17.2	17.3	17.4	17.5	40
41	15.2	15.3	15.4	15.5	15.6	15.7	15.8	15.9	16.0	16.1	16.2	16.3	16.4	16.5	16.6	16.6	16.7	16.8	41
42	14.6	14.7	14.8	14.9	15.0	15.1	15.2	15.3	15.4	15.5	15.5	15.6	15.7	15.8	15.9	16.0	16.1	16.2	42
43	14.0	14.1	14.2	14.3	14.4	14.5	14.6	14.7	14.8	14.9	14.9	15.0	15.1	15.2	15.3	15.4	15.5	15.6	43
44	13.4	13.5	13.6	13.7	13.8	13.8	13.9	14.0	14.1	14.2	14.3	14.4	14.5	14.6	14.7	14.7	14.8	14.9	44
45	12.8	12.9	13.0	13.0	13.1	13.2	13.3	13.4	13.5	13.6	13.6	13.7	13.8	13.9	14.0	14.1	14.2	14.3	45
46	12.1	12.2	12.3	12.4	12.5	12.6	12.7	12.7	12.8	12.9	13.0	13.1	13.2	13.2	13.3	13.4	13.5	13.6	46
	54′	.2	.4	.6	.8	55′	.2	.4	.6	.8	56′	.2	.4	.6	.8	57′	.2	.4	

For HEIGHT of EYE, always ADDITIVE to ALTITUDE

H.E. (feet)	10	12	14	16	18	20	22	24	26	28	30	32	34	36
Correction	6.7′	6.4′	6.1′	5.9′	5.6′	5.4′	5.2′	5.0′	4.8′	4.6′	4.4′	4.3′	4.1′	3.9′

Table 9   B

Correction to be applied to Obs. Alt.   to obtain True Alt.   **ADDITIVE SUBTRACTIVE**

HORIZONTAL PARALLAX

	54′	.2	.4	.6	.8	55′	.2	.4	.6	.8	56′	.2	.4	.6	.8	57′	.2	.4	
46	12.1	12.2	12.3	12.4	12.5	12.6	12.7	12.7	12.8	12.9	13.0	13.1	13.2	13.2	13.3	13.4	13.5	13.6	46
47	11.5	11.6	11.7	11.8	11.8	11.9	12.0	12.1	12.2	12.3	12.3	12.4	12.5	12.6	12.7	12.7	12.8	12.9	47
48	10.8	10.9	11.0	11.1	11.2	11.2	11.3	11.4	11.5	11.6	11.6	11.7	11.8	11.9	12.0	12.0	12.1	12.2	48
49	10.1	10.2	10.3	10.4	10.5	10.5	10.6	10.7	10.8	10.9	10.9	11.0	11.1	11.2	11.2	11.3	11.4	11.5	49
50	9.5	9.6	9.6	9.7	9.8	9.8	9.9	10.0	10.1	10.2	10.2	10.3	10.4	10.5	10.5	10.6	10.7	10.8	50
51	8.7	8.8	8.9	9.0	9.1	9.1	9.2	9.3	9.4	9.4	9.5	9.6	9.6	9.7	9.8	9.8	9.9	10.0	51
52	8.0	8.1	8.2	8.3	8.4	8.4	8.5	8.5	8.6	8.7	8.7	8.8	8.9	9.0	9.0	9.1	9.2	9.2	52
53	7.3	7.4	7.5	7.5	7.6	7.7	7.8	7.8	7.9	8.0	8.0	8.1	8.1	8.2	8.3	8.3	8.4	8.5	53
54	6.6	6.7	6.8	6.8	6.9	6.9	7.0	7.1	7.1	7.2	7.2	7.3	7.4	7.5	7.5	7.6	7.7	7.7	54
55	5.8	5.9	6.0	6.1	6.1	6.2	6.3	6.3	6.4	6.4	6.5	6.6	6.6	6.7	6.7	6.8	6.9	6.9	55
56	5.1	5.2	5.3	5.3	5.4	5.4	5.5	5.5	5.6	5.7	5.7	5.8	5.8	5.9	5.9	6.0	6.1	6.1	56
57	4.3	4.4	4.5	4.5	4.6	4.6	4.7	4.8	4.8	4.9	4.9	5.0	5.0	5.1	5.1	5.2	5.3	5.3	57
58	3.6	3.7	3.7	3.8	3.8	3.9	3.9	4.0	4.0	4.1	4.1	4.2	4.2	4.3	4.3	4.4	4.4	4.5	58
59	2.8	2.9	2.9	3.0	3.0	3.1	3.1	3.2	3.2	3.3	3.3	3.4	3.4	3.5	3.5	3.6	3.6	3.7	59
60	2.0	2.1	2.2	2.2	2.2	2.3	2.3	2.4	2.4	2.5	2.5	2.6	2.6	2.7	2.7	2.7	2.8	2.8	60
61	1.2	1.3	1.3	1.4	1.4	1.4	1.5	1.5	1.6	1.6	1.7	1.7	1.8	1.8	1.9	1.9	1.9	2.0	61
62	0.4	0.5	0.5	0.6	0.6	0.6	0.7	0.7	0.8	0.8	0.8	0.9	0.9	1.0	1.0	1.0	1.1	1.1	62
63	0.4	0.3	0.3	0.3	0.2	0.2	0.1	0.1	0.1	0.0	0.0	0.0	0.1	0.1	0.2	0.2	0.2	0.3	63
64	1.2	1.2	1.1	1.1	1.0	1.0	1.0	1.0	0.9	0.9	0.9	0.8	0.8	0.7	0.7	0.7	0.7	0.6	64
65	2.1	2.0	1.9	1.9	1.9	1.9	1.8	1.8	1.8	1.7	1.7	1.7	1.6	1.6	1.6	1.6	1.5	1.5	65
66	2.9	2.8	2.8	2.8	2.7	2.7	2.7	2.7	2.6	2.6	2.6	2.5	2.5	2.5	2.5	2.5	2.4	2.4	66
67	3.7	3.7	3.6	3.6	3.6	3.6	3.6	3.5	3.5	3.5	3.5	3.4	3.4	3.4	3.4	3.4	3.3	3.3	67
68	4.6	4.5	4.5	4.5	4.5	4.5	4.4	4.4	4.4	4.3	4.3	4.3	4.3	4.3	4.2	4.2	4.2	4.2	68
69	5.4	5.4	5.4	5.3	5.3	5.3	5.3	5.3	5.2	5.2	5.2	5.2	5.2	5.2	5.2	5.2	5.1	5.1	69
70	6.3	6.2	6.2	6.2	6.2	6.2	6.2	6.2	6.1	6.1	6.1	6.1	6.1	6.1	6.1	6.0	6.0	6.0	70
71	7.1	7.1	7.1	7.1	7.1	7.1	7.1	7.0	7.0	7.0	7.0	7.0	7.0	7.0	7.0	7.0	6.9	6.9	71
72	8.0	8.0	8.0	8.0	8.0	8.0	7.9	7.9	7.9	7.9	7.9	7.9	7.9	7.9	7.9	7.9	7.9	7.9	72
73	8.9	8.9	8.9	8.9	8.9	8.9	8.9	8.9	8.9	8.9	8.9	8.8	8.8	8.8	8.8	8.8	8.8	8.8	73
74	9.8	9.8	9.8	9.8	9.8	9.8	9.8	9.8	9.8	9.8	9.8	9.8	9.8	9.8	9.8	9.8	9.8	9.8	74
75	10.7	10.7	10.7	10.7	10.7	10.7	10.7	10.7	10.7	10.7	10.7	10.7	10.7	10.7	10.7	10.7	10.7	10.7	75
76	11.6	11.6	11.6	11.6	11.6	11.6	11.6	11.6	11.6	11.6	11.6	11.6	11.6	11.6	11.6	11.6	11.6	11.6	76
77	12.5	12.5	12.5	12.5	12.5	12.5	12.5	12.5	12.5	12.5	12.5	12.5	12.5	12.6	12.6	12.6	12.6	12.6	77
78	13.4	13.4	13.4	13.4	13.4	13.4	13.4	13.4	13.5	13.5	13.5	13.5	13.5	13.5	13.5	13.6	13.6	13.6	78
79	14.3	14.3	14.3	14.3	14.3	14.3	14.3	14.4	14.4	14.4	14.4	14.4	14.4	14.5	14.5	14.5	14.5	14.5	79
80	15.2	15.2	15.2	15.2	15.2	15.3	15.3	15.3	15.3	15.3	15.4	15.4	15.4	15.4	15.4	15.5	15.5	15.5	80
81	16.1	16.1	16.1	16.1	16.2	16.2	16.2	16.2	16.3	16.3	16.3	16.3	16.3	16.4	16.4	16.4	16.4	16.4	81
82	17.0	17.0	17.0	17.1	17.1	17.1	17.1	17.2	17.2	17.2	17.2	17.3	17.3	17.3	17.3	17.4	17.4	17.4	82
83	17.9	17.9	18.0	18.0	18.0	18.1	18.1	18.1	18.1	18.2	18.2	18.2	18.3	18.3	18.3	18.4	18.4	18.4	83
84	18.8	18.9	18.9	18.9	18.9	19.0	19.0	19.1	19.1	19.1	19.2	19.2	19.2	19.2	19.3	19.3	19.3	19.4	84
85	19.8	19.8	19.8	19.8	19.9	19.9	19.9	20.0	20.0	20.1	20.1	20.1	20.2	20.2	20.2	20.3	20.3	20.4	85
86	20.7	20.7	20.7	20.8	20.8	20.9	20.9	20.9	21.0	21.0	21.0	21.1	21.1	21.2	21.2	21.3	21.3	21.3	86
87	21.6	21.6	21.7	21.7	21.7	21.8	21.8	21.9	21.9	22.0	22.0	22.0	22.1	22.1	22.2	22.2	22.3	22.3	87
88	22.5	22.5	22.6	22.6	22.7	22.7	22.8	22.8	22.9	22.9	23.0	23.0	23.1	23.1	23.2	23.2	23.2	23.3	88
89	23.4	23.5	23.5	23.6	23.6	23.7	23.7	23.8	23.8	23.9	23.9	24.0	24.0	24.1	24.1	24.2	24.2	24.3	89
	54′	.2	.4	.6	.8	55′	.2	.4	.6	.8	56′	.2	.4	.6	.8	57′	.2	.4	

For HEIGHT of EYE, always ADDITIVE to ALTITUDE

38	40	42	44	46	48	50	52	54	56	58	60	65	70	75	80	85	90
′	′	′	′	′	′	′	′	′	′	′	′	′	′	′	′	′	′
3.8	3.6	3.5	3.3	3.2	3.0	2.9	2.7	2.6	2.5	2.3	2.2	1.9	1.6	1.3	1.0	.8	.5

Table 9

Table 9   C

☽ Correction to be applied to Obs. Alt.   to obtain True Alt.   **ADDITIVE**

HORIZONTAL PARALLAX

☽	57'.6	.8	58'	.2	.4	.6	.8	59'	.2	.4	.6	.8	60'	.2	.4	.6	.8	61'	☽
6°	23.2	23.4	23.5	23.7	23.8	23.9	24.1	24.2	24.4	24.5	24.7	24.8	25.0	25.1	25.3	25.4	25.5	25.7	6°
7	24.2	24.4	24.5	24.6	24.8	24.9	25.1	25.2	25.4	25.5	25.7	25.8	26.0	26.1	26.3	26.4	26.6	26.7	7
8	24.9	25.1	25.2	25.3	25.5	25.6	25.8	25.9	26.1	26.2	26.4	26.5	26.6	26.8	26.9	27.1	27.2	27.3	8
9	25.5	25.6	25.7	25.9	26.0	26.2	26.3	26.4	26.6	26.7	26.9	27.0	27.1	27.3	27.5	27.6	27.8	27.9	9
10	25.9	26.0	26.1	26.3	26.4	26.6	26.7	26.8	27.0	27.1	27.3	27.4	27.5	27.7	27.9	28.0	28.2	28.3	10
11	26.2	26.3	26.4	26.6	26.7	26.9	27.0	27.1	27.3	27.4	27.6	27.7	27.8	28.0	28.2	28.3	28.4	28.5	11
12	26.4	26.5	26.6	26.8	26.9	27.1	27.2	27.3	27.5	27.6	27.8	27.9	28.0	28.2	28.3	28.5	28.6	28.7	12
13	26.5	26.7	26.8	26.9	27.1	27.2	27.3	27.4	27.6	27.8	27.9	28.0	28.1	28.3	28.5	28.6	28.8	28.9	13
14	26.6	26.7	26.8	27.0	27.1	27.3	27.4	27.5	27.7	27.8	28.0	28.1	28.2	28.4	28.5	28.7	28.8	28.9	14
15	26.6	26.7	26.8	27.0	27.1	27.3	27.4	27.5	27.7	27.8	28.0	28.1	28.2	28.4	28.5	28.7	28.8	28.9	15
16	26.5	26.7	26.8	26.9	27.1	27.2	27.4	27.5	27.6	27.8	27.9	28.1	28.2	28.3	28.5	28.6	28.8	28.9	16
17	26.5	26.6	26.7	26.8	27.0	27.1	27.3	27.4	27.6	27.7	27.8	28.0	28.1	28.2	28.4	28.5	28.7	28.8	17
18	26.4	26.5	26.6	26.7	26.9	27.0	27.2	27.3	27.4	27.6	27.7	27.8	27.9	28.1	28.3	28.4	28.5	28.6	18
19	26.2	26.3	26.4	26.6	26.7	26.9	27.0	27.1	27.3	27.4	27.5	27.7	27.8	27.9	28.1	28.2	28.3	28.4	19
20	26.0	26.2	26.3	26.4	26.5	26.7	26.8	26.9	27.1	27.2	27.3	27.5	27.6	27.7	27.9	28.0	28.2	28.2	20
21	25.8	25.9	26.0	26.2	26.3	26.5	26.6	26.7	26.9	27.0	27.1	27.3	27.4	27.5	27.7	27.8	27.9	28.0	21
22	25.6	25.7	25.8	26.0	26.1	26.2	26.4	26.5	26.6	26.7	26.9	27.0	27.1	27.3	27.4	27.5	27.7	27.8	22
23	25.3	25.4	25.5	25.7	25.8	25.9	26.1	26.2	26.3	26.5	26.6	26.7	26.8	27.0	27.1	27.3	27.4	27.5	23
24	25.0	25.1	25.2	25.4	25.5	25.6	25.8	25.9	26.0	26.1	26.3	26.4	26.5	26.7	26.8	26.9	27.1	27.2	24
25	24.7	24.8	24.9	25.0	25.2	25.3	25.4	25.5	25.7	25.8	26.0	26.1	26.2	26.3	26.4	26.6	26.7	26.8	25
26	24.3	24.5	24.6	24.7	24.8	25.0	25.1	25.2	25.3	25.5	25.6	25.7	25.8	26.0	26.1	26.2	26.3	26.4	26
27	24.0	24.1	24.2	24.3	24.5	24.6	24.7	24.8	25.0	25.1	25.2	25.3	25.4	25.6	25.7	25.8	26.0	26.1	27
28	23.6	23.7	23.8	24.0	24.1	24.2	24.3	24.4	24.6	24.7	24.8	24.9	25.0	25.2	25.3	25.4	25.6	25.7	28
29	23.2	23.3	23.4	23.5	23.7	23.8	23.9	24.0	24.2	24.3	24.4	24.5	24.6	24.8	24.9	25.0	25.1	25.2	29
30	22.8	22.9	23.0	23.1	23.2	23.4	23.5	23.6	23.7	23.8	24.0	24.1	24.2	24.3	24.4	24.6	24.7	24.8	30
31	22.3	22.4	22.5	22.7	22.8	22.9	23.0	23.1	23.3	23.4	23.5	23.6	23.7	23.9	24.0	24.1	24.2	24.3	31
32	21.9	22.0	22.1	22.2	22.3	22.4	22.6	22.7	22.8	22.9	23.0	23.1	23.2	23.4	23.5	23.6	23.7	23.8	32
33	21.4	21.5	21.6	21.7	21.8	22.0	22.1	22.2	22.3	22.4	22.5	22.6	22.7	22.9	23.0	23.1	23.2	23.3	33
34	20.9	21.0	21.1	21.2	21.3	21.5	21.6	21.7	21.8	21.9	22.0	22.1	22.2	22.3	22.5	22.6	22.7	22.8	34
35	20.4	20.5	20.6	20.7	20.8	20.9	21.0	21.1	21.3	21.4	21.5	21.6	21.7	21.8	21.9	22.0	22.1	22.2	35
36	19.9	20.0	20.1	20.2	20.3	20.4	20.5	20.6	20.7	20.8	20.9	21.0	21.1	21.2	21.4	21.5	21.6	21.7	36
37	19.3	19.4	19.5	19.6	19.7	19.8	19.9	20.0	20.1	20.2	20.4	20.5	20.6	20.7	20.8	20.9	21.0	21.1	37
38	18.7	18.8	18.9	19.0	19.1	19.2	19.4	19.5	19.6	19.7	19.8	19.9	20.0	20.1	20.2	20.3	20.4	20.5	38
39	18.2	18.3	18.4	18.5	18.6	18.7	18.8	18.9	19.0	19.1	19.2	19.3	19.4	19.5	19.6	19.7	19.8	19.9	39
40	17.6	17.7	17.8	17.9	18.0	18.1	18.2	18.3	18.4	18.5	18.6	18.7	18.8	18.9	19.0	19.1	19.2	19.3	40
41	16.9	17.0	17.1	17.2	17.3	17.4	17.5	17.6	17.7	17.8	17.9	18.0	18.1	18.2	18.3	18.4	18.5	18.6	41
42	16.3	16.4	16.5	16.6	16.7	16.8	16.9	17.0	17.1	17.2	17.3	17.3	17.4	17.5	17.6	17.7	17.8	17.9	42
43	15.7	15.8	15.9	16.0	16.0	16.1	16.2	16.3	16.4	16.5	16.6	16.7	16.8	16.9	17.0	17.1	17.2	17.2	43
44	15.0	15.1	15.2	15.3	15.4	15.5	15.6	15.6	15.7	15.8	15.9	16.0	16.1	16.2	16.3	16.4	16.5	16.5	44
45	14.4	14.4	14.5	14.6	14.7	14.8	14.9	15.0	15.1	15.1	15.2	15.3	15.4	15.5	15.6	15.7	15.8	15.8	45
46	13.7	13.8	13.8	13.9	14.0	14.1	14.2	14.3	14.4	14.4	14.5	14.6	14.7	14.8	14.9	14.9	15.0	15.1	46
	57'.6	.8	58'	.2	.4	.6	.8	59'	.2	.4	.6	.8	60'	.2	.4	.6	.8	61'	

For HEIGHT of EYE, ALWAYS ADDITIVE to ALTITUDE

H.E. (feet)	10	12	14	16	18	20	22	24	26	28	30	32	34	36
Correction	6.7	6.4	6.1	5.9	5.6	5.4	5.2	5.0	4.8	4.6	4.4	4.3	4.1	3.9

Table 9

ADDITIVE
__SUBTRACTIVE__

Correction to be applied to Obs. Alt. ☽ to obtain True Alt.

HORIZONTAL PARALLAX

☽	57'.6	.8	58'	.2	.4	.6	.8	59'	.2	.4	.6	.8	60'	.2	.4	.6	.8	61'	☽
46	13.7	13.8	13.8	13.9	14.0	14.1	14.2	14.3	14.4	14.4	14.5	14.6	14.7	14.8	14.9	14.9	15.0	15.1	46
47	13.0	13.1	13.1	13.2	13.3	13.4	13.5	13.5	13.6	13.7	13.8	13.9	14.0	14.1	14.1	14.2	14.3	14.3	47
48	12.3	12.4	12.4	12.5	12.6	12.7	12.8	12.8	12.9	13.0	13.1	13.2	13.2	13.3	13.4	13.5	13.6	13.6	48
49	11.6	11.6	11.7	11.8	11.9	11.9	12.0	12.1	12.2	12.2	12.3	12.4	12.5	12.6	12.6	12.7	12.8	12.8	49
50	10.8	10.9	10.9	11.0	11.1	11.2	11.3	11.3	11.4	11.5	11.6	11.7	11.7	11.8	11.9	11.9	12.0	12.0	50
51	10.1	10.1	10.2	10.3	10.3	10.4	10.5	10.6	10.6	10.7	10.8	10.9	10.9	11.0	11.1	11.1	11.2	11.3	51
52	9.3	9.4	9.4	9.5	9.6	9.7	9.7	9.8	9.9	9.9	10.0	10.1	10.1	10.2	10.3	10.4	10.4	10.5	52
53	8.6	8.6	8.7	8.7	8.8	8.9	9.0	9.0	9.1	9.1	9.2	9.3	9.3	9.4	9.5	9.5	9.6	9.6	53
54	7.8	7.8	7.9	8.0	8.0	8.1	8.2	8.2	8.3	8.3	8.4	8.5	8.5	8.6	8.7	8.7	8.8	8.8	54
55	7.0	7.0	7.1	7.1	7.2	7.3	7.3	7.4	7.5	7.5	7.6	7.6	7.7	7.8	7.8	7.9	8.0	8.0	55
56	6.2	6.2	6.3	6.4	6.4	6.5	6.5	6.6	6.7	6.7	6.8	6.8	6.9	6.9	7.0	7.0	7.1	7.1	56
57	5.4	5.4	5.5	5.5	5.6	5.6	5.7	5.7	5.8	5.9	5.9	6.0	6.0	6.1	6.1	6.2	6.2	6.3	57
58	4.6	4.6	4.7	4.7	4.8	4.8	4.9	4.9	5.0	5.0	5.1	5.1	5.2	5.2	5.3	5.3	5.4	5.4	58
59	3.7	3.8	3.8	3.9	3.9	4.0	4.0	4.0	4.1	4.1	4.2	4.3	4.3	4.4	4.4	4.5	4.5	4.5	59
60	2.9	2.9	3.0	3.0	3.1	3.1	3.2	3.2	3.2	3.3	3.3	3.4	3.4	3.5	3.5	3.6	3.6	3.6	60
61	2.0	2.1	2.1	2.2	2.2	2.2	2.3	2.3	2.4	2.4	2.5	2.5	2.5	2.6	2.6	2.7	2.7	2.7	61
62	1.2	1.2	1.2	1.3	1.3	1.4	1.4	1.4	1.5	1.5	1.6	1.6	1.6	1.7	1.7	1.8	1.8	1.8	62
63	0.3	0.3	0.3	0.4	0.4	0.5	0.5	0.5	0.6	0.6	0.7	0.7	0.7	0.8	0.8	0.9	0.9	0.9	63
64	0.6	0.5	0.5	0.5	0.4	0.4	0.4	0.3	0.3	0.3	0.2	0.2	0.2	0.1	0.1	0.1	0.0	0.0	64
65	1.5	1.4	1.4	1.4	1.3	1.3	1.3	1.3	1.2	1.2	1.2	1.1	1.1	1.1	1.0	1.0	1.0	1.0	65
66	2.4	2.3	2.3	2.3	2.2	2.2	2.2	2.2	2.1	2.1	2.1	2.0	2.0	2.0	2.0	1.9	1.9	1.9	66
67	3.3	3.2	3.2	3.2	3.2	3.1	3.1	3.1	3.1	3.1	3.0	3.0	3.0	3.0	2.9	2.9	2.9	2.9	67
68	4.2	4.1	4.1	4.1	4.1	4.1	4.0	4.0	4.0	4.0	3.9	3.9	3.9	3.9	3.9	3.8	3.8	3.8	68
69	5.1	5.1	5.1	5.0	5.0	5.0	5.0	5.0	4.9	4.9	4.9	4.9	4.9	4.8	4.8	4.8	4.8	4.8	69
70	6.0	6.0	6.0	6.0	5.9	5.9	5.9	5.9	5.9	5.9	5.9	5.8	5.8	5.8	5.8	5.8	5.8	5.8	70
71	6.9	6.9	6.9	6.9	6.9	6.9	6.9	6.9	6.8	6.8	6.8	6.8	6.8	6.8	6.8	6.8	6.7	6.7	71
72	7.9	7.8	7.8	7.8	7.8	7.8	7.8	7.8	7.8	7.8	7.8	7.8	7.8	7.8	7.8	7.7	7.7	7.7	72
73	8.8	8.8	8.8	8.8	8.8	8.8	8.8	8.8	8.8	8.8	8.8	8.8	8.7	8.7	8.7	8.7	8.7	8.7	73
74	9.7	9.7	9.7	9.7	9.7	9.7	9.7	9.7	9.7	9.7	9.7	9.7	9.7	9.7	9.7	9.7	9.7	9.7	74
75	10.7	10.7	10.7	10.7	10.7	10.7	10.7	10.7	10.7	10.7	10.7	10.7	10.7	10.7	10.7	10.7	10.7	10.7	75
76	11.6	11.7	11.7	11.7	11.7	11.7	11.7	11.7	11.7	11.7	11.7	11.7	11.7	11.7	11.7	11.7	11.7	11.7	76
77	12.6	12.6	12.6	12.6	12.6	12.6	12.6	12.7	12.7	12.7	12.7	12.7	12.7	12.7	12.7	12.7	12.8	12.0	77
78	13.6	13.6	13.6	13.6	13.6	13.6	13.6	13.7	13.7	13.7	13.7	13.7	13.7	13.7	13.7	13.8	13.8	13.8	78
79	14.5	14.6	14.6	14.6	14.6	14.6	14.6	14.6	14.7	14.7	14.7	14.7	14.7	14.7	14.8	14.8	14.8	14.8	79
80	15.5	15.5	15.6	15.6	15.6	15.6	15.6	15.7	15.7	15.7	15.7	15.7	15.8	15.8	15.8	15.8	15.8	15.9	80
81	16.5	16.5	16.5	16.5	16.6	16.6	16.6	16.7	16.7	16.7	16.7	16.7	16.8	16.8	16.8	16.8	16.8	16.9	81
82	17.4	17.5	17.5	17.5	17.5	17.6	17.6	17.6	17.7	17.7	17.7	17.7	17.7	17.8	17.8	17.8	17.9	17.9	82
83	18.4	18.5	18.5	18.5	18.5	18.6	18.6	18.6	18.7	18.7	18.7	18.7	18.8	18.8	18.8	18.9	18.9	19.0	83
84	19.4	19.4	19.5	19.5	19.5	19.6	19.6	19.6	19.7	19.7	19.7	19.8	19.8	19.9	19.9	19.9	19.9	20.0	84
85	20.4	20.4	20.5	20.5	20.5	20.6	20.6	20.7	20.7	20.7	20.8	20.8	20.8	20.9	20.9	20.9	21.0	21.0	85
86	21.4	21.4	21.5	21.5	21.5	21.6	21.6	21.7	21.7	21.7	21.8	21.8	21.9	21.9	21.9	22.0	22.0	22.1	86
87	22.4	22.4	22.4	22.5	22.5	22.6	22.6	22.7	22.7	22.8	22.8	22.8	22.9	22.9	23.0	23.0	23.1	23.1	87
88	23.3	23.4	23.4	23.5	23.5	23.6	23.6	23.7	23.7	23.8	23.8	23.9	23.9	23.9	24.0	24.0	24.1	24.1	88
89	24.3	24.4	24.4	24.5	24.5	24.6	24.6	24.7	24.7	24.8	24.8	24.9	24.9	25.0	25.0	25.1	25.1	25.2	89
	57'.6	.8	58'	.2	.4	.6	.8	59'	.2	.4	.6	.8	60'	.2	.4	.6	.8	61'	

For HEIGHT of EYE, ALWAYS ADDITIVE to ALTITUDE

38	40	42	44		46	48	50	52		54	56	58	60		65	70	75		80	85	90
'	'	'	'		'	'	'	'		'	'	'	'		'	'	'		'	'	'
3.8	3.6	3.5	3.3		3.2	3.0	2.9	2.7		2.6	2.5	2.3	2.2		1.9	1.6	1.3		1.0	.8	.5

Table 9   A1

Correction to be applied to Obs. Alt. [moon symbol] to obtain True Alt.   **ADDITIVE**

HORIZONTAL PARALLAX

☾	54′	.2	.4	.6	.8	55′	.2	.4	.6	.8	56′	.2	.4	.6	.8	57′	.2	.4	☾
6°	50.1	50.3	50.6	50.8	51.1	51.3	51.6	51.8	52.1	52.3	52.6	52.9	53.1	53.4	53.6	53.9	54.1	54.4	6°
7	51.1	51.3	51.6	51.8	52.1	52.3	52.6	52.8	53.1	53.3	53.6	53.8	54.1	54.3	54.6	54.9	55.1	55.4	7
8	51.7	52.0	52.3	52.5	52.8	53.0	53.3	53.5	53.8	54.0	54.3	54.5	54.8	55.0	55.3	55.5	55.8	56.1	8
9	52.3	52.6	52.8	53.1	53.3	53.6	53.8	54.1	54.3	54.6	54.8	55.1	55.4	55.6	55.9	56.1	56.4	56.6	9
10	52.7	53.0	53.2	53.5	53.8	54.0	54.2	54.5	54.8	55.0	55.2	55.5	55.8	56.0	56.3	56.5	56.8	57.0	10
11	53.0	53.3	53.5	53.8	54.0	54.3	54.6	54.8	55.1	55.3	55.5	55.8	56.1	56.3	56.6	56.8	57.1	57.3	11
12	53.2	53.5	53.8	54.0	54.3	54.5	54.8	55.0	55.3	55.5	55.8	56.0	56.3	56.5	56.8	57.0	57.3	57.5	12
13	53.4	53.7	53.9	54.2	54.4	54.7	54.9	55.2	55.4	55.6	55.9	56.1	56.4	56.6	56.9	57.1	57.4	57.6	13
14	53.5	53.7	54.0	54.2	54.5	54.8	55.0	55.2	55.5	55.7	56.0	56.2	56.5	56.7	57.0	57.2	57.5	57.7	14
15	53.5	53.8	54.0	54.3	54.5	54.8	55.0	55.3	55.5	55.7	56.0	56.2	56.5	56.7	57.0	57.2	57.5	57.7	15
16	53.5	53.7	54.0	54.2	54.5	54.7	55.0	55.2	55.5	55.7	56.0	56.2	56.5	56.7	57.0	57.2	57.4	57.7	16
17	53.4	53.7	53.9	54.2	54.4	54.7	54.9	55.2	55.4	55.6	55.9	56.1	56.3	56.6	56.9	57.1	57.4	57.6	17
18	53.3	53.6	53.8	54.1	54.3	54.6	54.8	55.1	55.3	55.5	55.8	56.0	56.3	56.5	56.8	57.0	57.3	57.5	18
19	53.2	53.5	53.7	53.9	54.2	54.5	54.7	54.9	55.2	55.4	55.7	55.9	56.1	56.4	56.6	56.9	57.1	57.3	19
20	53.0	53.3	53.5	53.8	54.0	54.3	54.5	54.7	55.0	55.2	55.5	55.7	55.9	56.2	56.4	56.7	56.9	57.2	20
21	52.8	53.1	53.3	53.6	53.8	54.1	54.3	54.5	54.8	55.0	55.3	55.5	55.7	56.0	56.2	56.5	56.7	56.9	21
22	52.6	52.9	53.1	53.4	53.6	53.8	54.1	54.3	54.6	54.8	55.1	55.3	55.5	55.8	56.0	56.2	56.5	56.7	22
23	52.4	52.6	52.9	53.1	53.4	53.6	53.8	54.1	54.3	54.5	54.8	55.0	55.3	55.5	55.7	55.9	56.2	56.4	23
24	52.1	52.4	52.6	52.8	53.1	53.3	53.5	53.8	54.0	54.2	54.5	54.7	55.0	55.2	55.4	55.6	55.9	56.1	24
25	51.8	52.1	52.3	52.5	52.8	53.0	53.2	53.5	53.7	53.9	54.2	54.4	54.7	54.9	55.1	55.3	55.6	55.8	25
26	51.5	51.8	52.0	52.2	52.4	52.6	52.9	53.2	53.4	53.6	53.8	54.1	54.3	54.5	54.8	55.0	55.3	55.5	26
27	51.2	51.4	51.7	51.9	52.1	52.3	52.6	52.8	53.0	53.3	53.5	53.7	54.0	54.2	54.5	54.7	54.9	55.1	27
28	50.8	51.1	51.3	51.5	51.8	52.0	52.2	52.4	52.7	52.9	53.0	53.4	53.6	53.8	54.1	54.3	54.5	54.8	28
29	50.4	50.7	50.9	51.2	51.4	51.6	51.8	52.0	52.3	52.5	52.7	53.0	53.2	53.4	53.7	53.9	54.1	54.4	29
30	50.0	50.3	50.5	50.7	51.0	51.2	51.4	51.6	51.9	52.1	52.2	52.6	52.8	53.0	53.3	53.4	53.7	53.9	30
31	49.6	49.9	50.1	50.3	50.5	50.7	51.0	51.2	51.5	51.7	51.8	52.1	52.4	52.6	52.8	53.0	53.3	53.5	31
32	49.2	49.5	49.7	49.9	50.1	50.3	50.6	50.8	51.0	51.2	51.5	51.7	51.9	52.1	52.4	52.6	52.8	53.0	32
33	48.8	49.0	49.2	49.5	49.7	49.9	50.1	50.3	50.6	50.8	51.0	51.2	51.5	51.7	51.9	52.1	52.4	52.6	33
34	48.3	48.5	48.7	49.0	49.2	49.4	49.6	49.8	50.1	50.3	50.5	50.7	51.0	51.2	51.4	51.6	51.8	52.0	34
35	47.8	48.0	48.3	48.5	48.7	48.9	49.1	49.4	49.6	49.8	50.0	50.2	50.5	50.7	50.9	51.1	51.3	51.5	35
36	47.3	47.6	47.8	48.0	48.2	48.4	48.6	48.8	49.1	49.3	49.5	49.7	49.9	50.2	50.4	50.6	50.8	51.0	36
37	46.8	47.0	47.3	47.5	47.7	48.0	48.2	48.4	48.6	48.8	49.1	49.3	49.4	49.6	49.8	50.0	50.3	50.5	37
38	46.3	46.5	46.7	46.9	47.1	47.3	47.6	47.8	48.0	48.2	48.4	48.6	48.9	49.1	49.3	49.5	49.7	49.9	38
39	45.8	46.0	46.2	46.4	46.6	46.7	47.0	47.2	47.4	47.6	47.8	48.1	48.3	48.5	48.7	48.9	49.1	49.3	39
40	45.2	45.4	45.6	45.8	46.0	46.2	46.4	46.7	46.9	47.1	47.3	47.5	47.7	47.9	48.1	48.3	48.5	48.7	40
41	44.6	44.8	45.0	45.3	45.5	45.6	45.9	46.1	46.3	46.5	46.7	46.9	47.1	47.3	47.5	47.7	47.9	48.1	41
42	44.0	44.3	44.5	44.7	44.9	45.0	45.3	45.5	45.7	45.9	46.2	46.3	46.5	46.7	46.9	47.1	47.3	47.5	42
43	43.4	43.6	43.9	44.1	44.3	44.5	44.7	44.9	45.1	45.2	45.5	45.6	45.9	46.1	46.3	46.4	46.7	46.9	43
44	42.8	43.0	43.2	43.4	43.6	43.8	44.0	44.2	44.4	44.6	44.8	45.0	45.2	45.4	45.6	45.8	46.0	46.2	44
45	42.2	42.4	42.6	42.8	43.0	43.2	43.4	43.6	43.8	44.0	44.1	44.4	44.6	44.8	45.0	45.1	45.4	45.6	45
46	41.6	41.8	42.0	42.2	42.3	42.5	42.7	42.9	43.1	43.3	43.5	43.7	43.9	44.1	44.3	44.5	44.7	44.9	46
	54′	.2	.4	.6	.8	**55′**	.2	.4	.6	.8	**56′**	.2	.4	.6	.8	**57′**	.2	.4	

For HEIGHT of EYE, always ADDITIVE to ALTITUDE

H.E. (feet)	10	12	14	16	18	20	22	24	26	28	30	32	34	36
Correction	6.7	6.4	6.1	5.9	5.6	5.4	5.2	5.0	4.8	4.6	4.4	4.3	4.1	3.9

Table 9   B1

Correction to be applied to Obs. Alt. ☾ to obtain True Alt.   **ADDITIVE**

HORIZONTAL PARALLAX

☾	54′	.2	.4	.6	.8	55′	.2	.4	.6	.8	56′	.2	.4	.6	.8	57′	.2	.4	☾
46	41.6	41.8	42.0	42.2	42.3	42.5	42.7	42.9	43.1	43.3	43.5	43.7	43.9	44.1	44.3	44.5	44.7	44.9	46
47	40.9	41.1	41.3	41.5	41.7	41.8	42.1	42.3	42.5	42.6	42.8	43.0	43.2	43.4	43.6	43.8	44.0	44.2	47
48	40.3	40.5	40.7	40.8	41.0	41.2	41.4	41.6	41.8	42.0	42.2	42.3	42.5	42.7	42.9	43.1	43.3	43.5	48
49	39.6	39.8	40.0	40.2	40.4	40.5	40.7	40.9	41.1	41.3	41.5	41.6	41.8	42.0	42.2	42.3	42.6	42.8	49
50	38.9	39.1	39.3	39.5	39.7	39.8	40.0	40.2	40.4	40.6	40.8	40.9	41.1	41.3	41.5	41.7	41.9	42.0	50
51	38.2	38.4	38.6	38.8	38.9	39.1	39.3	39.5	39.7	39.8	40.0	40.2	40.4	40.6	40.7	40.9	41.1	41.3	51
52	37.5	37.7	37.9	38.0	38.2	38.4	38.6	38.8	38.9	39.1	39.3	39.5	39.6	39.8	40.0	40.2	40.4	40.5	52
53	36.8	37.0	37.1	37.3	37.5	37.6	37.8	38.0	38.2	38.4	38.5	38.7	38.9	39.1	39.3	39.4	39.6	39.8	53
54	36.1	36.3	36.4	36.6	36.8	36.9	37.1	37.3	37.4	37.6	37.8	38.0	38.1	38.3	38.5	38.7	38.8	39.0	54
55	35.3	35.5	35.7	35.8	36.0	36.2	36.3	36.5	36.7	36.8	37.0	37.2	37.4	37.5	37.7	37.9	38.0	38.2	55
56	34.6	34.7	34.9	35.1	35.2	35.4	35.6	35.7	35.9	36.1	36.2	36.4	36.6	36.7	36.9	37.1	37.3	37.4	56
57	33.8	34.0	34.1	34.3	34.5	34.7	34.8	35.0	35.1	35.3	35.5	35.6	35.8	35.9	36.1	36.3	36.4	36.6	57
58	33.1	33.2	33.4	33.5	33.7	33.9	34.0	34.2	34.3	34.5	34.7	34.8	35.0	35.1	35.3	35.5	35.6	35.8	58
59	32.3	32.4	32.6	32.7	32.9	33.1	33.2	33.4	33.5	33.7	33.8	34.0	34.2	34.3	34.5	34.7	34.8	35.0	59
60	31.5	31.6	31.8	32.0	32.1	32.3	32.4	32.6	32.7	32.9	33.0	33.2	33.4	33.5	33.7	33.8	34.0	34.1	60
61	30.7	30.8	31.0	31.1	31.3	31.4	31.6	31.7	31.9	32.0	32.2	32.4	32.5	32.7	32.8	32.9	33.1	33.3	61
62	29.9	30.0	30.2	30.3	30.5	30.6	30.8	30.9	31.1	31.2	31.4	31.5	31.7	31.8	32.0	32.1	32.3	32.4	62
63	29.1	29.2	29.4	29.5	29.7	29.8	29.9	30.1	30.2	30.4	30.5	30.7	30.8	31.0	31.1	31.2	31.4	31.5	63
64	28.3	28.4	28.5	28.7	28.8	29.0	29.1	29.2	29.4	29.5	29.7	29.8	30.0	30.1	30.2	30.4	30.5	30.7	64
65	27.4	27.6	27.7	27.8	28.0	28.1	28.2	28.4	28.5	28.7	28.8	29.0	29.1	29.2	29.4	29.5	29.6	29.8	65
66	26.6	26.7	26.9	27.0	27.1	27.2	27.4	27.5	27.7	27.8	28.0	28.1	28.2	28.4	28.5	28.6	28.8	28.9	66
67	25.7	25.9	26.0	26.1	26.3	26.4	26.5	26.7	26.8	26.9	27.1	27.2	27.4	27.5	27.6	27.7	27.9	28.0	67
68	24.9	25.0	25.1	25.3	25.4	25.6	25.7	25.8	25.9	26.1	26.2	26.3	26.5	26.6	26.7	26.8	27.0	27.1	68
69	24.0	24.2	24.3	24.4	24.5	24.6	24.8	24.9	25.1	25.2	25.3	25.4	25.6	25.7	25.8	25.9	26.1	26.2	69
70	23.2	23.3	23.4	23.5	23.7	23.8	23.9	24.0	24.2	24.3	24.4	24.5	24.7	24.8	24.9	25.0	25.2	25.3	70
71	22.3	22.4	22.5	22.7	22.8	22.9	23.0	23.1	23.3	23.4	23.5	23.6	23.7	23.9	24.0	24.1	24.2	24.3	71
72	21.4	21.5	21.7	21.8	21.9	22.0	22.1	22.3	22.4	22.5	22.6	22.7	22.8	23.0	23.1	23.2	23.3	23.4	72
73	20.5	20.7	20.8	20.9	21.0	21.1	21.2	21.3	21.5	21.6	21.7	21.8	21.9	22.0	22.1	22.2	22.4	22.5	73
74	19.7	19.8	19.9	20.0	20.1	20.2	20.3	20.4	20.5	20.7	20.8	20.9	21.0	21.1	21.2	21.3	21.4	21.5	74
75	18.8	18.9	19.0	19.1	19.2	19.3	19.4	19.5	19.6	19.7	19.8	19.9	20.1	20.2	20.3	20.4	20.5	20.6	75
76	17.9	18.0	18.1	18.2	18.3	18.4	18.5	18.6	18.7	18.8	18.9	19.0	19.1	19.2	19.3	19.4	19.5	19.6	76
77	17.0	17.1	17.2	17.3	17.4	17.5	17.6	17.7	17.8	17.9	18.0	18.1	18.2	18.3	18.4	18.5	18.6	18.7	77
78	16.1	16.2	16.3	16.4	16.5	16.6	16.7	16.8	16.9	17.0	17.0	17.1	17.2	17.3	17.4	17.5	17.6	17.7	78
79	15.2	15.3	15.4	15.5	15.6	15.6	15.7	15.8	15.9	16.0	16.1	16.2	16.3	16.4	16.5	16.6	16.7	16.8	79
80	14.3	14.4	14.5	14.5	14.6	14.7	14.8	14.9	15.0	15.1	15.2	15.3	15.4	15.4	15.5	15.6	15.7	15.8	80
81	13.4	13.5	13.5	13.6	13.7	13.8	13.9	14.0	14.1	14.1	14.2	14.3	14.4	14.5	14.6	14.6	14.7	14.8	81
82	12.5	12.5	12.6	12.7	12.8	12.9	12.9	13.0	13.1	13.2	13.3	13.4	13.4	13.5	13.6	13.7	13.8	13.9	82
83	11.6	11.6	11.7	11.8	11.9	12.0	12.0	12.1	12.2	12.2	12.3	12.4	12.5	12.6	12.6	12.7	12.8	12.9	83
84	10.6	10.7	10.8	10.8	10.9	11.0	11.1	11.2	11.2	11.3	11.4	11.4	11.5	11.6	11.7	11.7	11.8	11.9	84
85	9.7	9.8	9.8	9.9	10.0	10.1	10.1	10.2	10.3	10.3	10.4	10.5	10.6	10.6	10.7	10.7	10.8	10.9	85
86	8.8	8.9	8.9	9.0	9.1	9.1	9.2	9.3	9.3	9.4	9.5	9.5	9.6	9.7	9.7	9.8	9.9	10.0	86
87	7.9	7.9	8.0	8.1	8.1	8.2	8.2	8.3	8.4	8.4	8.5	8.6	8.7	8.7	8.8	8.8	8.9	9.0	87
88	6.9	7.0	7.1	7.1	7.2	7.3	7.3	7.4	7.4	7.5	7.6	7.6	7.7	7.7	7.8	7.9	7.9	8.0	88
89	6.0	6.1	6.1	6.2	6.2	6.3	6.4	6.4	6.5	6.5	6.6	6.7	6.7	6.8	6.8	6.9	7.0	7.0	89
	54′	.2	.4	.6	.8	55′	.2	.4	.6	.8	56′	.2	.4	.6	.8	57′	.2	.4	

For HEIGHT of EYE, always ADDITIVE to ALTITUDE

38	40	42	44	46	48	50	52	54	56	58	60	65	70	75	80	85	90
′	′	′	′	′	′	′	′	′	′	′	′	′	′	′	′	′	′
3.8	3.6	3.5	3.3	3.2	3.0	2.9	2.7	2.6	2.5	2.3	2.2	1.9	1.6	1.3	1.0	.8	.5

Table 9   C1

Correction to be applied to Obs. Alt. to obtain True Alt.   **ADDITIVE**

HORIZONTAL PARALLAX

(	57'.6	.8	58	.2	.4	.6	.8	59'	.2	.4	.6	.8	60'	.2	.4	.6	.8	61'	(
6°	54.6	54.9	55.1	55.4	55.6	55.9	56.1	56.4	56.7	56.9	57.2	57.4	57.7	57.9	58.1	58.4	58.7	58.9	6°
7	55.6	55.9	56.1	56.4	56.6	56.9	57.1	57.4	57.7	57.9	58.2	58.4	58.7	58.9	59.2	59.4	59.7	59.9	7
8	56.3	56.6	56.8	57.1	57.3	57.6	57.8	58.1	58.3	58.6	58.8	59.1	59.3	59.6	59.9	60.1	60.4	60.6	8
9	56.9	57.1	57.4	57.6	57.9	58.1	58.4	58.6	58.9	59.1	59.4	59.6	59.9	60.1	60.4	60.6	60.9	61.1	9
10	57.3	57.5	57.8	58.0	58.3	58.5	58.8	59.0	59.3	59.5	59.8	60.0	60.3	60.5	60.8	61.0	61.3	61.5	10
11	57.6	57.8	58.1	58.3	58.6	58.8	59.1	59.3	59.6	59.8	60.1	60.3	60.6	60.8	61.1	61.3	61.6	61.8	11
12	57.8	58.0	58.3	58.5	58.8	59.0	59.3	59.5	59.8	60.0	60.3	60.5	60.8	61.0	61.3	61.5	61.8	62.0	12
13	57.9	58.2	58.4	58.6	58.9	59.1	59.4	59.6	59.9	60.2	60.4	60.6	60.9	61.1	61.4	61.6	61.9	62.1	13
14	57.9	58.2	58.5	58.7	58.9	59.2	59.4	59.7	60.0	60.2	60.4	60.7	60.9	61.2	61.4	61.7	61.9	62.2	14
15	58.0	58.2	58.5	58.7	59.0	59.2	59.5	59.7	60.0	60.2	60.5	60.7	60.9	61.2	61.5	61.7	61.9	62.2	15
16	57.9	58.2	58.4	58.7	58.9	59.2	59.4	59.7	59.9	60.2	60.4	60.6	60.9	61.1	61.4	61.6	61.9	62.1	16
17	57.9	58.1	58.4	58.6	58.8	59.1	59.3	59.6	59.8	60.1	60.3	60.6	60.8	61.0	61.3	61.5	61.8	62.0	17
18	57.7	58.0	58.3	58.5	58.7	59.0	59.2	59.5	59.7	59.9	60.2	60.4	60.7	60.9	61.2	61.4	61.6	61.9	18
19	57.6	57.8	58.1	58.3	58.6	58.8	59.1	59.3	59.5	59.8	60.0	60.3	60.6	60.8	61.0	61.2	61.5	61.8	19
20	57.4	57.6	57.9	58.1	58.4	58.6	58.9	59.1	59.4	59.6	59.8	60.1	60.3	60.6	60.8	61.0	61.3	61.5	20
21	57.2	57.4	57.7	57.9	58.2	58.4	58.6	58.9	59.1	59.4	59.6	59.8	60.1	60.3	60.6	60.8	61.0	61.3	21
22	56.9	57.2	57.5	57.7	57.9	58.2	58.4	58.7	58.9	59.1	59.4	59.6	59.9	60.1	60.3	60.6	60.8	61.0	22
23	56.7	56.9	57.2	57.4	57.6	57.9	58.1	58.4	58.6	58.8	59.1	59.3	59.6	59.8	60.0	60.3	60.5	60.7	23
24	56.4	56.6	56.8	57.1	57.3	57.6	57.8	58.0	58.3	58.5	58.8	59.0	59.3	59.5	59.7	59.9	60.2	60.4	24
25	56.1	56.3	56.5	56.8	57.0	57.3	57.5	57.7	58.0	58.2	58.4	58.7	58.9	59.1	59.4	59.6	59.9	60.1	25
26	55.7	56.0	56.2	56.4	56.7	56.9	57.1	57.4	57.6	57.9	58.1	58.3	58.6	58.8	59.0	59.3	59.5	59.7	26
27	55.4	55.6	55.8	56.1	56.3	56.5	56.8	57.0	57.3	57.5	57.7	57.9	58.2	58.4	58.7	58.9	59.1	59.3	27
28	55.0	55.2	55.4	55.7	55.9	56.2	56.4	56.6	56.8	57.1	57.3	57.5	57.8	58.0	58.2	58.5	58.7	58.9	28
29	54.6	54.8	55.0	55.3	55.5	55.7	56.0	56.2	56.4	56.7	56.9	57.1	57.3	57.6	57.8	58.0	58.3	58.5	29
30	54.2	54.4	54.6	54.9	55.1	55.3	55.5	55.7	56.0	56.2	56.5	56.7	56.9	57.1	57.4	57.6	57.8	58.0	30
31	53.7	54.0	54.2	54.4	54.6	54.9	55.1	55.3	55.5	55.8	56.0	56.2	56.5	56.7	56.9	57.1	57.3	57.6	31
32	53.3	53.5	53.7	53.9	54.2	54.4	54.6	54.8	55.1	55.3	55.5	55.7	56.0	56.2	56.4	56.6	56.9	57.1	32
33	52.8	53.0	53.2	53.5	53.7	53.9	54.1	54.3	54.6	54.8	55.0	55.2	55.4	55.7	55.9	56.1	56.3	56.5	33
34	52.3	52.5	52.7	52.9	53.2	53.4	53.6	53.8	54.0	54.3	54.5	54.7	54.9	55.1	55.4	55.6	55.8	56.0	34
35	51.8	52.0	52.2	52.4	52.6	52.9	53.1	53.3	53.5	53.7	54.0	54.2	54.4	54.6	54.8	55.1	55.3	55.5	35
36	51.2	51.5	51.7	51.9	52.1	52.3	52.5	52.8	53.0	53.2	53.4	53.6	53.9	54.1	54.3	54.5	54.7	54.9	36
37	50.7	50.9	51.1	51.3	51.6	51.8	52.0	52.2	52.4	52.6	52.8	53.1	53.3	53.5	53.7	53.9	54.1	54.3	37
38	50.1	50.3	50.5	50.8	51.0	51.2	51.4	51.6	51.8	52.0	52.3	52.5	52.7	52.9	53.1	53.3	53.5	53.7	38
39	49.5	49.8	50.0	50.2	50.4	50.6	50.8	51.0	51.2	51.5	51.7	51.9	52.1	52.3	52.5	52.7	52.9	53.1	39
40	48.9	49.2	49.4	49.6	49.8	50.0	50.2	50.4	50.6	50.8	51.0	51.2	51.5	51.7	51.9	52.1	52.3	52.5	40
41	48.3	48.6	48.8	49.0	49.2	49.4	49.6	49.8	50.0	50.2	50.4	50.6	50.8	51.0	51.2	51.4	51.6	51.8	41
42	47.7	47.9	48.1	48.3	48.5	48.7	48.9	49.1	49.3	49.5	49.7	49.9	50.2	50.4	50.6	50.8	51.0	51.2	42
43	47.1	47.3	47.5	47.7	47.9	48.1	48.3	48.4	48.7	48.9	49.1	49.3	49.5	49.7	49.9	50.1	50.3	50.5	43
44	46.4	46.6	46.8	47.0	47.2	47.4	47.6	47.8	48.0	48.2	48.4	48.6	48.8	49.0	49.2	49.4	49.6	49.8	44
45	45.8	46.0	46.1	46.3	46.5	46.7	46.9	47.1	47.3	47.5	47.7	47.9	48.1	48.3	48.5	48.7	48.9	49.1	45
46	45.1	45.3	45.5	45.7	45.8	46.0	46.2	46.4	46.6	46.8	47.0	47.2	47.4	47.6	47.8	48.0	48.2	48.4	46
	57'.6	.8	58'	.2	.4	.6	.8	59'	.2	.4	.6	.8	60'	.2	.4	.6	.8	61'	

For HEIGHT of EYE, always ADDITIVE to ALTITUDE

H.E. (feet)	10	12	14	16	18	20	22	24	26	28	30	32	34	36
Correction	6.7	6.4	6.1	5.9	5.6	5.4	5.2	5.0	4.8	4.6	4.4	4.3	4.1	3.9

Table 9   D1

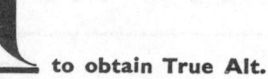

Correction to be applied to Obs. Alt. ◗ to obtain True Alt.   **ADDITIVE**

HORIZONTAL PARALLAX

◗	57'.6	.8	58'	.2	.4	.6	.8	59'	.2	.4	.6	.8	60'	.2	.4	.6	.8	61'	◗
46	45.1	45.3	45.5	45.7	45.8	46.0	46.2	46.4	46.6	46.8	47.0	47.2	47.4	47.6	47.8	48.0	48.2	48.4	46
47	44.4	44.6	44.7	45.0	45.2	45.4	45.5	45.7	45.9	46.1	46.3	46.5	46.7	46.9	47.1	47.3	47.5	47.7	47
48	43.7	43.9	44.0	44.2	44.4	44.6	44.8	45.0	45.2	45.4	45.6	45.8	46.0	46.1	46.3	46.5	46.7	46.9	48
49	42.9	43.2	43.3	43.5	43.7	43.9	44.1	44.2	44.4	44.6	44.8	45.0	45.2	45.4	45.6	45.7	45.9	46.1	49
50	42.2	42.4	42.6	42.8	42.9	43.1	43.3	43.5	43.7	43.9	44.1	44.2	44.4	44.6	44.8	45.0	45.2	45.4	50
51	41.5	41.7	41.8	42.0	42.2	42.4	42.5	42.7	42.9	43.1	43.3	43.5	43.6	43.8	44.0	44.2	44.4	44.6	51
52	40.7	40.9	41.1	41.2	41.4	41.6	41.8	42.0	42.1	42.3	42.5	42.7	42.8	43.0	43.2	43.4	43.6	43.8	52
53	39.9	40.1	40.3	40.5	40.7	40.8	41.0	41.2	41.4	41.5	41.7	41.9	42.0	42.2	42.4	42.6	42.8	42.9	53
54	39.2	39.4	39.5	39.7	39.9	40.0	40.2	40.4	40.6	40.7	40.9	41.1	41.2	41.4	41.6	41.8	41.9	42.1	54
55	38.4	38.6	38.7	38.9	39.0	39.2	39.4	39.6	39.7	39.9	40.1	40.2	40.4	40.6	40.8	40.9	41.1	41.3	55
56	37.6	37.7	37.9	38.1	38.2	38.4	38.6	38.7	38.9	39.1	39.2	39.4	39.6	39.7	39.9	40.1	40.3	40.4	56
57	36.8	36.9	37.1	37.2	37.4	37.6	37.7	37.9	38.1	38.2	38.4	38.6	38.8	38.9	39.1	39.2	39.4	39.5	57
58	35.9	36.1	36.3	36.4	36.6	36.8	36.9	37.1	37.2	37.4	37.6	37.7	37.9	38.0	38.2	38.4	38.5	38.7	58
59	35.1	35.3	35.5	35.6	35.7	35.9	36.1	36.3	36.4	36.5	36.7	36.8	37.0	37.2	37.3	37.5	37.6	37.8	59
60	34.3	34.4	34.6	34.7	34.9	35.1	35.2	35.4	35.5	35.7	35.8	36.0	36.1	36.3	36.5	36.6	36.8	36.9	60
61	33.5	33.6	33.7	33.9	34.0	34.2	34.3	34.5	34.6	34.8	34.9	35.1	35.2	35.4	35.6	35.7	35.9	36.0	61
62	32.5	32.7	32.9	33.0	33.2	33.3	33.5	33.6	33.7	33.9	34.0	34.2	34.4	34.5	34.6	34.8	34.9	35.1	62
63	31.7	31.8	32.0	32.1	32.3	32.4	32.6	32.7	32.9	33.0	33.2	33.3	33.4	33.6	33.7	33.9	34.0	34.2	63
64	30.8	31.0	31.1	31.2	31.4	31.5	31.7	31.8	32.0	32.1	32.3	32.4	32.5	32.7	32.8	32.9	33.1	33.2	64
65	29.9	30.1	30.2	30.3	30.5	30.6	30.8	30.9	31.0	31.2	31.3	31.5	31.6	31.7	31.9	32.0	32.2	32.3	65
66	29.0	29.2	29.3	29.4	29.6	29.7	29.8	30.0	30.1	30.3	30.4	30.5	30.7	30.8	30.9	31.1	31.2	31.4	66
67	28.1	28.3	28.4	28.5	28.7	28.8	28.9	29.1	29.2	29.3	29.5	29.6	29.8	29.9	30.0	30.1	30.3	30.4	67
68	27.2	27.4	27.5	27.6	27.7	27.9	28.0	28.1	28.3	28.4	28.5	28.7	28.8	28.9	29.0	29.2	29.3	29.4	68
69	26.3	26.4	26.5	26.7	26.8	27.0	27.1	27.2	27.3	27.5	27.6	27.7	27.8	27.9	28.1	28.2	28.3	28.5	69
70	25.4	25.5	25.6	25.8	25.9	26.0	26.1	26.3	26.4	26.5	26.6	26.8	26.9	27.0	27.1	27.2	27.4	27.5	70
71	24.5	24.6	24.7	24.8	24.9	25.1	25.2	25.3	25.4	25.6	25.7	25.8	25.9	26.0	26.2	26.3	26.4	26.5	71
72	23.5	23.7	23.8	23.9	24.0	24.1	24.2	24.4	24.5	24.6	24.7	24.8	25.0	25.1	25.2	25.3	25.4	25.5	72
73	22.6	22.7	22.8	22.9	23.0	23.2	23.3	23.4	23.5	23.6	23.7	23.8	24.0	24.1	24.2	24.3	24.4	24.5	73
74	21.6	21.8	21.9	22.0	22.1	22.2	22.3	22.4	22.5	22.6	22.7	22.9	23.0	23.1	23.2	23.3	23.4	23.5	74
75	20.7	20.8	20.9	21.0	21.1	21.2	21.3	21.4	21.6	21.7	21.8	21.9	22.0	22.1	22.2	22.3	22.4	22.5	75
76	19.7	19.8	19.9	20.1	20.2	20.3	20.4	20.5	20.6	20.7	20.8	20.9	21.0	21.1	21.2	21.3	21.4	21.5	76
77	18.8	18.9	19.0	19.1	19.2	19.3	19.4	19.5	19.6	19.7	19.8	19.9	20.0	20.1	20.2	20.3	20.4	20.5	77
78	17.8	17.9	18.0	18.1	18.2	18.3	18.4	18.5	18.6	18.7	18.8	18.9	19.0	19.1	19.2	19.3	19.4	19.5	78
79	16.9	17.0	17.1	17.1	17.2	17.3	17.4	17.5	17.6	17.7	17.8	17.9	18.0	18.1	18.2	18.3	18.3	18.4	79
80	15.9	16.0	16.1	16.2	16.2	16.3	16.4	16.5	16.6	16.7	16.8	16.9	17.0	17.1	17.1	17.2	17.3	17.4	80
81	14.9	15.0	15.1	15.2	15.3	15.3	15.4	15.5	15.6	15.7	15.8	15.9	16.0	16.0	16.1	16.2	16.3	16.4	81
82	13.9	14.0	14.1	14.2	14.3	14.4	14.4	14.5	14.6	14.7	14.8	14.9	15.0	15.0	15.1	15.2	15.3	15.4	82
83	13.0	13.0	13.1	13.2	13.3	13.4	13.4	13.5	13.6	13.7	13.7	13.8	13.9	14.0	14.1	14.1	14.2	14.3	83
84	12.0	12.1	12.1	12.2	12.3	12.4	12.4	12.5	12.6	12.7	12.7	12.8	12.9	13.0	13.0	13.1	13.2	13.3	84
85	11.0	11.1	11.1	11.2	11.3	11.4	11.4	11.5	11.6	11.7	11.7	11.8	11.9	11.9	12.0	12.1	12.2	12.2	85
86	10.0	10.1	10.1	10.2	10.3	10.4	10.4	10.5	10.6	10.6	10.7	10.8	10.9	10.9	11.0	11.1	11.1	11.2	86
87	9.0	9.1	9.1	9.2	9.3	9.4	9.4	9.5	9.6	9.6	9.7	9.8	9.9	9.9	10.0	10.0	10.1	10.2	87
88	8.1	8.1	8.2	8.2	8.3	8.4	8.4	8.5	8.5	8.6	8.7	8.7	8.8	8.9	8.9	9.0	9.0	9.1	88
89	7.1	7.1	7.2	7.2	7.3	7.4	7.4	7.5	7.5	7.6	7.6	7.7	7.8	7.8	7.9	7.9	8.0	8.0	89
	57'.6	.8	58'	.2	.4	.6	.8	59'	.2	.4	.6	.8	60'	.2	.4	.6	.8	61'	

For HEIGHT of EYE, always ADDITIVE to ALTITUDE

38	40	42	44		46	48	50	52		54	56	58	60		·65	70	75		80	85	90
'	'	'	'		'	'	'	'		'	'	'	'		'	'	'		'	'	'
3.8	3.6	3.5	3.3		3.2	3.0	2.9	2.7		2.6	2.5	2.3	2.2		1.9	1.6	1.3		1.0	.8	.5

Table 10

G.H.A. & Dec. MOON, Interpolation Tables

M. or S.	For G.H.A. — 1 For Minutes	2 For Secs.	3 M.	v or d .3	.6	.9	1.2	1.5	1.8	2.1	2.4	2.7	3.0	3.3	3.6	3.9	4.2	4.5	3 M.
1	0 14.3	.2	1	.0	.0	.0	.0	.0	.0	.0	.0	.0	.1	.1	.1	.1	.1	.1	1
2	0 28.6	.5	2	.0	.0	.0	.0	.1	.1	.1	.1	.1	.1	.1	.1	.1	.1	.2	2
3	0 42.9	.7	3	.0	.0	.0	.1	.1	.1	.1	.1	.1	.2	.2	.2	.2	.2	.2	3
4	0 57.3	1.0	4	.0	.0	.1	.1	.1	.1	.1	.2	.2	.2	.2	.2	.3	.3	.3	4
5	1 11.6	1.2	5	.0	.1	.1	.1	.1	.2	.2	.2	.2	.3	.3	.3	.3	.4	.4	5
6	1 25.9	1.4	6	.0	.1	.1	.1	.2	.2	.2	.2	.3	.3	.3	.4	.4	.4	.5	6
7	1 40.2	1.7	7	.0	.1	.1	.1	.2	.2	.2	.3	.3	.4	.4	.4	.5	.5	.5	7
8	1 54.5	1.9	8	.0	.1	.1	.2	.2	.2	.3	.3	.4	.4	.4	.5	.5	.6	.6	8
9	2 08.9	2.1	9	.0	.1	.1	.2	.2	.3	.3	.4	.4	.5	.5	.5	.6	.6	.7	9
10	2 23.2	2.4	10	.1	.1	.2	.2	.3	.3	.4	.4	.5	.5	.6	.6	.7	.7	.8	10
11	2 37.5	2.6	11	.1	.1	.2	.2	.3	.3	.4	.4	.5	.6	.6	.7	.7	.8	.8	11
12	2 51.8	2.9	12	.1	.1	.2	.2	.3	.4	.4	.5	.5	.6	.7	.7	.8	.8	.9	12
13	3 06.1	3.1	13	.1	.1	.2	.3	.3	.4	.5	.5	.6	.7	.7	.8	.8	.9	1.0	13
14	3 20.4	3.3	14	.1	.1	.2	.3	.4	.4	.5	.6	.6	.7	.8	.8	.9	1.0	1.1	14
15	3 34.8	3.6	15	.1	.2	.2	.3	.4	.5	.5	.6	.7	.8	.8	.9	1.0	1.1	1.1	15
16	3 49.1	3.8	16	.1	.2	.2	.3	.4	.5	.6	.6	.7	.8	.9	1.0	1.0	1.1	1.2	16
17	4 03.4	4.1	17	.1	.2	.3	.3	.4	.5	.6	.7	.8	.9	.9	1.0	1.1	1.2	1.3	17
18	4 17.7	4.3	18	.1	.2	.3	.4	.5	.5	.6	.7	.8	.9	1.0	1.1	1.2	1.3	1.4	18
19	4 32.0	4.5	19	.1	.2	.3	.4	.5	.6	.7	.8	.9	1.0	1.0	1.1	1.2	1.3	1.4	19
20	4 46.3	4.8	20	.1	.2	.3	.4	.5	.6	.7	.8	.9	1.0	1.1	1.2	1.3	1.4	1.5	20
21	5 00.7	5.0	21	.1	.2	.3	.4	.5	.6	.7	.8	.9	1.1	1.2	1.3	1.4	1.5	1.6	21
22	5 15.0	5.2	22	.1	.2	.3	.4	.6	.7	.8	.9	1.0	1.1	1.2	1.3	1.4	1.5	1.7	22
23	5 29.3	5.5	23	.1	.2	.3	.5	.6	.7	.8	.9	1.0	1.2	1.3	1.4	1.5	1.6	1.7	23
24	5 43.6	5.7	24	.1	.2	.4	.5	.6	.7	.8	1.0	1.1	1.2	1.3	1.4	1.6	1.7	1.8	24
25	5 57.9	6.0	25	.1	.3	.4	.5	.6	.8	.9	1.0	1.1	1.3	1.4	1.5	1.6	1.8	1.9	25
26	6 12.2	6.2	26	.1	.3	.4	.5	.7	.8	.9	1.0	1.2	1.3	1.4	1.6	1.7	1.8	2.0	26
27	6 26.6	6.4	27	.1	.3	.4	.5	.7	.8	.9	1.1	1.2	1.4	1.5	1.6	1.8	1.9	2.0	27
28	6 40.9	6.7	28	.1	.3	.4	.6	.7	.8	1.0	1.1	1.3	1.4	1.5	1.7	1.8	2.0	2.1	28
29	6 55.2	6.9	29	.1	.3	.4	.6	.7	.9	1.0	1.2	1.3	1.5	1.6	1.7	1.9	2.0	2.2	29
30	7 09.5	7.2	30	.2	.3	.5	.6	.8	.9	1.1	1.2	1.4	1.5	1.7	1.8	2.0	2.1	2.3	30
31	7 23.8	7.4	31	.2	.3	.5	.6	.8	.9	1.1	1.2	1.4	1.6	1.7	1.9	2.0	2.2	2.3	31
32	7 38.1	7.6	32	.2	.3	.5	.6	.8	1.0	1.1	1.3	1.4	1.6	1.8	1.9	2.1	2.2	2.4	32
33	7 52.5	7.9	33	.2	.3	.5	.7	.8	1.0	1.2	1.3	1.5	1.7	1.8	2.0	2.1	2.3	2.5	33
34	8 06.8	8.1	34	.2	.3	.5	.7	.9	1.0	1.2	1.4	1.5	1.7	1.9	2.0	2.2	2.4	2.6	34
35	8 21.1	8.4	35	.2	.4	.5	.7	.9	1.1	1.2	1.4	1.6	1.8	1.9	2.1	2.3	2.5	2.6	35
36	8 35.4	8.6	36	.2	.4	.5	.7	.9	1.1	1.3	1.4	1.6	1.8	2.0	2.2	2.3	2.5	2.7	36
37	8 49.7	8.8	37	.2	.4	.6	.7	.9	1.1	1.3	1.5	1.7	1.9	2.0	2.2	2.4	2.6	2.8	37
38	9 04.0	9.1	38	.2	.4	.6	.8	1.0	1.1	1.3	1.5	1.7	1.9	2.1	2.3	2.5	2.7	2.9	38
39	9 18.4	9.3	39	.2	.4	.6	.8	1.0	1.2	1.4	1.6	1.8	2.0	2.1	2.3	2.5	2.7	2.9	39
40	9 32.7	9.5	40	.2	.4	.6	.8	1.0	1.2	1.4	1.6	1.8	2.0	2.2	2.4	2.6	2.8	3.0	40
41	9 47.0	9.8	41	.2	.4	.6	.8	1.0	1.2	1.4	1.6	1.8	2.1	2.3	2.5	2.7	2.9	3.1	41
42	10 01.3	10.0	42	.2	.4	.6	.8	1.1	1.3	1.5	1.7	1.9	2.1	2.3	2.5	2.7	2.9	3.2	42
43	10 15.6	10.3	43	.2	.4	.6	.9	1.1	1.3	1.5	1.7	1.9	2.2	2.4	2.6	2.8	3.0	3.2	43
44	10 29.9	10.5	44	.2	.4	.7	.9	1.1	1.3	1.5	1.8	2.0	2.2	2.4	2.6	2.9	3.1	3.3	44
45	10 44.3	10.7	45	.2	.5	.7	.9	1.1	1.4	1.6	1.8	2.0	2.3	2.5	2.7	2.9	3.2	3.4	45
46	10 58.6	11.0	46	.2	.5	.7	.9	1.2	1.4	1.6	1.8	2.1	2.3	2.5	2.8	3.0	3.2	3.5	46
47	11 12.9	11.2	47	.2	.5	.7	.9	1.2	1.4	1.6	1.9	2.1	2.4	2.6	2.8	3.1	3.3	3.5	47
48	11 27.2	11.5	48	.2	.5	.7	1.0	1.2	1.4	1.7	1.9	2.2	2.4	2.6	2.9	3.1	3.4	3.6	48
49	11 41.5	11.7	49	.2	.5	.7	1.0	1.2	1.5	1.7	2.0	2.2	2.5	2.7	2.9	3.2	3.4	3.7	49
50	11 55.8	11.9	50	.3	.5	.8	1.0	1.3	1.5	1.8	2.0	2.3	2.5	2.8	3.0	3.3	3.5	3.8	50
51	12 10.1	12.2	51	.3	.5	.8	1.0	1.3	1.5	1.8	2.0	2.3	2.6	2.8	3.1	3.3	3.6	3.8	51
52	12 24.5	12.4	52	.3	.5	.8	1.0	1.3	1.6	1.8	2.1	2.3	2.6	2.9	3.1	3.4	3.6	3.9	52
53	12 38.8	12.6	53	.3	.5	.8	1.1	1.3	1.6	1.9	2.1	2.4	2.7	2.9	3.2	3.4	3.7	4.0	53
54	12 53.1	12.9	54	.3	.5	.8	1.1	1.4	1.6	1.9	2.2	2.4	2.7	3.0	3.2	3.5	3.8	4.1	54
55	13 07.4	13.1	55	.3	.6	.8	1.1	1.4	1.7	1.9	2.2	2.5	2.8	3.0	3.3	3.6	3.9	4.1	55
56	13 21.7	13.4	56	.3	.6	.8	1.1	1.4	1.7	2.0	2.2	2.5	2.8	3.1	3.4	3.6	3.9	4.2	56
57	13 36.1	13.6	57	.3	.6	.9	1.1	1.4	1.7	2.0	2.3	2.6	2.9	3.1	3.4	3.7	4.0	4.3	57
58	13 50.4	13.8	58	.3	.6	.9	1.2	1.5	1.7	2.0	2.3	2.6	2.9	3.2	3.5	3.8	4.1	4.4	58
59	14 04.7	14.1	59	.3	.6	.9	1.2	1.5	1.8	2.1	2.4	2.7	3.0	3.2	3.5	3.8	4.1	4.4	59
60	14 19.0	14.3	60	.3	.6	.9	1.2	1.5	1.8	2.1	2.4	2.7	3.0	3.3	3.6	3 9	4.2	4.5	60

Table 10

G.H.A. & Dec. MOON, Interpolation Tables

3   For G.H.A. & Dec.   3

M.	v or d																			M.
	4.8	5.1	5.4	5.7	6.0	6.3	6.6	6.9	7.2	7.5	7.8	8.1	8.4	8.7	9.0	9.3	9.6	9.9	10.2	
1	.1	.1	.1	.1	.1	.1	.1	.1	.1	.1	.1	.1	.1	.1	.2	.2	.2	.2	.2	1
2	.2	.2	.2	.2	.2	.2	.2	.2	.2	.3	.3	.3	.3	.3	.3	.3	.3	.3	.3	2
3	.2	.3	.3	.3	.3	.3	.3	.3	.4	.4	.4	.4	.4	.4	.5	.5	.5	.5	.5	3
4	.3	.3	.4	.4	.4	.4	.4	.5	.5	.5	.5	.5	.6	.6	.6	.6	.6	.7	.7	4
5	.4	.4	.5	.5	.5	.5	.6	.6	.6	.6	.7	.7	.7	.7	.8	.8	.8	.8	.9	5
6	.5	.5	.5	.6	.6	.6	.7	.7	.7	.8	.8	.8	.8	.9	.9	.9	1.0	1.0	1.0	6
7	.6	.6	.6	.7	.7	.7	.8	.8	.8	.9	.9	.9	1.0	1.0	1.1	1.1	1.1	1.2	1.2	7
8	.6	.7	.7	.8	.8	.8	.9	.9	1.0	1.0	1.0	1.1	1.1	1.2	1.2	1.2	1.3	1.3	1.4	8
9	.7	.8	.8	.9	.9	.9	1.0	1.0	1.1	1.1	1.2	1.2	1.3	1.3	1.4	1.4	1.4	1.5	1.5	9
10	.8	.9	.9	1.0	1.0	1.1	1.1	1.2	1.2	1.3	1.3	1.4	1.4	1.5	1.5	1.6	1.6	1.7	1.7	10
11	.9	.9	1.0	1.0	1.1	1.2	1.2	1.3	1.3	1.4	1.4	1.5	1.5	1.6	1.7	1.7	1.8	1.8	1.9	11
12	1.0	1.0	1.1	1.1	1.2	1.3	1.3	1.4	1.4	1.5	1.6	1.6	1.7	1.7	1.8	1.9	1.9	2.0	2.0	12
13	1.0	1.1	1.2	1.2	1.3	1.4	1.4	1.5	1.6	1.6	1.7	1.8	1.8	1.9	2.0	2.0	2.1	2.1	2.2	13
14	1.1	1.2	1.3	1.3	1.4	1.5	1.5	1.6	1.7	1.8	1.8	1.9	2.0	2.0	2.1	2.2	2.2	2.3	2.4	14
15	1.2	1.3	1.4	1.4	1.5	1.6	1.7	1.7	1.8	1.9	2.0	2.0	2.1	2.2	2.3	2.3	2.4	2.5	2.6	15
16	1.3	1.4	1.4	1.5	1.6	1.7	1.8	1.8	1.9	2.0	2.1	2.2	2.2	2.3	2.4	2.5	2.6	2.6	2.7	16
17	1.4	1.4	1.5	1.6	1.7	1.8	1.9	2.0	2.0	2.1	2.2	2.3	2.4	2.5	2.6	2.6	2.7	2.8	2.9	17
18	1.4	1.5	1.6	1.7	1.8	1.9	2.0	2.1	2.2	2.3	2.3	2.4	2.5	2.6	2.7	2.8	2.9	3.0	3.1	18
19	1.5	1.6	1.7	1.8	1.9	2.0	2.1	2.2	2.3	2.4	2.5	2.6	2.7	2.8	2.9	2.9	3.0	3.1	3.2	19
20	1.6	1.7	1.8	1.9	2.0	2.1	2.2	2.3	2.4	2.5	2.6	2.7	2.8	2.9	3.0	3.1	3.2	3.3	3.4	20
21	1.7	1.8	1.9	2.0	2.1	2.2	2.3	2.4	2.5	2.6	2.7	2.8	2.9	3.0	3.2	3.3	3.4	3.5	3.6	21
22	1.8	1.9	2.0	2.1	2.2	2.3	2.4	2.5	2.6	2.8	2.9	3.0	3.1	3.2	3.3	3.4	3.5	3.6	3.7	22
23	1.8	2.0	2.1	2.2	2.3	2.4	2.5	2.6	2.8	2.9	3.0	3.1	3.2	3.3	3.5	3.6	3.7	3.8	3.9	23
24	1.9	2.0	2.2	2.3	2.4	2.5	2.6	2.8	2.9	3.0	3.1	3.2	3.4	3.5	3.6	3.7	3.8	4.0	4.1	24
25	2.0	2.1	2.3	2.4	2.5	2.6	2.8	2.9	3.0	3.1	3.3	3.4	3.5	3.6	3.8	3.9	4.0	4.1	4.3	25
26	2.1	2.2	2.3	2.5	2.6	2.7	2.9	3.0	3.1	3.3	3.4	3.5	3.6	3.8	3.9	4.0	4.2	4.3	4.4	26
27	2.2	2.3	2.4	2.6	2.7	2.8	3.0	3.1	3.2	3.4	3.5	3.6	3.8	3.9	4.1	4.2	4.3	4.5	4.6	27
28	2.2	2.4	2.5	2.7	2.8	2.9	3.1	3.2	3.4	3.5	3.6	3.8	3.9	4.1	4.2	4.3	4.5	4.6	4.8	28
29	2.3	2.5	2.6	2.8	2.9	3.0	3.2	3.3	3.5	3.6	3.8	3.9	4.1	4.2	4.4	4.5	4.6	4.8	4.9	29
30	2.4	2.6	2.7	2.9	3.0	3.2	3.3	3.5	3.6	3.8	3.9	4.1	4.2	4.4	4.5	4.7	4.8	5.0	5.1	30
31	2.5	2.6	2.8	2.9	3.1	3.3	3.4	3.6	3.7	3.9	4.0	4.2	4.3	4.5	4.7	4.8	5.0	5.1	5.3	31
32	2.6	2.7	2.9	3.0	3.2	3.4	3.5	3.7	3.8	4.0	4.2	4.3	4.5	4.6	4.8	5.0	5.1	5.3	5.4	32
33	2.6	2.8	3.0	3.1	3.3	3.5	3.6	3.8	4.0	4.1	4.3	4.5	4.6	4.8	5.0	5.1	5.3	5.4	5.6	33
34	2.7	2.9	3.1	3.2	3.4	3.6	3.7	3.9	4.1	4.3	4.4	4.6	4.8	4.9	5.1	5.3	5.4	5.6	5.8	34
35	2.8	3.0	3.2	3.3	3.5	3.7	3.9	4.0	4.2	4.4	4.6	4.7	4.9	5.1	5.2	5.4	5.6	5.8	6.0	35
36	2.9	3.1	3.2	3.4	3.6	3.8	4.0	4.1	4.3	4.5	4.7	4.9	5.0	5.2	5.4	5.6	5.8	5.9	6.1	36
37	3.0	3.1	3.3	3.5	3.7	3.9	4.1	4.3	4.4	4.6	4.8	5.0	5.2	5.4	5.6	5.7	5.9	6.1	6.3	37
38	3.0	3.2	3.4	3.6	3.8	4.0	4.2	4.4	4.6	4.8	4.9	5.1	5.3	5.5	5.7	5.9	6.1	6.3	6.5	38
39	3.1	3.3	3.5	3.7	3.9	4.1	4.3	4.5	4.7	4.9	5.1	5.3	5.5	5.7	5.9	6.0	6.2	6.4	6.6	39
40	3.2	3.4	3.6	3.8	4.0	4.2	4.4	4.6	4.8	5.0	5.2	5.4	5.6	5.8	6.0	6.2	6.4	6.6	6.8	40
41	3.3	3.5	3.7	3.9	4.1	4.3	4.5	4.7	4.9	5.1	5.3	5.5	5.7	5.9	6.2	6.4	6.6	6.8	7.0	41
42	3.4	3.6	3.8	4.0	4.2	4.4	4.6	4.8	5.0	5.3	5.5	5.7	5.9	6.1	6.3	6.5	6.7	6.9	7.1	42
43	3.4	3.7	3.9	4.1	4.3	4.5	4.7	4.9	5.2	5.4	5.6	5.8	6.0	6.2	6.5	6.7	6.9	7.1	7.3	43
44	3.5	3.7	4.0	4.2	4.4	4.6	4.8	5.1	5.3	5.5	5.7	5.9	6.2	6.4	6.6	6.8	7.0	7.3	7.5	44
45	3.6	3.8	4.1	4.3	4.5	4.7	5.0	5.2	5.4	5.6	5.9	6.1	6.3	6.5	6.8	7.0	7.2	7.4	7.7	45
46	3.7	3.9	4.1	4.4	4.6	4.8	5.1	5.3	5.5	5.8	6.0	6.2	6.4	6.7	6.9	7.1	7.4	7.6	7.8	46
47	3.8	4.0	4.2	4.5	4.7	4.9	5.2	5.4	5.6	5.9	6.1	6.3	6.6	6.8	7.1	7.2	7.5	7.8	8.0	47
48	3.8	4.1	4.3	4.6	4.8	5.0	5.3	5.5	5.8	6.0	6.2	6.5	6.7	7.0	7.2	7.4	7.7	7.9	8.2	48
49	3.9	4.2	4.4	4.7	4.9	5.1	5.4	5.6	5.9	6.1	6.4	6.6	6.9	7.1	7.4	7.6	7.8	8.1	8.3	49
50	4.0	4.3	4.5	4.8	5.0	5.3	5.5	5.8	6.0	6.3	6.5	6.8	7.0	7.3	7.5	7.8	8.0	8.3	8.5	50
51	4.1	4.3	4.6	4.8	5.1	5.4	5.6	5.9	6.1	6.4	6.6	6.9	7.1	7.4	7.7	7.9	8.2	8.4	8.7	51
52	4.2	4.4	4.7	4.9	5.2	5.5	5.7	6.0	6.2	6.5	6.8	7.0	7.3	7.5	7.8	8.1	8.3	8.6	8.8	52
53	4.2	4.5	4.8	5.0	5.3	5.6	5.8	6.1	6.4	6.6	6.9	7.2	7.4	7.7	8.0	8.2	8.5	8.7	9.0	53
54	4.3	4.6	4.9	5.1	5.4	5.7	5.9	6.2	6.5	6.8	7.0	7.3	7.6	7.8	8.1	8.4	8.6	8.9	9.2	54
55	4.4	4.7	5.0	5.2	5.5	5.8	6.1	6.3	6.6	6.9	7.2	7.4	7.7	8.0	8.3	8.5	8.8	9.1	9.4	55
56	4.5	4.8	5.0	5.3	5.6	5.9	6.2	6.4	6.7	7.0	7.3	7.6	7.8	8.1	8.4	8.7	9.0	9.2	9.5	56
57	4.6	4.8	5.1	5.4	5.7	6.0	6.3	6.6	6.8	7.1	7.4	7.7	8.0	8.3	8.6	8.8	9.1	9.4	9.7	57
58	4.6	4.9	5.2	5.5	5.8	6.1	6.4	6.7	7.0	7.3	7.5	7.8	8.1	8.4	8.7	9.0	9.3	9.6	9.9	58
59	4.7	5.0	5.3	5.6	5.9	6.2	6.5	6.8	7.1	7.4	7.7	8.0	8.3	8.6	8.9	9.1	9.4	9.7	10.0	59
60	4.8	5.1	5.4	5.7	6.0	6.3	6.6	6.9	7.2	7.5	7.8	8.1	8.4	8.7	9.0	9.3	9.6	9.9	10.2	60

Table 10

G.H.A. & Dec. MOON, Interpolation Tables

3

For G.H.A. & Dec.

3

M.	10.5	10.8	11.1	11.4	11.7	12.0	12.3	12.6	12.9	13.2	13.5	13.8	14.1	14.4	14.7	15.0	15.3	15.6	15.9	M.
1	.2	.2	.2	.2	.2	.2	.2	.2	.2	.2	.2	.2	.2	.2	.2	.3	.3	.3	.3	1
2	.4	.4	.4	.4	.4	.4	.4	.4	.4	.4	.5	.5	.5	.5	.5	.5	.5	.5	.5	2
3	.5	.5	.6	.6	.6	.6	.6	.6	.6	.7	.7	.7	.7	.7	.7	.8	.8	.8	.8	3
4	.7	.7	.7	.8	.8	.8	.8	.8	.9	.9	.9	.9	.9	1.0	1.0	1.0	1.0	1.0	1.1	4
5	.9	.9	.9	1.0	1.0	1.0	1.0	1.1	1.1	1.1	1.1	1.2	1.2	1.2	1.2	1.3	1.3	1.3	1.3	5
6	1.1	1.1	1.1	1.1	1.2	1.2	1.2	1.3	1.3	1.3	1.4	1.4	1.4	1.4	1.5	1.5	1.5	1.6	1.6	6
7	1.2	1.3	1.3	1.3	1.4	1.4	1.4	1.5	1.5	1.5	1.6	1.6	1.6	1.7	1.7	1.8	1.8	1.8	1.9	7
8	1.4	1.4	1.5	1.5	1.6	1.6	1.6	1.7	1.7	1.8	1.8	1.8	1.9	1.9	2.0	2.0	2.0	2.1	2.1	8
9	1.6	1.6	1.7	1.7	1.8	1.8	1.8	1.9	1.9	2.0	2.0	2.1	2.1	2.2	2.2	2.3	2.3	2.3	2.4	9
10	1.8	1.8	1.9	1.9	2.0	2.0	2.1	2.1	2.2	2.2	2.3	2.3	2.4	2.4	2.5	2.5	2.6	2.6	2.7	10
11	1.9	2.0	2.0	2.1	2.1	2.2	2.3	2.3	2.4	2.4	2.5	2.5	2.6	2.6	2.7	2.8	2.8	2.9	2.9	11
12	2.1	2.2	2.2	2.3	2.3	2.4	2.5	2.5	2.6	2.6	2.7	2.8	2.8	2.9	2.9	3.0	3.1	3.1	3.2	12
13	2.3	2.3	2.4	2.5	2.5	2.6	2.7	2.7	2.8	2.9	2.9	3.0	3.1	3.1	3.2	3.3	3.3	3.4	3.4	13
14	2.5	2.5	2.6	2.7	2.7	2.8	2.9	2.9	3.0	3.1	3.2	3.2	3.3	3.4	3.4	3.5	3.6	3.6	3.7	14
15	2.6	2.7	2.8	2.9	2.9	3.0	3.1	3.2	3.2	3.3	3.4	3.5	3.5	3.6	3.7	3.8	3.8	3.9	4.0	15
16	2.8	2.9	3.0	3.0	3.1	3.2	3.3	3.4	3.4	3.5	3.6	3.7	3.8	3.8	3.9	4.0	4.1	4.2	4.2	16
17	3.0	3.1	3.1	3.2	3.3	3.4	3.5	3.6	3.7	3.7	3.8	3.9	4.0	4.1	4.2	4.3	4.3	4.4	4.5	17
18	3.2	3.2	3.3	3.4	3.5	3.6	3.7	3.8	3.9	3.9	4.1	4.1	4.2	4.3	4.4	4.5	4.6	4.7	4.8	18
19	3.3	3.4	3.5	3.6	3.7	3.8	3.9	4.0	4.1	4.2	4.3	4.4	4.5	4.6	4.7	4.8	4.8	4.9	5.0	19
20	3.5	3.6	3.7	3.8	3.9	4.0	4.1	4.2	4.3	4.4	4.5	4.6	4.7	4.8	4.9	5.0	5.1	5.2	5.3	20
21	3.7	3.8	3.9	4.0	4.1	4.2	4.3	4.4	4.5	4.6	4.7	4.8	4.9	5.0	5.1	5.3	5.4	5.5	5.6	21
22	3.9	4.0	4.1	4.2	4.3	4.4	4.5	4.6	4.7	4.8	5.0	5.1	5.2	5.3	5.4	5.5	5.6	5.7	5.8	22
23	4.0	4.1	4.3	4.4	4.5	4.6	4.7	4.8	4.9	5.1	5.2	5.3	5.4	5.5	5.6	5.8	5.9	6.0	6.1	23
24	4.2	4.3	4.4	4.6	4.7	4.8	4.9	5.0	5.2	5.3	5.4	5.5	5.6	5.8	5.9	6.0	6.1	6.2	6.4	24
25	4.4	4.5	4.6	4.8	4.9	5.0	5.1	5.3	5.4	5.5	5.6	5.8	5.9	6.0	6.1	6.3	6.4	6.5	6.6	25
26	4.6	4.7	4.8	4.9	5.1	5.2	5.3	5.5	5.6	5.7	5.9	6.0	6.1	6.2	6.4	6.5	6.6	6.8	6.9	26
27	4.7	4.9	5.0	5.1	5.3	5.4	5.5	5.7	5.8	5.9	6.1	6.2	6.3	6.5	6.6	6.8	6.9	7.0	7.2	27
28	4.9	5.0	5.2	5.3	5.5	5.6	5.7	5.9	6.0	6.2	6.3	6.4	6.6	6.7	6.9	7.0	7.1	7.3	7.4	28
29	5.1	5.2	5.4	5.5	5.7	5.8	5.9	6.1	6.2	6.4	6.5	6.7	6.8	7.0	7.1	7.3	7.4	7.5	7.7	29
30	5.3	5.4	5.6	5.7	5.9	6.0	6.2	6.3	6.4	6.6	6.8	6.9	7.1	7.2	7.4	7.5	7.7	7.8	8.0	30
31	5.4	5.6	5.7	5.9	6.0	6.2	6.4	6.5	6.7	6.8	7.0	7.1	7.3	7.4	7.6	7.8	7.9	8.0	8.2	31
32	5.6	5.8	5.9	6.1	6.2	6.4	6.6	6.7	6.9	7.0	7.2	7.4	7.5	7.7	7.8	8.0	8.2	8.3	8.5	32
33	5.8	5.9	6.1	6.3	6.4	6.6	6.8	6.9	7.1	7.3	7.4	7.6	7.8	7.9	8.1	8.3	8.4	8.6	8.7	33
34	6.0	6.1	6.3	6.5	6.6	6.8	7.0	7.1	7.3	7.5	7.7	7.8	8.0	8.2	8.3	8.5	8.7	8.8	9.0	34
35	6.1	6.3	6.5	6.7	6.8	7.0	7.2	7.4	7.5	7.7	7.9	8.1	8.2	8.4	8.6	8.8	8.9	9.1	9.3	35
36	6.3	6.5	6.7	6.8	7.0	7.2	7.4	7.6	7.7	7.9	8.1	8.3	8.5	8.6	8.8	9.0	9.2	9.4	9.5	36
37	6.5	6.7	6.8	7.0	7.2	7.4	7.6	7.8	8.0	8.1	8.3	8.5	8.7	8.9	9.1	9.3	9.4	9.6	9.8	37
38	6.7	6.8	7.0	7.2	7.4	7.6	7.8	8.0	8.2	8.4	8.6	8.7	8.9	9.1	9.3	9.5	9.7	9.9	10.0	38
39	6.8	7.0	7.2	7.4	7.6	7.8	8.0	8.2	8.4	8.6	8.8	9.0	9.2	9.4	9.6	9.8	9.9	10.1	10.3	39
40	7.0	7.2	7.4	7.6	7.8	8.0	8.2	8.4	8.6	8.8	9.0	9.2	9.4	9.6	9.8	10.0	10.2	10.4	10.6	40
41	7.2	7.4	7.6	7.8	8.0	8.2	8.4	8.6	8.8	9.0	9.2	9.4	9.6	9.8	10.0	10.3	10.5	10.7	10.9	41
42	7.4	7.6	7.8	8.0	8.2	8.4	8.6	8.8	9.0	9.2	9.5	9.7	9.9	10.1	10.3	10.5	10.7	10.9	11.1	42
43	7.5	7.7	8.0	8.2	8.4	8.6	8.8	9.0	9.2	9.5	9.7	9.9	10.1	10.3	10.5	10.8	11.0	11.2	11.4	43
44	7.7	7.9	8.1	8.4	8.6	8.8	9.0	9.2	9.5	9.7	9.9	10.1	10.3	10.6	10.8	11.0	11.2	11.4	11.7	44
45	7.9	8.1	8.3	8.6	8.8	9.0	9.2	9.5	9.7	9.9	10.1	10.4	10.6	10.8	11.0	11.3	11.5	11.7	11.9	45
46	8.1	8.3	8.5	8.7	9.0	9.2	9.4	9.7	9.9	10.1	10.4	10.6	10.8	11.0	11.3	11.5	11.7	12.0	12.2	46
47	8.2	8.5	8.7	8.9	9.2	9.4	9.6	9.9	10.1	10.3	10.6	10.8	11.0	11.3	11.5	11.8	12.0	12.2	12.5	47
48	8.4	8.6	8.9	9.1	9.4	9.6	9.8	10.1	10.3	10.6	10.8	11.0	11.3	11.5	11.8	12.0	12.2	12.5	12.7	48
49	8.6	8.8	9.1	9.3	9.6	9.8	10.0	10.3	10.5	10.8	11.0	11.3	11.5	11.8	12.0	12.3	12.5	12.7	13.0	49
50	8.8	9.0	9.3	9.5	9.8	10.0	10.3	10.5	10.8	11.0	11.3	11.5	11.8	12.0	12.3	12.5	12.8	13.0	13.3	50
51	8.9	9.2	9.4	9.7	9.9	10.2	10.5	10.7	11.0	11.2	11.5	11.7	12.0	12.2	12.5	12.8	13.0	13.3	13.5	51
52	9.1	9.4	9.6	9.9	10.1	10.4	10.7	10.9	11.2	11.4	11.7	12.0	12.2	12.5	12.7	13.0	13.3	13.5	13.8	52
53	9.3	9.5	9.8	10.1	10.3	10.6	10.9	11.1	11.4	11.7	11.9	12.2	12.5	12.7	13.0	13.3	13.5	13.8	14.0	53
54	9.5	9.7	10.0	10.3	10.5	10.8	11.1	11.3	11.6	11.9	12.2	12.4	12.7	13.0	13.2	13.5	13.8	14.0	14.3	54
55	9.6	9.9	10.2	10.5	10.7	11.0	11.3	11.6	11.8	12.1	12.4	12.7	12.9	13.2	13.5	13.8	14.0	14.3	14.6	55
56	9.8	10.1	10.4	10.6	10.9	11.2	11.5	11.8	12.0	12.3	12.6	12.9	13.2	13.4	13.7	14.0	14.3	14.6	14.8	56
57	10.0	10.3	10.5	10.8	11.1	11.4	11.7	12.0	12.3	12.5	12.8	13.1	13.4	13.7	14.0	14.3	14.5	14.8	15.1	57
58	10.2	10.4	10.7	11.0	11.3	11.6	11.9	12.2	12.5	12.8	13.1	13.3	13.6	13.9	14.2	14.5	14.8	15.1	15.4	58
59	10.3	10.6	10.9	11.2	11.5	11.8	12.1	12.4	12.7	13.0	13.3	13.6	13.9	14.2	14.5	14.8	15.0	15.3	15.6	59
60	10.5	10.8	11.1	11.4	11.7	12.0	12.3	12.6	12.9	13.2	13.5	13.8	14.1	14.4	14.7	15.0	15.3	15.6	15.9	60

Table 10

G.H.A. & Dec. MOON, Interpolation Tables

3

For G.H.A. & Dec.

3

M.	16.2	16.5	16.8	17.1	17.4	17.7	18.0	18.3	18.6	18.9	19.2	19.5	19.8	M.
						v or *d*								
1	.3	.3	.3	.3	.3	.3	.3	.3	.3	.3	.3	.3	.3	1
2	.5	.6	.6	.6	.6	.6	.6	.6	.6	.6	.6	.7	.7	2
3	.8	.8	.8	.9	.9	.9	.9	.9	.9	.9	1.0	1.0	1.0	3
4	1.1	1.1	1.1	1.1	1.2	1.2	1.2	1.2	1.2	1.3	1.3	1.3	1.3	4
5	1.4	1.4	1.4	1.4	1.5	1.5	1.5	1.5	1.6	1.6	1.6	1.6	1.7	5
6	1.6	1.7	1.7	1.7	1.7	1.8	1.8	1.8	1.9	1.9	1.9	2.0	2.0	6
7	1.9	1.9	2.0	2.0	2.0	2.1	2.1	2.1	2.2	2.2	2.2	2.3	2.3	7
8	2.2	2.2	2.2	2.3	2.3	2.4	2.4	2.4	2.5	2.5	2.6	2.6	2.6	8
9	2.4	2.5	2.5	2.6	2.6	2.7	2.7	2.7	2.8	2.8	2.9	2.9	3.0	9
10	2.7	2.8	2.8	2.9	2.9	3.0	3.0	3.1	3.1	3.2	3.2	3.3	3.3	10
11	3.0	3.0	3.1	3.1	3.2	3.2	3.3	3.4	3.4	3.5	3.5	3.6	3.6	11
12	3.2	3.3	3.4	3.4	3.5	3.5	3.6	3.7	3.7	3.8	3.8	3.9	4.0	12
13	3.5	3.6	3.6	3.7	3.8	3.8	3.9	4.0	4.0	4.1	4.2	4.2	4.3	13
14	3.8	3.9	3.9	4.0	4.1	4.1	4.2	4.3	4.3	4.4	4.5	4.6	4.6	14
15	4.1	4.1	4.2	4.3	4.4	4.4	4.5	4.6	4.7	4.7	4.8	4.9	5.0	15
16	4.3	4.4	4.5	4.6	4.6	4.7	4.8	4.9	5.0	5.0	5.1	5.2	5.3	16
17	4.6	4.7	4.8	4.8	4.9	5.0	5.1	5.2	5.3	5.4	5.4	5.5	5.6	17
18	4.9	5.0	5.0	5.1	5.2	5.3	5.4	5.5	5.6	5.7	5.8	5.9	5.9	18
19	5.1	5.2	5.3	5.4	5.5	5.6	5.7	5.8	5.9	6.0	6.1	6.2	6.3	19
20	5.4	5.5	5.6	5.7	5.8	5.9	6.0	6.1	6.2	6.3	6.4	6.5	6.6	20
21	5.7	5.8	5.9	6.0	6.1	6.2	6.3	6.4	6.5	6.6	6.7	6.8	6.9	21
22	5.9	6.1	6.2	6.3	6.4	6.5	6.6	6.7	6.8	6.9	7.0	7.2	7.3	22
23	6.2	6.3	6.4	6.6	6.7	6.8	6.9	7.0	7.1	7.2	7.4	7.5	7.6	23
24	6.5	6.6	6.7	6.8	7.0	7.1	7.2	7.3	7.4	7.6	7.7	7.8	7.9	24
25	6.8	6.9	7.0	7.1	7.3	7.4	7.5	7.6	7.8	7.9	8.0	8.1	8.3	25
26	7.0	7.2	7.3	7.4	7.5	7.7	7.8	7.9	8.1	8.2	8.3	8.5	8.6	26
27	7.3	7.4	7.6	7.7	7.8	8.0	8.1	8.2	8.4	8.5	8.6	8.8	8.9	27
28	7.6	7.7	7.8	8.0	8.1	8.3	8.4	8.5	8.7	8.8	9.0	9.1	9.2	28
29	7.8	8.0	8.1	8.3	8.4	8.6	8.7	8.8	9.0	9.1	9.3	9.4	9.6	29
30	8.1	8.3	8.4	8.6	8.7	8.9	9.0	9.2	9.3	9.5	9.6	9.8	9.9	30
31	8.4	8.5	8.7	8.8	9.0	9.1	9.3	9.5	9.6	9.8	9.9	10.1	10.2	31
32	8.6	8.8	9.0	9.1	9.3	9.4	9.6	9.8	9.9	10.1	10.2	10.4	10.6	32
33	8.9	9.1	9.2	9.4	9.6	9.7	9.9	10.1	10.2	10.4	10.6	10.7	10.9	33
34	9.2	9.4	9.5	9.7	9.9	10.0	10.2	10.4	10.5	10.7	10.9	11.1	11.2	34
35	9.5	9.6	9.8	10.0	10.2	10.3	10.5	10.7	10.9	11.0	11.2	11.4	11.6	35
36	9.7	9.9	10.1	10.3	10.4	10.6	10.8	11.0	11.2	11.3	11.5	11.7	11.9	36
37	10.0	10.2	10.4	10.5	10.7	10.9	11.1	11.3	11.5	11.7	11.8	12.0	12.2	37
38	10.3	10.5	10.6	10.8	11.0	11.2	11.4	11.6	11.8	12.0	12.2	12.4	12.5	38
39	10.5	10.7	10.9	11.1	11.3	11.5	11.7	11.9	12.1	12.3	12.5	12.7	12.9	39
40	10.8	11.0	11.2	11.4	11.6	11.8	12.0	12.2	12.4	12.6	12.8	13.0	13.2	40
41	11.1	11.3	11.5	11.7	11.9	12.1	12.3	12.5	12.7	12.9	13.1	13.3	13.5	41
42	11.3	11.6	11.8	12.0	12.2	12.4	12.6	12.8	13.0	13.2	13.4	13.7	13.9	42
43	11.6	11.8	12.0	12.3	12.5	12.7	12.9	13.1	13.3	13.5	13.8	14.0	14.2	43
44	11.9	12.1	12.3	12.5	12.8	13.0	13.2	13.4	13.6	13.9	14.1	14.3	14.5	44
45	12.2	12.4	12.6	12.8	13.1	13.3	13.5	13.7	14.0	14.2	14.4	14.6	14.9	45
46	12.4	12.7	12.9	13.1	13.3	13.6	13.8	14.0	14.3	14.5	14.7	15.0	15.2	46
47	12.7	12.9	13.2	13.4	13.6	13.9	14.1	14.3	14.6	14.8	15.0	15.3	15.5	47
48	13.0	13.2	13.4	13.7	13.9	14.2	14.4	14.6	14.9	15.1	15.4	15.6	15.8	48
49	13.2	13.5	13.7	14.0	14.2	14.5	14.7	14.9	15.2	15.4	15.7	15.9	16.2	49
50	13.5	13.8	14.0	14.3	14.5	14.8	15.0	15.3	15.5	15.8	16.0	16.3	16.5	50
51	13.8	14.0	14.3	14.5	14.8	15.0	15.3	15.6	15.8	16.1	16.3	16.6	16.8	51
52	14.0	14.3	14.6	14.8	15.1	15.3	15.6	15.8	16.1	16.4	16.6	16.9	17.2	52
53	14.3	14.6	14.8	15.1	15.4	15.6	15.9	16.2	16.4	15.7	17.0	17.2	17.5	53
54	14.6	14.9	15.1	15.4	15.7	15.9	16.2	16.5	16.7	17.0	17.3	17.6	17.8	54
55	14.9	15.1	15.4	15.7	16.0	16.2	16.5	16.8	17.1	17.3	17.6	17.9	18.2	55
56	15.1	15.4	15.7	16.0	16.2	16.5	16.8	17.1	17.4	17.6	17.9	18.2	18.5	56
57	15.4	15.7	16.0	16.2	16.5	16.8	17.1	17.4	17.7	18.0	18.2	18.5	18.8	57
58	15.7	16.0	16.2	16.5	16.8	17.1	17.4	17.7	18.0	18.3	18.6	18.9	19.1	58
59	15.9	16.2	16.5	16.8	17.1	17.4	17.7	18.0	18.3	18.6	18.9	19.2	19.5	59
60	16.2	16.5	16.8	17.1	17.4	17.7	18.0	18.3	18.6	18.9	19.2	19.5	19.8	60

Table 10a

Corrections to
BUBBLE SEXTANT
observations

For SUN or STAR	
observation by bubble sextant correct for refraction only, Table 15. The correction is always to be SUBTRACTED.	

See also " Notes ", p. vii.

To obtain the true altitude from a bubble sextant observation of the Moon, first correct as obs. alt. lower limb (☾) Table 9 (disregarding H.E.).

From this result *subtract* each of the two quantities given. i.e. these two quantities should be added together and their sum subtracted from the altitude corrected as for lower limb.

Second Correction
(See below)

H.P. '	Qty. '	Alt.	Qty. '
54.0	4.9		
.2	5.0		
.4	5.0	0°⎤	
.6	5.1		
.8	5.1	to⎬	.0
55.0	5.2		
.2	5.2	9°⎦	
.4	5.3		
.6	5.3		
.8	5.4		
56.0	5.5	10°⎤	
.2	5.5		
.4	5.6	to⎬	.1
.6	5.6		
.8	5.7	35°⎦	
57.0	5.7		
.2	5.8		
.4	5.8		
.6	5.9	36°⎤	
.8	5.9		
58.0	6.0	to⎬	.2
.2	6.1		
.4	6.1	70°⎦	
.6	6.2		
.8	6.2		
59.0	6.3		
.2	6.3	71°⎤	
.4	6.4		
.6	6.4	to⎬	.3
.8	6.5		
60.0	6.5	90°⎦	
.2	6.6		
.4	6.7		
.6	6.7		
.8	6.8		
61.0	6.8		

Table 11

AUGMENTATION OF THE MOON'S SEMI-DIAMETER

App. Alt.	Semi-diameter					
	14.5	15.0	15.5	16.0	16.5	17.0
°	'	'	'	'	'	'
0	.00	.00	.00	.00	.00	.00
5	.02	.02	.02	.03	.03	.03
10	.04	.04	.05	.05	.05	.05
15	.06	.06	.07	.07	.08	.08
20	.08	.08	.09	.09	.10	.11
30	.11	.12	.13	.14	.15	.16
40	.15	.16	.17	.18	.19	.20
50	.17	.19	.20	.21	.22	.24
60	.20	.21	.22	.24	.25	.27
70	.21	.23	.24	.26	.28	.29
90	.22	.24	.26	.28	.29	.31

Table 12

REDUCTION of the Moon's Equatorial Horizontal Parallax for the figure of the Earth

Lat.	Hor. Pax.		
	54'	57'	60'
°	'	'	'
0	.00	.00	.00
20	.02	.02	.02
30	.05	.05	.05
40	.08	.08	.08
50	.11	.11	.12
60	.13	.14	.15
70	.16	.17	.18
80	.17	.18	.19
90	.18	.19	.20

Table 13

CORRECTION OF TIME OF MOON'S MERIDIAN PASSAGE

West Long. Corr. **+**   East Long. Corr. **—**

Long.	Daily Variation of Meridian Passage (From Almanac)															Long.
	40m	42m	44m	46m	48m	50m	52m	54m	56m	58m	60m	62m	64m	66m		
°	m	m	m	m	m	m	m	m	m	m	m	m	m	m		°
5	.6	.6	.6	.6	.7	.7	.7	.8	.8	.8	.8	.9	.9	.9		5
10	1.1	1.2	1.2	1.3	1.3	1.4	1.4	1.5	1.6	1.6	1.7	1.7	1.8	1.8		10
15	1.7	1.8	1.8	1.9	2.0	2.1	2.2	2.2	2.3	2.4	2.5	2.6	2.7	2.8		15
20	2.2	2.3	2.4	2.6	2.7	2.8	2.9	3.0	3.1	3.2	3.3	3.4	3.6	3.7		20
25	2.8	2.9	3.1	3.2	3.3	3.5	3.6	3.8	3.9	4.0	4.2	4.3	4.4	4.6		25
30	3.3	3.5	3.7	3.8	4.0	4.2	4.3	4.5	4.7	4.8	5.0	5.2	5.3	5.5		30
35	3.9	4.1	4.3	4.5	4.7	4.9	5.1	5.3	5.4	5.6	5.8	6.0	6.2	6.4		35
40	4.4	4.7	4.9	5.1	5.3	5.6	5.8	6.0	6.2	6.4	6.7	6.9	7.1	7.3		40
45	5.0	5.2	5.5	5.8	6.0	6.2	6.5	6.8	7.0	7.2	7.5	7.8	8.0	8.2		45
50	5.6	5.8	6.1	6.4	6.7	6.9	7.2	7.5	7.8	8.1	8.3	8.6	8.9	9.2		50
55	6.1	6.4	6.7	7.0	7.3	7.6	7.9	8.3	8.6	8.9	9.2	9.5	9.8	10.1		55
60	6.7	7.0	7.3	7.7	8.0	8.3	8.7	9.0	9.3	9.7	10.0	10.3	10.7	11.0		60
65	7.2	7.6	7.9	8.3	8.7	9.0	9.4	9.8	10.1	10.5	10.8	11.2	11.6	11.9		65
70	7.8	8.2	8.6	8.9	9.3	9.7	10.1	10.5	10.9	11.3	11.7	12.1	12.4	12.8		70
75	8.3	8.8	9.2	9.6	10.0	10.4	10.8	11.2	11.7	12.1	12.5	12.9	13.3	13.8		75
80	8.9	9.3	9.8	10.2	10.7	11.1	11.5	12.0	12.4	12.9	13.3	13.8	14.2	14.7		80
85	9.4	9.9	10.4	10.9	11.3	11.8	12.3	12.8	13.2	13.7	14.2	14.6	15.1	15.6		85
90	10.0	10.5	11.0	11.5	12.0	12.5	13.0	13.5	14.0	14.5	15.0	15.5	16.0	16.5		90
95	10.6	11.1	11.6	12.1	12.7	13.2	13.7	14.3	14.8	15.3	15.8	16.3	16.9	17.4		95
100	11.1	11.7	12.2	12.8	13.3	13.9	14.4	15.0	15.6	16.1	16.7	17.2	17.8	18.3		100
105	11.7	12.2	12.8	13.4	14.0	14.6	15.2	15.8	16.3	16.9	17.5	18.1	18.7	19.2		105
110	12.2	12.8	13.4	14.1	14.7	15.3	15.9	16.5	17.1	17.7	18.3	18.9	19.5	20.2		110
115	12.8	13.4	14.1	14.7	15.3	16.0	16.6	17.3	17.9	18.5	19.2	19.8	20.4	21.1		115
120	13.3	14.0	14.7	15.3	16.0	16.7	17.3	18.0	18.7	19.3	20.0	20.7	21.3	22.0		120
125	13.8	14.6	15.3	16.0	16.7	17.4	18.1	18.8	19.4	20.1	20.8	21.5	22.2	22.9		125
130	14.4	15.2	15.9	16.6	17.3	18.1	18.8	19.5	20.2	20.9	21.7	22.4	23.1	23.8		130
135	15.0	15.8	16.5	17.2	18.0	18.8	19.5	20.2	21.0	21.7	22.5	23.2	24.0	24.8		135
140	15.6	16.3	17.1	17.9	18.7	19.4	20.2	21.0	21.8	22.6	23.3	24.1	24.9	25.7		140
145	16.1	16.9	17.7	18.5	19.3	20.1	20.9	21.8	22.6	23.4	24.2	25.0	25.8	26.6		145
150	16.7	17.5	18.3	19.2	20.0	20.8	21.7	22.5	23.3	24.2	25.0	25.8	26.7	27.5		150
155	17.2	18.1	18.9	19.8	20.7	21.5	22.4	23.3	24.1	25.0	25.8	26.7	27.6	28.4		155
160	17.8	18.7	19.6	20.4	21.3	22.2	23.1	24.0	24.9	25.8	26.7	27.6	28.4	29.3		160
165	18.3	19.2	20.2	21.1	22.0	22.9	23.8	24.8	25.7	26.6	27.5	28.4	29.3	30.2		165
170	18.9	19.8	20.8	21.7	22.7	23.6	24.6	25.5	26.5	27.4	28.3	29.3	30.2	31.2		170
175	19.4	20.4	21.4	22.4	23.3	24.3	25.3	26.3	27.2	28.2	29.2	30.1	31.1	32.1		175
180	20.0	21.0	22.0	23.0	24.0	25.0	26.0	27.0	28.0	29.0	30.0	31.0	32.0	33.0		180

Table 14

DIP OF SEA HORIZON

H.E. Ft.	Dip ′	H.E. Ft.	Dip ′	H.E. Ft.	Dip ′
4	1.9	58	7.4	160	12.3
5	2.2	59	7.5	165	12.5
6	2.4	60	7.5	170	12.6
7	2.6	61	7.6	175	12.8
8	2.7	62	7.6	180	13.0
9	2.9	63	7.7	185	13.2
10	3.1	64	7.8	190	13.4
11	3.2	65	7.8	195	13.5
12	3.4	66	7.9	200	13.7
13	3.5	67	7.9	205	13.9
14	3.6	68	8.0	210	14.1
15	3.8	69	8.1	215	14.2
16	3.9	70	8.1	220	14.4
17	4.0	71	8.2	225	14.6
18	4.1	72	8.2	230	14.7
19	4.2	73	8.3	235	14.9
20	4.3	74	8.3	240	15.0
21	4.4	75	8.4	245	15.2
22	4.5	76	8.5	250	15.3
23	4.7	77	8.5	255	15.5
24	4.8	78	8.6	260	15.6
25	4.9	79	8.6	265	15.8
26	4.9	80	8.7	270	15.9
27	5.0	81	8.7	275	16.1
28	5.1	82	8.8	280	16.2
29	5.2	83	8.8	285	16.4
30	5.3	84	8.9	290	16.5
31	5.4	85	8.9	295	16.7
32	5.5	86	9.0	300	16.8
33	5.6	87	9.0	305	16.9
34	5.7	88	9.1	310	17.1
35	5.7	89	9.2	315	17.2
36	5.8	90	9.2	320	17.4
37	5.9	91	9.3	325	17.5
38	6.0	92	9.3	330	17.6
39	6.1	93	9.4	335	17.8
40	6.1	94	9.4	340	17.9
41	6.2	95	9.5	345	18.0
42	6.3	96	9.5	350	18.1
43	6.4	97	9.6	360	18.4
44	6.4	98	9.6	370	18.7
45	6.5	99	9.7	380	18.9
46	6.6	100	9.7	390	19.2
47	6.6	105	9.9	400	19.4
48	6.7	110	10.2	410	19.7
49	6.8	115	10.4	420	19.9
50	6.9	120	10.6	430	20.1
51	6.9	125	10.8	440	20.3
52	7.0	130	11.1	450	20.6
53	7.1	135	11.3	460	20.8
54	7.1	140	11.5	470	21.0
55	7.2	145	11.7	480	21.3
56	7.3	150	11.9	490	21.5
57	7.3	155	12.1	500	21.7

Table 15

MEAN REFRACTION
(GARFINKEL)
Temp. 50°F. (10°C.)
Bar. 29.83 ins. (1010 mb.)

App. Alt.	Refr. ′	App. Alt.	Refr. ′	App. Alt.	Refr. ′
0 00	34.5	5 30	9.1	14 00	3.8
05	33.4	40	8.9	20	3.7
10	32.4	50	8.7	40	3.7
15	31.4				
20	30.5	6 00	8.5	15 00	3.6
25	29.6	10	8.3	20	3.5
		20	8.1	40	3.4
30	28.7	30	7.9		
35	27.9	40	7.7	16 00	3.3
40	27.1	50	7.6	30	3.2
45	26.4			17 00	3.1
50	25.7	7 00	7.4	30	3.0
55	25.0	10	7.2	18 00	3.0
		20	7.1	30	2.9
1 00	24.3	30	7.0	19 00	2.8
05	23.7	40	6.8	30	2.7
10	23.1	50	6.7		
15	22.5			20	2.6
20	22.0	8 00	6.6	21	2.5
25	21.5	10	6.4	22	2.4
		20	6.3	23	2.3
		30	6.2	24	2.2
30	20.9	40	6.1	25	2.1
35	20.5	50	6.0	26	2.0
40	20.0			27	1.9
45	19.5	9 00	5.9	28	1.8
50	19.1	10	5.8		
55	18.7	20	5.7	30	1.7
		30	5.6	32	1.6
2 00	18.3	40	5.5	34	1.4
10	17.5	50	5.4	36	1.3
20	16.8			38	1.2
30	16.1	10 00	5.3		
40	15.5	10	5.2	41	1.1
50	14.9	20	5.2	44	1.0
		30	5.1	47	0.9
3 00	14.4	40	5.0		
10	13.9	50	4.9	50	0.8
20	13.4			55	0.7
30	13.0	11 00	4.9	60	0.6
40	12.5	10	4.8	65	0.5
50	12.1	20	4.7	70	0.4
		30	4.6	75	0.3
		40	4.6	80	0.2
4 00	11.8	50	4.5	85	0.1
10	11.4				
20	11.1	12 00	4.5	90	0.0
30	10.7	10	4.4		
40	10.4	20	4.3		
50	10.1	40	4.2		
5 00	9.9	13 00	4.1		
10	9.6	20	4.0		
20	9.4	40	3.9		

Table 16

ADDITIONAL ALTITUDE CORRECTIONS
for
NON-STANDARD CONDITIONS OF REFRACTION

Bar. ins.	Tem. F.	Apparent Altitude												Tem. C.	Bar. mb.
		0 00	0 20	0 40	1 00	1 30	2 00	2 30	3 00	5 00	8 00	20 00	60		
	0	−8.5	−7.1	−6.0	−5.2	−4.2	−3.5	−3.0	−2.6	−1.7	−1.1	−0.4	−0.1	−18	
	10	−6.9	−5.8	−4.9	−4.3	−3.5	−2.9	−2.5	−2.1	−1.4	−0.9	−0.3	−0.1	−12	
	20	−5.4	−4.6	−3.9	−3.4	−2.8	−2.3	−2.0	−1.7	−1.1	−0.7	−0.3	−0.1	− 7	
	30	−4.0	−3.4	−2.9	−2.5	−2.1	−1.8	−1.5	−1.3	−0.9	−0.6	−0.2	0.0	− 1	
31.0	40	−2.7	−2.3	−2.0	−1.8	−1.5	−1.2	−1.1	−0.9	−0.6	−0.4	−0.2	0.0	+ 4	1050
	50	−1.5	−1.3	−1.1	−1.0	−0.9	−0.7	−0.6	−0.6	−0.4	−0.3	−0.1	0.0	+10	
	60	−0.3	−0.3	−0.3	−0.3	−0.3	−0.3	−0.2	−0.2	−0.2	−0.1	0.0	0.0	+16	
	70	+0.8	+0.6	+0.5	+0.4	+0.3	+0.2	+0.1	+0.1	0.0	0.0	0.0	0.0	+21	
	80	+1.8	+1.5	+1.2	+1.0	+0.8	+0.6	+0.5	+0.4	+0.2	+0.1	+0.1	0.0	+27	
	0	−7.7	−6.4	−5.4	−4.7	−3.8	−3.2	−2.7	−2.3	−1.5	−0.9	−0.4	−0.1	−18	
	10	−6.2	−5.1	−4.4	−3.8	−3.1	−2.6	−2.2	−1.9	−1.2	−0.8	−0.3	−0.1	−12	
	20	−4.7	−4.0	−3.4	−2.9	−2.4	−2.0	−1.7	−1.5	−0.9	−0.6	−0.2	0.0	− 7	
	30	−3.3	−2.8	−2.4	−2.1	−1.7	−1.4	−1.2	−1.1	−0.7	−0.4	−0.2	0.0	− 1	
30.5	40	−2.1	−1.8	−1.5	−1.3	−1.1	−0.9	−0.8	−0.7	−0.5	−0.3	−0.1	0.0	+ 4	1033
	50	−0.8	−0.8	−0.7	−0.6	−0.5	−0.4	−0.4	−0.3	−0.2	−0.1	−0.1	0.0	+10	
	60	+0.3	+0.2	+0.2	+0.1	+0.1	0.0	0.0	0.0	0.0	0.0	0.0	0.0	+16	
	70	+1.4	+1.1	+0.9	+0.8	+0.6	+0.5	+0.4	+0.3	+0.2	+0.1	+0.1	0.0	+21	
	80	+2.3	+2.0	+1.6	+1.4	+1.1	+0.9	+0.8	+0.7	+0.4	+0.2	+0.1	0.0	+27	
	0	−6.9	−5.8	−4.9	−4.2	−3.4	−2.8	−2.4	−2.0	−1.3	−0.8	−0.3	−0.1	−18	
	10	−5.4	−4.5	−3.8	−3.3	−2.7	−2.2	−1.9	−1.6	−1.0	−0.6	−0.2	0.0	−12	
	20	−4.0	−3.3	−2.8	−2.4	−2.0	−1.6	−1.4	−1.2	−0.8	−0.5	−0.2	0.0	− 7	
	30	−2.7	−2.2	−1.9	−1.6	−1.3	−1.1	−0.9	−0.8	−0.5	−0.3	−0.1	0.0	− 1	
30.0	40	−1.4	−1.2	−1.0	−0.9	−0.7	−0.6	−0.5	−0.4	−0.3	−0.2	−0.1	0.0	+ 4	1016
	50	−0.2	−0.2	−0.2	−0.2	−0.1	−0.1	−0.1	−0.1	−0.1	0.0	0.0	0.0	+10	
	60	+0.9	+0.7	+0.6	+0.5	+0.4	+0.4	+0.3	+0.3	+0.2	+0.1	+0.1	0.0	+16	
	70	+1.9	+1.6	+1.4	+1.2	+0.9	+0.8	+0.7	+0.6	+0.4	+0.2	+0.1	0.0	+21	
	80	+2.9	+2.5	+2.1	+1.8	+1.5	+1.2	+1.0	+0.9	+0.6	+0.3	+0.2	0.0	+27	
	0	−6.2	−5.1	−4.3	−3.6	−2.9	−2.4	−2.0	−1.7	−1.1	−0.7	−0.3	−0.1	−18	
	10	−4.7	−3.9	−3.3	−2.8	−2.2	−1.8	−1.5	−1.3	−0.8	−0.5	−0.2	0.0	−12	
	20	−3.3	−2.7	−2.3	−2.0	−1.6	−1.3	−1.1	−0.9	−0.6	−0.4	−0.2	0.0	− 7	
	30	−2.0	−1.6	−1.4	−1.2	−0.9	−0.8	−0.6	−0.5	−0.3	−0.2	−0.1	0.0	− 1	
29.5	40	−0.7	−0.6	−0.5	−0.4	−0.3	−0.3	−0.2	−0.2	−0.1	−0.1	0.0	0.0	+ 4	999
	50	+0.4	+0.4	+0.3	+0.3	+0.2	+0.2	+0.2	+0.2	+0.1	+0.1	0.0	0.0	+10	
	60	+1.5	+1.3	+1.1	+0.9	+0.8	+0.7	+0.6	+0.5	+0.3	+0.2	+0.1	0.0	+16	
	70	+2.5	+2.1	+1.8	+1.6	+1.3	+1.1	+0.9	+0.8	+0.5	+0.3	+0.1	0.0	+21	
	80	+3.5	+3.0	+2.5	+2.2	+1.8	+1.5	+1.3	+1.1	+0.7	+0.4	+0.2	0.0	+27	
	0	−5.4	−4.4	−3.7	−3.1	−2.5	−2.1	−1.7	−1.5	−0.9	−0.5	−0.2	0.0	−18	
	10	−3.9	−3.2	−2.7	−2.3	−1.8	−1.5	−1.2	−1.1	−0.6	−0.4	−0.1	0.0	−12	
	20	−2.6	−2.1	−1.8	−1.5	−1.2	−0.9	−0.8	−0.7	−0.4	−0.2	−0.1	0.0	− 7	
	30	−1.3	−1.0	−0.9	−0.7	−0.5	−0.4	−0.4	−0.3	−0.2	−0.1	0.0	0.0	− 1	
29.0	40	−0.1	0.0	0.0	0.0	0.0	+0.1	+0.1	+0.1	+0.1	0.0	0.0	0.0	+ 4	982
	50	+1.0	+0.9	+0.8	+0.7	+0.6	+0.5	+0.5	+0.4	+0.3	+0.2	+0.1	0.0	+10	
	60	+2.1	+1.8	+1.6	+1.4	+1.1	+1.0	+0.8	+0.7	+0.5	+0.3	+0.1	0.0	+16	
	70	+3.1	+2.7	+2.3	+2.0	+1.6	+1.4	+1.2	+1.0	+0.7	+0.4	+0.2	0.0	+21	
	80	+4.0	+3.5	+3.0	+2.6	+2.1	+1.8	+1.6	+1.3	+0.9	+0.5	+0.2	0.0	+27	
	0	−4.6	−3.8	−3.1	−2.6	−2.1	−1.7	−1.4	−1.2	−0.7	−0.4	−0.2	0.0	−18	
	10	−3.2	−2.6	−2.2	−1.8	−1.4	−1.1	−0.9	−0.8	−0.5	−0.3	−0.1	0.0	−12	
	20	−1.9	−1.5	−1.2	−1.0	−0.8	−0.6	−0.5	−0.4	−0.2	−0.1	−0.1	0.0	− 7	
	30	−0.6	−0.5	−0.3	−0.2	−0.2	−0.1	−0.1	0.0	0.0	0.0	0.0	0.0	− 1	
28.5	40	+0.6	+0.5	+0.5	+0.5	+0.4	+0.4	+0.4	+0.3	+0.2	+0.2	+0.1	0.0	+ 4	965
	50	+1.7	+1.4	+1.3	+1.1	+1.0	+0.8	+0.7	+0.7	+0.4	+0.3	+0.1	0.0	+10	
	60	+2.7	+2.3	+2.0	+1.8	+1.5	+1.3	+1.1	+1.0	+0.6	+0.4	+0.2	0.0	+16	
	70	+3.7	+3.2	+2.7	+2.4	+2.0	+1.7	+1.5	+1.3	+0.8	+0.5	+0.2	0.0	+21	
	80	+4.6	+4.0	+3.4	+3.0	+2.5	+2.1	+1.8	+1.6	+1.0	+0.6	+0.3	+0.1	+27	

The corrections in the above table are to be applied, with the sign given, as additional corrections to the altitude.

Table 17

DIP OF THE SHORE HORIZON
(or Dip at Different Distances from Observer)

Dist. M.	Height of Eye in Feet															Dist. Yds.
	10	15	20	25	30	35	40	45	50	55	60	65	70	75	80	
.1	56.6	84.9	113.1	141	170	198	226	254	283	310	339	367	396	424	452	203
.2	28.4	45.2	56.6	70.8	84.9	99.0	113	127	142	155	170	184	198	212	226	405
.3	19.0	28.4	37.8	47.2	56.7	66.1	75.5	84.9	94.4	104	113	123	132	141	151	608
.4	14.3	21.4	28.4	35.5	42.6	49.6	56.7	63.8	70.8	77.9	84.9	92.0	99.1	106	113	811
.5	11.5	17.2	22.8	28.5	34.1	39.8	45.4	51.1	56.7	62.4	68.0	73.7	79.3	85.0	90.6	1013
.6	9.7	14.4	19.1	23.8	28.5	33.2	37.9	42.7	47.4	52.0	56.8	61.5	66.2	70.9	75.6	1216
.7	8.4	12.4	16.4	20.5	24.5	28.6	32.6	36.6	40.7	44.7	48.7	52.8	56.8	60.8	64.9	1419
.8	7.4	10.9	14.5	18.0	21.5	25.1	28.6	32.1	35.7	39.2	42.7	46.2	49.8	53.3	56.8	1621
.9	6.6	9.8	12.9	16.1	19.2	22.4	25.5	28.6	31.8	34.8	38.1	41.2	44.3	47.5	50.6	1824
1.0	6.1	8.9	11.7	14.5	17.4	20.2	23.0	25.9	28.7	31.5	34.3	37.1	40.0	42.8	45.6	2027
1.1	5.6	8.2	10.7	13.3	15.9	18.4	21.0	23.6	26.1	28.7	31.3	33.9	36.4	39.0	41.6	2229
1.2	5.2	7.6	9.9	12.3	14.6	17.0	19.3	21.7	24.0	26.4	28.8	31.1	33.5	35.8	38.2	2432
1.3	4.9	7.1	9.2	11.4	13.6	15.8	17.9	20.1	22.3	24.5	26.6	28.8	31.0	33.2	35.3	2635
1.4	4.6	6.6	8.6	10.7	12.7	14.7	16.7	18.7	20.8	22.8	24.8	26.8	28.8	30.9	32.9	2837
1.5	4.4	6.3	8.2	10.1	11.9	13.8	15.7	17.6	19.5	21.4	23.2	25.1	27.0	28.9	30.8	3040
1.6	4.2	5.9	7.7	9.5	11.3	13.0	14.8	16.6	18.3	20.1	21.9	23.6	25.4	27.2	28.9	3243
1.7	4.0	5.7	7.4	9.0	10.7	12.4	14.0	15.7	17.3	19.0	20.7	22.3	24.0	25.7	27.3	3445
1.8	3.9	5.4	7.0	8.6	10.2	11.7	13.3	14.9	16.4	18.0	19.6	21.2	22.7	24.3	25.9	3648
1.9	3.7	5.3	6.8	8.2	9.7	11.1	12.7	14.2	15.7	17.2	18.6	20.1	21.6	23.1	24.6	3851
2.0	3.6	5.1	6.5	7.9	9.3	10.7	12.1	13.5	14.9	16.4	17.8	19.2	20.6	22.0	23.4	4053
2.2	3.5	4.8	6.1	7.4	8.6	9.9	11.2	12.5	13.8	15.1	16.3	17.7	18.9	20.2	21.5	4459
2.4	3.3	4.5	5.7	6.9	8.1	9.3	10.4	11.6	12.8	14.0	15.1	16.3	17.5	18.7	19.8	4864
2.6	3.3	4.4	5.4	6.5	7.6	8.7	9.8	10.9	12.0	13.1	14.1	15.2	16.3	17.4	18.5	5269
2.8	3.2	4.2	5.2	6.2	7.2	8.2	9.3	10.3	11.3	12.3	13.3	14.3	15.3	16.3	17.3	5675
3.0	*	4.0	5.0	5.9	6.9	7.8	8.8	9.7	10.6	11.6	12.6	13.5	14.5	15.4	16.3	6080
3.5	—	3.9	4.7	5.5	6.3	7.1	7.9	8.7	9.6	10.4	11.2	12.0	12.8	13.6	14.4	7093
4.0	—	*	—	5.2	5.9	6.6	7.3	8.0	8.7	9.5	10.2	10.9	11.6	12.3	13.0	8107
4.5	—	—	—	5.0	5.7	6.3	6.9	7.6	8.2	8.8	9.4	10.1	10.7	11.3	11.9	9120
5.0	—	—	—	—	5.5	6.1	6.6	7.2	7.8	8.3	8.9	9.5	10.0	10.6	11.2	10133
6.0	—	—	—	—	—	—	—	6.7	7.2	7.7	8.2	8.7	9.1	9.6	10.1	12160
7.0	—	—	—	—	—	—	—	—	7.0	7.4	7.8	8.2	8.6	9.0	9.4	14187
8.0	—	—	—	—	—	—	—	—	—	—	—	8.0	8.3	8.7	9.0	16213

* The dip in these columns ceases where the sea horizon intervenes, in which case the ordinary altitude correction tables may be used.

120

Table 18
LOGARITHMS

No.	Log.	No.	Log.	No.	Log.	No.	Log.
1	0.00000	26	1.41497	51	1.70757	76	1.88081
2	0.30103	27	1.43136	52	1.71600	77	1.88649
3	0.47712	28	1.44716	53	1.72428	78	1.89209
4	0.60206	29	1.46240	54	1.73239	79	1.89763
5	0.69897	30	1.47712	55	1.74036	80	1.90309
6	0.77815	31	1.49136	56	1.74819	81	1.90849
7	0.84510	32	1.50515	57	1.75587	82	1.91381
8	0.90309	33	1.51851	58	1.76343	83	1.91908
9	0.95424	34	1.53148	59	1.77085	84	1.92428
10	1.00000	35	1.54407	60	1.77815	85	1.92942
11	1.04139	36	1.55630	61	1.78533	86	1.93450
12	1.07918	37	1.56820	62	1.79239	87	1.93952
13	1.11394	38	1.57978	63	1.79934	88	1.94448
14	1.14613	39	1.59106	64	1.80618	89	1.94939
15	1.17609	40	1.60206	65	1.81291	90	1.95424
16	1.20412	41	1.61278	66	1.81954	91	1.95904
17	1.23045	42	1.62325	67	1.82607	92	1.96379
18	1.25527	43	1.63347	68	1.83251	93	1.96848
19	1.27875	44	1.64345	69	1.83885	94	1.97313
20	1.30103	45	1.65321	70	1.84510	95	1.97772
21	1.32222	46	1.66276	71	1.85126	96	1.98227
22	1.34242	47	1.67210	72	1.85733	97	1.98677
23	1.36173	48	1.68124	73	1.86332	98	1.99123
24	1.38021	49	1.69020	74	1.86923	99	1.99564
25	1.39794	50	1.69897	75	1.87506	100	2.00000

Table 18

LOGARITHMS

| Nos. { 1—
15— | | | | | | | | | | | Logs 00000
20385 |

No.	0	1	2	3	4	5	6	7	8	9	No.	5th Fig.	Log Diff.
100	.00000	.00043	.00087	.00130	.00173	.00217	.00260	.00303	.00346	.00389	100		
101	.00432	.00475	.00518	.00561	.00604	.00647	.00689	.00732	.00775	.00817	101	1	4
102	.00860	.00903	.00945	.00988	.01030	.01072	.01115	.01157	.01199	.01242	102	2	8
103	.01284	.01326	.01368	.01410	.01452	.01494	.01536	.01578	.01620	.01662	103	3	12
104	.01703	.01745	.01787	.01828	.01870	.01912	.01953	.01995	.02036	.02078	104	4	16
105	.02119	.02160	.02202	.02243	.02284	.02325	.02366	.02407	.02449	.02490	105	5	21
106	.02531	.02572	.02612	.02653	.02694	.02735	.02776	.02816	.02857	.02898	106	6	25
107	.02938	.02979	.03019	.03060	.03100	.03141	.03181	.03222	.03262	.03302	107	7	28
108	.03342	.03383	.03423	.03463	.03503	.03543	.03583	.03623	.03663	.03703	108	8	33
109	.03743	.03782	.03822	.03862	.03902	.03941	.03981	.04021	.04060	.04100	109	9	37
110	.04139	.04179	.04218	.04258	.04297	.04336	.04376	.04415	.04454	.04493	110		
111	.04532	.04571	.04610	.04650	.04689	.04727	.04766	.04805	.04844	.04883	111	1	4
112	.04922	.04961	.04999	.05038	.05077	.05115	.05154	.05192	.05231	.05269	112	2	8
113	.05308	.05346	.05385	.05423	.05461	.05500	.05538	.05576	.05614	.05652	113	3	11
114	.05690	.05729	.05767	.05805	.05843	.05881	.05918	.05956	.05994	.06032	114	4	15
115	.06070	.06108	.06145	.06183	.06221	.06258	.06296	.06333	.06371	.06408	115	5	19
116	.06446	.06483	.06521	.06558	.06595	.06633	.06670	.06707	.06744	.06781	116	6	23
117	.06819	.06856	.06893	.06930	.06967	.07004	.07041	.07078	.07115	.07151	117	7	26
118	.07188	.07225	.07262	.07298	.07335	.07372	.07408	.07445	.07482	.07518	118	8	30
119	.07555	.07591	.07628	.07664	.07700	.07737	.07773	.07809	.07846	.07882	119	9	34
120	.07918	.07954	.07990	.08027	.08063	.08099	.08135	.08171	.08207	.08243	120		
121	.08279	.08314	.08350	.08386	.08422	.08458	.08493	.08529	.08565	.08600	121	1	3
122	.08636	.08672	.08707	.08743	.08778	.08814	.08849	.08884	.08920	.08955	122	2	7
123	.08991	.09026	.09061	.09096	.09132	.09167	.09202	.09237	.09272	.09307	123	3	10
124	.09342	.09377	.09412	.09447	.09482	.09517	.09552	.09587	.09621	.09656	124	4	14
125	.09691	.09726	.09760	.09795	.09830	.09864	.09899	.09934	.09968	.10003	125	5	17
126	**.10037**	**.10072**	**.10106**	**.10140**	**.10175**	**.10209**	**.10243**	**.10278**	**.10312**	.10346	126	6	21
127	.10380	.10415	.10449	.10483	.10517	.10551	.10585	.10619	.10653	.10687	127	7	24
128	.10721	.10755	.10789	.10823	.10857	.10890	.10924	.10958	.10992	.11025	128	8	28
129	.11059	.11093	.11126	.11160	.11193	.11227	.11261	.11294	.11327	.11361	129	9	31
130	.11394	.11428	.11461	.11494	.11528	.11561	.11594	.11628	.11661	.11694	130		
131	.11727	.11760	.11793	.11826	.11860	.11893	.11926	.11959	.11992	.12024	131	1	3
132	.12057	.12090	.12123	.12156	.12189	.12222	.12254	.12287	.12320	.12352	132	2	6
133	.12385	.12418	.12450	.12483	.12516	.12548	.12581	.12613	.12646	.12678	133	3	10
134	.12710	.12743	.12775	.12808	.12840	.12872	.12905	.12937	.12969	.13001	134	4	13
135	.13033	.13066	.13098	.13130	.13162	.13194	.13226	.13258	.13290	.13322	135	5	16
136	.13354	.13386	.13418	.13450	.13481	.13513	.13545	.13577	.13609	.13640	136	6	19
137	.13672	.13704	.13735	.13767	.13799	.13830	.13862	.13893	.13925	.13956	137	7	22
138	.13988	.14019	.14051	.14082	.14114	.14145	.14176	.14208	.14239	.14270	138	8	26
139	.14301	.14333	.14364	.14395	.14426	.14457	.14489	.14520	.14551	.14582	139	9	29
140	.14613	.14644	.14675	.14706	.14737	.14768	.14799	.14829	.14860	.14891	140		
141	.14922	.14953	.14983	.15014	.15045	.15076	.15106	.15137	.15168	.15198	141	1	3
142	.15229	.15259	.15290	.15320	.15351	.15381	.15412	.15442	.15473	.15503	142	2	6
143	.15534	.15564	.15594	.15625	.15655	.15685	.15715	.15746	.15776	.15806	143	3	9
144	.15836	.15866	.15897	.15927	.15957	.15987	.16017	.16047	.16077	.16107	144	4	12
145	.16137	.16167	.16197	.16227	.16256	.16286	.16316	.16346	.16376	.16406	145	5	15
146	.16435	.16465	.16495	.16524	.16554	.16584	.16613	.16643	.16673	.16702	146	6	18
147	.16732	.16761	.16791	.16820	.16850	.16879	.16909	.16938	.16967	.16997	147	7	21
148	.17026	.17056	.17085	.17114	.17143	.17173	.17202	.17231	.17260	.17289	148	8	24
149	.17319	.17348	.17377	.17406	.17435	.17464	.17493	.17522	.17551	.17580	149	9	27
150	.17609	.17638	.17667	.17696	.17725	.17754	.17782	.17811	.17840	.17869	150		
151	.17898	.17926	.17955	.17984	.18013	.18041	.18070	.18099	.18127	.18156	151	1	3
152	.18184	.18213	.18241	.18270	.18298	.18327	.18355	.18384	.18412	.18441	152	2	6
153	.18469	.18498	.18526	.18554	.18583	.18611	.18639	.18667	.18696	.18724	153	3	8
154	.18752	.18780	.18808	.18837	.18865	.18893	.18921	.18949	.18977	.19005	154	4	11
155	.19033	.19061	.19089	.19117	.19145	.19173	.19201	.19229	.19257	.19285	155	5	14
156	.19312	.19340	.19368	.19396	.19424	.19451	.19479	.19507	.19535	.19562	156	6	17
157	.19590	.19618	.19645	.19673	.19700	.19728	.19756	.19783	.19811	.19838	157	7	20
158	.19866	.19893	.19921	.19948	.19976	**.20003**	**.20030**	**.20058**	**.20085**	**.20112**	158	8	22
159	**.20140**	**.20167**	**.20194**	**.20222**	**.20249**	.20276	.20303	.20330	.20358	.20385	159	9	25
	0	1	2	3	4	5	6	7	8	9			

Table 18

LOGARITHMS

No.	0	1	2	3	4	5	6	7	8	9	No.	5th Fig.	Log Diff.
160	.20412	.20439	.20466	.20493	.20520	.20548	.20575	.20602	.20629	.20656	160		
161	.20683	.20710	.20737	.20763	.20790	.20817	.20844	.20871	.20898	.20925	161	1	3
162	.20952	.20978	.21005	.21032	.21059	.21085	.21112	.21139	.21165	.21192	162	2	5
163	.21219	.21245	.21272	.21299	.21325	.21352	.21378	.21405	.21431	.21458	163	3	8
164	.21484	.21511	.21537	.21564	.21590	.21617	.21643	.21669	.21696	.21722	164	4	11
165	.21748	.21775	.21801	.21827	.21854	.21880	.21906	.21932	.21958	.21985	165	5	13
166	.22011	.22037	.22063	.22089	.22115	.22141	.22167	.22194	.22220	.22246	166	6	16
167	.22272	.22298	.22324	.22350	.22376	.22401	.22427	.22453	.22479	.22505	167	7	18
168	.22531	.22557	.22583	.22608	.22634	.22660	.22686	.22712	.22737	.22763	168	8	21
169	.22789	.22814	.22840	.22866	.22891	.22917	.22943	.22968	.22994	.23019	169	9	24
170	.23045	.23070	.23096	.23121	.23147	.23172	.23198	.23223	.23249	.23274	170		
171	.23300	.23325	.23350	.23376	.23401	.23426	.23452	.23477	.23502	.23528	171	1	2
172	.23553	.23578	.23603	.23629	.23654	.23679	.23704	.23729	.23754	.23779	172	2	5
173	.23805	.23830	.23855	.23880	.23905	.23930	.23955	.23980	.24005	.24030	173	3	7
174	.24055	.24080	.24105	.24130	.24155	.24180	.24204	.24229	.24254	.24279	174	4	10
175	.24304	.24329	.24353	.24378	.24403	.24428	.24452	.24477	.24502	.24527	175	5	12
176	.24551	.24576	.24601	.24625	.24650	.24674	.24699	.24724	.24748	.24773	176	6	15
177	.24797	.24822	.24846	.24871	.24895	.24920	.24944	.24969	.24993	.25018	177	7	17
178	.25042	.25066	.25091	.25115	.25139	.25164	.25188	.25212	.25237	.25261	178	8	20
179	.25285	.25310	.25334	.25358	.25382	.25406	.25431	.25455	.25479	.25503	179	9	22
180	.25527	.25551	.25575	.25600	.25624	.25648	.25672	.25696	.25720	.25744	180		
181	.25768	.25792	.25816	.25840	.25864	.25888	.25912	.25935	.25959	.25983	181	1	2
182	.26007	.26031	.26055	.26079	.26102	.26126	.26150	.26174	.26198	.26221	182	2	5
183	.26245	.26269	.26293	.26316	.26340	.26364	.26387	.26411	.26435	.26458	183	3	7
184	.26482	.26505	.26529	.26553	.26576	.26600	.26623	.26647	.26670	.26694	184	4	9
185	.26717	.26741	.26764	.26788	.26811	.26834	.26858	.26881	.26905	.26928	185	5	12
186	.26951	.26975	.26998	.27021	.27045	.27068	.27091	.27114	.27138	.27161	186	6	14
187	.27184	.27207	.27231	.27254	.27277	.27300	.27323	.27346	.27370	.27393	187	7	16
188	.27416	.27439	.27462	.27485	.27508	.27531	.27554	.27577	.27600	.27623	188	8	19
189	.27646	.27669	.27692	.27715	.27738	.27761	.27784	.27807	.27830	.27852	189	9	21
190	.27875	.27898	.27921	.27944	.27967	.27989	.28012	.28035	.28058	.28081	190		
191	.28103	.28126	.28149	.28171	.28194	.28217	.28240	.28262	.28285	.28307	191	1	2
192	.28330	.28353	.28375	.28398	.28421	.28443	.28466	.28488	.28511	.28533	192	2	4
193	.28556	.28578	.28601	.28623	.28646	.28668	.28691	.28713	.28735	.28758	193	3	7
194	.28780	.28803	.28825	.28847	.28870	.28892	.28914	.28937	.28959	.28981	194	4	9
195	.29003	.29026	.29048	.29070	.29092	.29115	.29137	.29159	.29181	.29203	195	5	11
196	.29226	.29248	.29270	.29292	.29314	.29336	.29358	.29380	.29403	.29425	196	6	13
197	.29447	.29469	.29491	.29513	.29535	.29557	.29579	.29601	.29623	.29645	197	7	16
198	.29667	.29688	.29710	.29732	.29754	.29776	.29798	.29820	.29842	.29863	198	8	18
199	.29885	.29907	.29929	.29951	.29973	.29994	**.30016**	**.30038**	**.30060**	**.30081**	199	9	20
200	**.30103**	**.30125**	**.30146**	**.30168**	**.30190**	**.30211**	.30233	.30255	.30276	.30298	200		
201	.30320	.30341	.30363	.30384	.30406	.30428	.30449	.30471	.30492	.30514	201	1	2
202	.30535	.30557	.30578	.30600	.30621	.30643	.30664	.30685	.30707	.30728	202	2	4
203	.30750	.30771	.30792	.30814	.30835	.30856	.30878	.30899	.30920	.30942	203	3	6
204	.30963	.30984	.31006	.31027	.31048	.31069	.31091	.31112	.31133	.31154	204	4	8
205	.31175	.31197	.31218	.31239	.31260	.31281	.31302	.31323	.31345	.31366	205	5	11
206	.31387	.31408	.31429	.31450	.31471	.31492	.31513	.31534	.31555	.31576	206	6	13
207	.31597	.31618	.31639	.31660	.31681	.31702	.31723	.31744	.31765	.31785	207	7	15
208	.31806	.31827	.31848	.31869	.31890	.31911	.31931	.31952	.31973	.31994	208	8	17
209	.32015	.32035	.32056	.32077	.32098	.32118	.32139	.32160	.32181	.32201	209	9	19
210	.32222	.32243	.32263	.32284	.32305	.32325	.32346	.32366	.32387	.32408	210		
211	.32428	.32449	.32469	.32490	.32510	.32531	.32552	.32572	.32593	.32613	211	1	2
212	.32634	.32654	.32675	.32695	.32715	.32736	.32756	.32777	.32797	.32818	212	2	4
213	.32838	.32858	.32879	.32899	.32919	.32940	.32960	.32980	.33001	.33021	213	3	6
214	.33041	.33062	.33082	.33102	.33122	.33143	.33163	.33183	.33203	.33224	214	4	8
215	.33244	.33264	.33284	.33304	.33325	.33345	.33365	.33385	.33405	.33425	215	5	10
216	.33445	.33465	.33486	.33506	.33526	.33546	.33566	.33586	.33606	.33626	216	6	12
217	.33646	.33666	.33686	.33706	.33726	.33746	.33766	.33786	.33806	.33826	217	7	14
218	.33846	.33866	.33885	.33905	.33925	.33945	.33965	.33985	.34005	.34025	218	8	16
219	.34044	.34064	.34084	.34104	.34124	.34143	.34163	.34183	.34203	.34223	219	9	18
	0	1	2	3	4	5	6	7	8	9			

Table 18

LOGARITHMS

No.	0	1	2	3	4	5	6	7	8	9	No.	5th Fig.	Log Diff.
220	.34242	.34262	.34282	.34301	.34321	.34341	.34361	.34380	.34400	.34420	220		
221	.34439	.34459	.34479	.34498	.34518	.34537	.34557	.34577	.34596	.34616	221	1	2
222	.34635	.34655	.34674	.34694	.34713	.34733	.34753	.34772	.34792	.34811	222	2	4
223	.34830	.34850	.34869	.34889	.34908	.34928	.34947	.34967	.34986	.35005	223	3	6
224	.35025	.35044	.35064	.35083	.35102	.35122	.35141	.35160	.35180	.35199	224	4	8
225	.35218	.35238	.35257	.35276	.35295	.35315	.35334	.35353	.35372	.35392	225	5	10
226	.35411	.35430	.35449	.35468	.35488	.35507	.35526	.35545	.35564	.35583	226	6	12
227	.35603	.35622	.35641	.35660	.35679	.35698	.35717	.35736	.35755	.35774	227	7	14
228	.35793	.35813	.35832	.35851	.35870	.35889	.35908	.35927	.35946	.35965	228	8	15
229	.35984	.36003	.36021	.36040	.36059	.36078	.36097	.36116	.36135	.36154	229	9	17
230	.36173	.36192	.36211	.36229	.36248	.36267	.36286	.36305	.36324	.36342	230		
231	.36361	.36380	.36399	.36418	.36436	.36455	.36474	.36493	.36511	.36530	231	1	2
232	.36549	.36568	.36586	.36605	.36624	.36642	.36661	.36680	.36698	.36717	232	2	4
233	.36736	.36754	.36773	.36791	.36810	.36829	.36847	.36866	.36884	.36903	233	3	6
234	.36922	.36940	.36959	.36977	.36996	.37014	.37033	.37051	.37070	.37088	234	4	7
235	.37107	.37125	.37144	.37162	.37181	.37199	.37218	.37236	.37254	.37273	235	5	9
236	.37291	.37310	.37328	.37346	.37365	.37383	.37401	.37420	.37438	.37457	236	6	11
237	.37475	.37493	.37511	.37530	.37548	.37566	.37585	.37603	.37621	.37639	237	7	13
238	.37658	.37676	.37694	.37712	.37731	.37749	.37767	.37785	.37803	.37822	238	8	15
239	.37840	.37858	.37876	.37894	.37912	.37931	.37949	.37967	.37985	.38003	239	9	17
240	.38021	.38039	.38057	.38075	.38093	.38112	.38130	.38148	.38166	.38184	240		
241	.38202	.38220	.38238	.38256	.38274	.38292	.38310	.38328	.38346	.38364	241	1	2
242	.38382	.38399	.38417	.38435	.38453	.38471	.38489	.38507	.38525	.38543	242	2	4
243	.38561	.38578	.38596	.38614	.38632	.38650	.38668	.38686	.38703	.38721	243	3	5
244	.38739	.38757	.38775	.38792	.38810	.38828	.38846	.38863	.38881	.38899	244	4	6
245	.38917	.38934	.38952	.38970	.38987	.39005	.39023	.39041	.39058	.39076	245	5	9
246	.39094	.39111	.39129	.39146	.39164	.39182	.39199	.39217	.39235	.39252	246	6	11
247	.39270	.39287	.39305	.39322	.39340	.39358	.39375	.39393	.39410	.39428	247	7	12
248	.39445	.39463	.39480	.39498	.39515	.39533	.39550	.39568	.39585	.39602	248	8	14
249	.39620	.39637	.39655	.39672	.39690	.39707	.39724	.39742	.39759	.39777	249	9	16
250	.39794	.39811	.39829	.39846	.39863	.39881	.39898	.39915	.39933	.39950	250		
251	.39967	.39985	.40002	.40019	.40037	.40054	.40071	.40088	.40106	.40123	251	1	2
252	.40140	.40157	.40175	.40192	.40209	.40226	.40243	.40261	.40278	.40295	252	2	3
253	.40312	.40329	.40346	.40364	.40381	.40398	.40415	.40432	.40449	.40466	253	3	5
254	.40483	.40500	.40518	.40535	.40552	.40569	.40586	.40603	.40620	.40637	254	4	7
255	.40654	.40671	.40688	.40705	.40722	.40739	.40756	.40773	.40790	.40807	255	5	9
256	.40824	.40841	.40858	.40875	.40892	.40909	.40926	.40943	.40960	.40976	256	6	10
257	.40993	.41010	.41027	.41044	.41061	.41078	.41095	.41111	.41128	.41145	257	7	12
258	.41162	.41179	.41196	.41212	.41229	.41246	.41263	.41280	.41296	.41313	258	8	14
259	.41330	.41347	.41363	.41380	.41397	.41414	.41430	.41447	.41464	.41481	259	9	15
260	.41497	.41514	.41531	.41547	.41564	.41581	.41597	.41614	.41631	.41647	260		
261	.41664	.41681	.41697	.41714	.41731	.41747	.41764	.41780	.41797	.41814	261	1	2
262	.41830	.41847	.41863	.41880	.41896	.41913	.41929	.41946	.41963	.41979	262	2	3
263	.41996	.42012	.42029	.42045	.42062	.42078	.42095	.42111	.42127	.42144	263	3	5
264	.42160	.42177	.42193	.42210	.42226	.42243	.42259	.42275	.42292	.42308	264	4	7
265	.42325	.42341	.42357	.42374	.42390	.42406	.42423	.42439	.42455	.42472	265	5	8
266	.42488	.42504	.42521	.42537	.42553	.42570	.42586	.42602	.42619	.42635	266	6	10
267	.42651	.42667	.42684	.42700	.42716	.42732	.42749	.42765	.42781	.42797	267	7	11
268	.42813	.42830	.42846	.42862	.42878	.42894	.42911	.42927	.42943	.42959	268	8	13
269	.42975	.42991	.43008	.43024	.43040	.43056	.43072	.43088	.43104	.43120	269	9	15
270	.43136	.43152	.43169	.43185	.43201	.43217	.43233	.43249	.43265	.43281	270		
271	.43297	.43313	.43329	.43345	.43361	.43377	.43393	.43409	.43425	.43441	271	1	2
272	.43457	.43473	.43489	.43505	.43521	.43537	.43553	.43569	.43584	.43600	272	2	3
273	.43616	.43632	.43648	.43664	.43680	.43696	.43712	.43727	.43743	.43759	273	3	5
274	.43775	.43791	.43807	.43823	.43838	.43854	.43870	.43886	.43902	.43917	274	4	6
275	.43933	.43949	.43965	.43981	.43996	.44012	.44028	.44044	.44059	.44075	275	5	8
276	.44091	.44107	.44122	.44138	.44154	.44170	.44185	.44201	.44217	.44232	276	6	10
277	.44248	.44264	.44279	.44295	.44311	.44326	.44342	.44358	.44373	.44389	277	7	11
278	.44404	.44420	.44436	.44451	.44467	.44483	.44498	.44514	.44529	.44545	278	8	13
279	.44560	.44576	.44592	.44607	.44623	.44638	.44654	.44669	.44685	.44700	279	9	14
	0	1	2	3	4	5	6	7	8	9			

Table 18

LOGARITHMS

No.	0	1	2	3	4	5	6	7	8	9	No.	5th Fig.	Log Diff.
280	.44716	.44731	.44747	.44762	.44778	.44793	.44809	.44824	.44840	.44855	280		
281	.44871	.44886	.44902	.44917	.44932	.44948	.44963	.44979	.44994	.45010	281	1	2
282	.45025	.45040	.45056	.45071	.45086	.45102	.45117	.45133	.45148	.45163	282	2	3
283	.45179	.45194	.45209	.45225	.45240	.45255	.45271	.45286	.45301	.45317	283	3	5
284	.45332	.45347	.45362	.45378	.45393	.45408	.45423	.45439	.45454	.45469	284	4	6
285	.45484	.45500	.45515	.45530	.45545	.45561	.45576	.45591	.45606	.45621	285	5	8
286	.45637	.45652	.45667	.45682	.45697	.45712	.45728	.45743	.45758	.45773	286	6	9
287	.45788	.45803	.45818	.45834	.45849	.45864	.45879	.45894	.45909	.45924	287	7	11
288	.45939	.45954	.45969	.45984	.46000	.46015	.46030	.46045	.46060	.46075	288	8	12
289	.46090	.46105	.46120	.46135	.46150	.46165	.46180	.46195	.46210	.46225	289	9	14
290	.46240	.46255	.46270	.46285	.46300	.46315	.46330	.46345	.46359	.46374	290		
291	.46389	.46404	.46419	.46434	.46449	.46464	.46479	.46494	.46509	.46523	291	1	1
292	.46538	.46553	.46568	.46583	.46598	.46613	.46627	.46642	.46657	.46672	292	2	3
293	.46687	.46702	.46716	.46731	.46746	.46761	.46776	.46790	.46805	.46820	293	3	4
294	.46835	.46850	.46864	.46879	.46894	.46909	.46923	.46938	.46953	.46967	294	4	6
295	.46982	.46997	.47012	.47026	.47041	.47056	.47070	.47085	.47100	.47114	295	5	7
296	.47129	.47144	.47159	.47173	.47188	.47202	.47217	.47232	.47246	.47261	296	6	9
297	.47276	.47290	.47305	.47319	.47334	.47349	.47363	.47378	.47392	.47407	297	7	10
298	.47422	.47436	.47451	.47465	.47480	.47494	.47509	.47524	.47538	.47553	298	8	12
299	.47567	.47582	.47596	.47611	.47625	.47640	.47654	.47669	.47683	.47698	299	9	13
300	.47712	.47727	.47741	.47756	.47770	.47784	.47799	.47813	.47828	.47842	300		
301	.47857	.47871	.47885	.47900	.47914	.47929	.47943	.47958	.47972	.47986	301	1	1
302	.48001	.48015	.48029	.48044	.48058	.48073	.48087	.48101	.48116	.48130	302	2	3
303	.48144	.48159	.48173	.48187	.48202	.48216	.48230	.48244	.48259	.48273	303	3	4
304	.48287	.48302	.48316	.48330	.48344	.48359	.48373	.48387	.48401	.48416	304	4	6
305	.48430	.48444	.48458	.48473	.48487	.48501	.48515	.48530	.48544	.48558	305	5	7
306	.48572	.48586	.48601	.48615	.48629	.48643	.48657	.48671	.48686	.48700	306	6	9
307	.48714	.48728	.48742	.48756	.48770	.48785	.48799	.48813	.48827	.48841	307	7	10
308	.48855	.48869	.48883	.48897	.48911	.48926	.48940	.48954	.48968	.48982	308	8	11
309	.48996	.49010	.49024	.49038	.49052	.49066	.49080	.49094	.49108	.49122	309	9	13
310	.49136	.49150	.49164	.49178	.49192	.49206	.49220	.49234	.49248	.49262	310		
311	.49276	.49290	.49304	.49318	.49332	.49346	.49360	.49374	.49388	.49402	311	1	1
312	.49415	.49429	.49443	.49457	.49471	.49485	.49499	.49513	.49527	.49541	312	2	3
313	.49554	.49568	.49582	.49596	.49610	.49624	.49638	.49651	.49665	.49679	313	3	4
314	.49693	.49707	.49721	.49734	.49748	.49762	.49776	.49790	.49803	.49817	314	4	6
315	.49831	.49845	.49859	.49872	.49886	.49900	.49914	.49927	.49941	.49955	315	5	7
316	.49969	.49982	.49996	.50010	.50024	.50037	.50051	.50065	.50079	.50092	316	6	8
317	.50106	.50120	.50133	.50147	.50161	.50174	.50188	.50202	.50215	.50229	317	7	10
318	.50243	.50256	.50270	.50284	.50297	.50311	.50325	.50338	.50352	.50365	318	8	11
319	.50379	.50393	.50406	.50420	.50433	.50447	.50461	.50474	.50488	.50501	319	9	12
320	.50515	.50529	.50542	.50556	.50569	.50583	.50596	.50610	.50623	.50637	320		
321	.50651	.50664	.50678	.50691	.50705	.50718	.50732	.50745	.50759	.50772	321	1	1
322	.50786	.50799	.50813	.50826	.50840	.50853	.50866	.50880	.50893	.50907	322	2	3
323	.50920	.50934	.50947	.50961	.50974	.50987	.51001	.51014	.51028	.51041	323	3	4
324	.51055	.51068	.51081	.51095	.51108	.51121	.51135	.51148	.51162	.51175	324	4	5
325	.51188	.51202	.51215	.51228	.51242	.51255	.51268	.51282	.51295	.51308	325	5	7
326	.51322	.51335	.51348	.51362	.51375	.51388	.51402	.51415	.51428	.51441	326	6	8
327	.51455	.51468	.51481	.51495	.51508	.51521	.51534	.51548	.51561	.51574	327	7	9
328	.51587	.51601	.51614	.51627	.51640	.51654	.51667	.51680	.51693	.51706	328	8	11
329	.51720	.51733	.51746	.51759	.51772	.51786	.51799	.51812	.51825	.51838	329	9	12
330	.51851	.51865	.51878	.51891	.51904	.51917	.51930	.51943	.51957	.51970	330		
331	.51983	.51996	.52009	.52022	.52035	.52048	.52061	.52075	.52088	.52101	331	1	1
332	.52114	.52127	.52140	.52153	.52166	.52179	.52192	.52205	.52218	.52231	332	2	3
333	.52244	.52257	.52270	.52284	.52297	.52310	.52323	.52336	.52349	.52362	333	3	4
334	.52375	.52388	.52401	.52414	.52427	.52440	.52453	.52466	.52479	.52492	334	4	5
335	.52504	.52517	.52530	.52543	.52556	.52569	.52582	.52595	.52608	.52621	335	5	6
336	.52634	.52647	.52660	.52673	.52686	.52699	.52711	.52724	.52737	.52750	336	6	8
337	.52763	.52776	.52789	.52802	.52815	.52827	.52840	.52853	.52866	.52879	337	7	9
338	.52892	.52905	.52917	.52930	.52943	.52956	.52969	.52982	.52994	.53007	338	8	10
339	.53020	.53033	.53046	.53058	.53071	.53084	.53097	.53110	.53122	.53135	339	9	12
	0	1	2	3	4	5	6	7	8	9			

Table 18

LOGARITHMS

Nos. { 34— / 39—

No.	0	1	2	3	4	5	6	7	8	9	No.	5th Fig.	Log Diff.
340	.53148	.53161	.53173	.53186	.53199	.53212	.53224	.53237	.53250	.53263	340		
341	.53275	.53288	.53301	.53314	.53326	.53339	.53352	.53364	.53377	.53390	341	1	1
342	.53403	.53415	.53428	.53441	.53453	.53466	.53479	.53491	.53504	.53517	342	2	3
343	.53529	.53542	.53555	.53567	.53580	.53593	.53605	.53618	.53631	.53643	343	3	4
344	.53656	.53668	.53681	.53694	.53706	.53719	.53732	.53744	.53757	.53769	344	4	5
345	.53782	.53794	.53807	.53820	.53832	.53845	.53857	.53870	.53882	.53895	345	5	6
346	.53908	.53920	.53933	.53945	.53958	.53970	.53983	.53995	.54008	.54020	346	6	8
347	.54033	.54045	.54058	.54070	.54083	.54095	.54108	.54120	.54133	.54145	347	7	9
348	.54158	.54170	.54183	.54195	.54208	.54220	.54233	.54245	.54258	.54270	348	8	10
349	.54283	.54295	.54307	.54320	.54332	.54345	.54357	.54370	.54382	.54394	349	9	11
350	.54407	.54419	.54432	.54444	.54456	.54469	.54481	.54494	.54506	.54518	350		
351	.54531	.54543	.54555	.54568	.54580	.54593	.54605	.54617	.54630	.54642	351	1	1
352	.54654	.54667	.54679	.54691	.54704	.54716	.54728	.54741	.54753	.54765	352	2	2
353	.54777	.54790	.54802	.54814	.54827	.54839	.54851	.54864	.54876	.54888	353	3	4
354	.54900	.54913	.54925	.54937	.54949	.54962	.54974	.54986	.54998	.55011	354	4	5
355	.55023	.55035	.55047	.55060	.55072	.55084	.55096	.55108	.55121	.55133	355	5	6
356	.55145	.55157	.55169	.55182	.55194	.55206	.55218	.55230	.55242	.55255	356	6	7
357	.55267	.55279	.55291	.55303	.55315	.55328	.55340	.55352	.55364	.55376	357	7	9
358	.55388	.55400	.55413	.55425	.55437	.55449	.55461	.55473	.55485	.55497	358	8	10
359	.55509	.55522	.55534	.55546	.55558	.55570	.55582	.55594	.55606	.55618	359	9	11
360	.55630	.55642	.55654	.55666	.55678	.55691	.55703	.55715	.55727	.55739	360		
361	.55751	.55763	.55775	.55787	.55799	.55811	.55823	.55835	.55847	.55859	361	1	1
362	.55871	.55883	.55895	.55907	.55919	.55931	.55943	.55955	.55967	.55979	362	2	2
363	.55991	.56003	.56015	.56027	.56038	.56050	.56062	.56074	.56086	.56098	363	3	4
364	.56110	.56122	.56134	.56146	.56158	.56170	.56182	.56194	.56205	.56217	364	4	5
365	.56229	.56241	.56253	.56265	.56277	.56289	.56301	.56312	.56324	.56336	365	5	6
366	.56348	.56360	.56372	.56384	.56396	.56407	56419	.56431	.56443	.56455	366	6	7
367	.56467	.56478	.56490	.56502	.56514	.56526	.56538	.56549	.56561	.56573	367	7	8
368	.56585	.56597	.56608	.56620	.56632	.56644	.56656	.56667	.56679	.56691	368	8	10
369	.56703	.56714	.56726	.56738	.56750	.56761	.56773	.56785	.56797	.56808	369	9	11
370	.56820	.56832	.56844	.56855	.56867	.56879	.56891	.56902	.56914	.56926	370		
371	.56937	.56949	.56961	.56972	.56984	.56996	.57008	.57019	.57031	.57043	371	1	1
372	.57054	.57066	.57078	.57089	.57101	.57113	.57124	.57136	.57148	.57159	372	2	2
373	.57171	.57183	.57194	.57206	.57217	.57229	.57241	.57252	.57264	.57276	373	3	4
374	.57287	.57299	.57310	.57322	.57334	.57345	.57357	.57368	.57380	.57392	374	4	5
375	.57403	.57415	.57426	.57438	.57449	.57461	.57473	.57484	.57496	.57507	375	5	6
376	.57519	.57530	.57542	.57553	.57565	.57576	.57588	.57600	.57611	.57623	376	6	7
377	.57634	.57646	.57657	.57669	.57680	.57692	.57703	.57715	.57726	.57738	377	7	8
378	.57749	.57761	.57772	.57784	.57795	.57807	.57818	.57830	.57841	.57852	378	8	9
379	.57864	.57875	.57887	.57898	.57910	.57921	.57933	.57944	.57955	.57967	379	9	10
380	.57978	.57990	.58001	.58013	.58024	.58035	.58047	.58058	.58070	.58081	380		
381	.58092	.58104	.58115	.58127	.58138	.58149	.58161	.58172	.58184	.58195	381	1	1
382	.58206	.58218	.58229	.58240	.58252	.58263	.58274	.58286	.58297	.58309	382	2	2
383	.58320	.58331	.58343	.58354	.58365	.58377	.58388	.58399	.58410	.58422	383	3	3
384	.58433	.58444	.58456	.58467	.58478	.58490	.58501	.58512	.58524	.58535	384	4	5
385	.58546	.58557	.58569	.58580	.58591	.58602	.58614	.58625	.58636	.58647	385	5	6
386	.58659	.58670	.58681	.58692	.58704	.58715	.58726	.58737	.58749	.58760	386	6	7
387	.58771	.58782	.58794	.58805	.58816	.58827	.58838	.58850	.58861	.58872	387	7	8
388	.58883	.58894	.58906	.58917	.58928	.58939	.58950	.58961	.58973	.58984	388	8	9
389	.58995	.59006	.59017	.59028	.59040	.59051	.59062	.59073	.59084	.59095	389	9	10
390	.59106	.59118	.59129	.59140	.59151	.59162	.59173	.59184	.59195	.59207	390		
391	.59218	.59229	.59240	.59251	.59262	.59273	.59284	.59295	.59306	.59318	391	1	1
392	.59329	.59340	.59351	.59362	.59373	.59384	.59395	.59406	.59417	.59428	392	2	2
393	.59439	.59450	.59461	.59472	.59483	.59494	.59506	.59517	.59528	.59539	393	3	3
394	.59550	.59561	.59572	.59583	.59594	.59605	.59616	.59627	.59638	.59649	394	4	4
395	.59660	.59671	.59682	.59693	.59704	.59715	.59726	.59737	.59748	.59759	395	5	6
396	.59770	.59780	.59791	.59802	.59813	.59824	.59835	.59846	.59857	.59868	396	6	7
397	.59879	.59890	.59901	.59912	.59923	.59934	.59945	.59956	.59966	.59977	397	7	8
398	.59988	.59999	.60010	.60021	.60032	.60043	.60054	.60065	.60076	.60086	398	8	9
399	.60097	.60108	.60119	.60130	.60141	.60152	.60163	.60173	.60184	.60195	399	9	10
	0	1	2	3	4	5	6	7	8	9			

Table 18

LOGARITHMS

Nos. { 40— 45— } Logs 60206 66266

No.	0	1	2	3	4	5	6	7	8	9	No.	5th Fig.	Log Diff.
400	.60206	.60217	.60228	.60239	.60249	.60260	.60271	.60282	.60293	.60304	400		
401	.60314	.60325	.60336	.60347	.60358	.60369	.60379	.60390	.60401	.60412	401	1	1
402	.60423	.60433	.60444	.60455	.60466	.60477	.60487	.60498	.60509	.60520	402	2	2
403	.60531	.60541	.60552	.60563	.60574	.60584	.60595	.60606	.60617	.60627	403	3	3
404	.60638	.60649	.60660	.60670	.60681	.60692	.60703	.60713	.60724	.60735	404	4	4
405	.60746	.60756	.60767	.60778	.60788	.60799	.60810	.60821	.60831	.60842	405	5	5
406	.60853	.60863	.60874	.60885	.60895	.60906	.60917	.60927	.60938	.60949	406	6	6
407	.60959	.60970	.60981	.60991	.61002	.61013	.61023	.61034	.61045	.61055	407	7	8
408	.61066	.61077	.61087	.61098	.61109	.61119	.61130	.61140	.61151	.61162	408	8	9
409	.61172	.61183	.61194	.61204	.61215	.61225	.61236	.61247	.61257	.61268	409	9	10
410	.61278	.61289	.61300	.61310	.61321	.61331	.61342	.61352	.61363	.61374	410		
411	.61384	.61395	.61405	.61416	.61426	.61437	.61448	.61458	.61469	.61479	411	1	1
412	.61490	.61500	.61511	.61521	.61532	.61542	.61553	.61563	.61574	.61584	412	2	2
413	.61595	.61606	.61616	.61627	.61637	.61648	.61658	.61669	.61679	.61690	413	3	3
414	.61700	.61711	.61721	.61731	.61742	.61752	.61763	.61773	.61784	.61794	414	4	4
415	.61805	.61815	.61826	.61836	.61847	.61857	.61868	.61878	.61888	.61899	415	5	5
416	.61909	.61920	.61930	.61941	.61951	.61962	.61972	.61982	.61993	.62003	416	6	6
417	.62014	.62024	.62034	.62045	.62055	.62066	.62076	.62086	.62097	.62107	417	7	7
418	.62118	.62128	.62138	.62149	.62159	.62170	.62180	.62190	.62201	.62211	418	8	8
419	.62221	.62232	.62242	.62252	.62263	.62273	.62284	.62294	.62304	.62315	419	9	9
420	.62325	.62335	.62346	.62356	.62366	.62377	.62387	.62397	.62408	.62418	420		
421	.62428	.62439	.62449	.62459	.62469	.62480	.62490	.62500	.62511	.62521	421	1	1
422	.62531	.62542	.62552	.62562	.62572	.62583	.62593	.62603	.62613	.62624	422	2	2
423	.62634	.62644	.62655	.62665	.62675	.62685	.62696	.62706	.62716	.62726	423	3	3
424	.62737	.62747	.62757	.62767	.62778	.62788	.62798	.62808	.62818	.62829	424	4	4
425	.62839	.62849	.62859	.62870	.62880	.62890	.62900	.62910	.62921	.62931	425	5	5
426	.62941	.62951	.62961	.62972	.62982	.62992	.63002	.63012	.63022	.63033	426	6	6
427	.63043	.63053	.63063	.63073	.63083	.63094	.63104	.63114	.63124	.63134	427	7	7
428	.63144	.63155	.63165	.63175	.63185	.63195	.63205	.63215	.63225	.63236	428	8	8
429	.63246	.63256	.63266	.63276	.63286	.63296	.63306	.63317	.63327	.63337	429	9	9
430	.63347	.63357	.63367	.63377	.63387	.63397	.63407	.63417	.63428	.63438	430		
431	.63448	.63458	.63468	.63478	.63488	.63498	.63508	.63518	.63528	.63538	431	1	1
432	.63548	.63558	.63568	.63579	.63589	.63599	.63609	.63619	.63629	.63639	432	2	2
433	.63649	.63659	.63669	.63679	.63689	.63699	.63709	.63719	.63729	.63739	433	3	3
434	.63749	.63759	.63769	.63779	.63789	.63799	.63809	.63819	.63829	.63839	434	4	4
435	.63849	.63859	.63869	.63879	.63889	.63899	.63909	.63919	.63929	.63939	435	5	5
436	.63949	.63959	.63969	.63979	.63988	.63998	.64008	.64018	.64028	.64038	436	6	6
437	.64048	.64058	.64068	.64078	.64088	.64098	.64108	.64118	.64128	.64137	437	7	7
438	.64147	.64157	.64167	.64177	.64187	.64197	.64207	.64217	.64227	.64237	438	8	8
439	.64246	.64256	.64266	.64276	.64286	.64296	.64306	.64316	.64326	.64335	439	9	9
440	.64345	.64355	.64365	.64375	.64385	.64395	.64404	.64414	.64424	.64434	440		
441	.64444	.64454	.64464	.64473	.64483	.64493	.64503	.64513	.64523	.64532	441	1	1
442	.64542	.64552	.64562	.64572	.64582	.64591	.64601	.64611	.64621	.64631	442	2	2
443	.64640	.64650	.64660	.64670	.64680	.64689	.64699	.64709	.64719	.64729	443	3	3
444	.64738	.64748	.64758	.64768	.64777	.64787	.64797	.64807	.64816	.64826	444	4	4
445	.64836	.64846	.64856	.64865	.64875	.64885	.64895	.64904	.64914	.64924	445	5	5
446	.64933	.64943	.64953	.64963	.64972	.64982	.64992	.65002	.65011	.65021	446	6	6
447	.65031	.65040	.65050	.65060	.65070	.65079	.65089	.65099	.65108	.65118	447	7	7
448	.65128	.65137	.65147	.65157	.65167	.65176	.65186	.65196	.65205	.65215	448	8	8
449	.65225	.65234	.65244	.65254	.65263	.65273	.65283	.65292	.65302	.65312	449	9	9
450	.65321	.65331	.65341	.65350	.65360	.65369	.65379	.65389	.65398	.65408	450		
451	.65418	.65427	.65437	.65447	.65456	.65466	.65475	.65485	.65495	.65504	451	1	1
452	.65514	.65523	.65533	.65543	.65552	.65562	.65571	.65581	.65591	.65600	452	2	2
453	.65610	.65619	.65629	.65639	.65648	.65658	.65667	.65677	.65686	.65696	453	3	3
454	.65706	.65715	.65725	.65734	.65744	.65753	.65763	.65772	.65782	.65792	454	4	4
455	.65801	.65811	.65820	.65830	.65839	.65849	.65858	.65868	.65877	.65887	455	5	5
456	.65896	.65906	.65916	.65925	.65935	.65944	.65954	.65963	.65973	.65982	456	6	6
457	.65992	.66001	.66011	.66020	.66030	.66039	.66049	.66058	.66068	.66077	457	7	7
458	.66087	.66096	.66106	.66115	.66124	.66134	.66143	.66153	.66162	.66172	458	8	8
459	.66181	.66191	.66200	.66210	.66219	.66229	.66238	.66247	.66257	.66266	459	9	9
	0	1	2	3	4	5	6	7	8	9			

Table 18

LOGARITHMS

Nos. { 46— / 51—   Logs 66276 71592

No.	0	1	2	3	4	5	6	7	8	9	No.	5th Fig.	Log Diff.
460	.66276	.66285	.66295	.66304	.66314	.66323	.66332	.66342	.66351	.66361	460		
461	.66370	.66380	.66389	.66398	.66408	.66417	.66427	.66436	.66445	.66455	461	1	1
462	.66464	.66474	.66483	.66492	.66502	.66511	.66521	.66530	.66539	.66549	462	2	2
463	.66558	.66567	.66577	.66586	.66596	.66605	.66614	.66624	.66633	.66642	463	3	3
464	.66652	.66661	.66671	.66680	.66689	.66699	.66708	.66717	.66727	.66736	464	4	4
465	.66745	.66755	.66764	.66773	.66783	.66792	.66801	.66811	.66820	.66829	465	5	5
466	.66839	.66848	.66857	.66867	.66876	.66885	.66894	.66904	.66913	.66922	466	6	6
467	.66932	.66941	.66950	.66960	.66969	.66978	.66987	.66997	.67006	.67015	467	7	7
468	.67025	.67034	.67043	.67052	.67062	.67071	.67080	.67089	.67099	.67108	468	8	7
469	.67117	.67127	.67136	.67145	.67154	.67164	.67173	.67182	.67191	.67201	469	9	8
470	.67210	.67219	.67228	.67237	.67247	.67256	.67265	.67274	.67284	.67293	470		
471	.67302	.67311	.67321	.67330	.67339	.67348	.67357	.67367	.67376	.67385	471	1	1
472	.67394	.67403	.67413	.67422	.67431	.67440	.67449	.67459	.67468	.67477	472	2	2
473	.67486	.67495	.67504	.67514	.67523	.67532	.67541	.67550	.67560	.67569	473	3	3
474	.67578	.67587	.67596	.67605	.67614	.67624	.67633	.67642	.67651	.67660	474	4	4
475	.67669	.67679	.67688	.67697	.67706	.67715	.67724	.67733	.67742	.67752	475	5	5
476	.67761	.67770	.67779	.67788	.67797	.67806	.67815	.67825	.67834	.67843	476	6	5
477	.67852	.67861	.67870	.67879	.67888	.67897	.67906	.67916	.67925	.67934	477	7	6
478	.67943	.67952	.67961	.67970	.67979	.67988	.67997	.68006	.68015	.68024	478	8	7
479	.68034	.68043	.68052	.68061	.68070	.68079	.68088	.68097	.68106	.68115	479	9	8
480	.68124	.68133	.68142	.68151	.68160	.68169	.68178	.68187	.68196	.68205	480		
481	.68215	.68224	.68233	.68242	.68251	.68260	.68269	.68278	.68287	.68296	481	1	1
482	.68305	.68314	.68323	.68332	.68341	.68350	.68359	.68368	.68377	.68386	482	2	2
483	.68395	.68404	.68413	.68422	.68431	.68440	.68449	.68458	.68467	.68476	483	3	3
484	.68485	.68494	.68502	.68511	.68520	.68529	.68538	.68547	.68556	.68565	484	4	4
485	.68574	.68583	.68592	.68601	.68610	.68619	.68628	.68637	.68646	.68655	485	5	4
486	.68664	.68673	.68681	.68690	.68699	.68708	.68717	.68726	.68735	.68744	486	6	5
487	.68753	.68762	.68771	.68780	.68789	.68797	.68806	.68815	.68824	.68833	487	7	6
488	.68842	.68851	.68860	.68869	.68878	.68886	.68895	.68904	.68913	.68922	488	8	7
489	.68931	.68940	.68949	.68958	.68966	.68975	.68984	.68993	.69002	.69011	489	9	8
490	.69020	.69028	.69037	.69046	.69055	.69064	.69073	.69082	.69090	.69099	490		
491	.69108	.69117	.69126	.69135	.69144	.69152	.69161	.69170	.69179	.69188	491	1	1
492	.69197	.69205	.69214	.69223	.69232	.69241	.69249	.69258	.69267	.69276	492	2	2
493	.69285	.69294	.69302	.69311	.69320	.69329	.69338	.69346	.69355	.69364	493	3	3
494	.69373	.69381	.69390	.69399	.69408	.69417	.69425	.69434	.69443	.69452	494	4	4
495	.69461	.69469	.69478	.69487	.69496	.69504	.69513	.69522	.69531	.69539	495	5	4
496	.69548	.69557	.69566	.69574	.69583	.69592	.69601	.69609	.69618	.69627	496	6	5
497	.69636	.69644	.69653	.69662	.69671	.69679	.69688	.69697	.69705	.69714	497	7	6
498	.69723	.69732	.69740	.69749	.69758	.69767	.69775	.69784	.69793	.69801	498	8	7
499	.69810	.69819	.69827	.69836	.69845	.69854	.69862	.69871	.69880	.69888	499	9	8
500	.69897	.69906	.69914	.69923	.69932	.69940	.69949	.69958	.69966	.69975	500		
501	.69984	.69992	.70001	.70010	.70018	.70027	.70036	.70044	.70053	.70062	501	1	1
502	.70070	.70079	.70088	.70096	.70105	.70114	.70122	.70131	.70140	.70148	502	2	2
503	.70157	.70165	.70174	.70183	.70191	.70200	.70209	.70217	.70226	.70234	503	3	3
504	.70243	.70252	.70260	.70269	.70278	.70286	.70295	.70303	.70312	.70321	504	4	4
505	.70329	.70338	.70346	.70355	.70364	.70372	.70381	.70389	.70398	.70406	505	5	5
506	.70415	.70424	.70432	.70441	.70449	.70458	.70467	.70475	.70484	.70492	506	6	5
507	.70501	.70509	.70518	.70526	.70535	.70544	.70552	.70561	.70569	.70578	507	7	6
508	.70586	.70595	.70603	.70612	.70621	.70629	.70638	.70646	.70655	.70663	508	8	7
509	.70672	.70680	.70689	.70697	.70706	.70714	.70723	.70731	.70740	.70749	509	9	8
510	.70757	.70766	.70774	.70783	.70791	.70800	.70808	.70817	.70825	.70834	510		
511	.70842	.70851	.70859	.70868	.70876	.70885	.70893	.70902	.70910	.70919	511	1	1
512	.70927	.70935	.70944	.70952	.70961	.70969	.70978	.70986	.70995	.71003	512	2	2
513	.71012	.71020	.71029	.71037	.71046	.71054	.71063	.71071	.71079	.71088	513	3	3
514	.71096	.71105	.71113	.71122	.71130	.71139	.71147	.71155	.71164	.71172	514	4	3
515	.71181	.71189	.71198	.71206	.71214	.71223	.71231	.71240	.71248	.71257	515	5	4
516	.71265	.71273	.71282	.71290	.71299	.71307	.71315	.71324	.71332	.71341	516	6	5
517	.71349	.71357	.71366	.71374	.71383	.71391	.71399	.71408	.71416	.71425	517	7	6
518	.71433	.71441	.71450	.71458	.71466	.71475	.71483	.71492	.71500	.71508	518	8	7
519	.71517	.71525	.71533	.71542	.71550	.71559	.71567	.71575	.71584	.71592	519	9	8
	0	1	2	3	4	5	6	7	8	9			

Table 18

LOGARITHMS

No.	0	1	2	3	4	5	6	7	8	9	No.	5th Fig.	Log Diff.
520	.71600	.71609	.71617	.71625	.71634	.71642	.71650	.71659	.71667	.71675	520		
521	.71684	.71692	.71700	.71709	.71717	.71725	.71734	.71742	.71750	.71759	521	1	1
522	.71767	.71775	.71784	.71792	.71800	.71809	.71817	.71825	.71834	.71842	522	2	2
523	.71850	.71858	.71867	.71875	.71883	.71892	.71900	.71908	.71917	.71925	523	3	3
524	.71933	.71941	.71950	.71958	.71966	.71975	.71983	.71991	.71999	.72008	524	4	3
525	.72016	.72024	.72032	.72041	.72049	.72057	.72066	.72074	.72082	.72090	525	5	4
526	.72099	.72107	.72115	.72123	.72132	.72140	.72148	.72156	.72165	.72173	526	6	5
527	.72181	.72189	.72198	.72206	.72214	.72222	.72230	.72239	.72247	.72255	527	7	6
528	.72263	.72272	.72280	.72288	.72296	.72304	.72313	.72321	.72329	.72337	528	8	7
529	.72346	.72354	.72362	.72370	.72378	.72387	.72395	.72403	.72411	.72419	529	9	8
530	.72428	.72436	.72444	.72452	.72460	.72469	.72477	.72485	.72493	.72501	530		
531	.72509	.72518	.72526	.72534	.72542	.72550	.72558	.72567	.72575	.72583	531	1	1
532	.72591	.72599	.72607	.72616	.72624	.72632	.72640	.72648	.72656	.72665	532	2	2
533	.72673	.72681	.72689	.72697	.72705	.72713	.72722	.72730	.72738	.72746	533	3	3
534	.72754	.72762	.72770	.72779	.72787	.72795	.72803	.72811	.72819	.72827	534	4	3
535	.72835	.72843	.72852	.72860	.72868	.72876	.72884	.72892	.72900	.72908	535	5	4
536	.72916	.72925	.72933	.72941	.72949	.72957	.72965	.72973	.72981	.72989	536	6	5
537	.72997	.73006	.73014	.73022	.73030	.73038	.73046	.73054	.73062	.73070	537	7	6
538	.73078	.73086	.73094	.73102	.73111	.73119	.73127	.73135	.73143	.73151	538	8	7
539	.73159	.73167	.73175	.73183	.73191	.73199	.73207	.73215	.73223	.73231	539	9	8
540	.73239	.73247	.73255	.73263	.73272	.73280	.73288	.73296	.73304	.73312	540		
541	.73320	.73328	.73336	.73344	.73352	.73360	.73368	.73376	.73384	.73392	541	1	1
542	.73400	.73408	.73416	.73424	.73432	.73440	.73448	.73456	.73464	.73472	542	2	2
543	.73480	.73488	.73496	.73504	.73512	.73520	.73528	.73536	.73544	.73552	543	3	2
544	.73560	.73568	.73576	.73584	.73592	.73600	.73608	.73616	.73624	.73632	544	4	3
545	.73640	.73648	.73656	.73664	.73672	.73679	.73687	.73695	.73703	.73711	545	5	4
546	.73719	.73727	.73735	.73743	.73751	.73759	.73767	.73775	.73783	.73791	546	6	5
547	.73799	.73807	.73815	.73823	.73830	.73838	.73846	.73854	.73862	.73870	547	7	6
548	.73878	.73886	.73894	.73902	.73910	.73918	.73926	.73933	.73941	.73949	548	8	6
549	.73957	.73965	.73973	.73981	.73989	.73997	.74005	.74013	.74020	.74028	549	9	7
550	.74036	.74044	.74052	.74060	.74068	.74076	.74084	.74092	.74099	.74107	550		
551	.74115	.74123	.74131	.74139	.74147	.74155	.74162	.74170	.74178	.74186	551	1	1
552	.74194	.74202	.74210	.74218	.74225	.74233	.74241	.74249	.74257	.74265	552	2	2
553	.74273	.74280	.74288	.74296	.74304	.74312	.74320	.74327	.74335	.74343	553	3	2
554	.74351	.74359	.74367	.74374	.74382	.74390	.74398	.74406	.74414	.74421	554	4	3
555	.74429	.74437	.74445	.74453	.74461	.74468	.74476	.74484	.74492	.74500	555	5	4
556	.74507	.74515	.74523	.74531	.74539	.74547	.74554	.74562	.74570	.74578	556	6	4
557	.74586	.74593	.74601	.74609	.74617	.74624	.74632	.74640	.74648	.74656	557	7	5
558	.74663	.74671	.74679	.74687	.74695	.74702	.74710	.74718	.74726	.74733	558	8	6
559	.74741	.74749	.74757	.74764	.74772	.74780	.74788	.74796	.74803	.74811	559	9	7
560	.74819	.74827	.74834	.74842	.74850	.74858	.74865	.74873	.74881	.74889	560		
561	.74896	.74904	.74912	.74920	.74927	.74935	.74943	.74950	.74958	.74966	561	1	1
562	.74974	.74981	.74989	.74997	.75005	.75012	.75020	.75028	.75035	.75043	562	2	2
563	.75051	.75059	.75066	.75074	.75082	.75089	.75097	.75105	.75113	.75120	563	3	2
564	.75128	.75136	.75143	.75151	.75159	.75166	.75174	.75182	.75189	.75197	564	4	3
565	.75205	.75213	.75220	.75228	.75236	.75243	.75251	.75259	.75266	.75274	565	5	4
566	.75282	.75289	.75297	.75305	.75312	.75320	.75328	.75335	.75343	.75351	566	6	5
567	.75358	.75366	.75374	.75381	.75389	.75397	.75404	.75412	.75420	.75427	567	7	5
568	.75435	.75442	.75450	.75458	.75465	.75473	.75481	.75488	.75496	.75504	568	8	6
569	.75511	.75519	.75526	.75534	.75542	.75549	.75557	.75565	.75572	.75580	569	9	7
570	.75587	.75595	.75603	.75610	.75618	.75626	.75633	.75641	.75648	.75656	570		
571	.75664	.75671	.75679	.75686	.75694	.75702	.75709	.75717	.75724	.75732	571	1	1
572	.75740	.75747	.75755	.75762	.75770	.75778	.75785	.75793	.75800	.75808	572	2	2
573	.75815	.75823	.75831	.75838	.75846	.75853	.75861	.75868	.75876	.75884	573	3	2
574	.75891	.75899	.75906	.75914	.75921	.75929	.75937	.75944	.75952	.75959	574	4	3
575	.75967	.75974	.75982	.75989	.75997	.76005	.76012	.76020	.76027	.76035	575	5	4
576	.76042	.76050	.76057	.76065	.76072	.76080	.76087	.76095	.76103	.76110	576	6	5
577	.76118	.76125	.76133	.76140	.76148	.76155	.76163	.76170	.76178	.76185	577	7	5
578	.76193	.76200	.76208	.76215	.76223	.76230	.76238	.76245	.76253	.76260	578	8	6
579	.76268	.76275	.76283	.76290	.76298	.76305	.76313	.76320	.76328	.76335	579	9	7
	0	1	2	3	4	5	6	7	8	9			

Table 18

LOGARITHMS

No.	0	1	2	3	4	5	6	7	8	9	No.	5th Fig.	Log Diff.
580	.76343	.76350	.76358	.76365	.76373	.76380	.76388	.76395	.76403	.76410	580		
581	.76418	.76425	.76433	.76440	.76448	.76455	.76462	.76470	.76477	.76485	581	1	1
582	.76492	.76500	.76507	.76515	.76522	.76530	.76537	.76545	.76552	.76559	582	2	2
583	.76567	.76574	.76582	.76589	.76597	.76604	.76612	.76619	.76626	.76634	583	3	2
584	.76641	.76649	.76656	.76664	.76671	.76678	.76686	.76693	.76701	.76708	584	4	3
585	.76716	.76723	.76730	.76738	.76745	.76753	.76760	.76768	.76775	.76782	585	5	4
586	.76790	.76797	.76805	.76812	.76819	.76827	.76834	.76842	.76849	.76856	586	6	5
587	.76864	.76871	.76879	.76886	.76893	.76901	.76908	.76916	.76923	.76930	587	7	5
588	.76938	.76945	.76953	.76960	.76967	.76975	.76982	.76989	.76997	.77004	588	8	6
589	.77012	.77019	.77026	.77034	.77041	.77048	.77056	.77063	.77070	.77078	589	9	7
590	.77085	.77093	.77100	.77107	.77115	.77122	.77129	.77137	.77144	.77151	590		
591	.77159	.77166	.77173	.77181	.77188	.77195	.77203	.77210	.77217	.77225	591	1	1
592	.77232	.77240	.77247	.77254	.77262	.77269	.77276	.77283	.77291	.77298	492	2	1
593	.77305	.77313	.77320	.77327	.77335	.77342	.77349	.77357	.77364	.77371	593	3	2
594	.77379	.77386	.77393	.77401	.77408	.77415	.77422	.77430	.77437	.77444	594	4	3
595	.77452	.77459	.77466	.77474	.77481	.77488	.77495	.77503	.77510	.77517	595	5	3
596	.77525	.77532	.77539	.77546	.77554	.77561	.77568	.77576	.77583	.77590	596	6	4
597	.77597	.77605	.77612	.77619	.77627	.77634	.77641	.77648	.77656	.77663	597	7	5
598	.77670	.77677	.77685	.77692	.77699	.77706	.77714	.77721	.77728	.77735	598	8	6
599	.77743	.77750	.77757	.77764	.77772	.77779	.77786	.77793	.77801	.77808	599	9	7
600	.77815	.77822	.77830	.77837	.77844	.77851	.77859	.77866	.77873	.77880	600		
601	.77887	.77895	.77902	.77909	.77916	.77924	.77931	.77938	.77945	.77952	601	1	1
602	.77960	.77967	.77974	.77981	.77988	.77996	.78003	.78010	.78017	.78025	602	2	1
603	.78032	.78039	.78046	.78053	.78061	.78068	.78075	.78082	.78089	.78097	603	3	2
604	.78104	.78111	.78118	.78125	.78132	.78140	.78147	.78154	.78161	.78168	604	4	3
605	.78176	.78183	.78190	.78197	.78204	.78211	.78219	.78226	.78233	.78240	605	5	4
606	.78247	.78254	.78262	.78269	.78276	.78283	.78290	.78297	.78305	.78312	606	6	5
607	.78319	.78326	.78333	.78340	.78347	.78355	.78362	.78369	.78376	.78383	607	7	5
608	.78390	.78398	.78405	.78412	.78419	.78426	.78433	.78440	.78447	.78455	608	8	6
609	.78462	.78469	.78476	.78483	.78490	.78497	.78504	.78512	.78519	.78526	609	9	7
610	.78533	.78540	.78547	.78554	.78561	.78569	.78576	.78583	.78590	.78597	610		
611	.78604	.78611	.78618	.78625	.78633	.78640	.78647	.78654	.78661	.78668	611	1	1
612	.78675	.78682	.78689	.78696	.78704	.78711	.78718	.78725	.78732	.78739	612	2	2
613	.78746	.78753	.78760	.78767	.78774	.78781	.78789	.78796	.78803	.78810	613	3	2
614	.78817	.78824	.78831	.78838	.78845	.78852	.78859	.78866	.78873	.78880	614	4	3
615	.78888	.78895	.78902	.78909	.78916	.78923	.78930	.78937	.78944	.78951	615	5	4
616	.78958	.78965	.78972	.78979	.78986	.78993	.79000	.79007	.79014	.79021	616	6	4
617	.79029	.79036	.79043	.79050	.79057	.79064	.79071	.79078	.79085	.79092	617	7	5
618	.79099	.79106	.79113	.79120	.79127	.79134	.79141	.79148	.79155	.79162	618	8	6
619	.79169	.79176	.79183	.79190	.79197	.79204	.79211	.79218	.79225	.79232	619	9	6
620	.79239	.79246	.79253	.79260	.79267	.79274	.79281	.79288	.79295	.79302	620		
621	.79309	.79316	.79323	.79330	.79337	.79344	.79351	.79358	.79365	.79372	621	1	1
622	.79379	.79386	.79393	.79400	.79407	.79414	.79421	.79428	.79435	.79442	622	2	1
623	.79449	.79456	.79463	.79470	.79477	.79484	.79491	.79498	.79505	.79511	623	3	2
624	.79518	.79525	.79532	.79539	.79546	.79553	.79560	.79567	.79574	.79581	624	4	3
625	.79588	.79595	.79602	.79609	.79616	.79623	.79630	.79637	.79644	.79650	625	5	3
626	.79657	.79664	.79671	.79678	.79685	.79692	.79699	.79706	.79713	.79720	626	6	4
627	.79727	.79734	.79741	.79748	.79754	.79761	.79768	.79775	.79782	.79789	627	7	5
628	.79796	.79803	.79810	.79817	.79824	.79831	.79837	.79844	.79851	.79858	628	8	6
629	.79865	.79872	.79879	.79886	.79893	.79900	.79906	.79913	.79920	.79927	629	9	6
630	.79934	.79941	.79948	.79955	.79962	.79969	.79975	.79982	.79989	.79996	630		
631	.80003	.80010	.80017	.80024	.80030	.80037	.80044	.80051	.80058	.80065	631	1	1
632	.80072	.80079	.80085	.80092	.80099	.80106	.80113	.80120	.80127	.80134	632	2	1
633	.80140	.80147	.80154	.80161	.80168	.80175	.80182	.80188	.80195	.80202	633	3	2
634	.80209	.80216	.80223	.80229	.80236	.80243	.80250	.80257	.80264	.80271	634	4	3
635	.80277	.80284	.80291	.80298	.80305	.80312	.80318	.80325	.80332	.80339	635	5	4
636	.80346	.80353	.80359	.80366	.80373	.80380	.80387	.80393	.80400	.80407	636	6	4
637	.80414	.80421	.80428	.80434	.80441	.80448	.80455	.80462	.80468	.80475	637	7	5
638	.80482	.80489	.80496	.80502	.80509	.80516	.80523	.80530	.80536	.80543	638	8	6
639	.80550	.80557	.80564	.80570	.80577	.80584	.80591	.80598	.80604	.80611	639	9	6
	0	1	2	3	4	5	6	7	8	9			

Table 18

LOGARITHMS

No.	0	1	2	3	4	5	6	7	8	9	No.	5th Fig.	Log Diff.
640	.80618	.80625	.80632	.80638	.80645	.80652	.80659	.80665	.80672	.80679	640		
641	.80686	.80693	.80699	.80706	.80713	.80720	.80726	.80733	.80740	.80747	641	1	1
642	.80754	.80760	.80767	.80774	.80781	.80787	.80794	.80801	.80808	.80814	642	2	1
643	.80821	.80828	.80835	.80841	.80848	.80855	.80862	.80868	.80875	.80882	643	3	2
644	.80889	.80895	.80902	.80909	.80916	.80922	.80929	.80936	.80943	.80949	644	4	3
645	.80956	.80963	.80969	.80976	.80983	.80990	.80996	.81003	.81010	.81017	645	5	4
646	.81023	.81030	.81037	.81043	.81050	.81057	.81064	.81070	.81077	.81084	646	6	4
647	.81090	.81097	.81104	.81111	.81117	.81124	.81131	.81137	.81144	.81151	647	7	5
648	.81158	.81164	.81171	.81178	.81184	.81191	.81198	.81204	.81211	.81218	648	8	6
649	.81224	.81231	.81238	.81245	.81251	.81258	.81265	.81271	.81278	.81285	649	9	6
650	.81291	.81298	.81305	.81311	.81318	.81325	.81331	.81338	.81345	.81351	650		
651	.81358	.81365	.81371	.81378	.81385	.81391	.81398	.81405	.81411	.81418	651	1	1
652	.81425	.81431	.81438	.81445	.81451	.81458	.81465	.81471	.81478	.81485	652	2	1
653	.81491	.81498	.81505	.81511	.81518	.81525	.81531	.81538	.81544	.81551	653	3	2
654	.81558	.81564	.81571	.81578	.81584	.81591	.81598	.81604	.81611	.81617	654	4	3
655	.81624	.81631	.81637	.81644	.81651	.81657	.81664	.81671	.81677	.81684	655	5	3
656	.81690	.81697	.81704	.81710	.81717	.81723	.81730	.81737	.81743	.81750	656	6	4
657	.81757	.81763	.81770	.81776	.81783	.81790	.81796	.81803	.81809	.81816	657	7	5
658	.81823	.81829	.81836	.81842	.81849	.81856	.81862	.81869	.81875	.81882	658	8	6
659	.81889	.81895	.81902	.81908	.81915	.81921	.81928	.81935	.81941	.81948	659	9	6
660	.81954	.81961	.81968	.81974	.81981	.81987	.81994	.82000	.82007	.82014	660		
661	.82020	.82027	.82033	.82040	.82046	.82053	.82060	.82066	.82073	.82079	661	1	1
662	.82086	.82092	.82099	.82105	.82112	.82119	.82125	.82132	.82138	.82145	662	2	1
663	.82151	.82158	.82164	.82171	.82178	.82184	.82191	.82197	.82204	.82210	663	3	2
664	.82217	.82223	.82230	.82236	.82243	.82249	.82256	.82263	.82269	.82276	664	4	3
665	.82282	.82289	.82295	.82302	.82308	.82315	.82321	.82328	.82334	.82341	665	5	3
666	.82347	.82354	.82360	.82367	.82373	.82380	.82387	.82393	.82400	.82406	666	6	4
667	.82413	.82419	.82426	.82432	.82439	.82445	.82452	.82458	.82465	.82471	667	7	5
668	.82478	.82484	.82491	.82497	.82504	.82510	.82517	.82523	.82530	.82536	668	8	5
669	.82543	.82549	.82556	.82562	.82569	.82575	.82582	.82588	.82595	.82601	669	9	6
670	.82607	.82614	.82620	.82627	.82633	.82640	.82646	.82653	.82659	.82666	670		
671	.82672	.82679	.82685	.82692	.82698	.82705	.82711	.82718	.82724	.82730	671	1	1
672	.82737	.82743	.82750	.82756	.82763	.82769	.82776	.82782	.82789	.82795	672	2	1
673	.82802	.82808	.82814	.82821	.82827	.82834	.82840	.82847	.82853	.82860	673	3	2
674	.82866	.82872	.82879	.82885	.82892	.82898	.82905	.82911	.82918	.82924	674	4	3
675	.82930	.82937	.82943	.82950	.82956	.82963	.82969	.82975	.82982	.82988	675	5	3
676	.82995	.83001	.83008	.83014	.83020	.83027	.83033	.83040	.83046	.83052	676	6	4
677	.83059	.83065	.83072	.83078	.83085	.83091	.83097	.83104	.83110	.83117	677	7	5
678	.83123	.83129	.83136	.83142	.83149	.83155	.83161	.83168	.83174	.83181	678	8	5
679	.83187	.83193	.83200	.83206	.83213	.83219	.83225	.83232	.83238	.83245	679	9	6
680	.83251	.83257	.83264	.83270	.83276	.83283	.83289	.83296	.83302	.83308	680		
681	.83315	.83321	.83327	.83334	.83340	.83347	.83353	.83359	.83366	.83372	681	1	1
682	.83378	.83385	.83391	.83398	.83404	.83410	.83417	.83423	.83429	.83436	682	2	1
683	.83442	.83448	.83455	.83461	.83467	.83474	.83480	.83487	.83493	.83499	683	3	2
684	.83506	.83512	.83518	.83525	.83531	.83537	.83544	.83550	.83556	.83563	684	4	3
685	.83569	.83575	.83582	.83588	.83594	.83601	.83607	.83613	.83620	.83626	685	5	3
686	.83632	.83639	.83645	.83651	.83658	.83664	.83670	.83677	.83683	.83689	686	6	4
687	.83696	.83702	.83708	.83715	.83721	.83727	.83734	.83740	.83746	.83753	687	7	5
688	.83759	.83765	.83771	.83778	.83784	.83790	.83797	.83803	.83809	.83816	688	8	5
689	.83822	.83828	.83835	.83841	.83847	.83853	.83860	.83866	.83872	.83879	689	9	6
690	.83885	.83891	.83897	.83904	.83910	.83916	.83923	.83929	.83935	.83942	690		
691	.83948	.83954	.83960	.83967	.83973	.83979	.83985	.83992	.83998	.84004	691	1	1
692	.84011	.84017	.84023	.84029	.84036	.84042	.84048	.84055	.84061	.84067	692	2	1
693	.84073	.84080	.84086	.84092	.84098	.84105	.84111	.84117	.84123	.84130	693	3	2
694	.84136	.84142	.84148	.84155	.84161	.84167	.84173	.84180	.84186	.84192	694	4	3
695	.84198	.84205	.84211	.84217	.84223	.84230	.84236	.84242	.84248	.84255	695	5	3
696	.84261	.84267	.84273	.84280	.84286	.84292	.84298	.84305	.84311	.84317	696	6	4
697	.84323	.84330	.84336	.84342	.84348	.84354	.84361	.84367	.84373	.84379	697	7	5
698	.84386	.84392	.84398	.84404	.84410	.84417	.84423	.84429	.84435	.84442	698	8	5
699	.84448	.84454	.84460	.84466	.84473	.84479	.84485	.84491	.84497	.84504	699	9	6
	0	1	2	3	4	5	6	7	8	9			

Table 18

LOGARITHMS

Nos. $\begin{cases} 70- \\ 75- \end{cases}$

Logs 84510
88076

No.	0	1	2	3	4	5	6	7	8	9	No.	5th Fig.	Log Diff.
700	.84510	.84516	.84522	.84528	.84535	.84541	.84547	.84553	.84559	.84566	700		
701	.84572	.84578	.84584	.84590	.84597	.84603	.84609	.84615	.84621	.84628	701	1	1
702	.84634	.84640	.84646	.84652	.84658	.84665	.84671	.84677	.84683	.84689	702	2	1
703	.84696	.84702	.84708	.84714	.84720	.84726	.84733	.84739	.84745	.84751	703	3	2
704	.84757	.84763	.84770	.84776	.84782	.84788	.84794	.84800	.84807	.84813	704	4	2
705	.84819	.84825	.84831	.84837	.84844	.84850	.84856	.84862	.84868	.84874	705	5	3
706	.84880	.84887	.84893	.84899	.84905	.84911	.84917	.84924	.84930	.84936	706	6	4
707	.84942	.84948	.84954	.84960	.84967	.84973	.84979	.84985	.84991	.84997	707	7	4
708	.85003	.85009	.85016	.85022	.85028	.85034	.85040	.85046	.85052	.85058	708	8	5
709	.85065	.85071	.85077	.85083	.85089	.85095	.85101	.85107	.85114	.85120	709	9	5
710	.85126	.85132	.85138	.85144	.85150	.85156	.85163	.85169	.85175	.85181	710		
711	.85187	.85193	.85199	.85205	.85211	.85217	.85224	.85230	.85236	.85242	711	1	1
712	.85248	.85254	.85260	.85266	.85272	.85278	.85285	.85291	.85297	.85303	712	2	1
713	.85309	.85315	.85321	.85327	.85333	.85339	.85345	.85352	.85358	.85364	713	3	2
714	.85370	.85376	.85382	.85388	.85394	.85400	.85406	.85412	.85418	.85425	714	4	2
715	.85431	.85437	.85443	.85449	.85455	.85461	.85467	.85473	.85479	.85485	715	5	3
716	.85491	.85497	.85503	.85509	.85516	.85522	.85528	.85534	.85540	.85546	716	6	4
717	.85552	.85558	.85564	.85570	.85576	.85582	.85588	.85594	.85600	.85606	717	7	4
718	.85612	.85618	.85625	.85631	.85637	.85643	.85649	.85655	.85661	.85667	718	8	5
719	.85673	.85679	.85685	.85691	.85697	.85703	.85709	.85715	.85721	.85727	719	9	5
720	.85733	.85739	.85745	.85751	.85757	.85763	.85769	.85775	.85781	.85788	720		
721	.85794	.85800	.85806	.85812	.85818	.85824	.85830	.85836	.85842	.85848	721	1	1
722	.85854	.85860	.85866	.85872	.85878	.85884	.85890	.85896	.85902	.85908	722	2	1
723	.85914	.85920	.85926	.85932	.85938	.85944	.85950	.85956	.85962	.85968	723	3	2
724	.85974	.85980	.85986	.85992	.85998	.86004	.86010	.86016	.86022	.86028	724	4	2
725	.86034	.86040	.86046	.86052	.86058	.86064	.86070	.86076	.86082	.86088	725	5	3
726	.86094	.86100	.86106	.86112	.86118	.86124	.86130	.86136	.86141	.86147	726	6	4
727	.86153	.86159	.86165	.86171	.86177	.86183	.86189	.86195	.86201	.86207	727	7	4
728	.86213	.86219	.86225	.86231	.86237	.86243	.86249	.86255	.86261	.86267	728	8	5
729	.86273	.86279	.86285	.86291	.86297	.86303	.86308	.86314	.86320	.86326	729	9	5
730	.86332	.86338	.86344	.86350	.86356	.86362	.86368	.86374	.86380	.86386	730		
731	.86392	.86398	.86404	.86410	.86415	.86421	.86427	.86433	.86439	.86445	731	1	1
732	.86451	.86457	.86463	.86469	.86475	.86481	.86487	.86493	.86499	.86504	732	2	1
733	.86510	.86516	.86522	.86528	.86534	.86540	.86546	.86552	.86558	.86564	733	3	2
734	.86570	.86576	.86581	.86587	.86593	.86599	.86605	.86611	.86617	.86623	734	4	2
735	.86629	.86635	.86641	.86646	.86652	.86658	.86664	.86670	.86676	.86682	735	5	3
736	.86688	.86694	.86700	.86705	.86711	.86717	.86723	.86729	.86735	.86741	736	6	4
737	.86747	.86753	.86759	.86764	.86770	.86776	.86782	.86788	.86794	.86800	737	7	4
738	.86806	.86812	.86817	.86823	.86829	.86835	.86841	.86847	.86853	.86859	738	8	5
739	.86864	.86870	.86876	.86882	.86888	.86894	.86900	.86906	.86911	.86917	739	9	5
740	.86923	.86929	.86935	.86941	.86947	.86953	.86958	.86964	.86970	.86976	740		
741	.86982	.86988	.86994	.86999	.87005	.87011	.87017	.87023	.87029	.87035	741	1	1
742	.87040	.87046	.87052	.87058	.87064	.87070	.87075	.87081	.87087	.87093	742	2	1
743	.87099	.87105	.87111	.87116	.87122	.87128	.87134	.87140	.87146	.87151	743	3	2
744	.87157	.87163	.87169	.87175	.87181	.87186	.87192	.87198	.87204	.87210	744	4	2
745	.87216	.87221	.87227	.87233	.87239	.87245	.87251	.87256	.87262	.87268	745	5	3
746	.87274	.87280	.87286	.87291	.87297	.87303	.87309	.87315	.87320	.87326	746	6	4
747	.87332	.87338	.87344	.87349	.87355	.87361	.87367	.87373	.87379	.87384	747	7	4
748	.87390	.87396	.87402	.87408	.87413	.87419	.87425	.87431	.87437	.87442	748	8	5
749	.87448	.87454	.87460	.87466	.87471	.87477	.87483	.87489	.87495	.87500	749	9	5
750	.87506	.87512	.87518	.87523	.87529	.87535	.87541	.87547	.87552	.87558	750		
751	.87564	.87570	.87576	.87581	.87587	.87593	.87599	.87604	.87610	.87616	751	1	1
752	.87622	.87628	.87633	.87639	.87645	.87651	.87656	.87662	.87668	.87674	752	2	1
753	.87679	.87685	.87691	.87697	.87703	.87708	.87714	.87720	.87726	.87731	753	3	2
754	.87737	.87743	.87749	.87754	.87760	.87766	.87772	.87777	.87783	.87789	754	4	2
755	.87795	.87800	.87806	.87812	.87818	.87823	.87829	.87835	.87841	.87846	755	5	3
756	.87852	.87858	.87864	.87869	.87875	.87881	.87887	.87892	.87898	.87904	756	6	4
757	.87910	.87915	.87921	.87927	.87933	.87938	.87944	.87950	.87955	.87961	757	7	4
758	.87967	.87973	.87978	.87984	.87990	.87996	.88001	.88007	.88013	.88018	758	8	5
759	.88024	.88030	.88036	.88041	.88047	.88053	.88058	.88064	.88070	.88076	759	9	5
	0	1	2	3	4	5	6	7	8	9			

Table 18

LOGARITHMS

No.	0	1	2	3	4	5	6	7	8	9	No.	5th Fig.	Log Diff.
760	.88081	.88087	.88093	.88098	.88104	.88110	.88116	.88121	.88127	.88133	760		
761	.88138	.88144	.88150	.88156	.88161	.88167	.88173	.88178	.88184	.88190	761	1	1
762	.88195	.88201	.88207	.88213	.88218	.88224	.88230	.88235	.88241	.88247	762	2	1
763	.88252	.88258	.88264	.88270	.88275	.88281	.88287	.88292	.88298	.88304	763	3	2
764	.88309	.88315	.88321	.88326	.88332	.88338	.88343	.88349	.88355	.88360	764	4	2
765	.88366	.88372	.88377	.88383	.88389	.88395	.88400	.88406	.88412	.88417	765	5	3
766	.88423	.88429	.88434	.88440	.88446	.88451	.88457	.88463	.88468	.88474	766	6	4
767	.88480	.88485	.88491	.88497	.88502	.88508	.88513	.88519	.88525	.88530	767	7	4
768	.88536	.88542	.88547	.88553	.88559	.88564	.88570	.88576	.88581	.88587	768	8	5
769	.88593	.88598	.88604	.88610	.88615	.88621	.88627	.88632	.88638	.88643	769	9	5
770	.88649	.88655	.88660	.88666	.88672	.88677	.88683	.88689	.88694	.88700	770		
771	.88705	.88711	.88717	.88722	.88728	.88734	.88739	.88745	.88750	.88756	771	1	1
772	.88762	.88767	.88773	.88779	.88784	.88790	.88795	.88801	.88807	.88812	772	2	1
773	.88818	.88824	.88829	.88835	.88840	.88846	.88852	.88857	.88863	.88868	773	3	2
774	.88874	.88880	.88885	.88891	.88897	.88902	.88908	.88913	.88919	.88925	774	4	2
775	.88930	.88936	.88941	.88947	.88953	.88958	.88964	.88969	.88975	.88981	775	5	3
776	.88986	.88992	.88997	.89003	.89009	.89014	.89020	.89025	.89031	.89037	776	6	3
777	.89042	.89048	.89053	.89059	.89064	.89070	.89076	.89081	.89087	.89092	777	7	4
778	.89098	.89104	.89109	.89115	.89120	.89126	.89131	.89137	.89143	.89148	778	8	4
779	.89154	.89159	.89165	.89170	.89176	.89182	.89187	.89193	.89198	.89204	779	9	5
780	.89209	.89215	.89221	.89226	.89232	.89237	.89243	.89248	.89254	.89260	780		
781	.89265	.89271	.89276	.89282	.89287	.89293	.89298	.89304	.89310	.89315	781	1	1
782	.89321	.89326	.89332	.89337	.89343	.89348	.89354	.89360	.89365	.89371	782	2	1
783	.89376	.89382	.89387	.89393	.89398	.89404	.89409	.89415	.89421	.89426	783	3	2
784	.89432	.89437	.89443	.89448	.89454	.89459	.89465	.89470	.89476	.89481	784	4	3
785	.89437	.89492	.89498	.89504	.89509	.89515	.89520	.89526	.89531	.89537	785	5	3
786	.89542	.89548	.89553	.89559	.89564	.89570	.89575	.89581	.89586	.89592	786	6	4
787	.89597	.89603	.89609	.89614	.89620	.89625	.89631	.89636	.89642	.89647	787	7	4
788	.89653	.89658	.89664	.89669	.89675	.89680	.89686	.89691	.89697	.89702	788	8	5
789	.89708	.89713	.89719	.89724	.89730	.89735	.89741	.89746	.89752	.89757	789	9	5
790	.89763	.89768	.89774	.89779	.89785	.89790	.89796	.89801	.89807	.89812	790		
791	.89818	.89823	.89829	.89834	.89840	.89845	.89851	.89856	.89862	.89867	791	1	1
792	.89873	.89878	.89883	.89889	.89894	.89900	.89905	.89911	.89916	.89922	792	2	1
793	.89927	.89933	.89938	.89944	.89949	.89955	.89960	.89966	.89971	.89977	793	3	2
794	.89982	.89988	.89993	.89998	.90004	.90009	.90015	.90020	.90026	.90031	794	4	2
795	.90037	.90042	.90048	.90053	.90059	.90064	.90069	.90075	.90080	.90086	795	5	3
796	.90091	.90097	.90102	.90108	.90113	.90119	.90124	.90129	.90135	.90140	796	6	4
797	.90146	.90151	.90157	.90162	.90168	.90173	.90179	.90184	.90189	.90195	797	7	4
798	.90200	.90206	.90211	.90217	.90222	.90227	.90233	.90238	.90244	.90249	798	8	5
799	.90255	.90260	.90266	.90271	.90276	.90282	.90287	.90293	.90298	.90304	799	9	5
800	.90309	.90314	.90320	.90325	.90331	.90336	.90342	.90347	.90352	.90358	800		
801	.90363	.90369	.90374	.90380	.90385	.90390	.90396	.90401	.90407	.90412	801	1	1
802	.90417	.90423	.90428	.90434	.90439	.90445	.90450	.90455	.90461	.90466	802	2	1
803	.90472	.90477	.90482	.90488	.90493	.90499	.90504	.90509	.90515	.90520	803	3	2
804	.90526	.90531	.90536	.90542	.90547	.90553	.90558	.90563	.90569	.90574	804	4	2
805	.90580	.90585	.90590	.90596	.90601	.90607	.90612	.90617	.90623	.90628	805	5	3
806	.90634	.90639	.90644	.90650	.90655	.90660	.90666	.90671	.90677	.90682	806	6	3
807	.90687	.90693	.90698	.90703	.90709	.90714	.90720	.90725	.90730	.90736	807	7	4
808	.90741	.90747	.90752	.90757	.90763	.90768	.90773	.90779	.90784	.90789	808	8	4
809	.90795	.90800	.90806	.90811	.90816	.90822	.90827	.90832	.90838	.90843	809	9	5
810	.90849	.90854	.90859	.90865	.90870	.90875	.90881	.90886	.90891	.90897	810		
811	.90902	.90907	.90913	.90918	.90924	.90929	.90934	.90940	.90945	.90950	811	1	1
812	.90956	.90961	.90966	.90972	.90977	.90982	.90988	.90993	.90998	.91004	812	2	1
813	.91009	.91014	.91020	.91025	.91030	.91036	.91041	.91046	.91052	.91057	813	3	2
814	.91062	.91068	.91073	.91078	.91084	.91089	.91094	.91100	.91105	.91110	814	4	2
815	.91116	.91121	.91126	.91132	.91137	.91142	.91148	.91153	.91158	.91164	815	5	3
816	.91169	.91174	.91180	.91185	.91190	.91196	.91201	.91206	.91212	.91217	816	6	3
817	.91222	.91228	.91233	.91238	.91243	.91249	.91254	.91259	.91265	.91270	817	7	4
818	.91275	.91281	.91286	.91291	.91297	.91302	.91307	.91312	.91318	.91323	818	8	4
819	.91328	.91334	.91339	.91344	.91350	.91355	.91360	.91365	.91371	.91376	819	9	5
	0	1	2	3	4	5	6	7	8	9			

Table 18

LOGARITHMS

No.	0	1	2	3	4	5	6	7	8	9	No.	5th Fig.	Log Diff.
820	.91381	.91387	.91392	.91397	.91403	.91408	.91413	.91418	.91424	.91429	820		
821	.91434	.91440	.91445	.91450	.91455	.91461	.91466	.91471	.91477	.91482	821	1	1
822	.91487	.91492	.91498	.91503	.91508	.91514	.91519	.91524	.91529	.91535	822	2	1
823	.91540	.91545	.91551	.91556	.91561	.91566	.91572	.91577	.91582	.91587	823	3	2
824	.91593	.91598	.91603	.91609	.91614	.91619	.91624	.91630	.91635	.91640	824	4	2
825	.91645	.91651	.91656	.91661	.91666	.91672	.91677	.91682	.91687	.91693	825	5	3
826	.91698	.91703	.91709	.91714	.91719	.91724	.91730	.91735	.91740	.91745	826	6	3
827	.91751	.91756	.91761	.91766	.91772	.91777	.91782	.91787	.91793	.91798	827	7	4
828	.91803	.91808	.91814	.91819	.91824	.91829	.91834	.91840	.91845	.91850	828	8	4
829	.91855	.91861	.91866	.91871	.91876	.91882	.91887	.91892	.91897	.91903	829	9	5
830	.91908	.91913	.91918	.91924	.91929	.91934	.91939	.91944	.91950	.91955	830		
831	.91960	.91965	.91971	.91976	.91981	.91986	.91991	.91997	.92002	.92007	831	1	1
832	.92012	.92018	.92023	.92028	.92033	.92038	.92044	.92049	.92054	.92059	832	2	1
833	.92065	.92070	.92075	.92080	.92085	.92091	.92096	.92101	.92106	.92111	833	3	2
834	.92117	.92122	.92127	.92132	.92137	.92143	.92148	.92153	.92158	.92163	834	4	2
835	.92169	.92174	.92179	.92184	.92189	.92195	.92200	.92205	.92210	.92215	835	5	3
836	.92221	.92226	.92231	.92236	.92241	.92247	.92252	.92257	.92262	.92267	836	6	3
837	.92273	.92278	.92283	.92288	.92293	.92298	.92304	.92309	.92314	.92319	837	7	4
838	.92324	.92330	.92335	.92340	.92345	.92350	.92355	.92361	.92366	.92371	838	8	4
839	.92376	.92381	.92387	.92392	.92397	.92402	.92407	.92412	.92418	.92423	839	9	5
840	.92428	.92433	.92438	.92443	.92449	.92454	.92459	.92464	.92469	.92474	840		
841	.92480	.92485	.92490	.92495	.92500	.92505	.92511	.92516	.92521	.92526	841	1	1
842	.92531	.92536	.92542	.92547	.92552	.92557	.92562	.92567	.92572	.92578	842	2	1
843	.92583	.92588	.92593	.92598	.92603	.92609	.92614	.92619	.92624	.92629	843	3	2
844	.92634	.92639	.92645	.92650	.92655	.92660	.92665	.92670	.92675	.92681	844	4	2
845	.92686	.92691	.92696	.92701	.92706	.92711	.92716	.92722	.92727	.92732	845	5	3
846	.92737	.92742	.92747	.92752	.92758	.92763	.92768	.92773	.92778	.92783	846	6	3
847	.92788	.92793	.92799	.92804	.92809	.92814	.92819	.92824	.92829	.92834	847	7	4
848	.92840	.92845	.92850	.92855	.92860	.92865	.92870	.92875	.92881	.92886	848	8	4
849	.92891	.92896	.92901	.92906	.92911	.92916	.92921	.92927	.92932	.92937	849	9	5
850	.92942	.92947	.92952	.92957	.92962	.92967	.92973	.92978	.92983	.92988	850		
851	.92993	.92998	.93003	.93008	.93013	.93018	.93024	.93029	.93034	.93039	851	1	1
852	.93044	.93049	.93054	.93059	.93064	.93069	.93075	.93080	.93085	.93090	852	2	1
853	.93095	.93100	.93105	.93110	.93115	.93120	.93125	.93131	.93136	.93141	853	3	2
854	.93146	.93151	.93156	.93161	.93166	.93171	.93176	.93181	.93186	.93192	854	4	2
855	.93197	.93202	.93207	.93212	.93217	.93222	.93227	.93232	.93237	.93242	855	5	3
856	.93247	.93252	.93258	.93263	.93268	.93273	.93278	.93283	.93288	.93293	856	6	3
857	.93298	.93303	.93308	.93313	.93318	.93323	.93328	.93334	.93339	.93344	857	7	3
858	.93349	.93354	.93359	.93364	.93369	.93374	.93379	.93384	.93389	.93394	858	8	4
859	.93399	.93404	.93409	.93414	.93420	.93425	.93430	.93435	.93440	.93445	859	9	4
860	.93450	.93455	.93460	.93465	.93470	.93475	.93480	.93485	.93490	.93495	860		
861	.93500	.93505	.93510	.93515	.93520	.93526	.93531	.93536	.93541	.93546	861	1	1
862	.93551	.93556	.93561	.93566	.93571	.93576	.93581	.93586	.93591	.93596	862	2	1
863	.93601	.93606	.93611	.93616	.93621	.93626	.93631	.93636	.93641	.93646	863	3	2
864	.93651	.93656	.93661	.93666	.93671	.93676	.93682	.93687	.93692	.93697	864	4	2
865	.93702	.93707	.93712	.93717	.93722	.93727	.93732	.93737	.93742	.93747	865	5	3
866	.93752	.93757	.93762	.93767	.93772	.93777	.93782	.93787	.93792	.93797	866	6	3
867	.93802	.93807	.93812	.93817	.93822	.93827	.93832	.93837	.93842	.93847	867	7	3
868	.93852	.93857	.93862	.93867	.93872	.93877	.93882	.93887	.93892	.93897	868	8	4
869	.93902	.93907	.93912	.93917	.93922	.93927	.93932	.93937	.93942	.93947	869	9	4
870	.93952	.93957	.93962	.93967	.93972	.93977	.93982	.93987	.93992	.93997	870		
871	.94002	.94007	.94012	.94017	.94022	.94027	.94032	.94037	.94042	.94047	871	1	0
872	.94052	.94057	.94062	.94067	.94072	.94077	.94082	.94086	.94091	.94096	872	2	1
873	.94101	.94106	.94111	.94116	.94121	.94126	.94131	.94136	.94141	.94146	873	3	1
874	.94151	.94156	.94161	.94166	.94171	.94176	.94181	.94186	.94191	.94196	874	4	2
875	.94201	.94206	.94211	.94216	.94221	.94226	.94231	.94236	.94240	.94245	875	5	2
876	.94250	.94255	.94260	.94265	.94270	.94275	.94280	.94285	.94290	.94295	876	6	3
877	.94300	.94305	.94310	.94315	.94320	.94325	.94330	.94335	.94340	.94345	877	7	3
878	.94349	.94354	.94359	.94364	.94369	.94374	.94379	.94384	.94389	.94394	878	8	4
879	.94399	.94404	.94409	.94414	.94419	.94424	.94429	.94433	.94438	.94443	879	9	4
	0	1	2	3	4	5	6	7	8	9			

Table 18

LOGARITHMS

No.	0	1	2	3	4	5	6	7	8	9	No.	5th Fig.	Log Diff.
880	.94448	.94453	.94458	.94463	.94468	.94473	.94478	.94483	.94488	.94493	880		
881	.94498	.94503	.94507	.94512	.94517	.94522	.94527	.94532	.94537	.94542	881	1	0
882	.94547	.94552	.94557	.94562	.94567	.94571	.94576	.94581	.94586	.94591	882	2	1
883	.94596	.94601	.94606	.94611	.94616	.94621	.94626	.94630	.94635	.94640	883	3	1
884	.94645	.94650	.94655	.94660	.94665	.94670	.94675	.94680	.94685	.94689	884	4	2
885	.94694	.94699	.94704	.94709	.94714	.94719	.94724	.94729	.94734	.94738	885	5	2
886	.94743	.94748	.94753	.94758	.94763	.94768	.94773	.94778	.94783	.94787	886	6	3
887	.94792	.94797	.94802	.94807	.94812	.94817	.94822	.94827	.94832	.94836	887	7	3
888	.94841	.94846	.94851	.94856	.94861	.94866	.94871	.94876	.94880	.94885	888	8	4
889	.94890	.94895	.94900	.94905	.94910	.94915	.94919	.94924	.94929	.94934	889	9	4
890	.94939	.94944	.94949	.94954	.94959	.94963	.94968	.94973	.94978	.94983	890		
891	.94988	.94993	.94998	.95002	.95007	.95012	.95017	.95022	.95027	.95032	891	1	0
892	.95036	.95041	.95046	.95051	.95056	.95061	.95066	.95071	.95075	.95080	892	2	1
893	.95085	.95090	.95095	.95100	.95105	.95109	.95114	.95119	.95124	.95129	893	3	1
894	.95134	.95139	.95143	.95148	.95153	.95158	.95163	.95168	.95173	.95177	894	4	2
895	.95182	.95187	.95192	.95197	.95202	.95207	.95211	.95216	.95221	.95226	895	5	2
896	.95231	.95236	.95240	.95245	.95250	.95255	.95260	.95265	.95270	.95274	896	6	3
897	.95279	.95284	.95289	.95294	.95299	.95303	.95308	.95313	.95318	.95323	897	7	3
898	.95328	.95332	.95337	.95342	.95347	.95352	.95357	.95361	.95366	.95371	898	8	4
899	.95376	.95381	.95386	.95390	.95395	.95400	.95405	.95410	.95415	.95419	899	9	4
900	.95424	.95429	.95434	.95439	.95444	.95448	.95453	.95458	.95463	.95468	900		
901	.95472	.95477	.95482	.95487	.95492	.95497	.95501	.95506	.95511	.95516	901	1	0
902	.95521	.95525	.95530	.95535	.95540	.95545	.95550	.95554	.95559	.95564	902	2	1
903	.95569	.95574	.95578	.95583	.95588	.95593	.95598	.95602	.95607	.95612	903	3	1
904	.95617	.95622	.95626	.95631	.95636	.95641	.95646	.95650	.95655	.95660	904	4	2
905	.95665	.95670	.95674	.95679	.95684	.95689	.95694	.95698	.95703	.95708	905	5	2
906	.95713	.95718	.95722	.95727	.95732	.95737	.95742	.95746	.95751	.95756	906	6	3
907	.95761	.95766	.95770	.95775	.95780	.95785	.95789	.95794	.95799	.95804	907	7	3
908	.95809	.95813	.95818	.95823	.95828	.95832	.95837	.95842	.95847	.95852	908	8	4
909	.95856	.95861	.95866	.95871	.95875	.95880	.95885	.95890	.95895	.95899	909	9	4
910	.95904	.95909	.95914	.95918	.95923	.95928	.95933	.95938	.95942	.95947	910		
911	.95952	.95957	.95961	.95966	.95971	.95976	.95980	.95985	.95990	.95995	911	1	0
912	.95999	.96004	.96009	.96014	.96019	.96023	.96028	.96033	.96038	.96042	912	2	1
913	.96047	.96052	.96057	.96061	.96066	.96071	.96076	.96080	.96085	.96090	913	3	1
914	.96095	.96099	.96104	.96109	.96114	.96118	.96123	.96128	.96133	.96137	914	4	2
915	.96142	.96147	.96152	.96156	.96161	.96166	.96171	.96175	.96180	.96185	915	5	2
916	.96190	.96194	.96199	.96204	.96209	.96213	.96218	.96223	.96227	.96232	916	6	3
917	.96237	.96242	.96246	.96251	.96256	.96261	.96265	.96270	.96275	.96280	917	7	3
918	.96284	.96289	.96294	.96298	.96303	.96308	.96313	.96317	.96322	.96327	918	8	4
919	.96332	.96336	.96341	.96346	.96350	.96355	.96360	.96365	.96369	.96374	919	9	4
920	.96379	.96384	.96388	.96393	.96398	.96402	.96407	.96412	.96417	.96421	920		
921	.96426	.96431	.96435	.96440	.96445	.96450	.96454	.96459	.96464	.96468	921	1	0
922	.96473	.96478	.96483	.96487	.96492	.96497	.96501	.96506	.96511	.96515	922	2	1
923	.96520	.96525	.96530	.96534	.96539	.96544	.96548	.96553	.96558	.96562	923	3	1
924	.96567	.96572	.96577	.96581	.96586	.96591	.96595	.96600	.96605	.96609	924	4	2
925	.96614	.96619	.96624	.96628	.96633	.96638	.96642	.96647	.96652	.96656	925	5	2
926	.96661	.96666	.96670	.96675	.96680	.96685	.96689	.96694	.96699	.96703	926	6	3
927	.96708	.96713	.96717	.96722	.96727	.96731	.96736	.96741	.96745	.96750	927	7	3
928	.96755	.96759	.96764	.96769	.96774	.96778	.96783	.96788	.96792	.96797	928	8	4
929	.96802	.96806	.96811	.96816	.96820	.96825	.96830	.96834	.96839	.96844	929	9	4
930	.96848	.96853	.96858	.96862	.96867	.96872	.96876	.96881	.96886	.96890	930		
931	.96895	.96900	.96904	.96909	.96914	.96918	.96923	.96928	.96932	.96937	931	1	0
932	.96942	.96946	.96951	.96956	.96960	.96965	.96970	.96974	.96979	.96984	932	2	1
933	.96988	.96993	.96997	.97002	.97007	.97011	.97016	.97021	.97025	.97030	933	3	1
934	.97035	.97039	.97044	.97049	.97053	.97058	.97063	.97067	.97072	.97077	934	4	2
935	.97081	.97086	.97090	.97095	.97100	.97104	.97109	.97114	.97118	.97123	935	5	2
936	.97128	.97132	.97137	.97142	.97146	.97151	.97155	.97160	.97165	.97169	936	6	3
937	.97174	.97179	.97183	.97188	.97192	.97197	.97202	.97206	.97211	.97216	937	7	3
938	.97220	.97225	.97230	.97234	.97239	.97243	.97248	.97253	.97257	.97262	938	8	4
939	.97267	.97271	.97276	.97280	.97285	.97290	.97294	.97299	.97304	.97308	939	9	4
	0	1	2	3	4	5	6	7	8	9			

Table 18

LOGARITHMS

No.	0	1	2	3	4	5	6	7	8	9	No.	5th Fig	Log Diff.
940	.97313	.97317	.97322	.97327	.97331	.97336	.97340	.97345	.97350	.97354	940		
941	.97359	.97364	.97368	.97373	.97377	.97382	.97387	.97391	.97396	.97400	941	1	0
942	.97405	.97410	.97414	.97419	.97424	.97428	.97433	.97437	.97442	.97447	942	2	1
943	.97451	.97456	.97460	.97465	.97470	.97474	.97479	.97483	.97488	.97493	943	3	1
944	.97497	.97502	.97506	.97511	.97516	.97520	.97525	.97529	.97534	.97539	944	4	2
945	.97543	.97548	.97552	.97557	.97562	.97566	.97571	.97575	.97580	.97585	945	5	2
946	.97589	.97594	.97598	.97603	.97607	.97612	.97617	.97621	.97626	.97630	946	6	3
947	.97635	.97640	.97644	.97649	.97653	.97658	.97663	.97667	.97672	.97676	947	7	3
948	.97681	.97685	.97690	.97695	.97699	.97704	.97708	.97713	.97717	.97722	948	8	4
949	.97727	.97731	.97736	.97740	.97745	.97749	.97754	.97759	.97763	.97768	949	9	4
950	.97772	.97777	.97782	.97786	.97791	.97795	.97800	.97804	.97809	.97813	950		
951	.97818	.97823	.97827	.97832	.97836	.97841	.97845	.97850	.97855	.97859	951	1	0
952	.97864	.97868	.97873	.97877	.97882	.97886	.97891	.97896	.97900	.97905	952	2	1
953	.97909	.97914	.97918	.97923	.97928	.97932	.97937	.97941	.97946	.97950	953	3	1
954	.97955	.97959	.97964	.97968	.97973	.97978	.97982	.97987	.97991	.97996	954	4	2
955	.98000	.98005	.98009	.98014	.98019	.98023	.98028	.98032	.98037	.98041	955	5	2
956	.98046	.98050	.98055	.98059	.98064	.98068	.98073	.98078	.98082	.98087	956	6	3
957	.98091	.98096	.98100	.98105	.98109	.98114	.98118	.98123	.98127	.98132	957	7	3
958	.98137	.98141	.98146	.98150	.98155	.98159	.98164	.98168	.98173	.98177	958	8	4
959	.98182	.98186	.98191	.98195	.98200	.98204	.98209	.98214	.98218	.98223	959	9	4
960	.98227	.98232	.98236	.98241	.98245	.98250	.98254	.98259	.98263	.98268	960		
961	.98272	.98277	.98281	.98286	.98290	.98295	.98299	.98304	.98308	.98313	961	1	0
962	.98318	.98322	.98327	.98331	.98336	.98340	.98345	.98349	.98354	.98358	962	2	1
963	.98363	.98367	.98372	.98376	.98381	.98385	.98390	.98394	.98399	.98403	963	3	1
964	.98408	.98412	.98417	.98421	.98426	.98430	.98435	.98439	.98444	.98448	964	4	2
965	.98453	.98457	.98462	.98466	.98471	.98475	.98480	.98484	.98489	.98493	965	5	2
966	.98498	.98502	.98507	.98511	.98516	.98520	.98525	.98529	.98534	.98538	966	6	3
967	.98543	.98547	.98552	.98556	.98561	.98565	.98570	.98574	.98579	.98583	967	7	3
968	.98588	.98592	.98597	.98601	.98605	.98610	.98614	.98619	.98623	.98628	968	8	4
969	.98632	.98637	.98641	.98646	.98650	.98655	.98659	.98664	.98668	.98673	969	9	4
970	.98677	.98682	.98686	.98691	.98695	.98700	.98704	.98709	.98713	.98717	970		
971	.98722	.98726	.98731	.98735	.98740	.98744	.98749	.98753	.98758	.98762	971	1	0
972	.98767	.98771	.98776	.98780	.98784	.98789	.98793	.98798	.98802	.98807	972	2	1
973	.98811	.98816	.98820	.98825	.98829	.98834	.98838	.98843	.98847	.98851	973	3	1
974	.98856	.98860	.98865	.98869	.98874	.98878	.98883	.98887	.98892	.98896	974	4	2
975	.98900	.98905	.98909	.98914	.98918	.98923	.98927	.98932	.98936	.98941	975	5	2
976	.98945	.98949	.98954	.98958	.98963	.98967	.98972	.98976	.98981	.98985	976	6	3
977	.98989	.98994	.98998	.99003	.99007	.99012	.99016	.99021	.99025	.99029	977	7	3
978	.99034	.99038	.99043	.99047	.99052	.99056	.99061	.99065	.99069	.99074	978	8	4
979	.99078	.99083	.99087	.99092	.99096	.99100	.99105	.99109	.99114	.99118	979	9	4
980	.99123	.99127	.99131	.99136	.99140	.99145	.99149	.99154	.99158	.99162	980		
981	.99167	.99171	.99176	.99180	.99185	.99189	.99193	.99198	.99202	.99207	981	1	0
982	.99211	.99216	.99220	.99224	.99229	.99233	.99238	.99242	.99247	.99251	982	2	1
983	.99255	.99260	.99264	.99269	.99273	.99277	.99282	.99286	.99291	.99295	983	3	1
984	.99300	.99304	.99308	.99313	.99317	.99322	.99326	.99330	.99335	.99339	984	4	2
985	.99344	.99348	.99352	.99357	.99361	.99366	.99370	.99374	.99379	.99383	985	5	2
986	.99388	.99392	.99396	.99401	.99405	.99410	.99414	.99419	.99423	.99427	986	6	3
987	.99432	.99436	.99441	.99445	.99449	.99454	.99458	.99463	.99467	.99471	987	7	3
988	.99476	.99480	.99484	.99489	.99493	.99498	.99502	.99506	.99511	.99515	988	8	4
989	.99520	.99524	.99528	.99533	.99537	.99542	.99546	.99550	.99555	.99559	989	9	4
990	.99564	.99568	.99572	.99577	.99581	.99585	.99590	.99594	.99599	.99603	990		
991	.99607	.99612	.99616	.99621	.99625	.99629	.99634	.99638	.99642	.99647	991	1	0
992	.99651	.99656	.99660	.99664	.99669	.99673	.99677	.99682	.99686	.99691	992	2	1
993	.99695	.99699	.99704	.99708	.99712	.99717	.99721	.99726	.99730	.99734	993	3	1
994	.99739	.99743	.99747	.99752	.99756	.99760	.99765	.99769	.99774	.99778	994	4	2
995	.99782	.99787	.99791	.99795	.99800	.99804	.99808	.99813	.99817	.99822	995	5	2
996	.99826	.99830	.99835	.99839	.99843	.99848	.99852	.99856	.99861	.99865	996	6	3
997	.99870	.99874	.99878	.99883	.99887	.99891	.99896	.99900	.99904	.99909	997	7	3
998	.99913	.99917	.99922	.99926	.99930	.99935	.99939	.99944	.99948	.99952	998	8	4
999	.99957	.99961	.99965	.99970	.99974	.99978	.99983	.99987	.99991	.99996	999	9	4
	0	1	2	3	4	5	6	7	8	9			

Table 19 — LOGARITHMIC FUNCTIONS

		0°				1°				2°				
′	Cos.	Sec.	Tan.	D.	Cos.	Sec.	Tan.	D.	Cos.	Sec.	Tan.	D.		
	0/$\bar{1}$. [0/9]	0.	[6, 7, 8]		$\bar{1}$. [9]	0.	$\bar{2}$. [8]		$\bar{1}$. [9]	0.	$\bar{2}$. [8]			
0	00000	00000	−∞		99993	00007	2419	73	99974	00026	5431	37	60	60
1	00000	00000	$\bar{4}$.464		99993	00007	2491	72	99973	00027	5467	37	59	56
2	00000	00000	$\bar{4}$.765		99993	00007	2562	71	99973	00027	5503	36	58	52
3	00000	00000	$\bar{4}$.941		99993	00007	2631	69	99972	00028	5538	35	57	48
4	00000	00000	$\bar{3}$.066		99992	00008	2700	69	99972	00028	5573	35	56	44
5	00000	00000	$\bar{3}$.163	97	99992	00008	2767	67	99971	00029	5608	35	55	40
6	00000	00000	$\bar{3}$.242	79	99992	00008	2833	66	99971	00029	5643	35	54	36
7	00000	00000	$\bar{3}$.309	67	99992	00008	2899	66	99970	00030	5677	34	53	32
8	00000	00000	$\bar{3}$.367	58	99992	00008	2963	64	99970	00030	5711	34	52	28
9	00000	00000	$\bar{3}$.418	51	99991	00009	3026	63	99969	00031	5745	34	51	24
10	00000	00000	$\bar{3}$.464	46	99991	00009	3089	63	99969	00031	5779	34	50	20
11	00000	00000	$\bar{3}$.505	41	99991	00009	3150	61	99968	00032	5812	33	49	16
12	00000	00000	$\bar{3}$.543	38	99990	00010	3211	61	99968	00032	5845	33	48	12
13	00000	00000	$\bar{3}$.578	35	99990	00010	3271	60	99967	00033	5878	33	47	8
14	00000	00000	$\bar{3}$.610	32	99990	00010	3330	59	99967	00033	5911	33	46	4
15	00000	00000	$\bar{3}$.640	30	99990	00010	3389	59	99967	00033	5943	32	45	+3m
16	00000	00000	$\bar{3}$.668	28	99989	00011	3446	57	99966	00034	5975	32	44	56
17	99999	00001	$\bar{3}$.694	26	99989	00011	3503	57	99966	00034	6007	32	43	52
18	99999	00001	$\bar{3}$.719	25	99989	00011	3559	56	99965	00035	6038	31	42	48
19	99999	00001	$\bar{3}$.742	23	99989	00011	3614	55	99964	00036	6070	32	41	44
20	99999	00001	$\bar{3}$.765	23	99988	00012	3669	55	99964	00036	6101	31	40	40
21	99999	00001	$\bar{3}$.786	21	99988	00012	3723	54	99963	00037	6132	31	39	36
22	99999	00001	$\bar{3}$.806	20	99988	00012	3776	53	99963	00037	6163	31	38	32
23	99999	00001	$\bar{3}$.825	19	99987	00013	3829	53	99962	00038	6193	30	37	28
24	99999	00001	$\bar{3}$.844	19	99987	00013	3881	52	99962	00038	6223	30	36	24
25	99999	00001	$\bar{3}$.862	18	99987	00013	3932	51	99961	00039	6254	31	35	20
26	99999	00001	$\bar{3}$.879	17	99986	00014	3983	51	99961	00039	6283	29	34	16
27	99999	00001	$\bar{3}$.895	16	99986	00014	4033	50	99960	00040	6313	30	33	12
28	99999	00001	$\bar{3}$.911	16	99986	00014	4083	50	99960	00040	6343	30	32	8
29	99998	00002	$\bar{3}$.926	15	99985	00015	4132	49	99959	00041	6372	29	31	4
30	99998	00002	$\bar{3}$.941	15	99985	00015	4181	49	99959	00041	6401	29	30	+2m
31	99998	00002	$\bar{3}$.955	14	99985	00015	4229	48	99958	00042	6430	29	29	56
32	99998	00002	$\bar{3}$.969	14	99984	00016	4276	47	99958	00042	6459	29	28	52
33	99998	00002	$\bar{3}$.982	13	99984	00016	4323	47	99957	00043	6487	28	27	48
34	99998	00002	$\bar{3}$.995	13	99984	00016	4370	47	99956	00044	6515	28	26	44
35	99998	00002	$\bar{2}$.008	13	99983	00017	4416	46	99956	00044	6544	29	25	40
36	99998	00002	$\bar{2}$.020	12	99983	00017	4461	45	99955	00045	6571	27	24	36
37	99997	00003	$\bar{2}$.032	12	99983	00017	4506	45	99955	00045	6599	28	23	32
38	99997	00003	$\bar{2}$.044	12	99982	00018	4551	45	99954	00046	6627	28	22	28
39	99997	00003	$\bar{2}$.055	11	99982	00018	4595	44	99954	00046	6654	27	21	24
40	99997	00003	$\bar{2}$.066	11	99982	00018	4638	43	99953	00047	6682	28	20	20
41	99997	00003	$\bar{2}$.077	11	99981	00019	4682	44	99952	00048	6709	27	19	16
42	99997	00003	$\bar{2}$.087	10	99981	00019	4725	43	99952	00048	6736	27	18	12
43	99997	00003	$\bar{2}$.097	10	99981	00019	4767	42	99951	00049	6762	26	17	8
44	99996	00004	$\bar{2}$.107	10	99980	00020	4809	42	99951	00049	6789	27	16	4
45	99996	00004	$\bar{2}$.117	10	99980	00020	4851	42	99950	00050	6815	26	15	+1m
46	99996	00004	$\bar{2}$.127	10	99979	00021	4892	41	99949	00051	6842	27	14	56
47	99996	00004	$\bar{2}$.136	9	99979	00021	4933	41	99949	00051	6868	26	13	52
48	99996	00004	$\bar{2}$.145	9	99979	00021	4973	40	99948	00052	6894	26	12	48
49	99996	00004	$\bar{2}$.154	9	99978	00022	5013	40	99948	00052	6920	26	11	44
50	99995	00005	$\bar{2}$.163	9	99978	00022	5053	40	99947	00053	6945	25	10	40
51	99995	00005	$\bar{2}$.171	8	99977	00023	5092	39	99946	00054	6971	26	9	36
52	99995	00005	$\bar{2}$.180	9	99977	00023	5131	39	99946	00054	6996	25	8	32
53	99995	00005	$\bar{2}$.188	8	99977	00023	5170	39	99945	00055	7021	25	7	28
54	99995	00005	$\bar{2}$.196	8	99976	00024	5208	38	99944	00056	7046	25	6	24
55	99994	00006	$\bar{2}$.204	8	99976	00024	5246	38	99944	00056	7071	25	5	20
56	99994	00006	$\bar{2}$.212	8	99975	00025	5283	37	99943	00057	7096	25	4	16
57	99994	00006	$\bar{2}$.220	8	99975	00025	5321	38	99942	00058	7121	25	3	12
58	99994	00006	$\bar{2}$.227	7	99974	00026	5358	37	99942	00058	7145	24	2	8
59	99994	00006	$\bar{2}$.235	8	99974	00026	5394	36	99941	00059	7170	25	1	4
60	99993	00007	$\bar{2}$.242	7	99974	00026	5431	37	99940	00060	7194	24	0	0
	$\bar{1}$/0. [9/0]	0.	[8, 7, 6]		$\bar{1}$. [9]	0.	$\bar{2}$. [8]		$\bar{1}$. [9]	0.	$\bar{2}$. [8]			
	Sin.	Cosec.	Cot.	D.	Sin.	Cosec.	Cot.	D.	Sin.	Cosec.	Cot.	D.	′	Secs.
		89°				88°				87°				
		5h 56m				5h 52m				5h 48m				

137

Table 19 — LOGARITHMIC FUNCTIONS

′	3° Cos.	D.	Sec.	Tan.	D.	4° Cos.	D.	Sec.	Tan.	D.	5° Cos.	D.	Sec.	Tan.	D.	′	Secs.
	Ī. [9]		0.	2̄. [8]		Ī. [9]		0.	2̄. [8]		Ī. [9]		0.	2̄/Ī. [8/9]			
0	99940	1	00060	7194	24	99894	1	00106	8446	18	99834	2	00166	9420	15	60	60
1	99940	0	00060	7218	24	99893	1	00107	8465	19	99833	1	00167	9434	14	59	56
2	99939	1	00061	7242	24	99892	1	00108	8483	18	99832	1	00168	9449	15	58	52
3	99938	1	00062	7266	24	99891	1	00109	8501	18	99831	1	00169	9463	14	57	48
4	99938	0	00062	7290	24	99891	0	00109	8518	17	99830	1	00170	9477	14	56	44
5	99937	1	00063	7313	23	99890	1	00110	8536	18	99829	1	00171	9492	15	55	40
6	99936	1	00064	7337	24	99889	1	00111	8554	18	99828	1	00172	9506	14	54	36
7	99936	0	00064	7360	23	99888	1	00112	8572	18	99827	1	00173	9520	14	53	32
8	99935	1	00065	7383	23	99887	1	00113	8589	17	99825	2	00175	9534	14	52	28
9	99934	1	00066	7406	23	99886	1	00114	8607	18	99824	1	00176	9549	15	51	24
10	99934	0	00066	7429	23	99885	1	00115	8624	17	99823	1	00177	9563	14	50	20
11	99933	1	00067	7452	23	99884	1	00116	8642	18	99822	1	00178	9577	14	49	16
12	99932	1	00068	7475	23	99883	1	00117	8659	17	99821	1	00179	9591	14	48	12
13	99932	0	00068	7497	22	99882	1	00118	8676	17	99820	1	00180	9605	14	47	8
14	99931	1	00069	7520	23	99881	1	00119	8694	18	99819	1	00181	9619	14	46	4
15	99930	1	00070	7542	22	99880	1	00120	8711	17	99817	2	00183	9633	14	45	+3m
16	99929	1	00071	7565	23	99879	1	00121	8728	17	99816	1	00184	9646	13	44	56
17	99929	0	00071	7587	22	99879	0	00121	8745	17	99815	1	00185	9660	14	43	52
18	99928	1	00072	7609	22	99878	1	00122	8762	17	99814	1	00186	9674	14	42	48
19	99927	1	00073	7631	22	99877	1	00123	8778	16	99813	1	00187	9688	14	41	44
20	99926	1	00074	7652	21	99876	1	00124	8795	17	99812	1	00188	9701	13	40	40
21	99926	0	00074	7674	22	99875	1	00125	8812	17	99810	2	00190	9715	14	39	36
22	99925	1	00075	7696	22	99874	1	00126	8829	17	99809	1	00191	9729	14	38	32
23	99924	1	00076	7717	21	99873	1	00127	8845	16	99808	1	00192	9742	13	37	28
24	99923	1	00077	7739	22	99872	1	00128	8862	17	99807	1	00193	9756	14	36	24
25	99923	0	00077	7760	21	99871	1	00129	8878	16	99806	1	00194	9769	13	35	20
26	99922	1	00078	7781	21	99870	1	00130	8895	17	99804	2	00196	9782	14	34	16
27	99921	1	00079	7802	21	99869	1	00131	8911	16	99803	1	00197	9796	14	33	12
28	99920	1	00080	7823	21	99868	1	00132	8927	16	99802	1	00198	9809	13	32	8
29	99920	0	00080	7844	21	99867	1	00133	8944	17	99801	1	00199	9823	14	31	4
30	99919	1	00081	7865	21	99866	1	00134	8960	16	99800	1	00200	9836	13	30	+2m
31	99918	1	00082	7886	21	99865	1	00135	8976	16	99798	2	00202	9849	13	29	56
32	99917	1	00083	7906	20	99864	1	00136	8992	16	99797	1	00203	9862	13	28	52
33	99917	0	00083	7927	21	99863	1	00137	9008	16	99796	1	00204	9875	13	27	48
34	99916	1	00084	7947	20	99862	1	00138	9024	16	99795	1	00205	9888	13	26	44
35	99915	1	00085	7967	20	99861	1	00139	9040	16	99793	2	00207	9901	13	25	40
36	99914	1	00086	7988	21	99860	1	00140	9056	16	99792	1	00208	9915	14	24	36
37	99913	1	00087	8008	20	99859	1	00141	9071	15	99791	1	00209	9928	13	23	32
38	99913	0	00087	8028	20	99858	1	00142	9087	16	99790	1	00210	9940	12	22	28
39	99912	1	00088	8048	20	99857	1	00143	9103	16	99788	2	00212	9953	13	21	24
40	99911	1	00089	8067	19	99856	1	00144	9118	15	99787	1	00213	9966	13	20	20
41	99910	1	00090	8087	20	99855	1	00145	9134	16	99786	1	00214	9979	13	19	16
42	99909	1	00091	8107	20	99854	1	00146	9150	16	99785	1	00215	9992	13	18	12
43	99909	0	00091	8126	19	99853	1	00147	9165	15	99783	2	00217	0̄005	13	17	8
44	99908	1	00092	8146	20	99852	1	00148	9180	15	99782	1	00218	0017	12	16	4
45	99907	1	00093	8165	19	99851	1	00149	9196	16	99781	1	00219	0030	13	15	+1m
46	99906	1	00094	8185	20	99850	1	00150	9211	15	99780	1	00220	0043	13	14	56
47	99905	1	00095	8204	19	99848	2	00152	9226	15	99778	2	00222	0055	12	13	52
48	99904	1	00096	8223	19	99847	1	00153	9241	15	99777	1	00223	0068	13	12	48
49	99904	0	00096	8242	19	99846	1	00154	9256	15	99776	1	00224	0080	12	11	44
50	99903	1	00097	8261	19	99845	1	00155	9272	16	99775	1	00225	0093	13	10	40
51	99902	1	00098	8280	19	99844	1	00156	9287	15	99773	2	00227	0105	12	9	36
52	99901	1	00099	8299	19	99843	1	00157	9302	15	99772	1	00228	0118	13	8	32
53	99900	1	00100	8317	18	99842	1	00158	9316	14	99771	1	00229	0130	12	7	28
54	99899	1	00101	8336	19	99841	1	00159	9331	15	99769	2	00231	0143	13	6	24
55	99898	1	00102	8355	19	99840	1	00160	9346	15	99768	1	00232	0155	12	5	20
56	99898	0	00102	8373	18	99839	1	00161	9361	15	99767	1	00233	0167	12	4	16
57	99897	1	00103	8392	19	99838	1	00162	9376	15	99765	2	00235	0180	13	3	12
58	99896	1	00104	8410	18	99837	1	00163	9390	14	99764	1	00236	0192	12	2	8
59	99895	1	00105	8428	18	99836	1	00164	9405	15	99763	1	00237	0204	12	1	4
60	99894	1	00106	8446	18	99834	2	00166	9420	15	99761	1	00239	0216	12	0	0
	Ī. [9]		0.	2̄. [8]		Ī. [9]		0.	2̄. [8]		Ī. [9]		0.	Ī/2̄. [9/8]			
	Sin.	D.	Cosec.	Cot.	D.	Sin.	D.	Cosec.	Cot.	D.	Sin.	D.	Cosec.	Cot.	D.	′	Secs.

86°	**85°**	**84°**
5h44m	5h40m	5h36m

138

Table 19   LOGARITHMIC FUNCTIONS

6°   7°   8°

′	Cos.	D.	Sec.	Tan.	D.	Cos.	D.	Sec.	Tan.	D.	Cos.	D.	Sec.	Tan.	D.		
	Ī. [9]		0.	Ī. [9]		Ī. [9]		0.	Ī. [9]		Ī. [9]		0.	Ī. [9]			
0	99761	2	00239	0216	12	99675	2	00325	0891	10	99575	2	00425	14780	92	60	60
1	99760	1	00240	0228	12	99674	1	00326	0902	11	99574	1	00426	14872	92	59	56
2	99759	1	00241	0240	12	99672	2	00328	0912	10	99572	2	00428	14963	91	58	52
3	99757	2	00243	0253	13	99670	2	00330	0923	11	99570	2	00430	15054	91	57	48
4	99756	1	00244	0265	12	99669	1	00331	0933	10	99568	2	00432	15145	91	56	44
5	99755	1	00245	0277	12	99667	2	00333	0943	10	99566	2	00434	15236	91	55	40
6	99753	2	00247	0289	12	99666	1	00334	0954	11	99565	1	00435	15327	91	54	36
7	99752	1	00248	0300	11	99664	2	00336	0964	10	99563	2	00437	15417	90	53	32
8	99751	1	00249	0312	12	99663	1	00337	0974	10	99561	2	00439	15508	91	52	28
9	99749	2	00251	0324	12	99661	2	00339	0984	11	99559	2	00441	15598	90	51	24
10	99748	1	00252	0336	12	99659	2	00341	0995	11	99557	2	00443	15688	90	50	20
11	99747	1	00253	0348	12	99658	1	00342	1005	10	99556	1	00444	15777	89	49	16
12	99745	2	00255	0360	12	99656	2	00344	1015	10	99554	2	00446	15867	90	48	12
13	99744	1	00256	0371	11	99655	1	00345	1025	10	99552	2	00448	15956	89	47	8
14	99742	2	00258	0383	12	99653	2	00347	1035	10	99550	2	00450	16046	90	46	4
15	99741	1	00259	0395	12	99651	2	00349	1045	10	99548	2	00452	16135	89	45	+ 3m
16	99740	1	00260	0407	12	99650	1	00350	1055	11	99546	2	00454	16224	89	44	56
17	99738	2	00262	0418	11	99648	2	00352	1066	11	99545	1	00455	16312	88	43	52
18	99737	1	00263	0430	11	99647	1	00353	1076	10	99543	2	00457	16401	89	42	48
19	99736	1	00264	0441	11	99645	2	00355	1086	10	99541	2	00459	16489	88	41	44
20	99734	2	00266	0453	12	99643	2	00357	1096	10	99539	2	00461	16577	88	40	40
21	99733	1	00267	0464	11	99642	1	00358	11056	10	99537	2	00463	16665	88	39	36
22	99731	2	00269	0476	12	99640	2	00360	11155	99	99535	2	00465	16753	88	38	32
23	99730	1	00270	0487	11	99638	2	00362	11254	99	99533	2	00467	16841	88	37	28
24	99728	2	00272	0499	12	99637	1	00363	11353	99	99532	1	00468	16928	87	36	24
25	99727	1	00273	0510	11	99635	2	00365	11452	99	99530	2	00470	17016	87	35	20
26	99726	1	00274	0521	11	99633	2	00367	11551	99	99528	2	00472	17103	87	34	16
27	99724	2	00276	0533	12	99632	1	00368	11649	98	99526	2	00474	17190	87	33	12
28	99723	1	00277	0544	11	99630	2	00370	11747	98	99524	2	00476	17277	87	32	8
29	99721	2	00279	0555	11	99629	1	00371	11845	98	99522	2	00478	17363	86	31	4
30	99720	1	00280	0567	12	99627	2	00373	11943	98	99520	2	00480	17450	87	30	+ 2m
31	99718	2	00282	0578	11	99625	2	00375	12040	97	99518	2	00482	17536	86	29	56
32	99717	1	00283	0589	11	99624	1	00376	12138	98	99517	1	00483	17622	86	28	52
33	99716	1	00284	0600	11	99622	2	00378	12235	97	99515	2	00485	17708	86	27	48
34	99714	2	00286	0611	11	99620	2	00380	12332	97	99513	2	00487	17794	86	26	44
35	99713	1	00287	0622	11	99618	2	00382	12428	96	99511	2	00489	17880	86	25	40
36	99711	2	00289	0633	11	99617	1	00383	12525	97	99509	2	00491	17965	86	24	36
37	99710	1	00290	0645	12	99615	2	00385	12621	96	99507	2	00493	18051	86	23	32
38	99708	2	00292	0656	11	99613	2	00387	12717	96	99505	2	00495	18136	85	22	28
39	99707	1	00293	0667	11	99612	1	00388	12813	96	99503	2	00497	18221	85	21	24
40	99705	2	00295	0678	11	99610	2	00390	12909	96	99501	2	00499	18306	85	20	20
41	99704	1	00296	0688	10	99608	2	00392	13004	95	99499	2	00501	18391	85	19	16
42	99702	2	00298	0699	11	99607	1	00393	13099	95	99497	2	00503	18475	84	18	12
43	99701	1	00299	0710	11	99605	2	00395	13194	95	99495	2	00505	18560	85	17	8
44	99699	2	00301	0721	11	99603	2	00397	13289	95	99494	1	00506	18644	84	16	4
45	99698	1	00302	0732	11	99601	2	00399	13384	95	99492	2	00508	18728	84	15	+ 1m
46	99696	2	00304	0743	11	99600	1	00400	13478	94	99490	2	00510	18812	84	14	56
47	99695	1	00305	0754	11	99598	2	00402	13573	95	99488	2	00512	18896	84	13	52
48	99693	2	00307	0764	10	99596	2	00404	13667	94	99486	2	00514	18979	83	12	48
49	99692	1	00308	0775	11	99595	1	00405	13761	94	99484	2	00516	19063	84	11	44
50	99690	2	00310	0786	11	99593	2	00407	13854	93	99482	2	00518	19146	83	10	40
51	99689	1	00311	0796	10	99591	2	00409	13948	94	99480	2	00520	19229	83	9	36
52	99687	2	00313	0807	11	99589	2	00411	14041	93	99478	2	00522	19312	83	8	32
53	99686	1	00314	0818	11	99588	1	00412	14134	93	99476	2	00524	19395	83	7	28
54	99684	2	00316	0828	10	99586	2	00414	14227	93	99474	2	00526	19478	83	6	24
55	99683	1	00317	0839	11	99584	2	00416	14320	93	99472	2	00528	19561	83	5	20
56	99681	2	00319	0849	10	99582	2	00418	14412	92	99470	2	00530	19643	82	4	16
57	99680	1	00320	0860	11	99581	1	00419	14504	92	99468	2	00532	19725	82	3	12
58	99678	2	00322	0871	11	99579	2	00421	14597	93	99466	2	00534	19807	82	2	8
59	99677	1	00323	0881	10	99577	2	00423	14688	91	99464	2	00536	19889	82	1	4
60	99675	2	00325	0891	10	99575	2	00425	14780	92	99462	2	00538	19971	82	0	0
	Ī. [9]		0.	Ī. [9]		Ī. [9]		0.	Ī. [9]		Ī. [9]		0.	Ī. [9]			
	Sin.	D.	Cosec.	Cot.	D.	Sin.	D.	Cosec.	Cot.	D.	Sin.	D.	Cosec.	Cot.	D.	′	Secs.

83°   82°   81°

5h32m   5h28m   5h24m

Table 19   **LOGARITHMIC FUNCTIONS**

	9°					10°					11°						
′	Cos.	D.	Sec.	Tan.	D.	Cos.	D.	Sec.	Tan.	D.	Cos.	D.	Sec.	Tan.	D.		
	Ī.[9]		0.	Ī.[9]		Ī.[9]		0.	Ī.[9]		Ī.[9]		0.	Ī.[9]			
0	99462	2	00538	19971	82	99335	2	00665	24632	74	99195	2	00805	28865	67	60	60
1	99460	2	00540	20053	82	99333	2	00667	24706	74	99192	3	00808	28933	68	59	56
2	99458	2	00542	20134	81	99331	2	00669	24779	73	99190	2	00810	29000	67	58	52
3	99456	2	00544	20216	82	99328	3	00672	24853	74	99187	3	00813	29067	67	57	48
4	99454	2	00546	20297	81	99326	2	00674	24926	73	99185	2	00815	29134	67	56	44
5	99452	2	00548	20378	81	99324	2	00676	25000	73	99182	3	00818	29201	67	55	40
6	99450	2	00550	20459	81	99322	2	00678	25073	73	99180	2	00820	29268	67	54	36
7	99448	2	00552	20540	81	99319	3	00681	25146	73	99177	3	00823	29335	67	53	32
8	99446	2	00554	20621	81	99317	2	00683	25219	73	99175	2	00825	29402	67	52	28
9	99444	2	00556	20701	80	99315	2	00685	25292	73	99172	3	00828	29468	66	51	24
10	99442	2	00558	20782	81	99313	2	00687	25365	73	99170	2	00830	29535	67	50	20
11	99440	2	00560	20862	80	99310	3	00690	25437	72	99167	3	00833	29601	66	49	16
12	99438	2	00562	20942	80	99308	2	00692	25510	73	99165	2	00835	29668	67	48	12
13	99436	2	00564	21022	80	99306	2	00694	25582	72	99162	3	00838	29734	66	47	8
14	99434	2	00566	21102	80	99304	2	00696	25655	72	99160	2	00840	29800	66	46	4
15	99432	2	00568	21182	80	99301	3	00699	25727	72	99157	3	00843	29866	66	45	+3m
16	99429	3	00571	21261	79	99299	2	00701	25799	72	99155	2	00845	29932	66	44	56
17	99427	2	00573	21341	80	99297	2	00703	25871	72	99152	3	00848	29998	66	43	52
18	99425	2	00575	21420	79	99294	2	00706	25943	72	99150	2	00850	30064	66	42	48
19	99423	2	00577	21499	79	99292	2	00708	26015	72	99147	3	00853	30130	66	41	44
20	99421	2	00579	21578	79	99290	2	00710	26086	71	99145	2	00855	30195	65	40	40
21	99419	2	00581	21657	79	99288	2	00712	26158	72	99142	3	00858	30261	66	39	36
22	99417	2	00583	21736	79	99285	3	00715	26229	71	99140	2	00860	30326	65	38	32
23	99415	2	00585	21814	78	99283	2	00717	26301	72	99137	3	00863	30391	65	37	28
24	99413	2	00587	21893	79	99281	2	00719	26372	71	99135	2	00865	30457	66	36	24
25	99411	2	00589	21971	78	99278	3	00722	26443	71	99132	3	00868	30522	65	35	20
26	99409	2	00591	22049	78	99276	2	00724	26514	71	99130	2	00870	30587	65	34	16
27	99407	2	00593	22127	78	99274	2	00726	26585	71	99127	3	00873	30652	65	33	12
28	99404	3	00596	22205	78	99271	3	00729	26655	70	99124	3	00876	30717	65	32	8
29	99402	2	00598	22283	78	99269	2	00731	26726	71	99122	2	00878	30782	65	31	4
30	99400	2	00600	22361	78	99267	2	00733	26797	71	99119	3	00881	30846	64	30	+2m
31	99398	2	00602	22438	77	99264	3	00736	26867	70	99117	2	00883	30911	65	29	56
32	99396	2	00604	22516	78	99262	2	00738	26937	70	99114	3	00886	30975	64	28	52
33	99394	2	00606	22593	77	99260	2	00740	27008	71	99112	2	00888	31040	65	27	48
34	99392	2	00608	22670	77	99257	3	00743	27078	70	99109	3	00891	31104	64	26	44
35	99390	2	00610	22747	77	99255	2	00745	27148	70	99106	3	00894	31168	64	25	40
36	99388	2	00612	22824	77	99252	3	00748	27218	70	99104	2	00896	31233	65	24	36
37	99385	3	00615	22901	77	99250	2	00750	27288	70	99101	3	00899	31297	64	23	32
38	99383	2	00617	22977	76	99248	2	00752	27357	69	99099	2	00901	31361	64	22	28
39	99381	2	00619	23054	77	99245	3	00755	27427	70	99096	3	00904	31425	64	21	24
40	99379	2	00621	23130	76	99243	2	00757	27496	69	99093	3	00907	31489	64	20	20
41	99377	2	00623	23206	76	99241	2	00759	27566	70	99091	2	00909	31552	63	19	16
42	99375	2	00625	23283	77	99238	3	00762	27635	69	99088	3	00912	31616	64	18	12
43	99372	3	00628	23359	76	99236	2	00764	27704	69	99086	2	00914	31679	63	17	8
44	99370	2	00630	23435	76	99233	3	00767	27773	69	99083	3	00917	31743	63	16	4
45	99368	2	00632	23510	75	99231	2	00769	27842	69	99080	3	00920	31806	63	15	+1m
46	99366	2	00634	23586	76	99229	2	00771	27911	69	99078	2	00922	31870	64	14	56
47	99364	2	00636	23661	75	99226	3	00774	27980	69	99075	3	00925	31933	63	13	52
48	99362	2	00638	23737	76	99224	2	00776	28049	69	99072	3	00928	31996	63	12	48
49	99359	3	00641	23812	75	99221	3	00779	28117	68	99070	2	00930	32059	63	11	44
50	99357	2	00643	23887	75	99219	2	00781	28186	69	99067	3	00933	32122	63	10	40
51	99355	2	00645	23962	75	99217	2	00783	28254	68	99064	3	00936	32185	63	9	36
52	99353	2	00647	24037	75	99214	3	00786	28323	69	99062	2	00938	32248	63	8	32
53	99351	2	00649	24112	75	99212	2	00788	28391	63	99059	3	00941	32311	63	7	28
54	99348	3	00652	24186	74	99209	3	00791	28459	68	99056	3	00944	32373	62	6	24
55	99346	2	00654	24261	75	99207	2	00793	28527	68	99054	2	00946	32436	63	5	20
56	99344	2	00656	24335	74	99204	3	00796	28595	68	99051	3	00949	32498	63	4	16
57	99342	2	00658	24410	75	99202	2	00798	28662	67	99048	3	00952	32561	63	3	12
58	99340	2	00660	24484	74	99200	2	00800	28730	68	99046	2	00954	32623	62	2	8
59	99337	3	00663	24558	74	99197	3	00803	28798	68	99043	3	00957	32685	62	1	4
60	99335	2	00665	24632	74	99195	2	00805	28865	67	99040	3	00960	32747	62	0	0
	Ī.[9]		0.	Ī.[9]		Ī.[9]		0.	Ī.[9]		Ī.[9]		0.	Ī.[9]			
	Sin.	D.	Cosec.	Cot.	D.	Sin.	D.	Cosec.	Cot.	D.	Sin.	D.	Cosec.	Cot.	D.	′	Secs.
	80°					**79°**					**78°**						

5h20m   5h16m   5h12m

Table 19   **LOGARITHMIC FUNCTIONS**

	12°					13°					14°						
′	Cos.	D.	Sec.	Tan.	D.	Cos.	D.	Sec.	Tan.	D.	Cos.	D.	Sec.	Tan.	D.		
	T. [9]		0.	T. [9]		T. [9]		0.	T. [9]		T. [9]		0.	T. [9]			
0	99040	3	00960	32747	62	98872	3	01128	36336	57	98690	4	01310	39677	54	60	60
1	99038	2	00962	32810	63	98869	3	01131	36394	58	98687	3	01313	39731	54	59	56
2	99035	3	00965	32872	62	98867	2	01133	36452	58	98684	3	01316	39785	54	58	52
3	99032	3	00968	32933	61	98864	3	01136	36509	57	98681	3	01319	39838	53	57	48
4	99030	2	00970	32995	62	98861	3	01139	36566	57	98678	3	01322	39892	54	56	44
5	99027	3	00973	33057	62	98858	3	01142	36624	58	98675	3	01325	39945	53	55	40
6	99024	3	00976	33119	62	98855	3	01145	36681	57	98671	4	01329	39999	54	54	36
7	99022	2	00978	33180	61	98852	3	01148	36738	57	98668	3	01332	40052	53	53	32
8	99019	3	00981	33242	62	98849	3	01151	36795	57	98665	3	01335	40106	54	52	28
9	99016	3	00984	33303	61	98846	3	01154	36852	57	98662	3	01338	40159	53	51	24
10	99013	3	00987	33365	62	98843	3	01157	36909	57	98659	3	01341	40212	53	50	20
11	99011	2	00989	33426	61	98840	3	01160	36966	57	98656	3	01344	40266	54	49	16
12	99008	3	00992	33487	61	98837	3	01163	37023	57	98652	4	01348	40319	53	48	12
13	99005	3	00995	33548	61	98834	3	01166	37080	57	98649	3	01351	40372	53	47	8
14	99002	3	00998	33609	61	98831	3	01169	37137	57	98646	3	01354	40425	53	46	4
15	99000	2	01000	33670	61	98828	3	01172	37193	56	98643	3	01357	40478	53	45	+3m
16	98997	3	01003	33731	61	98825	3	01175	37250	57	98640	3	01360	40531	53	44	56
17	98994	3	01006	33792	61	98822	3	01178	37306	57	98636	4	01364	40584	53	43	52
18	98991	3	01009	33853	61	98819	3	01181	37363	57	98633	3	01367	40636	53	42	48
19	98989	2	01011	33913	60	98816	3	01184	37419	56	98630	3	01370	40689	53	41	44
20	98986	3	01014	33974	61	98813	3	01187	37476	57	98627	3	01373	40742	53	40	40
21	98983	3	01017	34034	60	98810	3	01190	37532	56	98623	4	01377	40795	53	39	36
22	98980	3	01020	34095	61	98807	3	01193	37588	56	98620	3	01380	40847	52	38	32
23	98978	2	01022	34155	60	98804	3	01196	37644	56	98617	3	01383	40900	53	37	28
24	98975	3	01025	34215	60	98801	3	01199	37700	56	98614	3	01386	40952	53	36	24
25	98972	3	01028	34276	61	98798	3	01202	37756	56	98610	4	01390	41005	53	35	20
26	98969	3	01031	34336	60	98795	3	01205	37812	56	98607	3	01393	41057	52	34	16
27	98967	2	01033	34396	60	98792	3	01208	37868	56	98604	3	01396	41109	52	33	12
28	98964	3	01036	34456	60	98789	3	01211	37924	56	98601	3	01399	41161	53	32	8
29	98961	3	01039	34516	60	98786	3	01214	37980	56	98597	4	01403	41214	53	31	4
30	98958	3	01042	34576	60	98783	3	01217	38035	55	98594	3	01406	41266	52	30	+2m
31	98955	3	01045	34635	59	98780	3	01220	38091	56	98591	3	01409	41318	52	29	56
32	98953	2	01047	34695	60	98777	3	01223	38147	56	98588	4	01412	41370	52	28	52
33	98950	3	01050	34755	60	98774	3	01226	38202	55	98584	4	01416	41422	52	27	48
34	98947	3	01053	34814	59	98771	3	01229	38257	55	98581	3	01419	41474	52	26	44
35	98944	3	01056	34874	60	98768	3	01232	38313	56	98578	3	01422	41526	52	25	40
36	98941	3	01059	34933	59	98765	3	01235	38368	55	98574	4	01426	41578	52	24	36
37	98938	3	01062	34992	59	98762	3	01238	38423	55	98571	3	01429	41629	51	23	32
38	98936	2	01064	35051	59	98759	3	01241	38479	56	98568	3	01432	41681	52	22	28
39	98933	3	01067	35111	60	98756	3	01244	38534	55	98565	3	01435	41733	52	21	24
40	98930	3	01070	35170	59	98753	3	01247	38589	55	98561	4	01439	41784	51	20	20
41	98927	3	01073	35229	59	98750	3	01250	38644	55	98558	3	01442	41836	52	19	16
42	98924	3	01076	35288	59	98746	4	01254	38699	55	98555	3	01445	41887	51	18	12
43	98921	3	01079	35347	59	98743	3	01257	38754	55	98551	3	01449	41939	52	17	8
44	98919	2	01081	35405	58	98740	3	01260	38808	54	98548	3	01452	41990	51	16	4
45	98916	3	01084	35464	59	98737	3	01263	38863	55	98545	3	01455	42041	51	15	+1m
46	98913	3	01087	35523	59	98734	3	01266	38918	54	98541	4	01459	42093	52	14	56
47	98910	3	01090	35581	58	98731	3	01269	38972	54	98538	3	01462	42144	51	13	52
48	98907	3	01093	35640	59	98728	3	01272	39027	55	98535	3	01465	42195	51	12	48
49	98904	3	01096	35698	58	98725	3	01275	39082	54	98531	4	01469	42246	51	11	44
50	98901	3	01099	35757	59	98722	3	01278	39136	54	98528	3	01472	42297	51	10	40
51	98898	3	01102	35815	58	98719	3	01281	39190	54	98525	3	01475	42348	51	9	36
52	98896	2	01104	35873	58	98715	4	01285	39245	55	98521	4	01479	42399	51	8	32
53	98893	3	01107	35931	58	98712	3	01288	39299	54	98518	3	01482	42450	51	7	28
54	98890	3	01110	35989	58	98709	3	01291	39353	54	98515	3	01485	42501	51	6	24
55	98887	3	01113	36047	58	98706	3	01294	39407	54	98511	4	01489	42552	51	5	20
56	98884	3	01116	36105	58	98703	3	01297	39461	54	98508	3	01492	42603	51	4	16
57	98881	3	01119	36163	58	98700	3	01300	39515	54	98505	3	01495	42653	50	3	12
58	98878	3	01122	36221	58	98697	3	01303	39569	54	98501	4	01499	42704	51	2	8
59	98875	3	01125	36279	58	98694	3	01306	39623	54	98498	3	01502	42755	51	1	4
60	98872	3	01128	36336	57	98690	4	01310	39677	54	98494	4	01506	42805	50	0	0
	T. [9]		0.	T. [9]		T. [9]		0.	T. [9]		T. [9]		0.	T. [9]			
	Sin.	D.	Cosec.	Cot.	D.	Sin.	D.	Cosec.	Cot.	D.	Sin.	D.	Cosec.	Cot.	D.	′	Secs.
				77°					**76°**					**75°**			

Table 19 — LOGARITHMIC FUNCTIONS

15° 16° 17°

′	Cos.	D.	Sec.	Tan.	D.	Cos.	D.	Sec.	Tan.	D.	Cos.	D.	Sec.	Tan.	D.		
	T̄. [9]		0.	T̄. [9]		T̄. [9]		0.	T̄. [9]		T̄. [9]		0.	T̄. [9]			
0	98494	4	01506	42805	50	98284	4	01716	45750	48	98060	3	01940	48534	45	60	60
1	98491	3	01509	42856	51	98281	3	01719	45797	47	98056	4	01944	48579	45	59	56
2	98488	3	01512	42906	50	98277	4	01723	45845	48	98052	4	01948	48624	45	58	52
3	98484	3	01516	42957	51	98273	4	01727	45892	47	98048	4	01952	43669	45	57	48
4	98481	3	01519	43007	50	98270	3	01730	45940	48	98044	4	01956	48714	45	56	44
5	98477	4	01523	43057	50	98266	4	01734	45987	47	98040	4	01960	48759	45	55	40
6	98474	3	01526	43108	51	98262	4	01738	46035	48	98036	4	01964	48804	45	54	36
7	98471	4	01529	43158	50	98259	3	01741	46082	47	98032	4	01968	48849	45	53	32
8	98467	4	01533	43208	50	98255	4	01745	46130	48	98029	3	01971	48894	45	52	28
9	98464	3	01536	43258	50	98251	4	01749	46177	47	98025	4	01975	48939	45	51	24
10	98460	4	01540	43308	50	98248	3	01752	46224	47	98021	.4	01979	48984	45	50	20
11	98457	3	01543	43358	50	98244	4	01756	46271	47	98017	4	01983	49029	45	49	16
12	98453	4	01547	43408	50	98240	4	01760	46319	48	98013	4	01987	49073	44	48	12
13	98450	3	01550	43458	50	98237	3	01763	46366	47	98009	4	01991	49118	45	47	8
14	98447	4	01553	43508	50	98233	4	01767	46413	47	98005	4	01995	49163	44	46	4
15	98443	4	01557	43558	50	98229	4	01771	46460	47	98001	4	01999	49207	44	45	+3m
16	98440	3	01560	43607	49	98226	3	01774	46507	47	97997	4	02003	49252	45	44	56
17	98436	4	01564	43657	50	98222	4	01778	46554	47	97993	4	02007	49296	45	43	52
18	98433	4	01567	43707	50	98218	4	01782	46601	47	97989	4	02011	49341	45	42	48
19	98429	4	01571	43756	49	98215	3	01785	46648	47	97986	3	02014	49385	44	41	44
20	98426	3	01574	43806	50	98211	4	01789	46694	46	97982	4	02018	49430	45	40	40
21	98422	4	01578	43855	49	98207	4	01793	46741	47	97978	4	02022	49474	44	39	36
22	98419	3	01581	43905	50	98204	3	01796	46788	47	97974	4	02026	49519	45	38	32
23	98415	4	01585	43954	49	98200	4	01800	46835	47	97970	4	02030	49563	44	37	28
24	98412	3	01588	44004	50	98196	4	01804	46881	46	97966	4	02034	49607	44	36	24
25	98409	3	01591	44053	49	98192	4	01808	46928	47	97962	4	02038	49652	45	35	20
26	98405	4	01595	44102	49	98189	3	01811	46975	47	97958	4	02042	49696	44	34	16
27	98402	3	01598	44151	49	98185	4	01815	47021	46	97954	4	02046	49740	44	33	12
28	98398	4	01602	44201	50	98181	4	01819	47068	47	97950	4	02050	49784	44	32	8
29	98395	3	01605	44250	49	98177	4	01823	47114	46	97946	4	02054	49828	44	31	4
30	98391	4	01609	44299	49	98174	3	01826	47160	46	97942	4	02058	49872	44	30	+2m
31	98388	3	01612	44348	49	98170	4	01830	47207	47	97938	4	02062	49916	44	29	56
32	98384	4	01616	44397	49	98166	4	01834	47253	46	97934	4	02066	49960	44	28	52
33	98381	3	01619	44446	49	98162	4	01838	47299	46	97930	4	02070	50004	44	27	48
34	98377	4	01623	44495	49	98159	3	01841	47346	47	97926	4	02074	50048	44	26	44
35	98373	4	01627	44544	49	98155	4	01845	47392	46	97922	4	02078	50092	44	25	40
36	98370	3	01630	44592	49	98151	4	01849	47438	46	97918	4	02082	50136	44	24	36
37	98366	4	01634	44641	49	98147	4	01853	47484	46	97914	4	02086	50180	44	23	32
38	98363	3	01637	44690	49	98144	3	01856	47530	46	97910	4	02090	50223	43	22	28
39	98359	4	01641	44738	48	93140	4	01860	47576	46	97906	4	02094	50267	44	21	24
40	98356	3	01644	44787	49	98136	4	01864	47622	46	97902	4	02098	50311	44	20	20
41	98352	4	01648	44836	49	98132	4	01868	47668	46	97898	4	02102	50355	44	19	16
42	98349	3	01651	44884	48	98129	3	01871	47714	46	97894	4	02106	50398	43	18	12
43	98345	4	01655	44933	49	98125	4	01875	47760	46	97890	4	02110	50442	44	17	8
44	98342	3	01658	44981	48	98121	4	01879	47806	46	97886	4	02114	50485	43	16	4
45	98338	4	01662	45029	48	98117	4	01883	47852	46	97882	4	02118	50529	44	15	+1m
46	98334	4	01666	45078	49	98113	4	01887	47897	45	97878	4	02122	50572	43	14	56
47	98331	3	01669	45126	48	98110	3	01890	47943	46	97874	4	02126	50616	44	13	52
48	98327	4	01673	45174	48	98106	4	01894	47989	46	97870	4	02130	50659	43	12	48
49	98324	3	01676	45222	48	98102	4	01898	48035	46	97866	4	02134	50703	44	11	44
50	98320	4	01680	45271	49	98098	4	01902	48080	45	97861	5	02139	50746	43	10	40
51	98317	3	01683	45319	48	98094	4	01906	48126	46	97857	4	02143	50789	43	9	36
52	98313	4	01687	45367	48	98090	4	01910	48171	45	97853	4	02147	50833	44	8	32
53	98309	4	01691	45415	48	98087	3	01913	48217	46	97849	4	02151	50876	43	7	28
54	98306	3	01694	45463	48	98083	4	01917	48262	45	97845	4	02155	50919	43	6	24
55	98302	4	01698	45511	48	98079	4	01921	48307	45	97841	4	02159	50962	43	5	20
56	98299	3	01701	45559	48	98075	4	01925	48353	46	97837	4	02163	51005	43	4	16
57	98295	4	01705	45606	47	98071	4	01929	48398	45	97833	4	02167	51048	43	3	12
58	98291	4	01709	45654	48	98067	4	01933	48443	45	97829	4	02171	51092	44	2	8
59	98288	3	01712	45702	48	98063	4	01937	48489	46	97825	4	02175	51135	43	1	4
60	98284	4	01716	45750	48	98060	3	01940	48534	45	97821	4	02179	51178	43	0	0
	T̄. [9]		0.	T̄. [9]		T̄. [9]		0.	T̄. [9]		T̄. [9]		0.	T̄. [9]			
	Sin.	D.	Cosec.	Cot.	D.	Sin.	D.	Cosec.	Cot.	D.	Sin.	D.	Cosec.	Cot.	D.	′	Secs.

74° 73° 72°

4h56m   4h52m   4h48m

Table 19

LOGARITHMIC FUNCTIONS

	18°				19°				20°						
′	Cos.	D.	Sec.	Tan.	D.	Cos.	D.	Sec.	Tan.	D.	Cos.	D.	Sec.	Tan.	D.		
	Ī. [9]		0.	Ī. [9]		Ī. [9]		0.	Ī. [9]		Ī. [9]		0.	Ī. [9]			
0	97821	4	02179	51178	43	97567	4	02433	53697	41	97299	4	02701	56107	40	60	60
1	97817	4	02183	51221	43	97563	4	02437	53738	41	97294	5	02706	56146	39	59	56
2	97812	5	02188	51264	42	97558	5	02442	53779	41	97289	5	02711	56185	39	58	52
3	97808	4	02192	51306	43	97554	4	02446	53820	41	97285	5	02715	56224	39	57	48
4	97804	4	02196	51349	43	97550	4	02450	53861	41	97280	5	02720	56264	40	56	44
5	97800	4	02200	51392	43	97545	5	02455	53902	41	97276	4	02724	56303	39	55	40
6	97796	4	02204	51435	43	97541	4	02459	53943	41	97271	5	02729	56342	39	54	36
7	97792	4	02208	51478	43	97536	5	02464	53984	41	97266	5	02734	56381	39	53	32
8	97788	4	02212	51520	42	97532	4	02468	54025	41	97262	5	02738	56420	39	52	28
9	97784	4	02216	51563	43	97528	4	02472	54065	40	97257	5	02743	56459	39	51	24
10	97779	5	02221	51606	43	97523	5	02477	54106	41	97252	5	02748	56498	39	50	20
11	97775	4	02225	51648	42	97519	4	02481	54147	41	97248	4	02752	56537	39	49	16
12	97771	4	02229	51691	43	97515	4	02485	54187	40	97243	5	02757	56576	39	48	12
13	97767	4	02233	51734	43	97510	5	02490	54228	41	97238	4	02762	56615	39	47	8
14	97763	4	02237	51776	43	97506	4	02494	54269	40	97234	5	02766	56654	39	46	4
15	97759	4	02241	51819	42	97501	4	02499	54309	41	97229	5	02771	56693	39	45	+ 3m
16	97754	5	02246	51861	42	97497	4	02503	54350	40	97224	4	02776	56732	39	44	56
17	97750	4	02250	51903	43	97492	5	02508	54390	41	97220	5	02780	56771	39	43	52
18	97746	4	02254	51946	42	97488	4	02512	54431	40	97215	5	02785	56810	39	42	48
19	97742	4	02258	51988	43	97484	5	02516	54471	41	97210	4	02790	56849	38	41	44
20	97738	4	02262	52031	43	97479	5	02521	54512	41	97206	5	02794	56887	39	40	40
21	97734	4	02266	52073	42	97475	4	02525	54552	40	97201	5	02799	56926	39	39	36
22	97729	5	02271	52115	42	97470	5	02530	54593	41	97196	4	02804	56965	39	38	32
23	97725	4	02275	52157	43	97466	4	02534	54633	40	97192	5	02808	57004	38	37	28
24	97721	4	02279	52200	42	97461	5	02539	54673	41	97187	5	02813	57042	39	36	24
25	97717	4	02283	52242	42	97457	4	02543	54714	40	97182	4	02818	57081	39	35	20
26	97713	4	02287	52284	42	97453	4	02547	54754	40	97178	5	02822	57120	38	34	16
27	97708	5	02292	52326	42	97448	4	02552	54794	41	97173	5	02827	57158	39	33	12
28	97704	4	02296	52368	42	97444	4	02556	54835	41	97168	5	02832	57197	38	32	8
29	97700	4	02300	52410	42	97439	5	02561	54875	40	97163	4	02837	57235	39	31	4
30	97696	4	02304	52452	42	97435	4	02565	54915	40	97159	5	02841	57274	38	30	+ 2m
31	97691	5	02309	52494	42	97430	5	02570	54955	40	97154	5	02846	57312	39	29	56
32	97687	4	02313	52536	42	97426	4	02574	54995	40	97149	4	02851	57351	38	28	52
33	97683	4	02317	52578	42	97421	5	02579	55035	40	97145	5	02855	57389	39	27	48
34	97679	4	02321	52620	41	97417	4	02583	55075	40	97140	5	02860	57428	38	26	44
35	97674	5	02326	52661	42	97412	5	02588	55115	40	97135	5	02865	57466	38	25	40
36	97670	4	02330	52703	42	97408	4	02592	55155	40	97130	4	02870	57504	39	24	36
37	97666	4	02334	52745	42	97403	5	02597	55195	40	97126	5	02874	57543	38	23	32
38	97662	4	02338	52787	42	97399	4	02601	55235	40	97121	5	02879	57581	38	22	28
39	97657	5	02343	52829	42	97394	5	02606	55275	40	97116	5	02884	57619	39	21	24
40	97653	4	02347	52870	41	97390	4	02610	55315	40	97111	5	02889	57658	38	20	20
41	97649	4	02351	52912	42	97385	5	02615	55355	40	97107	4	02893	57696	38	19	16
42	97645	4	02355	52953	41	97381	4	02619	55395	40	97102	5	02898	57734	38	18	12
43	97640	5	02360	52995	42	97376	5	02624	55434	39	97097	5	02903	57772	38	17	8
44	97636	4	02364	53037	42	97372	4	02628	55474	40	97092	5	02908	57810	39	16	4
45	97632	4	02368	53078	41	97367	4	02633	55514	40	97087	4	02913	57849	38	15	+ 1m
46	97628	4	02372	53120	42	97363	4	02637	55554	39	97083	5	02917	57887	38	14	56
47	97623	5	02377	53161	41	97358	5	02642	55593	40	97078	5	02922	57925	38	13	52
48	97619	4	02381	53203	42	97353	4	02647	55633	40	97073	5	02927	57963	38	12	48
49	97615	4	02385	53244	42	97349	5	02651	55673	39	97068	5	02932	58001	38	11	44
50	97610	5	02390	53285	41	97344	4	02656	55712	39	97063	5	02937	58039	38	10	40
51	97606	4	02394	53327	42	97340	4	02660	55752	40	97059	4	02941	58077	38	9	36
52	97602	4	02398	53368	41	97335	5	02665	55791	39	97054	5	02946	58115	38	8	32
53	97597	5	02403	53409	41	97331	4	02669	55831	40	97049	5	02951	58153	38	7	28
54	97593	4	02407	53450	41	97326	5	02674	55870	39	97044	5	02956	58191	38	6	24
55	97589	4	02411	53492	42	97322	4	02678	55910	40	97039	4	02961	58229	38	5	20
56	97584	5	02416	53533	41	97317	5	02683	55949	39	97035	5	02965	58267	38	4	16
57	97580	4	02420	53574	41	97312	4	02688	55989	39	97030	5	02970	58304	37	3	12
58	97576	4	02424	53615	41	97308	4	02692	56028	39	97025	5	02975	58342	38	2	8
59	97571	5	02429	53656	41	97303	5	02697	56067	39	97020	5	02980	58380	38	1	4
60	97567	4	02433	53697	41	97299	4	02701	56107	40	97015	5	02985	58418	38	0	0
	Ī. [9]		0.	Ī. [9]		Ī. [9]		0.	Ī. [9]		Ī. [9]		0.	Ī. [9]			
	Sin.	D.	Cosec.	Cot.	D.	Sin.	D.	Cosec.	Cot.	D.	Sin.	D.	Cosec.	Cot.	D.	′	Secs.
				71°					70°					69°			

4h44m   4h40m   4h36m

143

Table 19 — LOGARITHMIC FUNCTIONS

′	21° Cos.	D.	Sec.	Tan.	D.	22° Cos.	D.	Sec.	Tan.	D.	23° Cos.	D.	Sec.	Tan.	D.		
	Ī.[9]		0.	Ī.[9]		Ī.[9]		0.	Ī.[9]		Ī.[9]		0.	Ī.[9]			
0	97015	5	02985	58418	38	96717	5	03283	60641	36	96403	5	03597	62785	35	60	60
1	97010	5	02990	58455	37	96711	6	03289	60677	36	96397	5	03603	62820	35	59	56
2	97005	5	02995	58493	38	96706	5	03294	60714	37	96392	5	03608	62855	35	58	52
3	97001	4	02999	58531	38	96701	5	03299	60750	36	96387	5	03613	62890	35	57	48
4	96996	5	03004	58569	38	96696	5	03304	60786	36	96381	6	03619	62926	36	56	44
5	96991	5	03009	58606	37	96691	5	03309	60823	37	96376	6	03624	62961	35	55	40
6	96986	5	03014	58644	38	96686	5	03314	60859	36	96370	6	03630	62996	35	54	36
7	96981	5	03019	58681	37	96681	5	03319	60895	36	96365	5	03635	63031	35	53	32
8	96976	5	03024	58719	38	96676	5	03324	60931	36	96360	5	03640	63066	35	52	28
9	96971	5	03029	58757	38	96670	6	03330	60967	36	96354	6	03646	63101	35	51	24
10	96966	5	03034	58794	37	96665	5	03335	61004	37	96349	5	03651	63135	34	50	20
11	96962	4	03038	58832	38	96660	5	03340	61040	36	96343	6	03657	63170	35	49	16
12	96957	5	03043	58869	37	96655	5	03345	61076	36	96338	5	03662	63205	35	48	12
13	96952	5	03048	58907	38	96650	5	03350	61112	36	96333	5	03667	63240	35	47	8
14	96947	5	03053	58944	37	96645	5	03355	61148	36	96327	6	03673	63275	35	46	4
15	96942	5	03058	58981	37	96640	5	03360	61184	36	96322	5	03678	63310	35	45	+3m
16	96937	5	03063	59019	38	96634	5	03366	61220	36	96316	6	03684	63345	34	44	56
17	96932	5	03068	59056	37	96629	5	03371	61256	36	96311	5	03689	63379	34	43	52
18	96927	5	03073	59094	38	96624	5	03376	61292	36	96305	6	03695	63414	35	42	48
19	96922	5	03078	59131	37	96619	5	03381	61328	36	96300	5	03700	63449	35	41	44
20	96917	5	03083	59168	37	96614	5	03386	61364	36	96294	6	03706	63484	35	40	40
21	96912	5	03088	59205	37	96608	6	03392	61400	36	96289	5	03711	63519	35	39	36
22	96907	5	03093	59243	38	96603	5	03397	61436	36	96284	5	03716	63553	34	38	32
23	96903	4	03097	59280	37	96598	5	03402	61472	36	96278	6	03722	63588	35	37	28
24	96898	5	03102	59317	37	96593	5	03407	61508	36	96273	5	03727	63623	34	36	24
25	96893	5	03107	59354	37	96588	5	03412	61544	36	96267	6	03733	63657	34	35	20
26	96888	5	03112	59391	37	96582	6	03418	61579	35	96262	5	03738	63692	35	34	16
27	96883	5	03117	59429	38	96577	5	03423	61615	36	96256	6	03744	63726	35	33	12
28	96878	5	03122	59466	37	96572	5	03428	61651	36	96251	5	03749	63761	35	32	8
29	96873	5	03127	59503	37	96567	5	03433	61687	36	96245	6	03755	63796	35	31	4
30	96868	5	03132	59540	37	96562	5	03438	61722	35	96240	5	03760	63830	34	30	+2m
31	96863	5	03137	59577	37	96556	6	03444	61758	36	96234	6	03766	63865	35	29	56
32	96858	5	03142	59614	37	96551	5	03449	61794	36	96229	5	03771	63899	34	28	52
33	96853	5	03147	59651	37	96546	5	03454	61830	36	96223	6	03777	63934	35	27	48
34	96848	5	03152	59688	37	96541	5	03459	61865	35	96218	5	03782	63968	34	26	44
35	96843	5	03157	59725	37	96535	6	03465	61901	36	96212	6	03788	64003	34	25	40
36	96838	5	03162	59762	37	96530	5	03470	61936	35	96207	5	03793	64037	34	24	36
37	96833	5	03167	59799	37	96525	5	03475	61972	36	96201	5	03799	64072	34	23	32
38	96828	5	03172	59835	36	96520	5	03480	62008	36	96196	5	03804	64106	34	22	28
39	96823	5	03177	59872	37	96514	6	03486	62043	35	96190	6	03810	64140	34	21	24
40	96818	5	03182	59909	37	96509	5	03491	62079	36	96185	5	03815	64175	35	20	20
41	96813	5	03187	59946	37	96504	5	03496	62114	35	96179	6	03821	64209	34	19	16
42	96808	5	03192	59983	37	96498	6	03502	62150	36	96174	5	03826	64243	34	18	12
43	96803	5	03197	60019	36	96493	5	03507	62185	35	96168	6	03832	64278	35	17	8
44	96798	5	03202	60056	37	96488	5	03512	62221	36	96162	5	03838	64312	34	16	4
45	96793	5	03207	60093	37	96483	5	03517	62256	35	96157	5	03843	64346	34	15	+1m
46	96788	5	03212	60130	37	96477	6	03523	62292	36	96151	6	03849	64381	35	14	56
47	96783	5	03217	60166	36	96472	5	03528	62327	35	96146	5	03854	64415	34	13	52
48	96778	5	03222	60203	37	96467	5	03533	62362	35	96140	6	03860	64449	34	12	48
49	96772	6	03228	60240	37	96461	6	03539	62398	36	96135	5	03865	64483	34	11	44
50	96767	5	03233	60276	36	96456	5	03544	62433	35	96129	6	03871	64517	34	10	40
51	96762	5	03238	60313	37	96451	5	03549	62468	35	96123	6	03877	64552	35	9	36
52	96757	5	03243	60349	36	96445	6	03555	62504	36	96118	5	03882	64586	34	8	32
53	96752	5	03248	60386	37	96440	5	03560	62539	35	96112	6	03888	64620	34	7	28
54	96747	5	03253	60422	36	96435	5	03565	62574	35	96107	5	03893	64654	34	6	24
55	96742	5	03258	60459	37	96429	6	03571	62609	35	96101	6	03899	64688	34	5	20
56	96737	5	03263	60495	36	96424	5	03576	62645	36	96095	6	03905	64722	34	4	16
57	96732	5	03268	60532	37	96419	5	03581	62680	35	96090	5	03910	64756	34	3	12
58	96727	5	03273	60568	36	96413	6	03587	62715	35	96084	6	03916	64790	34	2	8
59	96722	5	03278	60605	37	96408	5	03592	62750	35	96079	5	03921	64824	34	1	4
60	96717	5	03283	60641	36	96403	5	03597	62785	35	96073	6	03927	64858	34	0	0
	Ī.[9]		0.	Ī.[9]		Ī.[9]		0.	Ī.[9]		Ī.[9]		0.	Ī.[9]			
	Sin.	D.	Cosec.	Cot.	D.	Sin.	D.	Cosec.	Cot.	D.	Sin.	D.	Cosec.	Cot.	D.	′	Secs.

	68°	67°	66°
	4h32m	4h28m	4h24m

144

Table 19 — LOGARITHMIC FUNCTIONS

24° | 25° | 26°

′	Cos.	D.	Sec.	Tan.	D.	Cos.	D.	Sec.	Tan.	D.	Cos.	D.	Sec.	Tan.	D.	′	Secs
	Ī.[9]		0.	Ī.[9]		Ī.[9]		0.	Ī.[9]		Ī.[9]		0.	Ī.[9]			
0	96073	6	03927	64858	34	95728	5	04272	66867	33	95366	6	04634	68818	32	60	60
1	96067	6	03933	64892	34	95722	6	04278	66900	33	95360	6	04640	68850	32	59	56
2	96062	5	03938	64926	34	95716	6	04284	66933	33	95354	6	04646	68882	32	58	52
3	96056	6	03944	64960	34	95710	6	04290	66966	33	95348	6	04652	68914	32	57	48
4	96050	6	03950	64994	34	95704	6	04296	66999	33	95341	7	04659	68946	32	56	44
5	96045	5	03955	65028	34	95698	6	04302	67032	33	95335	6	04665	68978	32	55	40
6	96039	6	03961	65062	34	95692	6	04308	67065	33	95329	6	04671	69010	32	54	36
7	96034	5	03966	65096	34	95686	6	04314	67098	33	95323	6	04677	69042	32	53	32
8	96028	6	03972	65130	34	95680	6	04320	67131	33	95317	6	04683	69074	32	52	28
9	96022	6	03978	65164	34	95674	6	04326	67163	32	95310	7	04690	69106	32	51	24
10	96017	5	03983	65197	33	95668	6	04332	67196	33	95304	6	04696	69138	32	50	20
11	96011	6	03989	65231	34	95663	5	04337	67229	33	95298	6	04702	69170	32	49	16
12	96005	6	03995	65265	34	95657	6	04343	67262	33	95292	6	04708	69202	32	48	12
13	96000	5	04000	65299	34	95651	6	04349	67295	33	95286	6	04714	69234	32	47	8
14	95994	6	04006	65333	34	95645	6	04355	67327	33	95279	7	04721	69266	32	46	4
15	95988	6	04012	65366	33	95639	6	04361	67360	33	95273	6	04727	69298	31	45	+3m
16	95982	5	04018	65400	34	95633	6	04367	67393	33	95267	6	04733	69329	32	44	56
17	95977	5	04023	65434	34	95627	6	04373	67426	33	95261	6	04739	69361	32	43	52
18	95971	6	04029	65467	33	95621	6	04379	67458	32	95254	7	04746	69393	32	42	48
19	95965	6	04035	65501	34	95615	6	04385	67491	33	95248	6	04752	69425	32	41	44
20	95960	5	04040	65535	34	95609	6	04391	67524	33	95242	6	04758	69457	32	40	40
21	95954	6	04046	65568	33	95603	6	04397	67556	32	95236	6	04764	69488	31	39	36
22	95948	6	04052	65602	34	95597	6	04403	67589	33	95229	7	04771	69520	32	38	32
23	95942	6	04058	65636	34	95591	6	04409	67622	33	95223	6	04777	69552	32	37	28
24	95937	5	04063	65669	33	95585	6	04415	67654	32	95217	6	04783	69584	32	36	24
25	95931	6	04069	65703	34	95579	6	04421	67687	33	95211	6	04789	69615	31	35	20
26	95925	6	04075	65736	34	95573	6	04427	67719	33	95204	7	04796	69647	32	34	16
27	95920	5	04080	65770	34	95567	6	04433	67752	33	95198	6	04802	69679	31	33	12
28	95914	6	04086	65803	33	95561	6	04439	67785	33	95192	6	04808	69710	31	32	8
29	95908	6	04092	65837	34	95555	6	04445	67817	32	95185	7	04815	69742	32	31	4
30	95902	6	04098	65870	33	95549	6	04451	67850	33	95179	6	04821	69774	32	30	+2m
31	95897	5	04103	65904	34	95543	6	04457	67882	32	95173	6	04827	69805	31	29	56
32	95891	6	04109	65937	33	95537	6	04463	67915	33	95167	6	04833	69837	32	28	52
33	95885	6	04115	65971	34	95531	6	04469	67947	33	95160	7	04840	69868	31	27	48
34	95879	6	04121	66004	33	95525	6	04475	67980	33	95154	6	04846	69900	32	26	44
35	95873	6	04127	66038	34	95519	6	04481	68012	32	95148	6	04852	69932	32	25	40
36	95868	5	04132	66071	33	95513	6	04487	68044	33	95141	7	04859	69963	31	24	36
37	95862	6	04138	66104	34	95507	6	04493	68077	33	95135	6	04865	69995	32	23	32
38	95856	6	04144	66138	34	95500	7	04500	68109	33	95129	6	04871	70026	31	22	28
39	95850	6	04150	66171	33	95494	6	04506	68142	33	95122	7	04878	70058	32	21	24
40	95844	6	04156	66204	33	95488	6	04512	68174	32	95116	6	04884	70089	31	20	20
41	95839	5	04161	66238	34	95482	6	04518	68206	32	95110	6	04890	70121	32	19	16
42	95833	6	04167	66271	33	95476	6	04524	68239	33	95103	7	04897	70152	31	18	12
43	95827	6	04173	66304	33	95470	6	04530	68271	32	95097	6	04903	70184	32	17	8
44	95821	6	04179	66337	34	95464	6	04536	68303	33	95090	7	04910	70215	31	16	4
45	95815	6	04185	66371	34	95458	6	04542	68336	33	95084	6	04916	70247	32	15	+1m
46	95810	5	04190	66404	33	95452	6	04548	68368	32	95078	6	04922	70278	31	14	56
47	95804	6	04196	66437	33	95446	6	04554	68400	32	95071	7	04929	70309	31	13	52
48	95798	6	04202	66470	33	95440	6	04560	68432	33	95065	6	04935	70341	32	12	48
49	95792	6	04208	66503	33	95434	6	04566	68465	32	95059	6	04941	70372	31	11	44
50	95786	6	04214	66537	34	95427	7	04573	68497	32	95052	7	04948	70404	32	10	40
51	95780	6	04220	66570	33	95421	6	04579	68529	32	95046	6	04954	70435	31	9	36
52	95775	6	04225	66603	33	95415	6	04585	68561	32	95039	7	04961	70466	32	8	32
53	95769	6	04231	66636	33	95409	6	04591	68593	33	95033	6	04967	70498	32	7	28
54	95763	6	04237	66669	33	95403	6	04597	68626	32	95027	6	04973	70529	31	6	24
55	95757	6	04243	66702	33	95397	6	04603	68658	32	95020	7	04980	70560	31	5	20
56	95751	6	04249	66735	33	95391	6	04609	68690	32	95014	6	04986	70592	32	4	16
57	95745	6	04255	66768	33	95384	7	04616	68722	32	95007	7	04993	70623	31	3	12
58	95739	6	04261	66801	33	95378	6	04622	68754	32	95001	6	04999	70654	31	2	8
59	95733	6	04267	66834	33	95372	6	04628	68786	32	94995	6	05005	70685	31	1	4
60	95728	5	04272	66867	33	95366	6	04634	68818	32	94988	7	05012	70717	32	0	0
	Ī.[9]		0.	Ī.[9]		Ī.[9]		0.	Ī.[9]		Ī.[9]		0.	Ī.[9]			
	Sin.	D.	Cosec.	Cot.	D.	Sin.	D.	Cosec.	Cot.	D.	Sin.	D.	Cosec.	Cot.	D.	′	Secs.

| | **65°** | | | | | **64°** | | | | | **63°** | | | | | | |

4h 20m   4h 16m   4h 12m

145

Table 19 — LOGARITHMIC FUNCTIONS

27° | 28° | 29°

′	Cos.	D.	Sec.	Tan.	D.	Cos.	D.	Sec.	Tan.	D.	Cos.	D.	Sec.	Tan.	D.		
	Ī.[9]		0.	Ī.[9]		Ī.[9]		0.	Ī.[9]		Ī.[9]		0.	Ī.[9]			
0	94988	7	05012	70717	32	94593	7	05407	72567	30	94182	7	05818	74375	30	60	60
1	94982	6	05018	70748	31	94587	6	05413	72598	31	94175	7	05825	74405	30	59	56
2	94975	7	05025	70779	31	94580	7	05420	72628	30	94168	7	05832	74435	30	58	52
3	94969	6	05031	70810	31	94573	7	05427	72659	31	94161	7	05839	74465	30	57	48
4	94962	7	05038	70841	31	94567	6	05433	72689	30	94154	7	05846	74494	29	56	44
5	94956	6	05044	70873	32	94560	7	05440	72720	31	94147	7	05853	74524	30	55	40
6	94949	7	05051	70904	31	94553	7	05447	72750	30	94140	7	05860	74554	30	54	36
7	94943	6	05057	70935	31	94546	7	05454	72780	30	94133	7	05867	74583	29	53	32
8	94936	7	05064	70966	31	94540	6	05460	72811	31	94126	7	05874	74613	30	52	28
9	94930	6	05070	70997	31	94533	7	05467	72841	30	94119	7	05881	74643	30	51	24
10	94923	7	05077	71028	31	94526	7	05474	72872	31	94112	7	05888	74673	30	50	20
11	94917	6	05083	71059	31	94519	7	05481	72902	30	94105	7	05895	74702	29	49	16
12	94911	6	05089	71090	31	94513	6	05487	72932	30	94098	7	05902	74732	30	48	12
13	94904	7	05096	71121	31	94506	7	05494	72963	31	94090	8	05910	74762	30	47	8
14	94898	6	05102	71153	32	94499	7	05501	72993	30	94083	7	05917	74791	29	46	4
15	94891	7	05109	71184	31	94492	7	05508	73023	30	94076	7	05924	74821	30	45	+3m
16	94885	6	05115	71215	31	94485	7	05515	73054	31	94069	7	05931	74851	30	44	56
17	94878	7	05122	71246	31	94479	6	05521	73084	30	94062	7	05938	74880	29	43	52
18	94871	6	05129	71277	31	94472	7	05528	73114	30	94055	7	05945	74910	30	42	48
19	94865	6	05135	71308	31	94465	7	05535	73144	30	94048	7	05952	74939	29	41	44
20	94858	7	05142	71339	31	94458	7	05542	73175	31	94041	7	05959	74969	30	40	40
21	94852	6	05148	71370	31	94451	7	05549	73205	30	94034	7	05966	74998	29	39	36
22	94845	7	05155	71401	31	94445	6	05555	73235	30	94027	7	05973	75028	30	38	32
23	94839	6	05161	71431	30	94438	7	05562	73265	30	94020	7	05980	75058	30	37	28
24	94832	7	05168	71462	31	94431	7	05569	73295	30	94012	8	05988	75087	29	36	24
25	94826	6	05174	71493	31	94424	7	05576	73326	31	94005	7	05995	75117	30	35	20
26	94819	6	05181	71524	31	94417	7	05583	73356	30	93998	7	06002	75146	29	34	16
27	94813	6	05187	71555	31	94410	7	05590	73386	30	93991	7	06009	75176	30	33	12
28	94806	7	05194	71586	31	94404	6	05596	73416	30	93984	7	06016	75205	29	32	8
29	94799	7	05201	71617	31	94397	7	05603	73446	30	93977	7	06023	75235	30	31	4
30	94793	6	05207	71648	31	94390	7	05610	73476	31	93970	7	06030	75264	29	30	+2m
31	94786	7	05214	71679	31	94383	7	05617	73507	31	93963	7	06037	75294	30	29	56
32	94780	6	05220	71709	30	94376	7	05624	73537	30	93955	8	06045	75323	29	28	52
33	94773	6	05227	71740	31	94369	7	05631	73567	30	93948	7	06052	75353	29	27	48
34	94767	6	05233	71771	31	94362	7	05638	73597	30	93941	7	06059	75382	29	26	44
35	94760	7	05240	71802	31	94355	6	05645	73627	30	93934	7	06066	75411	29	25	40
36	94753	7	05247	71833	31	94349	6	05651	73657	30	93927	7	06073	75441	30	24	36
37	94747	6	05253	71863	30	94342	7	05658	73687	30	93920	7	06080	75470	29	23	32
38	94740	7	05260	71894	31	94335	7	05665	73717	30	93912	8	06088	75500	30	22	28
39	94734	6	05266	71925	31	94328	7	05672	73747	30	93905	7	06095	75529	29	21	24
40	94727	7	05273	71955	30	94321	7	05679	73777	30	93898	7	06102	75558	29	20	20
41	94720	7	05280	71986	31	94314	7	05686	73807	30	93891	7	06109	75588	30	19	16
42	94714	6	05286	72017	31	94307	7	05693	73837	30	93884	7	06116	75617	29	18	12
43	94707	7	05293	72048	31	94300	7	05700	73867	30	93876	8	06124	75647	30	17	8
44	94700	7	05300	72078	30	94293	7	05707	73897	30	93869	7	06131	75676	29	16	4
45	94694	6	05306	72109	31	94286	7	05714	73927	30	93862	7	06138	75705	29	15	+1m
46	94687	7	05313	72140	31	94279	7	05721	73957	30	93855	7	06145	75735	30	14	56
47	94680	7	05320	72170	30	94273	6	05727	73987	30	93847	8	06153	75764	29	13	52
48	94674	6	05326	72201	31	94266	7	05734	74017	30	93840	7	06160	75793	29	12	48
49	94667	7	05333	72231	31	94259	7	05741	74047	30	93833	7	06167	75822	29	11	44
50	94660	7	05340	72262	31	94252	7	05748	74077	30	93826	7	06174	75852	30	10	40
51	94654	6	05346	72293	31	94245	7	05755	74107	30	93819	7	06181	75881	29	9	36
52	94647	7	05353	72323	30	94238	7	05762	74137	30	93811	8	06189	75910	29	8	32
53	94640	7	05360	72354	31	94231	7	05769	74166	29	93804	7	06196	75939	29	7	28
54	94634	6	05366	72384	30	94224	7	05776	74196	30	93797	7	06203	75969	30	6	24
55	94627	7	05373	72415	31	94217	7	05783	74226	30	93789	8	06211	75998	29	5	20
56	94620	7	05380	72445	30	94210	7	05790	74256	30	93782	7	06218	76027	29	4	16
57	94614	6	05386	72476	31	94203	7	05797	74286	30	93775	7	06225	76056	29	3	12
58	94607	7	05393	72506	30	94196	7	05804	74316	30	93768	7	06232	76086	30	2	8
59	94600	7	05400	72537	31	94189	7	05811	74345	29	93760	8	06240	76115	29	1	4
60	94593	7	05407	72567	30	94182	7	05818	74375	30	93753	7	06247	76144	29	0	
	Ī.[9]		0.	Ī.[9]		Ī.[9]		0.	Ī.[9]		Ī.[9]		0.	Ī.[9]			
	Sin.	D.	Cosec.	Cot.	D.	Sin.	D.	Cosec.	Cot.	D.	Sin.	D.	Cosec.	Cot.	D.	′	Secs.

	62°	61°	60°
	4h08m	4h04m	4h00m

Table 19   **LOGARITHMIC FUNCTIONS**

30° 31° 32°

′	Cos.	D.	Sec.	Tan.	D.	Cos.	D.	Sec.	Tan.	D.	Cos.	D.	Sec.	Tan.	D.		
	Ī. [9]		0.	Ī. [9]		Ī. [9]		0.	Ī. [9]		Ī. [9]		0.	Ī. [9]			
0	93753	7	06247	76144	29	93307	7	06693	77877	28	92842	8	07158	79579	28	60	60
1	93746	7	06254	76173	29	93299	8	06701	77906	29	92834	8	07166	79607	28	59	56
2	93738	8	06262	76202	29	93291	8	06709	77935	29	92826	8	07174	79635	28	58	52
3	93731	7	06269	76231	29	93284	7	06716	77963	28	92818	8	07182	79663	28	57	48
4	93724	7	06276	76261	30	93276	8	06724	77992	29	92810	8	07190	79691	28	56	44
5	93717	7	06283	76290	29	93269	7	06731	78020	28	92803	7	07197	79719	28	55	40
6	93709	8	06291	76319	29	93261	8	06739	78049	29	92795	8	07205	79747	28	54	36
7	93702	7	06298	76348	29	93253	8	06747	78077	28	92787	8	07213	79776	29	53	32
8	93695	7	06305	76377	29	93246	7	06754	78106	29	92779	8	07221	79804	28	52	28
9	93687	8	06313	76406	29	93238	8	06762	78135	29	92771	8	07229	79832	28	51	24
10	93680	7	06320	76435	29	93230	8	06770	78163	28	92763	8	07237	79860	28	50	20
11	93673	7	06327	76464	29	93223	7	06777	78192	29	92755	8	07245	79888	28	49	16
12	93665	8	06335	76493	29	93215	8	06785	78220	28	92747	8	07253	79916	28	48	12
13	93658	7	06342	76522	29	93207	8	06793	78249	29	92739	8	07261	79944	28	47	8
14	93650	8	06350	76551	29	93200	7	06800	78277	28	92731	8	07269	79972	28	46	4
15	93643	7	06357	76580	29	93192	8	06808	78306	29	92723	8	07277	80000	28	45	+3m
16	93636	7	06364	76609	29	93184	8	06816	78334	28	92715	8	07285	80028	28	44	56
17	93628	8	06372	76639	30	93177	7	06823	78363	29	92707	8	07293	80056	28	43	52
18	93621	7	06379	76668	29	93169	8	06831	78391	28	92699	8	07301	80084	28	42	48
19	93614	7	06386	76697	29	93161	8	06839	78419	29	92691	8	07309	80112	28	41	44
20	93606	8	06394	76725	28	93154	7	06846	78448	29	92683	8	07317	80140	28	40	40
21	93599	7	06401	76754	29	93146	8	06854	78476	28	92675	8	07325	80168	28	39	36
22	93591	8	06409	76783	29	93138	8	06862	78505	29	92667	8	07333	80195	27	38	32
23	93584	7	06416	76812	29	93131	7	06869	78533	28	92659	8	07341	80223	28	37	28
24	93577	7	06423	76841	29	93123	8	06877	78562	28	92651	8	07349	80251	28	36	24
25	93569	8	06431	76870	29	93115	8	06885	78590	29	92643	8	07357	80279	28	35	20
26	93562	7	06438	76899	29	93108	7	06892	78618	29	92635	8	07365	80307	28	34	16
27	93554	8	06446	76928	29	93100	8	06900	78647	28	92627	8	07373	80335	28	33	12
28	93547	7	06453	76957	29	93092	8	06908	78675	29	92619	8	07381	80363	28	32	8
29	93539	8	06461	76986	29	93084	8	06916	78704	29	92611	8	07389	80391	28	31	4
30	93532	7	06468	77015	29	93077	7	06923	78732	28	92603	8	07397	80419	28	30	+2m
31	93525	7	06475	77044	29	93069	8	06931	78760	28	92595	8	07405	80447	28	29	56
32	93517	8	06483	77073	29	93061	8	06939	78789	29	92587	8	07413	80474	27	28	52
33	93510	7	06490	77101	28	93053	8	06947	78817	28	92579	8	07421	80502	28	27	48
34	93502	8	06498	77130	29	93046	7	06954	78845	28	92571	8	07429	80530	28	26	44
35	93495	7	06505	77159	29	93038	8	06962	78874	29	92563	8	07437	80558	28	25	40
36	93487	8	06513	77188	29	93030	8	06970	78902	28	92555	8	07445	80586	28	24	36
37	93480	7	06520	77217	29	93022	8	06978	78930	28	92546	9	07454	80614	28	23	32
38	93472	8	06528	77246	29	93014	8	06986	78959	29	92538	8	07462	80642	28	22	28
39	93465	7	06535	77274	28	93007	7	06993	78987	28	92530	8	07470	80669	27	21	24
40	93457	8	06543	77303	29	92999	8	07001	79015	28	92522	8	07478	80697	28	20	20
41	93450	7	06550	77332	29	92991	8	07009	79043	28	92514	8	07486	80725	28	19	16
42	93442	8	06558	77361	29	92983	7	07017	79072	29	92506	8	07494	80753	28	18	12
43	93435	7	06565	77390	29	92976	7	07024	79100	28	92498	8	07502	80781	28	17	8
44	93427	8	06573	77418	28	92968	8	07032	79128	28	92490	8	07510	80808	27	16	4
45	93420	7	06580	77447	29	92960	8	07040	79156	29	92482	8	07518	80836	28	15	+1m
46	93412	8	06588	77476	29	92952	8	07048	79185	29	92473	9	07527	80864	28	14	56
47	93405	7	06595	77505	28	92944	8	07056	79213	28	92465	8	07535	80892	28	13	52
48	93397	8	06603	77533	28	92936	8	07064	79241	28	92457	8	07543	80919	27	12	48
49	93390	7	06610	77562	29	92929	7	07071	79269	28	92449	8	07551	80947	28	11	44
50	93382	8	06618	77591	29	92921	8	07079	79297	29	92441	8	07559	80975	28	10	40
51	93375	7	06625	77619	28	92913	8	07087	79326	29	92433	8	07567	81003	28	9	36
52	93367	8	06633	77648	29	92905	8	07095	79354	28	92425	8	07575	81030	27	8	32
53	93360	7	06640	77677	29	92897	8	07103	79382	28	92416	9	07584	81058	28	7	28
54	93352	8	06648	77706	28	92889	8	07111	79410	28	92408	8	07592	81086	28	6	24
55	93344	8	06656	77734	28	92881	8	07119	79438	28	92400	8	07600	81113	27	5	20
56	93337	7	06663	77763	29	92874	7	07126	79466	29	92392	8	07608	81141	28	4	16
57	93329	8	06671	77791	28	92866	8	07134	79495	28	92384	8	07616	81169	28	3	12
58	93322	8	06678	77820	29	92858	8	07142	79523	28	92376	9	07624	81196	27	2	8
59	93314	8	06686	77849	29	92850	8	07150	79551	28	92367	9	07633	81224	28	1	4
60	93307	7	06693	77877	28	92842	8	07158	79579	28	92359	8	07641	81252	28	0	0
	Ī. [9]		0.	Ī. [9]		Ī. [9]		0.	Ī. [9]		Ī. [9]		0.	Ī. [9]			

	Sin.	D.	Cosec.	Cot.	D.	Sin.	D.	Cosec.	Cot.	D.	Sin.	D.	Cosec.	Cot.	D.	′	Secs.

59° 58° 57°

3ʰ56m   3ʰ52m   3ʰ48m

Table 19

LOGARITHMIC FUNCTIONS

33°   34°   35°

′	Cos.	D.	Sec.	Tan.	D.	Cos.	D.	Sec.	Tan.	D.	Cos.	D.	Sec.	Tan.	D.		
	Ī.[9]		0.	Ī.[9]		Ī.[9]		0.	Ī.[9]		Ī.[9]		0.	Ī.[9]			
0	92359	8	07641	81252	28	91857	9	08143	82899	28	91336	9	08664	84523	27	60	60
1	92351	8	07649	81279	27	91849	8	08151	82926	27	91328	8	08672	84550	27	59	56
2	92343	8	07657	81307	28	91840	9	08160	82953	27	91319	9	08681	84576	26	58	52
3	92335	8	07665	81335	28	91832	8	08168	82980	27	91310	9	08690	84603	27	57	48
4	92326	9	07674	81362	27	91823	9	08177	83008	28	91301	9	08699	84630	27	56	44
5	92318	8	07682	81390	28	91815	8	08185	83035	27	91292	9	08708	84657	27	55	40
6	92310	8	07690	81418	28	91806	9	08194	83062	27	91283	9	08717	84684	27	54	36
7	92302	8	07698	81445	27	91798	8	08202	83089	28	91274	9	08726	84711	27	53	32
8	92293	9	07707	81473	28	91789	9	08211	83117	27	91266	8	08734	84738	27	52	28
9	92285	8	07715	81500	27	91781	8	08219	83144	27	91257	9	08743	84764	26	51	24
10	92277	8	07723	81528	28	91772	9	08228	83171	27	91248	9	08752	84791	27	50	20
11	92269	8	07731	81556	28	91763	9	08237	83198	27	91239	9	08761	84818	27	49	16
12	92260	9	07740	81583	27	91755	8	08245	83225	27	91230	9	08770	84845	27	48	12
13	92252	8	07748	81611	28	91746	9	08254	83252	27	91221	9	08779	84872	27	47	8
14	92244	8	07756	81638	27	91738	8	08262	83280	28	91212	9	08788	84899	27	46	4
15	92235	9	07765	81666	28	91729	9	08271	83307	27	91203	9	08797	84925	26	45	+3m
16	92227	8	07773	81693	27	91720	8	08280	83334	27	91194	9	08806	84952	27	44	56
17	92219	8	07781	81721	28	91712	8	08288	83361	27	91185	9	08815	84979	27	43	52
18	92211	8	07789	81748	27	91703	9	08297	83388	27	91176	9	08824	85006	27	42	48
19	92202	9	07798	81776	28	91695	8	08305	83415	27	91167	9	08833	85033	27	41	44
20	92194	8	07806	81803	27	91686	9	08314	83442	27	91158	9	08842	85059	26	40	40
21	92186	8	07814	81831	28	91677	9	08323	83470	28	91149	9	08851	85086	27	39	36
22	92177	9	07823	81858	27	91669	8	08331	83497	27	91141	8	08859	85113	27	38	32
23	92169	8	07831	81886	28	91660	9	08340	83524	27	91132	9	08868	85140	27	37	28
24	92161	8	07839	81913	27	91651	9	08349	83551	27	91123	9	08877	85166	26	36	24
25	92152	9	07848	81941	28	91643	8	08357	83578	27	91114	9	08886	85193	27	35	20
26	92144	8	07856	81968	27	91634	9	08366	83605	27	91105	9	08895	85220	27	34	16
27	92136	8	07864	81996	28	91625	9	08375	83632	27	91096	9	08904	85247	26	33	12
28	92127	9	07873	82023	27	91617	8	08383	83659	27	91087	9	08913	85273	27	32	8
29	92119	8	07881	82051	28	91608	9	08392	83686	27	91078	9	08922	85300	27	31	4
30	92111	8	07889	82078	27	91599	9	08401	83713	27	91069	9	08931	85327	27	30	+2m
31	92102	9	07898	82106	28	91591	8	08409	83740	27	91060	9	08940	85354	27	29	56
32	92094	8	07906	82133	27	91582	9	08418	83768	28	91051	9	08949	85380	26	28	52
33	92086	8	07914	82161	28	91573	8	08427	83795	27	91042	9	08958	85407	27	27	48
34	92077	9	07923	82188	27	91565	9	08435	83822	27	91033	9	08967	85434	27	26	44
35	92069	8	07931	82215	27	91556	9	08444	83849	27	91023	10	08977	85460	27	25	40
36	92060	9	07940	82243	28	91547	9	08453	83876	27	91014	9	08986	85487	27	24	36
37	92052	8	07948	82270	27	91538	8	08462	83903	27	91005	9	08995	85514	27	23	32
38	92044	8	07956	82298	27	91530	8	08470	83930	27	90996	9	09004	85540	26	22	28
39	92035	9	07965	82325	27	91521	9	08479	83957	27	90987	9	09013	85567	27	21	24
40	92027	8	07973	82352	27	91512	8	08488	83984	27	90978	9	09022	85594	26	20	20
41	92018	9	07982	82380	28	91504	8	08496	84011	27	90969	9	09031	85620	27	19	16
42	92010	8	07990	82407	27	91495	9	08505	84038	27	90960	9	09040	85647	27	18	12
43	92002	8	07998	82435	28	91486	9	08514	84065	27	90951	9	09049	85674	26	17	8
44	91993	9	08007	82462	27	91477	9	08523	84092	27	90942	9	09058	85700	27	16	4
45	91985	8	08015	82489	27	91469	8	08531	84119	27	90933	9	09067	85727	27	15	+1m
46	91976	9	08024	82517	28	91460	9	08540	84146	27	90924	9	09076	85754	26	14	56
47	91968	8	08032	82544	27	91451	9	08549	84173	27	90915	9	09085	85780	27	13	52
48	91959	9	08041	82571	27	91442	9	08558	84200	27	90906	9	09094	85807	27	12	48
49	91951	8	08049	82599	28	91433	9	08567	84227	27	90896	10	09104	85834	27	11	44
50	91942	9	08058	82626	27	91425	8	08575	84254	27	90887	9	09113	85860	26	10	40
51	91934	8	08066	82653	27	91416	9	08584	84280	26	90878	9	09122	85887	27	9	36
52	91925	9	08075	82681	28	91407	9	08593	84307	27	90869	9	09131	85913	26	8	32
53	91917	8	08083	82708	27	91398	9	08602	84334	27	90860	9	09140	85940	27	7	28
54	91908	8	08092	82735	27	91389	8	08611	84361	27	90851	9	09149	85967	26	6	24
55	91900	8	08100	82762	27	91381	8	08619	84388	27	90842	9	09158	85993	27	5	20
56	91891	9	08109	82790	28	91372	9	08628	84415	27	90832	10	09168	86020	26	4	16
57	91883	8	08117	82817	27	91363	9	08637	84442	27	90823	9	09177	86046	27	3	12
58	91874	9	08126	82844	27	91354	9	08646	84469	27	90814	9	09186	86073	27	2	8
59	91866	8	08134	82871	27	91345	9	08655	84496	27	90805	9	09195	86100	26	1	4
60	91857	9	08143	82899	28	91336	9	08664	84523	27	90796	9	09204	86126	26	0	0
	Ī.[9]		0.	Ī.[9]		Ī.[9]		0.	Ī.[9]		Ī.[9]		0.	Ī.[9]			
	Sin.	D.	Cosec.	Cot.	D.	Sin.	D.	Cosec.	Cot.	D.	Sin.	D.	Cosec.	Cot.	D.	′	Secs.

56°   55°   54°

3h44m   3h40m   3h36m

Table 19   LOGARITHMIC FUNCTIONS

36°   37°   38°

′	Cos.	D.	Sec.	Tan.	D.	Cos.	D.	Sec.	Tan.	D.	Cos.	D.	Sec.	Tan.	D.	′	Secs
	1.[9]		0.	1.[9]		1.[9]		0.	1.[9]		1.[9]		0.	1.[9]			
0	90796	9	09204	86126	26	90235	9	09765	87711	26	89653	10	10347	89281	26	60	60
1	90787	9	09213	86153	27	90225	10	09775	87738	27	89643	10	10357	89307	26	59	56
2	90777	10	09223	86179	26	90216	9	09784	87764	26	89633	10	10367	89333	26	58	52
3	90768	9	09232	86206	27	90206	9	09794	87790	26	89624	9	10376	89359	26	57	48
4	90759	9	09241	86232		90197	9	09803	87817	27	89614	10	10386	89385	26	56	44
5	90750	9	09250	86259	27	90187	10	09813	87843	26	89604	10	10396	89411	26	55	40
6	90741	9	09259	86285	26	90178	9	09822	87869	26	89594	10	10406	89437	26	54	36
7	90731	10	09269	86312	27	90168	10	09832	87895	26	89584	10	10416	89463	26	53	32
8	90722	9	09278	86338	26	90159	9	09841	87922	27	89574	10	10426	89489	26	52	28
9	90713	9	09287	86365	27	90149	10	09851	87948	26	89564	10	10436	89515	26	51	24
10	90704	9	09296	86392	27	90139	10	09861	87974	26	89554	10	10446	89541	26	50	20
11	90694	10	09306	86418	26	90130	9	09870	88000	26	89544	10	10456	89567	26	49	16
12	90685	9	09315	86445	27	90120	10	09880	88027	27	89534	10	10466	89593	26	48	12
13	90676	9	09324	86471	26	90111	9	09889	88053	26	89524	10	10476	89619	26	47	8
14	90667	9	09333	86498	27	90101	10	09899	88079	26	89514	10	10486	89645	26	46	4
15	90657	10	09343	86524	26	90091	10	09909	88105	26	89504	10	10496	89671	26	45	+3m
16	90648	9	09352	86551	27	90082	9	09918	88131	26	89495	9	10505	89697	26	44	56
17	90639	9	09361	86577	26	90072	10	09928	88158	27	89485	10	10515	89723	26	43	52
18	90630	9	09370	86603	26	90063	9	09937	88184	26	89475	10	10525	89749	26	42	48
19	90620	10	09380	86630	27	90053	10	09947	88210	26	89465	10	10535	89775	26	41	44
20	90611	9	09389	86656	26	90043	10	09957	88236	26	89455	10	10545	89801	26	40	40
21	90602	9	09398	86683	27	90034	9	09966	88262	26	89445	10	10555	89827	26	39	36
22	90592	10	09408	86709	26	90024	10	09976	88289	27	89435	10	10565	89853	26	38	32
23	90583	9	09417	86736	27	90014	10	09986	88315	26	89425	10	10575	89879	26	37	28
24	90574	9	09426	86762	26	90005	9	09995	88341	26	89415	10	10585	89905	26	36	24
25	90565	9	09435	86789	27	89995	10	10005	88367	26	89405	10	10595	89931	26	35	20
26	90555	10	09445	86815	26	89985	10	10015	88393	26	89395	10	10605	89957	26	34	16
27	90546	9	09454	86842	27	89976	9	10024	88420	27	89385	10	10615	89983	26	33	12
28	90537	9	09463	86868	26	89966	10	10034	88446	26	89375	10	10625	90009	26	32	8
29	90527	10	09473	86894	26	89956	10	10044	88472	26	89364	11	10636	90035	26	31	4
30	90518	9	09482	86921	27	89947	9	10053	88498	26	89354	10	10646	90061	26	30	+2m
31	90509	9	09491	86947	26	89937	10	10063	88524	26	89344	10	10656	90086	25	29	56
32	90499	10	09501	86974	27	89927	10	10073	88550	26	89334	10	10666	90112	26	28	52
33	90490	9	09510	87000	26	89918	9	10082	88577	27	89324	10	10676	90138	26	27	48
34	90480	10	09520	87027	27	89908	10	10092	88603	26	89314	10	10686	90164	26	26	44
35	90471	9	09529	87053	26	89898	10	10102	88629	26	89304	10	10696	90190	26	25	40
36	90462	9	09538	87079	26	89888	10	10112	88655	26	89294	10	10706	90216	26	24	36
37	90452	10	09548	87106	27	89879	9	10121	88681	26	89284	10	10716	90242	26	23	32
38	90443	9	09557	87132	26	89869	10	10131	88707	26	89274	10	10726	90268	26	22	28
39	90434	9	09566	87158	26	89859	10	10141	88733	26	89264	10	10736	90294	26	21	24
40	90424	10	09576	87185	27	89849	10	10151	88759	26	89254	10	10746	90320	26	20	20
41	90415	9	09585	87211	26	89840	9	10160	88786	27	89244	10	10756	90346	26	19	16
42	90405	10	09595	87238	27	89830	10	10170	88812	26	89233	11	10767	90371	25	18	12
43	90396	9	09604	87264	26	89820	10	10180	88838	26	89223	10	10777	90397	26	17	8
44	90386	10	09614	87290	26	89810	10	10190	88864	26	89213	10	10787	90423	26	16	4
45	90377	9	09623	87317	27	89801	9	10199	88890	26	89203	10	10797	90449	26	15	+1m
46	90368	9	09632	87343	26	89791	10	10209	88916	26	89193	10	10807	90475	26	14	56
47	90358	10	09642	87369	26	89781	10	10219	88942	26	89183	10	10817	90501	26	13	52
48	90349	10	09651	87396	27	89771	10	10229	88968	26	89173	10	10827	90527	26	12	48
49	90339	10	09661	87422	26	89761	10	10239	88994	26	89162	11	10838	90553	26	11	44
50	90330	9	09670	87448	26	89752	9	10248	89020	26	89152	10	10848	90578	25	10	40
51	90320	10	09680	87475	27	89742	10	10258	89046	26	89142	10	10858	90604	26	9	36
52	90311	10	09689	87501	26	89732	10	10268	89073	27	89132	10	10868	90630	26	8	32
53	90301	10	09699	87527	26	89722	10	10278	89099	26	89122	10	10878	90656	26	7	28
54	90292	9	09708	87554	27	89712	10	10288	89125	26	89112	10	10888	90682	26	6	24
55	90282	10	09718	87580	26	89702	10	10298	89151	26	89101	11	10899	90708	26	5	20
56	90273	9	09727	87606	26	89693	9	10307	89177	26	89091	10	10909	90734	26	4	16
57	90263	10	09737	87633	27	89683	10	10317	89203	26	89081	10	10919	90759	25	3	12
58	90254	9	09746	87659	26	89673	10	10327	89229	26	89071	10	10929	90785	26	2	8
59	90244	10	09756	87685	26	89663	10	10337	89255	26	89060	11	10940	90811	26	1	4
60	90235	9	09765	87711	26	89653	10	10347	89281	26	89050	10	10950	90837	26	0	0
	1.[9]		0.	1.[9]		1.[9]		0.	1.[9]		1.[9]		0.	1.[9]			

	Sin.	D.	Cosec.	Cot.	D.	Sin.	D.	Cosec.	Cot.	D.	Sin.	D.	Cosec.	Cot.	D.	′	Secs.

53°   52°   51°

3h 32m   3h 28m   3h 24m

Table 19 — LOGARITHMIC FUNCTIONS

	39° Cos.	D.	Sec.	Tan.	D.	40° Cos.	D.	Sec.	Tan.	D.	41° Cos.	D.	Sec.	Tan.	D.		
'	T.[9]		0.	T.[9]		T.[9]		0.	T.[9]		T.[9]		0.	T.[9]			
0	89050	10	10950	90837	26	88425	11	11575	92381	25	87778	11	12222	93916	25	60	60
1	89040	10	10960	90863	26	88415	10	11585	92407	26	87767	11	12233	93942	26	59	56
2	89030	10	10970	90889	26	88404	11	11596	92433	26	87756	11	12244	93967	25	58	52
3	89020	10	10980	90914	25	88394	10	11606	92458	25	87745	11	12255	93993	26	57	48
4	89009	11	10991	90940	26	88383	11	11617	92484	26	87734	11	12266	94018	26	56	44
5	88999	10	11001	90966	26	88372	11	11628	92510	26	87723	11	12277	94044	26	55	40
6	88989	10	11011	90992	26	88362	10	11638	92535	25	87712	11	12288	94069	25	54	36
7	88978	11	11022	91018	26	88351	11	11649	92561	26	87701	11	12299	94095	25	53	32
8	88968	10	11032	91043	25	88340	11	11660	92587	26	87690	11	12310	94120	25	52	28
9	88958	10	11042	91069	26	88330	10	11670	92612	25	87679	11	12321	94146	26	51	24
10	88948	10	11052	91095	26	88319	11	11681	92638	26	87668	11	12332	94171	25	50	20
11	88937	11	11063	91121	26	88308	11	11692	92663	25	87657	11	12343	94197	26	49	16
12	88927	10	11073	91147	26	88298	10	11702	92689	26	87646	11	12354	94222	26	48	12
13	88917	10	11083	91172	25	88287	11	11713	92715	26	87635	11	12365	94248	26	47	8
14	88906	11	11094	91198	26	88276	11	11724	92740	25	87624	11	12376	94273	26	46	4
15	88896	10	11104	91224	26	88266	10	11734	92766	26	87613	11	12387	94299	26	45	+3m
16	88886	10	11114	91250	26	88255	11	11745	92792	26	87601	12	12399	94324	25	44	56
17	88875	11	11125	91276	26	88244	11	11756	92817	25	87590	11	12410	94350	26	43	52
18	88865	10	11135	91301	26	88234	10	11766	92843	26	87579	11	12421	94375	25	42	48
19	88855	10	11145	91327	26	88223	11	11777	92868	26	87568	11	12432	94401	26	41	44
20	88844	11	11156	91353	26	88212	11	11788	92894	26	87557	11	12443	94426	25	40	40
21	88834	10	11166	91379	26	88201	11	11799	92920	25	87546	11	12454	94452	26	39	36
22	88824	10	11176	91404	25	88191	10	11809	92945	25	87535	11	12465	94477	25	38	32
23	88813	11	11187	91430	26	88180	11	11820	92971	26	87524	11	12476	94503	26	37	28
24	88803	10	11197	91456	26	88169	11	11831	92996	25	87513	11	12487	94528	25	36	24
25	88793	10	11207	91482	26	88158	11	11842	93022	26	87501	12	12499	94554	26	35	20
26	88782	11	11218	91507	26	88148	10	11852	93048	25	87490	11	12510	94579	25	34	16
27	88772	10	11228	91533	26	88137	11	11863	93073	26	87479	11	12521	94604	25	33	12
28	88761	11	11239	91559	26	88126	11	11874	93099	25	87468	11	12532	94630	26	32	8
29	88751	10	11249	91585	26	88115	11	11885	93124	25	87457	11	12543	94655	25	31	4
30	88741	10	11259	91610	25	88105	10	11895	93150	26	87446	11	12554	94681	26	30	+2m
31	88730	11	11270	91636	26	88094	11	11906	93175	25	87434	12	12566	94706	25	29	56
32	88720	10	11280	91662	26	88083	11	11917	93201	26	87423	11	12577	94732	26	28	52
33	88709	11	11291	91688	26	88072	11	11928	93227	25	87412	11	12588	94757	25	27	48
34	88699	10	11301	91713	25	88061	11	11939	93252	26	87401	11	12599	94783	26	26	44
35	88688	11	11312	91739	26	88051	10	11949	93278	25	87390	11	12610	94808	25	25	40
36	88678	10	11322	91765	26	88040	11	11960	93303	25	87378	12	12622	94834	26	24	36
37	88668	10	11332	91791	26	88029	11	11971	93329	26	87367	11	12633	94859	25	23	32
38	88657	11	11343	91816	25	88018	11	11982	93354	26	87356	11	12644	94884	26	22	28
39	88647	10	11353	91842	26	88007	11	11993	93380	26	87345	11	12655	94910	26	21	24
40	88636	11	11364	91868	26	87996	11	12004	93406	26	87334	11	12666	94935	25	20	20
41	88626	10	11374	91893	25	87985	11	12015	93431	25	87322	12	12678	94961	26	19	16
42	88615	11	11385	91919	26	87975	10	12025	93457	25	87311	11	12689	94986	25	18	12
43	88605	10	11395	91945	26	87964	11	12036	93482	25	87300	11	12700	95012	26	17	8
44	88594	11	11406	91971	26	87953	11	12047	93508	26	87288	12	12712	95037	25	16	4
45	88584	11	11416	91996	26	87942	11	12058	93533	25	87277	11	12723	95062	26	15	+1m
46	88573	11	11427	92022	26	87931	11	12069	93559	25	87266	11	12734	95088	26	14	56
47	88563	10	11437	92048	26	87920	11	12080	93584	25	87255	11	12745	95113	25	13	52
48	88552	11	11448	92073	25	87909	11	12091	93610	26	87243	12	12757	95139	26	12	48
49	88542	10	11458	92099	26	87898	11	12102	93636	26	87232	11	12768	95164	25	11	44
50	88531	11	11469	92125	26	87887	11	12113	93661	25	87221	11	12779	95190	26	10	40
51	88521	10	11479	92150	25	87877	10	12123	93687	26	87209	12	12791	95215	25	9	36
52	88510	11	11490	92176	26	87866	11	12134	93712	25	87198	11	12802	95240	26	8	32
53	88499	11	11501	92202	26	87855	11	12145	93738	26	87187	11	12813	95266	25	7	28
54	88489	10	11511	92227	25	87844	11	12156	93763	26	87175	12	12825	95291	25	6	24
55	88478	11	11522	92253	26	87833	11	12167	93789	25	87164	11	12836	95317	26	5	20
56	88468	10	11532	92279	26	87822	11	12178	93814	26	87153	11	12847	95342	25	4	16
57	88457	11	11543	92304	25	87811	11	12189	93840	25	87141	12	12859	95368	26	3	12
58	88447	10	11553	92330	26	87800	11	12200	93865	26	87130	11	12870	95393	25	2	8
59	88436	11	11564	92356	26	87789	11	12211	93891	26	87119	11	12881	95418	25	1	4
60	88425	11	11575	92381	25	87778	11	12222	93916	25	87107	12	12893	95444	26	0	0
	T.[9]		0.	T.[9]		T.[9]		0.	T.[9]		T.[9]		0.	T.[9]			
	Sin.	D.	Cosec.	Cot.	D.	Sin.	D.	Cosec.	Cot.	D.	Sin.	D.	Cosec.	Cot.	D.	'	Secs.
				50°					**49°**					**48°**			

3h20m   3h16m   3h12m

Table 19   **LOGARITHMIC FUNCTIONS**

42°   43°   44°

′	Cos.	D.	Sec.	Tan.	D.	Cos.	D.	Sec.	Tan.	D.	Cos.	D.	Sec.	Tan.	D.		
	T̄.[9]		0.	T̄.[9]		T̄.[9]		0.	T̄.[9]		T̄.[9]		0.	T̄/0.[9/0]			
0	87107	12	12893	95444	26	86413	12	13587	96966	26	85693	13	14307	98484	26	60	60
1	87096	11	12904	95469	25	86401	12	13599	96991	25	85681	12	14319	98509	25	59	56
2	87085	11	12915	95495	26	86389	12	13611	97016	25	85669	12	14331	98534	25	58	52
3	87073	12	12927	95520	25	86377	12	13623	97042	26	85657	12	14343	98560	26	57	48
4	87062	11	12938	95545	25	86366	11	13634	97067	25	85645	12	14355	98585	25	56	44
5	87050	12	12950	95571	26	86354	12	13646	97092	26	85632	13	14368	98610	25	55	40
6	87039	11	12961	95596	25	86342	12	13658	97118	26	85620	12	14380	98635	25	54	36
7	87028	11	12972	95622	26	86330	12	13670	97143	25	85608	12	14392	98661	26	53	32
8	87016	12	12984	95647	25	86318	12	13682	97168	25	85596	12	14404	98686	25	52	28
9	87005	11	12995	95672	25	86306	12	13694	97193	25	85583	13	14417	98711	25	51	24
10	86993	12	13007	95698	26	86295	11	13705	97219	26	85571	12	14429	98737	26	50	20
11	86982	11	13018	95723	25	86283	12	13717	97244	25	85559	12	14441	98762	25	49	16
12	86970	12	13030	95748	25	86271	12	13729	97269	25	85547	12	14453	98787	25	48	12
13	86959	11	13041	95774	26	86259	12	13741	97295	26	85534	13	14466	98812	25	47	8
14	86947	12	13053	95799	25	86247	12	13753	97320	25	85522	12	14478	98838	26	46	4
15	86936	11	13064	95825	26	86235	12	13765	97345	25	85510	12	14490	98863	25	45	+3m
16	86924	12	13076	95850	25	86223	12	13777	97371	26	85497	13	14503	98888	25	44	56
17	86913	11	13087	95875	25	86211	12	13789	97396	25	85485	12	14515	98913	25	43	52
18	86902	11	13098	95901	26	86200	11	13800	97421	25	85473	12	14527	98939	26	42	48
19	86890	12	13110	95926	25	86188	12	13812	97447	25	85460	13	14540	98964	25	41	44
20	86879	11	13121	95952	25	86176	12	13824	97472	25	85448	12	14552	98989	25	40	40
21	86867	12	13133	95977	25	86164	12	13836	97497	25	85436	12	14564	99015	26	39	36
22	86855	12	13145	96002	25	86152	12	13848	97523	26	85423	13	14577	99040	25	38	32
23	86844	11	13156	96028	25	86140	12	13860	97548	25	85411	12	14589	99065	25	37	28
24	86832	12	13168	96053	25	86128	12	13872	97573	25	85399	12	14601	99090	25	36	24
25	86821	11	13179	96078	26	86116	12	13884	97598	26	85386	13	14614	99116	25	35	20
26	86809	12	13191	96104	25	86104	12	13896	97624	26	85374	12	14626	99141	25	34	16
27	86798	11	13202	96129	26	86092	12	13908	97649	25	85361	13	14639	99166	25	33	12
28	86786	12	13214	96155	26	86080	12	13920	97674	26	85349	12	14651	99191	26	32	8
29	86775	11	13225	96180	25	86068	12	13932	97700	25	85337	12	14663	99217	26	31	4
30	86763	12	13237	96205	25	86056	12	13944	97725	25	85324	13	14676	99242	25	30	+2m
31	86752	11	13248	96231	26	86044	12	13956	97750	26	85312	12	14688	99267	25	29	56
32	86740	12	13260	96256	25	86032	12	13968	97776	25	85299	13	14701	99293	26	28	52
33	86728	12	13272	96281	26	86020	12	13980	97801	25	85287	12	14713	99318	25	27	48
34	86717	11	13283	96307	25	86008	12	13992	97826	25	85274	13	14726	99343	25	26	44
35	86705	12	13295	96332	25	85996	12	14004	97851	26	85262	12	14738	99368	26	25	40
36	86694	11	13306	96357	25	85984	12	14016	97877	26	85250	12	14750	99394	25	24	36
37	86682	12	13318	96383	26	85972	12	14028	97902	25	85237	13	14763	99419	25	23	32
38	86670	12	13330	96408	25	85960	12	14040	97927	25	85225	12	14775	99444	25	22	28
39	86659	11	13341	96433	25	85948	12	14052	97953	25	85212	13	14788	99469	25	21	24
40	86647	12	13353	96459	26	85936	12	14064	97978	25	85200	12	14800	99495	26	20	20
41	86635	12	13365	96484	25	85924	12	14076	98003	26	85187	13	14813	99520	25	19	16
42	86624	11	13376	96510	26	85912	12	14088	98029	26	85175	12	14825	99545	25	18	12
43	86612	12	13388	96535	25	85900	12	14100	98054	25	85162	13	14838	99570	25	17	8
44	86600	12	13400	96560	25	85888	12	14112	98079	25	85150	12	14850	99596	26	16	4
45	86589	11	13411	96586	26	85876	12	14124	98104	26	85137	13	14863	99621	25	15	+1m
46	86577	12	13423	96611	25	85864	12	14136	98130	25	85125	12	14875	99646	25	14	56
47	86565	11	13435	96636	25	85851	13	14149	98155	25	85112	13	14888	99672	26	13	52
48	86554	11	13446	96662	26	85839	12	14161	98180	26	85100	12	14900	99697	25	12	48
49	86542	12	13458	96687	25	85827	12	14173	98206	25	85087	13	14913	99722	25	11	44
50	86530	12	13470	96712	25	85815	12	14185	98231	25	85074	12	14926	99747	25	10	40
51	86518	12	13482	96738	26	85803	12	14197	98256	25	85062	12	14938	99773	26	9	36
52	86507	11	13493	96763	25	85791	12	14209	98281	26	85049	13	14951	99798	25	8	32
53	86495	12	13505	96788	25	85779	12	14221	98307	25	85037	12	14963	99823	25	7	28
54	86483	12	13517	96814	26	85766	13	14234	98332	25	85024	12	14976	99848	25	6	24
55	86472	11	13528	96839	25	85754	12	14246	98357	26	85012	12	14988	99874	26	5	20
56	86460	12	13540	96864	25	85742	12	14258	98383	25	84999	13	15001	99899	25	4	16
57	86448	12	13552	96890	25	85730	12	14270	98408	25	84986	12	15014	99924	25	3	12
58	86436	12	13564	96915	25	85718	12	14282	98433	25	84974	13	15026	99949	25	2	8
59	86425	11	13575	96940	25	85706	12	14294	98458	25	84961	13	15039	99975	26	1	4
60	86413	12	13587	96966	26	85693	13	14307	98484	26	84949	12	15051	00000	25	0	0
	T̄.[9]		0.	T̄.[9]		T̄.[9]		0.	T̄.[9]		T̄.[9]		0.	0/T̄.[0|9]			
	Sin.	D.	Cosec.	Cot.	D.	Sin.	D.	Cosec.	Cot.	D.	Sin.	D.	Cosec.	Cot.	D.	′	Secs.

47°   46°   45°

3h08m   3h04m   3h00m

Table 19   LOGARITHMIC FUNCTIONS

45°   46°   47°

′	Cos.	D.	Sec.	Tan.	D.	Cos.	D.	Sec.	Tan.	D.	Cos.	D.	Sec.	Tan.	D.		
	Ī. [9]		0.	0.		Ī. [9]		0.	0.		Ī. [9]		0.	0.			
0	84949	12	15051	00000	25	84177	13	15823	01516	25	83378	14	16622	03034	26	60	60
1	84936	13	15064	00025	25	84164	13	15836	01542	26	83365	13	16635	03060	26	59	56
2	84923	13	15077	00051	26	84151	13	15849	01567	25	83351	14	16649	03085	25	58	52
3	84911	12	15089	00076	25	84138	13	15862	01592	25	83338	13	16662	03110	25	57	48
4	84898	13	15102	00101	25	84125	13	15875	01617	25	83324	14	16676	03136	26	56	44
5	84885	13	15115	00126	25	84112	13	15888	01643	26	83310	14	16690	03161	25	55	40
6	84873	12	15127	00152	26	84098	14	15902	01668	25	83297	13	16703	03186	25	54	36
7	84860	13	15140	00177	25	84085	13	15915	01693	25	83283	14	16717	03212	26	53	32
8	84847	13	15153	00202	25	84072	13	15928	01719	26	83270	13	16730	03237	25	52	28
9	84835	12	15165	00227	25	84059	13	15941	01744	25	83256	14	16744	03262	26	51	24
10	84822	13	15178	00253	26	84046	13	15954	01769	25	83242	14	16758	03288	26	50	20
11	84809	13	15191	00278	25	84033	13	15967	01794	25	83229	13	16771	03313	25	49	16
12	84796	13	15204	00303	25	84020	13	15980	01820	26	83215	14	16785	03338	26	48	12
13	84784	12	15216	00328	25	84006	14	15994	01845	25	83202	13	16798	03364	26	47	8
14	84771	13	15229	00354	26	83993	13	16007	01870	25	83188	14	16812	03389	25	46	4
15	84758	13	15242	00379	25	83980	13	16020	01896	25	83174	14	16826	03414	25	45	+3m
16	84745	13	15255	00404	25	83967	13	16033	01921	25	83161	13	16839	03440	25	44	56
17	84733	12	15267	00430	26	83954	13	16046	01946	25	83147	14	16853	03465	25	43	52
18	84720	13	15280	00455	25	83940	14	16060	01971	25	83133	14	16867	03490	26	42	48
19	84707	13	15293	00480	25	83927	13	16073	01997	26	83120	13	16880	03516	26	41	4
20	84694	13	15306	00505	25	83914	13	16086	02022	25	83106	14	16894	03541	25	40	40
21	84682	12	15318	00531	26	83901	13	16099	02047	25	83092	14	16908	03567	26	39	36
22	84669	13	15331	00556	25	83887	14	16113	02073	26	83078	14	16922	03592	25	38	32
23	84656	13	15344	00581	25	83874	13	16126	02098	25	83065	13	16935	03617	26	37	28
24	84643	13	15357	00606	25	83861	13	16139	02123	25	83051	14	16949	03643	25	36	24
25	84630	13	15370	00632	26	83848	13	16152	02149	26	83037	14	16963	03668	25	35	20
26	84618	12	15382	00657	25	83834	14	16166	02174	25	83023	14	16977	03693	25	34	16
27	84605	13	15395	00682	25	83821	13	16179	02199	25	83010	13	16990	03719	25	33	12
28	84592	13	15408	00707	25	83808	13	16192	02224	25	82996	14	17004	03744	25	32	8
29	84579	13	15421	00733	26	83795	13	16205	02250	26	82982	14	17018	03769	25	31	4
30	84566	13	15434	00758	25	83781	14	16219	02275	25	82968	14	17032	03795	26	30	+2m
31	84553	13	15447	00783	25	83768	13	16232	02300	25	82955	13	17045	03820	25	29	56
32	84540	13	15460	00809	26	83755	13	16245	02326	26	82941	14	17059	03845	25	28	52
33	84528	12	15472	00834	25	83741	14	16259	02351	25	82927	14	17073	03871	26	27	48
34	84515	13	15485	00859	25	83728	13	16272	02376	25	82913	14	17087	03896	26	26	44
35	84502	13	15498	00884	25	83715	13	16285	02402	26	82899	14	17101	03922	26	25	40
36	84489	13	15511	00910	26	83701	14	16299	02427	25	82885	14	17115	03947	25	24	36
37	84476	13	15524	00935	25	83688	13	16312	02452	25	82872	13	17128	03972	26	23	32
38	84463	13	15537	00960	25	83674	14	16326	02477	25	82858	14	17142	03998	26	22	28
39	84450	13	15550	00985	25	83661	13	16339	02503	26	82844	14	17156	04023	25	21	24
40	84437	13	15563	01011	26	83648	13	16352	02528	25	82830	14	17170	04048	25	20	20
41	84424	13	15576	01036	25	83634	14	16366	02553	25	82816	14	17184	04074	26	19	16
42	84411	13	15589	01061	25	83621	13	16379	02579	26	82802	14	17198	04099	25	18	12
43	84398	13	15602	01087	26	83608	13	16392	02604	25	82788	14	17212	04125	26	17	8
44	84385	13	15615	01112	25	83594	14	16406	02629	26	82775	13	17225	04150	25	16	4
45	84373	12	15627	01137	25	83581	13	16419	02655	25	82761	14	17239	04175	25	15	+1m
46	84360	13	15640	01162	25	83567	14	16433	02680	25	82747	14	17253	04201	26	14	56
47	84347	13	15653	01188	26	83554	14	16446	02705	25	82733	14	17267	04226	26	13	52
48	84334	13	15666	01213	25	83540	14	16460	02731	26	82719	14	17281	04252	26	12	48
49	84321	13	15679	01238	25	83527	13	16473	02756	25	82705	14	17295	04277	25	11	44
50	84308	13	15692	01263	25	83513	14	16487	02781	25	82691	14	17309	04302	25	10	40
51	84295	13	15705	01289	26	83500	13	16500	02807	26	82677	14	17323	04328	26	9	36
52	84282	13	15718	01314	25	83486	14	16514	02832	25	82663	14	17337	04353	25	8	32
53	84269	13	15731	01339	25	83473	13	16527	02857	25	82649	14	17351	04378	26	7	28
54	84255	14	15745	01365	26	83459	13	16541	02882	26	82635	14	17365	04404	26	6	24
55	84242	13	15758	01390	25	83446	13	16554	02908	26	82621	14	17379	04429	25	5	20
56	84229	13	15771	01415	25	83432	14	16568	02933	25	82607	14	17393	04455	26	4	16
57	84216	13	15784	01440	26	83419	13	16581	02958	26	82593	14	17407	04480	25	3	12
58	84203	13	15797	01466	25	83405	14	16595	02984	26	82579	14	17421	04505	26	2	8
59	84190	13	15810	01491	25	83392	13	16608	03009	25	82565	14	17435	04531	25	1	4
60	84177	13	15823	01516	25	83378	14	16622	03034	25	82551	14	17449	04556	25	0	0
	Ī. [9]		0.	0.		Ī. [9]		0.	0.		Ī. [9]		0.	0.			
	Sin.	D.	Cosec.	Cot.	D.	Sin.	D.	Cosec.	Cot.	D.	Sin.	D.	Cosec.	Cot.	D.	′	Secs

44°   43°   42°

2h56m   2h52m   2h48m

Table 19　　LOGARITHMIC FUNCTIONS

	48°					49°					50°						
′	Cos.	D.	Sec.	Tan.	D.	Cos.	D.	Sec.	Tan.	D.	Cos.	D.	Sec.	Tan.	D.		
	Ī.[9]		0.	0.		Ī.[9]		0.	0.		Ī.[9]		0.	0.			
0	82551	14	17449	04556	25	81694	15	18306	06084	26	80807	15	19193	07619	26	60	60
1	82537	14	17463	04582	26	81680	14	18320	06109	25	80792	15	19208	07644	25	59	56
2	82523	14	17477	04607	25	81665	15	18335	06135	26	80777	15	19223	07670	26	58	52
3	82509	14	17491	04632	25	81651	14	18349	06160	25	80762	15	19238	07696	25	57	48
4	82495	14	17505	04658	26	81636	15	18364	06186	25	80746	16	19254	07721	25	56	44
5	82481	14	17519	04683	25	81622	14	18378	06211	25	80731	15	19269	07747	26	55	40
6	82467	14	17533	04709	25	81607	15	18393	06237	25	80716	15	19284	07773	25	54	36
7	82453	14	17547	04734	25	81592	14	18408	06262	26	80701	15	19299	07798	26	53	32
8	82439	14	17561	04760	26	81578	14	18422	06288	25	80686	15	19314	07824	26	52	28
9	82424	15	17576	04785	25	81563	15	18437	06313	26	80671	15	19329	07850	26	51	24
10	82410	14	17590	04810	25	81549	14	18451	06339	25	80656	15	19344	07875	25	50	20
11	82396	14	17604	04836	26	81534	15	18466	06364	25	80641	15	19359	07901	26	49	16
12	82382	14	17618	04861	25	81519	15	18481	06390	26	80625	16	19375	07927	26	48	12
13	82368	14	17632	04887	26	81505	14	18495	06416	25	80610	15	19390	07952	25	47	8
14	82354	14	17646	04912	25	81490	15	18510	06441	26	80595	15	19405	07978	26	46	4
15	82340	14	17660	04938	26	81475	15	18525	06467	25	80580	15	19420	08004	26	45	+3m
16	82326	14	17674	04963	25	81461	14	18539	06492	26	80565	15	19435	08029	25	44	56
17	82311	15	17689	04988	26	81446	15	18554	06518	25	80550	15	19450	08055	26	43	52
18	82297	14	17703	05014	25	81431	15	18569	06543	26	80534	16	19466	08081	26	42	48
19	82283	14	17717	05039	26	81417	14	18583	06569	25	80519	15	19481	08107	25	41	44
20	82269	14	17731	05065	26	81402	15	18598	06594	25	80504	15	19496	08132	25	40	40
21	82255	14	17745	05090	25	81387	15	18613	06620	26	80489	15	19511	08158	26	39	36
22	82240	15	17760	05116	26	81372	15	18628	06646	26	80473	16	19527	08184	26	38	32
23	82226	14	17774	05141	25	81358	14	18642	06671	25	80458	15	19542	08209	25	37	28
24	82212	14	17788	05166	25	81343	15	18657	06697	26	80443	15	19557	08235	26	36	24
25	82198	14	17802	05192	26	81328	15	18672	06722	26	80428	15	19572	08261	26	35	20
26	82184	14	17816	05217	25	81314	14	18686	06748	25	80412	16	19588	08287	25	34	16
27	82169	15	17831	05243	26	81299	15	18701	06773	25	80397	15	19603	08312	25	33	12
28	82155	14	17845	05268	26	81284	15	18716	06799	26	80382	15	19618	08338	26	32	8
29	82141	14	17859	05294	25	81269	15	18731	06825	25	80366	16	19634	08364	26	31	4
30	82126	15	17874	05319	25	81254	14	18746	06850	26	80351	15	19649	08390	26	30	+2m
31	82112	14	17888	05345	26	81240	14	18760	06876	26	80336	15	19664	08415	25	29	56
32	82098	14	17902	05370	26	81225	15	18775	06901	26	80320	16	19680	08441	26	28	52
33	82084	14	17916	05396	26	81210	15	18790	06927	25	80305	15	19695	08467	26	27	48
34	82069	15	17931	05421	25	81195	15	18805	06952	26	80290	15	19710	08493	25	26	44
35	82055	14	17945	05446	25	81180	15	18820	06978	26	80274	16	19726	08518	25	25	40
36	82041	14	17959	05472	26	81166	14	18834	07004	25	80259	15	19741	08544	26	24	36
37	82026	15	17974	05497	26	81151	15	18849	07029	26	80244	15	19756	08570	26	23	32
38	82012	14	17988	05523	26	81136	15	18864	07055	25	80228	16	19772	08596	25	22	28
39	81998	14	18002	05548	25	81121	15	18879	07080	25	80213	15	19787	08621	26	21	24
40	81983	15	18017	05574	26	81106	15	18894	07106	26	80197	16	19803	08647	26	20	20
41	81969	14	18031	05599	26	81091	15	18909	07132	25	80182	15	19818	08673	26	19	16
42	81955	14	18045	05625	26	81076	15	18924	07157	26	80166	16	19834	08699	25	18	12
43	81940	15	18060	05650	25	81061	15	18939	07183	25	80151	15	19849	08724	26	17	8
44	81926	14	18074	05676	25	81047	14	18953	07208	26	80136	15	19864	08750	26	16	4
45	81911	15	18089	05701	25	81032	15	18968	07234	26	80120	16	19880	08776	26	15	+1m
46	81897	14	18103	05727	25	81017	15	18983	07260	25	80105	15	19895	08802	26	14	56
47	81882	15	18118	05752	25	81002	15	18998	07285	26	80089	16	19911	08828	25	13	52
48	81868	14	18132	05778	26	80987	15	19013	07311	26	80074	15	19926	08853	26	12	48
49	81854	14	18146	05803	25	80972	15	19028	07337	25	80058	16	19942	08879	26	11	44
50	81839	15	18161	05829	26	80957	15	19043	07362	25	80043	15	19957	08905	26	10	40
51	81825	14	18175	05854	25	80942	15	19058	07388	25	80027	16	19973	08931	26	9	36
52	81810	15	18190	05880	26	80927	15	19073	07413	25	80012	15	19988	08957	26	8	32
53	81796	14	18204	05905	25	80912	15	19088	07439	26	79996	16	20004	08982	25	7	28
54	81781	15	18219	05931	26	80897	15	19103	07465	25	79981	15	20019	09008	26	6	24
55	81767	14	18233	05956	25	80882	15	19118	07490	26	79965	16	20035	09034	26	5	20
56	81752	15	18248	05982	25	80867	15	19133	07516	26	79950	15	20050	09060	26	4	16
57	81738	14	18262	06007	25	80852	15	19148	07542	25	79934	16	20066	09086	25	3	12
58	81723	15	18277	06033	26	80837	15	19163	07567	26	79918	16	20082	09111	26	2	8
59	81709	14	18291	06058	25	80822	15	19178	07593	26	79903	15	20097	09137	26	1	4
60	81694	15	18306	06084	26	80807	15	19193	07619	26	79887	16	20113	09163	26	0	0
	Ī.[9]		0.	0.		Ī.[9]		0.	0.		Ī.[9]		0.	0.			
	Sin.	D.	Cosec.	Cot.	D.	Sin.	D.	Cosec.	Cot.	D.	Sin.	D.	Cosec.	Cot.	D.	′	Secs.
	41°					**40°**					**39°**						

2h44m　　　　　　2h40m　　　　　　2h36m

Table 19　　　　LOGARITHMIC FUNCTIONS

	51°					52°					53°						
′	Cos.	D.	Sec.	Tan.	D.	Cos.	D.	Sec.	Tan.	D.	Cos.	D.	Sec.	Tan.	D.		
	I̅. [9]		0.	0.		I̅. [9]		0.	0.		I̅. [9]		0.	0.			
0	79887	16	20113	09163	26	78934	16	21066	10719	26	77946	17	22054	12289	27	60	60
1	79872	15	20128	09189	26	78918	16	21082	10745	26	77930	16	22070	12315	26	59	56
2	79856	16	20144	09215	26	78902	16	21098	10771	26	77913	17	22087	12341	26	58	52
3	79840	16	20160	09241	26	78886	16	21114	10797	26	77896	17	22104	12367	27	57	48
4	79825	15	20175	09266	25	78869	17	21131	10823	26	77879	17	22121	12394	27	56	44
5	79809	16	20191	09292	26	78853	16	21147	10849	26	77862	17	22138	12420	26	55	40
6	79793	16	20207	09318	26	78837	16	21163	10875	26	77846	16	22154	12446	26	54	36
7	79778	15	20222	09344	26	78821	16	21179	10901	26	77829	17	22171	12473	27	53	32
8	79762	16	20238	09370	26	78805	16	21195	10927	26	77812	17	22188	12499	26	52	28
9	79746	16	20254	09396	26	78788	17	21212	10954	27	77795	17	22205	12525	26	51	24
10	79731	15	20269	09422	26	78772	16	21228	10980	26	77778	17	22222	12552	27	50	20
11	79715	16	20285	09447	25	78756	16	21244	11006	26	77761	17	22239	12578	26	49	16
12	79699	16	20301	09473	26	78739	17	21261	11032	26	77744	17	22256	12604	26	48	12
13	79684	15	20316	09499	26	78723	16	21277	11058	26	77728	16	22272	12631	27	47	8
14	79668	16	20332	09525	26	78707	16	21293	11084	26	77711	17	22289	12657	26	46	4
15	79652	16	20348	09551	26	78691	16	21309	11110	26	77694	17	22306	12683	26	45	+ 3m
16	79636	15	20364	09577	26	78674	17	21326	11136	26	77677	17	22323	12710	27	44	56
17	79621	15	20379	09603	26	78658	16	21342	11162	26	77660	17	22340	12736	26	43	52
18	79605	16	20395	09629	26	78642	16	21358	11188	26	77643	17	22357	12762	27	42	48
19	79589	16	20411	09654	25	78625	17	21375	11214	26	77626	17	22374	12789	26	41	44
20	79573	16	20427	09680	26	78609	16	21391	11241	27	77609	17	22391	12815	26	40	40
21	79558	15	20442	09706	26	78592	17	21408	11267	26	77592	17	22408	12842	27	39	36
22	79542	16	20458	09732	26	78576	16	21424	11293	26	77575	17	22425	12868	26	38	32
23	79526	16	20474	09758	26	78560	16	21440	11319	26	77558	17	22442	12894	26	37	28
24	79510	16	20490	09784	26	78543	17	21457	11345	26	77541	17	22459	12921	27	36	24
25	79494	16	20506	09810	26	78527	16	21473	11371	26	77524	17	22476	12947	26	35	20
26	79478	16	20522	09836	26	78510	17	21490	11397	26	77507	17	22493	12973	26	34	16
27	79463	15	20537	09862	26	78494	16	21506	11423	26	77490	17	22510	13000	27	33	12
28	79447	16	20553	09888	26	78478	16	21522	11450	27	77473	17	22527	13026	26	32	8
29	79431	16	20569	09914	26	78461	17	21539	11476	26	77456	17	22544	13053	27	31	4
30	79415	16	20585	09939	25	78445	16	21555	11502	26	77439	17	22561	13079	26	30	+ 2m
31	79399	16	20601	09965	26	78428	17	21572	11528	26	77422	17	22578	13106	27	29	56
32	79383	16	20617	09991	26	78412	16	21588	11554	26	77405	17	22595	13132	26	28	52
33	79367	16	20633	10017	26	78395	17	21605	11580	26	77387	18	22613	13158	26	27	48
34	79351	16	20649	10043	26	78379	16	21621	11607	27	77370	17	22630	13185	27	26	44
35	79335	16	20665	10069	26	78362	17	21638	11633	26	77353	17	22647	13211	26	25	40
36	79319	16	20681	10095	26	78346	16	21654	11659	26	77336	17	22664	13238	27	24	36
37	79304	15	20696	10121	26	78329	17	21671	11685	26	77319	17	22681	13264	26	23	32
38	79288	16	20712	10147	26	78313	16	21687	11711	26	77302	17	22698	13291	27	22	28
39	79272	16	20728	10173	26	78296	17	21704	11738	27	77285	17	22715	13317	26	21	24
40	79256	16	20744	10199	26	78280	16	21720	11764	26	77268	17	22732	13344	27	20	20
41	79240	16	20760	10225	26	78263	17	21737	11790	26	77250	18	22750	13370	26	19	16
42	79224	16	20776	10251	26	78246	17	21754	11816	26	77233	17	22767	13397	27	18	12
43	79208	16	20792	10277	26	78230	16	21770	11842	26	77216	17	22784	13423	26	17	8
44	79192	16	20808	10303	26	78213	17	21787	11869	27	77199	17	22801	13449	26	16	4
45	79176	16	20824	10329	26	78197	16	21803	11895	26	77181	18	22819	13476	27	15	+ 1m
46	79160	16	20840	10355	26	78180	17	21820	11921	26	77164	17	22836	13502	26	14	56
47	79144	16	20856	10381	26	78163	17	21837	11947	26	77147	17	22853	13529	27	13	52
48	79128	16	20872	10407	26	78147	16	21853	11973	26	77130	17	22870	13555	26	12	48
49	79111	17	20889	10433	26	78130	17	21870	12000	27	77112	18	22888	13582	26	11	44
50	79095	16	20905	10459	26	78113	17	21887	12026	26	77095	17	22905	13608	26	10	40
51	79079	16	20921	10485	26	78097	16	21903	12052	26	77078	17	22922	13635	27	9	36
52	79063	16	20937	10511	26	78080	17	21920	12078	26	77061	17	22939	13662	27	8	32
53	79047	16	20953	10537	26	78063	17	21937	12105	26	77043	18	22957	13688	26	7	28
54	79031	16	20969	10563	26	78047	16	21953	12131	26	77026	17	22974	13715	27	6	24
55	79015	16	20985	10589	26	78030	17	21970	12157	26	77009	17	22991	13741	26	5	20
56	78999	16	21001	10615	26	78013	17	21987	12183	26	76991	18	23009	13768	26	4	16
57	78983	16	21017	10641	26	77997	16	22003	12210	26	76974	17	23026	13794	27	3	12
58	78967	16	21033	10667	26	77980	17	22020	12236	26	76957	17	23043	13821	26	2	8
59	78950	17	21050	10693	26	77963	17	22037	12262	26	76939	18	23061	13847	27	1	4
60	78934	16	21066	10719	26	77946	17	22054	12289	27	76922	17	23078	13874	27	0	
	I̅. [9]		0.	0.		I̅. [9]		0.	0.		I̅. [9]		0.	0.			
	Sin.	D.	Cosec.	Cot.	D.	Sin.	D.	Cosec.	Cot.	D.	Sin.	D.	Cosec.	Cot.	D.	′	Secs.
				38°					**37°**					**36°**			

Table 19 — LOGARITHMIC FUNCTIONS

54° — 55° — 56°

′	Cos.	D.	Sec.	Tan.	D.	Cos.	D.	Sec.	Tan.	D.	Cos.	D.	Sec.	Tan.	D.	′	Secs.
	Ī. [9]		0.	0.		Ī. [9]		0.	0.		Ī. [19]		0.	0.			
0	76922	17	23078	13874	27	75859	18	24141	15477	27	74756	19	25244	17101	27	60	60
1	76904	18	23096	13900	26	75841	18	24159	15504	27	74737	19	25263	17129	28	59	56
2	76887	17	23113	13927	27	75823	18	24177	15531	27	74719	18	25281	17156	27	58	52
3	76870	17	23130	13954	27	75805	18	24195	15558	27	74700	19	25300	17183	27	57	48
4	76852	18	23148	13980	26	75787	18	24213	15585	27	74681	19	25319	17210	28	56	44
5	76835	17	23165	14007	27	75769	18	24231	15612	27	74662	18	25338	17238	28	55	40
6	76817	18	23183	14033	26	75751	18	24249	15639	27	74644	18	25356	17265	27	54	36
7	76800	17	23200	14060	27	75733	18	24267	15666	27	74625	19	25375	17292	27	53	32
8	76782	18	23218	14087	27	75714	19	24286	15693	27	74606	19	25394	17319	28	52	28
9	76765	17	23235	14113	26	75696	18	24304	15720	27	74587	19	25413	17347	28	51	24
10	76747	18	23253	14140	27	75678	18	24322	15746	26	74568	19	25432	17374	27	50	20
11	76730	17	23270	14166	26	75660	18	24340	15773	27	74549	19	25451	17401	27	49	16
12	76712	18	23288	14193	27	75642	18	24358	15800	27	74531	18	25469	17429	28	48	12
13	76695	17	23305	14220	27	75624	18	24376	15827	27	74512	19	25488	17456	27	47	8
14	76677	18	23323	14246	27	75605	19	24395	15854	27	74493	19	25507	17483	27	46	4
15	76660	17	23340	14273	27	75587	18	24413	15881	27	74474	19	25526	17511	27	45	+3m
16	76642	17	23358	14300	27	75569	18	24431	15908	27	74455	19	25545	17538	27	44	56
17	76625	17	23375	14326	26	75551	18	24449	15935	27	74436	19	25564	17565	27	43	52
18	76607	18	23393	14353	27	75533	18	24467	15962	27	74417	19	25583	17593	28	42	48
19	76590	17	23410	14380	27	75514	19	24486	15989	27	74398	19	25602	17620	27	41	44
20	76572	18	23428	14406	26	75496	18	24504	16016	27	74379	19	25621	17648	28	40	40
21	76554	18	23446	14433	27	75478	18	24522	16043	27	74360	19	25640	17675	27	39	36
22	76537	17	23463	14460	27	75459	19	24541	16070	27	74341	19	25659	17702	27	38	32
23	76519	18	23481	14486	26	75441	18	24559	16097	27	74322	19	25678	17730	28	37	28
24	76501	18	23499	14513	27	75423	18	24577	16124	27	74303	19	25697	17757	27	36	24
25	76484	17	23516	14540	27	75405	19	24595	16151	27	74284	19	25716	17785	28	35	20
26	76466	18	23534	14566	26	75386	18	24614	16178	27	74265	19	25735	17812	27	34	16
27	76448	18	23552	14593	27	75368	18	24632	16205	27	74246	19	25754	17839	28	33	12
28	76431	17	23569	14620	27	75350	18	24650	16232	27	74227	19	25773	17867	28	32	8
29	76413	18	23587	14646	26	75331	19	24669	16260	28	74208	19	25792	17894	27	31	4
30	76395	18	23605	14673	27	75313	18	24687	16287	27	74189	19	25811	17922	28	30	+2m
31	76378	17	23622	14700	27	75294	19	24706	16314	27	74170	19	25830	17949	27	29	56
32	76360	18	23640	14727	27	75276	18	24724	16341	27	74151	19	25849	17977	28	28	52
33	76342	18	23658	14753	26	75258	18	24742	16368	27	74132	19	25868	18004	27	27	48
34	76324	18	23676	14780	27	75239	19	24761	16395	27	74113	19	25887	18032	27	26	44
35	76307	17	23693	14807	27	75221	18	24779	16422	27	74093	20	25907	18059	27	25	40
36	76289	18	23711	14834	27	75202	19	24798	16449	27	74074	19	25926	18087	28	24	36
37	76271	18	23729	14860	26	75184	19	24816	16476	27	74055	19	25945	18114	27	23	32
38	76253	18	23747	14887	27	75165	19	24835	16503	27	74036	19	25964	18142	27	22	28
39	76236	17	23764	14914	27	75147	18	24853	16530	27	74017	19	25983	18169	27	21	24
40	76218	18	23782	14941	27	75128	19	24872	16558	28	73997	20	26003	18197	28	20	20
41	76200	18	23800	14967	26	75110	18	24890	16585	27	73978	19	26022	18224	27	19	16
42	76182	18	23818	14994	27	75091	19	24909	16612	27	73959	19	26041	18252	28	18	12
43	76164	18	23836	15021	27	75073	18	24927	16639	27	73940	19	26060	18279	27	17	8
44	76146	18	23854	15048	27	75054	19	24946	16666	27	73921	19	26079	18307	28	16	4
45	76129	17	23871	15075	27	75036	18	24964	16693	27	73901	20	26099	18334	28	15	+1m
46	76111	18	23889	15101	26	75017	19	24983	16720	27	73882	19	26118	18362	28	14	56
47	76093	18	23907	15128	27	74999	18	25001	16748	28	73863	19	26137	18389	27	13	52
48	76075	18	23925	15155	27	74980	19	25020	16775	27	73843	20	26157	18417	27	12	48
49	76057	18	23943	15182	27	74961	19	25039	16802	27	73824	19	26176	18444	28	11	44
50	76039	18	23961	15209	27	74943	18	25057	16829	27	73805	19	26195	18472	28	10	40
51	76021	18	23979	15236	27	74924	19	25076	16856	27	73785	20	26215	18500	28	9	36
52	76003	18	23997	15262	26	74906	18	25094	16883	27	73766	19	26234	18527	27	8	32
53	75985	18	24015	15289	27	74887	19	25113	16911	28	73747	19	26253	18555	28	7	28
54	75967	18	24033	15316	27	74868	18	25132	16938	27	73727	20	26273	18582	27	6	24
55	75949	18	24051	15343	27	74850	18	25150	16965	27	73708	19	26292	18610	28	5	20
56	75931	18	24069	15370	27	74831	19	25169	16992	27	73689	19	26311	18638	27	4	16
57	75913	18	24087	15397	27	74812	19	25188	17020	28	73659	20	26331	18665	27	3	12
58	75895	18	24105	15424	27	74794	18	25206	17047	27	73650	19	26350	18693	28	2	8
59	75877	18	24123	15450	26	74775	19	25225	17074	27	73630	20	26370	18721	28	1	4
60	75859	18	24141	15477	27	74756	19	25244	17101	27	73611	19	26389	18748	27	0	0
	Ī. [9]		0.	0.		Ī. [9]		0.	0.		Ī. [9]		0.	0.			

	Sin.	D.	Cosec.	Cot.	D.	Sin.	D.	Cosec.	Cot.	D.	Sin.	D.	Cosec.	Cot.	D.	′	Secs.
				35°					**34°**					**33°**			

2h 20m   2h 16m   2h 12m

Table 19

LOGARITHMIC FUNCTIONS

	57°					58°					59°						
'	**Cos.**	**D.**	**Sec.**	**Tan.**	**D.**	**Cos.**	**D.**	**Sec.**	**Tan.**	**D.**	**Cos.**	**D.**	**Sec.**	**Tan.**	**D.**		
	Ī. [9]		0.	0.		Ī. [9]		0.	0.		Ī. [9]		0.	0.			
0	73611	19	26389	18748	27	72421	20	27579	20421	28	71184	21	28816	22123	29	60	60
1	73591	20	26409	18776	28	72401	20	27599	20449	28	71163	21	28837	22151	28	59	56
2	73572	19	26428	18804	27	72381	20	27619	20477	28	71142	21	28858	22180	29	58	52
3	73552	20	26448	18831	27	72360	21	27640	20505	28	71121	21	28879	22209	28	57	48
4	73533	19	26467	18859	28	72340	20	27660	20534	29	71100	21	28900	22237	28	56	44
5	73513	20	26487	18887	28	72320	20	27680	20562	28	71079	21	28921	22266	29	55	40
6	73494	19	26506	18914	27	72299	21	27701	20590	28	71058	21	28942	22294	29	54	36
7	73474	20	26526	18942	28	72279	20	27721	20618	28	71036	22	28964	22323	29	53	32
8	73455	19	26545	18970	28	72259	20	27741	20646	28	71015	21	28985	22352	29	52	28
9	73435	20	26565	18997	27	72238	21	27762	20674	28	70994	21	29006	22381	28	51	24
10	73416	19	26584	19025	28	72218	20	27782	20703	29	70973	21	29027	22409	28	50	50
11	73396	20	26604	19053	28	72198	20	27802	20731	28	70952	21	29048	22438	29	49	16
12	73377	19	26623	19081	28	72177	21	27823	20759	28	70931	21	29069	22467	28	48	12
13	73357	20	26643	19108	27	72157	20	27843	20787	28	70909	22	29091	22495	29	47	8
14	73337	20	26663	19136	28	72137	20	27863	20815	28	70888	21	29112	22524	29	46	4
15	73318	19	26682	19164	28	72116	21	27884	20844	29	70867	21	29133	22553	29	45	+ 3m
16	73298	20	26702	19192	27	72096	20	27904	20872	28	70846	21	29154	22582	29	44	56
17	73278	20	26722	19219	28	72075	21	27925	20900	28	70824	22	29176	22610	29	43	52
18	73259	19	26741	19247	28	72055	20	27945	20928	29	70803	21	29197	22639	29	42	48
19	73239	20	26761	19275	28	72034	21	27966	20957	29	70782	21	29218	22668	29	41	44
20	73219	20	26781	19303	28	72014	20	27986	20985	28	70761	21	29239	22697	29	40	40
21	73200	19	26800	19331	28	71994	20	28006	21013	28	70739	22	29261	22726	29	39	36
22	73180	20	26820	19358	27	71973	21	28027	21041	28	70718	21	29282	22754	28	38	32
23	73160	20	26840	19386	28	71952	21	28048	21070	29	70697	21	29303	22783	29	37	28
24	73140	20	26860	19414	28	71932	20	28068	21098	28	70675	22	29325	22812	29	36	24
25	73121	19	26879	19442	28	71911	21	28089	21126	28	70654	21	29346	22841	29	35	20
26	73101	20	26899	19470	28	71891	20	28109	21155	29	70633	21	29367	22870	29	34	16
27	73081	20	26919	19498	28	71870	21	28130	21183	28	70611	22	29389	22899	29	33	12
28	73061	20	26939	19526	28	71850	20	28150	21211	28	70590	21	29410	22927	28	32	8
29	73041	20	26959	19553	27	71829	21	28171	21240	29	70568	22	29432	22956	29	31	4
30	73022	19	26978	19581	28	71809	20	28191	21268	28	70547	21	29453	22985	29	30	+ 2m
31	73002	20	26998	19609	28	71788	21	28212	21296	28	70525	22	29475	23014	29	29	56
32	72982	20	27018	19637	28	71767	21	28233	21325	29	70504	21	29496	23043	29	28	52
33	72962	20	27038	19665	28	71747	21	28253	21353	28	70482	22	29518	23072	29	27	48
34	72942	20	27058	19693	28	71726	21	28274	21382	29	70461	21	29539	23101	29	26	44
35	72922	20	27078	19721	28	71705	21	28295	21410	28	70439	22	29561	23130	29	25	40
36	72902	20	27098	19749	28	71685	20	28315	21438	29	70418	21	29582	23159	29	24	36
37	72883	19	27117	19777	28	71664	21	28336	21467	29	70396	22	29604	23188	29	23	32
38	72863	20	27137	19805	28	71643	21	28357	21495	28	70375	21	29625	23217	29	22	28
39	72843	20	27157	19832	27	71622	21	28378	21524	29	70353	22	29647	23246	29	21	24
40	72823	20	27177	19860	28	71602	20	28398	21552	29	70332	21	29668	23275	29	20	20
41	72803	20	27197	19888	28	71581	21	28419	21581	29	70310	22	29690	23303	28	19	16
42	72783	20	27217	19916	28	71560	21	28440	21609	28	70288	22	29712	23332	29	18	12
43	72763	20	27237	19944	28	71539	21	28461	21637	29	70267	21	29733	23361	29	17	8
44	72743	20	27257	19972	28	71519	20	28481	21666	28	70245	21	29755	23391	30	16	4
45	72723	20	27277	20000	28	71498	21	28502	21694	28	70224	21	29776	23420	29	15	+ 1m
46	72703	20	27297	20028	28	71477	21	28523	21723	29	70202	22	29798	23449	29	14	56
47	72683	20	27317	20056	28	71456	21	28544	21751	28	70180	21	29820	23478	29	13	52
48	72663	20	27337	20084	28	71435	21	28565	21780	28	70159	21	29841	23507	29	12	48
49	72643	20	27357	20112	28	71414	21	28586	21808	28	70137	22	29863	23536	29	11	44
50	72622	21	27378	20140	28	71393	21	28607	21837	29	70115	22	29885	23565	29	10	40
51	72602	20	27398	20168	28	71373	20	28627	21865	28	70093	22	29907	23594	29	9	36
52	72582	20	27418	20196	28	71352	21	28648	21894	29	70072	21	29928	23623	29	8	32
53	72562	20	27438	20224	28	71331	21	28669	21923	28	70050	22	29950	23652	29	7	28
54	72542	20	27458	20253	29	71310	21	28690	21951	28	70028	22	29972	23681	29	6	24
55	72522	20	27478	20281	28	71289	21	28711	21980	29	70006	22	29994	23710	29	5	20
56	72502	20	27498	20309	28	71268	21	28732	22008	29	69984	21	30016	23739	29	4	16
57	72482	20	27518	20337	28	71247	21	28753	22037	29	69963	21	30037	23769	30	3	12
58	72461	21	27539	20365	28	71226	21	28774	22065	28	69941	22	30059	23798	29	2	8
59	72441	20	27559	20393	28	71205	21	28795	22094	29	69919	22	30081	23827	29	1	4
60	72421	20	27579	20421	28	71184	21	28816	22123	29	69897	22	30103	23856	29	0	0
	Ī. [9]		0.	0.		Ī. [9]		0.	0.		Ī. [9]		0.	0.			
	Sin.	**D.**	**Cosec.**	**Cot.**	**D.**	**Sin.**	**D.**	**Cosec.**	**Cot.**	**D.**	**Sin.**	**D.**	**Cosec.**	**Cot.**	**D.**	**'**	Secs

32°	31°	30°
2ʰ08m	2ʰ04m	2ʰ00m

Table 19 LOGARITHMIC FUNCTIONS

	60°					61°					62°						
′	Cos.	D.	Sec.	Tan.	D.	Cos.	D.	Sec.	Tan.	D.	Cos.	D.	Sec.	Tan.	D.		
	Ī. [9]		0.	0.		Ī. [9]		0.	0.		Ī. [9]		0.	0.			
0	69897	22	30103	23856	29	68557	23	31443	25625	30	67161	24	32839	27433	31	60	60
1	69875	22	30125	23885	29	68534	23	31466	25655	30	67137	24	32863	27463	30	59	56
2	69853	22	30147	23914	29	68512	22	31488	25684	30	67113	24	32887	27494	31	58	52
3	69831	22	30169	23944	30	68489	23	31511	25714	30	67090	23	32910	27524	30	57	48
4	69809	22	30191	23973	29	68466	23	31534	25744	30	67066	24	32934	27555	30	56	44
5	69787	22	30213	24002	29	68443	23	31557	25774	30	67042	24	32958	27585	30	55	40
6	69765	22	30235	24031	29	68420	23	31580	25804	30	67018	24	32982	27616	31	54	36
7	69743	22	30257	24061	29	68397	23	31603	25834	30	66994	24	33006	27646	30	53	32
8	69721	22	30279	24090	29	68374	23	31626	25863	29	66970	24	33030	27677	30	52	28
9	69699	22	30301	24119	29	68351	23	31649	25893	30	66946	24	33054	27707	30	51	24
10	69677	22	30323	24148	29	68328	23	31672	25923	30	66922	24	33078	27738	31	50	20
11	69655	22	30345	24178	30	68305	23	31695	25953	30	66899	23	33101	27769	31	49	16
12	69633	22	30367	24207	29	68283	22	31717	25983	30	66875	24	33125	27799	30	48	12
13	69611	22	30389	24236	29	68260	23	31740	26013	30	66851	24	33149	27830	31	47	8
14	69589	22	30411	24265	29	68237	23	31763	26043	30	66827	24	33173	27860	30	46	4
15	69567	22	30433	24295	30	68213	24	31787	26073	30	66803	24	33197	27891	31	45	+3m
16	69545	22	30455	24324	29	68190	23	31810	26103	30	66779	24	33221	27922	31	44	56
17	69523	22	30477	24353	29	68167	23	31833	26133	30	66755	24	33245	27952	30	43	52
18	69501	22	30499	24383	30	68144	23	31856	26163	30	66731	24	33269	27983	31	42	48
19	69479	22	30521	24412	29	68121	23	31879	26193	30	66706	25	33294	28014	31	41	44
20	69456	23	30544	24442	30	68098	23	31902	26223	30	66682	24	33318	28045	31	40	40
21	69434	22	30566	24471	29	68075	23	31925	26253	30	66658	24	33342	28075	30	39	36
22	69412	22	30588	24500	29	68052	23	31948	26283	30	66634	24	33366	28106	31	38	32
23	69390	22	30610	24530	30	68029	23	31971	26313	30	66610	24	33390	28137	31	37	28
24	69368	22	30632	24559	29	68006	23	31994	26343	30	66586	24	33414	28167	30	36	24
25	69345	23	30655	24589	30	67982	24	32018	26373	30	66562	25	33438	28198	31	35	20
26	69323	22	30677	24618	29	67959	23	32041	26403	30	66537	25	33463	28229	31	34	16
27	69301	22	30699	24647	29	67936	23	32064	26433	30	66513	24	33487	28260	31	33	12
28	69279	22	30721	24677	30	67913	23	32087	26463	30	66489	24	33511	28291	31	32	8
29	69256	23	30744	24706	29	67890	23	32110	26493	30	66465	24	33535	28321	30	31	4
30	69234	22	30766	24736	30	67866	24	32134	26524	31	66441	24	33559	28352	31	30	+2m
31	69212	22	30788	24765	29	67843	23	32157	26554	30	66416	25	33584	28383	31	29	56
32	69189	23	30811	24795	30	67820	23	32180	26584	30	66392	24	33608	28414	31	28	52
33	69167	23	30833	24824	29	67796	24	32204	26614	30	66368	24	33632	28445	31	27	48
34	69144	23	30856	24854	29	67773	23	32227	26644	30	66343	25	33657	28476	31	26	44
35	69122	22	30878	24883	29	67750	23	32250	26674	31	66319	24	33681	28507	31	25	40
36	69100	22	30900	24913	30	67726	24	32274	26705	30	66295	24	33705	28538	31	24	36
37	69077	23	30923	24942	29	67703	23	32297	26735	30	66270	24	33730	28569	31	23	32
38	69055	22	30945	24972	30	67680	23	32320	26765	30	66246	24	33754	28599	30	22	28
39	69032	23	30968	25002	30	67656	24	32344	26795	30	66221	25	33779	28630	31	21	24
40	69010	22	30990	25031	29	67633	23	32367	26825	30	66197	24	33803	28661	31	20	20
41	68987	23	31013	25061	30	67609	24	32391	26856	31	66173	24	33827	28692	31	19	16
42	68965	22	31035	25090	29	67586	23	32414	26886	30	66148	25	33852	28723	31	18	12
43	68942	23	31058	25120	30	67562	24	32438	26916	30	66124	24	33876	28754	31	17	8
44	68920	22	31080	25149	29	67539	23	32461	26946	30	66099	25	33901	28785	31	16	4
45	68897	23	31103	25179	30	67515	24	32485	26977	31	66075	24	33925	28816	31	15	+1m
46	68875	22	31125	25209	29	67492	24	32508	27007	30	66050	24	33950	28847	31	14	56
47	68852	23	31148	25238	29	67468	24	32532	27037	30	66025	24	33975	28879	32	13	52
48	68829	23	31171	25268	30	67445	23	32555	27068	31	66001	24	33999	28910	31	12	48
49	68807	22	31193	25298	30	67421	24	32579	27098	30	65976	24	34024	28941	31	11	44
50	68784	23	31216	25327	29	67398	23	32602	27128	30	65952	24	34048	28972	31	10	40
51	68762	22	31238	25357	30	67374	24	32626	27159	31	65927	25	34073	29003	31	9	36
52	68739	23	31261	25387	30	67350	23	32650	27189	30	65902	25	34098	29034	31	8	32
53	68716	23	31284	25417	29	67327	23	32673	27220	31	65878	24	34122	29065	31	7	28
54	68694	22	31306	25446	29	67303	24	32697	27250	30	65853	25	34147	29096	31	6	24
55	68671	23	31329	25476	30	67280	23	32720	27280	30	65828	25	34172	29127	31	5	20
56	68648	23	31352	25506	30	67256	24	32744	27311	31	65804	24	34196	29159	32	4	16
57	68625	23	31375	25535	29	67232	24	32768	27341	30	65779	25	34221	29190	31	3	12
58	68603	22	31397	25565	30	67208	24	32792	27372	31	65754	25	34246	29221	31	2	8
59	68580	23	31420	25595	30	67185	23	32815	27402	30	65729	25	34271	29252	31	1	4
60	68557	23	31443	25625	30	67161	24	32839	27433	31	65705	24	34295	29283	31	0	0
	Ī. [9]		0.	0.		Ī. [9]		0.	0.		Ī. [9]		0.	0.			
	Sin.	D.	Cosec.	Cot.	D.	Sin.	D.	Cosec.	Cot.	D.	Sin.	D.	Cosec.	Cot.	D.	′	Secs.
				29°					28°					27°			

1h56m   1h52m   1h48m

Table 19 — LOGARITHMIC FUNCTIONS

′	**63°** Cos.	D.	Sec.	Tan.	D.	**64°** Cos.	D.	Sec.	Tan.	D.	**65°** Cos.	D.	Sec.	Tan.	D.		
	Ī.[9]		0.	0.		Ī.[9]		0.	0.		Ī.[9]		0.	0.			
0	65705	24	34295	29283	31	64184	26	35816	31182	32	62595	27	37405	33133	33	60	60
1	65680	25	34320	29315	32	64158	26	35842	31214	32	62568	27	37432	33166	33	59	56
2	65655	25	34345	29346	31	64132	26	35868	31246	32	62541	27	37459	33199	33	58	52
3	65630	25	34370	29377	31	64106	26	35894	31278	32	62513	28	37487	33232	33	57	48
4	65605	25	34395	29408	32	64080	26	35920	31310	32	62486	27	37514	33265	33	56	44
5	65580	25	34420	29440	32	64054	26	35946	31342	32	62459	27	37541	33298	33	55	40
6	65556	24	34444	29471	31	64028	26	35972	31374	32	62432	27	37568	33331	33	54	36
7	65531	25	34469	29502	31	64002	26	35998	31407	33	62405	27	37595	33364	33	53	32
8	65506	25	34494	29534	32	63976	26	36024	31439	32	62377	28	37623	33397	33	52	28
9	65481	25	34519	29565	31	63950	26	36050	31471	32	62350	27	37650	33430	33	51	24
10	65456	25	34544	29596	31	63924	26	36076	31503	32	62323	27	37677	33463	33	50	20
11	65431	25	34569	29628	32	63898	26	36102	31535	32	62296	27	37704	33497	34	49	16
12	65406	25	34594	29659	31	63872	26	36128	31568	33	62268	28	37732	33530	33	48	12
13	65381	25	34619	29691	32	63846	26	36154	31600	32	62241	27	37759	33563	33	47	8
14	65356	25	34644	29722	31	63820	26	36180	31632	32	62214	27	37786	33596	33	46	4
15	65331	25	34669	29753	31	63794	26	36206	31664	32	62186	28	37814	33629	33	45	+3m
16	65306	25	34694	29785	32	63767	27	36233	31697	33	62159	28	37841	33663	34	44	56
17	65281	25	34719	29816	31	63741	26	36259	31729	32	62131	28	37869	33696	33	43	52
18	65255	26	34745	29848	32	63715	26	36285	31761	33	62104	27	37896	33729	33	42	48
19	65230	25	34770	29879	31	63689	26	36311	31794	33	62076	28	37924	33762	33	41	44
20	65205	25	34795	29911	32	63662	27	36338	31826	32	62049	27	37951	33796	34	40	40
21	65180	25	34820	29942	31	63636	26	36364	31858	32	62021	28	37979	33829	33	39	36
22	65155	25	34845	29974	32	63610	26	36390	31891	33	61994	27	38006	33862	33	38	32
23	65130	25	34870	30005	31	63583	27	36417	31923	32	61966	28	38034	33896	34	37	28
24	65104	26	34896	30037	32	63557	26	36443	31956	33	61939	27	38061	33929	33	36	24
25	65079	25	34921	30068	31	63531	26	36469	31988	32	61911	28	38089	33962	33	35	20
26	65054	25	34946	30100	32	63504	27	36496	32020	33	61883	28	38117	33996	34	34	16
27	65029	25	34971	30132	32	63478	26	36522	32053	33	61856	28	38144	34029	33	33	12
28	65003	26	34997	30163	31	63451	27	36549	32085	32	61828	28	38172	34063	34	32	8
29	64978	25	35022	30195	32	63425	26	36575	32118	33	61800	28	38200	34096	33	31	4
30	64953	25	35047	30226	31	63398	27	36602	32150	32	61773	27	38227	34130	34	30	+2m
31	64927	26	35073	30258	32	63372	26	36628	32183	33	61745	28	38255	34163	33	29	56
32	64902	25	35098	30290	32	63345	27	36655	32215	32	61717	28	38283	34197	34	28	52
33	64877	25	35123	30321	31	63319	26	36681	32248	33	61689	28	38311	34230	33	27	48
34	64851	26	35149	30353	32	63292	27	36708	32281	32	61662	27	38338	34264	34	26	44
35	64826	25	35174	30385	32	63266	26	36734	32313	32	61634	28	38366	34297	34	25	40
36	64800	26	35200	30416	31	63239	27	36761	32346	33	61606	28	38394	34331	34	24	36
37	64775	25	35225	30448	32	63213	26	36787	32378	32	61578	28	38422	34364	34	23	32
38	64749	26	35251	30480	32	63186	27	36814	32411	33	61550	28	38450	34398	34	22	28
39	64724	25	35276	30512	32	63159	27	36841	32444	33	61522	28	38478	34432	34	21	24
40	64698	26	35302	30543	31	63133	26	36867	32476	32	61494	28	38506	34465	33	20	20
41	64673	25	35327	30575	32	63106	27	36894	32509	33	61466	28	38534	34499	34	19	16
42	64647	26	35353	30607	32	63079	27	36921	32542	32	61438	28	38562	34533	34	18	12
43	64622	25	35378	30639	32	63052	27	36948	32574	32	61411	27	38589	34566	33	17	8
44	64596	26	35404	30671	32	63026	26	36974	32607	33	61382	29	38618	34600	34	16	4
45	64571	26	35429	30702	31	62999	27	37001	32640	33	61354	28	38646	34634	34	15	+1m
46	64545	26	35455	30734	32	62972	27	37028	32673	33	61326	28	38674	34667	33	14	56
47	64519	26	35481	30766	32	62945	27	37055	32705	32	61298	28	38702	34701	34	13	52
48	64494	25	35506	30798	32	62918	27	37082	32738	33	61270	28	38730	34735	34	12	48
49	64468	26	35532	30830	32	62892	26	37108	32771	33	61242	28	38758	34769	34	11	44
50	64442	26	35558	30862	32	62865	27	37135	32804	33	61214	28	38786	34803	34	10	40
51	64417	25	35583	30894	32	62838	27	37162	32837	33	61186	28	38814	34836	33	9	36
52	64391	26	35609	30926	32	62811	27	37189	32869	32	61158	28	38842	34870	34	8	32
53	64365	26	35635	30958	32	62784	27	37216	32902	33	61129	29	38871	34904	34	7	28
54	64339	26	35661	30990	32	62757	27	37243	32935	33	61101	28	38899	34938	34	6	24
55	64313	25	35687	31022	32	62730	27	37270	32968	33	61073	28	38927	34972	34	5	20
56	64288	25	35712	31054	32	62703	27	37297	33001	33	61045	28	38955	35006	34	4	16
57	64262	26	35738	31086	32	62676	27	37324	33034	33	61016	29	38984	35040	34	3	12
58	64236	26	35764	31118	32	62649	27	37351	33067	33	60988	28	39012	35074	34	2	8
59	64210	26	35790	31150	32	62622	27	37378	33100	33	60960	28	39040	35108	34	1	4
60	64184	26	35816	31182	32	62595	27	37405	33133	33	60931	29	39069	35142	34	0	
	Ī.[9]		0.	0.		Ī.[9]		0.	0.		Ī.[9]		0.	0.			
	Sin.	D.	Cosec.	Cot.	D.	Sin.	D.	Cosec.	Cot.	D.	Sin.	D.	Cosec.	Cot.	D.	′	Secs.
	26°					**25°**					**24°**						

Table 19   LOGARITHMIC FUNCTIONS

66°   67°   68°

′	Cos.	D.	Sec.	Tan.	D.	Cos.	D.	Sec.	Tan.	D.	Cos.	D.	Sec.	Tan.	D.		
	Ī. [9]		0.	0.		Ī. [9]		0.	0.		Ī. [9]		0.	0.			
0	60931	29	39069	35142	34	59188	30	40812	37215	35	57358	31	42642	39359	36	60	60
1	60903	28	39097	35176	34	59158	30	40842	37250	35	57326	32	42674	39395	36	59	56
2	60875	28	39125	35210	34	59128	30	40872	37285	35	57295	31	42705	39432	37	58	52
3	60846	29	39154	35244	34	59098	30	40902	37320	35	57264	31	42736	39468	37	57	48
4	60818	28	39182	35278	34	59069	29	40931	37355	35	57232	32	42768	39505	37	56	44
5	60789	29	39211	35312	34	59039	30	40961	37391	36	57201	31	42799	39541	36	55	40
6	60761	29	39239	35346	34	59009	30	40991	37426	35	57169	32	42831	39578	37	54	36
7	60732	29	39268	35380	34	58979	30	41021	37461	35	57138	31	42862	39614	37	53	32
8	60704	28	39296	35414	34	58949	30	41051	37496	36	57107	31	42893	39651	37	52	28
9	60675	29	39325	35448	34	58919	30	41081	37532	36	57075	32	42925	39687	36	51	24
10	60646	29	39354	35483	35	58889	30	41111	37567	35	57044	31	42956	39724	37	50	20
11	60618	28	39382	35517	34	58859	30	41141	37602	35	57012	32	42988	39760	36	49	16
12	60589	29	39411	35551	34	58829	30	41171	37638	36	56980	32	43020	39797	37	48	12
13	60561	28	39439	35585	34	58799	30	41201	37673	35	56949	31	43051	39834	37	47	8
14	60532	29	39468	35619	34	58769	30	41231	37708	36	56917	32	43083	39870	36	46	4
15	60503	29	39497	35654	35	58739	30	41261	37744	36	56886	31	43114	39907	37	45	+3m
16	60474	29	39526	35688	34	58709	30	41291	37779	35	56854	32	43146	39944	37	44	56
17	60446	28	39554	35722	34	58678	31	41322	37815	36	56822	32	43178	39981	37	43	52
18	60417	29	39583	35757	35	58648	30	41352	37850	36	56790	32	43210	40017	36	42	48
19	60388	29	39612	35791	34	58618	30	41382	37886	35	56759	31	43241	40054	37	41	44
20	60359	29	39641	35825	34	58588	30	41412	37921	35	56727	32	43273	40091	37	40	40
21	60331	28	39669	35860	35	58557	31	41443	37957	36	56695	32	43305	40128	37	39	36
22	60302	29	39698	35894	34	58527	30	41473	37992	35	56663	32	43337	40165	37	38	32
23	60273	29	39727	35928	34	58497	30	41503	38028	36	56631	32	43369	40201	36	37	28
24	60244	29	39756	35963	35	58467	30	41533	38064	36	56599	31	43401	40238	37	36	24
25	60215	29	39785	35997	35	58436	31	41564	38099	36	56568	31	43432	40275	37	35	20
26	60186	29	39814	36032	35	58406	31	41594	38135	36	56536	32	43464	40312	37	34	16
27	60157	29	39843	36066	34	58375	31	41625	38170	36	56504	32	43496	40349	37	33	12
28	60128	29	39872	36101	35	58345	30	41655	38206	36	56472	32	43528	40385	37	32	8
29	60099	29	39901	36135	34	58314	31	41686	38242	36	56440	32	43560	40423	37	31	4
30	60070	29	39930	36170	35	58284	30	41716	38278	36	56408	32	43592	40460	37	30	+2m
31	60041	29	39959	36204	34	58253	31	41747	38313	35	56375	33	43625	40497	37	29	56
32	60012	29	39988	36239	35	58223	30	41777	38349	36	56343	32	43657	40534	37	28	52
33	59983	29	40017	36274	35	58192	30	41808	38385	36	56311	32	43689	40571	37	27	48
34	59954	29	40046	36308	34	58162	30	41838	38421	35	56279	32	43721	40609	38	26	44
35	59924	30	40076	36343	35	58131	31	41869	38456	36	56247	32	43753	40646	37	25	40
36	59895	29	40105	36377	34	58101	30	41899	38492	36	56215	32	43785	40683	37	24	36
37	59866	29	40134	36412	35	58070	31	41930	38528	36	56182	33	43818	40720	37	23	32
38	59837	29	40163	36447	35	58039	31	41961	38564	36	56150	32	43850	40757	37	22	28
39	59808	29	40192	36481	34	58008	31	41992	38600	36	56118	32	43882	40795	38	21	24
40	59778	30	40222	36516	35	57978	30	42022	38636	36	56085	33	43915	40832	37	20	20
41	59749	29	40251	36551	35	57947	31	42053	38672	36	56053	32	43947	40869	37	19	16
42	59720	29	40280	36586	35	57916	31	42084	38708	36	56021	32	43979	40906	37	18	12
43	59690	30	40310	36621	35	57885	31	42115	38744	36	55988	33	44012	40944	38	17	8
44	59661	29	40339	36655	34	57855	30	42145	38780	36	55956	32	44044	40981	37	16	4
45	59632	29	40368	36690	35	57824	31	42176	38816	36	55923	33	44077	41019	37	15	+1m
46	59602	30	40398	36725	35	57793	31	42207	38852	36	55891	32	44109	41056	37	14	56
47	59573	29	40427	36760	35	57762	31	42238	38888	36	55858	33	44142	41093	37	13	52
48	59543	30	40457	36795	35	57731	31	42269	38924	36	55826	32	44174	41131	38	12	48
49	59514	30	40486	36830	35	57700	31	42300	38960	36	55793	33	44207	41168	38	11	44
50	59484	30	40516	36865	35	57669	31	42331	38996	37	55761	32	44239	41206	37	10	40
51	59455	29	40545	36899	34	57638	31	42362	39033	37	55728	33	44272	41243	37	9	36
52	59425	30	40575	36934	35	57607	31	42393	39069	36	55695	33	44305	41281	38	8	32
53	59396	29	40604	36969	35	57576	31	42424	39105	36	55663	33	44337	41319	38	7	28
54	59366	30	40634	37004	35	57545	31	42455	39141	36	55630	33	44370	41356	37	6	24
55	59336	30	40664	37039	35	57514	31	42486	39177	36	55597	33	44403	41394	38	5	20
56	59307	30	40693	37074	35	57482	32	42518	39214	37	55564	32	44436	41431	38	4	16
57	59277	30	40723	37110	36	57451	31	42549	39250	36	55532	33	44468	41469	38	3	12
58	59247	30	40753	37145	35	57420	31	42580	39286	36	55499	33	44501	41507	38	2	8
59	59218	29	40782	37180	35	57389	31	42611	39323	37	55466	33	44534	41545	38	1	4
60	59188	30	40812	37215	35	57358	31	42642	39359	36	55433	33	44567	41582	37	0	0
	Ī. [9]		0.	0.		Ī. [9]		0.	0.		Ī. [9]		0.	0.			
	Sin.	D.	Cosec.	Cot.	D.	Sin.	D.	Cosec.	Cot.	D.	Sin.	D.	Cosec.	Cot.	D.	′	Secs.

23°   22°   21°

1h32m   1h28m   1h24m

Table 19　　　　　LOGARITHMIC FUNCTIONS

′	69° Cos.	D.	Sec.	Tan.	D.	70° Cos.	D.	Sec.	Tan.	D.	71° Cos.	D.	Sec.	Tan.	D.		
	T.[9]		0.	0.		T.[9]		0.	0.		T.[9]		0.	0.		60	60
0	55433	33	44567	41582	37	53405	35	46595	43893	39	51264	37	48736	46303	41	60	60
1	55400	33	44600	41620	38	53370	35	46630	43933	40	51227	37	48773	46344	41	59	56
2	55367	33	44633	41658	38	53336	34	46664	43972	39	51191	36	48809	46385	41	58	52
3	55334	33	44666	41696	38	53301	35	46699	44011	39	51154	37	48846	46426	41	57	48
4	55301	33	44699	41733	37	53266	35	46734	44051	40	51117	37	48883	46467	41	56	44
5	55268	33	44732	41771	38	53231	35	46769	44090	39	51080	37	48920	46508	41	55	40
6	55235	33	44765	41809	38	53196	35	46804	44130	40	51043	37	48957	46550	42	54	36
7	55202	33	44798	41847	38	53161	35	46839	44169	39	51007	36	48993	46591	41	53	32
8	55169	33	44831	41885	38	53126	35	46874	44209	40	50970	37	49030	46632	41	52	28
9	55136	33	44864	41923	38	53092	34	46908	44248	39	50933	37	49067	46673	41	51	24
10	55102	34	44898	41961	38	53056	36	46944	44288	40	50896	37	49104	46715	42	50	20
11	55069	33	44931	41999	38	53021	35	46979	44327	39	50858	38	49142	46756	41	49	16
12	55036	33	44964	42037	38	52986	35	47014	44367	40	50821	37	49179	46798	42	48	12
13	55003	33	44997	42075	38	52951	35	47049	44407	40	50784	37	49216	46839	41	47	8
14	54969	34	45031	42113	38	52916	35	47084	44446	39	50747	37	49253	46880	41	46	4
15	54936	33	45064	42151	38	52881	35	47119	44486	40	50710	37	49290	46922	42	45	+3m
16	54903	33	45097	42190	39	52846	35	47154	44526	40	50673	37	49327	46963	41	44	56
17	54869	34	45131	42228	38	52811	35	47189	44566	40	50635	38	49365	47005	42	43	52
18	54836	33	45164	42266	38	52775	36	47225	44605	39	50598	37	49402	47047	42	42	48
19	54802	34	45198	42304	38	52740	35	47260	44645	40	50561	37	49439	47088	41	41	44
20	54769	33	45231	42342	38	52705	35	47295	44685	40	50523	38	49477	47130	42	40	40
21	54735	34	45265	42381	39	52669	36	47331	44725	40	50486	37	49514	47171	41	39	36
22	54702	33	45298	42419	38	52634	35	47366	44765	40	50449	37	49551	47213	42	38	32
23	54668	34	45332	42457	38	52598	36	47402	44805	40	50411	38	49589	47255	42	37	28
24	54635	33	45365	42496	39	52563	35	47437	44845	40	50374	37	49626	47297	42	36	24
25	54601	34	45399	42534	38	52527	36	47473	44885	40	50336	38	49664	47339	42	35	20
26	54567	33	45433	42572	38	52492	35	47508	44925	40	50298	38	49702	47380	41	34	16
27	54534	33	45466	42611	39	52456	36	47544	44965	40	50261	37	49739	47422	42	33	12
28	54500	34	45500	42649	38	52421	35	47579	45005	40	50223	38	49777	47464	42	32	8
29	54466	34	45534	42688	39	52385	36	47615	45045	40	50185	38	49815	47506	42	31	4
30	54433	33	45567	42726	38	52350	35	47650	45085	40	50148	37	49852	47548	42	30	+2m
31	54399	34	45601	42765	39	52314	36	47686	45125	40	50110	38	49890	47590	42	29	56
32	54365	34	45635	42803	38	52278	36	47722	45165	40	50072	38	49928	47632	42	28	52
33	54331	34	45669	42842	39	52242	36	47758	45206	41	50034	38	49966	47674	42	27	48
34	54297	34	45703	42880	38	52207	35	47793	45246	40	49996	38	50004	47716	42	26	44
35	54263	34	45737	42919	39	52171	36	47829	45286	40	49958	38	50042	47758	42	25	40
36	54229	34	45771	42958	39	52135	36	47865	45327	41	49920	38	50080	47800	42	24	36
37	54195	34	45805	42996	39	52099	36	47901	45367	40	49882	38	50118	47843	43	23	32
38	54161	34	45839	43035	39	52063	36	47937	45407	40	49844	38	50156	47885	42	22	28
39	54127	34	45873	43074	39	52027	36	47973	45448	41	49806	38	50194	47927	42	21	24
40	54093	34	45907	43113	39	51991	36	48009	45488	40	49768	38	50232	47969	42	20	20
41	54059	34	45941	43151	38	51955	36	48045	45529	41	49730	38	50270	48012	43	19	16
42	54025	34	45975	43190	39	51919	36	48081	45569	40	49692	38	50308	48054	42	18	12
43	53991	34	46009	43229	39	51883	36	48117	45610	41	49654	38	50346	48097	43	17	8
44	53957	34	46043	43268	39	51847	36	48153	45650	40	49615	39	50385	48139	42	16	4
45	53922	35	46078	43307	39	51811	36	48189	45691	41	49577	38	50423	48181	43	15	+1m
46	53888	34	46112	43346	39	51774	37	48226	45731	40	49539	38	50461	48224	43	14	56
47	53854	34	46146	43385	39	51738	36	48262	45772	41	49500	39	50500	48266	42	13	52
48	53819	35	46181	43424	39	51702	36	48298	45813	41	49462	38	50538	48309	43	12	48
49	53785	34	46215	43463	39	51666	36	48334	45853	40	49424	39	50576	48352	42	11	44
50	53751	34	46249	43502	39	51629	37	48371	45894	41	49385	39	50615	48394	42	10	40
51	53716	35	46284	43541	39	51593	36	48407	45935	41	49347	38	50653	48437	43	9	36
52	53682	34	46318	43580	39	51557	36	48443	45975	40	49308	39	50692	48480	43	8	32
53	53647	35	46353	43619	39	51520	37	48480	46016	41	49269	39	50731	48522	42	7	28
54	53613	34	46387	43658	39	51484	36	48516	46057	41	49231	38	50769	48565	43	6	24
55	53578	35	46422	43697	39	51447	37	48553	46098	41	49192	39	50808	48608	43	5	20
56	53544	34	46456	43736	39	51411	36	48589	46139	41	49153	39	50847	48651	43	4	16
57	53509	35	46491	43776	40	51374	37	48626	46180	41	49115	38	50885	48694	43	3	12
58	53475	34	46525	43815	39	51338	36	48662	46221	41	49076	39	50924	48736	42	2	8
59	53440	35	46560	43854	39	51301	37	48699	46262	41	49037	39	50963	48779	43	1	4
60	53405	35	46595	43893	39	51264	37	48736	46303	41	48998	39	51002	48822	43	0	0
	T.[9]		0.	0.		T.[9]		0.	0.		T.[9]		0.	0.			
	Sin.	D.	Cosec.	Cot.	D.	Sin.	D.	Cosec.	Cot.	D.	Sin.	D.	Cosec.	Cot.	D.	′	Secs
	20°					19°					18°						

1h20m　　　　　1h16m　　　　　1h12m

Table 19   LOGARITHMIC FUNCTIONS

72°   73°   74°

′	Cos.	D.	Sec.	Tan.	D.	Cos.	D.	Sec.	Tan.	D.	Cos.	D.	Sec.	Tan.	D.		
	Ī.[9]		0.	0.		Ī.[9]		0.	0.		Ī.[9]		0.	0.			
0	48998	39	51002	48822	43	46594	41	53406	51466	45	44034	44	55966	54250	47	60	60
1	48959	39	51041	48865	43	46552	42	53448	51511	45	43990	44	56010	54298	48	59	56
2	48920	39	51080	48908	43	46511	41	53489	51557	46	43946	44	56054	54346	48	58	52
3	48881	39	51119	48952	44	46469	42	53531	51602	45	43901	45	56099	54394	48	57	48
4	48842	39	51158	48995	43	46428	41	53572	51647	45	43857	44	56143	54441	47	56	44
5	48803	39	51197	49038	43	46386	42	53614	51693	46	43813	44	56187	54489	48	55	40
6	48764	39	51236	49081	43	46345	41	53655	51738	45	43769	44	56231	54537	48	54	36
7	48725	39	51275	49124	43	46303	42	53697	51783	45	43724	45	56276	54585	48	53	32
8	48686	39	51314	49167	43	46262	41	53738	51829	46	43680	44	56320	54633	48	52	28
9	48647	39	51353	49211	44	46220	42	53780	51874	45	43635	44	56365	54681	48	51	24
10	48607	40	51393	49254	43	46178	42	53822	51920	46	43591	44	56409	54729	48	50	20
11	48568	39	51432	49297	43	46136	42	53864	51965	45	43546	45	56454	54778	49	49	16
12	48529	39	51471	49341	44	46095	41	53905	52011	46	43502	44	56498	54826	48	48	12
13	48490	39	51510	49384	43	46053	42	53947	52057	46	43457	45	56543	54874	48	47	8
14	48450	40	51550	49428	44	46011	42	53989	52103	46	43412	45	56588	54922	48	46	4
15	48411	39	51589	49471	43	45969	42	54031	52148	45	43367	44	56633	54971	48	45	+3m
16	48371	40	51629	49515	43	45927	42	54073	52194	46	43323	44	56677	55019	48	44	56
17	48332	39	51668	49558	44	45885	42	54115	52240	46	43278	45	56722	55067	48	43	52
18	48292	40	51708	49602	43	45843	42	54157	52286	46	43233	45	56767	55116	49	42	48
19	48252	40	51748	49645	43	45801	42	54199	52332	46	43188	45	56812	55164	48	41	44
20	48213	39	51787	49689	44	45758	43	54242	52378	46	43143	45	56857	55213	49	40	40
21	48173	40	51827	49733	44	45716	42	54284	52424	46	43098	45	56902	55262	49	39	36
22	48133	40	51867	49777	44	45674	42	54326	52470	46	43053	45	56947	55310	49	38	32
23	48094	39	51906	49820	43	45632	42	54368	52516	46	43008	45	56992	55359	49	37	28
24	48054	40	51946	49864	44	45589	42	54411	52562	46	42962	46	57038	55408	49	36	24
25	48014	40	51986·	49908	44	45547	42	54453	52608	46	42917	45	57083	55456	48	35	20
26	47974	40	52026	49952	44	45504	43	54496	52654	46	42872	45	57128	55505	49	34	16
27	47934	40	52066	49996	44	45462	42	54538	52701	47	42826	46	57174	55554	49	33	12
28	47894	40	52106	50040	44	45419	43	54581	52747	46	42781	45	57219	55603	49	32	8
29	47854	40	52146	50084	44	45377	42	54623	52793	46	42735	46	57265	55652	49	31	4
30	47814	40	52186	50128	44	45334	43	54666	52840	47	42690	45	57310	55701	49	30	+2m
31	47774	40	52226	50172	44	45292	42	54708	52886	46	42644	46	57356	55750	49	29	56
32	47734	40	52266	50216	44	45249	43	54751	52932	46	42599	45	57401	55799	49	28	52
33	47694	40	52306	50260	44	45206	43	54794	52979	47	42553	46	57447	55849	50	27	48
34	47654	40	52346	50304	44	45163	43	54837	53025	46	42507	46	57493	55898	49	26	44
35	47613	41	52387	50348	44	45120	43	54880	53072	47	42461	45	57539	55947	49	25	40
36	47573	40	52427	50393	45	45077	43	54923	53119	47	42416	45	57584	55996	49	24	36
37	47533	40	52467	50437	44	45035	42	54965	53165	46	42370	46	57630	56046	50	23	32
38	47492	41	52508	50481	44	44992	44	55008	53212	47	42324	46	57676	56095	49	22	28
39	47452	40	52548	50526	45	44948	43	55052	53259	47	42278	46	57722	56145	50	21	24
40	47411	41	52589	50570	44	44905	43	55095	53306	47	42232	46	57768	56194	49	20	20
41	47371	40	52629	50615	45	44862	43	55138	53352	46	42186	46	57814	56244	50	19	16
42	47330	41	52670	50659	44	44819	43	55181	53399	47	42140	46	57860	56293	49	18	12
43	47290	40	52710	50704	45	44776	43	55224	53446	47	42093	47	57907	56343	50	17	8
44	47249	41	52751	50748	44	44733	43	55267	53493	47	42047	46	57953	56393	50	16	4
45	47209	40	52791	50793	45	44689	44	55311	53540	47	42001	46	57999	56442	49	15	+1m
46	47168	41	52832	50837	44	44646	43	55354	53587	47	41954	47	58046	56492	50	14	56
47	47127	41	52873	50882	45	44602	44	55398	53634	47	41908	46	58092	56542	50	13	52
48	47086	41	52914	50927	44	44559	43	55441	53681	47	41861	47	58139	56592	50	12	48
49	47045	41	52955	50971	44	44516	43	55484	53729	48	41815	46	58185	56642	50	11	44
50	47005	40	52995	51016	45	44472	44	55528	53776	47	41768	47	58232	56692	50	10	40
51	46964	41	53036	51061	45	44428	44	55572	53823	47	41722	46	58278	56742	50	9	36
52	46923	41	53077	51106	45	44385	43	55615	53870	47	41675	47	58325	56792	50	8	32
53	46882	41	53118	51151	45	44341	44	55659	53918	48	41628	47	58372	56842	50	7	28
54	46841	41	53159	51196	45	44297	44	55703	53965	48	41582	46	58418	56892	50	6	24
55	46800	41	53200	51241	45	44253	44	55747	54013	48	41535	47	58465	56943	51	5	20
56	46758	42	53242	51286	45	44210	43	55790	54060	47	41488	47	58512	56993	50	4	16
57	46717	41	53283	51331	45	44166	44	55834	54108	48	41441	47	58559	57043	50	3	12
58	46676	41	53324	51376	45	44122	44	55878	54155	47	41394	47	58606	57094	51	2	8
59	46635	41	53365	51421	45	44078	44	55922	54203	48	41347	47	58653	57144	50	1	4
60	46594	41	53406	51466	45	44034	44	55966	54250	47	41300	47	58700	57195	51	0	0
	Ī.[9]		0.	0.		Ī.[9]		0.	0.		Ī.[9]		0.	0.			
	Sin.	D.	Cosec.	Cot.	D.	Sin.	D.	Cosec.	Cot.	D.	Sin.	D.	Cosec.	Cot.	D.	′	Secs.

17°   16°   15°

1h 08m   1h 04m   1h 00m

Table 19   LOGARITHMIC FUNCTIONS

	75°					76°					77°						
′	Cos.	D.	Sec.	Tan.	D.	Cos.	D.	Sec.	Tan.	D.	Cos.	D.	Sec.	Tan.	D.		
	Ī. [9]		0.	0.		Ī. [9]		0.	0.		Ī. [9]		0.	0.			
0	41300	47	58700	57195	51	38368	50	61632	60323	54	35209	54	64791	63664	58	60	60
1	41252	48	58748	57245	50	38317	51	61683	60377	54	35154	55	64846	63721	57	59	56
2	41205	47	58795	57296	51	38266	51	61734	60431	54	35099	55	64901	63779	58	58	52
3	41158	47	58842	57347	51	38215	51	61785	60485	54	35044	55	64956	63837	58	57	48
4	41111	47	58889	57397	50	38164	51	61836	60539	54	34989	55	65011	63895	58	56	44
5	41063	48	58937	57448	51	38113	51	61887	60593	54	34934	55	65066	63953	58	55	40
6	41016	47	58984	57499	51	38062	51	61938	60647	54	34879	55	65121	64011	58	54	36
7	40968	48	59032	57550	51	38011	51	61989	60701	54	34824	55	65176	64069	58	53	32
8	40921	47	59079	57601	51	37960	51	62040	60755	54	34769	55	65231	64127	58	52	28
9	40873	48	59127	57652	51	37909	51	62091	60810	55	34713	56	65287	64185	58	51	24
10	40825	48	59175	57703	51	37858	51	62142	60864	54	34658	55	65342	64243	58	50	20
11	40778	47	59222	57754	51	37806	52	62194	60918	54	34602	56	65398	64302	59	49	16
12	40730	48	59270	57805	51	37755	51	62245	60973	55	34547	55	65453	64360	58	48	12
13	40682	48	59318	57856	51	37703	52	62297	61028	55	34491	56	65509	64419	58	47	8
14	40634	48	59366	57907	51	37652	51	62348	61082	55	34436	55	65564	64477	58	46	4
15	40586	48	59414	57959	52	37600	52	62400	61137	55	34380	56	65620	64536	59	45	+3m
16	40538	48	59462	58010	51	37549	51	62451	61192	55	34324	56	65676	64595	59	44	56
17	40490	48	59510	58061	51	37497	52	62503	61246	54	34268	56	65732	64653	58	43	52
18	40442	48	59558	58113	52	37445	52	62555	61301	55	34212	56	65788	64712	59	42	48
19	40394	48	59606	58164	51	37393	52	62607	61356	55	34156	56	65844	64771	59	41	44
20	40346	48	59654	58216	52	37341	52	62659	61411	55	34100	56	65900	64830	59	40	40
21	40297	49	59703	58267	51	37289	52	62711	61466	55	34043	57	65957	64889	59	39	36
22	40249	48	59751	58319	52	37237	52	62763	61521	55	33987	56	66013	64949	60	38	32
23	40200	49	59800	58371	52	37185	52	62815	61577	56	33931	56	66069	65008	59	37	28
24	40152	48	59848	58422	51	37133	52	62867	61632	55	33874	57	66126	65067	59	36	24
25	40103	49	59897	58474	52	37081	52	62919	61687	55	33818	56	66182	65126	59	35	20
26	40055	48	59945	58526	52	37028	53	62972	61743	56	33761	57	66239	65186	60	34	16
27	40006	49	59994	58578	52	36976	52	63024	61798	55	33704	57	66296	65245	59	33	12
28	39958	48	60042	58630	52	36924	52	63076	61853	55	33647	56	66353	65305	60	32	8
29	39909	49	60091	58682	52	36871	53	63129	61909	56	33591	56	66409	65365	60	31	4
30	39860	49	60140	58734	52	36819	52	63181	61965	56	33534	57	66466	65424	59	30	+2m
31	39811	49	60189	58786	52	36766	53	63234	62020	55	33477	57	66523	65484	60	29	56
32	39762	49	60238	58839	53	36713	53	63287	62076	56	33420	57	66580	65544	60	28	52
33	39713	49	60287	58891	52	36660	52	63340	62132	56	33362	58	66638	65604	60	27	48
34	39664	49	60336	58943	52	36608	52	63392	62188	56	33305	57	66695	65664	60	26	44
35	39615	49	60385	58995	52	36555	53	63445	62244	56	33248	57	66752	65724	60	25	40
36	39566	49	60434	59048	53	36502	53	63498	62300	56	33190	58	66810	65785	61	24	36
37	39517	49	60483	59100	52	36449	53	63551	62356	56	33133	57	66867	65845	60	23	32
38	39467	50	60533	59153	53	36395	54	63605	62412	56	33075	58	66925	65905	60	22	28
39	39418	49	60582	59205	52	36342	53	63658	62468	56	33018	57	66982	65966	61	21	24
40	39369	49	60631	59258	53	36289	53	63711	62524	56	32960	58	67040	66026	60	20	20
41	39319	50	60681	59311	53	36236	53	63764	62581	57	32902	58	67098	66087	61	19	16
42	39270	49	60730	59364	53	36182	54	63818	62637	56	32844	58	67156	66147	60	18	12
43	39220	50	60780	59416	52	36129	53	63871	62694	57	32786	58	67214	66208	61	17	8
44	39170	50	60830	59469	53	36075	54	63925	62750	56	32728	58	67272	66269	61	16	4
45	39121	49	60879	59522	53	36022	53	63978	62807	57	32670	58	67330	66330	61	15	+1m
46	39071	50	60929	59575	53	35968	54	64032	62863	56	32612	58	67388	66391	61	14	56
47	39021	50	60979	59628	53	35914	54	64086	62920	57	32553	59	67447	66452	61	13	52
48	38971	50	61029	59681	53	35860	54	64140	62977	57	32495	58	67505	66513	61	12	48
49	38921	50	61079	59734	53	35806	54	64194	63034	57	32437	58	67563	66574	61	11	44
50	38871	50	61129	59788	54	35752	54	64248	63091	57	32378	59	67622	66635	61	10	40
51	38821	50	61179	59841	53	35698	54	64302	63148	57	32319	59	67681	66697	62	9	36
52	38771	50	61229	59894	53	35644	54	64356	63205	57	32261	58	67739	66758	61	8	32
53	38721	50	61279	59948	54	35590	54	64410	63262	57	32202	59	67798	66820	62	7	28
54	38670	51	61330	60001	53	35536	54	64464	63319	57	32143	59	67857	66881	61	6	24
55	38620	50	61380	60055	53	35481	55	64519	63376	57	32084	59	67916	66943	62	5	20
56	38570	51	61430	60108	53	35427	54	64573	63434	58	32025	59	67975	67005	62	4	16
57	38519	51	61481	60162	54	35373	54	64627	63491	57	31966	59	68034	67067	62	3	12
58	38469	50	61531	60215	53	35318	55	64682	63548	57	31907	59	68093	67128	61	2	8
59	38418	51	61582	60269	54	35263	55	64737	63606	58	31847	60	68153	67190	62	1	4
60	38368	50	61632	60323	54	35209	54	64791	63664	58	31788	59	68212	67253	63	0	0
	Ī. [9]		0.	0.		Ī. [9]		0.	0.		Ī. [9]		0.	0.			
	Sin.	D.	Cosec.	Cot.	D.	Sin.	D.	Cosec.	Cot.	D.	Sin.	D.	Cosec.	Cot.	D.	′	Secs.
	14°					**13°**					**12°**						

0h56m   0h52m   0h48m

Table 19 LOGARITHMIC FUNCTIONS

78° 79° 80°

′	Cos.	D.	Sec.	Tan.	D.	Cos.	D.	Sec.	Tan.	D.	Cos.	D.	Sec.	Tan.	D.	′	Secs.
	Ī. [9]		0·	0·		Ī. [9]		0·	0·		Ī. [9]		0·	0·			
0	31788	59	68212	67253	63	28060	65	71940	71135	68	23967	72	76033	75368	74	60	60
1	31728	60	68272	67315	62	27995	65	72005	71202	67	23895	72	76105	75442	74	59	56
2	31669	59	68331	67377	62	27930	65	72070	71270	68	23823	72	76177	75516	74	58	52
3	31609	60	68391	67439	62	27864	66	72136	71338	68	23752	71	76248	75590	74	57	48
4	31549	60	68451	67502	63	27799	65	72201	71405	67	23679	73	76321	75665	75	56	44
5	31490	59	68510	67564	62	27734	65	72266	71473	68	23607	72	76393	75739	74	55	40
6	31430	60	68570	67627	63	27668	66	72332	71541	68	23535	72	76465	75814	75	54	36
7	31370	60	68630	67689	62	27602	66	72398	71609	68	23462	73	76538	75888	75	53	32
8	31310	60	68690	67752	63	27537	65	72463	71677	68	23390	72	76610	75963	75	52	28
9	31250	60	68750	67815	63	27471	66	72529	71746	69	23317	73	76683	76038	75	51	24
10	31189	61	68811	67878	63	27405	66	72595	71814	68	23244	73	76756	76113	75	50	20
11	31129	60	68871	67941	63	27339	66	72661	71883	69	23171	73	76829	76188	75	49	16
12	31068	61	68932	68004	63	27273	66	72727	71951	68	23098	73	76902	76263	75	48	12
13	31008	60	68992	68067	63	27206	67	72794	72020	69	23025	73	76975	76339	76	47	8
14	30947	60	69053	68130	63	27140	66	72860	72089	69	22952	73	77048	76414	75	46	4
15	30887	60	69113	68194	64	27073	67	72927	72158	69	22878	74	77122	76490	75	45	+3m
16	30826	61	69174	68257	63	27007	67	72993	72227	69	22805	73	77195	76565	75	44	56
17	30765	61	69235	68321	64	26940	67	73060	72296	69	22731	74	77269	76641	76	43	52
18	30704	61	69296	68384	63	26873	67	73127	72365	69	22657	74	77343	76717	76	42	48
19	30643	61	69357	68448	64	26806	67	73194	72434	69	22583	74	77417	76794	77	41	44
20	30582	61	69418	68511	63	26739	67	73261	72504	70	22509	74	77491	76870	76	40	40
21	30521	61	69479	68575	64	26672	67	73328	72573	69	22435	74	77565	76946	76	39	36
22	30459	62	69541	68639	64	26605	67	73395	72643	70	22361	74	77639	77023	77	38	32
23	30398	61	69602	68703	64	26538	67	73462	72712	69	22286	75	77714	77099	76	37	28
24	30336	62	69664	68767	64	26470	68	73530	72782	70	22211	75	77789	77176	77	36	24
25	30275	61	69725	68832	65	26403	67	73597	72852	70	22137	74	77863	77253	77	35	20
26	30213	62	69787	68896	64	26335	68	73665	72922	70	22062	75	77938	77330	77	34	16
27	30151	62	69849	68960	64	26267	68	73733	72992	70	21987	75	78013	77407	77	33	12
28	30090	61	69910	69025	65	26199	68	73801	73063	71	21912	75	78088	77484	77	32	8
29	30028	62	69972	69089	64	26131	68	73869	73133	70	21836	76	78164	77562	78	31	4
30	29966	62	70034	69154	65	26063	68	73937	73203	70	21761	75	78239	77639	77	30	+2m
31	29903	63	70097	69218	64	25995	68	74005	73274	71	21685	76	78315	77717	78	29	56
32	29841	62	70159	69283	65	25927	68	74073	73345	71	21610	75	78390	77795	78	28	52
33	29779	62	70221	69348	65	25858	69	74142	73415	70	21534	76	78466	77873	78	27	48
34	29716	63	70284	69413	65	25790	69	74210	73486	71	21458	76	78542	77951	78	26	44
35	29654	62	70346	69478	65	25721	69	74279	73557	71	21382	76	78618	78029	78	25	40
36	29591	63	70409	69543	65	25652	69	74348	73628	71	21306	76	78694	78107	78	24	36
37	29529	62	70471	69609	66	25583	69	74417	73699	71	21229	77	78771	78186	79	23	32
38	29466	63	70534	69674	65	25514	69	74486	73771	72	21153	76	78847	78264	78	22	28
39	29403	63	70597	69739	65	25445	69	74555	73842	71	21076	77	78924	78343	79	21	24
40	29340	63	70660	69805	66	25376	69	74624	73914	72	20999	77	79001	78422	79	20	20
41	29277	63	70723	69870	65	25307	69	74693	73985	71	20922	77	79078	78501	79	19	16
42	29214	63	70786	69936	66	25237	70	74763	74057	72	20845	77	79155	78580	79	18	12
43	29150	64	70850	70002	66	25168	69	74832	74129	72	20768	77	79232	78659	79	17	8
44	29087	63	70913	70068	66	25098	70	74902	74201	72	20691	77	79309	78739	80	16	4
45	29024	63	70976	70134	66	25028	70	74972	74273	72	20613	78	79387	78818	79	15	+1m
46	28960	64	71040	70200	66	24958	70	75042	74345	72	20535	77	79465	78898	80	14	56
47	28896	64	71104	70266	66	24888	70	75112	74418	73	20458	77	79542	78978	80	13	52
48	28833	63	71167	70332	66	24818	70	75182	74490	72	20380	78	79620	79058	80	12	48
49	28769	64	71231	70399	67	24748	70	75252	74563	73	20302	78	79698	79138	80	11	44
50	28705	64	71295	70465	66	24677	71	75323	74635	72	20223	79	79777	79218	80	10	40
51	28641	64	71359	70532	67	24607	70	75393	74708	73	20145	78	79855	79299	81	9	36
52	28577	64	71423	70598	66	24536	71	75464	74781	73	20067	78	79933	79379	80	8	32
53	28512	65	71488	70665	67	24466	70	75534	74854	73	19988	79	80012	79460	81	7	28
54	28448	64	71552	70732	67	24395	71	75605	74927	73	19909	79	80091	79541	81	6	24
55	28384	64	71616	70799	67	24324	71	75676	75000	73	19830	79	80170	79622	81	5	20
56	28319	65	71681	70866	67	24253	71	75747	75074	74	19751	79	80249	79703	81	4	16
57	28254	64	71746	70933	67	24181	72	75819	75147	73	19672	79	80328	79784	81	3	12
58	28190	64	71810	71000	67	24110	71	75890	75221	74	19592	80	80408	79866	82	2	8
59	28125	65	71875	71067	67	24039	71	75961	75294	73	19513	79	80487	79947	81	1	4
60	28060	65	71940	71135	68	23967	72	76033	75368	74	19433	80	80567	80029	82	0	0
	Ī. [9]		0·	0·		Ī. [9]		0·	0·		Ī. [9]		0·	0·			

	Sin.	D.	Cosec.	Cot.	D.	Sin.	D.	Cosec.	Cot.	D.	Sin.	D.	Cosec.	Cot.	D.	′	Secs.

11° 10° 9°

0ʰ44m   0ʰ40m   0ʰ36m

M

163

Table 19

LOGARITHMIC FUNCTIONS

81° | 82° | 83°

′	Cos.	D.	Sec.	Tan.	D.	Cos.	D.	Sec.	Tan.	D.	Cos.	D.	Sec.	Tan.	D.	′	Secs
	Ī.[9]		0·	0·		Ī.[9]		0·	0·		Ī.[9]		0·	0·			
0	19433	80	80567	80029	82	14356	89	85644	85220	92	0859	10	9141	9109	11	60	60
1	19353	80	80647	80111	82	14266	90	85734	85312	92	0849	10	9151	9119	10	59	56
2	19273	80	80727	80193	82	14175	91	85825	85403	91	0838	11	9162	9129	10	58	52
3	19193	80	80807	80275	82	14085	90	85915	85496	93	0828	10	9172	9140	11	57	48
4	19113	80	80887	80357	82	13994	91	86006	85588	92	0818	10	9182	9151	10	56	44
5	19033	80	80967	80439	82	13904	90	86096	85680	92	0807	11	9193	9161	10	55	40
6	18952	81	81048	80522	83	13813	91	86187	85773	93	0797	10	9203	9172	11	54	36
7	18871	81	81129	80605	83	13722	91	86278	85866	93	0786	11	9214	9182	10	53	32
8	18790	81	81210	80688	83	13630	92	86370	85959	93	0776	10	9224	9193	11	52	28
9	18709	81	81291	80771	83	13539	91	86461	86052	93	0765	11	9235	9204	11	51	24
10	18628	81	81372	80854	83	13447	92	86553	86146	94	0755	10	9245	9214	10	50	20
11	18547	81	81453	80937	83	13355	92	86645	86239	93	0744	11	9256	9225	11	49	16
12	18465	82	81535	81021	84	13263	92	86737	86333	94	0734	10	9266	9236	11	48	12
13	18383	82	81617	81104	83	13171	92	86829	86427	94	0723	11	9277	9246	10	47	8
14	18302	81	81698	81188	84	13078	93	86922	86522	95	0712	11	9288	9257	11	46	4
15	18220	82	81780	81272	84	12985	93	87015	86616	94	0702	10	9298	9268	11	45	+3m
16	18137	83	81863	81356	84	12892	93	87108	86711	95	0691	11	9309	9279	11	44	56
17	18055	82	81945	81440	84	12799	93	87201	86806	95	0680	11	9320	9290	11	43	52
18	17973	82	82027	81525	85	12706	93	87294	86901	95	0670	10	9330	9301	11	42	48
19	17890	83	82110	81609	84	12612	94	87388	86996	95	0659	11	9341	9312	11	41	44
20	17807	83	82193	81694	85	12519	93	87481	87091	95	0648	11	9352	9322	10	40	40
21	17724	83	82276	81779	85	12425	94	87575	87187	96	0637	11	9363	9333	11	39	36
22	17641	83	82359	81864	85	12331	94	87669	87283	96	0626	11	9374	9344	11	38	32
23	17558	83	82442	81949	85	12236	95	87764	87379	96	0616	10	9384	9355	11	37	28
24	17474	84	82526	82035	86	12142	94	87858	87475	96	0605	11	9395	9367	12	36	24
25	17391	83	82609	82120	85	12047	95	87953	87572	97	0594	11	9406	9378	11	35	20
26	17307	84	82693	82206	86	11952	95	88048	87668	96	0583	11	9417	9389	11	34	16
27	17223	84	82777	82292	86	11857	95	88143	87765	97	0572	11	9428	9400	11	33	12
28	17139	84	82861	82378	86	11761	96	88239	87862	97	0561	11	9439	9411	11	32	8
29	17055	84	82945	82464	86	11666	95	88334	87960	98	0550	11	9450	9422	11	31	4
30	16970	85	83030	82550	86	11570	96	88430	88057	97	0539	11	9461	9433	11	30	+2m
31	16886	84	83114	82637	87	11474	96	88526	88155	98	0527	12	9473	9445	12	29	56
32	16801	85	83199	82723	86	11377	97	88623	88253	58	0516	11	9484	9456	11	28	52
33	16716	85	83284	82810	87	11281	96	88719	88351	98	0505	11	9495	9467	11	27	48
34	16631	85	83369	82897	87	11184	97	88816	88449	98	0494	11	9506	9479	12	26	44
35	16545	86	83455	82984	87	11087	97	88913	88548	99	0483	11	9517	9490	11	25	40
36	16460	85	83540	83072	88	10990	97	89010	88647	99	0472	11	9528	9501	11	24	36
37	16374	86	83626	83159	87	10893	97	89107	88746	99	0460	12	9540	9513	12	23	32
38	16289	86	83711	83247	88	10795	98	89205	88845	99	0449	11	9551	9524	11	22	28
39	16203	86	83797	83335	88	10697	98	89303	88944	99	0438	11	9562	9536	12	21	24
40	16116	87	83884	83423	88	10599	98	89401	8904	10	0426	12	9574	9547	11	20	20
41	16030	86	83970	83511	88	10501	98	89499	8914	10	0415	11	9585	9559	12	19	16
42	15944	86	84056	83599	88	10402	99	89598	8924	10	0403	12	9597	9570	11	18	12
43	15857	87	84143	83688	89	10304	98	89696	8934	10	0392	11	9608	9582	12	17	8
44	15770	87	84230	83776	88	10205	99	89795	8944	10	0380	12	9620	9593	11	16	4
45	15683	87	84317	83865	89	10106	99	89894	8955	11	0369	11	9631	9605	12	15	+1m
46	15596	87	84404	83954	89	1001	10	8999	8965	10	0357	12	9643	9617	12	14	56
47	15508	88	84492	84044	90	0991	10	9009	8975	10	0346	11	9654	9629	12	13	52
48	15421	87	84579	84133	89	0981	10	9019	8985	10	0334	12	9666	9640	11	12	48
49	15333	88	84667	84223	90	0971	10	9029	8995	10	0323	11	9677	9652	12	11	44
50	15245	88	84755	84312	89	0961	10	9039	9005	10	0311	12	9689	9664	12	10	40
51	15157	88	84843	84402	90	0951	10	9049	9016	11	0299	12	9701	9676	12	9	36
52	15069	88	84931	84492	90	0940	11	9060	9026	10	0287	12	9713	9688	12	8	32
53	14980	89	85020	84583	91	0930	10	9070	9036	10	0276	11	9724	9700	12	7	28
54	14891	89	85109	84673	90	0920	10	9080	9046	10	0264	12	9736	9711	11	6	24
55	14803	88	85197	84764	91	0910	10	9090	9057	11	0252	12	9748	9723	12	5	20
56	14714	89	85286	84855	91	0900	10	9100	9067	10	0240	12	9760	9735	12	4	16
57	14624	90	85376	84946	91	0890	10	9110	9077	10	0228	12	9772	9747	12	3	12
58	14535	89	85465	85037	91	0879	11	9121	9088	11	0216	12	9784	9760	13	2	8
59	14445	90	85555	85128	91	0869	10	9131	9098	10	0204	12	9796	9772	12	1	4
60	14356	89	85644	85220	92	0859	10	9141	9109	11	0192	12	9808	9784	12	0	0
	Ī.[9]		0·	0·		Ī.[9]		0·	0·		Ī.[9]		0·	0·			

| | Sin. | D. | Cosec. | Cot. | D. | Sin. | D. | Cosec. | Cot. | D. | Sin. | D. | Cosec. | Cot. | D. | ′ | Secs |

8°	7°	6°
0h32m	0h28m	0h24m

Table 19

LOGARITHMIC FUNCTIONS

84° | 85° | 86°

Sub-header rows (below column headers): 84°: $\overline{1}/\overline{2}$. [9/8] | 0/$\overline{1}$· | 0/$\overline{1}$· — 85°: $\overline{2}$. [8] | $\overline{1}$· | $\overline{1}$· — 86°: $\overline{2}$. [8] | $\overline{1}$· | $\overline{1}$·

′	Cos.	D.	Sec.	Tan.	D.	Cos.	D.	Sec.	Tan.	D.	Cos.	D.	Sec.	Tan.	D.	′	Secs
0	0192	12	9808	9784	12	9403	14	0597	0580	14	8436	18	1564	1554	19	60	60
1	0180	12	9820	9796	12	9388	15	0612	0595	15	8418	18	1582	1572	18	59	56
2	0168	12	9832	9808	12	9374	14	0626	0610	15	8400	18	1600	1590	18	58	52
3	0156	12	9844	9820	12	9359	15	0641	0624	14	8381	19	1619	1608	18	57	48
4	0144	12	9856	9833	13	9345	14	0655	0639	15	8363	18	1637	1627	19	56	44
5	0132	12	9868	9845	12	9330	15	0670	0654	15	8345	19	1655	1645	18	55	40
6	0120	12	9880	9857	12	9315	15	0685	0669	15	8326	19	1674	1664	19	54	36
7	0107	13	9893	9870	13	9301	14	0699	0684	15	8307	19	1693	1683	19	53	32
8	0095	12	9905	9882	12	9286	15	0714	0698	14	8289	18	1711	1701	18	52	28
9	0083	12	9917	9895	13	9271	15	0729	0713	15	8270	19	1730	1720	19	51	24
10	0070	13	9930	9907	12	9256	15	0744	0728	15	8251	19	1749	1739	19	50	20
11	0058	12	9942	9920	13	9241	15	0759	0744	16	8232	19	1768	1758	19	49	16
12	0046	12	9954	9932	12	9226	15	0774	0759	15	8213	19	1787	1777	19	48	12
13	0033	13	9967	9945	13	9211	15	0789	0774	15	8194	19	1806	1796	19	47	8
14	0021	12	9979	9957	12	9196	15	0804	0789	15	8175	19	1825	1815	19	46	4
15	0008	13	9992	9970	13	9181	15	0819	0804	15	8156	19	1844	1835	20	45	+3m
16	9996	12	0004	9983	12	9166	15	0834	0820	16	8137	19	1863	1854	19	44	56
17	9983	13	0017	9995	12	9150	16	0850	0835	15	8117	20	1883	1874	20	43	52
18	9970	13	0030	0008	13	9135	15	0865	0850	15	8098	19	1902	1893	19	42	48
19	9958	12	0042	0021	13	9119	16	0881	0866	16	8078	20	1922	1913	20	41	44
20	9945	13	0055	0034	13	9104	15	0896	0882	16	8059	19	1941	1933	20	40	40
21	9932	13	0068	0047	13	9089	15	0911	0897	15	8039	20	1961	1952	19	39	36
22	9919	13	0081	0060	13	9073	16	0927	0913	16	8019	20	1981	1972	20	38	32
23	9907	12	0093	0072	12	9057	16	0943	0929	16	7999	20	2001	1992	20	37	28
24	9894	13	0106	0085	13	9042	15	0958	0944	15	7979	20	2021	2012	20	36	24
25	9881	13	0119	0099	14	9026	16	0974	0960	16	7959	20	2041	2033	21	35	20
26	9868	13	0132	0112	13	9010	16	0990	0976	16	7939	20	2061	2053	20	34	16
27	9855	13	0145	0125	13	8994	16	1006	0992	16	7918	21	2082	2073	20	33	12
28	9842	13	0158	0138	13	8978	16	1022	1008	16	7898	21	2102	2094	21	32	8
29	9829	13	0171	0151	13	8962	16	1038	1024	16	7877	21	2123	2114	20	31	4
30	9816	13	0184	0164	13	8946	16	1054	1040	16	7857	20	2143	2135	21	30	+2m
31	9803	13	0197	0177	13	8930	16	1070	1056	16	7836	21	2164	2156	21	29	56
32	9789	14	0211	0191	14	8914	16	1086	1073	17	7815	21	2185	2177	21	28	52
33	9776	13	0224	0204	13	8898	16	1102	1089	16	7794	21	2206	2198	21	27	48
34	9763	13	0237	0218	14	8882	16	1118	1105	17	7773	21	2227	2219	21	26	44
35	9750	14	0250	0231	13	8865	17	1135	1122	17	7752	21	2248	2240	21	25	40
36	9736	14	0264	0244	13	8849	16	1151	1138	16	7731	21	2269	2261	21	24	36
37	9723	13	0277	0258	14	8833	16	1167	1155	17	7710	21	2290	2283	22	23	32
38	9709	14	0291	0271	13	8816	17	1184	1171	17	7688	22	2312	2304	21	22	28
39	9696	13	0304	0285	14	8799	17	1201	1188	17	7667	22	2333	2326	22	21	24
40	9682	14	0318	0299	14	8783	16	1217	1205	17	7645	22	2355	2348	22	20	20
41	9669	13	0331	0312	13	8766	17	1234	1222	17	7623	22	2377	2369	21	19	16
42	9655	14	0345	0326	14	8749	17	1251	1238	16	7602	21	2398	2391	22	18	12
43	9642	13	0358	0340	14	8733	16	1267	1255	17	7580	22	2420	2413	22	17	8
44	9628	14	0372	0354	14	8716	17	1284	1272	17	7557	23	2443	2435	22	16	4
45	9614	14	0386	0367	13	8699	17	1301	1289	17	7535	22	2465	2458	23	15	+1m
46	9601	13	0399	0381	14	8682	17	1318	1306	17	7513	22	2487	2480	22	14	56
47	9587	14	0413	0395	14	8665	17	1335	1324	18	7491	22	2509	2503	23	13	52
48	9573	14	0427	0409	14	8647	18	1353	1341	17	7468	23	2532	2525	22	12	48
49	9559	14	0441	0423	14	8630	17	1370	1358	17	7445	23	2555	2548	23	11	44
50	9545	14	0455	0437	14	8613	17	1387	1376	18	7423	22	2577	2571	23	10	40
51	9531	14	0469	0451	14	8595	18	1405	1393	17	7400	23	2600	2594	23	9	36
52	9517	14	0483	0466	15	8578	17	1422	1411	18	7377	23	2623	2617	23	8	32
53	9503	14	0497	0480	14	8560	18	1440	1428	18	7354	24	2646	2640	23	7	28
54	9489	14	0511	0494	14	8543	17	1457	1446	18	7330	24	2670	2663	23	6	24
55	9475	14	0525	0508	14	8525	18	1475	1464	18	7307	23	2693	2687	24	5	20
56	9460	15	0540	0523	15	8508	17	1492	1482	18	7283	24	2717	2710	23	4	16
57	9446	14	0554	0537	14	8490	18	1510	1499	17	7260	24	2740	2734	24	3	12
58	9432	14	0568	0551	14	8472	18	1528	1517	18	7236	24	2764	2758	24	2	8
59	9417	15	0583	0566	15	8454	18	1546	1535	18	7212	24	2788	2782	24	1	4
60	9403	14	0597	0580	14	8436	18	1564	1554	19	7188	24	2812	2806	24	0	0

Bottom sub-header rows: 84°: $\overline{2}/\overline{1}$. [8'9] | 0 $\overline{1}$· | 0 $\overline{1}$· — 85°: $\overline{2}$. [8] | $\overline{1}$· | $\overline{1}$· — 86°: $\overline{2}$. [8] | $\overline{1}$· | $\overline{1}$·

Sin.	D.	Cosec.	Cot.	D.	Sin.	D.	Cosec.	Cot.	D.	Sin.	D.	Cosec.	Cot.	D.	′	Secs

5°	4°	3°

0h 20m   0h 16m   0h 12m

Table 19 — LOGARITHMIC FUNCTIONS

LOGARITHMIC FUNCTIONS

87° | 88° | 89°

′	Cos.	D.	Sec.	Tan.	D.	Cos.	D.	Sec.	Tan.	D.	Cos.	D.	Sec.	Tan.	D.		
	2̄.[8]		1·	1·		2̄.[8]		1·	1·		[8/6]						
0	7188	24	2812	2806	24	5428	36	4572	4569	36	2̄.242	7	1.758	1.758	7	60	60
1	7164	24	2836	2830	24	5392	36	4608	4606	37	2̄.235	7	1.765	1.765	7	59	56
2	7140	24	2860	2855	25	5355	37	4645	4642	36	2̄.227	8	1.773	1.773	8	58	52
3	7115	25	2885	2879	24	5318	37	4682	4679	37	2̄.220	7	1.780	1.780	7	57	48
4	7090	25	2910	2904	25	5281	37	4719	4717	38	2̄.212	8	1.788	1.788	8	56	44
5	7066	24	2934	2929	25	5243	38	4757	4754	37	2̄.204	8	1.796	1.796	8	55	40
6	7041	25	2959	2954	25	5206	37	4794	4792	38	2̄.196	8	1.804	1.804	8	54	36
7	7016	25	2984	2979	25	5167	39	4833	4830	38	2̄.188	8	1.812	1.812	8	53	32
8	6991	25	3009	3004	25	5129	38	4871	4869	39	2̄.180	8	1.820	1.820	8	52	28
9	6965	26	3035	3029	25	5090	39	4910	4908	39	2̄.171	9	1.829	1.829	9	51	24
10	6940	25	3060	3055	26	5050	40	4950	4947	39	2̄.163	8	1.837	1.837	8	50	20
11	6914	26	3086	3080	25	5011	39	4989	4987	40	2̄.154	9	1.846	1.846	9	49	16
12	6889	25	3111	3106	26	4971	40	5029	5027	40	2̄.145	9	1.855	1.855	9	48	12
13	6863	26	3137	3132	26	4930	41	5070	5067	40	2̄.136	9	1.864	1.864	9	47	8
14	6837	26	3163	3158	26	4890	40	5110	5108	41	2̄.126	10	1.874	1.873	9	46	4
15	6810	27	3190	3185	27	4848	42	5152	5149	41	2̄.117	9	1.883	1.883	10	45	+3m
16	6784	26	3216	3211	26	4807	41	5193	5191	42	2̄.107	10	1.893	1.893	10	44	56
17	6758	26	3242	3238	27	4765	42	5235	5233	42	2̄.097	10	1.903	1.903	10	43	52
18	6731	27	3269	3264	26	4723	42	5277	5275	42	2̄.087	10	1.913	1.913	10	42	48
19	6704	27	3296	3291	27	4680	43	5320	5318	43	2̄.076	11	1.924	1.923	10	41	44
20	6677	27	3323	3318	27	4637	43	5363	5362	44	2̄.066	10	1.934	1.934	11	40	40
21	6650	27	3350	3346	28	4593	44	5407	5405	43	2̄.055	11	1.945	1.945	11	39	36
22	6622	28	3378	3373	27	4549	44	5451	5449	44	2̄.044	11	1.956	1.956	11	38	32
23	6595	27	3405	3401	28	4504	45	5496	5494	45	2̄.032	12	1.968	1.968	12	37	28
24	6567	28	3433	3429	28	4459	45	5541	5539	45	2̄.020	12	1.980	1.980	12	36	24
25	6539	28	3461	3456	27	4414	45	5586	5584	45	2̄.008	12	1.992	1.992	12	35	20
26	6511	28	3489	3485	29	4368	46	5632	5630	46	3̄.995	13	2.005	2.005	13	34	16
27	6483	28	3517	3513	28	4322	46	5678	5677	47	3̄.982	13	2.018	2.018	13	33	12
28	6454	29	3546	3541	28	4275	47	5725	5724	47	3̄.969	13	2.031	2.031	13	32	8
29	6426	28	3574	3570	29	4227	48	5773	5771	47	3̄.955	14	2.045	2.045	14	31	4
30	6397	29	3603	3599	29	4179	48	5821	5819	48	3̄.941	14	2.059	2.059	14	30	+2m
31	6368	29	3632	3628	29	4131	48	5869	5868	49	3̄.926	15	2.074	2.074	15	29	56
32	6339	29	3661	3657	29	4082	49	5918	5917	49	3̄.911	15	2.089	2.089	15	28	52
33	6309	30	3691	3687	30	4032	50	5968	5967	50	3̄.895	16	2.105	2.105	16	27	48
34	6279	30	3721	3717	30	3982	50	6018	6017	50	3̄.879	16	2.121	2.121	16	26	44
35	6250	29	3750	3746	29	3931	51	6069	6068	51	3̄.862	17	2.138	2.138	17	25	40
36	6220	30	3780	3777	31	3880	51	6120	6119	51	3̄.844	18	2.156	2.156	18	24	36
37	6189	31	3811	3807	30	3828	52	6172	6171	52	3̄.825	19	2.175	2.175	19	23	32
38	6159	30	3841	3837	30	3775	53	6225	6224	53	3̄.806	19	2.194	2.194	19	22	28
39	6128	31	3872	3868	31	3722	53	6278	6277	53	3̄.786	20	2.214	2.214	20	21	24
40	6097	31	3903	3899	31	3668	54	6332	6331	54	3̄.765	21	2.235	2.235	21	20	20
41	6066	31	3934	3930	31	3613	55	6387	6386	55	3̄.742	23	2.258	2.258	23	19	16
42	6035	31	3965	3962	32	3558	55	6442	6441	55	3̄.719	23	2.281	2.281	23	18	12
43	6003	32	3997	3993	31	3502	56	6498	6497	56	3̄.694	25	2.306	2.306	25	17	8
44	5972	31	4028	4025	32	3445	57	6555	6554	57	3̄.668	26	2.332	2.332	26	16	4
45	5939	33	4061	4057	32	3388	57	6612	6611	57	3̄.640	28	2.360	2.360	28	15	+1m
46	5907	32	4093	4089	32	3329	59	6671	6670	59	3̄.610	30	2.390	2.390	30	14	56
47	5875	32	4125	4122	33	3270	59	6730	6729	59	3̄.578	32	2.422	2.422	32	13	52
48	5842	33	4158	4155	33	3210	60	6790	6789	60	3̄.543	35	2.457	2.457	35	12	48
49	5809	33	4191	4188	33	3150	60	6850	6850	61	3̄.505	38	2.495	2.495	38	11	44
50	5776	33	4224	4221	33	3088	62	6912	6911	61	3̄.464	41	2.536	2.536	41	10	40
51	5742	34	4258	4255	34	3025	63	6975	6974	63	3̄.418	46	2.582	2.582	46	9	36
52	5708	34	4292	4289	34	2962	63	7038	7037	63	3̄.367	51	2.633	2.633	51	8	32
53	5674	34	4326	4323	34	2898	64	7102	7101	64	3̄.309	58	2.691	2.691	58	7	28
54	5640	34	4360	4357	34	2832	66	7168	7167	66	3̄.242	67	2.758	2.758	67	6	24
55	5605	35	4395	4392	35	2766	66	7234	7233	66	3̄.163	79	2.837	2.837	79	5	20
56	5571	34	4429	4427	35	2699	67	7301	7300	67	3̄.066	97	2.934	2.934	97	4	16
57	5535	36	4465	4462	35	2630	69	7370	7369	69	4̄.941		3.059	3.059		3	12
58	5500	35	4500	4497	35	2561	69	7439	7438	69	4̄.765		3.235	3.235		2	8
59	5464	36	4536	4533	36	2490	71	7510	7509	71	4̄.464		3.536	3.536		1	4
60	5428	36	4572	4569	36	2419	71	7581	7581	72	−∞		∞	∞		0	0
	2̄.[8]	1·		1·		2̄.[8]	1·		1·		[6/8]						

	Sin.	D.	Cosec.	Cot.	D.	Sin.	D.	Cosec.	Cot.	D.	Sin.	D.	Cosec.	Cot.	D.	′	Secs
					2°					**1°**					**0°**		

0h08m   0h04m   0h00m

Table 20

HAVERSINES

Grouping of columns: **0°** (00′, 30′), **1°** (00′, 30′), **2°** (00′, 30′).

′	0° 00′ Nat	0° 00′ Log	0° 30′ Nat	0° 30′ Log	1° 00′ Nat	1° 00′ Log	1° 30′ Nat	1° 30′ Log	2° 00′ Nat	2° 00′ Log	2° 30′ Nat	2° 30′ Log	′
		[1–5]		[5]		5̄/4̄.[5/6]		4̄. [6]		4̄. [6]		4̄. [6]	
0	000000		000019		000076	88168	000171	23385	000305	48371	000476	67751	30
	0000	$\overline{9}.7233$	0020	$\overline{5}.2940$	0077	88889	0173	23866	0307	48732	0479	68040	
1	000000	$\overline{8}.3254$	000020	$\overline{5}.3081$	000079	89604	000175	24345	000310	49092	000482	68328	29
	0000	$\overline{8}.6776$	0021	$\overline{5}.3220$	0080	90313	0177	24821	0312	49450	0485	68615	
2	000000	$\overline{8}.9275$	000022	$\overline{5}.3357$	000081	91016	000179	25294	000315	49807	000489	68901	28
	0000	$\overline{7}.1213$	0022	$\overline{5}.3492$	0083	91714	0181	25765	0317	50162	0492	69186	
3	000000	$\overline{7}.2796$	000023	$\overline{5}.3624$	000084	92406	000183	26233	000320	50516	000495	69470	27
	0000	$\overline{7}.4135$	0024	$\overline{5}.3755$	0085	93093	0185	26699	0323	50868	0498	69754	
4	000000	$\overline{7}.5295$	000024	$\overline{5}.3883$	000087	93774	000187	27162	000325	51219	000502	70036	26
	0000	$\overline{7}.6318$	0025	$\overline{5}.4010$	0088	94450	0189	27623	0328	51568	0505	70318	
5	000001	$\overline{7}.7233$	000026	$\overline{5}.4135$	000089	95211	000191	28081	000330	51916	000508	70598	25
	0001	$\overline{7}.8061$	0027	$\overline{5}.4258$	0091	95786	0193	28537	0333	52263	0511	70878	
6	000001	$\overline{7}.8817$	000027	$\overline{5}.4380$	000092	96447	000195	28991	000336	52608	000515	71157	24
	0001	$\overline{7}.9512$	0028	$\overline{5}.4500$	0094	97102	0197	29442	0338	52952	0518	71435	
7	000001	$\overline{6}.0156$	000029	$\overline{5}.4618$	000095	97753	000199	29891	000341	53295	000521	71712	23
	0001	$\overline{6}.0755$	0030	$\overline{5}.4735$	0096	98399	0201	30337	0344	53636	0525	71988	
8	000001	$\overline{6}.1316$	000031	$\overline{5}.4850$	000098	99040	000203	30781	000347	53976	000528	72263	22
	0002	$\overline{6}.1842$	0031	$\overline{5}.4963$	0099	99676	0205	31223	0349	54315	0531	72537	
9	000002	$\overline{6}.2339$	000032	$\overline{5}.5075$	000101	00308	000207	31663	000352	54652	000535	72811	21
	0002	$\overline{6}.2808$	0033	$\overline{5}.5186$	0102	00935	0209	32101	0355	54988	0538	73083	
10	000002	$\overline{6}.3254$	000034	$\overline{5}.5295$	000104	01557	000212	32536	000357	55323	000541	73355	20
11	0002	$\overline{6}.3678$	0035	$\overline{5}.5403$	0105	02176	0214	32969	0360	55656	0545	73626	19
	000003	$\overline{6}.4082$	000036	$\overline{5}.5510$	000107	02789	000216	33400	000363	55988	000548	73896	
12	0003	$\overline{6}.4468$	0036	$\overline{5}.5615$	0108	03399	0218	33829	0366	56319	0552	74166	18
	000003	$\overline{6}.4838$	000037	$\overline{5}.5719$	000110	04004	000220	34256	000369	56649	000555	74434	
13	0003	$\overline{6}.5192$	0038	$\overline{5}.5822$	0111	04605	0222	34681	0371	56977	0558	74702	17
	000004	$\overline{6}.5533$	000039	$\overline{5}.5923$	000113	05202	000224	35103	000374	57304	000562	74969	
14	0004	$\overline{6}.5861$	0040	$\overline{5}.6024$	0114	05795	0227	35524	0377	57630	0565	75235	16
	000004	$\overline{6}.6176$	000041	$\overline{5}.6123$	000116	06384	000229	35943	000380	57955	000569	75500	
15	0004	$\overline{6}.6481$	0042	$\overline{5}.6221$	0117	06969	0231	36359	0383	58278	0572	75764	15
	000005	$\overline{6}.6776$	000043	$\overline{5}.6318$	000119	07550	000233	36774	000385	58600	000576	76028	
16	0005	$\overline{6}.7061$	0044	$\overline{5}.6414$	0121	08127	0235	37186	0388	58921	0579	76290	14
	000005	$\overline{6}.7336$	000045	$\overline{5}.6509$	000122	08700	000238	37597	000391	59241	000583	76552	
17	0006	$\overline{6}.7604$	0046	$\overline{5}.6603$	0124	09270	0240	38006	0394	59560	0586	76814	13
	000006	$\overline{6}.7863$	000047	$\overline{5}.6696$	000125	09836	000242	38412	000397	59878	000590	77074	
18	0006	$\overline{6}.8115$	0048	$\overline{5}.6788$	0127	10398	0244	38817	0400	60194	0593	77334	12
	000007	$\overline{6}.8359$	000049	$\overline{5}.6879$	000129	10956	000247	39220	000403	60509	000597	77593	
19	0007	$\overline{6}.8597$	0050	$\overline{5}.6969$	0130	11511	0249	39621	0406	60823	0600	77851	11
	000008	$\overline{6}.8829$	000051	$\overline{5}.7058$	000132	12064	000251	40021	000409	61136	000604	78108	
20	0008	$\overline{6}.9055$	0052	$\overline{5}.7146$	0134	12611	0253	40418	0412	61448	0608	78364	10
	000008	$\overline{6}.9275$	000053	$\overline{5}.7233$	000135	13155	000256	40814	000415	61759	000611	78620	
21	0009	$\overline{6}.9489$	0054	$\overline{5}.7320$	0137	13696	0258	41208	0418	62069	0615	78875	9
	000009	$\overline{6}.9698$	000055	$\overline{5}.7405$	000139	14234	000261	41600	000421	62377	000618	79129	
22	0010	$\overline{6}.9903$	0056	$\overline{5}.7490$	0140	14769	0263	41990	0424	62684	0622	79383	8
	000010	$\overline{5}.0102$	000057	$\overline{5}.7574$	000142	15300	000265	42379	000427	62991	000626	79636	
23	0011	$\overline{5}.0298$	0058	$\overline{5}.7657$	0144	15828	0268	42766	0430	63296	0629	79888	7
	000011	$\overline{5}.0488$	000059	$\overline{5}.7739$	000146	16353	000270	43151	000433	63600	000633	80139	
24	0012	$\overline{5}.0675$	0061	$\overline{5}.7821$	0147	16874	0273	43534	0436	63903	0637	80390	6
	000012	$\overline{5}.0858$	000062	$\overline{5}.7902$	000149	17393	000275	43916	000439	64205	000640	80640	
25	0013	$\overline{5}.1037$	0063	$\overline{5}.7982$	0151	17908	0277	44296	0442	64506	0644	80889	5
	000013	$\overline{5}.1213$	000064	$\overline{5}.8061$	000153	18421	000280	44675	000445	64806	000648	81137	
26	0014	$\overline{5}.1385$	0065	$\overline{5}.8140$	0155	18930	0282	45052	0448	65105	0651	81385	4
	000014	$\overline{5}.1553$	000066	$\overline{5}.8218$	000156	19437	000285	45427	000451	65403	000655	81632	
27	0015	$\overline{5}.1719$	0068	$\overline{5}.8295$	0158	19940	0287	45800	0454	65700	0659	81879	3
	000015	$\overline{5}.1881$	000069	$\overline{5}.8371$	000160	20441	000290	46172	000457	65996	000663	82124	
28	0016	$\overline{5}.2041$	0070	$\overline{5}.8447$	0162	20938	0292	46543	0460	66291	0666	82369	2
	000016	$\overline{5}.2197$	000071	$\overline{5}.8522$	000164	21433	000295	46912	000463	66585	000670	82613	
29	0017	$\overline{5}.2351$	0072	$\overline{5}.8597$	0166	21925	0297	47279	0466	66878	0674	82857	1
	000018	$\overline{5}.2502$	000074	$\overline{5}.8671$	000168	22415	000300	47644	000470	67170	000678	83100	
30	0018	$\overline{5}.2650$	0075	$\overline{5}.8744$	0169	22901	0302	48008	0473	67461	0681	83342	0
	000019	$\overline{5}.2796$	000076	$\overline{5}.8817$	000171	23385	000305	48371	000476	67751	000685	83584	
		[5–1]		[5]		4̄/5̄.[6/5]		4̄. [6]		4̄. [6]		4̄. [6]	

30′		00′		30′		00′		30′		00′			′

359°			**358°**			**357°**		

Table 20   **HAVERSINES**

| | 3° | | | | 4° | | | | 5° | | | | |
| | 00′ | | 30′ | | 00′ | | 30′ | | 00′ | | 30′ | | |
′	Nat.	Log.	Nat.	Log.	Nat.	Log.	Nat.	Log.	Nat.	Log.	Nat.	Log.	′
		4̄. [6]		4̄/3̄.[6/7]		3̄. [7]		3̄. [7]		3̄. [7]		3̄. [7]	
0	000685	83584	000933	96970	001218	08564	001541	18790	001903	27936	002302	36209	30
	0689	83825	0937	97176	1223	08745	1547	18950	1909	28080	2309	36340	
1	000693	84065	000941	97382	001228	08925	001553	19111	001915	28225	002316	36471	29
	0697	84304	0946	97588	1233	09105	1558	19271	1922	28369	2323	36602	
2	000701	84543	000950	97793	001238	09284	001564	19430	001928	28513	002330	36733	28
	0704	84782	0955	97997	1243	09464	1570	19590	1934	28656	2337	36864	
3	000708	85019	000959	98201	001249	09642	001576	19749	001941	28800	002344	36994	27
	0712	85256	0964	98405	1254	09821	1582	19908	1947	28943	2351	37124	
4	000716	85492	000968	98608	001259	09999	001587	20066	001954	29086	002358	37254	26
	0720	85728	0973	98811	1264	10177	1593	20225	1960	29228	2365	37384	
5	000724	85963	000977	99013	001269	10354	001599	20383	001967	29371	002372	37514	25
	0728	86197	0982	99214	1274	10531	1605	20540	1973	29513	2379	37643	
6	000732	86431	000987	99416	001280	10708	001611	20698	001979	29655	002386	37772	24
	0736	86664	0991	99617	1285	10884	1616	20855	1986	29797	2393	37901	
7	000740	86897	000996	99817	001290	11060	001622	21012	001992	29938	002400	38030	23
	0744	87129	1000	00017	1295	11235	1628	21168	1999	30079	2408	38159	
8	000747	87360	001005	00216	001300	11411	001634	21325	002005	30220	002415	38288	22
	0751	87591	1010	00415	1306	11586	1640	21481	2012	30361	2422	38416	
9	000755	87821	001014	00613	001311	11760	001646	21636	002018	30501	002429	38544	21
	0759	88050	1019	00811	1316	11934	1652	21792	2025	30642	2436	38672	
10	000763	88279	001023	01009	001322	12108	001658	21947	002031	30782	002443	38800	20
	0767	88507	1028	01206	1327	12282	1663	22102	2038	30922	2451	38927	
11	000771	88735	001033	01403	001332	12455	001669	22256	002045	31062	002458	39054	19
	0775	88962	1038	01599	1337	12627	1675	22411	2051	31201	2465	39182	
12	000780	89188	001042	01795	001343	12800	001681	22565	002058	31340	002472	39309	18
	0784	89414	1047	01990	1348	12972	1687	22719	2064	31479	2479	39435	
13	000788	89639	001052	02185	001353	13144	001693	22872	002071	31618	002487	39562	17
	0792	89864	1056	02379	1359	13315	1699	23025	2078	31757	2494	39688	
14	000796	90088	001061	02573	001364	13486	001705	23178	002084	31895	002501	39815	16
	0800	90312	1066	02767	1370	13657	1711	23331	2091	32033	2508	39941	
15	000804	90535	001071	02960	001375	13827	001717	23483	002098	32171	002516	40067	15
	0808	90757	1075	03153	1380	13997	1723	23635	2104	32309	2523	40192	
16	000812	90979	001080	03345	001386	14167	001729	23787	002111	32446	002530	40318	14
	0817	91200	1085	03537	1391	14337	1735	23939	2118	32583	2538	40443	
17	000821	91421	001090	03729	001397	14506	001741	24090	002124	32720	002545	40568	13
	0825	91641	1094	03920	1402	14674	1747	24241	2131	32857	2552	40693	
18	000829	91860	001099	04110	001407	14843	001754	24392	002138	32994	002560	40818	12
	0833	92079	1104	04300	1413	15011	1760	24543	2144	33130	2567	40943	
19	000837	92298	001109	04490	001418	15179	001766	24693	002151	33266	002574	41067	11
	0842	92516	1114	04680	1423	15346	1772	24843	2158	33402	2582	41191	
20	000846	92733	001119	04869	001429	15513	001778	24993	002165	33538	002589	41315	10
	0850	92950	1123	05057	1435	15680	1784	25143	2171	33673	2597	41439	
21	000854	93166	001128	05245	001440	15846	001790	25292	002178	33809	002604	41563	9
	0859	93382	1133	05433	1446	16012	1796	25441	2185	33944	2611	41686	
22	000863	93597	001138	05620	001451	16178	001803	25590	002192	34079	002619	41810	8
	0867	93812	1143	05807	1457	16344	1809	25738	2199	34213	2626	41933	
23	000871	94026	001148	05994	001462	16509	001815	25886	002205	34348	002634	42056	7
	0876	94240	1153	06180	1468	16674	1821	26034	2212	34482	2641	42179	
24	000880	94453	001158	06366	001474	16839	001827	26182	002219	34616	002649	42301	6
	0884	94665	1163	06551	1479	17003	1834	26330	2226	34750	2656	42424	
25	000889	94877	001168	06736	001485	17167	001840	26477	002233	34884	002664	42546	5
	0893	95089	1173	06921	1490	17331	1846	26624	2240	35017	2671	42668	
26	000897	95300	001178	07105	001496	17494	001852	26771	002246	35150	002679	42790	4
	0902	95510	1183	07288	1502	17657	1858	26917	2253	35283	2686	42912	
27	000906	95720	001188	07472	001507	17820	001865	27063	002260	35416	002694	43034	3
	0911	95930	1193	07655	1513	17982	1871	27209	2267	35549	2701	43155	
28	000915	96139	001198	07837	001519	18144	001877	27355	002274	35681	002709	43277	2
	0919	96347	1203	08019	1524	18306	1884	27501	2281	35813	2716	43398	
29	000924	96555	001208	08201	001530	18468	001890	27646	002288	35945	002724	43519	1
	0928	96763	1213	08383	1536	18629	1896	27791	2295	36077	2731	43639	
30	000933	96970	001218	08564	001541	18790	001903	27936	002302	36209	002739	43760	0
		4̄. [6]		3̄/4̄.[7/6]		3̄. [7]		3̄. [7]		3̄. [7]		3̄. [7]	
	30′		00′		30′		00′		30′		00′		′

Table 20 — HAVERSINES

	6°				7°				8°				
	00′		30′		00′		30′		00′		30′		
′	Nat.	Log.	Nat.	Log.	Nat.	Log.	Nat.	Log.	Nat.	Log.	Nat.	Log.	
0	002739	3̄.[7] 43760	003214	3̄.[7] 50706	003727	3̄.[7] 57135	004278	3̄.[7] 63120	004866	3̄.[7] 68717	005492	3̄.[7] 73974	30
	2747	43880	3222	50817	3736	57238	4287	63216	4876	68807	5503	74059	
1	002754	44001	003231	50928	003745	57341	004297	63312	004886	68897	005514	74143	29
	2762	44121	3239	51039	3754	57444	4306	63408	4896	68987	5524	74228	
2	002770	44241	003247	51149	003762	57547	004316	63504	004907	69077	005535	74313	28
	2777	44361	3255	51260	3771	57650	4325	63600	4917	69167	5546	74398	
3	002785	44480	003264	51370	003780	57752	004335	63696	004927	69257	005557	74482	27
	2793	44600	3272	51481	3789	57855	4344	63792	4937	69347	5568	74567	
4	002800	44719	003280	51591	003798	57957	004354	63887	004947	69437	005578	74651	26
	2808	44838	3289	51701	3807	58060	4363	63983	4957	69526	5589	74735	
5	002816	44957	003297	51811	003816	58162	004373	64078	004968	69616	005600	74819	25
	2823	45076	3305	51921	3825	58264	4383	64173	4978	69705	5611	74904	
6	002831	45194	003314	52030	003834	58366	004392	64269	004988	69794	005622	74988	24
	2839	45313	3322	52140	3843	58467	4402	64364	4998	69883	5633	75072	
7	002846	45431	003330	52249	003852	58569	004411	64458	005009	69972	005644	75155	23
	2854	45549	3339	52358	3861	58670	4421	64553	5019	70061	5654	75239	
8	002862	45667	003347	52467	003870	58772	004431	64648	005029	70150	005665	75323	22
	2870	45785	3356	52576	3879	58873	4440	64743	5040	70239	5676	75407	
9	002878	45903	003364	52685	003888	58974	004450	64837	005050	70328	005687	75490	21
	2885	46020	3372	52794	3897	59075	4460	64932	5060	70416	5698	75574	
10	002893	46138	003381	52902	003906	59176	004469	65026	005071	70505	005709	75657	20
	2901	46255	3389	53011	3915	59277	4479	65120	5081	70593	5720	75740	
11	002909	46372	003398	53119	003924	59378	004489	65214	005091	70682	005731	75824	19
	2917	46489	3406	53227	3934	59478	4499	65308	5102	70770	5742	75907	
12	002924	46605	003415	53335	003943	59579	004508	65402	005112	70858	005753	75990	18
	2932	46722	3423	53443	3952	59679	4518	65496	5122	70946	5764	76073	
13	002940	46838	003432	53550	003961	59779	004528	65590	005133	71034	005775	76156	17
	2948	46955	3440	53658	3970	59879	4538	65683	5143	71122	5786	76239	
14	002956	47071	003449	53765	003979	59979	004547	65777	005153	71210	005797	76321	16
	2964	47187	3457	53873	3988	60079	4557	65870	5164	71298	5808	76404	
15	002972	47302	003466	53980	003998	60179	004567	65964	005174	71385	005819	76487	15
	2980	47418	3474	54087	4007	60279	4577	66057	5185	71473	5830	76569	
16	002988	47533	003483	54194	004016	60378	004587	66150	005195	71560	005841	76652	14
	2996	47649	3491	54301	4025	60478	4597	66243	5206	71648	5852	76734	
17	003004	47764	003500	54407	004034	60577	004606	66336	005216	71735	005864	76816	13
	3012	47879	3509	54514	4044	60676	4616	66429	5227	71822	5875	76898	
18	003020	47994	003517	54620	004053	60775	004626	66521	005237	71909	005886	76981	12
	3028	48109	3526	54727	4062	60874	4636	66614	5248	71996	5897	77063	
19	003036	48223	003534	54833	004071	60973	004646	66706	005258	72083	005908	77145	11
	3044	48337	3543	54939	4081	61072	4656	66799	5269	72170	5919	77227	
20	003052	48452	003552	55045	004090	61170	004666	66891	005279	72257	005930	77308	10
	3060	48566	3560	55150	4099	61269	4676	66983	5290	72343	5942	77390	
21	003068	48680	003569	55256	004108	61367	004685	67075	005300	72430	005953	77472	9
	3076	48794	3578	55361	4118	61466	4695	67167	5311	72516	5964	77553	
22	003084	48907	003586	55467	004127	61564	004705	67259	005321	72603	005975	77635	8
	3092	49021	3595	55572	4136	61662	4715	67351	5332	72689	5986	77716	
23	003100	49134	003604	55677	004146	61760	004725	67443	005343	72775	005998	77798	7
	3108	49247	3613	55782	4155	61858	4735	67535	5353	72861	6009	77879	
24	003116	49360	003621	55887	004164	61955	004745	67626	005364	72947	006020	77960	6
	3124	49473	3630	55992	4174	62053	4755	67717	5374	73033	6031	78041	
25	003132	49586	003639	56096	004183	62151	004765	67809	005385	73119	006043	78122	5
	3140	49699	3648	56201	4193	62248	4775	67900	5396	73205	6054	78203	
26	003149	49811	003656	56305	004202	62345	004785	67991	005406	73291	006065	78284	4
	3157	49923	3665	56409	4211	62442	4795	68082	5417	73377	6076	78365	
27	003165	50036	003674	56513	004221	62539	004805	68173	005428	73462	006088	78446	3
	3173	50148	3683	56617	4230	62636	4815	68264	5438	73548	6099	78526	
28	003181	50259	003692	56721	004240	62733	004826	68355	005449	73633	006110	78607	2
	3189	50371	3700	56825	4249	62830	4836	68445	5460	73718	6122	78688	
29	003198	50483	003709	56928	004259	62927	004846	68536	005471	73803	006133	78768	1
	3206	50594	3718	57032	4268	63023	4856	68627	5481	73889	6144	78848	
30	003214	50706	003727	57135	004278	63120	004866	68717	005492	73974	006156	78929	0
		3̄.[7]		3̄.[7]		3̄.[7]		3̄.[7]		3̄.[7]		3̄.[7]	
	30′		00′		30′		00′		30′		00′		′

353°	352°	351°

Table 20 HAVERSINES

	9° 00′ Nat.	Log.	9° 30′ Nat.	Log.	10° 00′ Nat.	Log.	10° 30′ Nat.	Log.	11° 00′ Nat.	Log.	11° 30′ Nat.	Log.	
′		3̄. [7]		3̄. [7]		3̄. [7]		3̄. [7]		3̄/2̄. [7/8]		2̄. [8]	′
0	00616	78929	00686	83615	00760	88059	00837	92286	00919	96315	01004	00163	30
	617	79009	687	83691	761	88131	839	92354	920	96380	005	00226	
1	00618	79089	00688	83767	00762	88203	00840	92423	00921	96446	01007	00289	29
	619	79169	689	83842	763	88275	841	92492	923	96511	008	00351	
2	00620	79249	00691	83918	00765	88347	00843	92560	00924	96577	01010	00414	28
	621	79329	692	83994	766	88419	844	92629	926	96642	011	00476	
3	00622	79409	00693	84070	00767	88491	00845	92697	00927	96707	01012	00539	27
	624	79489	694	84145	768	88563	847	92766	928	96773	014	00601	
4	00625	79568	00695	84221	00770	88635	00848	92834	00930	96838	01015	00664	26
	626	79648	697	84296	771	88707	849	92902	931	96903	017	00726	
5	00627	79728	00698	84372	00772	88778	00851	92970	00933	96968	01018	00788	25
	628	79807	699	84447	774	88850	852	93039	934	97033	020	00851	
6	00629	79886	00700	84522	00775	88921	00853	93107	00935	97098	01021	00913	24
	630	79966	701	84597	776	88993	855	93175	937	97163	023	00975	
7	00632	80045	00703	84672	00777	89064	00856	93243	00938	97228	01024	01037	23
	633	80124	704	84747	779	89135	857	93311	940	97293	026	01099	
8	00634	80203	00705	84822	00780	89207	00859	93379	00941	97358	01027	01161	22
	635	80282	706	84897	781	89278	860	93447	942	97423	029	01223	
9	00636	80361	00707	84972	00783	89349	00861	93514	00944	97487	01030	01285	21
	637	80440	709	85047	784	89420	863	93582	945	97552	032	01347	
10	00639	80519	00710	85122	00785	89491	00864	93650	00947	97617	01033	01409	20
	640	80598	711	85196	786	89562	865	93717	948	97681	034	01471	
11	00641	80677	00712	85271	00788	89633	00867	93785	00949	97746	01036	01532	19
	642	80755	714	85346	789	89704	868	93852	951	97810	037	01594	
12	00643	80834	00715	85420	00790	89775	00869	93920	00952	97875	01039	01656	18
	644	80912	716	85494	792	89846	871	93987	954	97939	040	01717	
13	00646	80991	00717	85569	00793	89916	00872	94055	00955	98003	01042	01779	17
	647	81069	719	85643	794	89987	873	94122	956	98068	043	01840	
14	00648	81147	00720	85717	00795	90057	00875	94189	00958	98132	01045	01902	16
	649	81225	721	85791	797	90128	876	94257	959	98196	046	01963	
15	00650	81303	00722	85866	00798	90198	00877	94324	00961	98260	01048	02025	15
	651	81382	723	85940	799	90269	879	94391	962	98325	049	02086	
16	00653	81459	00725	86014	00801	90339	00880	94458	00964	98389	01051	02147	14
	654	81537	726	86087	802	90409	882	94525	965	98453	052	02209	
17	00655	81615	00727	86161	00803	90480	00883	94592	00966	98517	01054	02270	13
	656	81693	728	86235	804	90550	884	94659	968	98581	055	02331	
18	00657	81771	00730	86309	00806	90620	00886	94726	00969	98644	01057	02392	12
	658	81848	731	86382	807	90690	887	94792	971	98708	058	02453	
19	00660	81926	00732	86456	00808	90760	00888	94859	00972	98772	01060	02514	11
	661	82003	733	86530	810	90830	890	94926	974	98836	061	02575	
20	00662	82081	00735	86603	00811	90900	00891	94992	00975	98899	01063	02636	10
	663	82158	736	86676	812	90970	892	95059	976	98963	064	02697	
21	00664	82235	00737	86750	00814	91039	00894	95126	00978	99027	01066	02758	9
	665	82313	738	86823	815	91109	895	95192	979	99090	067	02819	
22	00667	82390	00740	86896	00816	91179	00897	95259	00981	99154	01069	02880	8
	668	82467	741	86969	817	91248	898	95325	982	99217	070	02941	
23	00669	82544	00742	87042	00819	91318	00899	95391	00984	99280	01072	03001	7
	670	82621	743	87115	820	91387	901	95458	985	99344	073	03062	
24	00671	82698	00745	87188	00821	91457	00902	95524	00986	99407	01075	03123	6
	673	82774	746	87261	823	91526	903	95590	988	99470	076	03183	
25	00674	82851	00747	87334	00824	91596	00905	95656	00989	99534	01078	03244	5
	675	82928	748	87407	825	91665	906	95722	991	99597	079	03304	
26	00676	83004	00750	87480	00827	91734	00908	95788	00992	99660	01081	03365	4
	677	83081	751	87552	828	91803	909	95854	994	99723	082	03425	
27	00679	83157	00752	87625	00829	91872	00910	95920	00995	99786	01084	03486	3
	680	83234	753	87697	831	91941	912	95986	997	99849	085	03546	
28	00681	83310	00755	87770	00832	92010	00913	96052	00998	99912	01087	03606	2
	682	83386	756	87842	833	92079	914	96118	00999	99975	088	03666	
29	00683	83462	00757	87915	00835	92148	00916	96183	01001	00038	01090	03727	1
	685	83539	758	87987	836	92217	917	96249	002	00100	091	03787	
30	00686	83615	00760	88059	00837	92286	00919	96315	01004	00163	01093	03847	0
		3̄. [7]		3̄. [7]		3̄. [7]		3̄. [7]		2̄/3̄. [8/7]		2̄. [8]	′
		30′		00′		30′		00′		30′		00′	

| | 350° | | | | 349° | | | | 348° | | | | |

Table 20   HAVERSINES

′	12° 00′ Nat.	12° 00′ Log.	12° 30′ Nat.	12° 30′ Log.	13° 00′ Nat.	13° 00′ Log.	13° 30′ Nat.	13° 30′ Log.	14° 00′ Nat.	14° 00′ Log.	14° 30′ Nat.	14° 30′ Log.	′
		$\overline{2}$. [8]		$\overline{2}$. [8]		$\overline{2}$. [8]		$\overline{2}$. [8]		$\overline{2}$. [8]		$\overline{2}$. [8]	
0	01093	03847	01185	07379	01281	10772	01382	14035	01485	17179	01593	20211	30
	094	907	187	437	283	827	383	089	487	230	594	261	
1	01096	03967	01188	07494	01285	10883	01385	14142	01489	17282	01596	20310	29
	097	04027	190	552	286	938	387	195	490	333	598	360	
2	01099	04087	01192	07610	01288	10993	01388	14248	01492	17384	01600	20410	28
	100	147	193	667	290	11049	390	302	494	436	602	459	
3	01102	04207	01195	07725	01291	11104	01392	14355	01496	17487	01604	20509	27
	103	267	196	782	293	159	393	408	498	538	605	558	
4	01105	04326	01198	07839	01295	11214	01395	14461	01499	17589	01607	20607	26
	106	386	199	897	296	269	397	514	501	641	609	657	
5	01108	04446	01201	07954	01298	11324	01399	14567	01503	17692	01611	20706	25
	109	505	203	08011	300	379	400	620	505	743	613	756	
6	01111	04565	01204	08068	01301	11434	01402	14673	01506	17794	01615	20805	24
	112	625	206	126	303	489	404	726	508	845	616	854	
7	01114	04684	01207	08183	01305	11544	01405	14779	01510	17896	01618	20903	23
	115	744	209	240	306	599	407	832	512	947	620	20953	
8	01117	04803	01211	08297	01308	11654	01409	14885	01513	17998	01622	21002	22
	118	863	212	354	309	709	411	938	515	18049	624	051	
9	01120	04922	01214	08411	01311	11764	01412	14991	01517	18100	01626	21100	21
	122	04981	215	468	313	819	414	15043	519	151	627	149	
10	01123	05041	01217	08525	01314	11873	01416	15096	01521	18202	01629	21198	20
	125	100	218	582	316	928	417	149	522	253	631	248	
11	01126	05159	01220	08639	01318	11983	01419	15201	01524	18303	01633	21297	19
	128	218	222	696	319	12038	421	254	526	354	635	346	
12	01129	05277	01223	08752	01321	12092	01423	15307	01528	18405	01637	21395	18
	131	336	225	809	323	147	424	359	530	455	638	444	
13	01132	05395	01226	08866	01324	12201	01426	15412	01531	18506	01640	21492	17
	134	454	228	922	326	256	428	464	533	557	642	541	
14	01135	05513	01230	08979	01328	12310	01429	15517	01535	18607	01644	21590	16
	137	572	231	09036	329	365	431	569	537	658	646	639	
15	01138	05631	01233	09092	01331	12419	01433	15621	01538	18708	01648	21688	15
	140	690	234	149	333	473	435	674	540	759	650	737	
16	01142	05749	01236	09205	01334	12528	01436	15726	01542	18809	01651	21785	14
	143	808	238	262	336	582	438	779	544	860	653	834	
17	01145	05866	01239	09318	01338	12636	01440	15831	01546	18910	01655	21883	13
	146	925	241	374	339	691	442	883	547	18961	657	932	
18	01148	05984	01243	09431	01341	12745	01443	15935	01549	19011	01659	21980	12
	149	06042	244	487	343	799	445	15987	551	062	661	22029	
19	01151	06101	01246	09543	01344	12853	01447	16040	01553	19112	01663	22077	11
	152	159	247	600	346	907	448	092	555	162	664	126	
20	01154	06218	01249	09656	01348	12961	01450	16144	01556	19212	01666	22175	10
	155	276	251	712	349	13015	452	196	558	263	668	223	
21	01157	06335	01252	09768	01351	13069	01454	16248	01560	19313	01670	22272	9
	159	393	254	824	353	123	455	300	562	363	672	320	
22	01160	06451	01255	09880	01354	13177	01457	16352	01564	19413	01674	22368	8
	162	510	257	936	356	231	459	404	565	463	676	417	
23	01163	06568	01259	09992	01358	13285	01461	16456	01567	19513	01677	22465	7
	165	626	260	10048	360	339	462	508	569	563	679	514	
24	01166	06684	01262	10104	01361	13392	01464	16559	01571	19613	01681	22562	6
	168	742	264	160	363	446	466	611	573	663	683	610	
25	01170	06800	01265	10216	01365	13500	01468	16663	01574	19713	01685	22658	5
	171	858	267	271	366	554	469	715	576	763	687	707	
26	01173	06916	01268	10327	01368	13607	01471	16766	01578	19813	01689	22755	4
	174	06974	270	383	370	661	473	818	580	863	691	803	
27	01176	07032	01272	10438	01371	13714	01475	16870	01582	19913	01692	22851	3
	177	090	273	494	373	768	476	921	584	19963	694	899	
28	01179	07148	01275	10550	01375	13821	01478	16973	01585	20012	01696	22947	2
	180	206	277	605	376	875	480	17024	587	062	698	22996	
29	01182	07264	01278	10661	01378	13928	01482	17076	01589	20112	01700	23044	1
	184	322	280	716	380	13982	483	127	591	162	702	092	
30	01185	07379	01281	10772	01382	14035	01485	17179	01593	20211	01704	23140	0
		$\overline{2}$. [8]		$\overline{2}$. [8]		$\overline{2}$. [8]		$\overline{2}$. [8]		$\overline{2}$. [8]		$\overline{2}$. [8]	
	30′		00′		30′		00′		30′		00′		′
	347°				**346°**				**345°**				

Table 20   **HAVERSINES**

′	15° 00′ Nat.	15° 00′ Log.	15° 30′ Nat.	15° 30′ Log.	16° 00′ Nat.	16° 00′ Log.	16° 30′ Nat.	16° 30′ Log.	17° 00′ Nat.	17° 00′ Log.	17° 30′ Nat.	17° 30′ Log.	′
		$\overline{2}$. [8]		$\overline{2}$. [8]		$\overline{2}$. [8]		$\overline{2}$. [8]		$\overline{2}$. [8]		$\overline{2}$. [8]	
0	01704	23140	01818	25971	01937	28711	02059	31366	02185	33940	02314	36439	30
	706	188	820	26017	939	756	061	409	187	33983	316	480	
1	01707	23235	01822	26064	01941	28801	02063	31453	02189	34025	02319	36521	29
	709	283	824	110	943	846	065	497	191	067	321	562	
2	01711	23331	01826	26156	01945	28891	02067	31540	02193	34109	02323	36603	28
	713	379	828	203	947	935	069	583	195	152	325	644	
3	01715	23427	01830	26249	01949	28980	02071	31627	02198	34194	02327	36685	27
	717	475	832	295	951	29025	073	670	200	236	329	726	
4	01719	23523	01834	26341	01953	29070	02076	31714	02202	34278	02332	36767	26
	721	570	836	388	955	115	078	757	204	320	334	808	
5	01723	23618	01838	26434	01957	29159	02080	31800	02206	34362	02336	36849	25
	724	666	840	480	959	204	082	844	208	404	338	889	
6	01726	23713	01842	26526	01961	29249	02084	31887	02210	34446	02340	36930	24
	728	761	844	572	963	293	086	930	212	488	343	36971	
7	01730	23809	01846	26618	01965	29338	02088	31974	02215	34530	02345	37012	23
	732	856	848	664	967	383	090	32017	217	572	347	053	
8	01734	23904	01850	26710	01969	29427	02092	32060	02219	34614	02349	37093	22
	736	951	852	756	971	472	094	103	221	656	351	134	
9	01738	23999	01854	26802	01973	29516	02096	32146	02223	34698	02354	37175	21
	740	24046	856	848	975	561	098	190	225	740	356	215	
10	01742	24094	01858	26894	01977	29605	02101	32233	02227	34782	02358	37256	20
	743	141	860	940	979	650	103	276	230	823	360	297	
11	01745	24189	01861	26986	01981	29694	02105	32319	02232	34865	02363	37337	19
	747	236	863	27032	983	739	107	362	234	907	365	378	
12	01749	24283	01865	27078	01985	29783	02109	32405	02236	34949	02367	37418	18
	751	331	867	123	987	827	111	448	238	34991	369	459	
13	01753	24378	01869	27169	01989	29872	02113	32491	02240	35032	02371	37500	17
	755	425	871	215	991	916	115	534	243	074	374	540	
14	01757	24472	01873	27261	01993	29960	02117	32577	02245	35116	02376	37581	16
	759	520	875	306	995	30005	119	620	247	157	378	621	
15	01761	24567	01877	27352	01998	30049	02121	32663	02249	35199	02380	37662	15
	763	614	879	398	02000	093	124	706	251	241	382	702	
16	01764	24661	01881	27443	02002	30137	02126	32749	02253	35282	02385	37742	14
	766	708	883	489	004	182	128	792	255	324	387	783	
17	01768	24755	01885	27534	02006	30226	02130	32834	02258	35365	02389	37823	13
	770	803	887	580	008	270	132	877	260	407	391	864	
18	01772	24850	01889	27626	02010	30314	02134	32920	02262	35448	02394	37904	12
	774	897	891	671	012	358	136	32963	264	490	396	944	
19	01776	24944	01893	27717	02014	30402	02138	33005	02266	35531	02398	37985	11
	778	24991	895	762	016	446	140	048	268	573	400	38025	
20	01780	25037	01897	27807	02018	30490	02142	33091	02271	35614	02402	38065	10
	782	084	899	853	020	534	145	134	273	656	405	105	
21	01784	25131	01901	27898	02022	30578	02147	33176	02275	35697	02407	38146	9
	786	178	903	944	024	622	149	219	277	739	409	186	
22	01788	25225	01905	27989	02026	30666	02151	33262	02279	35780	02411	38226	8
	789	272	907	28034	028	710	153	304	281	821	414	266	
23	01791	25319	01909	28080	02030	30754	02155	33347	02284	35863	02416	38306	7
	793	365	911	125	032	798	157	389	286	904	418	346	
24	01795	25412	01913	28170	02034	30842	02159	33432	02288	35945	02420	38387	6
	797	459	915	215	036	885	161	474	290	35987	423	427	
25	01799	25505	01917	28260	02038	30929	02164	33517	02292	36028	02425	38467	5
	801	552	919	306	040	30973	166	559	295	069	427	507	
26	01803	25599	01921	28351	02043	31017	02168	33602	02297	36110	02429	38547	4
	805	645	923	396	045	060	170	644	299	151	431	587	
27	01807	25692	01925	28441	02047	31104	02172	33686	02301	36193	02434	38627	3
	809	738	927	486	049	148	174	729	303	234	436	667	
28	01811	25785	01929	28531	02051	31191	02176	33771	02305	36275	02438	38707	2
	813	831	931	576	053	235	178	814	308	316	440	747	
29	01815	25878	01933	28621	02055	31279	02181	33856	02310	36357	02443	38787	1
	817	924	935	666	057	322	183	898	312	398	445	827	
30	01818	25971	01937	28711	02059	31366	02185	33940	02314	36439	02447	38867	0
		$\overline{2}$. [8]		$\overline{2}$. [8]		$\overline{2}$. [8]		$\overline{2}$. [8]		$\overline{2}$. [8]		$\overline{2}$. [8]	

	30′		00′		30′		00′		30′		00′	′
	344°				**343°**				**342°**			

Table 20 — HAVERSINES

	18° 00′ Nat.	18° 00′ Log.	18° 30′ Nat.	18° 30′ Log.	19° 00′ Nat.	19° 00′ Log.	19° 30′ Nat.	19° 30′ Log.	20° 00′ Nat.	20° 00′ Log.	20° 30′ Nat.	20° 30′ Log.	
		2̄.[8]		2̄.[8]		2̄.[8]		2̄.[8]		2̄.[8]		2̄.[8]	
0	02447	38867	02584	41226	02724	43522	02868	45757	03015	47934	03166	50056	30
	449	906	586	265	726	560	870	794	018	47970	169	091	
1	02452	38946	02588	41304	02729	43597	02873	45830	03020	48006	03171	50126	29
	454	38986	591	342	731	635	875	867	023	041	174	161	
2	02456	39026	02593	41381	02734	43673	02878	45904	03025	48077	03177	50196	28
	458	066	595	420	736	710	880	940	028	113	179	231	
3	02461	39105	02598	41459	02738	43748	02883	45977	03030	48149	03182	50266	27
	463	145	600	497	741	786	885	46014	033	184	184	301	
4	02465	39185	02602	41536	02743	43823	02887	46050	03035	48220	03187	50335	26
	467	225	605	575	745	861	890	087	038	256	189	370	
5	02470	39264	02607	41613	02748	43898	02892	46124	03040	48292	03192	50405	25
	472	304	609	652	750	936	895	160	043	327	194	440	
6	02474	39344	02612	41690	02753	43974	02897	46197	03045	48363	03197	50475	24
	476	383	614	729	755	44011	900	233	048	399	200	509	
7	02479	39423	02616	41767	02757	44049	02902	46270	03050	48434	03202	50544	23
	481	463	619	806	760	086	904	306	053	470	205	579	
8	02483	39502	02621	41844	02762	44124	02907	46343	03055	48505	03207	50613	22
	486	542	623	883	764	161	909	379	058	541	210	648	
9	02488	39581	02626	41921	02767	44199	02912	46416	03060	48576	03212	50683	21
	490	621	628	960	769	236	914	452	063	612	215	718	
10	02492	39660	02630	41998	02772	44273	02917	46489	03065	48647	03218	50752	20
	495	700	632	42037	774	311	919	525	068	683	220	787	
11	02497	39739	02635	42075	02776	44348	02922	46562	03070	48718	03223	50821	19
	499	779	637	114	779	386	924	598	073	754	225	856	
12	02501	39818	02639	42152	02781	44423	02926	46634	03075	48789	03228	50891	18
	504	858	642	190	784	460	929	671	078	825	230	925	
13	02506	39897	02644	42229	02786	44498	02931	46707	03080	48860	03233	50960	17
	508	936	646	267	788	535	934	744	083	896	236	50994	
14	02510	39976	02649	42305	02791	44572	02936	46780	03085	48931	03238	51029	16
	513	40015	651	344	793	609	939	816	088	48967	241	063	
15	02515	40055	02653	42382	02796	44647	02941	46852	03090	49002	03243	51098	15
	517	094	656	420	798	684	944	889	093	037	246	132	
16	02520	40133	02658	42458	02800	44721	02946	46925	03095	49073	03248	51167	14
	522	172	661	496	803	758	949	961	098	108	251	201	
17	02524	40212	02663	42535	02805	44796	02951	46997	03101	49143	03254	51236	13
	526	251	665	573	808	833	953	47034	103	179	256	270	
18	02529	40290	02668	42611	02810	44870	02956	47070	03106	49214	03259	51305	12
	531	329	670	649	812	907	958	106	108	249	261	339	
19	02533	40369	02672	42687	02815	44944	02961	47142	03111	49284	03264	51373	11
	536	408	675	725	817	44981	963	178	113	320	266	408	
20	02538	40447	02677	42764	02820	45018	02966	47215	03116	49355	03269	51442	10
	540	486	679	802	822	055	968	251	118	390	272	477	
21	02542	40525	02682	42840	02824	45092	02971	47287	03121	49425	03274	51511	9
	545	564	684	878	827	130	973	323	123	461	277	545	
22	02547	40603	02686	42916	02829	45167	02976	47359	03126	49496	03279	51580	8
	549	642	689	954	832	204	978	395	128	531	282	614	
23	02552	40681	02691	42992	02834	45241	02981	47431	03131	49566	03285	51648	7
	554	720	693	43030	836	278	983	467	133	601	287	682	
24	02556	40759	02696	43068	02839	45314	02986	47503	03136	49636	03290	51717	6
	558	798	698	106	841	351	988	539	138	671	292	751	
25	02561	40837	02700	43144	02844	45388	02991	47575	03141	49706	03295	51785	5
	563	876	703	181	846	425	993	611	144	742	298	819	
26	02565	40915	02705	43219	02849	45462	02996	47647	03146	49777	03300	51854	4
	568	954	708	257	851	499	02998	683	149	812	303	888	
27	02570	40993	02710	43295	02853	45536	03000	47719	03151	49847	03305	51922	3
	572	41032	712	333	856	573	003	755	154	882	308	956	
28	02575	41071	02715	43371	02858	45610	03005	47791	03156	49917	03311	51990	2
	577	110	717	409	861	646	008	827	159	952	313	52024	
29	02579	41149	02719	43446	02863	45683	03010	47862	03161	49987	03316	52058	1
	582	187	722	484	865	720	013	898	164	50022	318	093	
30	02584	41226	02724	43522	02868	45757	03015	47934	03166	50056	03321	52127	0
		2̄.[8]		2̄.[8]		2̄.[8]		2̄.[8]		2̄.[8]		2̄.[8]	
	30′		00′		30′		00′		30′		00′		′
	341°				**340°**				**339°**				

173

Table 20 — HAVERSINES

′	21° 00′ Nat.	Log.	21° 30′ Nat.	Log.	22° 00′ Nat.	Log.	22° 30′ Nat.	Log.	23° 00′ Nat.	Log.	23° 30′ Nat.	Log.	′
		2̄.[8]		2̄.[8]		2̄.[8]		2̄.[8]		2̄.[8]		2̄.[8]	
0	03321	52127	03479	54147	03641	56120	03806	58047	03975	59931	04147	61773	30
	324	161	482	180	644	152	809	079	978	962	150	804	
1	03326	52195	03484	54213	03646	56185	03812	58111	03980	59993	04153	61834	29
	329	229	487	247	649	217	814	142	983	60024	156	864	
2	03331	52263	03490	54280	03652	56250	03817	58174	03986	60055	04159	61895	28
	334	297	492	313	654	282	820	206	989	086	162	925	
3	03337	52331	03495	54346	03657	56315	03823	58237	03992	60117	04164	61955	27
	339	365	498	380	660	347	826	269	995	148	167	61986	
4	03342	52399	03500	54413	03663	56379	03828	58301	03998	60179	04170	62016	26
	344	433	503	446	665	412	831	333	04000	210	173	046	
5	03347	52467	03506	54479	03668	56444	03834	58364	04003	60241	04176	62076	25
	350	501	509	512	671	476	837	396	006	272	179	107	
6	03352	52535	03511	54545	03674	56509	03839	58427	04009	60303	04182	62137	24
	355	569	514	578	676	541	842	459	012	334	185	167	
7	03358	52602	03517	54611	03679	56573	03845	58491	04015	60365	04188	62197	23
	360	636	519	645	682	606	848	522	018	396	191	228	
8	03363	52670	03522	54678	03685	56638	03851	58554	04020	60426	04194	62258	22
	365	704	525	711	687	670	853	585	023	457	196	288	
9	03368	52738	03527	54744	03690	56703	03856	58617	04026	60488	04199	62318	21
	371	772	530	777	693	735	859	648	029	519	202	348	
10	03373	52805	03533	54810	03695	56767	03862	58680	04032	60550	04205	62379	20
	376	839	535	843	698	799	865	711	035	581	208	409	
11	03379	52873	03538	54876	03701	56832	03867	58743	04038	60611	04211	62439	19
	381	907	541	909	704	864	870	774	040	642	214	469	
12	03384	52941	03543	54942	03706	56896	03873	58806	04043	60673	04217	62499	18
	386	52974	546	54975	709	928	876	837	046	704	220	529	
13	03389	53008	03549	55008	03712	56960	03879	58869	04049	60734	04223	62559	17
	392	042	551	041	715	56993	882	900	052	765	226	589	
14	03394	53075	03554	55073	03717	57025	03884	58932	04055	60796	04229	62619	16
	397	109	557	106	720	057	887	963	058	827	231	649	
15	03400	53143	03560	55139	03723	57089	03890	58994	04060	60857	04234	62679	15
	402	177	562	172	726	121	893	59026	063	888	237	710	
16	03405	53210	03565	55205	03728	57153	03896	59057	04066	60919	04240	62740	14
	408	244	568	238	731	185	898	089	069	949	243	770	
17	03410	53277	03570	55271	03734	57217	03901	59120	04072	60980	04246	62800	13
	413	311	573	303	737	250	904	151	075	61011	249	830	
18	03415	53345	03576	55336	03740	57282	03907	59183	04078	61041	04252	62859	12
	418	378	578	369	742	314	910	214	081	072	255	889	
19	03421	53412	03581	55402	03745	57346	03912	59245	04083	61103	04258	62919	11
	423	445	584	435	748	378	915	277	086	133	261	949	
20	03426	53479	03587	55467	03751	57410	03918	59308	04089	61164	04264	62979	10
	429	512	589	500	753	442	921	339	092	194	267	63009	
21	03431	53546	03592	55533	03756	57474	03924	59370	04095	61225	04270	63039	9
	434	579	595	566	759	506	927	402	098	256	273	069	
22	03437	53613	03597	55598	03762	57537	03929	59433	04101	61286	04276	63099	8
	439	646	600	631	764	569	932	464	104	317	278	129	
23	03442	53680	03603	55664	03767	57601	03935	59495	04106	61347	04281	63159	7
	445	713	605	696	770	633	938	526	109	378	284	189	
24	03447	53747	03608	55729	03773	57665	03941	59558	04112	61408	04287	63218	6
	450	780	611	762	775	697	944	589	115	439	290	248	
25	03453	53814	03614	55794	03778	57729	03946	59620	04118	61469	04293	63278	5
	455	847	616	827	781	761	949	651	121	500	296	308	
26	03458	53880	03619	55859	03784	57793	03952	59682	04124	61530	04299	63338	4
	460	914	622	892	787	825	955	713	127	561	302	368	
27	03463	53947	03624	55925	03789	57856	03958	59745	04130	61591	04305	63397	3
	466	53980	627	957	792	888	961	776	133	621	308	427	
28	03468	54014	03630	55990	03795	57920	03963	59807	04135	61652	04311	63457	2
	471	047	633	56022	798	952	966	838	138	682	314	487	
29	03474	54080	03635	56055	03800	57984	03969	59869	04141	61713	04317	63516	1
	476	114	638	087	803	58015	972	900	144	743	320	546	
30	03479	54147	03641	56120	03806	58047	03975	59931	04147	61773	04323	63576	0
		2̄.[8]		2̄.[8]		2̄.[8]		2̄.[8]		2̄.[8]		2̄.[8]	
′		30′		00′		30′		00′		30′		00′	′

| 338° | 337° | 336° |

174

Table 20 — HAVERSINES

′	24° 00′ Nat.	Log.	24° 30′ Nat.	Log.	25° 00′ Nat.	Log.	25° 30′ Nat.	Log.	26° 00′ Nat.	Log.	26° 30′ Nat.	Log.	′
		$\overline{2}$. [8]		$\overline{2}$. [8]		$\overline{2}$. [8]		$\overline{2}$. [8]		$\overline{2}$. [8]		$\overline{2}$. [8]	
0	04323	63576	04502	65340	04685	67067	04871	68759	05060	70418	05253	72043	30
	326	606	505	369	688	096	874	787	063	445	257	070	
1	04329	63635	04508	65398	04691	67124	04877	68815	05067	70472	05260	72097	29
	332	665	511	427	694	153	880	843	070	500	263	124	
2	04335	63695	04514	65456	04697	67181	04883	68871	05073	70527	05266	72150	28
	338	724	517	485	700	210	886	899	076	554	270	177	
3	04340	63754	04520	65514	04703	67238	04890	68927	05079	70582	05273	72204	27
	343	784	523	543	706	267	893	955	083	609	276	231	
4	04346	63813	04526	65572	04709	67295	04896	68982	05086	70636	05279	72257	26
	349	843	529	601	712	323	899	69010	089	664	283	284	
5	04352	63872	04532	65630	04715	67352	04902	69038	05092	70691	05286	72311	25
	355	902	535	659	718	380	905	066	095	718	289	338	
6	04358	63932	04538	65688	04722	67409	04908	69094	05099	70745	05292	72364	24
	361	961	541	717	725	437	912	122	102	773	296	391	
7	04364	63991	04544	65746	04728	67465	04915	69149	05105	70800	05299	72418	23
	367	64020	547	775	731	494	918	177	108	827	302	445	
8	04370	64050	04550	65804	04734	67522	04921	69205	05111	70854	05305	72471	22
	373	079	553	833	737	550	924	233	115	881	309	498	
9	04376	64109	04556	65862	04740	67579	04927	69260	05118	70909	05312	72525	21
	379	139	559	891	743	607	930	288	121	936	315	551	
10	04382	64168	04562	65920	04746	67635	04934	69316	05124	70963	05318	72578	20
	385	198	565	949	749	664	937	344	127	70990	322	605	
11	04388	64227	04569	65978	04752	67692	04940	69371	05131	71017	05325	72631	19
	391	257	572	66006	756	720	943	399	134	045	328	658	
12	04394	64286	04575	66035	04759	67748	04946	69427	05137	71072	05331	72684	18
	397	315	578	064	762	777	949	454	140	099	335	711	
13	04400	64345	04581	66093	04765	67805	04952	69482	05144	71126	05338	72738	17
	403	374	584	122	768	833	956	510	147	153	341	764	
14	04406	64404	04587	66151	04771	67861	04959	69537	05150	71180	05345	72791	16
	409	433	590	179	774	890	962	565	153	207	348	817	
15	04412	64463	04593	66208	04777	67918	04965	69593	05156	71234	05351	72844	15
	415	492	596	237	780	946	968	620	160	261	354	871	
16	04418	64521	04599	66266	04783	67974	04971	69648	05163	71289	05358	72897	14
	421	551	602	295	787	68002	975	676	166	316	361	924	
17	04424	64580	04605	66323	04790	68030	04978	69703	05169	71343	05364	72950	13
	427	609	608	352	793	059	981	731	172	370	367	72977	
18	04430	64639	04611	66381	04796	68087	04984	69758	05176	71397	05371	73003	12
	433	668	614	409	799	115	987	786	179	424	374	030	
19	04436	64697	04617	66438	04802	68143	04990	69813	05182	71451	05377	73056	11
	439	727	620	467	805	171	994	841	185	478	381	083	
20	04442	64756	04623	66496	04808	68199	04997	69869	05189	71505	05384	73109	10
	445	785	626	524	811	227	05000	896	192	532	387	136	
21	04448	64815	04629	66553	04815	68255	05003	69924	05195	71559	05390	73162	9
	451	844	633	582	818	284	006	951	198	586	394	189	
22	04454	64873	04636	66610	04821	68312	05009	69979	05201	71613	05397	73215	8
	457	902	639	639	824	340	013	70006	205	640	400	241	
23	04460	64932	04642	66667	04827	68368	05016	70034	05208	71667	05404	73268	7
	463	961	645	696	830	396	019	061	211	694	407	294	
24	04466	64990	04648	66725	04833	68424	05022	70089	05214	71721	05410	73321	6
	469	65019	651	753	836	452	025	116	218	748	413	347	
25	04472	65049	04654	66782	04839	68480	05028	70144	05221	71774	05417	73374	5
	475	078	657	811	843	508	032	171	224	801	420	400	
26	04478	65107	04660	66839	04846	68536	05035	70198	05227	71828	05423	73426	4
	481	136	663	868	849	564	038	226	231	855	427	453	
27	04484	65165	04666	66896	04852	68592	05041	70253	05234	71882	05430	73479	3
	487	194	669	925	855	620	044	281	237	909	433	505	
28	04490	65223	04672	66953	04858	68648	05048	70308	05240	71936	05436	73532	2
	493	253	675	66982	861	676	051	336	244	963	440	558	
29	04496	65282	04678	67010	04864	68704	05054	70363	05247	71989	05443	73584	1
	499	311	682	039	868	732	057	390	250	72016	446	611	
30	04502	65340	04685	67067	04871	68759	05060	70418	05253	72043	05450	73637	0
		$\overline{2}$. [8]		$\overline{2}$. [8]		$\overline{2}$. [8]		$\overline{2}$. [8]		$\overline{2}$. [8]		$\overline{2}$. [8]	
	30′		00′		30′		00′		30′		00′		′
	335°				**334°**				**333°**				

Table 20 HAVERSINES

′	27° 00′ Nat.	Log.	27° 30′ Nat.	Log.	28° 00′ Nat.	Log.	28° 30′ Nat.	Log.	29° 00′ Nat.	Log.	29° 30′ Nat.	Log.	′
		$\overline{2}$. [8]		$\overline{2}$. [8]		$\overline{2}$. [8]		$\overline{2}$. [8]		$\overline{2}$. [8]		$\overline{2}$. [8]	
0	05450	73637	05649	75201	05853	76735	06059	78241	06269	79720	06482	81172	30
	453	663	653	226	856	760	063	266	273	744	486	196	
1	05456	73690	05656	75252	05859	76786	06066	78291	06276	79769	06489	81220	29
	460	716	660	278	863	811	070	316	280	793	493	244	
2	05463	73742	05663	75304	05866	76836	06073	78341	06283	79818	06497	81268	28
	466	769	666	330	870	862	077	365	287	842	500	292	
3	05470	73795	05670	75355	05873	76887	06080	78390	06290	79866	06504	81316	27
	473	821	673	381	877	912	083	415	294	891	507	340	
4	05476	73847	05676	75407	05880	76937	06087	78440	06297	79915	06511	81364	26
	479	874	680	433	883	963	090	465	301	939	514	388	
5	05483	73900	05683	75458	05887	76988	06094	78489	06304	79964	06518	81412	25
	486	926	686	484	890	77013	097	514	308	79988	522	436	
6	05489	73952	05690	75510	05894	77038	06101	78539	06311	80012	06525	81460	24
	493	73978	693	536	897	064	104	564	315	037	529	484	
7	05496	74005	05697	75561	05901	77089	06108	78589	06318	80061	06532	81508	23
	499	031	700	587	904	114	111	613	322	086	536	531	
8	05503	74057	05703	75613	05907	77139	06115	78638	06326	80110	06540	81555	22
	506	083	707	638	911	165	118	663	329	134	543	579	
9	05509	74109	05710	75664	05914	77190	06122	78688	06333	80158	06547	81603	21
	513	135	713	690	918	215	125	712	336	183	550	627	
10	05516	74162	05717	75715	05921	77240	06129	78737	06340	80207	06554	81651	20
	519	188	720	741	925	265	132	762	343	231	558	675	
11	05523	74214	05724	75767	05928	77290	06136	78786	06347	80255	06561	81698	19
	526	240	727	792	931	316	139	811	350	280	565	722	
12	05529	74266	05730	75818	05935	77341	06143	78836	06354	80304	06568	81746	18
	533	292	734	844	938	366	146	861	357	328	572	770	
13	05536	74318	05737	75869	05942	77391	06150	78885	06361	80352	06576	81794	17
	539	344	740	895	945	416	153	910	365	377	579	818	
14	05542	74370	05744	75920	05949	77441	06157	78935	06368	80401	06583	81841	16
	546	397	747	946	952	466	160	959	372	425	586	865	
15	05549	74423	05751	75971	05855	77492	06164	78984	06375	80449	06590	81889	15
	552	449	754	75997	959	517	167	79009	379	474	594	913	
16	05556	74475	05757	76023	05962	77542	06171	79033	06382	80498	06597	81936	14
	559	501	761	048	966	567	174	058	386	522	601	960	
17	05562	74527	05764	76074	05969	77592	06178	79082	06389	80546	06605	81984	13
	566	553	768	099	973	617	181	107	393	570	608	82008	
18	05569	74579	05771	76125	05976	77642	06185	79132	06397	80594	06612	82031	12
	572	605	774	150	980	667	188	156	400	619	615	055	
19	05576	74631	05778	76176	05983	77692	06192	79181	06404	80643	06619	82079	11
	579	657	781	201	986	717	195	205	407	667	623	103	
20	05582	74683	05785	76227	05990	77742	06199	79230	06411	80691	06626	82126	10
	586	709	788	252	993	767	202	255	414	715	630	150	
21	05589	74735	05791	76278	05997	77792	06206	79279	06418	80739	06633	82174	9
	593	761	795	303	06000	817	209	304	421	763	637	198	
22	05596	74787	05798	76329	06004	77842	06213	79328	06425	80788	06641	82221	8
	599	813	802	354	007	867	216	353	429	812	644	245	
23	05603	74838	05805	76380	06011	77892	06220	79377	06432	80836	06648	82269	7
	606	864	808	405	014	917	223	402	436	860	652	292	
24	05609	74890	05812	76430	06018	77942	06227	79426	06439	80884	06655	82316	6
	613	916	815	456	021	967	230	451	443	908	659	340	
25	05616	74942	05819	76481	06024	77992	06234	79475	06446	80932	06662	82363	5
	619	968	822	507	028	78017	237	500	450	956	666	387	
26	05623	74994	05825	76532	06031	78042	06241	79524	06454	80980	06670	82410	4
	626	75020	829	558	035	067	244	549	457	81004	673	434	
27	05629	75046	05832	76583	06038	78092	06248	79573	06461	81028	06677	82458	3
	633	072	836	608	042	117	251	598	464	052	681	481	
28	05636	75097	05839	76634	06045	78142	06255	79622	06468	81076	06684	82505	2
	639	123	842	659	049	167	258	647	471	100	688	528	
29	05643	75149	05846	76684	06052	78191	06262	79671	06475	81124	06691	82552	1
	646	175	849	710	056	216	265	695	479	148	695	576	
30	05649	75201	05853	76735	06059	78241	06269	79720	06482	81172	06699	82599	0
		$\overline{2}$. [8]		$\overline{2}$. [8]		$\overline{2}$. [8]		$\overline{2}$. [8]		$\overline{2}$. [8]		$\overline{2}$. [8]	
′	30′		00′		30′		00′		30′		00′		′

| 332° | 331° | 330° |

Table 20 — HAVERSINES

	30° 00' Nat.	Log.	30° 30' Nat.	Log.	31° 00' Nat.	Log.	31° 30' Nat.	Log.	32° 00' Nat.	Log.	32° 30' Nat.	Log.	
		2̄. [8]		2̄. [8]		2̄. [8]		2̄. [8]		2̄. [8]		2̄. [8]	
0	06699	82599	06919	84001	07142	85380	07368	86735	07598	88068	07830	89379	30
	702	623	922	025	145	403	372	757	601	090	834	400	
1	06706	82646	06926	84048	07149	85425	07376	86780	07605	88112	07838	89422	29
	710	670	930	071	153	448	379	802	609	134	842	444	
2	06713	82693	06933	84094	07157	85471	07383	86824	07613	88156	07846	89465	28
	717	717	937	117	160	494	387	847	617	178	850	487	
3	06721	82741	06941	84140	07164	85516	07391	86869	07621	88200	07854	89508	27
	724	764	944	164	168	539	395	892	625	222	858	530	
4	06728	82788	06948	84187	07172	85562	07398	86914	07628	88244	07862	89552	26
	731	811	952	210	175	585	402	936	632	266	866	573	
5	06735	82835	06955	84233	07179	85607	07406	86959	07636	88288	07870	89595	25
	739	858	959	256	183	630	410	86981	640	310	873	617	
6	06742	82882	06963	84279	07187	85653	07414	87003	07644	88332	07877	89638	24
	746	905	967	302	190	675	417	026	648	353	881	660	
7	06750	82929	06970	84325	07194	85698	07421	87048	07652	88375	07885	89681	23
	753	952	974	348	198	721	425	070	656	397	889	703	
8	06757	82976	06978	84371	07202	85743	07429	87092	07659	88419	07893	89725	22
	761	82999	981	394	205	766	433	115	663	441	897	746	
9	06764	83022	06985	84417	07209	85789	07437	87137	07667	88463	07901	89768	21
	768	046	989	441	213	811	440	159	671	485	905	789	
10	06772	83069	06993	84464	07217	85834	07444	87182	07675	88507	07909	89811	20
	775	093	06996	487	220	857	448	204	679	529	913	832	
11	06779	83116	07000	84510	07224	85879	07452	87226	07683	88551	07917	89854	19
	783	140	004	533	228	902	456	248	686	573	921	875	
12	06786	83163	07007	84556	07232	85925	07459	87271	07690	88595	07924	89897	18
	790	186	011	579	236	947	463	293	694	616	928	919	
13	06794	83210	07015	84602	07239	85970	07467	87315	07698	88638	07932	89940	17
	797	233	019	625	243	85992	471	337	702	660	936	962	
14	06801	83257	07022	84648	07247	86015	07475	87360	07706	88682	07940	89983	16
	805	280	026	671	251	038	479	382	710	704	944	90005	
15	06808	83303	07030	84694	07254	86060	07482	87404	07714	88726	07948	90026	15
	812	327	033	717	258	083	486	426	717	748	952	048	
16	06816	83350	07037	84739	07262	86105	07490	87448	07721	88769	07956	90069	14
	819	374	041	762	266	128	494	471	725	791	960	091	
17	06823	83397	07045	84785	07270	86150	07498	87493	07729	88813	07964	90112	13
	827	420	048	808	273	173	502	515	733	835	968	134	
18	06830	83443	07052	84831	07277	86196	07505	87537	07737	88857	07972	90155	12
	834	467	056	854	281	218	509	559	741	879	976	176	
19	06838	83490	07059	84877	07285	86241	07513	87582	07745	88900	07980	90198	11
	841	513	063	900	288	263	517	604	749	922	983	219	
20	06845	83537	07067	84923	07292	86286	07521	87626	07752	88944	07987	90241	10
	849	560	071	946	296	308	525	648	756	966	991	262	
21	06852	83583	07074	84969	07300	86331	07528	87670	07760	88988	07995	90284	9
	856	607	078	84992	304	353	532	692	764	89009	07999	305	
22	06860	83630	07082	85015	07307	86376	07536	87714	07768	89031	08003	90326	8
	863	653	086	037	311	398	540	737	772	053	007	348	
23	06867	83676	07089	85060	07315	86421	07544	87759	07776	89075	08011	90369	7
	871	700	093	083	319	443	548	781	780	096	015	391	
24	06874	83723	07097	85106	07322	86466	07551	87803	07784	89118	08019	90412	6
	878	746	100	129	326	488	555	825	788	140	023	433	
25	06882	83769	07104	85152	07330	86511	07559	87847	07791	89162	08027	90455	5
	885	793	108	175	334	533	563	869	795	183	031	476	
26	06889	83816	07112	85197	07338	86556	07567	87891	07799	89205	08035	90498	4
	893	839	115	220	341	578	571	913	803	227	039	519	
27	06896	83862	07119	85243	07345	86600	07574	87935	07807	89248	08043	90540	3
	900	886	123	266	349	623	578	957	811	270	047	562	
28	06904	83909	07127	85289	07353	86645	07582	87979	07815	89292	08051	90583	2
	907	932	130	311	357	668	586	88002	819	314	055	604	
29	06911	83955	07134	85334	07360	86690	07590	88024	07823	89335	08059	90626	1
	915	83978	138	357	364	713	594	046	827	357	063	647	
30	06919	84001	07142	85380	07368	86735	07598	88068	07830	89379	08066	90668	0
		2̄. [8]		2̄. [8]		2̄. [8]		2̄. [8]		2̄. [8]		2̄. [8]	
'	30'		00'		30'		00'		30'		00'		'
	329°				**328°**				**327°**				

Table 20 HAVERSINES

′	33° 00′ Nat.	Log.	33° 30′ Nat.	Log.	34° 00′ Nat.	Log.	34° 30′ Nat.	Log.	35° 00′ Nat.	Log.	35° 30′ Nat.	Log.	′
		$\overline{2}$. [8]		$\overline{2}$. [8]		$\overline{2}$. [8]		$\overline{2}$. [8]		$\overline{2}$. [8]		$\overline{2}$. [8]	
0	08066	90668	08306	91938	08548	93187	08794	94417	09042	95628	09294	96821	30
	070	690	310	959	552	208	798	438	047	648	298	841	
1	08074	90711	08314	91980	08556	93228	08802	94458	09051	95668	09303	96861	29
	078	732	318	92001	560	249	806	478	055	688	307	880	
2	08082	90754	08322	92022	08564	93270	08810	94498	09059	95708	09311	96900	28
	086	775	326	043	568	290	814	519	063	728	315	920	
3	08090	90796	08330	92063	08573	93311	08818	94539	09067	95748	09320	96940	27
	094	818	334	084	577	332	823	559	072	768	324	959	
4	08098	90839	08338	92105	08581	93352	08827	94580	09076	95788	09328	96979	26
	102	860	342	126	585	373	831	600	080	808	332	96999	
5	08106	90881	08346	92147	08589	93393	08835	94620	09084	95828	09336	97018	25
	110	903	350	168	593	414	839	641	088	848	341	038	
6	08114	90924	08354	92189	08597	93435	08843	94661	09093	95868	09345	97058	24
	118	945	358	210	601	455	847	681	097	888	349	077	
7	08122	90966	08362	92231	08605	93476	08851	94701	09101	95908	09353	97097	23
	126	90988	366	252	609	496	856	722	105	928	358	117	
8	08130	91009	08370	92273	08613	93517	08860	94742	09109	95948	09362	97136	22
	134	030	374	294	617	538	864	762	113	968	366	156	
9	08138	91051	08378	92315	08621	93558	08868	94782	09118	95988	09370	97176	21
	142	073	382	335	626	579	872	803	122	96008	375	195	
10	08146	91094	08386	92356	08630	93599	08876	94823	09126	96028	09379	97215	20
	150	115	390	377	634	620	880	843	130	048	383	235	
11	08154	91136	08394	92398	08638	93640	08885	94863	09134	96068	09387	97254	19
	158	157	398	419	642	661	889	884	139	088	392	274	
12	08162	91179	08402	92440	08646	93681	08893	94904	09143	96108	09396	97293	18
	166	200	406	461	650	702	897	924	147	128	400	313	
13	08170	91221	08410	92481	08654	93722	08901	94944	09151	96148	09404	97333	17
	174	242	414	502	658	743	905	965	155	167	409	352	
14	08178	91263	08418	92523	08662	93763	08909	94985	09160	96187	09413	97372	16
	182	284	422	544	666	784	914	95005	164	207	417	392	
15	08186	91306	08427	92565	08671	93804	08918	95025	09168	96227	09421	97411	15
	190	327	431	586	675	825	922	045	172	247	426	431	
16	08194	91348	08435	92606	08679	93845	08926	95065	09176	96267	09430	97450	14
	198	369	439	627	683	866	930	086	181	287	434	470	
17	08202	91390	08443	92648	03687	93886	08934	95106	09185	96307	09438	97489	13
	206	411	447	669	691	907	938	126	189	326	443	509	
18	08210	91432	08451	92690	08695	93927	08943	95146	09193	96346	09447	97529	12
	214	454	455	710	699	948	947	166	197	366	451	548	
19	08218	91475	08459	92731	08703	93968	08951	95186	09202	96386	09455	97568	11
	222	496	463	752	707	93989	955	207	206	406	460	587	
20	08226	91517	08467	92773	08711	94009	08959	95227	09210	96426	09464	97607	10
	230	538	471	794	716	030	963	247	214	445	468	626	
21	08234	91559	08475	92814	08720	94050	08967	95267	09218	96465	09472	97646	9
	238	580	479	835	724	071	972	287	223	485	477	665	
22	08242	91601	08483	92856	08728	94091	08976	95307	09227	96505	09481	97685	8
	246	622	487	877	732	111	980	327	231	525	485	704	
23	08250	91643	08491	92897	08736	94132	08984	95347	09235	96545	09489	97724	7
	254	664	495	918	740	152	988	368	239	564	494	743	
24	08258	91685	08499	92939	08744	94173	08992	95388	09244	96584	09498	97763	6
	262	707	503	960	748	193	08997	408	248	604	502	782	
25	08266	91728	08508	92980	08753	94213	09001	95428	09252	96624	09506	97802	5
	270	749	512	93001	757	234	005	448	256	644	511	821	
26	08274	91770	08516	93022	08761	94254	09009	95468	09260	96663	09515	97841	4
	278	791	520	042	765	275	013	488	265	683	519	860	
27	08282	91812	08524	93063	08769	94295	09017	95508	09269	96703	09524	97880	3
	286	833	528	084	773	315	022	528	273	723	528	899	
28	08290	91854	08532	93104	08777	94336	09026	95548	09277	96742	09532	97919	2
	294	875	536	125	781	356	030	568	282	762	536	938	
29	08298	91896	08540	93146	08785	94376	09034	95588	09286	96782	09541	97958	1
	302	917	544	166	790	397	038	608	290	802	545	977	
30	08306	91938	08548	93187	08794	94417	09042	95628	09294	96821	09549	97996	0
		$\overline{2}$. [8]		$\overline{2}$. [8]		$\overline{2}$. [8]		$\overline{2}$. [8]		$\overline{2}$. [8]		$\overline{2}$. [8]	

	30′		00′		30′		00′		30′		00′		′
	326°				**325°**				**324°**				

Table 20   HAVERSINES

′	36° 00′ Nat.	Log.	36° 30′ Nat.	Log.	37° 00′ Nat.	Log.	37° 30′ Nat.	Log.	38° 00′ Nat.	Log.	38° 30′ Nat.	Log.	′
		$\overline{2}$. [8]		$\overline{2}/\overline{1}$.[8/9]		$\overline{1}$. [9]		$\overline{1}$. [9]		$\overline{1}$. [9]		$\overline{1}$. [9]	
0	09549	97996	09807	99154	10068	00295	10332	01420	10599	02528	10870	03621	30
	553	98016	811	173	073	314	337	438	604	547	874	639	
1	09558	98035	09816	99193	10077	00333	10341	01457	10608	02565	10879	03658	29
	562	055	820	212	081	352	346	476	613	583	883	676	
2	09566	98074	09824	99231	10086	00371	10350	01494	10617	02602	10888	03694	28
	571	094	829	250	090	390	354	513	622	620	892	712	
3	09575	98113	09833	99269	10095	00408	10359	01531	10626	02638	10897	03730	27
	579	132	837	288	099	427	363	550	631	657	901	748	
4	09583	98152	09842	99307	10103	00446	10368	01569	10635	02675	10906	03766	26
	588	171	846	327	108	465	372	587	640	693	910	784	
5	09592	98191	09850	99346	10112	00484	10377	01606	10644	02712	10915	03802	25
	596	210	855	365	116	503	381	624	649	730	919	820	
6	09601	98229	09859	99384	10121	00522	10386	01643	10653	02748	10924	03838	24
	605	249	863	403	125	540	390	661	658	767	929	856	
7	09609	98268	09868	99422	10130	00559	10394	01680	10662	02785	10933	03874	23
	613	288	872	441	134	578	399	698	667	803	938	892	
8	09618	98307	09876	99460	10138	00597	10403	01717	10671	02821	10942	03910	22
	622	326	881	479	143	616	408	736	676	840	947	928	
9	09626	98346	09885	99498	10147	00634	10412	01754	10680	02858	10951	03946	21
	631	365	889	517	152	653	417	773	685	876	956	964	
10	09635	98384	09894	99536	10156	00672	10421	01791	10689	02894	10960	03982	20
	639	404	898	556	160	691	425	810	694	913	965	04000	
11	09643	98423	09903	99575	10165	00710	10430	01828	10698	02931	10969	04018	19
	648	442	907	594	169	728	434	847	703	949	974	036	
12	09652	98462	09911	99613	10174	00747	10439	01865	10707	02967	10978	04054	18
	656	481	916	632	178	766	443	884	712	02986	983	072	
13	09661	98500	09920	99651	10182	00785	10448	01902	10716	03004	10988	04090	17
	665	520	924	670	187	803	452	921	721	022	992	108	
14	09669	98539	09929	99689	10191	00822	10457	01939	10725	03040	10997	04126	16
	673	558	933	,708	196	841	461	958	730	059	11001	144	
15	09678	98578	09937	99727	10200	00860	10466	01976	10734	03077	11006	04162	15
	682	597	942	746	204	878	470	01995	739	095	010	180	
16	09686	98616	09946	99765	10209	00897	10474	02013	10743	03113	11015	04198	14
	691	635	950	784	213	916	479	031	748	131	019	216	
17	09695	98655	09955	99803	10218	00935	10483	02050	10752	03150	11024	04234	13
	699	674	959	822	222	953	488	068	757	168	029	252	
18	09704	98693	09963	99841	10226	00972	10492	02087	10761	03186	11033	04270	12
	708	712	968	860	231	00991	497	105	766	204	038	288	
19	09712	98732	09972	99879	10235	01009	10501	02124	10770	03222	11042	04306	11
	717	751	977	898	240	028	506	142	775	241	047	324	
20	09721	98770	09981	99917	10244	01047	10510	02161	10779	03259	11051	04341	10
	725	790	985	936	248	065	515	179	784	277	056	359	
21	09729	98809	09990	99955	10253	01084	10519	02197	10788	03295	11060	04377	9
	734	828	994	974	257	103	523	216	793	313	065	395	
22	09738	98847	09998	99993	10262	01122	10528	02234	10797	03331	11070	04413	8
	742	866	10003	00012	266	140	532	253	802	350	074	431	
23	09747	98886	10007	00031	10270	01159	10537	02271	10806	03368	11079	04449	7
	751	905	011	049	275	178	541	290	811	386	083	467	
24	09755	98924	10016	00068	10279	01196	10546	02308	10815	03404	11088	04485	6
	760	943	020	087	284	215	550	326	820	422	092	503	
25	09764	98963	10025	00106	10288	01234	10555	02345	10824	03440	11097	04520	5
	768	98982	029	125	293	252	559	363	829	458	102	538	
26	09773	99001	10033	00144	10297	01271	10564	02381	10833	03476	11106	04556	4
	777	020	038	163	301	289	568	400	838	495	111	574	
27	09781	99039	10042	00182	10306	01308	10573	02418	10842	03513	11115	04592	3
	786	058	046	201	310	327	577	437	847	531	120	610	
28	09790	99078	10051	00220	10315	01345	10582	02455	10851	03549	11124	04628	2
	794	097	055	239	319	364	586	473	856	567	129	646	
29	09799	99116	10059	00258	10323	01383	10591	02492	10861	03585	11134	04663	1
	803	135	064	276	328	401	595	510	865	603	138	681	
30	09807	99154	10068	00295	10332	01420	10599	02528	10870	03621	11143	04699	0
		$\overline{2}$. [8]		$\overline{1}/\overline{2}$.[9/8]		$\overline{1}$. [9]		$\overline{1}$. [9]		$\overline{1}$. [9]		$\overline{1}$. [9]	
′	30′		00′		30′		00′		30′		00′		′

Table 20 — HAVERSINES

′	39° 00′ Nat.	Log.	39° 30′ Nat.	Log.	40° 00′ Nat.	Log.	40° 30′ Nat.	Log.	41° 00′ Nat.	Log.	41° 30′ Nat.	Log.	′
		T. [9]		T. [9]		T. [9]		T. [9]		T. [9]		T. [9]	
0	11143	04699	11419	05762	11698	06810	11980	07845	12265	08865	12552	09872	30
	147	717	423	780	702	828	984	862	269	882	557	889	
1	11152	04735	11428	05797	11707	06845	11989	07879	12274	08899	12562	09905	29
	156	753	433	815	712	862	994	896	279	916	567	922	
2	11161	04770	11437	05832	11716	06880	11999	07913	12284	08933	12571	09939	28
	166	788	442	850	721	897	12003	930	288	950	576	955	
3	11170	04806	11447	05867	11726	06914	12008	07947	12293	08966	12581	09972	27
	175	824	451	885	731	932	013	964	298	08983	586	09989	
4	11179	04842	11456	05903	11735	06949	12018	07981	12303	09000	12591	10005	26
	184	859	460	920	740	966	022	07999	307	017	596	022	
5	11189	04877	11465	05938	11745	06984	12027	08016	12312	09034	12600	10039	25
	193	895	470	955	749	07001	032	033	317	051	605	055	
6	11198	04913	11474	05973	11754	07018	12036	08050	12322	09068	12610	10072	24
	202	931	479	05990	759	036	041	067	327	084	615	088	
7	11207	04948	11484	06008	11763	07053	12046	08084	12331	09101	12620	10105	23
	211	966	488	025	768	070	051	101	336	118	625	122	
8	11216	04984	11493	06043	11773	07087	12055	08118	12341	09135	12629	10138	22
	221	05002	498	060	777	105	060	135	346	152	634	155	
9	11225	05019	11502	06078	11782	07122	12065	08152	12351	09169	12639	10172	21
	230	037	507	095	787	139	070	169	355	185	644	188	
10	11234	05055	11511	06113	11791	07157	12074	08186	12360	09202	12649	10205	20
	239	073	516	131	796	174	079	203	365	219	654	221	
11	11244	05090	11521	06148	11801	07191	12084	08220	12370	09236	12658	10238	19
	248	108	525	166	806	208	089	237	374	253	663	255	
12	11253	05126	11530	06183	11810	07226	12093	08254	12379	09269	12668	10271	18
	257	144	535	201	815	243	098	271	384	286	673	288	
13	11262	05161	11539	06218	11820	07260	12103	08288	12389	09303	12678	10304	17
	267	179	544	235	824	277	108	306	394	320	683	321	
14	11271	05197	11549	06253	11829	07295	12112	08323	12398	09337	12687	10337	16
	276	215	553	270	834	312	117	340	403	353	692	354	
15	11280	05232	11558	06288	11838	07329	12122	08357	12408	09370	12697	10371	15
	285	250	563	305	843	346	127	374	413	387	702	387	
16	11290	05268	11567	06323	11848	07364	12131	08391	12418	09404	12707	10404	14
	294	285	572	340	852	381	136	408	422	421	712	420	
17	11299	05303	11576	06358	11857	07398	12141	08425	12427	09437	12717	10437	13
	303	321	581	375	862	415	146	442	432	454	721	453	
18	11308	05339	11586	06393	11867	07433	12150	08459	12437	09471	12726	10470	12
	313	356	590	410	871	450	155	476	442	488	731	487	
19	11317	05374	11595	06428	11876	07467	12160	08492	12446	09504	12736	10503	11
	322	392	600	445	881	484	165	509	451	521	741	520	
20	11326	05409	11604	06462	11885	07501	12169	08526	12456	09538	12746	10536	10
	331	427	609	480	890	519	174	543	461	555	750	553	
21	11336	05445	11614	06497	11895	07536	12179	08560	12466	09571	12755	10569	9
	340	462	618	515	900	553	184	577	470	588	760	586	
22	11345	05480	11623	06532	11904	07570	12188	08594	12475	09605	12765	10602	8
	349	498	628	550	909	587	193	611	480	622	770	619	
23	11354	05515	11632	06567	11914	07605	12198	08628	12485	09638	12775	10635	7
	359	533	637	584	918	622	203	645	490	655	780	652	
24	11363	05551	11642	06602	11923	07639	12207	08662	12494	09672	12784	10668	6
	368	568	646	619	928	656	212	679	499	688	789	685	
25	11373	05586	11651	06637	11933	07673	12217	08696	12504	09705	12794	10701	5
	377	603	656	654	937	690	222	713	509	722	799	718	
26	11382	05621	11660	06671	11942	07707	12226	08730	12514	09739	12804	10734	4
	386	639	665	689	947	725	231	747	519	755	809	751	
27	11391	05656	11670	06706	11951	07742	12236	08764	12523	09772	12814	10767	3
	396	674	674	724	956	759	241	780	528	789	818	784	
28	11400	05692	11679	06741	11961	07776	12245	08797	12533	09805	12823	10800	2
	405	709	684	758	966	793	250	814	538	822	828	816	
29	11410	05727	11688	06776	11970	07810	12255	08831	12543	09839	12833	10833	1
	414	744	693	793	975	828	260	848	547	855	838	849	
30	11419	05762	11698	06810	11980	07845	12265	08865	12552	09872	12843	10866	0
		T. [9]		T. [9]		T. [9]		T. [9]		T. [9]		T. [9]	
	30′		00′		30′		00′		30′		00′		′
	320°				**319°**				**318°**				

Table 20 — HAVERSINES

'	42° 00′ Nat.	Log.	42° 30′ Nat.	Log.	43° 00′ Nat.	Log.	43° 30′ Nat.	Log.	44° 00′ Nat.	Log.	44° 30′ Nat.	Log.	'
		T.[9]		T.[9]		T.[9]		T.[9]		T.[9]		T.[9]	
0	12843	10866	13136	11847	13432	12815	13731	13771	14033	14715	14337	15647	30
	848	882	141	863	437	831	736	787	038	731	343	663	
1	12852	10899	13146	11879	13442	12847	13741	13803	14043	14746	14348	15678	29
	857	915	151	895	447	863	746	819	048	762	353	694	
2	12862	10932	13156	11912	13452	12879	13751	13834	14053	14778	14358	15709	28
	867	948	161	928	457	895	756	850	058	793	363	724	
3	12872	10964	13166	11944	13462	12911	13761	13866	14063	14809	14368	15740	27
	877	981	171	960	467	927	766	882	068	824	373	755	
4	12882	10997	13175	11977	13472	12943	13771	13898	14073	14840	14378	15771	26
	887	11014	180	11993	477	959	776	913	079	856	383	786	
5	12891	11030	13185	12009	13482	12975	13781	13929	14084	14871	14388	15802	25
	896	047	190	025	487	12991	786	945	089	887	394	817	
6	12901	11063	13195	12041	13492	13007	13791	13961	14094	14902	14399	15832	24
	906	079	200	058	497	023	796	977	099	918	404	848	
7	12911	11096	13205	12074	13502	13039	13801	13992	14104	14934	14409	15863	23
	916	112	210	090	507	055	806	14008	109	949	414	879	
8	12921	11129	13215	12106	13512	13071	13811	14024	14114	14965	14419	15894	22
	926	145	220	122	517	087	816	040	119	980	424	909	
9	12930	11161	13225	12139	13522	13103	13822	14056	14124	14996	14429	15925	21
	935	178	230	155	527	119	827	071	129	15012	434	940	
10	12940	11194	13235	12171	13532	13135	13832	14087	14134	15027	14440	15955	20
	945	211	239	187	537	151	837	103	139	043	445	971	
11	12950	11227	13244	12203	13542	13167	13842	14119	14144	15058	14450	15986	19
	955	243	249	219	547	183	847	134	149	074	455	16002	
12	12960	11260	13254	12236	13552	13199	13852	14150	14154	15089	14460	16017	18
	965	276	259	252	557	215	857	166	160	105	465	032	
13	12970	11292	13264	12268	13562	13231	13862	14182	14165	15120	14470	16048	17
	974	309	269	284	567	247	867	197	170	136	475	063	
14	12979	11325	13274	12300	13571	13263	13872	14213	14175	15152	14480	16078	16
	984	342	279	316	576	279	877	229	180	167	486	094	
15	12989	11358	13284	12332	13581	13295	13882	14245	14185	15183	14491	16109	15
	994	374	289	349	586	311	887	260	190	198	496	124	
16	12999	11391	13294	12365	13591	13326	13892	14276	14195	15214	14501	16140	14
	13004	407	299	381	596	342	897	292	200	229	506	155	
17	13009	11423	13304	12397	13601	13358	13902	14307	14205	15245	14511	16170	13
	014	440	309	413	606	374	907	323	210	260	516	186	
18	13018	11456	13314	12429	13611	13390	13912	14339	14215	15276	14521	16201	12
	023	472	318	445	616	406	917	355	220	291	527	216	
19	13028	11489	13323	12461	13621	13422	13922	14370	14226	15307	14532	16232	11
	033	505	328	478	626	438	927	386	231	322	537	247	
20	13038	11521	13333	12494	13631	13454	13932	14402	14236	15338	14542	16262	10
	043	538	338	510	636	470	937	417	241	353	547	278	
21	13048	11554	13343	12526	13641	13486	13942	14433	14246	15369	14552	16293	9
	053	570	348	542	646	502	947	449	251	384	557	308	
22	13058	11586	13353	12558	13651	13517	13952	14465	14256	15400	14562	16324	8
	063	603	358	574	656	533	957	480	261	415	568	339	
23	13067	11619	13363	12590	13661	13549	13962	14496	14266	15431	14573	16354	7
	072	635	368	606	666	565	967	512	271	446	578	369	
24	13077	11652	13373	12622	13671	13581	13972	14527	14276	15462	14583	16385	6
	082	668	378	639	676	597	977	543	281	477	588	400	
25	13087	11684	13383	12655	13681	13613	13983	14559	14287	15493	14593	16415	5
	092	700	388	671	686	629	988	574	292	508	598	431	
26	13097	11717	13393	12687	13691	13644	13993	14590	14297	15524	14604	16446	4
	102	733	398	703	696	660	13998	606	302	539	609	461	
27	13107	11749	13403	12719	13701	13676	14003	14621	14307	15555	14614	16476	3
	112	766	408	735	706	692	008	637	312	570	619	492	
28	13116	11782	13412	12751	13711	13708	14013	14653	14317	15585	14624	16507	2
	121	798	417	767	716	724	018	668	322	601	629	522	
29	13126	11814	13422	12783	13721	13739	14023	14684	14327	15616	14634	16537	1
	131	831	427	799	726	755	028	699	332	632	639	553	
30	13136	11847	13432	12815	13731	13771	14033	14715	14337	15647	14645	16568	0
		T.[9]		T.[9]		T.[9]		T.[9]		T.[9]		T.[9]	
	30′		00′		30′		00′		30′		00′		'

317°	316°	315°

Table 20 — HAVERSINES

′	45° 00′ Nat.	Log.	45° 30′ Nat.	Log.	46° 00′ Nat.	Log.	46° 30′ Nat.	Log.	47° 00′ Nat.	Log.	47° 30′ Nat.	Log.	′
0	14645	16568 T.[9]	14955	17477 T.[9]	15267	18376 T.[9]	15582	19263 T.[9]	15900	20140 T.[9]	16220	21006 T.[9]	30
	650	583	960	492	272	391	588	278	905	154	226	021	
1	14655	16598	14965	17507	15278	18405	15593	19292	15911	20169	16231	21035	29
	660	614	970	523	283	420	598	307	916	183	237	049	
2	14665	16629	14975	17538	15288	18435	15603	19322	15921	20198	16242	21064	28
	670	644	980	553	293	450	609	337	927	213	247	078	
3	14676	16659	14986	17568	15298	18465	15614	19351	15932	20227	16253	21092	27
	681	675	991	583	304	480	619	366	937	242	258	107	
4	14686	16690	14996	17598	15309	18495	15624	19381	15943	20256	16263	21121	26
	691	705	15001	613	314	509	630	395	948	271	269	135	
5	14696	16720	15006	17628	15319	18524	15635	19410	15953	20285	16274	21150	25
	701	736	012	643	325	539	640	425	959	300	280	164	
6	14706	16751	15017	17658	15330	18554	15646	19439	15964	20314	16285	21178	24
	712	766	022	673	335	569	651	454	969	329	290	193	
7	14717	16781	15027	17688	15340	18584	15656	19469	15975	20343	16296	21207	23
	722	796	032	703	346	599	661	483	980	358	301	221	
8	14727	16812	15038	17718	15351	18613	15667	19498	15985	20372	16306	21236	22
	732	827	043	733	356	628	672	513	991	386	312	250	
9	14737	16842	15048	17748	15361	18643	15677	19527	15996	20401	16317	21264	21
	742	857	053	763	367	658	683	542	16001	415	322	279	
10	14748	16872	15058	17778	15372	18673	15688	19557	16007	20430	16328	21293	20
	753	887	064	793	377	687	693	571	012	444	333	307	
11	14758	16903	15069	17808	15382	18702	15699	19586	16017	20459	16339	21322	19
	763	918	074	823	388	717	704	600	023	473	344	336	
12	14768	16933	15079	17838	15393	18732	15709	19615	16028	20488	16349	21350	18
	773	948	084	853	398	747	714	630	033	502	355	364	
13	14779	16963	15090	17868	15403	18761	15720	19644	16039	20517	16360	21379	17
	784	979	095	883	409	776	725	659	044	531	366	393	
14	14789	16994	15100	17898	15414	18791	15730	19674	16049	20546	16371	21407	16
	794	17009	105	913	419	806	736	688	055	560	376	422	
15	14799	17024	15110	17928	15424	18821	15741	19703	16060	20574	16382	21436	15
	804	039	116	943	430	835	746	717	065	589	387	450	
16	14810	17054	15121	17958	15435	18850	15751	19732	16071	20603	16392	21464	14
	815	069	126	973	440	865	757	747	076	618	398	479	
17	14820	17085	15131	17988	15445	18880	15762	19761	16081	20632	16403	21493	13
	825	100	137	18003	451	895	767	776	087	647	409	507	
18	14830	17115	15142	18018	15456	18909	15773	19790	16092	20661	16414	21521	12
	835	130	147	033	461	924	778	805	097	675	419	536	
19	14841	17145	15152	18047	15466	18939	15783	19820	16103	20690	16425	21550	11
	846	160	157	062	472	954	789	834	108	704	430	564	
20	14851	17175	15163	18077	15477	18968	15794	19849	16113	20719	16436	21578	10
	856	191	168	092	482	983	799	863	119	733	441	593	
21	14861	17206	15173	18107	15487	18998	15804	19878	16124	20748	16446	21607	9
	866	221	178	122	493	19013	810	893	129	762	452	621	
22	14872	17236	15183	18137	15498	19027	15815	19907	16135	20776	16457	21635	8
	877	251	189	152	503	042	820	922	140	791	462	650	
23	14882	17266	15194	18167	15508	19057	15826	19936	16145	20805	16468	21664	7
	887	281	199	182	514	072	831	951	151	820	473	678	
24	14892	17296	15204	18197	15519	19086	15836	19965	16156	20834	16479	21692	6
	898	311	210	212	524	101	842	980	162	848	484	706	
25	14903	17327	15215	18227	15530	19116	15847	19995	16167	20863	16489	21721	5
	908	342	220	242	535	131	852	20009	172	877	495	735	
26	14913	17357	15225	18256	15540	19145	15858	20024	16178	20891	16500	21749	4
	918	372	230	271	545	160	863	038	183	906	506	763	
27	14923	17387	15236	18286	15551	19175	15868	20053	16188	20920	16511	21777	3
	929	402	241	301	556	190	874	067	194	935	516	792	
28	14934	17417	15246	18316	15561	19204	15879	20082	16199	20949	16522	21806	2
	939	432	251	331	566	219	884	096	204	963	527	820	
29	14944	17447	15257	18346	15572	19234	15889	20111	16210	20978	16533	21834	1
	949	462	262	361	577	248	895	125	215	20992	538	848	
30	14955	17477	15267	18376	15582	19263	15900	20140	16220	21006	16543	21863	0
		T.[9]		T.[9]		T.[9]		T.[9]		T.[9]		T.[9]	

	30′		00′		30′		00′		30′		00′		′
	314°				**313°**				**312°**				

Table 20   HAVERSINES

	48° 00′ Nat.	Log.	48° 30′ Nat.	Log.	49° 00′ Nat.	Log.	49° 30′ Nat.	Log.	50° 00′ Nat.	Log.	50° 30′ Nat.	Log.	′
		T̄. [9]		T̄. [9]		T̄. [9]		T̄. [9]		T̄. [9]		T̄. [9]	
0	16543	21863	16869	22709	17197	23545	17528	24372	17861	25190	18196	25998	30
	549	877	874	723	203	559	533	386	866	203	202	26011	
1	16554	21891	16880	22737	17208	23573	17539	24400	17872	25217	18207	26025	29
	560	905	885	751	214	587	544	413	877	230	213	038	
2	16565	21919	16891	22765	17219	23601	17550	24427	17883	25244	18219	26051	28
	571	934	896	779	225	615	555	441	888	257	224	065	
3	16576	21948	16902	22793	17230	23629	17561	24454	17894	25271	18230	26078	27
	581	962	907	807	235	642	566	468	900	284	235	091	
4	16587	21976	16913	22821	17241	23656	17572	24482	17905	25298	18241	26105	26
	592	21990	918	835	246	670	577	495	911	311	247	118	
5	16598	22004	16924	22849	17252	23684	17583	24509	17916	25325	18252	26132	25
	603	019	929	863	257	698	588	523	922	339	258	145	
6	16608	22033	16934	22877	17263	23712	17594	24536	17928	25352	18263	26158	24
	614	047	940	891	268	725	600	550	933	366	269	172	
7	16619	22061	16945	22905	17274	23739	17605	24564	17939	25379	18275	26185	23
	625	075	951	919	279	753	611	577	944	393	280	198	
8	16630	22089	16956	22933	17285	23767	17616	24591	17950	25406	18286	26212	22
	635	103	962	947	290	781	622	605	955	420	292	225	
9	16641	22118	16967	22961	17296	23794	17627	24618	17961	25433	18297	26238	21
	646	132	973	975	301	808	633	632	967	447	303	252	
10	16652	22146	16978	22989	17307	23822	17638	24646	17972	25460	18308	26265	20
	657	160	984	23003	312	836	644	659	978	474	314	279	
11	16663	22174	16989	23017	17318	23850	17649	24673	17983	25487	18320	26292	19
	668	188	16994	031	323	863	655	687	989	501	325	305	
12	16673	22202	17000	23045	17329	23877	17661	24700	17995	25514	18331	26319	18
	679	216	005	059	334	891	666	714	18000	527	337	332	
13	16684	22231	17011	23073	17340	23905	17672	24728	18006	25541	18342	26345	17
	690	245	016	087	345	919	677	741	011	554	348	358	
14	16695	22259	17022	23100	17351	23932	17683	24755	18017	25568	18353	26372	16
	700	273	027	114	357	946	688	768	022	581	359	385	
15	16706	22287	17033	23128	17362	23960	17694	24782	18028	25595	18365	26398	15
	711	301	038	142	368	974	699	796	034	608	370	412	
16	16717	22315	17044	23156	17373	23988	17705	24809	18039	25622	18376	26425	14
	722	329	049	170	379	24001	710	823	045	635	382	438	
17	16728	22343	17055	23184	17384	24015	17716	24837	18050	25649	18387	26452	13
	733	358	060	198	390	029	722	850	056	662	393	465	
18	16738	22372	17066	23212	17395	24043	17727	24864	18062	25676	18399	26478	12
	744	386	071	226	401	056	733	877	067	689	404	492	
19	16749	22400	17076	23240	17406	24070	17738	24891	18073	25703	18410	26505	11
	755	414	082	254	412	084	744	905	078	716	415	518	
20	16760	22428	17087	23268	17417	24098	17749	24918	18084	25729	18421	26532	10
	766	442	093	282	423	111	755	932	090	743	427	545	
21	16771	22456	17098	23295	17428	24125	17760	24945	18095	25756	18432	26558	9
	777	470	104	309	434	139	766	959	101	770	438	571	
22	16782	22484	17109	23323	17439	24153	17772	24973	18106	25783	18444	26585	8
	787	498	115	337	445	166	777	24986	112	797	449	598	
23	16793	22512	17120	23351	17450	24180	17783	25000	18118	25810	18455	26611	7
	798	526	126	365	456	194	788	013	123	823	461	624	
24	16804	22540	17131	23379	17461	24208	17794	25027	18129	25837	18466	26638	6
	809	555	137	393	467	221	799	040	134	850	472	651	
25	16815	22569	17142	23407	17472	24235	17805	25054	18140	25864	18478	26664	5
	820	583	148	421	478	249	811	068	146	877	483	678	
26	16825	22597	17153	23434	17483	24263	17816	25081	18151	25891	18489	26691	4
	831	611	159	448	489	276	822	095	157	904	494	704	
27	16836	22625	17164	23462	17494	24290	17827	25108	18162	25917	18500	26717	3
	842	639	170	476	500	304	833	122	168	931	506	731	
28	16847	22653	17175	23490	17505	24317	17838	25135	18174	25944	18511	26744	2
	853	667	181	504	511	331	844	149	179	958	517	757	
29	16858	22681	17186	23518	17517	24345	17849	25163	18185	25971	18523	26770	1
	864	695	192	532	522	359	855	176	190	984	528	784	
30	16869	22709	17197	23545	17528	24372	17861	25190	18196	25998	18534	26797	0
		T̄. [9]		T̄. [9]		T̄. [9]		T̄. [9]		T̄. [9]		T̄. [9]	
	30′		00′		30′		00′		30′		00′		′
	311°				310°				309°				

183

Table 20 — HAVERSINES

′	51° 00′ Nat	Log	51° 30′ Nat	Log	52° 00′ Nat	Log	52° 30′ Nat	Log	53° 00′ Nat	Log	53° 30′ Nat	Log	′
		T̄. [9]		T̄. [9]		T̄. [9]		T̄. [9]		T̄. [9]		T̄. [9]	
0	18534	26797	18874	27587	19217	28368	19562	29141	19909	29905	20259	30662	30
	540	810	880	600	223	381	568	154	915	918	265	674	
1	18545	26823	18886	27613	19228	28394	19573	29167	19921	29931	20271	30687	29
	551	837	891	626	234	407	579	180	927	943	276	699	
2	18557	26850	18897	27639	19240	28420	19585	29192	19932	29956	20282	30712	28
	562	863	903	652	246	433	591	205	938	969	288	724	
3	18568	26876	18908	27666	19251	28446	19597	29218	19944	29981	20294	30737	27
	574	890	914	679	257	459	602	231	950	29994	300	749	
4	18579	26903	18920	27692	19263	28472	19608	29244	19956	30007	20306	30762	26
	585	916	926	705	269	485	614	256	962	019	311	774	
5	18591	26929	18931	27718	19274	28498	19620	29269	19967	30032	20317	30787	25
	596	942	937	731	280	511	625	282	973	045	323	799	
6	18602	26956	18943	27744	19286	28524	19631	29295	19979	30057	20329	30812	24
	608	969	948	757	291	537	637	307	985	070	335	824	
7	18613	26982	18954	27770	19297	28549	19643	29320	19991	30083	20341	30837	23
	619	26995	960	783	303	562	649	333	19996	095	347	849	
8	18624	27008	18965	27796	19309	28575	19654	29346	20002	30108	20352	30862	22
	630	022	971	809	314	588	660	359	008	121	358	874	
9	18636	27035	18977	27822	19320	28601	19666	29371	20014	30133	20364	30887	21
	641	048	983	835	326	614	672	384	020	146	370	899	
10	18647	27061	18988	27848	19332	28627	19677	29397	20026	30158	20376	30912	20
	653	074	18994	861	337	640	683	410	031	171	382	924	
11	18658	27088	19000	27875	19343	28653	19689	29422	20037	30184	20388	30937	19
	664	101	005	888	349	666	695	435	043	196	393	949	
12	18670	27114	19011	27901	19355	28679	19701	29448	20049	30209	20399	30962	18
	675	127	017	914	360	691	706	461	055	221	405	974	
13	18681	27140	19022	27927	19366	28704	19712	29473	20060	30234	20411	30987	17
	687	154	028	940	372	717	718	486	066	247	417	30999	
14	18692	27167	19034	27953	19378	28730	19724	29499	20072	30259	20423	31012	16
	698	180	040	966	383	743	730	512	078	272	429	024	
15	18704	27193	19045	27979	19389	28756	19735	29524	20084	30285	20435	31036	15
	709	206	051	27992	395	769	741	537	090	297	440	049	
16	18715	27219	19057	28005	19401	28782	19747	29550	20095	30310	20446	31061	14
	721	233	062	018	406	794	753	563	101	322	452	074	
17	18727	27246	19068	28031	19412	28807	19758	29575	20107	30335	20458	31086	13
	732	259	074	044	418	820	764	588	113	348	464	099	
18	18738	27272	19080	28057	19424	28833	19770	29601	20119	30360	20470	31111	12
	744	285	085	070	429	846	776	613	125	373	476	124	
19	18749	27298	19091	28083	19435	28859	19782	29626	20130	30385	20481	31136	11
	755	311	097	096	441	872	787	639	136	398	487	149	
20	18761	27325	19102	28109	19447	28885	19793	29652	20142	30410	20493	31161	10
	766	338	108	122	452	897	799	664	148	423	499	173	
21	18772	27351	19114	28135	19458	28910	19805	29677	20154	30436	20505	31186	9
	778	364	120	148	464	923	811	690	160	448	511	198	
22	18783	27377	19125	28161	19470	28936	19816	29702	20165	30461	20517	31211	8
	789	390	131	174	475	949	822	715	171	473	523	223	
23	18795	27403	19137	28187	19481	28962	19828	29728	20177	30486	20528	31236	7
	800	417	142	200	487	974	834	741	183	498	534	248	
24	18806	27430	19148	28213	19493	28987	19840	29753	20189	30511	20540	31260	6
	812	443	154	226	499	29000	845	766	195	524	546	273	
25	18817	27456	19160	28239	19504	29013	19851	29779	20200	30536	20552	31285	5
	823	469	165	252	510	026	857	791	206	549	558	298	
26	18829	27482	19171	28265	19516	29039	19863	29804	20212	30561	20564	31310	4
	834	495	177	278	522	051	869	817	218	574	570	323	
27	18840	27508	19183	28291	19527	29064	19874	29829	20224	30586	20575	31335	3
	846	522	188	304	533	077	880	842	230	599	581	347	
28	18852	27535	19194	28317	19539	29090	19886	29855	20235	30611	20587	31360	2
	857	548	200	330	545	103	892	867	241	624	593	372	
29	18863	27561	19205	28342	19550	29116	19898	29880	20247	30636	20599	31385	1
	869	574	211	355	556	128	903	893	253	649	605	397	
30	18874	27587	19217	28368	19562	29141	19909	29905	20259	30662	20611	31409	0
		T̄. [9]		T̄. [9]		T̄. [9]		T̄. [9]		T̄. [9]		T̄. [9]	
′	30′		00′		30′		00′		30′		00′		′
	308°				307°				306°				

Table 20 — HAVERSINES

′	54° 00′ Nat.	Log.	54° 30′ Nat.	Log.	55° 00′ Nat.	Log.	55° 30′ Nat.	Log.	56° 00′ Nat.	Log.	56° 30′ Nat.	Log.	′
		T. [9]		T. [9]		T. [9]		T. [9]		T. [9]		T. [9]	
0	20611	31409	20965	32149	21321	32881	21680	33605	22040	34322	22403	35031	30
	617	422	971	161	327	893	686	617	046	334	409	043	
1	20623	31434	20977	32174	21333	32905	21692	33629	22052	34346	22415	35054	29
	628	447	983	186	339	918	698	641	058	357	421	066	
2	20634	31459	20989	32198	21345	32930	21704	33653	22064	34369	22427	35078	28
	640	471	20994	210	351	942	710	665	071	381	433	090	
3	20646	31484	21000	32223	21357	32954	21716	33677	22077	34393	22440	35101	27
	652	496	006	235	363	966	722	689	083	405	446	113	
4	20658	31508	21012	32247	21369	32978	21728	33701	22089	34417	22452	35125	26
	664	521	018	259	375	32990	734	713	095	429	458	137	
5	20670	31533	21024	32272	21381	33002	21740	33725	22101	34441	22464	35148	25
	675	546	030	284	387	014	746	737	107	452	470	160	
6	20681	31558	21036	32296	21393	33027	21752	33749	22113	34464	22476	35172	24
	687	570	042	308	399	039	758	761	119	476	482	184	
7	20693	31583	21048	32321	21405	33051	21764	33773	22125	34488	22488	35195	23
	699	595	054	333	411	063	770	785	131	500	494	207	
8	20705	31607	21060	32345	21417	33075	21776	33797	22137	34512	22500	35219	22
	711	620	066	357	423	087	782	809	143	524	506	230	
9	20717	31632	21072	32370	21429	33099	21788	33821	22149	34535	22512	35242	21
	723	644	077	382	434	111	794	833	155	547	518	254	
10	20729	31657	21083	32394	21440	33123	21800	33845	22161	34559	22525	35266	20
	734	669	089	406	446	135	806	857	167	571	531	277	
11	20740	31682	21095	32418	21452	33148	21812	33869	22173	34583	22537	35289	19
	746	694	101	431	458	160	818	881	179	595	543	301	
12	20752	31706	21107	32443	21464	33172	21824	33893	22185	34606	22549	35312	18
	758	719	113	455	470	184	830	905	191	618	555	324	
13	20764	31731	21119	32467	21476	33196	21836	33917	22197	34630	22561	35336	17
	770	743	125	480	482	208	842	929	203	642	567	348	
14	20776	31756	21131	32492	21488	33220	21848	33941	22209	34654	22573	35359	16
	782	768	137	504	494	232	854	953	215	665	579	371	
15	20788	31780	21143	32516	21500	33244	21860	33965	22221	34677	22585	35383	15
	793	793	149	528	506	256	866	976	228	689	591	394	
16	20799	31805	21155	32541	21512	33268	21872	33988	22234	34701	22598	35406	14
	805	817	161	553	518	280	878	34000	240	713	604	418	
17	20811	31830	21167	32565	21524	33292	21884	34012	22246	34725	22610	35429	13
	817	842	172	577	530	304	890	024	252	736	616	441	
18	20823	31854	21178	32589	21536	33317	21896	34036	22258	34748	22622	35453	12
	829	867	184	601	542	329	902	048	264	760	628	464	
19	20835	31879	21190	32614	21548	33341	21908	34060	22270	34772	22634	35476	11
	841	891	196	626	554	353	914	072	276	784	640	488	
20	20847	31903	21202	32638	21560	33365	21920	34084	22282	34795	22646	35500	10
	852	916	208	650	566	377	926	096	288	807	652	511	
21	20858	31928	21214	32662	21572	33389	21932	34108	22294	34819	22658	35523	9
	864	940	220	675	578	401	938	120	300	831	664	535	
22	20870	31953	21226	32687	21584	33413	21944	34132	22306	34843	22671	35546	8
	876	965	232	699	590	425	950	143	312	854	677	558	
23	20882	31977	21238	32711	21596	33437	21956	34155	22318	34866	22683	35570	7
	888	31990	244	723	602	449	962	167	324	878	689	581	
24	20894	32002	21250	32735	21608	33461	21968	34179	22330	34890	22695	35593	6
	900	014	256	748	614	473	974	191	336	901	701	604	
25	20906	32026	21262	32760	21620	33485	21980	34203	22343	34913	22707	35616	5
	912	039	268	772	626	497	986	215	349	925	713	628	
26	20918	32051	21274	32784	21632	33509	21992	34227	22355	34937	22719	35639	4
	923	063	280	796	638	521	21998	239	361	949	725	651	
27	20929	32076	21285	32808	21644	33533	22004	34251	22367	34960	22731	35663	3
	935	088	291	820	650	545	010	262	373	972	738	674	
28	20941	32100	21297	32833	21656	33557	22016	34274	22379	34984	22744	35686	2
	947	112	303	845	662	569	022	286	385	34996	750	698	
29	20953	32125	21309	32857	21668	33581	22028	34298	22391	35007	22756	35709	1
	959	137	315	869	674	593	034	310	397	019	762	721	
30	20965	32149	21321	32881	21680	33605	22040	34322	22403	35031	22768	35733	0
		T. [9]		T. [9]		T. [9]		T. [9]		T. [9]		T. [9]	
	30′		00′		30′		00′		30′		00′		′

Table 20 — HAVERSINES

′	57° 00′ Nat.	Log.	57° 30′ Nat.	Log.	58° 00′ Nat.	Log.	58° 30′ Nat.	Log.	59° 00′ Nat.	Log.	59° 30′ Nat.	Log.	′
0	22768	35733 T̄.[9]	23135	36427 T̄.[9]	23504	37114 T̄.[9]	23875	37794 T̄.[9]	24248	38468 T̄.[9]	24623	39134 T̄.[9]	30
	774	744	141	438	510	126	881	806	254	479	629	145	
1	22780	35756	23147	36450	23516	37137	23887	37817	24261	38490	24636	39156	29
	786	767	153	462	523	148	894	828	267	501	642	167	
2	22792	35779	23160	36473	23529	37160	23900	37840	24273	38512	24648	39178	28
	799	791	166	485	535	171	906	851	279	524	654	189	
3	22805	35802	23172	36496	23541	37183	23912	37862	24286	38535	24661	39201	27
	811	814	178	508	547	194	918	873	292	546	667	212	
4	22817	35826	23184	36519	23553	37205	23925	37885	24298	38557	24673	39223	26
	823	837	190	531	560	217	931	896	304	568	679	234	
5	22829	35849	23196	36542	23566	37228	23937	37907	24310	38579	24686	39245	25
	835	860	203	554	572	239	943	918	317	590	692	256	
6	22841	35872	23209	36565	23578	37251	23950	37930	24323	38602	24698	39267	24
	847	884	215	576	584	262	956	941	329	613	705	278	
7	22853	35895	23221	36588	23590	37274	23962	37952	24335	38624	24711	39289	23
	860	907	227	599	597	285	968	963	342	635	717	300	
8	22866	35918	23233	36611	23603	37296	23974	37975	24348	38646	24723	39311	22
	872	930	239	622	609	308	981	986	354	657	730	322	
9	22878	35942	23246	36634	23615	37319	23987	37997	24360	38668	24736	39333	21
	884	953	252	645	621	330	993	38008	367	680	742	344	
10	22890	35965	23258	36657	23627	37342	23999	38020	24373	38691	24749	39355	20
	896	976	264	668	634	353	24005	031	379	702	755	366	
11	22902	35988	23270	36680	23640	37364	24012	38042	24385	38713	24761	39377	19
	903	36000	276	691	646	376	018	053	392	724	767	388	
12	22915	36011	23282	36703	23652	37387	24024	38065	24398	38735	24774	39399	18
	921	023	289	714	658	399	030	076	404	746	780	410	
13	22927	36034	23295	36726	23665	37410	24036	38087	24410	38757	24786	39421	17
	933	046	301	737	671	421	043	098	417	769	792	432	
14	22939	36058	23307	36749	23677	37433	24049	38110	24423	38780	24799	39443	16
	945	069	313	760	683	444	055	121	429	791	805	454	
15	22951	36081	23319	36771	23689	37455	24061	38132	24435	38802	24811	39465	15
	957	092	325	783	695	467	068	143	442	813	818	476	
16	22964	36104	23332	36794	23702	37478	24074	38154	24448	38824	24824	39487	14
	970	115	338	806	708	489	080	166	454	835	830	498	
17	22976	36127	23344	36817	23714	37501	24086	38177	24460	38846	24836	39509	13
	982	138	350	829	720	512	092	188	467	857	843	520	
18	22988	36150	23356	36840	23726	37523	24099	38199	24473	38868	24849	39531	12
	22994	162	362	852	733	535	105	210	479	880	855	542	
19	23000	36173	23368	36863	23739	37546	24111	38222	24485	38891	24862	39553	11
	006	185	375	875	745	557	117	233	492	902	868	564	
20	23012	36196	23381	36886	23751	37568	24124	38244	24498	38913	24874	39575	10
	019	208	387	897	757	580	130	255	504	924	880	586	
21	23025	36219	23393	36909	23764	37591	24136	38266	24510	38935	24887	39597	9
	031	231	399	920	770	602	142	278	517	946	893	608	
22	23037	36243	23405	36932	23776	37614	24148	38289	24523	38957	24899	39619	8
	043	254	412	943	782	625	155	300	529	968	906	630	
23	23049	36266	23418	36955	23788	37636	24161	38311	24535	38979	24912	39641	7
	055	277	424	966	795	648	167	322	542	38990	918	652	
24	23061	36289	23430	36977	23801	37659	24173	38334	24548	39001	24924	39663	6
	068	300	436	36989	807	670	180	345	554	013	931	674	
25	23074	36312	23442	37000	23813	37682	24186	38356	24560	39024	24937	39684	5
	080	323	449	012	819	693	192	367	567	035	943	695	
26	23086	36335	23455	37023	23825	37704	24198	38378	24573	39046	24950	39706	4
	092	346	461	034	832	715	204	390	579	057	956	717	
27	23098	36358	23467	37046	23838	37727	24211	38401	24585	39068	24962	39728	3
	104	369	473	057	844	738	217	412	592	079	969	739	
28	23110	36381	23479	37069	23850	37749	24223	38423	24598	39090	24975	39750	2
	117	392	486	080	856	761	229	434	604	101	981	761	
29	23123	36404	23492	37091	23863	37772	24236	38445	24611	39112	24987	39772	1
	129	415	498	103	869	783	242	457	617	123	24994	783	
30	23135	36427	23504	37114	23875	37794	24248	38468	24623	39134	25000	39794	0
		T̄.[9]		T̄.[9]		T̄.[9]		T̄.[9]		T̄.[9]		T̄.[9]	
′	30′		00′		30′		00′		30′		00′		′
	302°				**301°**				**300°**				

Table 20 — HAVERSINES

	60°				61°				62°				
	00′		30′		00′		30′		00′		30′		
′	Nat.	Log.	Nat.	Log.	Nat.	Log.	Nat.	Log.	Nat.	Log.	Nat.	Log.	′
		T̄. [9]		T̄. [9]		T̄. [9]		T̄. [9]		T̄. [9]		T̄. [9]	
0	25000	39794	25379	40447	25760	41094	26142	41734	26526	42368	26913	42996	30
	006	805	385	458	766	104	148	745	533	378	919	43006	
1	25013	39816	25391	40469	25772	41115	26155	41755	26539	42389	26925	43016	29
	019	827	398	480	779	126	161	766	546	399	932	027	
2	25025	39838	25404	40490	25785	41137	26168	41776	26552	42410	26938	43037	28
	031	849	410	501	791	147	174	787	559	420	945	048	
3	25038	39860	25417	40512	25798	41158	26180	41798	26565	42431	26951	43058	27
	044	871	423	523	804	169	187	808	571	441	958	068	
4	25050	39881	25429	40534	25810	41180	26193	41819	26578	42452	26964	43079	26
	057	892	436	545	817	190	200	829	584	462	971	089	
5	25063	39903	25442	40555	25823	41201	26206	41840	26591	42473	26977	43100	25
	069	914	448	566	830	212	212	851	597	483	984	110	
6	25076	39925	25455	40577	25836	41222	26219	41861	26604	42494	26990	43120	24
	082	936	461	588	842	233	225	872	610	504	26996	131	
7	25088	39947	25467	40599	25849	41244	26232	41882	26616	42515	27003	43141	23
	095	958	474	609	855	254	238	893	623	525	009	151	
8	25101	39969	25480	40620	25861	41265	26244	41904	26629	42536	27016	43162	22
	107	980	486	631	868	276	251	914	636	546	022	172	
9	25113	39991	25493	40642	25874	41287	26257	41925	26642	42557	27029	43183	21
	120	40001	499	653	880	297	264	935	649	567	035	193	
10	25126	40012	25506	40663	25887	41308	26270	41946	26655	42578	27042	43203	20
	132	023	512	674	893	319	276	957	661	588	048	214	
11	25139	40034	25518	40685	25900	41329	26283	41967	26668	42599	27055	43224	19
	145	045	525	696	906	340	289	978	674	609	061	234	
12	25151	40056	25531	40707	25912	41351	26296	41988	26681	42620	27068	43245	18
	158	067	537	717	919	361	302	41999	687	630	074	255	
13	25164	40078	25544	40728	25925	41372	26308	42009	26694	42641	27080	43266	17
	170	089	550	739	931	383	315	020	700	651	087	276	
14	25177	40100	25556	40750	25938	41393	26321	42031	26706	42662	27093	43286	16
	183	111	563	760	944	404	328	041	713	672	100	297	
15	25189	40121	25569	40771	25951	41415	26334	42052	26719	42682	27106	43307	15
	195	132	575	782	957	425	340	062	726	693	113	317	
16	25202	40143	25582	40793	25963	41436	26347	42073	26732	42703	27119	43328	14
	208	154	588	804	970	447	353	083	739	714	126	338	
17	25214	40165	25594	40814	25976	41457	26360	42094	26745	42724	27132	43348	13
	221	176	601	825	982	468	366	105	751	735	139	359	
18	25227	40187	25607	40836	25989	41479	26372	42115	26758	42745	27145	43369	12
	233	198	613	847	25995	489	379	126	764	756	152	379	
19	25240	40208	25620	40857	26002	41500	26385	42136	26771	42766	27158	43390	11
	246	219	626	868	008	511	392	147	777	777	165	400	
20	25252	40230	25632	40879	26014	41521	26398	42157	26784	42787	27171	43411	10
	259	241	639	890	021	532	405	168	790	797	177	421	
21	25265	40252	25645	40900	26027	41543	26411	42178	26797	42808	27184	43431	9
	271	263	651	911	033	553	417	189	803	818	190	442	
22	25278	40274	25658	40922	26040	41564	26424	42199	26809	42829	27197	43452	8
	284	284	664	933	046	575	430	210	816	839	203	462	
23	25290	40295	25671	40943	26053	41585	26437	42221	26822	42850	27210	43473	7
	297	306	677	954	059	596	443	231	829	860	216	483	
24	25303	40317	25683	40965	26065	41606	26449	42242	26835	42870	27223	43493	6
	309	328	690	976	072	617	456	252	842	881	229	504	
25	25316	40339	25696	40986	26078	41628	26462	42263	26848	42891	27236	43514	5
	322	350	702	40997	085	638	469	273	855	902	242	524	
26	25328	40360	25709	41008	26091	41649	26475	42284	26861	42912	27249	43535	4
	335	371	715	019	097	660	481	294	867	923	255	545	
27	25341	40382	25721	41029	26104	41670	26488	42305	26874	42933	27262	43555	3
	347	393	728	040	110	681	494	315	880	943	268	565	
28	25354	40404	25734	41051	26117	41692	26501	42326	26887	42954	27275	43576	2
	360	415	740	062	123	702	507	336	893	964	281	586	
29	25366	40425	25747	41072	26129	41713	26514	42347	26900	42975	27288	43596	1
	372	436	753	083	136	723	520	357	906	985	294	607	
30	25379	40447	25760	41094	26142	41734	26526	42368	26913	42996	27300	43617	0
		T̄. [9]		T̄. [9]		T̄. [9]		T̄. [9]		T̄. [9]		T̄. [9]	
	30′		00′		30′		00′		30′		00′		′
	299°				298°				297°				

Table 20   **HAVERSINES**

′	63° 00′ Nat.	Log.	63° 30′ Nat.	Log.	64° 00′ Nat.	Log.	64° 30′ Nat.	Log.	65° 00′ Nat.	Log.	65° 30′ Nat.	Log.	′
		T. [9]		T. [9]		T. [9]		T. [9]		T. [9]		T. [9]	
0	27300	43617	27690	44232	28081	44842	28474	45446	28869	46043	29265	46635	30
	307	627	697	243	088	852	481	456	876	053	272	645	
1	27313	43638	27703	44253	28095	44862	28488	45466	28882	46063	29279	46655	29
	320	648	710	263	101	872	494	476	889	073	285	665	
2	27326	43658	27716	44273	28108	44882	28501	45486	28895	46083	29292	46675	28
	333	669	723	283	114	892	507	496	902	093	298	684	
3	27339	43679	27729	44294	28121	44903	28514	45506	28909	46103	29305	46694	27
	346	689	736	304	127	913	520	516	915	113	312	704	
4	27352	43699	27742	44314	28134	44923	28527	45526	28922	46123	29318	46714	26
	359	710	749	324	140	933	534	536	928	132	325	724	
5	27365	43720	27755	44334	28147	44943	28540	45546	28935	46142	29332	46733	25
	372	730	762	345	153	953	547	556	942	152	338	743	
6	27378	43741	27768	44355	28160	44963	28553	45566	28948	46162	29345	46753	24
	385	751	775	365	166	973	560	576	955	172	351	763	
7	27391	43761	27781	44375	28173	44983	28566	45586	28961	46182	29358	46773	23
	398	771	788	385	180	44993	573	596	968	192	365	782	
8	27404	43782	27794	44396	28186	45003	28580	45606	28975	46202	29371	46792	22
	411	792	801	406	193	014	586	615	981	212	378	802	
9	27417	43802	27807	44416	28199	45024	28593	45625	28988	46222	29385	46812	21
	424	813	814	426	206	034	599	635	28994	231	391	822	
10	27430	43823	27820	44436	28212	45044	28606	45645	29001	46241	29398	46831	20
	437	833	827	446	219	054	612	655	008	251	404	841	
11	27443	43843	27833	44457	28225	45064	28619	45665	29014	46261	29411	46851	19
	450	854	840	467	232	074	626	675	021	271	418	861	
12	27456	43864	27846	44477	28238	45084	28632	45685	29027	46281	29424	46871	18
	463	874	853	487	245	094	639	695	034	291	431	880	
13	27469	43884	27859	44497	28252	45104	28645	45705	29041	46301	29438	46890	17
	476	895	866	507	258	114	652	715	047	310	444	900	
14	27482	43905	27873	44518	28265	45124	28658	45725	29054	46320	29451	46910	16
	489	915	879	528	271	134	665	735	060	330	457	919	
15	27495	43925	27886	44538	28278	45144	28672	45745	29067	46340	29464	46929	15
	502	936	892	548	284	155	678	755	074	350	471	939	
16	27508	43946	27899	44558	28291	45165	28685	45765	29080	46360	29477	46949	14
	515	956	905	568	297	175	691	775	087	370	484	959	
17	27521	43966	27912	44579	28304	45185	28698	45785	29093	46380	29491	46968	13
	528	977	918	589	310	195	704	795	100	389	497	978	
18	27534	43987	27925	44599	28317	45205	28711	45805	29107	46399	29504	46988	12
	541	43997	931	609	324	215	718	815	113	409	510	46998	
19	27547	44007	27938	44619	28330	45225	28724	45825	29120	46419	29517	47007	11
	554	018	944	629	337	235	731	835	126	429	524	017	
20	27560	44028	27951	44639	28343	45245	28737	45845	29133	46439	29530	47027	10
	567	038	957	650	350	255	744	855	140	448	537	037	
21	27573	44048	27964	44660	28356	45265	28751	45865	29146	46458	29544	47046	9
	580	059	970	670	363	275	757	875	153	468	550	056	
22	27586	44069	27977	44680	28369	45285	28764	45884	29160	46478	29557	47066	8
	593	079	983	690	376	295	770	894	166	488	564	076	
23	27599	44089	27990	44700	28383	45305	28777	45904	29173	46498	29570	47085	7
	606	100	27997	710	389	315	783	914	179	508	577	095	
24	27612	44110	28003	44721	28396	45325	28790	45924	29186	46517	29583	47105	6
	619	120	010	731	402	335	797	934	193	527	590	115	
25	27625	44130	28016	44741	28409	45345	28803	45944	29199	46537	29597	47124	5
	632	141	023	751	415	355	810	954	206	547	603	134	
26	27638	44151	28029	44761	28422	45365	28816	45964	29212	46557	29610	47144	4
	645	161	036	771	429	375	823	974	219	567	617	154	
27	27651	44171	28042	44781	28435	45385	28830	45984	29226	46576	29623	47163	3
	658	181	049	791	442	395	836	45994	232	586	630	173	
28	27664	44192	28055	44801	28448	45405	28843	46004	29239	46596	29637	47183	2
	671	202	062	812	455	415	849	014	245	606	643	193	
29	27677	44212	28068	44822	28461	45425	28856	46023	29252	46616	29650	47202	1
	684	222	075	832	468	436	862	033	259	626	657	212	
30	27690	44232	28081	44842	28474	45446	28869	46043	29265	46635	29663	47222	0
		T. [9]		T. [9]		T. [9]		T. [9]		T. [9]		T. [9]	
		30′		00′		30′		00′		30′		00′	′
	296°				**295°**				**294°**				

Table 20   HAVERSINES

	66° 00′ Nat.	66° 00′ Log.	66° 30′ Nat.	66° 30′ Log.	67° 00′ Nat.	67° 00′ Log.	67° 30′ Nat.	67° 30′ Log.	68° 00′ Nat.	68° 00′ Log.	68° 30′ Nat.	68° 30′ Log.	
		Ī. [9]		Ī. [9]		Ī. [9]		Ī. [9]		Ī. [9]		Ī. [9]	
0	29663	47222	30063	47803	30463	48378	30866	48948	31270	49512	31675	50072	30
	670	231	069	812	470	387	873	957	276	522	682	081	
1	29676	47241	30076	47822	30477	48397	30879	48967	31283	49531	31688	50090	29
	683	251	083	831	484	407	886	976	290	540	695	099	
2	29690	47261	30089	47841	30490	48416	30893	48986	31297	49550	31702	50109	28
	696	270	096	851	497	426	899	48995	303	559	709	118	
3	29703	47280	30103	47860	30504	48435	30906	49004	31310	49568	31716	50127	27
	710	290	109	870	510	445	913	014	317	578	722	136	
4	29716	47300	30116	47880	30517	48454	30920	49023	31324	49587	31729	50146	26
	723	309	123	889	524	464	926	033	330	597	736	155	
5	29730	47319	30129	47899	30530	48473	30933	49042	31337	49606	31743	50164	25
	736	329	136	908	537	483	940	052	344	615	749	174	
6	29743	47338	30143	47918	30544	48492	30946	49061	31351	49625	31756	50183	24
	750	348	149	928	551	502	953	071	357	634	763	192	
7	29756	47358	30156	47937	30557	48511	30960	49080	31364	49643	31770	50201	23
	763	367	163	947	564	521	967	089	371	653	776	211	
8	29770	47377	30169	47957	30571	48530	30973	49099	31378	49662	31783	50220	22
	776	387	176	966	577	540	980	108	384	671	790	229	
9	29783	47397	30183	47976	30584	48549	30987	49118	31391	49681	31797	50238	21
	789	406	189	985	591	559	30994	127	398	690	804	248	
10	29796	47416	30196	47995	30597	48568	31000	49137	31405	49699	31810	50257	20
	803	426	203	48005	604	578	007	146	411	709	817	266	
11	29809	47435	30209	48014	30611	48587	31014	49155	31418	49718	31824	50275	19
	816	445	216	024	618	597	020	165	425	727	831	285	
12	29823	47455	30223	48033	30624	48607	31027	49174	31432	49737	31837	50294	18
	829	464	229	043	631	616	034	184	438	746	844	303	
13	29836	47474	30236	48053	30638	48626	31041	49193	31445	49755	31851	50312	17
	843	484	243	062	644	635	047	202	452	765	858	322	
14	29849	47493	30249	48072	30651	48645	31054	49212	31459	49774	31865	50331	16
	856	503	256	081	658	654	061	221	465	783	871	340	
15	29863	47513	30263	48091	30664	48664	31068	49231	31472	49793	31878	50349	15
	869	523	269	101	671	673	074	240	479	802	885	358	
16	29876	47532	30276	48110	30678	48683	31081	49250	31486	49811	31892	50368	14
	883	542	283	120	685	692	088	259	492	821	898	377	
17	29889	47552	30290	48129	30691	48702	31094	49268	31499	49830	31905	50386	13
	896	561	296	139	698	711	101	278	506	839	912	395	
18	29903	47571	30303	48148	30705	48720	31108	49287	31513	49849	31919	50405	12
	909	581	310	158	711	730	115	297	519	858	926	414	
19	29916	47590	30316	48168	30718	48739	31121	49306	31526	49867	31932	50423	11
	923	600	323	177	725	749	128	315	533	876	939	432	
20	29929	47610	30330	48187	30732	48758	31135	49325	31540	49886	31946	50442	10
	936	619	336	196	738	768	142	334	546	895	953	451	
21	29943	47629	30343	48206	30745	48777	31148	49344	31553	49904	31959	50460	9
	949	639	350	215	752	787	155	353	560	914	966	469	
22	29956	47648	30356	48225	30758	48796	31162	49362	31567	49923	31973	50478	8
	963	658	363	235	765	806	169	372	573	932	980	488	
23	29969	47668	30370	48244	30772	48815	31175	49381	31580	49942	31987	50497	7
	976	677	376	254	779	825	182	390	587	951	31993	506	
24	29983	47687	30383	48263	30785	48834	31189	49400	31594	49960	32000	50515	6
	989	697	390	273	792	844	196	409	601	969	007	524	
25	29996	47706	30397	48282	30799	48853	31202	49419	31607	49979	32014	50534	5
	30003	716	403	292	805	863	209	428	614	988	021	543	
26	30009	47725	30410	48302	30812	48872	31216	49437	31621	49997	32027	50552	4
	016	735	417	311	819	882	222	447	628	50007	034	561	
27	30023	47745	30423	48321	30826	48891	31229	49456	31634	50016	32041	50570	3
	029	754	430	330	832	901	236	465	641	025	048	580	
28	30036	47764	30437	48340	30839	48910	31243	49475	31648	50034	32054	50589	2
	043	774	443	349	846	919	249	484	655	044	061	598	
29	30049	47783	30450	48359	30852	48929	31256	49494	31661	50053	32068	50607	1
	056	793	457	368	859	938	263	503	668	062	075	616	
30	30063	47803	30463	48378	30866	48948	31270	49512	31675	50072	32082	50626	0
		Ī. [9]		Ī. [9]		Ī. [9]		Ī. [9]		Ī. [9]		Ī. [9]	
′	30′		00′		30′		00′		30′		00′		′

293°   292°   291°

Table 20

HAVERSINES

′	69° 00′ Nat.	Log.	69° 30′ Nat.	Log.	70° 00′ Nat.	Log.	70° 30′ Nat.	Log.	71° 00′ Nat.	Log.	71° 30′ Nat.	Log.	′
		Ī.[9]		Ī.[9]		Ī.[9]		Ī.[9]		Ī.[9]		Ī.[9]	
0	32082	50626	32490	51174	32899	51718	33310	52257	33722	52791	34135	53320	30
	088	635	496	184	906	727	317	266	728	800	142	328	
1	32095	50644	32503	51193	32913	51736	33323	52275	33735	52809	34149	53337	29
	102	653	510	202	919	745	330	284	742	817	155	346	
2	32109	50662	32517	51211	32926	51754	33337	52293	33749	52826	34162	53355	28
	116	672	524	220	933	763	344	302	756	835	169	364	
3	32122	50681	32531	51229	32940	51772	33351	52311	33763	52844	34176	53372	27
	129	690	537	238	947	781	358	320	770	853	183	381	
4	32136	50699	32544	51247	32954	51790	33365	52328	33777	52862	34190	53390	26
	143	708	551	256	961	799	371	337	783	870	197	399	
5	32150	50717	32558	51265	32967	51808	33378	52346	33790	52879	34204	53407	25
	156	727	565	275	974	817	385	355	797	888	211	416	
6	32163	50736	32571	51284	32981	51826	33392	52364	33804	52897	34218	53425	24
	170	745	578	293	988	835	399	373	811	906	224	434	
7	32177	50754	32585	51302	32995	51844	33406	52382	33818	52915	34231	53442	23
	183	763	592	311	33002	853	413	391	825	923	238	451	
8	32190	50772	32599	51320	33008	51862	33419	52400	33832	52932	34245	53460	22
	197	782	605	329	015	871	426	409	839	941	252	469	
9	32204	50791	32612	51338	33022	51880	33433	52418	33845	52950	34259	53477	21
	211	800	619	347	029	889	440	427	852	959	266	486	
10	32217	50809	32626	51356	33036	51898	33447	52435	33859	52968	34273	53495	20
	224	818	633	365	043	907	454	444	866	976	280	504	
11	32231	50827	32640	51374	33049	51916	33461	52453	33873	52985	34287	53512	19
	238	837	646	384	056	925	467	462	880	52994	293	521	
12	32245	50846	32653	51393	33063	51934	33474	52471	33887	53003	34300	53530	18
	251	855	660	402	070	943	481	480	894	012	307	539	
13	32258	50864	32667	51411	33077	51952	33488	52489	33900	53021	34314	53547	17
	265	873	674	420	084	961	495	498	907	029	321	556	
14	32272	50882	32681	51429	33090	51970	33502	52507	33914	53038	34328	53565	16
	279	892	687	438	097	979	509	516	921	047	335	574	
15	32285	50901	32694	51447	33104	51988	33515	52525	33928	53056	34342	53582	15
	292	910	701	456	111	51997	522	533	935	065	349	591	
16	32299	50919	32708	51465	33118	52006	33529	52542	33942	53073	34356	53600	14
	306	928	715	474	125	015	536	551	949	082	363	609	
17	32313	50937	32721	51483	33132	52024	33543	52560	33956	53091	34369	53617	13
	319	946	728	492	138	033	550	569	962	100	376	626	
18	32326	50956	32735	51501	33145	52042	33557	52578	33969	53109	34383	53635	12
	333	965	742	510	152	051	564	587	976	118	390	643	
19	32340	50974	32749	51519	33159	52060	33570	52596	33983	53126	34397	53652	11
	347	983	756	529	166	069	577	605	990	135	404	661	
20	32353	50992	32762	51538	33173	52078	33584	52613	33997	53144	34411	53670	10
	360	51001	769	547	179	087	591	622	34004	153	418	678	
21	32367	51010	32776	51556	33186	52096	33598	52631	34011	53162	34425	53687	9
	374	019	783	565	193	105	605	640	018	170	432	696	
22	32381	51029	32790	51574	33200	52114	33612	52649	34024	53179	34439	53704	8
	387	038	797	583	207	123	618	658	031	188	445	713	
23	32394	51047	32803	51592	33214	52132	33625	52667	34038	53197	34452	53722	7
	401	056	810	601	221	141	632	676	045	206	459	731	
24	32408	51065	32817	51610	33227	52150	33639	52684	34052	53214	34466	53739	6
	415	074	824	619	234	159	646	693	059	223	473	748	
25	32422	51083	32831	51628	33241	52168	33653	52702	34066	53232	34480	53757	5
	428	092	838	637	248	177	660	711	073	241	487	765	
26	32435	51102	32844	51646	33255	52185	33667	52720	34080	53249	34494	53774	4
	442	111	851	655	262	194	673	729	087	258	501	783	
27	32449	51120	32858	51664	33269	52203	33680	52738	34093	53267	34508	53792	3
	456	129	865	673	275	212	687	747	100	276	515	800	
28	32462	51138	32872	51682	33282	52221	33694	52755	34107	53285	34521	53809	2
	469	147	878	691	289	230	701	764	114	293	528	818	
29	32476	51156	32885	51700	33296	52239	33708	52773	34121	53302	34535	53826	1
	483	165	892	709	303	248	715	782	128	311	542	835	
30	32490	51174	32899	51718	33310	52257	33722	52791	34135	53320	34549	53844	0
		Ī.[9]		Ī.[9]		Ī.[9]		Ī.[9]		Ī.[9]		Ī.[9]	
	30′		00′		30′		00′		30′		00′		′
	290°				289°				288°				

Table 20   HAVERSINES

′	72° 00′ Nat.	Log.	72° 30′ Nat.	Log.	73° 00′ Nat.	Log.	73° 30′ Nat.	Log.	74° 00′ Nat.	Log.	74° 30′ Nat.	Log.	
		T̄.[9]		T̄.[9]		T̄.[9]		T̄.[9]		T̄.[9]		T̄.[9]	
0	34549	53844	34965	54363	35381	54878	35799	55387	36218	55893	36638	56393	30
	556	852	972	372	388	886	806	396	225	901	645	402	
1	34563	53861	34979	54380	35395	54895	35813	55404	36232	55909	36652	56410	29
	570	870	986	389	402	903	820	413	239	918	659	418	
2	34577	53879	34992	54397	35409	54912	35827	55421	36246	55926	36666	56426	28
	584	887	34999	406	416	920	834	430	253	934	673	435	
3	34591	53896	35006	54415	35423	54929	35841	55438	36260	55943	36680	56443	27
	598	905	013	423	430	937	848	447	267	951	687	451	
4	34604	53913	35020	54432	35437	54946	35855	55455	36274	55960	36694	56460	26
	611	922	027	440	444	954	862	463	281	968	701	468	
5	34618	53931	35034	54449	35451	54963	35869	55472	36288	55976	36708	56476	25
	625	939	041	458	458	971	876	480	295	985	715	485	
6	34632	53948	35048	54466	35465	54980	35883	55489	36302	55993	36722	56493	24
	639	957	055	475	472	988	890	497	309	56001	729	501	
7	34646	53965	35062	54483	35479	54997	35897	55506	36316	56010	36736	56509	23
	653	974	069	492	486	55005	904	514	323	018	743	518	
8	34660	53983	35076	54501	35493	55014	35911	55523	36330	56027	36750	56526	22
	667	53991	083	509	500	022	918	531	337	035	757	534	
9	34674	54000	35090	54518	35507	55031	35925	55539	36344	56043	36764	56543	21
	681	009	097	526	514	039	932	548	351	052	771	551	
10	34688	54017	35103	54535	35521	55048	35939	55556	36358	56060	36778	56559	20
	694	026	110	544	528	056	946	565	365	068	785	567	
11	34701	54035	35117	54552	35534	55065	35953	55573	36372	56077	36792	56576	19
	708	043	124	561	541	074	960	582	379	085	799	584	
12	34715	54052	35131	54569	35548	55082	35967	55590	36386	56093	36806	56592	18
	722	061	138	578	555	091	974	598	393	102	813	601	
13	34729	54069	35145	54587	35562	55099	35981	55607	36400	56110	36820	56609	17
	736	078	152	595	569	108	988	615	407	118	827	617	
14	34743	54087	35159	54604	35576	55116	35995	55624	36414	56127	36834	56625	16
	750	095	166	612	583	125	36002	632	421	135	841	634	
15	34757	54104	35173	54621	35590	55133	36009	55641	36428	56144	36848	56642	15
	764	113	180	629	597	142	016	649	435	152	855	650	
16	34771	54121	35187	54638	35604	55150	36023	55657	36442	56160	36862	56658	14
	778	130	194	647	611	159	029	666	449	169	869	667	
17	34784	54139	35201	54655	35618	55167	36036	55674	36456	56177	36877	56675	13
	791	147	208	664	625	175	043	683	463	185	884	683	
18	34798	54156	35215	54672	35632	55184	36050	55691	36470	56194	36891	56692	12
	805	165	222	681	639	192	057	699	477	202	898	700	
19	34812	54173	35228	54689	35646	55201	36064	55708	36484	56210	36905	56708	11
	819	182	235	698	653	209	071	716	491	219	912	716	
20	34826	54190	35242	54707	35660	55218	36078	55725	36498	56227	36919	56725	10
	833	199	249	715	667	226	085	733	505	235	926	733	
21	34840	54208	35256	54724	35674	55235	36092	55742	36512	56244	36933	56741	9
	847	216	263	732	681	243	099	750	519	252	940	749	
22	34854	54225	35270	54741	35688	55252	36106	55758	36526	56260	36947	56758	8
	861	234	277	749	695	260	113	767	533	269	954	766	
23	34868	54242	35284	54758	35702	55269	36120	55775	36540	56277	36961	56774	7
	875	251	291	766	709	277	127	784	547	285	968	782	
24	34882	54260	35298	54775	35716	55286	36134	55792	36554	56294	36975	56791	6
	888	268	305	784	723	294	141	800	561	302	982	799	
25	34895	54277	35312	54792	35730	55303	36148	55809	36568	56310	36989	56807	5
	902	285	319	801	736	311	155	817	575	318	36996	815	
26	34909	54294	35326	54809	35743	55320	36162	55826	36582	56327	37003	56824	4
	916	303	333	818	750	328	169	834	589	335	010	832	
27	34923	54311	35340	54826	35757	55337	36176	55842	36596	56343	37017	56840	3
	930	320	347	835	764	345	183	851	603	352	024	848	
28	34937	54329	35354	54843	35771	55354	36190	55859	36610	56360	37031	56856	2
	944	337	361	852	778	362	197	867	617	368	038	865	
29	34951	54346	35368	54860	35785	55370	36204	55876	36624	56377	37045	56873	1
	958	354	374	869	792	379	211	884	631	385	052	881	
30	34965	54363	35381	54878	35799	55387	36218	55893	36638	56393	37059	56889	0
		T̄.[9]		T̄.[9]		T̄.[9]		T̄.[9]		T̄.[9]		T̄.[9]	
	30′		00′		30′		00′		30′		00′		′
	287°				286°				285°				

Table 20 — HAVERSINES

	75° 00′ Nat.	75° 00′ Log.	75° 30′ Nat.	75° 30′ Log.	76° 00′ Nat.	76° 00′ Log.	76° 30′ Nat.	76° 30′ Log.	77° 00′ Nat.	77° 00′ Log.	77° 30′ Nat.	77° 30′ Log.	
		Ī. [9]		Ī. [9]		Ī. [9]		Ī. [9]		Ī. [9]		Ī. [9]	30
0	37059	56889	37481	57381	37904	57868	38328	58351	38752	58830	39178	59304	
	066	898	488	389	911	876	335	359	760	838	185	312	29
1	37073	56906	37495	57397	37918	57885	38342	58367	38767	58846	39192	59320	
	080	914	502	406	925	893	349	375	774	854	199	328	28
2	37087	56922	37509	57414	37932	57901	38356	58383	38781	58862	39206	59336	
	094	931	516	422	939	909	363	391	788	870	214	344	27
3	37101	56939	37523	57430	37946	57917	38370	58399	38795	58878	39221	59351	
	108	947	530	438	953	925	377	407	802	885	228	359	26
4	37115	56955	37537	57446	37960	57933	38384	58415	38809	58893	39235	59367	
	122	963	544	454	967	941	391	423	816	901	242	375	25
5	37129	56972	37551	57463	37974	57949	38398	58431	38823	58909	39249	59383	
	136	980	558	471	982	957	406	439	830	917	256	391	24
6	37143	56988	37566	57479	37989	57965	38413	58447	38837	58925	39263	59399	
	150	56996	573	487	37996	973	420	455	845	933	270	406	23
7	37157	57005	37580	57495	38003	57981	38427	58463	38852	58941	39277	59414	
	164	013	587	503	010	990	434	471	859	949	285	422	22
8	37171	57021	37594	57511	38017	57998	38441	58479	38866	58957	39292	59430	
	179	029	601	520	024	58006	448	487	873	965	299	438	21
9	37186	57037	37608	57528	38031	58014	38455	58495	38880	58973	39306	59446	
	193	046	615	536	038	022	462	503	887	981	313	454	20
10	37200	57054	37622	57544	38045	58030	38469	58511	38894	58988	39320	59461	
	207	062	629	552	052	038	476	519	901	58996	327	469	19
11	37214	57070	37636	57560	38059	58046	38483	58527	38908	59004	39334	59477	
	221	078	643	568	066	054	490	535	915	012	341	485	18
12	37228	57087	37650	57577	38073	58062	38498	58543	38923	59020	39348	59493	
	235	095	657	585	080	070	505	551	930	028	356	501	17
13	37242	57103	37664	57593	38087	58078	38512	58559	38937	59036	39363	59508	
	249	111	671	601	095	086	519	567	944	044	370	516	16
14	37256	57119	37678	57609	38102	58094	38526	58575	38951	59052	39377	59524	
	263	128	685	617	109	102	533	583	958	060	384	532	15
15	37270	57136	37692	57625	38116	58110	38540	58591	38965	59068	39391	59540	
	277	144	699	633	123	118	547	599	972	076	398	548	14
16	37284	57152	37706	57642	38130	58126	38554	58607	38979	59083	39405	59555	
	291	160	713	650	137	135	561	615	986	091	412	563	13
17	37298	57169	37721	57658	38144	58143	38568	58623	38993	59099	39420	59571	
	305	177	728	666	151	151	575	631	39001	107	427	579	12
18	37312	57185	37735	57674	38158	58159	38582	58639	39008	59115	39434	59587	
	319	193	742	682	165	167	590	647	015	123	441	595	11
19	37326	57201	37749	57690	38172	58175	38597	58655	39022	59131	39448	59602	
	333	210	756	698	179	183	604	663	029	139	455	610	10
20	37340	57218	37763	57706	38186	58191	38611	58671	39036	59147	39462	59618	
	347	226	770	715	193	199	618	679	043	154	469	626	9
21	37354	57234	37777	57723	38200	58207	38625	58687	39050	59162	39476	59634	
	361	242	784	731	208	215	632	695	057	170	484	642	8
22	37368	57250	37791	57739	38215	58223	38639	58703	39064	59178	39491	59649	
	375	259	798	747	222	231	646	711	072	186	498	657	7
23	37382	57267	37805	57755	38229	58239	38653	58719	39079	59194	39505	59665	
	389	275	812	763	236	247	660	727	086	202	512	673	6
24	37397	57283	37819	57771	38243	58255	38667	58735	39093	59210	39519	59681	
	404	291	826	779	250	263	675	742	100	218	526	688	5
25	37411	57299	37833	57787	38257	58271	38682	58750	39107	59225	39533	59696	
	418	308	840	796	264	279	689	758	114	233	540	704	4
26	37425	57316	37847	57804	38271	58287	38696	58766	39121	59241	39548	59712	
	432	324	855	812	278	295	703	774	128	249	555	720	3
27	37439	57332	37862	57820	38285	58303	38710	58782	39135	59257	39562	59728	
	446	340	869	828	292	311	717	790	143	265	569	735	2
28	37453	57348	37876	57836	38299	58319	38724	58793	39150	59273	39576	59743	
	460	357	883	844	307	327	731	806	157	281	583	751	1
29	37467	57365	37890	57852	38314	58335	38738	58814	39164	59289	39590	59759	
	474	373	897	860	321	343	745	822	171	296	597	767	0
30	37481	57381	37904	57868	38328	58351	38752	58830	39178	59304	39604	59774	
		Ī. [9]		Ī. [9]		Ī. [9]		Ī. [9]		Ī. [9]		Ī. [9]	

	30′	00′	30′	00′	30′	00′	′
	284°		283°		282°		

Table 20   **HAVERSINES**

	78°				79°				80°				
	00′		**30′**		**00′**		**30′**		**00′**		**30′**		
′	Nat.	Log.	Nat.	Log.	Nat.	Log.	Nat.	Log.	Nat.	Log.	Nat.	Log.	
		T. [9]		T. [9]		T. [9]		T. [9]		T. [9]		T. [9]	
0	39604	59774	40032	60240	40460	60702	40888	61160	41318	61614	41748	62063	30
	612	782	039	248	467	710	895	167	325	621	755	071	
1	39619	59790	40046	60256	40474	60717	40903	61175	41332	61629	41762	62078	29
	626	798	053	263	481	725	910	183	339	636	769	086	
2	39633	59806	40060	60271	40488	60733	40917	61190	41346	61644	41776	62093	28
	640	813	067	279	495	740	924	198	353	651	783	100	
3	39647	59821	40074	60287	40502	60748	40931	61205	41361	61659	41791	62108	27
	654	829	081	294	510	756	938	213	368	666	798	115	
4	39661	59837	40089	60302	40517	60763	40945	61221	41375	61674	41805	62123	26
	668	845	096	310	524	771	953	228	382	681	812	130	
5	39676	59852	40103	60318	40531	60779	40960	61236	41389	61689	41819	62138	25
	683	860	110	325	538	786	967	243	396	696	827	145	
6	39690	59868	40117	60333	40545	60794	40974	61251	41404	61704	41834	62153	24
	697	876	124	341	552	802	981	258	411	711	841	160	
7	39704	59883	40131	60348	40560	60809	40988	61266	41418	61719	41848	62168	23
	711	891	139	356	567	817	40996	274	425	726	855	175	
8	39718	59899	40146	60364	40574	60825	41003	61281	41432	61734	41862	62182	22
	725	907	153	372	581	832	010	289	439	741	870	190	
9	39732	59915	40160	60379	40588	60840	41017	61296	41447	61749	41877	62197	21
	740	922	167	387	595	847	024	304	454	756	884	205	
10	39747	59930	40174	60395	40602	60855	41031	61311	41461	61764	41891	62212	20
	754	938	181	402	610	863	038	319	468	771	898	220	
11	39761	59946	40188	60410	40617	60870	41046	61327	41475	61779	41905	62227	19
	768	953	196	418	624	878	053	334	482	786	913	234	
12	39775	59961	40203	60426	40631	60886	41060	61342	41490	61794	41920	62242	18
	782	969	210	433	638	893	067	349	497	801	927	249	
13	39789	59977	40217	60441	40645	60901	41074	61357	41504	61809	41934	62257	17
	797	985	224	449	652	909	081	364	511	816	941	264	
14	39804	59992	40231	60456	40660	60916	41089	61372	41518	61824	41949	62272	16
	811	60000	238	464	667	924	096	380	525	831	956	279	
15	39818	60008	40245	60472	40674	60931	41103	61387	41533	61839	41963	62287	15
	825	016	253	479	681	939	110	395	540	846	970	294	
16	39832	60023	40260	60487	40688	60947	41117	61402	41547	61854	41977	62301	14
	839	031	267	495	695	954	124	410	554	861	984	309	
17	39846	60039	40274	60502	40702	60962	41131	61417	41561	61869	41992	62316	13
	854	047	281	510	710	970	139	425	568	876	41999	324	
18	39861	60054	40288	60518	40717	60977	41146	61433	41576	61884	42006	62331	12
	868	062	295	526	724	985	153	440	583	891	013	338	
19	39875	60070	40303	60533	40731	60992	41160	61448	41590	61899	42020	62346	11
	882	078	310	541	738	61000	167	455	597	906	027	353	
20	39889	60085	40317	60549	40745	61008	41174	61463	41604	61914	42035	62361	10
	896	093	324	556	752	015	182	470	611	921	042	368	
21	39903	60101	40331	60564	40760	61023	41189	61478	41619	61929	42049	62376	9
	910	109	338	572	767	031	196	485	626	936	056	383	
22	39918	60116	40345	60579	40774	61038	41203	61493	41633	61944	42063	62390	8
	925	124	352	587	781	046	210	500	640	951	071	398	
23	39932	60132	40360	60595	40788	61053	41217	61508	41647	61959	42078	62405	7
	939	140	367	602	795	061	225	516	654	966	085	413	
24	39946	60147	40374	60610	40802	61069	41232	61523	41662	61974	42092	62420	6
	953	155	381	618	810	076	239	531	669	981	099	427	
25	39960	60163	40388	60625	40817	61084	41246	61538	41676	61989	42106	62435	5
	967	171	395	633	824	091	253	546	683	61996	114	442	
26	39975	60178	40402	60641	40831	61099	41260	61553	41690	62003	42121	62450	4
	982	186	410	648	838	107	267	561	697	011	128	457	
27	39989	60194	40417	60656	40845	61114	41275	61568	41705	62018	42135	62464	3
	39996	202	424	664	852	122	282	576	712	026	142	472	
28	40003	60209	40431	60671	40860	61129	41289	61583	41719	62033	42150	62479	2
	010	217	438	679	867	137	296	591	726	041	157	487	
29	40017	60225	40445	60687	40874	61145	41303	61598	41733	62048	42164	62494	1
	024	233	452	694	881	152	310	606	740	056	171	501	
30	40032	60240	40460	60702	40888	61160	41318	61614	41748	62063	42178	62509	0
		T. [9]		T. [9]		T. [9]		T. [9]		T. [9]		T. [9]	
	30′		**00′**		**30′**		**00′**		**30′**		**00′**		′

281°		**280°**		**279°**	

Table 20 — HAVERSINES

′	81° 00′ Nat.	Log.	81° 30′ Nat.	Log.	82° 00′ Nat.	Log.	82° 30′ Nat.	Log.	83° 00′ Nat.	Log.	83° 30′ Nat.	Log.	′
		T̄. [9]		T̄. [9]		T̄. [9]		T̄. [9]		T̄. [9]		T̄. [9]	
0	42178	62509	42610	62951	43041	63389	43474	63823	43907	64253	44340	64679	30
	185	516	617	958	049	396	481	830	914	260	347	686	
1	42193	62524	42624	62965	43056	63403	43488	63837	43921	64267	44354	64694	29
	200	531	631	973	063	410	495	844	928	274	362	701	
2	42207	62538	42638	62980	43070	63418	43503	63851	43935	64281	44369	64708	28
	214	546	645	987	077	425	510	859	943	289	376	715	
3	42221	62553	42653	62995	43085	63432	43517	63866	43950	64296	44383	64722	27
	229	561	660	63002	092	439	524	873	957	303	390	729	
4	42236	62568	42667	63009	43099	63447	43531	63880	43964	64310	44398	64736	26
	243	575	674	017	106	454	539	887	972	317	405	743	
5	42250	62583	42681	63024	43113	63461	43546	63895	43979	64324	44412	64750	25
	257	590	689	031	121	468	553	902	986	331	419	757	
6	42264	62598	42696	63039	43128	63476	43560	63909	43993	64339	44427	64764	24
	272	605	703	046	135	483	567	916	44000	346	434	771	
7	42279	62612	42710	63053	43142	63490	43575	63923	44008	64353	44441	64778	23
	286	620	717	061	149	497	582	931	015	360	448	785	
8	42293	62627	42725	63068	43157	63505	43589	63938	44022	64367	44455	64793	22
	300	634	732	075	164	512	596	945	029	374	463	800	
9	42308	62642	42739	63082	43171	63519	43603	63952	44036	64381	44470	64807	21
	315	649	746	090	178	526	611	959	044	388	477	814	
10	42322	62657	42753	63097	43185	63534	43618	63966	44051	64396	44484	64821	20
	329	664	761	104	193	541	625	974	058	403	492	828	
11	42336	62671	42768	63112	43200	63548	43632	63981	44065	64410	44499	64835	19
	344	679	775	119	207	555	640	988	073	417	506	842	
12	42351	62686	42782	63126	43214	63563	43647	63995	44080	64424	44513	64849	18
	358	693	789	134	221	570	654	64002	087	431	521	856	
13	42365	62701	42797	63141	43229	63577	43661	64010	44094	64438	44528	64863	17
	372	708	804	148	236	584	668	017	101	445	535	870	
14	42379	62716	42811	63156	43243	63592	43676	64024	44109	64452	44542	64877	16
	387	723	818	163	250	599	683	031	116	460	549	884	
15	42394	62730	42825	63170	43257	63606	43690	64038	44123	64467	44557	64891	15
	401	738	833	177	265	613	697	045	130	474	564	898	
16	42408	62745	42840	63185	43272	63621	43704	64053	44138	64481	44571	64905	14
	415	752	847	192	279	628	712	060	145	488	578	912	
17	42423	62760	42854	63199	43286	63635	43719	64067	44152	64495	44586	64919	13
	430	767	861	207	293	642	726	074	159	502	593	926	
18	42437	62774	42869	63214	43301	63649	43733	64081	44166	64509	44600	64934	12
	444	782	876	221	308	657	741	088	174	516	607	941	
19	42451	62789	42883	63228	43315	63664	43748	64096	44181	64523	44614	64948	11
	459	796	890	236	322	671	755	103	188	531	622	955	
20	42466	62804	42897	63243	43330	63678	43762	64110	44195	64538	44629	64962	10
	473	811	905	250	337	686	769	117	203	545	636	969	
21	42480	62819	42912	63258	43344	63693	43777	64124	44210	64552	44643	64976	9
	487	826	919	265	351	700	784	131	217	559	651	983	
22	42494	62833	42926	63272	43358	63707	43791	64139	44224	64566	44658	64990	8
	502	841	933	279	366	714	798	146	231	573	665	64997	
23	42509	62848	42941	63287	43373	63722	43805	64153	44239	64580	44672	65004	7
	516	855	948	294	380	729	813	160	246	587	680	011	
24	42523	62863	42955	63301	43387	63736	43820	64167	44253	64594	44687	65018	6
	530	870	962	309	394	743	827	174	260	602	694	025	
25	42538	62877	42969	63316	43402	63751	43834	64181	44268	64609	44701	65032	5
	545	885	977	323	409	758	842	189	275	616	708	039	
26	42552	62892	42984	63330	43416	63765	43849	64196	44282	64623	44716	65046	4
	559	899	991	338	423	772	856	203	289	630	723	053	
27	42566	62907	42998	63345	43430	63779	43863	64210	44296	64637	44730	65060	3
	574	914	43005	352	438	787	870	217	304	644	737	067	
28	42581	62921	43013	63360	43445	63794	43878	64224	44311	64651	44745	65074	2
	588	929	020	367	452	801	885	231	318	658	752	081	
29	42595	62936	43027	63374	43459	63808	43892	64239	44325	64665	44759	65088	1
	602	943	034	381	466	815	899	246	333	672	766	095	
30	42610	62951	43041	63389	43474	63823	43907	64253	44340	64679	44774	65102	0
		T̄. [9]		T̄. [9]		T̄. [9]		T̄. [9]		T̄. [9]		T̄. [9]	
′	30′		00′		30′		00′		30′		00′		′
	278°				**277°**				**276°**				

Table 20   HAVERSINES   195

	84° 00' Nat.	Log. T.[9]	84° 30' Nat.	Log. T.[9]	85° 00' Nat.	Log. T.[9]	85° 30' Nat.	Log. T.[9]	86° 00' Nat.	Log. T.[9]	86° 30' Nat.	Log. T.[9]	
0	44774	65102	45208	65521	45642	65937	46077	66348	46512	66757	46948	67161	30
	781	109	215	528	649	944	084	355	519	763	955	168	
1	44788	65116	45222	65535	45657	65950	46092	66362	46527	66770	46962	67175	29
	795	123	229	542	664	957	099	369	534	777	969	181	
2	44803	65130	45237	65549	45671	65964	46106	66376	46541	66784	46977	67188	28
	810	137	244	556	678	971	113	383	548	791	984	195	
3	44817	65144	45251	65563	45686	65978	46121	66389	46556	66797	46991	67202	27
	824	151	258	570	693	985	128	396	563	804	46998	208	
4	44831	65158	45266	65577	45700	65992	46135	66403	46570	66811	47006	67215	26
	839	165	273	584	707	65999	142	410	577	818	013	222	
5	44846	65172	45280	65591	45715	66006	46150	66417	46585	66824	47020	67228	25
	853	179	287	598	722	012	157	424	592	831	027	235	
6	44860	65186	45295	65605	45729	66019	46164	66430	46599	66838	47035	67242	24
	868	193	302	612	736	026	171	437	606	845	042	249	
7	44875	65200	45309	65619	45744	66033	46179	66444	46614	66851	47049	67255	23
	882	207	316	625	751	040	186	451	621	858	056	262	
8	44889	65214	45324	65632	45758	66047	46193	66458	46628	66865	47064	67269	22
	897	221	331	639	765	054	200	464	636	872	071	275	
9	44904	65228	45338	65646	45773	66061	46208	66471	46643	66878	47078	67282	21
	911	235	345	653	780	067	215	478	650	885	086	289	
10	44918	65242	45353	65660	45787	66074	46222	66485	46657	66892	47093	67295	20
	925	249	360	667	794	081	229	492	665	899	100	302	
11	44933	65256	45367	65674	45802	66088	46237	66499	46672	66905	47107	67309	19
	940	263	374	681	809	095	244	505	679	912	115	315	
12	44947	65270	45381	65688	45816	66102	46251	66512	46686	66919	47122	67322	18
	954	277	389	695	823	109	258	519	694	926	129	329	
13	44962	65284	45396	65702	45831	66116	46266	66526	46701	66932	47136	67336	17
	969	291	403	709	838	122	273	533	708	939	144	342	
14	44976	65298	45410	65716	45845	66129	46280	66539	46715	66946	47151	67349	16
	983	305	418	722	852	136	287	546	723	953	158	356	
15	44991	65312	45425	65729	45860	66143	46295	66553	46730	66959	47165	67362	15
	44998	319	432	736	867	150	302	560	737	966	173	369	
16	45005	65326	45439	65743	45874	66157	46309	66567	46744	66973	47180	67376	14
	012	333	447	750	881	164	316	573	752	980	187	382	
17	45020	65340	45454	65757	45889	66170	46324	66580	46759	66986	47194	67389	13
	027	347	461	764	896	177	331	587	766	66993	202	396	
18	45034	65354	45468	65771	45903	66184	46338	66594	46773	67000	47209	67402	12
	041	361	476	778	910	191	345	601	781	007	216	409	
19	45048	65368	45483	65785	45918	66198	46353	66607	46788	67013	47223	67416	11
	056	375	490	792	925	205	360	614	795	020	231	422	
20	45063	65382	45497	65799	45932	66212	46367	66621	46802	67027	47238	67429	10
	070	389	505	806	939	218	374	628	810	034	245	436	
21	45077	65396	45512	65812	45947	66225	46382	66635	46817	67040	47252	67442	9
	085	403	519	819	954	232	389	641	824	047	260	449	
22	45092	65410	45526	65826	45961	66239	46396	66648	46831	67054	47267	67456	8
	099	417	534	833	968	246	403	655	839	060	274	462	
23	45106	65424	45541	65840	45976	66253	46411	66662	46846	67067	47282	67469	7
	114	431	548	847	983	260	418	669	853	074	289	476	
24	45121	65438	45555	65854	45990	66266	46425	66675	46860	67081	47296	67482	6
	128	445	563	861	45997	273	432	682	868	087	303	489	
25	45135	65452	45570	65868	46005	66280	46440	66689	46875	67094	47311	67496	5
	143	459	577	875	012	287	447	696	882	101	318	502	
26	45150	65466	45584	65881	46019	66294	46454	66702	46890	67108	47325	67509	4
	157	473	592	888	026	301	461	709	897	114	332	516	
27	45164	65480	45599	65895	46034	66307	46469	66716	46904	67121	47340	67522	3
	172	486	606	902	041	314	476	723	911	128	347	529	
28	45179	65493	45613	65909	46048	66321	46483	66730	46919	67134	47354	67536	2
	186	500	620	916	055	328	490	736	926	141	361	542	
29	45193	65507	45628	65923	46063	66335	46498	66743	46933	67148	47369	67549	1
	200	514	635	930	070	342	505	750	940	155	376	556	
30	45208	65521	45642	65937	46077	66348	46512	66757	46948	67161	47383	67562	0
		T.[9]		T.[9]		T.[9]		T.[9]		T.[9]		T.[9]	
	30'		00'		30'		00'		30'		00'		'
	275°				274°				273°				

Table 20   HAVERSINES

	87° 00′ Nat.	87° 00′ Log.	87° 30′ Nat.	87° 30′ Log.	88° 00′ Nat.	88° 00′ Log.	88° 30′ Nat.	88° 30′ Log.	89° 00′ Nat.	89° 00′ Log.	89° 30′ Nat.	89° 30′ Log.	′
		T̄. [9]		T̄. [9]		T̄. [9]		T̄. [9]		T̄. [9]		T̄. [9]	
0	47383	67562	47819	67960	48255	68354	48691	68745	49127	69132	49564	69516	30
	390	569	826	967	262	361	698	751	135	139	571	523	
1	47398	67576	47834	67973	48270	68367	48706	68758	49142	69145	49578	69529	29
	405	582	841	980	277	374	713	764	149	152	585	535	
2	47412	67589	47848	67986	48284	68380	48720	68771	49156	69158	49593	69542	28
	420	596	855	67993	291	387	727	777	164	164	600	548	
3	47427	67602	47863	68000	48299	68393	48735	68784	49171	69171	49607	69555	27
	434	609	870	006	306	400	742	790	178	177	615	561	
4	47441	67616	47877	68013	48313	68407	48749	68797	49186	69184	49622	69567	26
	449	622	884	019	320	413	757	803	193	190	629	574	
5	47456	67629	47892	68026	48328	68420	48764	68810	49200	69197	49636	69580	25
	463	636	899	033	335	426	771	816	207	203	644	586	
6	47470	67642	47906	68039	48342	68433	48778	68823	49215	69209	49651	69593	24
	478	649	913	046	350	439	786	829	222	216	658	599	
7	47485	67656	47921	68052	48357	68446	48793	68836	49229	69222	49665	69605	23
	492	662	928	059	364	452	800	842	236	229	673	612	
8	47499	67669	47935	68066	48371	68459	48807	68849	49244	69235	49680	69618	22
	507	675	943	072	379	465	815	855	251	241	687	625	
9	47514	67682	47950	68079	48386	68472	48822	68862	49258	69248	49695	69631	21
	521	689	957	085	393	478	829	868	266	254	702	637	
10	47528	67695	47964	68092	48400	68485	48837	68874	49273	69261	49709	69644	20
	536	702	972	098	408	491	844	881	280	267	716	650	
11	47543	67709	47979	68105	48415	68498	48851	68887	49287	69274	49724	69656	19
	550	715	986	112	422	504	858	894	295	280	731	663	
12	47558	67722	47993	68118	48429	68511	48866	68900	49302	69286	49738	69669	18
	565	729	48001	125	437	517	873	907	309	293	745	675	
13	47572	67735	48008	68131	48444	68524	48880	68913	49316	69299	49753	69682	17
	579	742	015	138	451	531	887	920	324	306	760	688	
14	47587	67748	48022	68144	48459	68537	48895	68926	49331	69312	49767	69694	16
	594	755	030	151	466	544	902	933	338	318	775	701	
15	47601	67762	48037	68158	48473	68550	48909	68939	49346	69325	49782	69707	15
	608	768	044	164	480	557	917	946	353	331	789	713	
16	47616	67775	48052	68171	48488	68563	48924	68952	49360	69338	49796	69720	14
	623	782	059	177	495	570	931	958	367	344	804	726	
17	47630	67788	48066	68184	48502	68576	48938	68965	49375	69350	49811	69732	13
	637	795	073	190	509	583	946	971	382	357	818	739	
18	47645	67801	48081	68197	48517	68589	48953	68978	49389	69363	49825	69745	12
	652	808	088	204	524	596	960	984	396	370	833	751	
19	47659	67815	48095	68210	48531	68602	48967	68991	49404	69376	49840	69758	11
	666	821	102	217	538	609	975	68997	411	382	847	764	
20	47674	67828	48110	68223	48546	68615	48982	69004	49418	69389	49855	69770	10
	681	835	117	230	553	622	989	010	426	395	862	777	
21	47688	67841	48124	68236	48560	68628	48997	69017	49433	69402	49869	69783	9
	696	848	131	243	568	635	49004	023	440	408	876	789	
22	47703	67854	48139	68249	48575	68641	49011	69029	49447	69414	49884	69796	8
	710	861	146	256	582	648	018	036	455	421	891	802	
23	47717	67868	48153	68263	48589	68654	49026	69042	49462	69427	49898	69808	7
	725	874	161	269	597	661	033	049	469	433	905	815	
24	47732	67881	48168	68276	48604	68667	49040	69055	49476	69440	49913	69821	6
	739	887	175	282	611	674	047	062	484	446	920	827	
25	47746	67894	48182	68289	48618	68680	49055	69068	49491	69453	49927	69834	5
	754	901	190	295	626	687	062	074	498	459	935	840	
26	47761	67907	48197	68302	48633	68693	49069	69081	49505	69465	49942	69846	4
	768	914	204	308	640	700	076	087	513	472	949	853	
27	47775	67920	48211	68315	48648	68706	49084	69094	49520	69478	49956	69859	3
	783	927	219	322	655	713	091	100	527	484	964	865	
28	47790	67934	48226	68328	48662	68719	49098	69107	49535	69491	49971	69872	2
	797	940	233	335	669	726	106	113	542	497	978	878	
29	47804	67947	48240	68341	48677	68732	49113	69120	49549	69504	49985	69884	1
	812	953	248	348	684	739	120	126	556	510	49993	891	
30	47819	67960	48255	68354	48691	68745	49127	69132	49564	69516	50000	69897	0
		T̄. [9]		T̄. [9]		T̄. [9]		T̄. [9]		T̄. [9]		T̄. [9]	

| | 30′ | | 00′ | | 30′ | | 00′ | | 30′ | | 00′ | | ′ |

272°   271°   270°

Table 20 HAVERSINES

′	90° 00′ Nat.	Log.	90° 30′ Nat.	Log.	91° 00′ Nat.	Log.	91° 30′ Nat.	Log.	92° 00′ Nat.	Log.	92° 30′ Nat.	Log.	′
		T. [9]		T. [9]		T. [9]		T. [9]		T. [9]		T. [9]	
0	50000	69897	50436	70274	50873	70648	51309	71019	51745	71387	52181	71751	30
	007	903	444	281	880	655	316	025	752	393	188	757	
1	50015	69910	50451	70287	50887	70661	51323	71032	51760	71399	52195	71763	29
	022	916	458	293	894	667	331	038	767	405	203	769	
2	50029	69922	50465	70299	50902	70673	51338	71044	51774	71411	52210	71775	28
	036	929	473	306	909	679	345	050	781	417	217	781	
3	50044	69935	50480	70312	50916	70686	51352	71056	51789	71423	52225	71787	27
	051	941	487	318	924	692	360	062	796	429	232	794	
4	50058	69948	50494	70324	50931	70698	51367	71068	51803	71436	52239	71800	26
	065	954	502	331	938	704	374	075	810	442	246	806	
5	50073	69960	50509	70337	50945	70710	51382	71081	51818	71448	52254	71812	25
	080	966	516	343	953	717	389	087	825	454	261	818	
6	50087	69973	50524	70349	50960	70723	51396	71093	51832	71460	52268	71824	24
	095	979	531	356	967	729	403	099	839	466	275	830	
7	50102	69985	50538	70362	50974	70735	51411	71105	51847	71472	52283	71836	23
	109	992	545	368	982	741	418	111	854	478	290	842	
8	50116	69998	50553	70374	50989	70748	51425	71118	51861	71484	52297	71848	22
	124	70004	560	381	50996	754	432	124	869	490	304	854	
9	50131	70011	50567	70387	51003	70760	51440	71130	51876	71496	52312	71860	21
	138	017	574	393	011	766	447	136	883	503	319	866	
10	50145	70023	50582	70399	51018	70772	51454	71142	51890	71509	52326	71872	20
	153	029	589	406	025	779	462	148	898	515	334	878	
11	50160	70036	50596	70412	51033	70785	51469	71154	51905	71521	52341	71884	19
	167	042	604	418	040	791	476	161	912	527	348	890	
12	50175	70048	50611	70424	51047	70797	51483	71167	51919	71533	52355	71896	18
	182	055	618	431	054	803	491	173	927	539	363	902	
13	50189	70061	50625	70437	51062	70809	51498	71179	51934	71545	52370	71908	17
	196	067	633	443	069	816	505	185	941	551	377	914	
14	50204	70074	50640	70449	51076	70822	51512	71191	51948	71557	52384	71920	16
	211	080	647	456	083	828	520	197	956	563	392	926	
15	50218	70086	50654	70462	51091	70834	51527	71203	51963	71569	52399	71932	15
	225	092	662	468	098	840	534	210	970	575	406	938	
16	50233	70099	50669	70474	51105	70847	51541	71216	51978	71582	52413	71944	14
	240	105	676	480	113	853	549	222	985	588	421	950	
17	50247	70111	50684	70487	51120	70859	51556	71228	51997	71591	52428	71956	13
	255	118	691	493	127	865	563	234	51999	600	435	962	
18	50262	70124	50698	70499	51134	70871	51571	71240	52007	71606	52442	71968	12
	269	130	705	505	142	877	578	246	014	612	450	974	
19	50276	70136	50713	70512	51149	70884	51585	71252	52021	71618	52457	71980	11
	284	143	720	518	156	890	592	259	028	624	464	986	
20	50291	70149	50727	70524	51163	70896	51600	71265	52036	71630	52472	71992	10
	298	155	734	530	171	902	607	271	043	636	479	71998	
21	50305	70161	50742	70537	51178	70908	51614	71277	52050	71642	52486	72004	9
	313	168	749	543	185	914	621	283	057	648	493	010	
22	50320	70174	50756	70549	51193	70921	51629	71289	52065	71654	52501	72016	8
	327	180	764	555	200	927	636	295	072	660	508	022	
23	50335	70187	50771	70561	51207	70933	51643	71301	52079	71666	52515	72028	7
	342	193	778	568	214	939	650	307	087	673	522	034	
24	50349	70199	50785	70574	51222	70945	51658	71314	52094	71679	52530	72040	6
	356	205	793	580	229	951	665	320	101	685	537	046	
25	50364	70212	50800	70586	51236	70958	51672	71326	52108	71691	52544	72052	5
	371	218	807	593	243	964	680	332	116	697	551	058	
26	50378	70224	50814	70599	51251	70970	51687	71338	52123	71703	52559	72064	4
	385	230	822	605	258	976	694	344	130	709	566	070	
27	50393	70237	50829	70611	51265	70982	51701	71350	52137	71715	52573	72076	3
	400	243	836	617	272	988	709	356	145	721	580	082	
28	50407	70249	50844	70624	51280	70995	51716	71362	52152	71727	52588	72088	2
	415	256	851	630	287	71001	723	369	159	733	595	094	
29	50422	70262	50858	70636	51294	71007	51730	71375	52166	71739	52602	72100	1
	429	268	865	642	302	013	738	381	174	745	610	106	
30	50436	70274	50873	70648	51309	71019	51745	71387	52181	71751	52617	72112	0
		T. [9]		T. [9]		T. [9]		T. [9]		T. [9]		T. [9]	

30′		00′		30′		00′		30′		00′		′
269°			268°			267°						

Table 20

HAVERSINES

′	93° 00′ Nat.	Log.	93° 30′ Nat.	Log.	94° 00′ Nat.	Log.	94° 30′ Nat.	Log.	95° 00′ Nat.	Log.	95° 30′ Nat.	Log.	
		$\bar{1}$. [9]		$\bar{1}$. [9]		$\bar{1}$. [9]		$\bar{1}$. [9]		$\bar{1}$. [9]		$\bar{1}$. [9]	
0	52617	72112	53052	72471	53488	72825	53923	73177	54358	73526	54792	73872	30
	624	118	060	476	495	831	930	183	365	532	800	878	
1	52631	72124	53067	72482	53502	72837	53937	73189	54372	73538	54807	73883	29
	639	130	074	488	510	843	945	195	380	544	814	889	
2	52646	72136	53081	72494	53517	72849	53952	73201	54387	73549	54821	73895	28
	653	142	089	500	524	855	959	207	394	555	828	901	
3	52660	72148	53096	72506	53531	72861	53966	73212	54401	73561	54836	73906	27
	668	154	103	512	539	867	974	218	408	567	843	912	
4	52675	72160	53110	72518	53546	72873	53981	73224	54416	73572	54850	73918	26
	682	166	118	524	553	878	988	230	423	578	857	924	
5	52689	72172	53125	72530	53560	72884	53995	73236	54430	73584	54865	73929	25
	697	178	132	536	568	890	54003	242	437	590	872	935	
6	52704	72184	53140	72542	53575	72896	54010	73247	54445	73596	54879	73941	24
	711	190	147	548	582	902	017	253	452	601	886	946	
7	52718	72196	53154	72554	53589	72908	54024	73259	54459	73607	54894	73952	23
	726	202	161	560	597	914	032	265	466	613	901	958	
8	52733	72208	53169	72565	53604	72920	54039	73271	54474	73619	54908	73964	22
	740	214	176	571	611	925	046	277	481	624	915	969	
9	52748	72220	53183	72577	53618	72931	54053	73282	54488	73630	54923	73975	21
	755	226	190	583	626	937	061	288	495	636	930	981	
10	52762	72232	53198	72589	53633	72943	54068	73294	54503	73642	54937	73987	20
	769	238	205	595	640	949	075	300	510	648	944	992	
11	52777	72244	53212	72601	53647	72955	54082	73306	54517	73653	54952	73998	19
	784	250	219	607	655	961	090	311	524	659	959	74004	
12	52791	72256	53227	72613	53662	72967	54097	73317	54532	73665	54966	74009	18
	798	262	234	619	669	972	104	323	539	671	973	015	
13	52806	72268	53241	72625	53676	72978	54111	73329	54546	73676	54980	74021	17
	813	274	248	631	684	984	119	335	553	682	988	027	
14	52820	72280	53256	72637	53691	72990	54126	73341	54561	73688	54995	74032	16
	827	286	263	642	698	72996	133	346	568	694	55002	038	
15	52835	72292	53270	72648	53705	73002	54140	73352	54575	73699	55009	74044	15
	842	298	277	654	713	008	148	358	582	705	017	049	
16	52849	72304	53285	72660	53720	73014	54155	73364	54590	73711	55024	74055	14
	856	310	292	666	727	019	162	370	597	717	031	061	
17	52864	72316	53299	72672	53734	73025	54169	73375	54604	73722	55038	74067	13
	871	322	306	678	742	031	177	381	611	728	046	072	
18	52878	72328	53314	72684	53749	73037	54184	73387	54619	73734	55053	74078	12
	885	334	321	690	756	043	191	393	626	740	060	084	
19	52893	72340	53328	72696	53763	73049	54198	73399	54633	73746	55067	74089	11
	900	346	335	702	771	055	206	404	640	751	075	095	
20	52907	72352	53343	72708	53778	73060	54213	73410	54647	73757	55082	74101	10
	914	357	350	713	785	066	220	416	655	763	089	106	
21	52922	72363	53357	72719	53792	73072	54227	73422	54662	73769	55096	74112	9
	929	369	364	725	800	078	235	428	669	774	103	118	
22	52936	72375	53372	72731	53807	73084	54242	73433	54676	73780	55111	74124	8
	944	381	379	737	814	090	249	439	684	786	118	129	
23	52951	72387	53386	72743	53821	73096	54256	73445	54691	73792	55125	74135	7
	958	393	394	749	829	101	264	451	698	797	132	141	
24	52965	72399	53401	72755	53836	73107	54271	73457	54705	73803	55140	74146	6
	973	405	408	761	843	113	278	462	713	809	147	152	
25	52980	72411	53415	72767	53850	73119	54285	73468	54720	73815	55154	74158	5
	987	417	423	772	858	125	293	474	727	820	161	163	
26	52994	72423	53430	72778	53865	73131	54300	73480	54734	73826	55169	74169	4
	53002	429	437	784	872	136	307	486	742	832	176	175	
27	53009	72435	53444	72790	53879	73142	54314	73491	54749	73838	55183	74181	3
	016	441	452	796	887	148	322	497	756	843	190	186	
28	53023	72447	53459	72802	53894	73154	54329	73503	54763	73849	55197	74192	2
	031	453	466	808	901	160	336	509	771	855	205	198	
29	53038	72459	53473	72814	53908	73166	54343	73515	54778	73860	55212	74203	1
	045	465	481	820	916	172	351	520	785	866	219	209	
30	53052	72471	53488	72825	53923	73177	54358	73526	54792	73872	55226	74215	0
		$\bar{1}$. [9]		$\bar{1}$. [9]		$\bar{1}$. [9]		$\bar{1}$. [9]		$\bar{1}$. [9]		$\bar{1}$. [9]	
	30′		00′		30′		00′		30′		00′		′
	266°				**265°**				**264°**				

Table 20   **HAVERSINES**

	96° 00′ Nat.	Log. Ī.[9]	96° 30′ Nat.	Log. Ī.[9]	97° 00′ Nat.	Log. Ī.[9]	97° 30′ Nat.	Log. Ī.[9]	98° 00′ Nat.	Log. Ī.[9]	98° 30′ Nat.	Log. Ī.[9]	
0	55226	74215	55660	74554	56093	74891	56526	75225	56959	75556	57390	75884	30
	234	220	667	560	101	897	534	231	966	561	398	889	
1	55241	74226	55675	74566	56108	74902	56541	75236	56973	75567	57405	75895	29
	248	232	682	571	115	908	548	242	980	572	412	900	
2	55255	74237	55689	74577	56122	74914	56555	75247	56987	75578	57419	75906	28
	263	243	696	583	130	919	562	253	56995	583	426	911	
3	55270	74249	55704	74588	56137	74925	56570	75258	57002	75589	57434	75917	27
	277	254	711	594	144	930	577	264	009	594	441	922	
4	55284	74260	55718	74600	56151	74936	56584	75269	57016	75600	57448	75927	26
	292	266	725	605	158	941	591	275	023	605	455	933	
5	55299	74272	55732	74611	56166	74947	56598	75280	57031	75611	57462	75938	25
	306	277	740	616	173	953	606	286	038	616	470	944	
6	55313	74283	55747	74622	56180	74958	56613	75291	57045	75622	57477	75949	24
	320	289	754	628	187	964	620	297	052	627	484	955	
7	55328	74294	55761	74633	56195	74969	56627	75303	57059	75633	57491	75960	23
	335	300	769	639	202	975	634	308	067	638	498	966	
8	55342	74306	55776	74645	56209	74981	56642	75314	57074	75644	57506	75971	22
	349	311	783	650	216	986	649	319	081	649	513	976	
9	55357	74317	55790	74656	56223	74992	56656	75325	57088	75655	57520	75982	21
	364	323	797	661	231	74997	663	330	095	660	527	987	
10	55371	74328	55805	74667	56238	75003	56670	75336	57103	75666	57534	75993	20
	378	334	812	673	245	008	678	341	110	671	541	75998	
11	55386	74340	55819	74678	56252	75014	56685	75347	57117	75677	57549	76004	19
	393	345	826	684	259	020	692	352	124	682	556	009	
12	55400	74351	55834	74690	56267	75025	56699	75358	57131	75688	57563	76014	18
	407	357	841	695	274	031	707	363	139	693	570	020	
13	55414	74362	55848	74701	56281	75036	56714	75369	57146	75698	57577	76025	17
	422	368	855	706	288	042	721	374	153	704	585	031	
14	55429	74374	55862	74712	56296	75047	56728	75380	57160	75709	57592	76036	16
	436	379	870	718	303	053	735	385	167	715	599	041	
15	55443	74385	55877	74723	56310	75059	56743	75391	57175	75720	57606	76047	15
	451	391	884	729	317	064	750	396	182	726	613	052	
16	55458	74396	55891	74734	56324	75070	56757	75402	57189	75731	57621	76058	14
	465	402	899	740	332	075	764	407	196	737	628	063	
17	55472	74408	55906	74746	56339	75081	56771	75413	57203	75742	57635	76069	13
	479	413	913	751	346	086	779	418	211	748	642	074	
18	55487	74419	55920	74757	56353	75092	56786	75424	57218	75753	57649	76079	12
	494	425	927	762	360	097	793	429	225	759	656	085	
19	55501	74430	55935	74768	56368	75103	56800	75435	57232	75764	57664	76090	11
	508	436	942	774	375	109	807	440	239	770	671	096	
20	55516	74442	55949	74779	56382	75114	56815	75446	57247	75775	57678	76101	10
	523	447	956	785	389	120	822	452	254	780	685	106	
21	55530	74453	55964	74791	56397	75125	56829	75457	57261	75786	57692	76112	9
	537	458	971	796	404	131	836	463	268	791	700	117	
22	55545	74464	55978	74802	56411	75136	56843	75468	57275	75797	57707	76123	8
	552	470	985	807	418	142	851	474	283	802	714	128	
23	55559	74475	55992	74813	56425	75147	56858	75479	57290	75808	57721	76133	7
	566	481	56000	74819	433	153	865	485	297	813	728	139	
24	55573	74487	56007	74824	56440	75159	56872	75490	57304	75819	57736	76144	6
	581	492	014	830	447	164	879	496	311	824	743	150	
25	55588	74498	56021	74835	56454	75170	56887	75501	57319	75830	57750	76155	5
	595	504	029	841	461	175	894	507	326	835	757	161	
26	55602	74509	56036	74847	56469	75181	56901	75512	57333	75840	57764	76166	4
	610	515	043	852	476	186	908	518	340	846	771	171	
27	55617	74521	56050	74858	56483	75192	56915	75523	57347	75851	57779	76177	3
	624	526	057	863	490	197	923	529	355	857	786	182	
28	55631	74532	56065	74869	56497	75203	56930	75534	57362	75862	57793	76188	2
	638	538	072	874	505	208	937	540	369	868	800	193	
29	55646	74543	56079	74880	56512	75214	56944	75545	57376	75873	57807	76198	1
	653	549	086	886	519	220	951	550	383	879	815	204	
30	55660	74554	56093	74891	56526	75225	56959	75556	57390	75884	57822	76209	0
		Ī.[9]		Ī.[9]		Ī.[9]		Ī.[9]		Ī.[9]		Ī.[9]	
	30′		00′		30′		00′		30′		00′		′

	263°	262°	261°

Table 20

HAVERSINES

	99°				100°				101°				
	00′		30′		00′		30′		00′		30′		
′	Nat.	Log.	Nat.	Log.	Nat.	Log.	Nat.	Log.	Nat.	Log.	Nat.	Log.	
		Ī. [9]		Ī. [9]		Ī. [9]		Ī. [9]		Ī. [9]		Ī. [9]	
0	57822	76209	58252	76531	58682	76851	59112	77167	59540	77481	59968	77792	30
	829	214	260	537	690	856	119	173	548	486	976	797	
1	57836	76220	58267	76542	58697	76861	59126	77178	59555	77492	59983	77803	29
	843	225	274	547	704	867	133	183	562	497	990	808	
2	57850	76231	58281	76553	58711	76872	59140	77188	59569	77502	59997	77813	28
	858	236	288	558	718	877	148	194	576	507	60004	818	
3	57865	76241	58295	76563	58725	76883	59155	77199	59583	77512	60011	77823	27
	872	247	303	569	733	888	162	204	590	518	018	828	
4	57879	76252	58310	76574	58740	76893	59169	77209	59598	77523	60025	77834	26
	886	258	317	579	747	898	176	215	605	528	033	839	
5	57894	76263	58324	76585	58754	76904	59183	77220	59612	77533	60040	77844	25
	901	268	331	590	761	909	190	225	619	538	047	849	
6	57908	76274	58338	76595	58768	76914	59198	77230	59626	77544	60054	77854	24
	915	279	346	601	775	920	205	236	633	549	061	859	
7	57922	76285	58353	76606	58783	76925	59212	77241	59640	77554	60068	77864	23
	929	290	360	611	790	930	219	246	648	559	075	870	
8	57937	76295	58367	76617	58797	76936	59226	77251	59655	77564	60082	77875	22
	944	301	374	622	804	941	233	257	662	570	090	880	
9	57951	76306	58381	76627	58811	76946	59240	77262	59669	77575	60097	77885	21
	958	311	389	633	818	951	248	267	676	580	104	890	
10	57965	76317	58396	76638	58826	76957	59255	77272	59683	77585	60111	77895	20
	973	322	403	643	833	962	262	278	690	590	118	900	
11	57980	76328	58410	76649	58840	76967	59269	77283	59697	77596	60125	77906	19
	987	333	417	654	847	972	276	288	705	601	132	911	
12	57994	76338	58424	76659	58854	76978	59283	77293	59712	77606	60139	77916	18
	58001	344	432	665	861	983	290	298	719	611	146	921	
13	58008	76349	58439	76670	58869	76988	59298	77304	59726	77616	60154	77926	17
	016	354	446	675	876	994	305	309	733	622	161	931	
14	58023	76360	58453	76681	58883	76999	59312	77314	59740	77627	60168	77936	16
	030	365	460	686	890	77004	319	319	747	632	175	942	
15	58037	76371	58467	76691	58897	77009	59326	77325	59755	77637	60182	77947	15
	044	376	475	697	904	015	333	330	762	642	189	952	
16	58051	76381	58482	76702	58911	77020	59340	77335	59769	77647	60196	77957	14
	059	387	489	707	919	025	348	340	776	653	203	962	
17	58066	76392	58496	76713	58926	77031	59355	77346	59783	77658	60211	77967	13
	073	397	503	718	933	036	362	351	790	663	218	972	
18	58080	76403	58510	76723	58940	77041	59369	77356	59797	77668	60225	77978	12
	087	408	518	729	947	046	376	361	804	673	232	983	
19	58095	76414	58525	76734	58954	77052	59383	77366	59812	77679	60239	77988	11
	102	419	532	739	962	057	390	372	819	684	246	993	
20	58109	76424	58539	76745	58969	77062	59398	77377	59826	77689	60253	77998	10
	116	430	546	750	976	067	405	382	833	694	260	78003	
21	58123	76435	58553	76755	58983	77073	59412	77387	59840	77699	60268	78008	9
	130	440	561	761	990	078	419	393	847	704	275	013	
22	58138	76446	58568	76766	58997	77083	59426	77398	59854	77710	60282	78019	8
	145	451	575	771	59004	089	433	403	861	715	289	024	
23	58152	76456	58582	76777	59012	77094	59440	77408	59869	77720	60296	78029	7
	159	462	589	782	019	099	448	413	876	725	303	034	
24	58166	76467	58596	76787	59026	77104	59455	77419	59883	77730	60310	78039	6
	173	472	604	792	033	110	462	424	890	735	317	044	
25	58181	76478	58611	76798	59040	77115	59469	77429	59897	77741	60324	78049	5
	188	483	618	803	047	120	476	434	904	746	332	054	
26	58195	76489	58625	76808	59055	77125	59483	77440	59911	77751	60339	78060	4
	202	494	632	814	062	131	490	445	919	756	346	065	
27	58209	76499	58639	76819	59069	77136	59498	77450	59926	77761	60353	78070	3
	217	505	647	824	076	141	505	455	933	766	360	075	
28	58224	76510	58654	76830	59083	77146	59512	77460	59940	77772	60367	78080	2
	231	515	661	835	090	152	519	466	947	777	374	085	
29	58238	76521	58668	76840	59097	77157	59526	77471	59954	77782	60381	78090	1
	245	526	675	845	105	162	533	476	961	787	388	095	
30	58252	76531	58682	76851	59112	77167	59540	77481	59968	77792	60396	78101	0
		Ī. [9]		Ī. [9]		Ī. [9]		Ī. [9]		Ī. [9]		Ī. [9]	
	30′		00′		30′		00′		30′		00′		′
	260°				259°				258°				

Table 20   HAVERSINES

′	102° 00′ Nat.	Log.	102° 30′ Nat.	Log.	103° 00′ Nat.	Log.	103° 30′ Nat.	Log.	104° 00′ Nat.	Log.	104° 30′ Nat.	Log.	′
		T̄. [9]		T̄. [9]		T̄. [9]		T̄. [9]		T̄. [9]		T̄. [9]	
0	60396	78101	60822	78406	61248	78709	61672	79009	62096	79306	62519	79601	30
	403	106	829	411	255	714	679	014	103	311	526	606	
1	60410	78111	60836	78416	61262	78719	61686	79019	62110	79316	62533	79611	29
	417	116	843	421	269	724	693	024	117	321	540	616	
2	60424	78121	60850	78426	61276	78729	61701	79029	62124	79326	62547	79621	28
	431	126	857	431	283	734	708	034	131	331	554	626	
3	60438	78131	60865	78436	61290	78739	61715	79039	62138	79336	62561	79631	27
	445	136	872	442	297	744	722	044	145	341	568	635	
4	60452	78141	60879	78447	61304	78749	61729	79049	62153	79346	62575	79640	26
	460	147	886	452	311	754	736	054	160	351	582	645	
5	60467	78152	60893	78457	61318	78759	61743	79059	62167	79356	62589	79650	25
	474	157	900	462	325	764	750	064	174	361	596	655	
6	60481	78162	60907	78467	61333	78769	61757	79069	62181	79366	62603	79660	24
	488	167	914	472	340	774	764	074	188	371	611	665	
7	60495	78172	60921	78477	61347	78779	61771	79079	62195	79375	62618	79670	23
	502	177	928	482	354	784	778	084	202	380	625	673	
8	60509	78182	60936	78487	61361	78789	61785	79089	62209	79385	62632	79679	22
	516	187	943	492	368	794	792	094	216	390	639	684	
9	60524	78192	60950	78497	61375	78799	61800	79099	62223	79395	62646	79689	21
	531	198	957	502	382	804	807	103	230	400	653	694	
10	60538	78203	60964	78507	61389	78809	61814	79108	62237	79405	62660	79699	20
	545	208	971	512	396	814	821	113	244	410	667	704	
11	60552	78213	60978	78517	61403	78819	61828	79118	62251	79415	62674	79709	19
	559	218	985	522	410	824	835	123	258	420	681	714	
12	60566	78223	60992	78528	61418	78829	61842	79128	62265	79425	62688	79718	18
	573	228	60999	533	425	834	849	133	272	430	695	723	
13	60580	78233	61007	78538	61432	78839	61856	79138	62279	79434	62702	79728	17
	588	238	014	543	439	844	863	143	287	439	709	733	
14	60595	78243	61021	78548	61446	78849	61870	79148	62294	79444	62716	79738	16
	602	249	028	553	453	854	877	153	301	449	723	743	
15	60609	78254	61035	78558	61460	78859	61884	79158	62308	79454	62730	79748	15
	616	259	042	563	467	864	891	163	315	459	737	752	
16	60623	78264	61049	78568	61474	78869	61898	79168	62322	79464	62744	79757	14
	630	269	056	573	481	874	905	173	329	469	751	762	
17	60637	78274	61063	78578	61488	78879	61913	79178	62336	79474	62758	79767	13
	644	279	070	583	495	884	920	183	343	479	765	772	
18	60652	78284	61077	78588	61502	78889	61927	79188	62350	79484	62772	79777	12
	659	289	085	593	510	894	934	193	357	489	779	782	
19	60666	78294	61092	78598	61517	78899	61941	79198	62364	79493	62786	79787	11
	673	299	099	603	524	904	948	203	371	498	793	791	
20	60680	78305	61106	78608	61531	78909	61955	79208	62378	79503	62800	79796	10
	687	310	113	613	538	914	962	213	385	508	807	801	
21	60694	78315	61120	78618	61545	78919	61969	79217	62392	79513	62814	79806	9
	701	320	127	623	552	924	976	222	399	518	821	811	
22	60708	78325	61134	78628	61559	78929	61983	79227	62406	79523	62829	79816	8
	715	330	141	633	566	934	990	232	413	528	836	821	
23	60723	78335	61148	78638	61573	78939	61997	79237	62420	79533	62843	79825	7
	730	340	155	643	580	944	62004	242	427	538	850	830	
24	60737	78345	61163	78649	61587	78949	62011	79247	62434	79542	62857	79835	6
	744	350	170	654	594	954	018	252	442	547	864	840	
25	60751	78355	61177	78659	61602	78959	62026	79257	62449	79552	62871	79845	5
	758	360	184	664	609	964	033	262	456	557	878	850	
26	60765	78365	61191	78669	61616	78969	62040	79267	62463	79562	62885	79855	4
	772	371	198	674	623	974	047	272	470	567	892	859	
27	60779	78376	61205	78679	61630	78979	62054	79277	62477	79572	62899	79864	3
	786	381	212	684	637	984	061	282	484	577	906	869	
28	60794	78386	61219	78689	61644	78989	62068	79287	62491	79582	62913	79874	2
	801	391	226	694	651	994	075	292	498	587	920	879	
29	60808	78396	61233	78699	61658	78999	62082	79297	62505	79591	62927	79884	1
	815	401	240	704	665	79004	089	301	512	596	934	888	
30	60822	78406	61248	78709	61672	79009	62096	79306	62519	79601	62941	79893	0
		T̄. [9]		T̄. [9]		T̄. [9]		T̄. [9]		T̄. [9]		T̄. [9]	
	30′		00′		30′		00′		30′		00′		′

Table 20   HAVERSINES

′	105° 00′ Nat.	Log.	105° 30′ Nat.	Log.	106° 00′ Nat.	Log.	106° 30′ Nat.	Log.	107° 00′ Nat.	Log.	107° 30′ Nat.	Log.	′
		T̄.[9]		T̄.[9]		T̄.[9]		T̄.[9]		T̄.[9]		T̄.[9]	
0	62941	79893	63362	80183	63782	80470	64201	80754	64619	81036	65035	81315	30
	948	898	369	188	789	474	208	759	626	040	042	320	
1	62955	79903	63376	80192	63796	80479	64215	80763	64632	81045	65049	81324	29
	962	908	383	197	803	484	222	768	639	050	056	329	
2	62969	79913	63390	80202	63810	80489	64229	80773	64646	81054	65063	81333	28
	976	918	397	207	817	494	236	778	653	059	070	338	
3	62983	79922	63404	80212	63824	80498	64243	80782	64660	81064	65077	81343	27
	990	927	411	216	831	503	250	787	667	068	084	347	
4	62997	79932	63418	80221	63838	80508	64257	80792	64674	81073	65091	81352	26
	63004	937	425	226	845	513	264	796	681	078	098	357	
5	63011	79942	63432	80231	63852	80517	64270	80801	64688	81082	65105	81361	25
	018	947	439	236	859	522	277	806	695	087	112	366	
6	63025	79951	63446	80240	63866	80527	64284	80811	64702	81092	65118	81370	24
	032	956	453	245	873	532	291	815	709	096	125	375	
7	63039	79961	63460	80250	63880	80536	64298	80820	64716	81101	65132	81380	23
	046	966	467	255	887	541	305	825	723	106	139	384	
8	63053	79971	63474	80260	63894	80546	64312	80829	64730	81110	65146	81389	22
	060	976	481	264	901	551	319	834	737	115	153	394	
9	63067	79980	63488	80269	63908	80555	64326	80839	64744	81120	65160	81398	21
	074	985	495	274	915	560	333	844	751	124	167	403	
10	63081	79990	63502	80279	63922	80565	64340	80848	64758	81129	65174	81407	20
	088	79995	509	284	929	570	347	853	765	134	181	412	
11	63095	80000	63516	80288	63936	80574	64354	80858	64772	81138	65188	81417	19
	102	005	523	293	943	579	361	862	778	143	195	421	
12	63109	80009	63530	80298	63950	80584	64368	80867	64785	81148	65202	81426	18
	116	014	537	303	957	588	375	872	792	152	209	430	
13	63123	80019	63544	80307	63964	80593	64382	80876	64799	81157	65216	81435	17
	131	024	551	312	971	598	389	881	806	162	222	440	
14	63138	80029	63558	80317	63977	80603	64396	80886	64813	81166	65229	81444	16
	145	034	565	322	984	607	403	891	820	171	236	449	
15	63152	80038	63572	80327	63991	80612	64410	80895	64827	81176	65243	81454	15
	159	043	579	331	63998	617	417	900	834	180	250	458	
16	63166	80048	63586	80336	64005	80622	64424	80905	64841	81185	65257	81463	14
	173	053	593	341	012	626	431	909	848	190	264	467	
17	63180	80058	63600	80346	64019	80631	64438	80914	64855	81194	65271	81472	13
	187	063	607	350	026	636	445	919	862	199	278	477	
18	63194	80067	63614	80355	64033	80641	64452	80923	64869	81204	65285	81481	12
	201	072	621	360	040	645	459	928	876	208	292	486	
19	63208	80077	63628	80365	64047	80650	64466	80933	64883	81213	65299	81490	11
	215	082	635	370	054	655	472	937	890	217	306	495	
20	63222	80087	63642	80374	64061	80659	64479	80942	64897	81222	65312	81500	10
	229	091	649	379	068	664	486	947	903	227	319	504	
21	63236	80096	63656	80384	64075	80669	64493	80951	64910	81231	65326	81509	9
	243	101	663	389	082	674	500	956	917	236	333	513	
22	63250	80106	63670	80393	64089	80678	64507	80961	64924	81241	65340	81518	8
	257	111	677	398	096	683	514	966	931	245	347	523	
23	63264	80116	63684	80403	64103	80688	64521	80970	64938	81250	65354	81527	7
	271	120	691	408	110	693	528	975	945	255	361	532	
24	63278	80125	63698	80413	64117	80697	64535	80980	64952	81259	65368	81536	6
	285	130	705	417	124	702	542	984	959	264	375	541	
25	63292	80135	63712	80422	64131	80707	64549	80989	64966	81269	65382	81546	5
	299	140	719	427	138	712	556	994	973	273	389	550	
26	63306	80144	63726	80432	64145	80716	64563	80998	64980	81278	65396	81555	4
	313	149	733	436	152	721	570	81003	987	282	402	559	
27	63320	80154	63740	80441	64159	80726	64577	81008	64994	81287	65409	81564	3
	327	159	747	446	166	730	584	012	65001	292	416	569	
28	63334	80164	63754	80451	64173	80735	64591	81017	65008	81296	65423	81573	2
	341	168	761	455	180	740	598	022	014	301	430	578	
29	63348	80173	63768	80460	64187	80745	64605	81026	65021	81306	65437	81582	1
	355	178	775	465	194	749	612	031	028	310	444	587	
30	63362	80183	63782	80470	64201	80754	64619	81036	65035	81315	65451	81592	0
		T̄.[9]		T̄.[9]		T̄.[9]		T̄.[9]		T̄.[9]		T̄.[9]	
	30′		00′		30′		00′		30′		00′		′
	254°				**253°**				**252°**				

Table 20   **HAVERSINES**

′	108° 00′ Nat.	Log.	108° 30′ Nat.	Log.	109° 00′ Nat.	Log.	109° 30′ Nat.	Log.	110° 00′ Nat.	Log.	110° 30′ Nat.	Log.	′
		T̄.[9]		T̄.[9]		T̄.[9]		T̄.[9]		T̄.[9]		T̄.[9]	
0	65451	81592	65865	81866	66278	82137	66690	82406	67101	82673	67510	82937	30
	458	596	872	870	285	142	697	411	108	677	517	941	
1	65465	81601	65879	81875	66292	82146	66704	82415	67115	82682	67524	82946	29
	472	605	886	879	299	151	711	420	122	686	531	950	
2	65479	81610	65893	81884	66306	82155	66718	82424	67128	82691	67538	82955	28
	485	614	900	888	313	160	725	429	135	695	544	959	
3	65492	81619	65907	81893	66320	82164	66731	82433	67142	82699	67551	82963	27
	499	624	914	897	327	169	738	438	149	704	558	968	
4	65506	81628	65920	81902	66333	82173	66745	82442	67156	82708	67565	82972	26
	513	633	927	907	340	178	752	446	162	713	572	976	
5	65520	81637	65934	81911	66347	82182	66759	82451	67169	82717	67578	82981	25
	527	642	941	916	354	187	766	455	176	722	585	985	
6	65534	81647	65948	81920	66361	82191	66773	82460	67183	82726	67592	82990	24
	541	651	955	925	368	196	779	464	190	730	599	994	
7	65548	81656	65962	81929	66375	82200	66786	82469	67197	82735	67606	82998	23
	555	660	969	934	382	205	793	473	203	739	613	83003	
8	65561	81665	65976	81938	66388	82209	66800	82478	67210	82744	67619	83007	22
	568	669	982	943	395	214	807	482	217	748	626	011	
9	65575	81674	65989	81947	66402	82218	66814	82487	67224	82752	67633	83016	21
	582	679	65996	952	409	223	821	491	231	757	640	020	
10	65589	81683	66003	81956	66416	82227	66827	82495	67238	82761	67647	83025	20
	596	688	010	961	423	232	834	500	244	766	653	029	
11	65603	81692	66017	81965	66430	82236	66841	82504	67251	82770	67660	83033	19
	610	697	024	970	436	241	848	509	258	774	667	038	
12	65617	81701	66031	81975	66443	82245	66855	82513	67265	82779	67674	83042	18
	624	706	038	979	450	250	862	518	272	783	681	046	
13	65631	81711	66044	81984	66457	82254	66868	82522	67279	82788	67687	83051	17
	637	715	051	988	464	259	875	527	285	792	694	055	
14	65644	81720	66058	81993	66471	82263	66882	82531	67292	82796	67701	83059	16
	651	724	065	81997	478	268	889	535	299	801	708	064	
15	65658	81729	66072	82002	66485	82272	66896	82540	67306	82805	67715	83068	15
	665	733	079	006	491	277	903	544	313	810	721	073	
16	65672	81738	66086	82011	66498	82281	66910	82549	67320	82814	67728	83077	14
	679	743	093	015	505	286	916	553	326	818	735	081	
17	65686	81747	66100	82020	66512	82290	66923	82558	67333	82823	67742	83086	13
	693	752	106	024	519	294	930	562	340	827	749	090	
18	65700	81756	66113	82029	66526	82299	66937	82567	67347	82832	67755	83094	12
	707	761	120	033	533	303	944	571	354	836	762	099	
19	65713	81765	66127	82038	66539	82308	66951	82575	67360	82840	67769	83103	11
	720	770	134	042	546	312	957	580	367	845	776	107	
20	65727	81775	66141	82047	66553	82317	66964	82584	67374	82849	67783	83112	10
	734	779	148	051	560	321	971	589	381	854	789	116	
21	65741	81784	66155	82056	66567	82326	66978	82593	67388	82858	67796	83120	9
	748	788	161	061	574	330	985	598	395	862	803	125	
22	65755	81793	66168	82065	66581	82335	66992	82602	67401	82867	67810	83129	8
	762	797	175	070	587	339	66998	606	408	871	817	134	
23	65769	81802	66182	82074	66594	82344	67005	82611	67415	82876	67823	83138	7
	776	806	189	079	601	348	012	615	422	880	830	142	
24	65782	81811	66196	82083	66608	82353	67019	82620	67429	82884	67837	83147	6
	789	816	203	088	615	357	026	624	435	889	844	151	
25	65796	81820	66210	82092	66622	82362	67033	82629	67442	82893	67850	83155	5
	803	825	217	097	629	366	039	633	449	898	857	160	
26	65810	81829	66223	82101	66635	82371	67046	82638	67456	82902	67864	83164	4
	817	834	230	106	642	375	053	642	463	906	871	168	
27	65824	81838	66237	82110	66649	82379	67060	82646	67469	82911	67878	83173	3
	831	843	244	115	656	384	067	651	476	915	884	177	
28	65838	81847	66251	82119	66663	82388	67074	82655	67483	82920	67891	83181	2
	845	852	258	124	670	393	081	660	490	924	898	186	
29	65851	81857	66265	82128	66677	82397	67087	82664	67497	82928	67905	83190	1
	858	861	272	133	683	402	094	668	504	933	912	194	
30	65865	81866	66278	82137	66690	82406	67101	82673	67510	82937	67918	83199	0
		T̄.[9]		T̄.[9]		T̄.[9]		T̄.[9]		T̄.[9]		T̄.[9]	
	30′		00′		30′		00′		30′		00′		′

Table 20 — HAVERSINES

′	111° 00′ Nat.	Log. Ī.[9]	111° 30′ Nat.	Log. Ī.[9]	112° 00′ Nat.	Log. Ī.[9]	112° 30′ Nat.	Log. Ī.[9]	113° 00′ Nat.	Log. Ī.[9]	113° 30′ Nat.	Log. Ī.[9]	′
0	67918	83199	68325	83458	68730	83715	69134	83969	69537	84221	69937	84471	30
	925	203	332	462	737	719	141	974	543	225	944	475	
1	67932	83207	68339	83467	68744	83723	69148	83978	69550	84230	69951	84479	29
	939	212	345	471	751	728	154	982	557	234	957	483	
2	67946	83216	68352	83475	68757	83732	69161	83986	69563	84238	69964	84488	28
	952	220	359	479	764	736	168	990	570	242	971	492	
3	67959	83225	68366	83484	68771	83740	69174	83995	69577	84246	69977	84496	27
	966	229	372	488	778	745	181	83999	583	251	984	500	
4	67973	83233	68379	83492	68784	83749	69188	84003	69590	84255	69991	84504	26
	979	238	386	497	791	753	195	007	597	259	69997	508	
5	67986	83242	68393	83501	68798	83757	69201	84011	69603	84263	70004	84512	25
	67993	246	399	505	804	762	208	016	610	267	011	517	
6	68000	83251	68406	83510	68811	83766	69215	84020	69617	84271	70017	84521	24
	007	255	413	514	818	770	221	024	624	276	024	525	
7	68013	83259	68420	83518	68825	83774	69228	84028	69630	84280	70031	84529	23
	020	264	427	522	831	779	235	033	637	284	037	533	
8	68027	83268	68433	83527	68838	83783	69242	84037	69644	84288	70044	84537	22
	034	272	440	531	845	787	248	041	650	292	051	541	
9	68041	83277	68447	83535	68852	83791	69255	84045	69657	84296	70057	84545	21
	047	281	454	540	858	796	262	049	664	301	064	550	
10	68054	83285	68460	83544	68865	83800	69268	84054	69670	84305	70071	84554	20
	061	290	467	548	872	804	275	058	677	309	077	558	
11	68068	83294	68474	83552	68879	83808	69282	84062	69684	84313	70084	84562	19
	074	298	481	557	885	813	289	066	690	317	091	566	
12	68081	83303	68487	83561	68892	83817	69295	84070	69697	84321	70097	84570	18
	088	307	494	565	899	821	302	075	704	326	104	574	
13	68095	83311	68501	83570	68906	83825	69309	84079	69710	84330	70111	84578	17
	102	316	508	574	912	830	315	083	717	334	117	583	
14	68108	83320	68514	83578	68919	83834	69322	84087	69724	84338	70124	84587	16
	115	324	521	582	926	838	329	091	731	342	131	591	
15	68122	83329	68528	83587	68932	83842	69336	84096	69737	84346	70137	84595	15
	129	333	535	591	939	847	342	100	744	351	144	599	
16	68135	83337	68541	83595	68946	83851	69349	84104	69751	84355	70151	84603	14
	142	342	548	600	953	855	356	108	757	359	157	607	
17	68149	83346	68555	83604	68959	83859	69362	84112	69764	84363	70164	84611	13
	156	350	562	608	966	864	369	117	771	367	171	616	
18	68163	83355	68568	83612	68973	83868	69376	84121	69777	84371	70177	84620	12
	169	359	575	617	980	872	382	125	784	376	184	624	
19	68176	83363	68582	83621	68986	83876	69389	84129	69791	84380	70191	84628	11
	183	368	589	625	993	881	396	133	797	384	197	632	
20	68190	83372	68595	83629	69000	83885	69403	84138	69804	84388	70204	84636	10
	196	376	602	634	006	889	409	142	811	392	211	640	
21	68203	83380	68609	83638	69013	83893	69416	84146	69817	84396	70217	84644	9
	210	385	616	642	020	897	423	150	824	400	224	648	
22	68217	83389	68622	83647	69027	83902	69429	84154	69831	84405	70230	84653	8
	224	393	629	651	033	906	436	159	837	409	237	657	
23	68230	83398	68636	83655	69040	83910	69443	84163	69844	84413	70244	84661	7
	237	402	643	659	047	914	450	167	851	417	250	665	
24	68244	83406	68649	83664	69054	83919	69456	84171	69857	84421	70257	84669	6
	251	411	656	668	060	923	463	175	864	425	264	673	
25	68257	83415	68663	83672	69067	83927	69470	84179	69871	84430	70270	84677	5
	264	419	670	676	074	931	476	184	877	434	277	681	
26	68271	83424	68676	83681	69080	83935	69483	84188	69884	84438	70284	84685	4
	278	428	683	685	087	940	490	192	891	442	290	690	
27	68284	83432	68690	83689	69094	83944	69496	84196	69897	84446	70297	84694	3
	291	436	697	694	101	948	503	200	904	450	304	698	
28	68298	83441	68703	83698	69107	83952	69510	84205	69911	84454	70310	84702	2
	305	445	710	702	114	957	516	209	917	459	317	706	
29	68312	83449	68717	83706	69121	83961	69523	84213	69924	84463	70324	84710	1
	318	454	724	711	127	965	530	217	931	467	330	714	
30	68325	83458	68730	83715	69134	83969	69537	84221	69937	84471	70337	84718	0
		Ī.[9]		Ī.[9]		Ī.[9]		Ī.[9]		Ī.[9]		Ī.[9]	
	30′		00′		30′		00′		30′		00′		′

248°	247°	246°

Table 20 — HAVERSINES

Table 20

′	114° 00′ Nat.	Log.	114° 30′ Nat.	Log.	115° 00′ Nat.	Log.	115° 30′ Nat.	Log.	116° 00′ Nat.	Log.	116° 30′ Nat.	Log.	′
		1̄.[9]		1̄.[9]		1̄.[9]		1̄.[9]		1̄.[9]		1̄.[9]	
0	70337	84718	70735	84963	71131	85206	71526	85446	71919	85684	72310	85920	30
	343	722	741	967	138	210	532	450	925	688	316	924	
1	70350	84726	70748	84971	71144	85214	71539	85454	71932	85692	72323	85928	29
	357	731	755	975	151	218	545	458	938	696	329	931	
2	70363	84735	70761	84979	71157	85222	71552	85462	71945	85700	72336	85935	28
	370	739	768	984	164	226	558	466	951	704	342	939	
3	70377	84743	70774	84988	71170	85230	71565	85470	71958	85708	72349	85943	27
	383	747	781	992	177	234	571	474	964	712	355	947	
4	70390	84751	70788	84996	71184	85238	71578	85478	71971	85716	72362	85951	26
	397	755	794	85000	190	242	585	482	977	720	368	955	
5	70403	84759	70801	85004	71197	85246	71591	85486	71984	85724	72375	85959	25
	410	763	807	008	203	250	598	490	990	727	381	963	
6	70417	84767	70814	85012	71210	85254	71604	85494	71997	85731	72388	85967	24
	423	772	821	016	217	258	611	498	72003	735	394	971	
7	70430	84776	70827	85020	71223	85262	71617	85502	72010	85739	72401	85974	23
	436	780	834	024	230	266	624	506	017	743	407	978	
8	70443	84784	70840	85028	71236	85270	71631	85510	72023	85747	72414	85982	22
	450	788	847	032	243	274	637	514	030	751	420	986	
9	70456	84792	70854	85036	71249	85278	71644	85518	72036	85755	72427	85990	21
	463	796	860	040	256	282	650	522	043	759	433	994	
10	70470	84800	70867	85044	71263	85286	71657	85526	72049	85763	72440	85998	20
	476	804	874	048	269	290	663	530	056	767	446	86002	
11	70483	84808	70880	85052	71276	85294	71670	85534	72062	85771	72453	86006	19
	490	812	887	057	282	298	676	538	069	775	459	010	
12	70496	84817	70893	85061	71289	85302	71683	85542	72075	85779	72466	86013	18
	503	821	900	065	296	306	690	546	082	783	472	017	
13	70509	84825	70907	85069	71302	85310	71696	85550	72088	85787	72479	86021	17
	516	829	913	073	309	314	703	553	095	790	485	025	
14	70523	84833	70920	85077	71315	85318	71709	85557	72101	85794	72492	86029	16
	529	837	926	081	322	322	716	561	108	798	498	033	
15	70536	84841	70933	85085	71328	85326	71722	85565	72114	85802	72505	86037	15
	543	845	940	089	335	330	729	569	121	806	511	041	
16	70549	84849	70946	85093	71342	85334	71735	85573	72127	85810	72518	86045	14
	556	853	953	097	348	338	742	577	134	814	524	048	
17	70562	84857	70959	85101	71355	85342	71748	85581	72141	85818	72531	86052	13
	569	861	966	105	361	346	755	585	147	822	537	056	
18	70576	84866	70973	85109	71368	85350	71762	85589	72154	85826	72544	86060	12
	582	870	979	113	374	354	768	593	160	830	550	064	
19	70589	84874	70986	85117	71381	85358	71775	85597	72167	85834	72557	86068	11
	596	878	992	121	388	362	781	601	173	838	563	072	
20	70602	84882	70999	85125	71394	85366	71788	85605	72180	85841	72570	86076	10
	609	886	71006	129	401	370	794	609	186	845	576	079	
21	70615	84890	71012	85133	71407	85374	71801	85613	72193	85849	72583	86083	9
	622	894	019	137	414	378	807	617	199	853	589	087	
22	70629	84898	71025	85141	71420	85382	71814	85621	72206	85857	72596	86091	8
	635	902	032	145	427	386	820	625	212	861	602	095	
23	70642	84906	71039	85149	71434	85390	71827	85629	72219	85865	72609	86099	7
	649	910	045	153	440	394	834	633	225	869	615	103	
24	70655	84914	71052	85158	71447	85398	71840	85637	72232	85873	72622	86107	6
	662	918	058	162	453	402	847	641	238	877	628	111	
25	70668	84923	71065	85166	71460	85406	71853	85645	72245	85881	72635	86114	5
	675	927	072	170	466	410	860	649	251	885	641	118	
26	70682	84931	71078	85174	71473	85414	71866	85653	72258	85888	72648	86122	4
	688	935	085	178	480	418	873	656	264	892	654	126	
27	70695	84939	71091	85182	71486	85422	71879	85660	72271	85896	72661	86130	3
	702	943	098	186	493	426	886	664	277	900	667	134	
28	70708	84947	71105	85190	71499	85430	71892	85668	72284	85904	72674	86138	2
	715	951	111	194	506	434	899	672	290	908	680	142	
29	70721	84955	71118	85198	71512	85438	71905	85676	72297	85912	72687	86145	1
	728	959	124	202	519	442	912	680	303	916	693	149	
30	70735	84963	71131	85206	71526	85446	71919	85684	72310	85920	72700	86153	0
		1̄.[9]		1̄.[9]		1̄.[9]		1̄.[9]		1̄.[9]		1̄.[9]	
	30′		00′		30′		00′		30′		00′		′

245°	244°	243°

Table 20 **HAVERSINES**

	117°				118°				119°				
	00′		**30′**		**00′**		**30′**		**00′**		**30′**		
′	Nat.	Log.	Nat.	Log.	Nat.	Log.	Nat.	Log.	Nat.	Log.	Nat.	Log.	
		Ī. [9]		Ī. [9]		Ī. [9]		Ī. [9]		Ī. [9]		Ī. [9]	
0	72700	86153	73087	86384	73474	86613	73858	86840	74240	87064	74621	87286	30
	706	157	094	388	480	617	864	843	247	068	628	290	
1	72712	86161	73100	86392	73486	86621	73871	86847	74253	87072	74634	87294	29
	719	165	107	396	493	625	877	851	260	075	640	297	
2	72725	86169	73113	86400	73499	86628	73884	86855	74266	87079	74646	87301	28
	732	173	120	403	506	632	890	858	272	083	653	305	
3	72738	86176	73126	86407	73512	86636	73896	86862	74279	87086	74659	87308	27
	745	180	133	411	519	640	903	866	285	090	665	312	
4	72751	86184	73139	86415	73525	86643	73909	86870	74291	87094	74672	87316	26
	758	188	145	419	531	647	915	874	298	098	678	319	
5	72764	86192	73152	86423	73538	86651	73922	86877	74304	87101	74684	87323	25
	771	196	158	426	544	655	928	881	310	105	691	327	
6	72777	86200	73165	86430	73551	86659	73935	86885	74317	87109	74697	87330	24
	784	203	171	434	557	662	941	889	323	112	703	334	
7	72790	86207	73178	86438	73563	86666	73947	86892	74329	87116	74710	87338	23
	797	211	184	442	570	670	954	896	336	120	716	341	
8	72803	86215	73191	86446	73576	86674	73960	86900	74342	87124	74722	87345	22
	810	219	197	449	583	678	967	904	349	127	729	349	
9	72816	86223	73203	86453	73589	86681	73973	86907	74355	87131	74735	87352	21
	823	227	210	457	595	685	979	911	361	135	741	356	
10	72829	86230	73216	86461	73602	86689	73986	86915	74368	87138	74748	87360	20
	835	234	223	465	608	693	992	919	374	142	754	363	
11	72842	86238	73229	86468	73615	86696	73998	86922	74380	87146	74760	87367	19
	848	242	236	472	621	700	74005	926	387	149	767	371	
12	72855	86246	73242	86476	73628	86704	74011	86930	74393	87153	74773	87374	18
	861	250	249	480	634	708	018	933	399	157	779	378	
13	72868	86254	73255	86484	73640	86712	74024	86937	74406	87161	74786	87382	17
	874	257	261	488	647	715	030	941	412	164	792	385	
14	72881	86261	73268	86491	73653	86719	74037	86945	74418	87168	74798	87389	16
	887	265	274	495	660	723	043	948	425	172	805	393	
15	72894	86269	73281	86499	73666	86727	74049	86952	74431	87175	74811	87396	15
	900	273	287	503	672	730	056	956	437	179	817	400	
16	72907	86277	73294	86507	73679	86734	74062	86960	74444	87183	74823	87404	14
	913	281	300	510	685	738	069	963	450	187	830	407	
17	72920	86284	73306	86514	73692	86742	74075	86967	74456	87190	74836	87411	13
	926	288	313	518	698	746	081	971	463	194	842	415	
18	72932	86292	73319	86522	73704	86749	74088	86975	74469	87198	74849	87418	12
	939	296	326	526	711	753	094	978	475	201	855	422	
19	72945	86300	73332	86529	73717	86757	74100	86982	74482	87205	74861	87426	11
	952	304	339	533	724	761	107	986	488	209	868	429	
20	72958	86307	73345	86537	73730	86764	74113	86990	74494	87212	74874	87433	10
	965	311	351	541	736	768	120	993	501	216	880	437	
21	72971	86315	73358	86545	73743	86772	74126	86997	74507	87220	74887	87440	9
	978	319	364	549	749	776	132	87001	514	224	893	444	
22	72984	86323	73371	86552	73756	86780	74139	87004	74520	87227	74899	87448	8
	991	327	377	556	762	783	145	008	526	231	905	451	
23	72997	86331	73384	86560	73768	86787	74151	87012	74533	87235	74912	87455	7
	73004	334	390	564	775	791	158	016	539	238	918	459	
24	73010	86338	73396	86568	73781	86795	74164	87019	74545	87242	74924	87462	6
	016	342	403	571	788	798	170	023	552	246	931	466	
25	73023	86346	73409	86575	73794	86802	74177	87027	74558	87249	74937	87470	5
	029	350	416	579	800	806	183	031	564	253	943	473	
26	73036	86354	73422	86583	73807	86810	74190	87034	74571	87257	74950	87477	4
	042	357	429	587	813	813	196	038	577	260	956	481	
27	73049	86361	73435	86590	73820	86817	74202	87042	74583	87264	74962	87484	3
	055	365	441	594	826	821	209	045	590	268	969	488	
28	73062	86369	73448	86598	73832	86825	74215	87049	74596	87271	74975	87492	2
	068	373	454	602	839	828	221	053	602	275	981	495	
29	73075	86377	73461	86606	73845	86832	74228	87057	74609	87279	74987	87499	1
	081	380	467	609	852	836	234	060	615	283	74994	502	
30	73087	86384	73474	86613	73858	86840	74240	87064	74621	87286	75000	87506	0
		Ī. [9]		Ī. [9]		Ī. [9]		Ī. [9]		Ī. [9]		Ī. [9]	
	30′		**00′**		**30′**		**00′**		**30′**		**00′**		′

242°		**241°**		**240°**

Table 20   **HAVERSINES**

′	120° Nat.	120° Log.	121° Nat.	121° Log.	122° Nat.	122° Log.	123° Nat.	123° Log.	124° Nat.	124° Log.	125° Nat.	125° Log.	
		T̄. [9]		T̄. [9]		T̄. [9]		T̄. [9]		T̄. [9]		T̄. [9]	
0	75000	87506	75752	87939	76496	88364	77232	88780	77960	89187	78679	89586	60
1	75013	87513	75764	87947	76508	88371	77244	88787	77972	89194	78691	89592	59
2	75025	87521	75777	87954	76521	88378	77256	88793	77984	89200	78703	89599	58
3	75038	87528	75789	87961	76533	88385	77269	88800	77996	89207	78715	89606	57
4	75050	87535	75802	87968	76545	88392	77281	88807	78008	89214	78726	89612	56
5	75063	87543	75814	87975	76558	88399	77293	88814	78020	89221	78738	89619	55
6	75076	87550	75827	87982	76570	88406	77305	88821	78032	89227	78750	89625	54
7	75088	87557	75839	87989	76582	88413	77317	88828	78044	89234	78762	89632	53
8	75101	87564	75852	87996	76595	88420	77329	88834	78056	89241	78774	89638	52
9	75113	87572	75864	88004	76607	88427	77342	88841	78068	89247	78786	89645	51
10	75126	87579	75876	88011	76619	88434	77354	88848	78080	89254	78798	89651	50
11	75138	87586	75889	88018	76632	88441	77366	88855	78092	89261	78810	89658	49
12	75151	87593	75901	88025	76644	88448	77378	88862	78104	89267	78822	89665	48
13	75164	87601	75914	88032	76656	88455	77390	88869	78116	89274	78834	89671	47
14	75176	87608	75926	88039	76668	88462	77402	88875	78128	89281	78845	89678	46
15	75189	87615	75939	88046	76681	88469	77415	88882	78140	89287	78857	89684	45
16	75201	87623	75951	88053	76693	88476	77427	88889	78152	89294	78869	89691	44
17	75214	87630	75964	88061	76705	88483	77439	88896	78164	89301	78881	89697	43
18	75226	87637	75976	88068	76718	88490	77451	88903	78176	89308	78893	89704	42
19	75239	87644	75988	88075	76730	88496	77463	88910	78188	89314	78905	89710	41
20	75251	87652	76001	88082	76742	88503	77475	88916	78200	89321	78917	89717	40
21	75264	87659	76013	88089	76754	88510	77488	88923	78212	89328	78928	89723	39
22	75277	87666	76026	88096	76767	88517	77500	88930	78224	89334	78940	89730	38
23	75289	87673	76038	88103	76779	88524	77512	88937	78236	89341	78952	89736	37
24	75302	87680	76050	88110	76791	88531	77524	88944	78248	89348	78964	89743	36
25	75314	87688	76063	88117	76804	88538	77536	88950	78260	89354	78976	89749	35
26	75327	87695	76075	88124	76816	88545	77548	88957	78272	89361	78988	89756	34
27	75339	87702	76088	88131	76828	88552	77560	88964	78284	89368	79000	89762	33
28	75352	87709	76100	88139	76840	88559	77573	88971	78296	89374	79011	89769	32
29	75364	87717	76113	88146	76853	88566	77585	88978	78308	89381	79023	89776	31
30	75377	87724	76125	88153	76865	88573	77597	88984	78320	89387	79035	89782	30
31	75389	87731	76137	88160	76877	88580	77609	88991	78332	89394	79047	89789	29
32	75402	87738	76150	88167	76890	88587	77621	88998	78344	89401	79059	89795	28
33	75415	87745	76162	88174	76902	88594	77633	89005	78356	89407	79071	89802	27
34	75427	87753	76175	88181	76914	88601	77645	89012	78368	89414	79082	89808	26
35	75440	87760	76187	88188	76926	88607	77657	89018	78380	89421	79094	89815	25
36	75452	87767	76199	88195	76939	88614	77670	89025	78392	89427	79106	89821	24
37	75465	87774	76212	88202	76951	88621	77682	89032	78404	89434	79118	89828	23
38	75477	87782	76224	88209	76963	88628	77694	89039	78416	89441	79130	89834	22
39	75490	87789	76236	88216	76975	88635	77706	89045	78428	89447	79142	89840	21
40	75502	87796	76249	88223	76988	88642	77718	89052	78440	89454	79153	89847	20
41	75515	87803	76261	88230	77000	88649	77730	89059	78452	89460	79165	89853	19
42	75527	87810	76274	88237	77012	88656	77742	89066	78464	89467	79177	89860	18
43	75540	87818	76286	88244	77024	88663	77754	89072	78476	89474	79189	89866	17
44	75552	87825	76298	88251	77036	88670	77766	89079	78488	89480	79201	89873	16
45	75565	87832	76311	88259	77049	88677	77779	89086	78500	89487	79212	89879	15
46	75577	87839	76323	88266	77061	88683	77791	89093	78512	89493	79224	89886	14
47	75590	87846	76335	88273	77073	88690	77803	89099	78524	89500	79236	89892	13
48	75602	87853	76348	88280	77085	88697	77815	89106	78536	89507	79248	89899	12
49	75615	87861	76360	88287	77098	88704	77827	89113	78548	89513	79260	89905	11
50	75627	87868	76373	88294	77110	88711	77839	89120	78560	89520	79271	89912	10
51	75640	87875	76385	88301	77122	88718	77851	89126	78571	89527	79283	89918	9
52	75652	87882	76397	88308	77134	88725	77863	89133	78583	89533	79295	89925	8
53	75665	87889	76410	88315	77147	88732	77875	89140	78595	89540	79307	89931	7
54	75677	87896	76422	88322	77159	88738	77887	89147	78607	89546	79319	89938	6
55	75690	87904	76434	88329	77171	88745	77899	89153	78619	89553	79330	89944	5
56	75702	87911	76447	88336	77183	88752	77911	89160	78631	89559	79342	89950	4
57	75714	87918	76459	88343	77195	88759	77923	89167	78643	89566	79354	89957	3
58	75727	87925	76471	88350	77208	88766	77936	89174	78655	89573	79366	89963	2
59	75739	87932	76484	88357	77220	88773	77948	89180	78667	89579	79377	89970	1
60	75752	87939	76496	88364	77232	88780	77960	89187	78679	89586	79389	89976	0
		T̄. [9]		T̄. [9]		T̄. [9]		T̄. [9]		T̄. [9]		T̄. [9]	
	239°		**238°**		**237°**		**236°**		**235°**		**234°**		′

Table 20   **HAVERSINES**

′	126° Nat.	126° Log.	127° Nat.	127° Log.	128° Nat.	128° Log.	129° Nat.	129° Log.	130° Nat.	130° Log.	131° Nat.	131° Log.	′
		T. [9]		T. [9]		T. [9]		T. [9]		T. [9]		T. [9]	
0	79389	89976	80091	90358	80783	90732	81466	91098	82139	91455	82803	91805	60
1	79401	89983	80102	90365	80795	90738	81477	91104	82151	91461	82814	91810	59
2	79413	89989	80114	90371	80806	90744	81489	91110	82162	91467	82825	91816	58
3	79425	89995	80126	90377	80817	90751	81500	91116	82173	91473	82836	91822	57
4	79436	90002	80137	90383	80829	90757	81511	91122	82184	91479	82847	91828	56
5	79448	90008	80149	90390	80840	90763	81523	91128	82195	91485	82858	91833	55
6	79460	90015	80160	90396	80852	90769	81534	91134	82206	91490	82869	91839	54
7	79472	90021	80172	90402	80863	90775	81545	91140	82217	91496	82880	91845	53
8	79483	90028	80184	90409	80875	90781	81556	91146	82228	91502	82891	91851	52
9	79495	90034	80195	90415	80886	90787	81568	91152	82240	91508	82902	91856	51
10	79507	90040	80207	90421	80898	90794	81579	91158	82251	91514	82913	91862	50
11	79519	90047	80218	90427	80909	90800	81590	91164	82262	91520	82924	91868	49
12	79530	90053	80230	90434	80920	90806	81601	91170	82273	91526	82934	91874	48
13	79542	90060	80242	90440	80932	90812	81613	91176	82284	91532	82945	91879	47
14	79554	90066	80253	90446	80943	90818	81624	91182	82295	91537	82956	91885	46
15	79565	90072	80265	90452	80955	90824	81635	91188	82306	91543	82967	91891	45
16	79577	90079	80276	90459	80966	90830	81647	91194	82317	91549	82978	91896	44
17	79589	90085	80288	90465	80978	90836	81658	91200	82328	91555	82989	91902	43
18	79601	90092	80299	90471	80989	90843	81669	91206	82339	91561	83000	91908	42
19	79612	90098	80311	90477	81000	90849	81680	91212	82351	91567	83011	91914	41
20	79624	90104	80323	90484	81012	90855	81692	91218	82362	91573	83022	91919	40
21	79636	90111	80334	90490	81023	90861	81703	91224	82373	91578	83033	91925	39
22	79648	90117	80346	90496	81035	90867	81714	91230	82384	91584	83044	91931	38
23	79659	90124	80357	90502	81046	90873	81725	91236	82395	91590	83055	91936	37
24	79671	90130	80369	90509	81057	90879	81737	91242	82406	91596	83066	91942	36
25	79683	90136	80380	90515	81069	90885	81748	91248	82417	91602	83077	91948	35
26	79694	90143	80392	90521	81080	90891	81759	91254	82428	91608	83087	91954	34
27	79706	90149	80403	90527	81092	90898	81770	91260	82439	91613	83098	91959	33
28	79718	90156	80415	90534	81103	90904	81781	91265	82450	91619	83109	91965	32
29	79729	90162	80427	90540	81114	90910	81793	91271	82461	91625	83120	91971	31
30	79741	90168	80438	90546	81126	90916	81804	91277	82472	91631	83131	91976	30
31	79753	90175	80450	90552	81137	90922	81815	91283	82483	91637	83142	91982	29
32	79765	90181	80461	90559	81148	90928	81826	91289	82495	91643	83153	91988	28
33	79776	90187	80473	90565	81160	90934	81838	91295	82506	91648	83164	91993	27
34	79788	90194	80484	90571	81171	90940	81849	91301	82517	91654	83175	91999	26
35	79800	90200	80496	90577	81183	90946	81860	91307	82528	91660	83185	92005	25
36	79811	90206	80507	90584	81194	90952	81871	91313	82539	91666	83196	92010	24
37	79823	90213	80519	90590	81205	90958	81882	91319	82550	91672	83207	92016	23
38	79835	90219	80530	90596	81217	90965	81894	91325	82561	91677	83218	92022	22
39	79846	90225	80542	90602	81228	90971	81905	91331	82572	91683	83229	92027	21
40	79858	90232	80553	90608	81239	90977	81916	91337	82583	91689	83240	92033	20
41	79870	90238	80565	90615	81251	90983	81927	91343	82594	91695	83251	92039	19
42	79881	90244	80576	90621	81262	90989	81938	91349	82605	91701	83262	92044	18
43	79893	90251	80588	90627	81273	90995	81950	91355	82616	91706	83272	92050	17
44	79905	90257	80599	90633	81285	91001	81961	91361	82627	91712	83283	92056	16
45	79916	90263	80611	90639	81296	91007	81972	91367	82638	91718	83294	92061	15
46	79928	90270	80622	90646	81308	91013	81983	91372	82649	91724	83305	92067	14
47	79940	90276	80634	90652	81319	91019	81994	91378	82660	91730	83316	92073	13
48	79951	90282	80645	90658	81330	91025	82005	91384	82671	91735	83327	92078	12
49	79963	90289	80657	90664	81342	91031	82017	91390	82682	91741	83337	92084	11
50	79974	90295	80668	90670	81353	91037	82028	91396	82693	91747	83348	92090	10
51	79986	90301	80680	90676	81364	91043	82039	91402	82704	91753	83359	92095	9
52	79998	90308	80691	90683	81376	91049	82050	91408	82715	91758	83370	92101	8
53	80009	90314	80703	90689	81387	91055	82061	91414	82726	91764	83381	92107	7
54	80021	90320	80714	90695	81398	91061	82072	91420	82737	91770	83392	92112	6
55	80033	90327	80726	90701	81409	91067	82084	91426	82748	91776	83402	92118	5
56	80044	90333	80737	90707	81421	91074	82095	91432	82759	91782	83413	92124	4
57	80056	90339	80749	90714	81432	91080	82106	91437	82770	91787	83424	92129	3
58	80068	90346	80760	90720	81443	91086	82117	91443	82781	91793	83435	92135	2
59	80079	90352	80772	90726	81455	91092	82128	91449	82792	91799	83446	92140	1
60	80091	90358	80783	90732	81466	91098	82139	91455	82803	91805	83457	92146	0
		T. [9]		T. [9]		T. [9]		T. [9]		T. [9]		T. [9]	
	233°		232°		231°		230°		229°		228°		′

Table 20

HAVERSINES

′	132° Nat.	132° Log.	133° Nat.	133° Log.	134° Nat.	134° Log.	135° Nat.	135° Log.	136° Nat.	136° Log.	137° Nat.	137° Log.	
		T̄. [9]		T̄. [9]		T̄. [9]		T̄. [9]		T̄. [9]		T̄. [9]	
0	83457	92146	84100	92480	84733	92805	85355	93123	85967	93433	86568	93736	60
1	83467	92152	84111	92485	84743	92811	85366	93128	85977	93438	86578	93741	59
2	83478	92157	84121	92491	84754	92816	85376	93134	85987	93443	86588	93746	58
3	83489	92163	84132	92496	84764	92821	85386	93139	85997	93448	86597	93750	57
4	83500	92169	84142	92502	84775	92827	85396	93144	86007	93454	86607	93755	56
5	83511	92174	84153	92507	84785	92832	85407	93149	86017	93459	86617	93760	55
6	83521	92180	84164	92512	84796	92837	85417	93154	86028	93464	86627	93765	54
7	83532	92185	84174	92518	84806	92843	85427	93160	86038	93469	86637	93770	53
8	83543	92191	84185	92523	84817	92848	85438	93165	86048	93474	86647	93775	52
9	83554	92197	84196	92529	84827	92853	85448	93170	86058	93479	86657	93780	51
10	83564	92202	84206	92534	84837	92859	85458	93175	86068	93484	86667	93785	50
11	83575	92208	84217	92540	84848	92864	85468	93181	86078	93489	86677	93790	49
12	83586	92213	84227	92545	84858	92869	85479	93186	86088	93494	86686	93795	48
13	83597	92219	84238	92551	84869	92875	85489	93191	86098	93499	86696	93800	47
14	83608	92225	84249	92556	84879	92880	85499	93196	86108	93504	86706	93805	46
15	83618	92230	84259	92562	84890	92885	85509	93201	86118	93509	86716	93810	45
16	83629	92236	84270	92567	84900	92891	85520	93207	86128	93515	86726	93815	44
17	83640	92241	84280	92573	84910	92896	85530	93212	86138	93520	86736	93820	43
18	83651	92247	84291	92578	84921	92901	85540	93217	86148	93525	86746	93825	42
19	83661	92253	84302	92584	84931	92907	85550	93222	86158	93530	86756	93830	41
20	83672	92258	84312	92589	84942	92912	85560	93227	86168	93535	86765	93835	40
21	83683	92264	84323	92594	84952	92917	85571	93232	86178	93540	86775	93840	39
22	83694	92269	84333	92600	84962	92923	85581	93238	86189	93545	86785	93845	38
23	83704	92275	84344	92605	84973	92928	85591	93243	86199	93550	86795	93849	37
24	83715	92280	84354	92611	84983	92933	85601	93248	86209	93555	86805	93854	36
25	83726	92286	84365	92616	84994	92939	85612	93253	86219	93560	86815	93859	35
26	83737	92292	84376	92622	85004	92944	85622	93258	86229	93565	86825	93864	34
27	83747	92297	84386	92627	85014	92949	85632	93264	86239	93570	86834	93869	33
28	83758	92303	84397	92633	85025	92955	85642	93269	86249	93575	86844	93874	32
29	83769	92308	84407	92638	85035	92960	85652	93274	86259	93580	86854	93879	31
30	83780	92314	84418	92643	85045	92965	85663	93279	86269	93585	86864	93884	30
31	83790	92319	84428	92649	85056	92970	85673	93284	86279	93590	86874	93889	29
32	83801	92325	84439	92654	85066	92976	85683	93289	86289	93595	86884	93894	28
33	83812	92330	84449	92660	85077	92981	85693	93295	86299	93600	86893	93899	27
34	83822	92336	84460	92665	85087	92986	85703	93300	86309	93605	86903	93904	26
35	83833	92342	84470	92670	85097	92992	85713	93305	86319	93611	86913	93908	25
36	83844	92347	84481	92676	85108	92997	85724	93310	86329	93616	86923	93913	24
37	83855	92353	84492	92681	85118	93002	85734	93315	86339	93621	86933	93918	23
38	83865	92358	84502	92687	85128	93007	85744	93320	86349	93626	86942	93923	22
39	83876	92364	84513	92692	85139	93013	85754	93326	86359	93631	86952	93928	21
40	83887	92369	84523	92698	85149	93018	85764	93331	86369	93636	86962	93933	20
41	83897	92375	84534	92703	85159	93023	85774	93336	86379	93641	86972	93938	19
42	83908	92380	84544	92708	85170	93029	85785	93341	86389	93646	86982	93943	18
43	83919	92386	84555	92714	85180	93034	85795	93346	86399	93651	86991	93948	17
44	83929	92391	84565	92719	85190	93039	85805	93351	86409	93656	87001	93952	16
45	83940	92397	84576	92725	85201	93044	85815	93356	86419	93661	87011	93957	15
46	83951	92402	84586	92730	85211	93050	85825	93362	86429	93666	87021	93962	14
47	83961	92408	84597	92735	85221	93055	85835	93367	86438	93671	87030	93967	13
48	83972	92413	84607	92741	85232	93060	85846	93372	86448	93676	87040	93972	12
49	83983	92419	84618	92746	85242	93065	85856	93377	86458	93681	87050	93977	11
50	83993	92425	84628	92751	85252	93071	85866	93382	86468	93686	87060	93982	10
51	84004	92430	84639	92757	85263	93076	85876	93387	86478	93691	87070	93987	9
52	84015	92436	84649	92762	85273	93081	85886	93392	86488	93696	87079	93991	8
53	84025	92441	84660	92768	85283	93086	85896	93397	86498	93701	87089	93996	7
54	84036	92447	84670	92773	85294	93092	85906	93403	86508	93706	87099	94001	6
55	84047	92452	84681	92778	85304	93097	85916	93408	86518	93711	87109	94006	5
56	84057	92458	84691	92784	85314	93102	85927	93413	86528	93716	87118	94011	4
57	84068	92463	84702	92789	85324	93107	85937	93418	86538	93721	87128	94016	3
58	84079	92469	84712	92794	85335	93113	85947	93423	86548	93726	87138	94021	2
59	84089	92474	84722	92800	85345	93118	85957	93428	86558	93731	87148	94025	1
60	84100	92480	84733	92805	85355	93123	85967	93433	86568	93736	87157	94030	0
		T̄. [9]		T̄. [9]		T̄. [9]		T̄. [9]		T̄. [9]		T̄. [9]	
	227°		226°		225°		224°		223°		222°		′

Table 20   HAVERSINES

′	138° Nat.	138° Log.	139° Nat.	139° Log.	140° Nat.	140° Log.	141° Nat.	141° Log.	142° Nat.	142° Log.	143° Nat.	143° Log.	′
		T. [9]		T. [9]		T. [9]		T. [9]		T. [9]		T. [9]	
0	87157	94030	87735	94318	88302	94597	88857	94869	89401	95134	89932	95391	60
1	87167	94035	87745	94322	88312	94602	88866	94874	89409	95138	89941	95396	59
2	87177	94040	87755	94327	88321	94606	88876	94878	89418	95143	89949	95400	58
3	87186	94045	87764	94332	88330	94611	88885	94883	89427	95147	89958	95404	57
4	87196	94050	87774	94336	88340	94616	88894	94887	89436	95151	89967	95408	56
5	87206	94055	87783	94341	88349	94620	88903	94892	89445	95156	89976	95412	55
6	87216	94059	87793	94346	88358	94625	88912	94896	89454	95160	89984	95417	54
7	87225	94064	87802	94351	88368	94629	88921	94901	89463	95164	89993	95421	53
8	87235	94069	87812	94355	88377	94634	88930	94905	89472	95169	90002	95425	52
9	87245	94074	87821	94360	88386	94638	88940	94909	89481	95173	90010	95429	51
10	87254	94079	87831	94365	88396	94643	88949	94914	89490	95177	90019	95433	50
11	87264	94084	87840	94369	88405	94648	88958	94918	89499	95182	90028	95438	49
12	87274	94088	87850	94374	88414	94652	88967	94923	89508	95186	90037	95442	48
13	87283	94093	87859	94379	88423	94657	88976	94927	89517	95190	90045	95446	47
14	87293	94098	87869	94383	88433	94661	88985	94932	89526	95195	90054	95450	46
15	87303	94103	87878	94388	88442	94666	88994	94936	89534	95199	90063	95454	45
16	87313	94108	87888	94393	88451	94670	89003	94941	89543	95203	90071	95459	44
17	87322	94112	87897	94398	88461	94675	89012	94945	89552	95208	90080	95463	43
18	87332	94117	87907	94402	88470	94680	89022	94949	89561	95212	90089	95467	42
19	87342	94122	87916	94407	88479	94684	89031	94954	89570	95216	90097	95471	41
20	87351	94127	87926	94412	88489	94689	89040	94958	89579	95221	90106	95475	40
21	87361	94132	87935	94416	88498	94693	89049	94963	89588	95225	90115	95480	39
22	87371	94137	87945	94421	88507	94698	89058	94967	89597	95229	90124	95484	38
23	87380	94141	87954	94426	88516	94702	89067	94972	89606	95234	90132	95488	37
24	87390	94146	87964	94430	88526	94707	89076	94976	89614	95238	90141	95492	36
25	87400	94151	87973	94435	88535	94711	89085	94981	89623	95242	90150	95496	35
26	87409	94156	87982	94440	88544	94716	89094	94985	89632	95246	90158	95501	34
27	87419	94161	87992	94444	88553	94721	89103	94989	89641	95251	90167	95505	33
28	87429	94165	88001	94449	88563	94725	89112	94994	89650	95255	90176	95509	32
29	87438	94170	88011	94454	88572	94730	89121	94998	89659	95259	90184	95513	31
30	87448	94175	88020	94458	88581	94734	89130	95003	89668	95264	90193	95517	30
31	87457	94180	88030	94463	88590	94739	89139	95007	89677	95268	90201	95521	29
32	87467	94184	88039	94468	88600	94743	89149	95011	89685	95272	90210	95526	28
33	87477	94189	88049	94472	88609	94748	89158	95016	89694	95276	90219	95530	27
34	87486	94194	88058	94477	88618	94752	89167	95020	89703	95281	90227	95534	26
35	87496	94199	88067	94482	88627	94757	89176	95025	89712	95285	90236	95538	25
36	87506	94204	88077	94486	88637	94761	89185	95029	89721	95289	90245	95542	24
37	87515	94208	88086	94491	88646	94766	89194	95033	89730	95294	90253	95546	23
38	87525	94213	88096	94496	88655	94770	89203	95038	89738	95298	90262	95550	22
39	87534	94218	88105	94500	88664	94775	89212	95042	89747	95302	90271	95555	21
40	87544	94223	88115	94505	88674	94779	89221	95047	89756	95306	90279	95559	20
41	87554	94227	88124	94509	88683	94784	89230	95051	89765	95311	90288	95563	19
42	87563	94232	88133	94514	88692	94788	89239	95055	89774	95315	90296	95567	18
43	87573	94237	88143	94519	88701	94793	89248	95060	89782	95319	90305	95571	17
44	87582	94242	88152	94523	88710	94797	89257	95064	89791	95323	90314	95575	16
45	87592	94246	88162	94528	88720	94802	89266	95069	89800	95328	90322	95579	15
46	87602	94251	88171	94533	88729	94806	89275	95073	89809	95332	90331	95584	14
47	87611	94256	88180	94537	88738	94811	89284	95077	89818	95336	90339	95588	13
48	87621	94261	88190	94542	88747	94815	89293	95082	89826	95340	90348	95592	12
49	87630	94265	88199	94546	88756	94820	89302	95086	89835	95345	90357	95596	11
50	87640	94270	88209	94551	88766	94824	89311	95090	89844	95349	90365	95600	10
51	87649	94275	88218	94556	88775	94829	89320	95095	89853	95353	90374	95604	9
52	87659	94280	88227	94560	88784	94833	89329	95099	89862	95357	90382	95608	8
53	87669	94284	88237	94565	88793	94838	89338	95104	89870	95362	90391	95612	7
54	87678	94289	88246	94570	88802	94842	89347	95108	89879	95366	90399	95617	6
55	87688	94294	88255	94574	88811	94847	89356	95112	89888	95370	90408	95621	5
56	87697	94299	88265	94579	88821	94851	89365	95117	89897	95374	90417	95625	4
57	87707	94303	88274	94583	88830	94856	89374	95121	89906	95379	90425	95629	3
58	87716	94308	88284	94588	88839	94860	89383	95125	89914	95383	90434	95633	2
59	87726	94313	88293	94593	88848	94865	89392	95130	89923	95387	90442	95637	1
60	87735	94318	88302	94597	88857	94869	89401	95134	89932	95391	90451	95641	0
		T. [9]		T. [9]		T. [9]		T. [9]		T. [9]		T. [9]	
	221°		220°		219°		218°		217°		216°		′

Table 20   **HAVERSINES**

′	144° Nat.	144° Log.	145° Nat.	145° Log.	146° Nat.	146° Log.	147° Nat.	147° Log.	148° Nat.	148° Log.	149° Nat.	149° Log.	
		Ī. [9]		Ī. [9]		Ī. [9]		Ī. [9]		Ī. [9]		Ī. [9]	
0	90451	95641	90958	95884	91452	96119	91934	96347	92402	96568	92858	96782	60
1	90459	95645	90966	95888	91460	96123	91941	96351	92410	96572	92866	96786	59
2	90468	95649	90974	95892	91468	96127	91949	96355	92418	96576	92873	96789	58
3	90476	95654	90983	95896	91476	96131	91957	96359	92426	96579	92881	96793	57
4	90485	95658	90991	95900	91484	96135	91965	96362	92433	96583	92888	96796	56
5	90494	95662	90999	95904	91493	96139	91973	96366	92441	96586	92896	96800	55
6	90502	95666	91008	95908	91501	96142	91981	96370	92449	96590	92903	96803	54
7	90511	95670	91016	95912	91509	96146	91989	96374	92456	96594	92911	96807	53
8	90519	95674	91024	95916	91517	96150	91997	96377	92464	96597	92918	96810	52
9	90528	95678	91033	95920	91525	96154	92005	96381	92472	96601	92926	96814	51
10	90536	95682	91041	95924	91533	96158	92013	96385	92479	96604	92933	96817	50
11	90545	95686	91049	95928	91541	96162	92020	96388	92487	96608	92941	96821	49
12	90553	95690	91057	95932	91549	96165	92028	96392	92495	96612	92948	96824	48
13	90562	95694	91066	95936	91557	96169	92036	96396	92502	96615	92955	96827	47
14	90570	95699	91074	95939	91565	96173	92044	96400	92510	96619	92963	96831	46
15	90579	95703	91082	95943	91573	96177	92052	96403	92518	96622	92970	96834	45
16	90587	95707	91091	95947	91582	96181	92060	96407	92525	96626	92978	96838	44
17	90596	95711	91099	95951	91590	96185	92068	96411	92533	96630	92985	96841	43
18	90604	95715	91107	95955	91598	96188	92076	96414	92541	96633	92993	96845	42
19	90613	95719	91115	95959	91606	96192	92083	96418	92548	96637	93000	96848	41
20	90621	95723	91124	95963	91614	96196	92091	96422	92556	96640	93007	96852	40
21	90630	95727	91132	95967	91622	96200	92099	96426	92563	96644	93015	96855	39
22	90638	95731	91140	95971	91630	96204	92107	96429	92571	96648	93022	96859	38
23	90647	95735	91149	95975	91638	96208	92115	96433	92579	96651	93030	96862	37
24	90655	95739	91157	95979	91646	96211	92123	96437	92586	96655	93037	96866	36
25	90664	95743	91165	95983	91654	96215	92130	96440	92594	96658	93045	96869	35
26	90672	95747	91173	95987	91662	96219	92138	96444	92602	96662	93052	96873	34
27	90680	95751	91182	95991	91670	96223	92146	96448	92609	96665	93059	96876	33
28	90689	95755	91190	95995	91678	96227	92154	96451	92617	96669	93067	96879	32
29	90697	95759	91198	95999	91686	96230	92162	96455	92624	96673	93074	96883	31
30	90706	95763	91206	96002	91694	96234	92170	96459	92632	96676	93081	96886	30
31	90714	95768	91215	96006	91702	96238	92177	96462	92640	96680	93089	96890	29
32	90723	95772	91223	96010	91710	96242	92185	96466	92647	96683	93096	96893	28
33	90731	95776	91231	96014	91718	96246	92193	96470	92655	96687	93104	96897	27
34	90740	95780	91239	96018	91726	96249	92201	96473	92662	96690	93111	96900	26
35	90748	95784	91247	96022	91734	96253	92209	96477	92670	96694	93118	96904	25
36	90756	95788	91256	96026	91742	96257	92216	96481	92678	96697	93126	96907	24
37	90765	95792	91264	96030	91750	96261	92224	96484	92685	96701	93133	96910	23
38	90773	95796	91272	96034	91758	96265	92232	96488	92693	96705	93140	96914	22
39	90782	95800	91280	96038	91766	96268	92240	96492	92700	96708	93148	96917	21
40	90790	95804	91289	96042	91774	96272	92248	96495	92708	96712	93155	96921	20
41	90798	95808	91297	96046	91782	96276	92255	96499	92715	96715	93162	96924	19
42	90807	95812	91305	96049	91790	96280	92263	96503	92723	96719	93170	96928	18
43	90815	95816	91313	96053	91798	96283	92271	96506	92730	96722	93177	96931	17
44	90824	95820	91321	96057	91806	96287	92279	96510	92738	96726	93184	96934	16
45	90832	95824	91329	96061	91814	96291	92286	96514	92746	96729	93192	96938	15
46	90840	95828	91338	96065	91822	96295	92294	96517	92753	96733	93199	96941	14
47	90849	95832	91346	96069	91830	96299	92302	96521	92761	96736	93206	96945	13
48	90857	95836	91354	96073	91838	96302	92310	96525	92768	96740	93214	96948	12
49	90866	95840	91362	96077	91846	96306	92317	96528	92776	96743	93221	96951	11
50	90874	95844	91370	96081	91854	96310	92325	96532	92783	96747	93228	96955	10
51	90882	95848	91379	96084	91862	96314	92333	96536	92791	96750	93236	96958	9
52	90891	95852	91387	96088	91870	96317	92341	96539	92798	96754	93243	96962	8
53	90899	95856	91395	96092	91878	96321	92348	96543	92806	96758	93250	96965	7
54	90907	95860	91403	96096	91886	96325	92356	96547	92813	96761	93258	96968	6
55	90916	95864	91411	96100	91894	96329	92364	96550	92821	96765	93265	96972	5
56	90924	95868	91419	96104	91902	96332	92372	96554	92828	96768	93272	96975	4
57	90933	95872	91427	96108	91910	96336	92379	96557	92836	96772	93279	96979	3
58	90941	95876	91436	96112	91918	96340	92387	96561	92843	96775	93287	96982	2
59	90949	95880	91444	96115	91926	96344	92395	96565	92851	96779	93294	96985	1
60	90958	95884	91452	96119	91934	96347	92402	96568	92858	96782	93301	96989	0
		Ī. [9]		Ī. [9]		Ī. [9]		Ī. [9]		Ī. [9]		Ī. [9]	
	215°		214°		213°		212°		211°		210°		′

Table 20   HAVERSINES

′	150° Nat.	150° Log.	151° Nat.	151° Log.	152° Nat.	152° Log.	153° Nat.	153° Log.	154° Nat.	154° Log.	155° Nat.	155° Log.	′
		T. [9]		T. [9]		T. [9]		T. [9]		T. [9]		T. [9]	
0	93301	96989	93731	97188	94147	97381	94550	97566	94940	97745	95315	97916	60
1	93309	96992	93738	97192	94154	97384	94557	97569	94946	97748	95322	97919	59
2	93316	96996	93745	97195	94161	97387	94564	97572	94952	97751	95328	97922	58
3	93323	96999	93752	97198	94168	97390	94570	97575	94959	97754	95334	97925	57
4	93330	97002	93759	97201	94175	97393	94577	97578	94965	97756	95340	97927	56
5	93338	97006	93766	97205	94181	97397	94583	97581	94972	97759	95346	97930	55
6	93345	97009	93773	97208	94188	97400	94590	97584	94978	97762	95352	97933	54
7	93352	97012	93780	97211	94195	97403	94596	97587	94984	97765	95358	97936	53
8	93359	97016	93787	97214	94202	97406	94603	97591	94991	97768	95364	97939	52
9	93367	97019	93794	97218	94209	97409	94610	97594	94997	97771	95371	97941	51
10	93374	97023	93801	97221	94215	97412	94616	97597	95003	97774	95377	97944	50
11	93381	97026	93808	97224	94222	97415	94623	97600	95010	97777	95383	97947	49
12	93388	97029	93815	97227	94229	97418	94629	97603	95016	97780	95389	97950	48
13	93396	97033	93822	97231	94236	97422	94636	97606	95022	97783	95395	97953	47
14	93403	97036	93829	97234	94243	97425	94642	97609	95029	97785	95401	97955	46
15	93410	97039	93836	97237	94249	97428	94649	97612	95035	97788	95407	97958	45
16	93417	97043	93843	97240	94256	97431	94655	97615	95041	97791	95413	97961	44
17	93424	97046	93850	97244	94263	97434	94662	97618	95048	97794	95419	97964	43
18	93432	97049	93857	97247	94270	97437	94669	97621	95054	97797	95425	97966	42
19	93439	97053	93864	97250	94276	97440	94675	97624	95060	97800	95431	97969	41
20	93446	97056	93871	97253	94283	97443	94682	97627	95066	97803	95438	97972	40
21	93453	97059	93878	97256	94290	97447	94688	97630	95073	97806	95444	97975	39
22	93460	97063	93885	97260	94297	97450	94695	97633	95079	97808	95450	97977	38
23	93468	97066	93892	97263	94303	97453	94701	97636	95085	97811	95456	97980	37
24	93475	97069	93899	97266	94310	97456	94708	97639	95092	97814	95462	97983	36
25	93482	97073	93906	97269	94317	97459	94714	97642	95098	97817	95468	97986	35
26	93489	97076	93913	97273	94324	97462	94721	97645	95104	97820	95474	97988	34
27	93496	97079	93920	97276	94330	97465	94727	97647	95110	97823	95480	97991	33
28	93503	97083	93927	97279	94337	97468	94734	97650	95117	97826	95486	97994	32
29	93511	97086	93934	97282	94344	97471	94740	97653	95123	97829	95492	97997	31
30	93518	97089	93941	97285	94351	97474	94747	97656	95129	97831	95498	97999	30
31	93525	97093	93948	97289	94357	97478	94753	97659	95136	97834	95504	98002	29
32	93532	97096	93955	97292	94364	97481	94760	97662	95142	97837	95510	98005	28
33	93539	97099	93962	97295	94371	97484	94766	97665	95148	97840	95516	98008	27
34	93546	97103	93969	97298	94377	97487	94773	97668	95154	97843	95522	98010	26
35	93554	97106	93976	97301	94384	97490	94779	97671	95161	97846	95528	98013	25
36	93561	97109	93982	97305	94391	97493	94786	97674	95167	97849	95534	98016	24
37	93568	97113	93989	97308	94397	97496	94792	97677	95173	97851	95540	98019	23
38	93575	97116	93996	97311	94404	97499	94799	97680	95179	97854	95546	98021	22
39	93582	97119	94003	97314	94411	97502	94805	97683	95185	97857	95552	98024	21
40	93589	97123	94010	97317	94418	97505	94811	97686	95192	97860	95558	98027	20
41	93596	97126	94017	97321	94424	97508	94818	97689	95198	97863	95564	98030	19
42	93603	97129	94024	97324	94431	97511	94824	97692	95204	97866	95570	98032	18
43	93611	97132	94031	97327	94438	97514	94831	97695	95210	97868	95576	98035	17
44	93618	97136	94038	97330	94444	97518	94837	97698	95217	97871	95582	98038	16
45	93625	97139	94045	97333	94451	97521	94844	97701	95223	97874	95588	98040	15
46	93632	97142	94051	97337	94458	97524	94850	97704	95229	97877	95594	98043	14
47	93639	97146	94058	97340	94464	97527	94856	97707	95235	97880	95600	98046	13
48	93646	97149	94065	97343	94471	97530	94863	97710	95241	97883	95606	98049	12
49	93653	97152	94072	97346	94477	97533	94869	97713	95248	97885	95612	98051	11
50	93660	97156	94079	97349	94484	97536	94876	97716	95254	97888	95618	98054	10
51	93667	97159	94086	97352	94491	97539	94882	97718	95260	97891	95624	98057	9
52	93674	97162	94093	97356	94497	97542	94889	97721	95266	97894	95630	98059	8
53	93682	97165	94099	97359	94504	97545	94895	97724	95272	97897	95636	98062	7
54	93689	97169	94106	97362	94511	97548	94901	97727	95278	97899	95642	98065	6
55	93696	97172	94113	97365	94517	97551	94908	97730	95285	97902	95648	98067	5
56	93703	97175	94120	97368	94524	97554	94914	97733	95291	97905	95654	98070	4
57	93710	97179	94127	97371	94531	97557	94921	97736	95297	97908	95660	98073	3
58	93717	97182	94134	97375	94537	97560	94927	97739	95303	97911	95665	98076	2
59	93724	97185	94141	97378	94544	97563	94933	97742	95309	97914	95671	98078	1
60	93731	97188	94147	97381	94550	97566	94940	97745	95315	97916	95677	98081	0
		T. [9]		T. [9]		T. [9]		T. [9]		T. [9]		T. [9]	

209°	208°	207°	206°	205°	204°	′

Table 20 — HAVERSINES

′	156° Nat.	156° Log.	157° Nat.	157° Log.	158° Nat.	158° Log.	159° Nat.	159° Log.	160° Nat.	160° Log.	161° Nat.	161° Log.	′
		$\bar{1}$. [9]		$\bar{1}$. [9]		$\bar{1}$. [9]		$\bar{1}$. [9]		$\bar{1}$. [9]		$\bar{1}$. [9]	
0	95677	98081	96025	98239	96359	98389	96679	98533	96985	98670	97276	98801	60
1	95683	98084	96031	98241	96365	98392	96684	98536	96990	98673	97281	98803	59
2	95689	98086	96037	98244	96370	98394	96689	98538	96995	98675	97285	98805	58
3	95695	98089	96042	98246	96376	98397	96695	98540	97000	98677	97290	98807	57
4	95701	98092	96048	98249	96381	98399	96700	98543	97004	98679	97295	98809	56
5	95707	98094	96054	98251	96386	98402	96705	98545	97009	98681	97300	98811	55
6	95713	98097	96059	98254	96392	98404	96710	98547	97014	98684	97304	98813	54
7	95719	98100	96065	98256	96397	98406	96715	98550	97019	98686	97309	98815	53
8	95724	98102	96071	98259	96403	98409	96721	98552	97024	98688	97314	98817	52
9	95730	98105	96076	98262	96408	98411	96726	98554	97029	98690	97318	98819	51
10	95736	98108	96082	98264	96413	98414	96731	98557	97034	98692	97323	98822	50
11	95742	98110	96088	98267	96419	98416	96736	98559	97039	98695	97328	98824	49
12	95748	98113	96093	98269	96424	98419	96741	98561	97044	98697	97332	98826	48
13	95754	98116	96099	98272	96430	98421	96746	98564	97049	98699	97337	98828	47
14	95760	98118	96104	98274	96435	98424	96752	98566	97054	98701	97342	98830	46
15	95766	98121	96110	98277	96440	98426	96757	98568	97059	98703	97347	98832	45
16	95771	98124	96116	98279	96446	98428	96762	98570	97064	98706	97351	98834	44
17	95777	98126	96121	98282	96451	98431	96767	98573	97069	98708	97356	98836	43
18	95783	98129	96127	98284	96457	98433	96772	98575	97074	98710	97361	98838	42
19	95789	98132	96133	98287	96462	98436	96777	98577	97078	98712	97365	98840	41
20	95795	98134	96138	98290	96467	98438	96782	98580	97083	98714	97370	98842	40
21	95801	98137	96144	98292	96473	98440	96788	98582	97088	98717	97374	98845	39
22	95806	98139	96149	98295	96478	98443	96793	98584	97093	98719	97379	98847	38
23	95812	98142	96155	98297	96483	98445	96798	98587	97098	98721	97384	98849	37
24	95818	98145	96161	98300	96489	98448	96803	98589	97103	98723	97388	98851	36
25	95824	98147	96166	98302	96494	98450	96808	98591	97108	98725	97393	98853	35
26	95830	98150	96172	98305	96500	98453	96813	98593	97113	98728	97398	98855	34
27	95836	98153	96177	98307	96505	98455	96818	98596	97117	98730	97402	98857	33
28	95841	98155	96183	98310	96510	98457	96823	98598	97122	98732	97407	98859	32
29	95847	98158	96188	98312	96516	98460	96829	98600	97127	98734	97412	98861	31
30	95853	98161	96194	98315	96521	98462	96834	98603	97132	98736	97416	98863	30
31	95859	98163	96200	98317	96526	98465	96839	98605	97137	98738	97421	98865	29
32	95865	98166	96205	98320	96532	98467	96844	98607	97142	98741	97425	98867	28
33	95870	98168	96211	98322	96537	98469	96849	98609	97147	98743	97430	98869	27
34	95876	98171	96216	98325	96542	98472	96854	98612	97151	98745	97435	98871	26
35	95882	98174	96222	98327	96547	98474	96859	98614	97156	98747	97439	98873	25
36	95888	98176	96227	98330	96553	98476	96864	98616	97161	98749	97444	98875	24
37	95894	98179	96233	98332	96558	98479	96869	98619	97166	98751	97448	98877	23
38	95899	98182	96238	98335	96563	98481	96874	98621	97171	98754	97453	98880	22
39	95905	98184	96244	98337	96569	98484	96879	98623	97176	98756	97458	98882	21
40	95911	98187	96249	98340	96574	98486	96884	98625	97180	98758	97462	98884	20
41	95917	98189	96255	98342	96579	98488	96889	98628	97185	98760	97467	98886	19
42	95922	98192	96260	98345	96585	98491	96894	98630	97190	98762	97471	98888	18
43	95928	98195	96266	98347	96590	98493	96899	98632	97195	98764	97476	98890	17
44	95934	98197	96272	98350	96595	98496	96905	98634	97200	98766	97480	98892	16
45	95940	98200	96277	98352	96600	98498	96910	98637	97204	98769	97485	98894	15
46	95945	98202	96283	98355	96606	98500	96915	98639	97209	98771	97490	98896	14
47	95951	98205	96288	98357	96611	98503	96920	98641	97214	98773	97494	98898	13
48	95957	98208	96294	98360	96616	98505	96925	98643	97219	98775	97499	98900	12
49	95962	98210	96299	98362	96621	98507	96930	98646	97224	98777	97503	98902	11
50	95968	98213	96305	98365	96627	98510	96935	98648	97228	98779	97508	98904	10
51	95974	98215	96310	98367	96632	98512	96940	98650	97233	98781	97512	98906	9
52	95980	98218	96315	98370	96637	98514	96945	98652	97238	98784	97517	98908	8
53	95985	98221	96321	98372	96642	98517	96950	98655	97243	98786	97521	98910	7
54	95991	98223	96326	98375	96648	98519	96955	98657	97247	98788	97526	98912	6
55	95997	98226	96332	98377	96653	98521	96960	98659	97252	98790	97530	98914	5
56	96002	98228	96337	98379	96658	98524	96965	98661	97257	98792	97535	98916	4
57	96008	98231	96343	98382	96663	98526	96970	98664	97262	98794	97539	98918	3
58	96014	98233	96348	98384	96669	98529	96975	98666	97266	98796	97544	98920	2
59	96020	98236	96354	98387	96674	98531	96980	98668	97271	98798	97548	98922	1
60	96025	98239	96359	98389	96679	98533	96985	98670	97276	98801	97553	98924	0
		$\bar{1}$. [9]		$\bar{1}$. [9]		$\bar{1}$. [9]		$\bar{1}$. [9]		$\bar{1}$. [9]		$\bar{1}$. [9]	
	203°		**202°**		**201°**		**200°**		**199°**		**198°**		′

Table 20   HAVERSINES

′	162° Nat.	Log.	163° Nat.	Log.	164° Nat.	Log.	165° Nat.	Log.	166° Nat.	Log.	167° Nat.	Log.	′
		T̄. [9]		T̄. [9]		T̄. [9]		T̄. [9]		T̄. [9]		T̄. [9]	
0	97553	98924	97815	99041	98063	99151	98296	99254	98515	99350	98719	99440	60
1	97557	98926	97819	99043	98067	99152	98300	99255	98518	99352	98722	99441	59
2	97562	98928	97824	99044	98071	99154	98304	99257	98522	99353	98725	99443	58
3	97566	98930	97828	99046	98075	99156	98308	99259	98525	99355	98728	99444	57
4	97571	98932	97832	99048	98079	99158	98311	99260	98529	99356	98732	99446	56
5	97575	98934	97836	99050	98083	99159	98315	99262	98532	99358	98735	99447	55
6	97580	98936	97841	99052	98087	99161	98319	99264	98536	99359	98738	99448	54
7	97584	98938	97845	99054	98091	99163	98323	99265	98539	99361	98741	99450	53
8	97589	98940	97849	99056	98095	99165	98326	99267	98543	99362	98745	99451	52
9	97593	98942	97853	99058	98099	99166	98330	99269	98546	99364	98748	99453	51
10	97598	98944	97858	99059	98103	99168	98334	99270	98550	99366	98751	99454	50
11	97602	98946	97862	99061	98107	99170	98337	99272	98553	99367	98754	99456	49
12	97606	98948	97866	99063	98111	99172	98341	99274	98557	99369	98757	99457	48
13	97611	98950	97870	99065	98115	99173	98345	99275	98560	99370	98761	99458	47
14	97615	98952	97874	99067	98119	99175	98349	99277	98564	99372	98764	99460	46
15	97620	98954	97879	99069	98123	99177	98352	99278	98567	99373	98767	99461	45
16	97624	98956	97883	99071	98127	99179	98356	99280	98571	99375	98770	99463	44
17	97629	98958	97887	99072	98131	99180	98360	99282	98574	99376	98774	99464	43
18	97633	98960	97891	99074	98135	99182	98363	99283	98577	99378	98777	99465	42
19	97637	98962	97895	99076	98139	99184	98367	99285	98581	99379	98780	99467	41
20	97642	98964	97899	99078	98142	99186	98371	99287	98584	99381	98783	99468	40
21	97646	98966	97904	99080	98146	99187	98374	99288	98588	99382	98786	99470	39
22	97651	98968	97908	99082	98150	99189	98378	99290	98591	99384	98789	99471	38
23	97655	98970	97912	99084	98154	99191	98382	99291	98595	99385	98793	99472	37
24	97660	98971	97916	99085	98158	99193	98385	99293	98598	99387	98796	99473	36
25	97664	98973	97920	99087	98162	99194	98389	99295	98601	99388	98799	99475	35
26	97668	98975	97924	99089	98166	99196	98393	99296	98605	99390	98802	99477	34
27	97673	98977	97929	99091	98170	99198	98396	99298	98608	99391	98805	99478	33
28	97677	98979	97933	99093	98174	99200	98400	99300	98612	99393	98808	99479	32
29	97681	98981	97937	99095	98178	99201	98404	99301	98615	99394	98812	99481	31
30	97686	98983	97941	99096	98182	99203	98407	99303	98618	99396	98815	99482	30
31	97690	98985	97945	99098	98185	99205	98411	99304	98622	99397	98818	99484	29
32	97695	98987	97949	99100	98189	99206	98415	99306	98625	99399	98821	99485	28
33	97699	98989	97953	99102	98193	99208	98418	99308	98629	99400	98824	99486	27
34	97703	98991	97957	99104	98197	99210	98422	99309	98632	99402	98827	99488	26
35	97708	98993	97962	99106	98201	99212	98426	99311	98635	99403	98830	99489	25
36	97712	98995	97966	99107	98205	99213	98429	99312	98639	99405	98834	99490	24
37	97716	98997	97970	99109	98209	99215	98433	99314	98642	99406	98837	99492	23
38	97721	98999	97974	99111	98212	99217	98436	99316	98646	99408	98840	99493	22
39	97725	99001	97978	99113	98216	99218	98440	99317	98649	99409	98843	99495	21
40	97729	99003	97982	99115	98220	99220	98444	99319	98652	99411	98846	99496	20
41	97734	99004	97986	99116	98224	99222	98447	99320	98656	99412	98849	99497	19
42	97738	99006	97990	99118	98228	99223	98451	99322	98659	99414	98852	99499	18
43	97742	99008	97994	99120	98232	99225	98454	99324	98662	99415	98855	99500	17
44	97747	99010	97998	99122	98236	99227	98458	99325	98666	99417	98858	99501	16
45	97751	99012	98002	99124	98239	99229	98462	99327	98669	99418	98862	99503	15
46	97755	99014	98007	99126	98243	99230	98465	99328	98672	99420	98865	99504	14
47	97760	99016	98011	99127	98247	99232	98469	99330	98676	99421	98868	99505	13
48	97764	99018	98015	99129	98251	99234	98472	99331	98679	99422	98871	99507	12
49	97768	99020	98019	99131	98255	99235	98476	99333	98682	99424	98874	99508	11
50	97773	99022	98023	99133	98258	99237	98479	99335	98686	99425	98877	99510	10
51	97777	99024	98027	99134	98262	99239	98483	99336	98689	99427	98880	99511	9
52	97781	99025	98031	99136	98266	99240	98487	99338	98692	99428	98883	99512	8
53	97785	99027	98035	99138	98270	99242	98490	99339	98696	99430	98886	99514	7
54	97790	99029	98039	99140	98274	99244	98494	99341	98699	99431	98889	99515	6
55	97794	99031	98043	99142	98277	99245	98497	99342	98702	99433	98892	99516	5
56	97798	99033	98047	99143	98281	99247	98501	99344	98705	99434	98895	99518	4
57	97802	99035	98051	99145	98285	99249	98504	99345	98709	99436	98898	99519	3
58	97807	99037	98055	99147	98289	99250	98508	99347	98712	99437	98901	99520	2
59	97811	99039	98059	99149	98293	99252	98511	99349	98715	99438	98904	99522	1
60	97815	99041	98063	99151	98296	99254	98515	99350	98719	99440	98907	99523	0
		T̄. [9]		T̄. [9]		T̄. [9]		T̄. [9]		T̄. [9]		T̄. [9]	
	197°		196°		195°		194°		193°		192°		′

Table 20   HAVERSINES

′	168° Nat.	Log.	169° Nat.	Log.	170° Nat.	Log.	171° Nat.	Log.	172° Nat.	Log.	173° Nat.	Log.	
		$\overline{1}$. [9]		$\overline{1}$. [9]		$\overline{1}$. [9]		$\overline{1}$. [9]		$\overline{1}$. [9]		$\overline{1}$. [9]	
0	98907	99523	99081	99599	99240	99669	99384	99732	99513	99788	99627	99838	60
1	98910	99524	99084	99600	99243	99670	99387	99733	99515	99789	99629	99839	59
2	98913	99526	99087	99602	99245	99671	99389	99734	99517	99790	99631	99839	58
3	98916	99527	99090	99603	99248	99672	99391	99735	99519	99791	99633	99840	57
4	98919	99528	99092	99604	99250	99673	99393	99736	99521	99792	99634	99841	56
5	98922	99529	99095	99605	99253	99674	99396	99737	99523	99793	99636	99842	55
6	98925	99531	99098	99606	99255	99675	99398	99738	99525	99793	99638	99842	54
7	98928	99532	99101	99608	99258	99677	99400	99739	99527	99794	99640	99843	53
8	98931	99533	99103	99609	99260	99678	99402	99740	99529	99795	99641	99844	52
9	98934	99535	99106	99610	99263	99679	99405	99741	99531	99796	99643	99845	51
10	98937	99536	99109	99611	99265	99680	99407	99742	99533	99797	99645	99845	50
11	98940	99537	99112	99612	99268	99681	99409	99743	99535	99798	99647	99846	49
12	98943	99539	99114	99614	99270	99682	99411	99744	99537	99799	99648	99847	48
13	98946	99540	99117	99615	99273	99683	99414	99745	99539	99799	99650	99848	47
14	98949	99541	99120	99616	99275	99684	99416	99746	99541	99800	99652	99848	46
15	98952	99543	99123	99617	99278	99685	99418	99747	99543	99801	99653	99849	45
16	98955	99544	99125	99618	99280	99686	99420	99748	99545	99802	99655	99850	44
17	98958	99545	99128	99620	99283	99687	99422	99748	99547	99803	99657	99851	43
18	98961	99546	99131	99621	99285	99688	99425	99749	99549	99804	99659	99851	42
19	98964	99548	99133	99622	99288	99690	99427	99750	99551	99805	99660	99852	41
20	98967	99549	99136	99623	99290	99691	99429	99751	99553	99805	99662	99853	40
21	98970	99550	99139	99624	99293	99692	99431	99752	99555	99806	99664	99854	39
22	98973	99552	99141	99626	99295	99693	99433	99753	99557	99807	99665	99854	38
23	98976	99553	99144	99627	99297	99694	99436	99754	99559	99808	99667	99855	37
24	98979	99554	99147	99628	99300	99695	99438	99755	99561	99809	99669	99856	36
25	98982	99555	99149	99629	99302	99696	99440	99756	99563	99810	99670	99857	35
26	98985	99557	99152	99630	99305	99697	99442	99757	99565	99811	99672	99857	34
27	98988	99558	99155	99631	99307	99698	99444	99758	99567	99811	99674	99858	33
28	98990	99559	99157	99633	99309	99699	99446	99759	99568	99812	99675	99859	32
29	98993	99561	99160	99634	99312	99700	99449	99760	99570	99813	99677	99859	31
30	98996	99562	99163	99635	99314	99701	99451	99761	99572	99814	99679	99860	30
31	98999	99563	99165	99636	99317	99702	99453	99762	99574	99815	99680	99861	29
32	99002	99564	99168	99637	99319	99703	99455	99763	99576	99815	99682	99862	28
33	99005	99566	99171	99638	99321	99704	99457	99764	99578	99816	99684	99862	27
34	99008	99567	99173	99639	99324	99705	99459	99765	99580	99817	99685	99863	26
35	99011	99568	99176	99641	99326	99706	99461	99765	99582	99818	99687	99864	25
36	99014	99569	99179	99642	99329	99707	99464	99766	99584	99819	99688	99864	24
37	99016	99571	99181	99643	99331	99708	99466	99767	99585	99820	99690	99865	23
38	99019	99572	99184	99644	99333	99710	99468	99768	99587	99820	99692	99866	22
39	99022	99573	99186	99645	99336	99711	99470	99769	99589	99821	99693	99867	21
40	99025	99574	99189	99646	99338	99712	99472	99770	99591	99822	99695	99867	20
41	99028	99576	99192	99648	99340	99713	99474	99771	99593	99823	99696	99868	19
42	99031	99577	99194	99649	99343	99714	99476	99772	99595	99824	99698	99869	18
43	99034	99578	99197	99650	99345	99715	99478	99773	99597	99824	99700	99869	17
44	99036	99579	99199	99651	99347	99716	99480	99774	99598	99825	99701	99870	16
45	99039	99581	99202	99652	99350	99717	99483	99775	99600	99826	99703	99871	15
46	99042	99582	99205	99653	99352	99718	99485	99776	99602	99827	99704	99871	14
47	99045	99583	99207	99654	99354	99719	99487	99777	99604	99828	99706	99872	13
48	99048	99584	99210	99655	99357	99720	99489	99777	99606	99828	99708	99873	12
49	99051	99586	99212	99657	99359	99721	99491	99778	99608	99829	99709	99873	11
50	99053	99587	99215	99658	99361	99722	99493	99779	99609	99830	99711	99874	10
51	99056	99588	99217	99659	99364	99723	99495	99780	99611	99831	99712	99875	9
52	99059	99589	99220	99660	99366	99724	99497	99781	99613	99832	99714	99876	8
53	99062	99591	99223	99661	99368	99725	99499	99782	99615	99832	99715	99876	7
54	99065	99592	99225	99662	99371	99726	99501	99783	99617	99833	99717	99877	6
55	99067	99593	99228	99663	99373	99727	99503	99784	99618	99834	99718	99878	5
56	99070	99594	99230	99664	99375	99728	99505	99785	99620	99835	99720	99878	4
57	99073	99596	99233	99666	99378	99729	99507	99785	99622	99836	99722	99879	3
58	99076	99597	99235	99667	99380	99730	99509	99786	99624	99836	99723	99880	2
59	99079	99598	99238	99668	99382	99731	99511	99787	99626	99837	99725	99880	1
60	99081	99599	99240	99669	99384	99732	99513	99788	99627	99838	99726	99881	0
		$\overline{1}$. [9]		$\overline{1}$. [9]		$\overline{1}$. [9]		$\overline{1}$. [9]		$\overline{1}$. [9]		$\overline{1}$. [9]	
	191°		190°		189°		188°		187°		186°		′

Table 20   HAVERSINES

′	174° Nat.	Log.	175° Nat.	Log.	176° Nat.	Log.	177° Nat.	Log.	178° Nat.	Log.	179° Nat.	Log.	
		Ī. [9]		Ī. [9]		Ī. [9]		Ī. [9]		Ī. [9]		Ī/0.[9/0]	
0	99726	99881	99810	99917	99878	99947	99931	99970	99970	99987	99992	99997	60
1	99728	99882	99811	99918	99879	99948	99932	99971	99970	99987	99993	99997	59
2	99729	99882	99812	99918	99880	99948	99933	99971	99971	99987	99993	99997	58
3	99731	99883	99814	99919	99881	99948	99934	99971	99971	99987	99993	99997	57
4	99732	99884	99815	99919	99882	99949	99934	99972	99972	99988	99993	99997	56
5	99734	99884	99816	99920	99883	99949	99935	99972	99972	99988	99994	99997	55
6	99735	99885	99817	99921	99884	99950	99936	99972	99973	99988	99994	99997	54
7	99737	99885	99819	99921	99885	99950	99937	99973	99973	99988	99994	99997	53
8	99738	99886	99820	99922	99886	99951	99937	99973	99973	99988	99994	99998	52
9	99740	99887	99821	99922	99887	99951	99938	99973	99974	99989	99995	99998	51
10	99741	99887	99822	99923	99888	99951	99939	99973	99974	99989	99995	99998	50
11	99743	99888	99823	99923	99889	99952	99940	99974	99975	99989	99995	99998	49
12	99744	99889	99825	99924	99890	99952	99940	99974	99975	99989	99995	99998	48
13	99746	99889	99826	99924	99891	99953	99941	99974	99976	99989	99995	99998	47
14	99747	99890	99827	99925	99892	99953	99942	99975	99976	99990	99996	99998	46
15	99748	99891	99828	99925	99893	99953	99942	99975	99977	99990	99996	99998	45
16	99750	99891	99829	99926	99894	99954	99943	99975	99977	99990	99996	99998	44
17	99751	99892	99831	99926	99895	99954	99944	99976	99978	99990	99996	99998	43
18	99753	99893	99832	99927	99896	99955	99944	99976	99978	99990	99996	99998	42
19	99754	99893	99833	99927	99897	99955	99945	99976	99978	99991	99996	99998	41
20	99756	99894	99834	99928	99898	99956	99946	99977	99979	99991	99997	99999	40
21	99757	99894	99835	99928	99899	99956	99947	99977	99979	99991	99997	99999	39
22	99759	99895	99837	99929	99900	99956	99947	99977	99980	99991	99997	99999	38
23	99760	99896	99838	99929	99900	99957	99948	99977	99980	99991	99997	99999	37
24	99761	99896	99839	99930	99901	99957	99949	99978	99981	99992	99997	99999	36
25	99763	99897	99840	99931	99902	99958	99949	99978	99981	99992	99997	99999	35
26	99764	99897	99841	99931	99903	99958	99950	99978	99981	99992	99998	99999	34
27	99766	99898	99842	99932	99904	99958	99950	99978	99982	99992	99998	99999	33
28	99767	99899	99844	99932	99905	99959	99951	99979	99982	99992	99998	99999	32
29	99768	99899	99845	99933	99906	99959	99952	99979	99982	99992	99998	99999	31
30	99770	99900	99846	99933	99907	99959	99952	99979	99983	99993	99998	99999	30
31	99771	99901	99847	99934	99908	99960	99953	99980	99983	99993	99998	99999	29
32	99773	99901	99848	99934	99909	99960	99954	99980	99984	99993	99998	99999	28
33	99774	99902	99849	99935	99909	99961	99954	99980	99984	99993	99998	99999	27
34	99775	99902	99850	99935	99910	99961	99955	99980	99984	99993	99999	99999	26
35	99777	99903	99852	99935	99911	99961	99956	99981	99985	99993	99999	99999	25
36	99778	99904	99853	99936	99912	99962	99956	99981	99985	99994	99999	99999	24
37	99780	99904	99854	99936	99913	99962	99957	99981	99985	99994	99999	00000	23
38	99781	99905	99855	99937	99914	99963	99957	99981	99986	99994	99999	00000	22
39	99782	99905	99856	99937	99915	99963	99958	99982	99986	99994	99999	00000	21
40	99784	99906	99857	99938	99915	99963	99959	99982	99986	99994	99999	00000	20
41	99785	99906	99858	99938	99916	99964	99959	99982	99987	99994	99999	00000	19
42	99786	99907	99859	99939	99917	99964	99960	99982	99987	99994	99999	00000	18
43	99788	99908	99860	99939	99918	99964	99960	99983	99987	99995	99999	00000	17
44	99789	99908	99861	99940	99919	99965	99961	99983	99988	99995	99999	00000	16
45	99790	99909	99863	99940	99920	99965	99961	99983	99988	99995	1.000	00000	15
46	99792	99909	99864	99941	99920	99965	99962	99983	99988	99995	1.000	00000	14
47	99793	99910	99865	99941	99921	99966	99963	99984	99989	99995	1.000	00000	13
48	99794	99911	99866	99942	99922	99966	99963	99984	99989	99995	1.000	00000	12
49	99796	99911	99867	99942	99923	99966	99964	99984	99989	99995	1.000	00000	11
50	99797	99912	99868	99943	99924	99967	99964	99984	99990	99995	1.000	00000	10
51	99798	99912	99869	99943	99924	99967	99965	99985	99990	99996	1.000	00000	9
52	99799	99913	99870	99943	99925	99968	99965	99985	99990	99996	1.000	00000	8
53	99801	99913	99871	99944	99926	99968	99966	99985	99991	99996	1.000	00000	7
54	99802	99914	99872	99944	99927	99968	99966	99985	99991	99996	1.000	00000	6
55	99803	99915	99873	99945	99928	99969	99967	99986	99991	99996	1.000	00000	5
56	99805	99915	99874	99945	99928	99969	99967	99986	99991	99996	1.000	00000	4
57	99806	99916	99875	99946	99929	99969	99968	99986	99992	99996	1.000	00000	3
58	99807	99916	99876	99946	99930	99970	99969	99986	99992	99996	1.000	00000	2
59	99808	99917	99877	99947	99931	99970	99969	99987	99992	99997	1.000	00000	1
60	99810	99917	99878	99947	99931	99970	99970	99987	99992	99997	1.000	00000	0
		Ī. [9]		Ī. [9]		Ī. [9]		Ī. [9]		Ī. [9]		0/Ī.[0/9]	′

185°	184°	183°	182°	181°	180°

216

Table 21

EX-MERIDIAN Containing Values of F (Ex-Meridian Factor) Table I

Dec.	0°	1°	2°	3°	4°	5°	6°	7°	8°	9°	10°	11°	12°	13°	14°	15°	Dec.
	LATITUDE, SAME name as declination																

LATITUDE, **SAME** name as declination

Dec.	0°	1°	2°	3°	4°	5°	6°	7°	8°	9°	10°	11°	12°	13°	14°	15°	Dec.
0°					28.1	22.4	18.7	16.0	14.0	12.4	11.1	10.1	9.24	8.50	7.88	7.33	0°
1						28.0	22.4	18.6	16.0	13.9	12.4	11.1	10.1	9.20	8.47	7.84	1
2							28.0	22.3	18.6	15.9	13.9	12.3	11.1	10.0	9.16	8.43	2
3								27.9	22.3	18.5	15.8	13.8	12.3	11.0	10.0	9.11	3
4	28.1								27.8	22.2	18.5	15.8	13.8	12.2	10.9	9.92	4
5	22.4	28.0								27.7	22.1	18.4	15.7	13.7	12.1	10.9	5
6	18.7	22.4	28.0								27.6	22.0	18.3	15.6	13.6	12.1	6
7	16.0	18.6	22.3	27.9								27.4	21.9	18.2	15.5	13.5	7
8	14.0	16.0	18.6	22.3	27.8								27.3	21.7	18.0	15.4	8
9	12.4	13.9	15.9	18.5	22.2	27.7								27.1	21.6	17.9	9
10	11.1	12.4	13.9	15.8	18.5	22.1	27.6								26.9	21.4	10
11	10.1	11.1	12.3	13.8	15.8	18.4	22.0	27.4								26.7	11
12	9.24	10.1	11.1	12.3	13.8	15.7	18.3	21.9	27.3								12
13	8.50	9.20	10.0	11.0	12.2	13.7	15.6	18.2	21.7	27.1							13
14	7.88	8.47	9.16	10.0	10.9	12.1	13.6	15.5	18.0	21.6	26.9						14
15	7.33	7.84	8.43	9.11	9.92	10.9	12.1	13.5	15.4	17.9	21.4	26.7					15
16	6.85	7.29	7.80	8.38	9.06	9.85	10.8	12.0	13.4	15.3	17.8	21.3	26.5				16
17	6.42	6.81	7.25	7.75	8.33	9.00	9.79	10.7	11.9	13.3	15.2	17.6	21.1	26.2			17
18	6.04	6.39	6.77	7.21	7.70	8.27	8.93	9.71	10.6	11.8	13.2	15.0	17.5	20.9	26.0		18
19	5.70	6.01	6.35	6.73	7.16	7.64	8.21	8.86	9.64	10.6	11.7	13.1	14.9	17.3	20.7	25.7	19
20	5.39	5.67	5.97	6.30	6.68	7.10	7.58	8.14	8.79	9.55	10.5	11.6	13.0	14.8	17.1	20.4	20
21	5.12	5.36	5.63	5.92	6.25	6.63	7.04	7.52	8.07	8.71	9.46	10.4	11.5	12.8	14.6	16.9	21
22	4.86	5.08	5.32	5.58	5.88	6.20	6.57	6.98	7.45	7.99	8.62	9.37	10.3	11.3	12.7	14.4	22
23	4.63	4.82	5.04·	5.28	5.54	5.83	6.15	6.51	6.92	7.38	7.91	8.53	9.27	10.1	11.2	12.5	23
24	4.41	4.59	4.79	5.00	5.23	5.49	5.77	6.09	6.44	6.85	7.30	7.83	8.44	9.16	10.0	11.1	24
25	4.21	4.37	4.55	4.74	4.95	5.18	5.44	5.72	6.03	6.38	6.77	7.22	7.74	8.34	9.05	9.90	25
26	4.03	4.18	4.34	4.51	4.70	4.91	5.13	5.38	5.66	5.96	6.31	6.69	7.14	7.64	8.24	8.93	26
27	3.85	3.99	4.14	4.30	4.47	4.65	4.86	5.08	5.32	5.59	5.89	6.23	6.61	7.05	7.55	8.13	27
28	3.69	3.82	3.95	4.10	4.25	4.42	4.60	4.80	5.02	5.26	5.53	5.82	6.15	6.53	6.95	7.44	28
29	3.54	3.66	3.78	3.91	4.05	4.21	4.37	4.55	4.75	4.96	5.19	5.46	5.75	6.07	6.44	6.86	29
30	3.40	3.51	3.62	3.74	3.87	4.01	4.16	4.32	4.50	4.69	4.90	5.13	5.38	5.67	5.99	6.35	30
31	3.27	3.37	3.47	3.58	3.70	3.82	3.96	4.11	4.27	4.44	4.63	4.83	5.06	5.31	5.56	5.90	31
32	3.14	3.23	3.33	3.43	3.54	3.65	3.78	3.91	4.05	4.21	4.38	4.56	4.76	4.98	5.23	5.50	32
33	3.02	3.11	3.20	3.29	3.39	3.49	3.61	3.73	3.86	4.00	4.15	4.32	4.49	4.69	4.91	5.15	33
34	2.91	2.99	3.07	3.16	3.25	3.34	3.45	3.56	3.68	3.80	3.94	4.09	4.25	4.43	4.62	4.83	34
35	2.80	2.88	2.95	3.03	3.12	3.20	3.30	3.40	3.51	3.62	3.75	3.88	4.03	4.18	4.35	4.54	35
36	2.70	2.77	2.84	2.91	2.99	3.07	3.16	3.25	3.35	3.46	3.57	3.69	3.82	3.96	4.11	4.28	36
37	2.61	2.67	2.73	2.80	2.87	2.95	3.03	3.11	3.20	3.30	3.40	3.51	3.63	3.76	3.89	4.04	37
38	2.51	2.57	2.63	2.69	2.76	2.83	2.90	2.98	3.06	3.15	3.25	3.35	3.45	3.57	3.69	3.82	38
39	2.42	2.48	2.53	2.59	2.65	2.72	2.79	2.86	2.93	3.01	3.10	3.19	3.29	3.39	3.50	3.62	39
40	2.34	2.39	2.44	2.50	2.55	2.61	2.68	2.74	2.81	2.88	2.96	3.05	3.13	3.23	3.33	3.44	40
41	2.26	2.31	2.35	2.40	2.46	2.51	2.57	2.63	2.69	2.76	2.83	2.91	2.99	3.08	3.17	3.27	41
42	2.18	2.22	2.27	2.32	2.36	2.42	2.47	2.53	2.58	2.65	2.71	2.78	2.85	2.93	3.02	3.10	42
43	2.11	2.15	2.19	2.23	2.28	2.32	2.37	2.42	2.48	2.54	2.60	2.66	2.73	2.80	2.87	2.95	43
44	2.03	2.07	2.11	2.15	2.19	2.24	2.28	2.33	2.38	2.43	2.49	2.55	2.61	2.67	2.74	2.81	44
45	1.96	2.00	2.03	2.07	2.11	2.15	2.19	2.24	2.28	2.33	2.38	2.44	2.49	2.55	2.62	2.68	45
46	1.90	1.93	1.96	2.00	2.03	2.07	2.11	2.15	2.19	2.24	2.29	2.33	2.39	2.44	2.50	2.56	46
47	1.83	1.86	1.89	1.93	1.96	1.99	2.03	2.07	2.11	2.15	2.19	2.24	2.28	2.33	2.39	2.44	47
48	1.77	1.80	1.83	1.86	1.89	1.92	1.95	1.99	2.02	2.06	2.10	2.14	2.19	2.23	2.28	2.33	48
49	1.71	1.73	1.76	1.79	1.82	1.85	1.88	1.91	1.94	1.98	2.02	2.05	2.09	2.13	2.18	2.23	49
50	1.65	1.67	1.70	1.72	1.75	1.78	1.81	1.84	1.87	1.90	1.93	1.97	2.01	2.04	2.08	2.13	50
51	1.59	1.61	1.64	1.66	1.69	1.71	1.74	1.77	1.79	1.82	1.85	1.89	1.92	1.96	1.99	2.03	51
52	1.53	1.56	1.58	1.60	1.62	1.65	1.67	1.70	1.72	1.75	1.78	1.81	1.84	1.87	1.91	1.94	52
53	1.48	1.50	1.52	1.54	1.56	1.58	1.61	1.63	1.65	1.68	1.71	1.73	1.76	1.79	1.82	1.85	53
54	1.43	1.44	1.46	1.48	1.50	1.52	1.54	1.57	1.59	1.61	1.64	1.66	1.69	1.71	1.74	1.77	54
55	1.37	1.39	1.41	1.43	1.45	1.46	1.48	1.50	1.52	1.55	1.57	1.59	1.62	1.64	1.67	1.69	55
56	1.32	1.34	1.36	1.37	1.39	1.41	1.43	1.44	1.46	1.48	1.50	1.52	1.55	1.57	1.59	1.62	56
57	1.28	1.29	1.30	1.32	1.34	1.35	1.37	1.39	1.40	1.42	1.44	1.46	1.48	1.50	1.52	1 54	57
58	1.23	1.24	1.25	1.27	1.28	1.30	1.31	1.33	1.35	1.36	1.38	1.40	1.41	1.43	1.45	1.47	58
59	1.18	1.19	1.21	1.22	1.23	1.25	1.26	1.27	1.29	1.30	1.32	1.34	1.35	1.37	1.39	1.41	59
60	1.13	1.15	1.16	1.17	1.18	1.19	1.21	1.22	1.23	1.25	1.26	1.28	1.29	1.31	1.32	1.34	60
61	1.09	1.10	1.11	1.12	1.13	1.14	1.16	1.17	1.18	1.19	1.21	1.22	1.23	1.25	1.26	1.28	61
62	1.04	1.05	1.06	1.07	1.08	1.09	1.11	1.12	1.13	1.14	1.15	1.16	1.18	1.19	1.20	1.22	62
63	1.00	1.01	1.02	1.03	1.04	1.05	1.06	1.07	1.08	1.09	1.10	1.11	1.12	1.13	1.15	1.16	63

| | 0° | 1° | 2° | 3° | 4° | 5° | 6° | 7° | 8° | 9° | 10° | 11° | 12° | 13° | 14° | 15° | |

Table 21

LATITUDE, SAME name as declination

Dec.	15°	16°	17°	18°	19°	20°	21°	22°	23°	24°	25°	26°	27°	28°	29°	30°	Dec.
0°	7.33	6.85	6.42	6.04	5.70	5.39	5.12	4.86	4.63	4.41	4.21	4.03	3.85	3.69	3.54	3.40	0°
1	7.84	7.29	6.81	6.39	6.01	5.67	5.36	5.08	4.82	4.59	4.37	4.18	3.99	3.82	3.66	3.51	1
2	8.43	7.80	7.25	6.77	6.35	5.97	5.63	5.32	5.04	4.79	4.55	4.34	4.14	3.95	3.78	3.62	2
3	9.11	8.38	7.75	7.21	6.73	6.30	5.92	5.58	5.28	5.00	4.74	4.51	4.30	4.10	3.91	3.74	3
4	9.92	9.06	8.33	7.70	7.16	6.68	6.25	5.88	5.54	5.23	4.95	4.70	4.47	4.25	4.05	3.87	4
5	10.9	9.85	9.00	8.27	7.64	7.10	6.63	6.20	5.83	5.49	5.18	4.91	4.65	4.42	4.21	4.01	5
6	12.1	10.8	9.79	8.93	8.21	7.58	7.04	6.57	6.15	5.77	5.44	5.13	4.86	4.60	4.37	4.16	6
7	13.5	12.0	10.7	9.71	8.86	8.14	7.52	6.98	6.51	6.09	5.72	5.38	5.08	4.80	4.55	4.32	7
8	15.4	13.4	11.9	10.6	9.64	8.79	8.07	7.45	6.92	6.44	6.03	5.66	5.32	5.02	4.75	4.50	8
9	17.9	15.3	13.3	11.8	10.6	9.55	8.71	7.99	7.38	6.85	6.38	5.96	5.59	5.26	4.96	4.69	9
10	21.4	17.8	15.2	13.2	11.7	10.5	9.46	8.62	7.91	7.30	6.77	6.31	5.89	5.53	5.19	4.90	10
11	26.7	21.3	17.6	15.0	13.1	11.6	10.4	9.37	8.53	7.83	7.22	6.69	6.23	5.82	5.46	5.13	11
12		26.5	21.1	17.5	14.9	13.0	11.5	10.3	9.27	8.44	7.74	7.14	6.61	6.15	5.75	5.38	12
13			26.2	20.9	17.3	14.8	12.8	11.3	10.1	9.16	8.34	7.64	7.05	6.53	6.07	5.67	13
14				26.0	20.7	17.1	14.6	12.7	11.2	10.0	9.05	8.24	7.55	6.95	6.44	5.99	14
15					25.7	20.4	16.9	14.4	12.5	11.1	9.90	8.93	8.13	7.44	6.86	6.35	15
16						25.4	20.2	16.7	14.3	12.4	10.9	9.77	8.81	8.02	7.34	6.76	16
17							25.1	20.0	16.5	14.1	12.2	10.8	9.63	8.69	7.90	7.23	17
18								24.8	19.7	16.3	13.9	12.1	10.6	9.50	8.56	7.78	18
19	25.7								24.5	19.5	16.1	13.7	11.9	10.5	9.35	8.43	19
20	20.4	25.4								24.2	19.2	15.9	13.5	11.7	10.3	9.20	20
21	16.9	20.2	25.1								23.8	18.9	15.6	13.3	11.5	10.1	21
22	14.4	16.7	20.0	24.8								23.5	18.1	15.4	13.1	11.3	22
23	12.5	14.3	16.5	19.7	24.5								23.1	18.3	15.1	12.8	23
24	11.1	12.4	14.1	16.3	19.5	24.2								22.7	18.0	14.9	24
25	9.90	10.9	12.2	13.9	16.1	19.2	23.8								22.3	17.7	25
26	8.93	9.77	10.8	12.1	13.7	15.9	18.9	23.5	23.1						21.9		26
27	8.13	8.81	9.63	10.6	11.9	13.5	15.6	18.6	23.1								27
28	7.44	8.02	8.69	9.50	10.5	11.7	13.3	15.4	18.3	22.7							28
29	6.86	7.34	7.90	8.56	9.35	10.3	11.5	13.1	15.1	18.0	22.3						29
30	6.35	6.76	7.23	7.78	8.43	9.20	10.1	11.3	12.8	14.9	17.7	21.9					30
31	5.90	6.25	6.65	7.12	7.65	8.29	9.05	10.0	11.1	12.6	14.6	17.4	21.5				31
32	5.50	5.81	6.15	6.55	7.00	7.53	8.15	8.89	9.80	10.9	12.4	14.3	17.0	21.1			32
33	5.15	5.41	5.71	6.05	6.44	6.88	7.39	8.00	8.73	9.62	10.7	12.1	14.0	16.7	20.6		33
34	4.83	5.06	5.32	5.61	5.95	6.32	6.76	7.26	7.85	8.56	9.43	10.5	11.9	13.8	16.3	20.2	34
35	4.54	4.75	4.98	5.23	5.52	5.84	6.21	6.63	7.12	7.70	8.39	9.24	10.3	11.7	13.5	16.0	35
36	4.28	4.46	4.67	4.89	5.14	5.42	5.73	6.09	6.50	6.98	7.54	8.22	9.05	10.1	11.4	13.2	36
37	4.04	4.21	4.38	4.58	4.80	5.04	5.31	5.62	5.97	6.37	6.84	7.39	8.05	8.85	9.85	11.1	37
38	3.82	3.97	4.13	4.30	4.49	4.70	4.94	5.20	5.50	5.84	6.23	6.69	7.23	7.87	8.65	9.63	38
39	3.62	3.75	3.90	4.05	4.22	4.40	4.61	4.84	5.10	5.39	5.72	6.10	6.54	7.06	7.69	8.45	39
40	3.44	3.55	3.68	3.82	3.97	4.13	4.31	4.51	4.74	4.99	5.27	5.59	5.96	6.39	6.90	7.50	40
41	3.27	3.37	3.48	3.61	3.74	3.89	4.04	4.22	4.41	4.63	4.87	5.15	5.46	5.82	6.23	6.73	41
42	3.10	3.20	3.30	3.41	3.53	3.66	3.80	3.96	4.13	4.31	4.52	4.76	5.02	5.33	5.67	6.08	42
43	2.95	3.04	3.13	3.23	3.34	3.45	3.58	3.72	3.86	4.03	4.21	4.41	4.64	4.90	5.19	5.53	43
44	2.81	2.89	2.98	3.06	3.16	3.26	3.37	3.50	3.63	3.77	3.93	4.11	4.30	4.52	4.77	5.06	44
45	2.68	2.75	2.83	2.91	2.99	3.09	3.19	3.29	3.41	3.54	3.68	3.83	4.00	4.20	4.41	4.65	45
46	2.56	2.62	2.69	2.76	2.84	2.92	3.01	3.11	3.21	3.33	3.45	3.58	3.73	3.90	4.08	4.29	46
47	2.44	2.50	2.56	2.63	2.69	2.77	2.85	2 94	3.03	3.13	3.25	3.36	3.49	3.63	3.79	3.97	47
48	2.33	2.38	2.44	2.50	2.56	2.63	2.70	2.78	2.86	2.95	3.05	3.15	3.27	3.39	3.53	3.68	48
49	2.23	2.27	2.32	2.38	2.44	2.50	2.56	2.63	2.70	2.78	2.88	2.97	3.06	3.17	3.29	3.43	49
50	2.13	2.17	2.22	2.27	2.32	2.37	2.43	2.49	2.56	2.63	2.71	2.79	2.88	2.97	3.08	3.20	50
51	2.03	2.07	2.11	2.16	2.20	2.25	2.31	2.36	2.42	2.49	2.56	2.63	2.71	2.79	2.89	2.99	51
52	1.94	1.98	2.02	2.06	2.10	2.14	2.19	2.24	2.30	2.35	2.41	2.48	2.55	2.62	2.71	2.79	52
53	1.85	1.89	1.92	1.96	2.00	2.04	2.08	2.13	2.18	2.23	2.27	2.34	2.40	2.47	2.54	2.62	53
54	1.77	1.80	1.83	1.87	1.90	1.94	1.98	2.02	2.06	2.11	2.16	2.21	2.27	2.32	2.39	2.46	54
55	1.69	1.72	1.75	1.78	1.81	1.85	1.88	1.92	1.96	2.00	2.03	2.09	2.14	2.19	2.25	2.31	55
56	1.62	1.64	1.67	1.70	1.73	1.76	1.79	1.82	1.86	1.89	1.93	1.97	2.02	2.06	2.11	2.17	56
57	1.54	1.57	1.59	1.62	1.64	1.67	1.70	1.73	1.76	1.79	1.82	1.87	1.91	1.95	1.99	2.04	57
58	1.47	1.49	1.52	1.54	1.56	1.59	1.61	1.64	1.67	1.70	1.73	1.76	1.80	1.84	1.88	1.92	58
59	1.41	1.43	1.45	1.47	1.49	1.51	1.53	1.56	1.58	1.61	1.63	1.67	1.70	1.73	1.77	1.81	59
60	1.34	1.36	1.38	1.40	1.42	1.44	1.46	1.48	1.50	1.53	1.55	1.58	1.61	1.64	1.67	1.70	60
61	1.28	1.29	1.31	1.33	1.35	1.36	1.38	1.40	1.42	1.45	1.46	1.49	1.52	1.54	1.57	1.60	61
62	1.22	1.23	1.25	1.26	1.28	1.29	1.31	1.33	1.35	1.37	1.39	1.41	1.43	1.46	1.48	1.51	62
63	1.16	1.17	1.19	1.20	1.21	1.23	1.24	1.26	1.28	1.29	1.31	1.33	1.35	1.37	1.39	1.42	63
	15°	16°	17°	18°	19°	20°	21°	22°	23°	24°	25°	26°	27°	28°	29°	30°	

Table 21

EX-MERIDIAN   Containing Values of **F** (Ex-Meridian Factor)   Table I

Dec.	LATITUDE, **SAME** name as declination																Dec.
	30°	31°	32°	33°	34°	35°	36°	37°	38°	39°	40°	41°	42°	43°	44°	45°	
0°	3.40	3.27	3.14	3.02	2.91	2.80	2.70	2.61	2.51	2.42	2.34	2.26	2.18	2.11	2.03	1.96	0°
1	3.51	3.37	3.23	3.11	2.99	2.88	2.77	2.67	2.57	2.48	2.39	2.31	2.22	2.15	2.07	2.00	1
2	3.62	3.47	3.33	3.20	3.07	2.95	2.84	2.73	2.63	2.53	2.44	2.35	2.27	2.19	2.11	2.03	2
3	3.74	3.58	3.43	3.29	3.16	3.03	2.91	2.80	2.69	2.59	2.50	2.40	2.32	2.23	2.15	2.07	3
4	3.87	3.70	3.54	3.39	3.25	3.12	2.99	2.87	2.76	2.65	2.55	2.46	2.36	2.28	2.19	2.11	4
5	4.01	3.82	3.65	3.49	3.34	3.20	3.07	2.95	2.83	2.72	2.61	2.51	2.42	2.32	2.24	2.15	5
6	4.16	3.96	3.78	3.61	3.45	3.30	3.16	3.03	2.90	2.79	2.68	2.57	2.47	2.37	2.28	2.19	6
7	4.32	4.11	3.91	3.73	3.56	3.40	3.25	3.11	2.98	2.86	2.74	2.63	2.53	2.42	2.33	2.24	7
8	4.50	4.27	4.05	3.86	3.68	3.51	3.35	3.20	3.06	2.93	2.81	2.69	2.58	2.48	2.38	2.28	8
9	4.69	4.44	4.21	4.00	3.80	3.62	3.46	3.30	3.15	3.01	2.88	2.76	2.65	2.54	2.43	2.33	9
10	4.90	4.63	4.38	4.15	3.94	3.75	3.57	3.40	3.25	3.10	2.96	2.83	2.71	2.60	2.49	2.38	10
11	5.13	4.83	4.56	4.32	4.09	3.88	3.69	3.51	3.35	3.19	3.05	2.91	2.78	2.66	2.55	2.44	11
12	5.38	5.06	4.76	4.49	4.25	4.03	3.82	3.63	3.45	3.29	3.13	2.99	2.85	2.73	2.61	2.49	12
13	5.67	5.31	4.98	4.69	4.43	4.18	3.96	3.76	3.57	3.39	3.23	3.08	2.93	2.80	2.67	2.55	13
14	5.99	5.56	5.23	4.91	4.62	4.35	4.11	3.89	3.69	3.50	3.33	3.17	3.02	2.87	2.74	2.62	14
15	6.35	5.90	5.50	5.15	4.83	4.54	4.28	4.04	3.82	3.62	3.44	3.27	3.10	2.95	2.81	2.68	15
16	6.76	6.25	5.81	5.41	5.06	4.75	4.46	4.21	3.97	3.75	3.55	3.37	3.20	3.04	2.89	2.75	16
17	7.23	6.65	6.15	5.71	5.32	4.98	4.67	4.38	4.13	3.90	3.68	3.48	3.30	3.13	2.98	2.83	17
18	7.78	7.12	6.55	6.05	5.61	5.23	4.89	4.58	4.30	4.05	3.82	3.61	3.41	3.23	3.06	2.91	18
19	8.43	7.65	7.00	6.44	5.95	5.52	5.14	4.80	4.49	4.22	3.97	3.74	3.53	3.34	3.16	2.99	19
20	9.20	8.29	7.53	6.88	6.32	5.84	5.42	5.04	4.70	4.40	4.13	3.89	3.66	3.45	3.26	3.09	20
21	10.1	9.05	8.15	7.39	6.76	6.21	5.73	5.31	4.94	4.61	4.31	4.04	3.80	3.58	3.37	3.19	21
22	11.3	10.0	8.89	8.00	7.26	6.63	6.09	5.62	5.20	4.84	4.51	4.22	3.96	3.72	3.50	3.29	22
23	12.8	11.1	9.80	8.73	7.85	7.12	6.50	5.97	5.50	5.10	4.74	4.41	4.13	3.86	3.63	3.41	23
24	14.9	12.6	10.9	9.62	8.56	7.70	6.98	6.37	5.84	5.39	4.99	4.63	4.31	4.03	3.77	3.54	24
25	17.7	14.6	12.4	10.7	9.43	8.39	7.54	6.84	6.23	5.72	5.27	4.87	4.52	4.21	3.93	3.68	25
26		17.4	14.3	12.1	10.5	9.24	8.22	7.39	6.69	6.10	5.59	5.15	4.76	4.41	4.11	3.83	26
27			17.0	14.0	11.9	10.3	9.05	8.05	7.23	6.54	5.96	5.46	5.02	4.64	4.30	4.00	27
28				16.7	13.7	11.7	10.1	8.85	7.87	7.06	6.39	5.82	5.33	4.90	4.52	4.20	28
29					16.3	13.5	11.4	9.85	8.65	7.69	6.90	6.23	5.67	5.19	4.77	4.41	29
30						16.0	13.2	11.1	9.63	8.45	7.50	6.73	6.08	5.53	5.06	4.65	30
31							15.6	12.9	10.9	9.40	8.24	7.31	6.56	5.92	5.38	4.92	31
32								15.3	12.6	10.6	9.16	8.03	7.13	6.38	5.76	5.23	32
33									14.9	12.2	10.4	8.93	7.82	6.94	6.21	5.60	33
34										14.5	11.9	10.1	8.69	7.61	6.74	6.03	34
35	16.0										14.1	11.6	9.81	8.45	7.40	6.55	35
36	13.2	15.6										13.8	11.3	9.53	8.21	7.18	36
37	11.1	12.9	15.3										13.4	11.0	9.26	7.97	37
38	9.63	10.9	12.6	14.9										13.0	10.6	8.98	38
39	8.45	9.40	10.6	12.2	14.5										12.6	10.3	39
40	7.50	8.24	9.16	10.4	11.9	14.1										12.2	40
41	6.73	7.31	8.03	8.93	10.1	11.6	13.8										41
42	6.08	6.56	7.13	7.82	8.69	9.81	11.3	13.4									42
43	5.53	5.92	6.38	6.94	7.61	8.45	9.53	11.0	13.0								43
44	5.06	5.38	5.76	6.21	6.74	7.40	8.21	9.26	10.6	12.6							44
45	4.65	4.92	5.23	5.60	6.03	6.55	7.18	7.97	8.98	10.3	12.2						45
46	4.29	4.52	4.78	5.08	5.44	5.86	6.36	6.96	7.72	8.70	10.0	11.8					46
47	3.97	4.16	4.39	4.64	4.93	5.28	5.68	6.16	6.75	7.47	8.42	9.67	11.4				47
48	3.68	3.85	4.04	4.26	4.50	4.78	5.11	5.50	5.96	6.52	7.23	8.14	9.34	11.0			48
49	3.43	3.57	3.74	3.92	4.12	4.36	4.63	4.95	5.31	5.76	6.31	6.98	7.85	9.01	10.6		49
50	3.20	3.32	3.46	3.62	3.80	3.99	4.22	4.48	4.78	5.14	5.57	6.09	6.74	7.57	8.69	10.2	50
51	2.99	3.10	3.22	3.35	3.50	3.67	3.86	4.08	4.33	4.62	4.96	5.37	5.87	6.49	7.29	8.35	51
52	2.79	2.89	3.00	3.11	3.24	3.39	3.55	3.73	3.94	4.18	4.45	4.78	5.17	5.65	6.25	7.01	52
53	2.62	2.70	2.80	2.90	3.01	3.13	3.27	3.42	3.60	3.80	4.02	4.29	4.60	4.98	5.44	6.00	53
54	2.46	2.53	2.61	2.70	2.80	2.90	3.02	3.15	3.30	3.47	3.65	3.87	4.12	4.42	4.78	5.22	54
55	2.31	2.37	2.44	2.52	2.60	2.70	2.79	2.91	3.04	3.18	3.33	3.51	3.72	3.96	4.25	4.59	55
56	2.17	2.23	2.29	2.36	2.43	2.51	2.60	2.69	2.80	2.92	3.05	3.20	3.37	3.57	3.80	4.07	56
57	2.04	2.09	2.15	2.21	2.27	2.34	2.41	2.50	2.59	2.69	2.80	2.93	3.07	3.23	3.42	3.64	57
58	1.92	1.96	2.01	2.06	2.12	2.18	2.25	2.32	2.40	2.48	2.58	2.68	2.80	2.94	3.09	3.27	58
59	1.81	1.85	1.89	1.93	1.98	2.04	2.09	2.16	2.22	2.30	2.38	2.47	2.58	2.68	2.81	2.96	59
60	1.70	1.74	1.77	1.81	1.86	1.90	1.95	2.00	2.07	2.13	2.20	2.28	2.36	2.46	2.56	2.68	60
61	1.60	1.63	1.67	1.70	1.74	1.78	1.82	1.87	1.92	1.97	2.03	2.10	2.17	2.25	2.34	2.44	61
62	1.51	1.53	1.56	1.59	1.63	1.66	1.70	1.74	1.79	1.83	1.89	1.94	2.00	2.07	2.15	2.23	62
63	1.42	1.44	1.47	1.50	1.52	1.56	1.59	1.62	1.66	1.70	1.75	1.80	1.85	1.91	1.97	2.04	63
	30°	31°	32°	33°	34°	35°	36°	37°	38°	39°	40°	41°	42°	43°	44°	45°	

Table 21

LATITUDE, **SAME** name as declination

Dec.	45°	46°	47°	48°	49°	50°	51°	52°	53°	54°	55°	56°	57°	58°	59°	60°	Dec.
0°	1.96	1.90	1.83	1.77	1.71	1.65	1.59	1.53	1.48	1.43	1.37	1.32	1.28	1.23	1.18	1.13	0°
1	2.00	1.93	1.86	1.80	1.73	1.67	1.61	1.56	1.50	1.44	1.39	1.34	1.29	1.24	1.19	1.15	1
2	2.03	1.96	1.89	1.83	1.76	1.70	1.64	1.58	1.52	1.46	1.41	1.36	1.30	1.25	1.21	1.16	2
3	2.07	2.00	1.93	1.86	1.79	1.72	1.66	1.60	1.54	1.48	1.43	1.37	1.32	1.27	1.22	1.17	3
4	2.11	2.03	1.96	1.89	1.82	1.75	1.69	1.62	1.56	1.50	1.45	1.39	1.34	1.28	1.23	1.18	4
5	2.15	2.07	1.99	1.92	1.85	1.78	1.71	1.65	1.58	1.52	1.46	1.41	1.35	1.30	1.25	1.19	5
6	2.19	2.11	2.03	1.95	1.88	1.81	1.74	1.67	1.61	1.54	1.48	1.43	1.37	1.31	1.26	1.21	6
7	2.24	2.15	2.07	1.99	1.91	1.84	1.77	1.70	1.63	1.57	1.50	1.44	1.39	1.33	1.27	1.22	7
8	2.28	2.19	2.11	2.02	1.94	1.87	1.79	1.72	1.65	1.59	1.52	1.46	1.40	1.35	1.29	1.23	8
9	2.33	2.24	2.15	2.06	1.98	1.90	1.82	1.75	1.68	1.61	1.55	1.48	1.42	1.36	1.30	1.25	9
10	2.38	2.29	2.19	2.10	2.02	1.93	1.85	1.78	1.71	1.64	1.57	1.50	1.44	1.38	1.32	1.26	10
11	2.44	2.33	2.24	2.14	2.05	1.97	1.89	1.81	1.73	1.66	1.59	1.52	1.46	1.40	1.34	1.28	11
12	2.49	2.39	2.28	2.19	2.09	2.01	1.92	1.84	1.76	1.69	1.62	1.55	1.48	1.41	1.35	1.29	12
13	2.55	2.44	2.33	2.23	2.13	2.04	1.96	1.87	1.79	1.71	1.64	1.57	1.50	1.43	1.37	1.31	13
14	2.62	2.50	2.39	2.28	2.18	2.08	1.99	1.91	1.82	1.74	1.67	1.59	1.52	1.45	1.39	1.32	14
15	2.68	2.56	2.44	2.33	2.23	2.13	2.03	1.94	1.85	1.77	1.69	1.62	1.54	1.47	1.41	1.34	15
16	2.75	2.62	2.50	2.38	2.27	2.17	2.07	1.98	1.89	1.80	1.72	1.64	1.57	1.49	1.43	1.36	16
17	2.83	2.69	2.56	2.44	2.32	2.22	2.11	2.02	1.92	1.83	1.75	1.67	1.59	1.52	1.45	1.38	17
18	2.91	2.76	2.63	2.50	2.38	2.27	2.16	2.06	1.96	1.87	1.78	1.70	1.62	1.54	1.47	1.40	18
19	2.99	2.84	2.69	2.56	2.44	2.32	2.20	2.10	2.00	1.90	1.81	1.73	1.64	1.56	1.49	1.42	19
20	3.09	2.92	2.77	2.63	2.50	2.37	2.25	2.14	2.04	1.94	1.85	1.76	1.67	1.59	1.51	1.44	20
21	3.19	3.01	2.85	2.70	2.56	2.43	2.31	2.19	2.08	1.98	1.88	1.79	1.70	1.61	1.53	1.46	21
22	3.29	3.11	2.94	2.78	2.63	2.49	2.36	2.24	2.13	2.02	1.92	1.82	1.73	1.64	1.56	1.48	22
23	3.41	3.21	3.03	2.86	2.70	2.56	2.42	2.30	2.18	2.06	1.96	1.86	1.76	1.67	1.58	1.50	23
24	3.54	3.33	3.13	2.95	2.78	2.63	2.49	2.35	2.23	2.11	2.00	1.89	1.79	1.70	1.61	1.53	24
25	3.68	3.45	3.25	3.05	2.88	2.71	2.56	2.41	2.27	2.16	2.03	1.93	1.82	1.73	1.63	1.55	25
26	3.83	3.58	3.36	3.15	2.97	2.79	2.63	2.48	2.34	2.21	2.09	1.97	1.87	1.76	1.67	1.58	26
27	4.00	3.73	3.49	3.27	3.06	2.88	2.71	2.55	2.40	2.27	2.14	2.02	1.91	1.80	1.70	1.61	27
28	4.20	3.90	3.63	3.39	3.17	2.97	2.79	2.62	2.47	2.32	2.19	2.06	1.95	1.84	1.73	1.64	28
29	4.41	4.08	3.79	3.53	3.29	3.08	2.89	2.71	2.54	2.39	2.25	2.11	1.99	1.88	1.77	1.67	29
30	4.65	4.29	3.97	3.68	3.43	3.20	2.99	2.79	2.62	2.46	2.31	2.17	2.04	1.92	1.81	1.70	30
31	4.92	4.52	4.16	3.85	3.57	3.32	3.10	2.89	2.70	2.53	2.37	2.23	2.09	1.96	1.85	1.74	31
32	5.23	4.78	4.39	4.04	3.74	3.46	3.22	3.00	2.80	2.61	2.44	2.29	2.15	2.01	1.89	1.77	32
33	5.60	5.08	4.64	4.26	3.92	3.62	3.35	3.11	2.90	2.70	2.52	2.36	2.21	2.06	1.93	1.81	33
34	6.03	5.44	4.93	4.50	4.12	3.80	3.50	3.24	3.00	2.80	2.60	2.43	2.27	2.12	1.98	1.86	34
35	6.55	5.86	5.28	4.78	4.36	3.99	3.67	3.39	3.13	2.90	2.70	2.51	2.34	2.18	2.04	1.90	35
36	7.18	6.36	5.68	5.11	4.63	4.22	3.86	3.55	3.27	3.02	2.79	2.60	2.41	2.25	2.09	1.95	36
37	7.97	6.96	6.16	5.50	4.95	4.48	4.08	3.73	3.42	3.15	2.91	2.69	2.50	2.32	2.16	2.00	37
38	8.98	7.72	6.75	5.96	5.31	4.78	4.33	3.94	3.60	3.30	3.04	2.80	2.59	2.40	2.22	2.07	38
39	10.3	8.70	7.47	6.52	5.76	5.14	4.62	4.18	3.80	3.47	3.18	2.92	2.69	2.48	2.30	2.13	39
40	12.2	10.0	8.42	7.23	6.31	5.57	4.96	4.45	4.02	3.65	3.33	3.05	2.80	2.58	2.38	2.20	40
41		11.8	9.67	8.14	6.98	6.09	5.37	4.78	4.29	3.87	3.51	3.20	2.93	2.68	2.47	2.28	41
42			11.4	9.34	7.85	6.74	5.87	5.17	4.60	4.12	3.72	3.37	3.07	2.80	2.58	2.36	42
43				11.0	9.01	7.57	6.49	5.65	4.97	4.42	3.96	3.57	3.23	2.94	2.68	2.46	43
44					10.6	8.69	7.29	6.25	5.44	4.78	4.25	3.80	3.42	3.09	2.81	2.56	44
45						10.2	8.35	7.01	6.00	5.22	4.59	4.07	3.64	3.27	2.96	2.68	45
46							9.85	8.03	6.74	5.76	5.00	4.39	3.89	3.48	3.12	2.82	46
47								9.46	7.71	6.46	5.52	4.79	4.20	3.72	3.32	2.98	47
48									9.07	7.39	6.18	5.28	4.57	4.01	3.55	3.16	48
49										8.69	7.07	5.91	5.04	4.36	3.82	3.38	49
50	10.2										8.31	6.75	5.64	4.81	4.16	3.63	50
51	8.35	9.85										7.93	6.44	5.37	4.57	3.96	51
52	7.01	8.03	9.46										7.55	6.13	5.11	4.34	52
53	6.00	6.74	7.71	9.07										7.19	5.88	4.85	53
54	5.22	5.76	6.46	7.39	8.69										6.82	5.52	54
55	4.59	5.00	5.52	6.18	7.07	8.31										6.46	55
56	4.07	4.39	4.79	5.28	5.91	6.75	7.93										56
57	3.64	3.89	4.20	4.57	5.04	5.64	6.44	7.55									57
58	3.27	3.48	3.72	4.01	4.36	4.81	5.37	6.13	7.19								58
59	2.96	3.12	3.32	3.55	3.82	4.16	4.57	5.11	5.88	6.82							59
60	2.68	2.82	2.98	3.16	3.38	3.63	3.96	4.34	4.85	5.52	6.46						60
61	2.44	2.56	2.68	2.83	3.00	3.21	3.45	3.75	4.12	4.59	5.25	6.11					61
62	2.23	2.32	2.43	2.55	2.69	2.85	3.04	3.27	3.55	3.89	4.34	4.98	5.76				62
63	2.04	2.12	2.21	2.30	2.42	2.55	2.71	2.88	3.09	3.35	3.67	4.09	4.69	5.42			63
	45°	46°	47°	48°	49°	50°	51°	52°	53°	54°	55°	56°	57°	58°	59°	60°	

Table 21

EX-MERIDIAN Containing Values of **F** (Ex-Meridian Factor) Table I

LATITUDE, SAME name as declination

Dec.	60°	61°	62°	63°	64°	65°	66°	67°	68°	69°	70°	71°	72°	73°	74°	75°	76°	77°	78°	79°	80°	81°	82°	Dec.
0°	1.13	1.09	1.04	1.00	.96	.92	.87	.83	.79	.75	.71	.68	.64	.60	.56	.53	.49	.45	.42	.38	.35	.31	.28	0°
1	1.15	1.10	1.05	1.01	.97	.92	.88	.84	.80	.76	.72	.68	.64	.60	.57	.53	.49	.46	.42	.38	.35	.31	.28	1
2	1.16	1.11	1.06	1.02	.97	.93	.89	.85	.80	.76	.72	.68	.65	.61	.57	.53	.49	.46	.42	.38	.35	.31	.28	2
3	1.17	1.12	1.07	1.03	.98	.94	.90	.85	.81	.77	.73	.69	.65	.61	.57	.53	.50	.46	.42	.39	.35	.31	.28	3
4	1.18	1.13	1.08	1.04	.99	.95	.90	.86	.82	.77	.73	.69	.65	.61	.57	.54	.50	.46	.42	.39	.35	.31	.28	4
5	1.19	1.14	1.09	1.05	1.00	.95	.91	.87	.82	.78	.74	.70	.66	.62	.58	.54	.50	.46	.43	.39	.35	.32	.28	5
6	1.21	1.16	1.11	1.06	1.01	.96	.92	.87	.83	.79	.74	.70	.66	.62	.58	.54	.50	.46	.43	.39	.35	.32	.28	6
7	1.22	1.17	1.12	1.07	1.02	.97	.92	.88	.83	.79	.75	.71	.66	.62	.58	.54	.51	.47	.43	.39	.35	.32	.28	7
8	1.23	1.18	1.13	1.08	1.03	.98	.93	.89	.84	.80	.75	.71	.67	.63	.59	.55	.51	.47	.43	.39	.36	.32	.28	8
9	1.25	1.19	1.14	1.09	1.04	.99	.94	.89	.85	.80	.76	.72	.67	.63	.59	.55	.51	.47	.43	.39	.36	.32	.28	9
10	1.26	1.21	1.15	1.10	1.05	1.00	.95	.90	.85	.81	.76	.72	.68	.63	.59	.55	.51	.47	.43	.40	.36	.32	.28	10
11	1.28	1.22	1.16	1.11	1.06	1.01	.96	.91	.86	.81	.77	.72	.68	.64	.60	.56	.51	.47	.44	.40	.36	.32	.28	11
12	1.29	1.23	1.18	1.12	1.07	1.02	.97	.92	.87	.82	.77	.73	.69	.64	.60	.56	.52	.48	.44	.40	.36	.32	.28	12
13	1.31	1.25	1.19	1.13	1.08	1.03	.97	.92	.87	.83	.78	.73	.69	.65	.60	.56	.52	.48	.44	.40	.36	.33	.29	13
14	1.32	1.26	1.20	1.15	1.09	1.04	.98	.93	.88	.83	.79	.74	.70	.65	.61	.56	.52	.48	.44	.40	.36	.33	.29	14
15	1.34	1.28	1.22	1.16	1.10	1.05	.99	.94	.89	.84	.79	.75	.70	.65	.61	.57	.52	.48	.44	.40	.36	.33	.29	15
16	1.36	1.30	1.23	1.17	1.11	1.06	1.00	.95	.90	.85	.80	.75	.70	.66	.61	.57	.53	.49	.44	.40	.36	.33	.29	16
17	1.38	1.31	1.25	1.19	1.13	1.07	1.01	.96	.91	.85	.80	.76	.71	.66	.62	.57	.53	.49	.45	.41	.37	.33	.29	17
18	1.40	1.33	1.26	1.20	1.14	1.08	1.02	.97	.91	.86	.81	.76	.71	.67	.62	.58	.53	.49	.45	.41	.37	.33	.29	18
19	1.42	1.35	1.28	1.21	1.15	1.09	1.03	.98	.92	.87	.82	.77	.72	.67	.62	.58	.54	.49	.45	.41	.37	.33	.29	19
20	1.44	1.37	1.29	1.23	1.16	1.10	1.04	.99	.93	.88	.83	.77	.72	.68	.63	.58	.54	.49	.45	.41	.37	.33	.29	20
21	1.46	1.39	1.31	1.24	1.18	1.12	1.05	1.00	.94	.88	.83	.78	.73	.68	.63	.59	.54	.50	.45	.41	.37	.33	.29	21
22	1.48	1.41	1.33	1.26	1.19	1.13	1.07	1.01	.95	.89	.84	.79	.73	.68	.64	.59	.54	.50	.46	.41	.37	.33	.29	22
23	1.50	1.43	1.35	1.28	1.21	1.14	1.08	1.02	.96	.90	.85	.79	.74	.69	.64	.59	.55	.50	.46	.42	.37	.33	.29	23
24	1.53	1.45	1.37	1.30	1.22	1.16	1.09	1.03	.97	.91	.85	.80	.75	.69	.65	.60	.55	.51	.46	.42	.38	.33	.29	24
25	1.55	1.47	1.39	1.31	1.24	1.17	1.10	1.04	.98	.92	.86	.81	.75	.70	.65	.60	.55	.51	.46	.42	.38	.34	.30	25
26	1.58	1.49	1.41	1.33	1.26	1.19	1.12	1.05	.99	.93	.87	.81	.76	.71	.66	.61	.56	.51	.47	.42	.38	.34	.30	26
27	1.61	1.52	1.43	1.35	1.27	1.20	1.13	1.07	1.00	.94	.88	.82	.76	.71	.66	.61	.56	.51	.47	.42	.38	.34	.30	27
28	1.64	1.55	1.46	1.37	1.29	1.22	1.15	1.08	1.01	.95	.89	.83	.77	.72	.66	.61	.56	.52	.47	.43	.38	.34	.30	28
29	1.67	1.57	1.48	1.40	1.31	1.24	1.16	1.09	1.02	.96	.90	.84	.78	.72	.67	.62	.57	.52	.47	.43	.38	.34	.30	29
30	1.70	1.60	1.51	1.42	1.33	1.25	1.18	1.10	1.03	.97	.91	.85	.79	.73	.68	.62	.57	.52	.48	.43	.39	.34	.30	30
31	1.74	1.63	1.53	1.44	1.35	1.27	1.19	1.12	1.05	.98	.92	.85	.79	.74	.68	.63	.58	.53	.48	.43	.39	.34	.30	31
32	1.77	1.67	1.56	1.47	1.38	1.29	1.21	1.14	1.06	1.00	.93	.86	.80	.74	.69	.63	.58	.53	.48	.43	.39	.35	.30	32
33	1.81	1.70	1.59	1.50	1.40	1.32	1.23	1.15	1.08	1.01	.94	.87	.81	.75	.69	.64	.58	.53	.48	.44	.39	.35	.30	33
34	1.86	1.74	1.63	1.53	1.43	1.34	1.25	1.17	1.09	1.02	.95	.88	.82	.76	.70	.64	.59	.54	.49	.44	.39	.35	.30	34
35	1.90	1.78	1.66	1.56	1.45	1.36	1.27	1.19	1.11	1.03	.96	.89	.83	.77	.71	.65	.59	.54	.49	.44	.39	.35	.31	35
36	1.95	1.82	1.70	1.59	1.48	1.39	1.29	1.21	1.12	1.05	.97	.90	.83	.77	.71	.65	.60	.54	.49	.44	.40	.35	.31	36
37	2.00	1.87	1.74	1.62	1.51	1.41	1.32	1.23	1.14	1.06	.98	.91	.84	.78	.72	.66	.60	.55	.50	.45	.40	.35	.31	37
38	2.07	1.92	1.79	1.66	1.55	1.44	1.34	1.25	1.16	1.08	1.00	.93	.86	.79	.73	.67	.61	.55	.50	.45	.40	.35	.31	38
39	2.13	1.97	1.83	1.70	1.58	1.47	1.37	1.27	1.18	1.10	1.01	.94	.87	.80	.74	.67	.61	.56	.50	.45	.40	.36	.31	39
40	2.20	2.03	1.89	1.75	1.62	1.50	1.40	1.29	1.20	1.11	1.03	.95	.88	.81	.75	.68	.62	.56	.51	.46	.41	.36	.31	40
41	2.28	2.10	1.94	1.80	1.66	1.54	1.43	1.32	1.22	1.13	1.05	.97	.89	.82	.76	.69	.63	.57	.51	.46	.41	.36	.31	41
42	2.36	2.17	2.00	1.85	1.71	1.58	1.46	1.35	1.25	1.15	1.06	.98	.90	.84	.77	.69	.63	.57	.52	.46	.41	.36	.32	42
43	2.46	2.25	2.07	1.91	1.76	1.62	1.49	1.38	1.27	1.18	1.08	1.00	.92	.85	.78	.70	.64	.58	.52	.47	.41	.36	.32	43
44	2.56	2.34	2.15	1.97	1.81	1.67	1.53	1.41	1.30	1.20	1.10	1.02	.93	.86	.79	.71	.64	.58	.53	.47	.42	.37	.32	44
45	2.68	2.44	2.23	2.04	1.87	1.72	1.58	1.45	1.33	1.23	1.12	1.04	.95	.87	.80	.72	.65	.59	.53	.47	.42	.37	.32	45
46	2.82	2.55	2.32	2.12	1.93	1.77	1.62	1.49	1.36	1.25	1.15	1.06	.97	.89	.81	.73	.66	.60	.54	.48	.42	.37	.32	46
47	2.98	2.68	2.43	2.21	2.01	1.83	1.67	1.53	1.40	1.28	1.17	1.08	.98	.90	.82	.74	.67	.60	.54	.48	.43	.37	.32	47
48	3.16	2.83	2.55	2.30	2.09	1.90	1.73	1.58	1.44	1.32	1.20	1.10	1.00	.91	.83	.75	.68	.61	.55	.49	.43	.38	.33	48
49	3.38	3.00	2.69	2.42	2.18	1.98	1.79	1.63	1.48	1.35	1.23	1.12	1.02	.93	.84	.76	.69	.62	.55	.49	.43	.38	.33	49
50	3.63	3.21	2.85	2.55	2.29	2.06	1.86	1.69	1.53	1.39	1.26	1.15	1.04	.94	.86	.77	.70	.63	.56	.50	.44	.38	.33	50
51	3.96	3.45	3.04	2.70	2.41	2.16	1.94	1.75	1.58	1.40	1.30	1.18	1.07	.96	.87	.79	.71	.64	.57	.50	.44	.39	.33	51
52	4.34	3.75	3.27	2.88	2.55	2.27	2.03	1.82	1.64	1.48	1.34	1.21	1.09	.99	.89	.80	.72	.65	.57	.51	.45	.39	.34	52
53	4.85	4.12	3.55	3.09	2.71	2.40	2.14	1.91	1.71	1.54	1.38	1.24	1.12	1.01	.91	.82	.73	.66	.58	.52	.45	.39	.34	53
54	5.52	4.59	3.89	3.35	2.91	2.56	2.26	2.00	1.79	1.60	1.43	1.29	1.15	1.04	.93	.83	.75	.67	.59	.52	.46	.40	.34	54
55	6.46	5.25	4.34	3.67	3.16	2.74	2.40	2.12	1.88	1.67	1.49	1.33	1.19	1.07	.95	.85	.76	.68	.60	.53	.46	.40	.35	55
56		6.11	4.93	4.09	3.46	2.97	2.57	2.25	1.98	1.75	1.55	1.38	1.23	1.10	.98	.87	.78	.69	.61	.54	.47	.41	.35	56
57			5.80	4.65			2.78	2.41	2.10	1.84	1.63	1.44	1.28	1.13	1.01	.90	.79	.71	.62	.55	.48	.41	.35	57
58			5.42		4.36	3.61	3.04	2.60	2.24	1.95	1.71	1.51	1.33	1.18	1.04	.92	.81	.72	.63	.56	.48	.42	.36	58
59					5.09	4.09	3.38	2.84	2.42	2.09	1.81	1.58	1.39	1.22	1.08	.95	.84	.74	.65	.57	.49	.42	.36	59
60					4.76		3.82	3.15	2.64	2.25	1.93	1.68	1.46	1.28	1.12	.98	.86	.76	.66	.58	.50	.43	.36	60
61							4.44	3.56	2.90	2.45	2.09	1.78	1.54	1.34	1.17	1.02	.89	.78	.68	.59	.51	.44	.37	61
62							4.13		3.30	2.69	2.27	1.92	1.64	1.41	1.22	1.06	.92	.80	.70	.61	.52	.44	.38	62
63									3.83	3.06	2.48	2.09	1.76	1.50	1.29	1.11	.96	.83	.72	.62	.53	.45	.38	63
64									3.54		2.82	2.28	1.91	1.61	1.37	1.17	1.00	.86	.74	.63	.54	.46	.39	64
68	2.64	2.90	3.30	3.83									2.47		1.94	1.56	1.28	1.06	.88	.74	.61	.51	.42	68
69	2.25	2.45	2.69	3.06	3.54										2.23	1.74	1.40	1.14	.94	.77	.64	.53	.44	69
70	1.93	2.09	2.27	2.48	2.82	3.26										1.99	1.55	1.24	1.00	.82	.67	.55	.45	70
74	1.12	1.17	1.22	1.29	1.37	1.46	1.58	1.74	1.94	2.23											.90	.69	.54	74
75	.98	1.02	1.06	1.11	1.17	1.24	1.19	1.43	1.56	1.74	1.99										1.01	.76	.58	75

| | 60° | 61° | 62° | 63° | 64° | 65° | 66° | 67° | 68° | 69° | 70° | 71° | 72° | 73° | 74° | 75° | 76° | 77° | 78° | 79° | 80° | 81° | 82° | |

Table 21

EX-MERIDIAN   Containing Values of **F** (Ex-Meridian Factor)   Table I

Dec.	LATITUDE, **CONTRARY** name to declination																Dec.
	0°	1°	2°	3°	4°	5°	6°	7°	8°	9°	10°	11°	12°	13°	14°	15°	
0°						22.4	18.7	16.0	14.0	12.4	11.1	10.1	9.24	8.50	7.88	7.33	0°
1					22.5	18.7	16.0	14.0	12.4	11.2	10.1	9.27	8.54	7.91	7.36	6.88	1
2				22.5	18.7	16.0	14.0	12.5	11.2	10.2	9.29	8.56	7.93	7.39	6.91	6.48	2
3			22.5	18.7	16.1	14.0	12.5	11.2	10.2	9.31	8.58	7.96	7.41	6.93	6.51	6.13	3
4		22.5	18.7	16.1	14.0	12.5	11.2	10.2	9.33	8.60	7.97	7.43	6.95	6.53	6.15	5.81	4
5	22.4	18.7	16.0	14.0	12.5	11.2	10.2	9.34	8.61	7.99	7.44	6.97	6.54	6.17	5.83	5.52	5
6	18.7	16.0	14.0	12.5	11.2	10.2	9.39	8.62	7.99	7.45	6.98	6.56	6.18	5.84	5.54	5.26	6
7	16.0	14.0	12.5	11.2	10.2	9.34	8.62	8.00	7.46	6.98	6.56	6.19	5.86	5.55	5.28	5.03	7
8	14.0	12.4	11.2	10.2	9.33	8.61	7.99	7.46	6.99	6.57	6.20	5.86	5.56	5.29	5.04	4.81	8
9	12.4	11.2	10.2	9.31	8.60	7.99	7.45	6.98	6.57	6.20	5.87	5.57	5.29	5.04	4.82	4.61	9
10	11.1	10.1	9.29	8.58	7.97	7.44	6.98	6.56	6.20	5.87	5.57	5.30	5.05	4.82	4.61	4.42	10
11	10.1	9.27	8.56	7.96	7.43	6.97	6.56	6.19	5.86	5.57	5.30	5.05	4.83	4.62	4.43	4 25	11
12	9.24	8.54	7.93	7.41	6.95	6.54	6.18	5.86	5.56	5.29	5.05	4.83	4.62	4.43	4.25	4.09	12
13	8.50	7.91	7.39	6.93	6.53	6.17	5.84	5.55	5.29	5.04	4.82	4.62	4.43	4.25	4.09	3.94	13
14	7.88	7.36	6.91	6.51	6.15	5.83	5.54	5.28	5.04	4.82	4.61	4.43	4.25	4.09	3.94	3.80	14
15	7.33	6.88	6.48	6.13	5.81	5.52	5.26	5.03	4.81	4.61	4.42	4.25	4.09	3.94	3.80	3.66	15
16	6.85	6.45	6.10	5.79	5.51	5.25	5.01	4.79	4.60	4.41	4.24	4.08	3.93	3.79	3.66	3.54	16
17	6.42	6.08	5.76	5.48	5.23	4.99	4.78	4.58	4.40	4.23	4.07	3.93	3.79	3.66	3.54	3.42	17
18	6.04	5.73	5.46	5.20	4.97	4.76	4.57	4.39	4.22	4.06	3.92	3.78	3.65	3.53	3.42	3.31	18
19	5.70	5.43	5.18	4.95	4.74	4.55	4.37	4.20	4.05	3.91	3.77	3.64	3.53	3.41	3.31	3.21	19
20	5.39	5.15	4.92	4.72	4.53	4.35	4.19	4.03	3.89	3.76	3.63	3.52	3.41	3.30	3.20	3.11	20
21	5.12	4.89	4.69	4.50	4.33	4.17	4.02	3.88	3.74	3.62	3.51	3.40	3.29	3.19	3.10	3.01	21
22	4.86	4.66	4.47	4.30	4.14	3.99	3.86	3.73	3.61	3.49	3.38	3.28	3.18	3.09	3.01	2.92	22
23	4.63	4.44	4.27	4.12	3.97	3.84	3.71	3.59	3.48	3.37	3.27	3.17	3.08	3.00	2.91	2.84	23
24	4.41	4.24	4.09	3.95	3.81	3.69	3.57	3.46	3.35	3.25	3.16	3.07	2.99	2.90	2.83	2.75	24
25	4.21	4.06	3.92	3.79	3.66	3.55	3.44	3.33	3.24	3.14	3.06	2.97	2.89	2.82	2.74	2.67	25
26	4.03	3.89	3.76	3.64	3.52	3.41	3.31	3.22	3.13	3.04	2.96	2.88	2.80	2.73	2.66	2.60	26
27	3.85	3.73	3.61	3.49	3.39	3.29	3.19	3.11	3.02	2.94	2.86	2.79	2.72	2.65	2.59	2.53	27
28	3.69	3.58	3.47	3.36	3.26	3.17	3.08	3.00	2.92	2.85	2.77	2.70	2.64	2.57	2.51	2.46	28
29	3.54	3.43	3.33	3.24	3.15	3.06	2.98	2.90	2.83	2.76	2.69	2.62	2.56	2.50	2.44	2.39	29
30	3.40	3.30	3.21	3.12	3.03	2.95	2.88	2.80	2.74	2.67	2.61	2.54	2.49	2.43	2.38	2.32	30
31	3.27	3.18	3.09	3.01	2.93	2.85	2.78	2.71	2.65	2.59	2.53	2.47	2.41	2.36	2.31	2.26	31
32	3.14	3.06	2.98	2.90	2.83	2.76	2.69	2.63	2.57	2.51	2.45	2.40	2.34	2.29	2.25	2.20	32
33	3.02	2.94	2.87	2.80	2.73	2.66	2.60	2.54	2.49	2.43	2.38	2.33	2.28	2.23	2.18	2.14	33
34	2.91	2.84	2.77	2.70	2.64	2.58	2.52	2.46	2.41	2.36	2.31	2.26	2.21	2.17	2.13	2.08	34
35	2.80	2.74	2.67	2.61	2.55	2.49	2.44	2.39	2.34	2.29	2.24	2.19	2.15	2.11	2.07	2.03	35
36	2.70	2.64	2.58	2.52	2.47	2.41	2.36	2.31	2.26	2.22	2.17	2.13	2.09	2.05	2.01	1.97	36
37	2.61	2.55	2.49	2.44	2.38	2.33	2.29	2.24	2.20	2.15	2.11	2.07	2.03	1.99	1.96	1.92	37
38	2.51	2.46	2.41	2.36	2.31	2.26	2.22	2.17	2.13	2.09	2.05	2.01	1.98	1.94	1.91	1.87	38
39	2.42	2.37	2.32	2.28	2.23	2.19	2.15	2.11	2.07	2.03	1.99	1.96	1.92	1.89	1.85	1.82	39
40	2.34	2.29	2.25	2.20	2.16	2.12	2.08	2.04	2.00	1.97	1.93	1.90	1.87	1.83	1.80	1.77	40
41	2.26	2.21	2.17	2.13	2.09	2.05	2.01	1.98	1.94	1.91	1.87	1.84	1.81	1.78	1.75	1.72	41
42	2.18	2.14	2.10	2.06	2.02	1.99	1.95	1.92	1.89	1.85	1.82	1.79	1.76	1.74	1.71	1.68	42
43	2.10	2.07	2.03	1.99	1.96	1.92	1.89	1.86	1.83	1.80	1.77	1.74	1.71	1.69	1.66	1.63	43
44	2.03	2.00	1.96	1.93	1.90	1.86	1.83	1.80	1.77	1.75	1.72	1.69	1.67	1.64	1.62	1.59	44
45	1.96	1.93	1.90	1.87	1.84	1.81	1.78	1.75	1.72	1.70	1.67	1.64	1.62	1.60	1.57	1.55	45
46	1.90	1.86	1.83	1.80	1.78	1.75	1.72	1.70	1.67	1.64	1.62	1.60	1.57	1.55	1.53	1.51	46
47	1.83	1.80	1.77	1.75	1.72	1.69	1.67	1.64	1.62	1.60	1.57	1.55	1.53	1.51	1.49	1.46	47
48	1.77	1.74	1.71	1.69	1.66	1.64	1.62	1.59	1.57	1.55	1.53	1.50	1.48	1.46	1.44	1.42	48
49	1.71	1.68	1.66	1.63	1.61	1.59	1.56	1.54	1.52	1.50	1.48	1.46	1.44	1.42	1.40	1.38	49
50	1.65	1.62	1.60	1.58	1.56	1.53	1.51	1.49	1.47	1.45	1.44	1.42	1.40	1.38	1.36	1.35	50
51	1.59	1.56	1.54	1.52	1.50	1.48	1.46	1.44	1.42	1.41	1.39	1.37	1.36	1.34	1.32	1.31	51
52	1.53	1.51	1.49	1.47	1.45	1.44	1.42	1.40	1.38	1.37	1.35	1.33	1.32	1.30	1.28	1.27	52
53	1.48	1.46	1.44	1.42	1.41	1.39	1.37	1.35	1.34	1.32	1.31	1.29	1.28	1.26	1.25	1.23	53
54	1.43	1.41	1.39	1.37	1.36	1.34	1.32	1.31	1.29	1.28	1.26	1.25	1.24	1.22	1.21	1.19	54
55	1.37	1.36	1.34	1.32	1.31	1.29	1.28	1.26	1.25	1.24	1.22	1.21	1.20	1.18	1.17	1.15	55
56	1.32	1.31	1.29	1.28	1.26	1.25	1.24	1.22	1.21	1.20	1.18	1.17	1.16	1.15	1.13	1.12	56
57	1.28	1.26	1.25	1.23	1.22	1.21	1.19	1.18	1.17	1.16	1.14	1.13	1.12	1.11	1.10	1.09	57
58	1.23	1.21	1.20	1.19	1.18	1.16	1.15	1.14	1.13	1.12	1.11	1.09	1.08	1.07	1.06	1.05	58
59	1.18	1.17	1.16	1.14	1.13	1.12	1.11	1.10	1.09	1.08	1.07	1.06	1.05	1.04	1.03	1.02	59
60	1.13	1.12	1.11	1.10	1.09	1.08	1.07	1.06	1.05	1.04	1.03	1.02	1.01	1.00	.991	.982	60
61	1.09	1.08	1.07	1.06	1.05	1.04	1.03	1.02	1.01	1.00	.991	.983	.974	.965	.956	.948	61
62	1.04	1.03	1.02	1.02	1.01	1.00	.989	.980	.971	.963	.955	.946	.938	.930	.922	.914	62
63	1.00	.992	.983	.974	.966	.958	.950	.942	.934	.926	.918	.910	.903	.895	.888	.880	63
	0°	1°	2°	3°	4°	5°	6°	7°	8°	9°	10°	11°	12°	13°	14°	15°	

Table 21

EX-MERIDIAN Containing Values of **F** (Ex-Meridian Factor) Table I

LATITUDE, CONTRARY name to declination

Dec.	15°	16°	17°	18°	19°	20°	21°	22°	23°	24°	25°	26°	27°	28°	29°	30°	Dec.
0°	7.33	6.85	6.42	6.04	5.70	5.39	5.12	4.86	4.63	4.41	4.21	4.03	3.85	3.69	3.54	3.40	0°
1	6.88	6.45	6.08	5.73	5.43	5.15	4.89	4.66	4.44	4.24	4.06	3.89	3.73	3.58	3.43	3.30	1
2	6.48	6.10	5.76	5.46	5.18	4.92	4.69	4.47	4.27	4.09	3.92	3.76	3.61	3.47	3.33	3.21	2
3	6.13	5.79	5.48	5.20	4.95	4.72	4.50	4.30	4.12	3.95	3.79	3.64	3.49	3.36	3.24	3.12	3
4	5.81	5.51	5.23	4.97	4.74	4.53	4.33	4.14	3.97	3.81	3.66	3.52	3.39	3.26	3.15	3.03	4
5	5.52	5.25	4.99	4.76	4.55	4.35	4.17	3.99	3.84	3.69	3.55	3.41	3.29	3.17	3.06	2.95	5
6	5.26	5.01	4.78	4.57	4.37	4.19	4.02	3.86	3.71	3.57	3.44	3.31	3.19	3.08	2.98	2.88	6
7	5.03	4.79	4.58	4.39	4.20	4.03	3.88	3.73	3.59	3.46	3.33	3.22	3.11	3.00	2.90	2.80	7
8	4.81	4.60	4.40	4.22	4.05	3.89	3.74	3.61	3.48	3.35	3.24	3.13	3.02	2.92	2.83	2.74	8
9	4.61	4.41	4.23	4.06	3.91	3.76	3.62	3.49	3.37	3.25	3.14	3.04	2.94	2.85	2.76	2.67	9
10	4.42	4.24	4.07	3.92	3.77	3.63	3.51	3.38	3.27	3.16	3.06	2.96	2.86	2.77	2.69	2.61	10
11	4.25	4.08	3.93	3.78	3.64	3.52	3.40	3.28	3.17	3.07	2.97	2.88	2.79	2.70	2.62	2.54	11
12	4.09	3.93	3.79	3.65	3.53	3.41	3.29	3.18	3.08	2.99	2.89	2.80	2.72	2.64	2.56	2.49	12
13	3.94	3.79	3.66	3.53	3.41	3.30	3.19	3.09	3.00	2.90	2.82	2.73	2.65	2.57	2.50	2.43	13
14	3.80	3.66	3.54	3.42	3.31	3.20	3.10	3.01	2.91	2.83	2.74	2.66	2.59	2.51	2.44	2.38	14
15	3.66	3.54	3.42	3.31	3.21	3.11	3.01	2.92	2.84	2.75	2.67	2.60	2.53	2.46	2.39	2.32	15
16	3.54	3.42	3.31	3.21	3.11	3.02	2.93	2.84	2.76	2.68	2.61	2.54	2.47	2.40	2.33	2.27	16
17	3.42	3.31	3.21	3.11	3.02	2.93	2.85	2.77	2.69	2.61	2.54	2.47	2.41	2.34	2.28	2.22	17
18	3.31	3.21	3.11	3.02	2.93	2.85	2.77	2.69	2.62	2.55	2.48	2.42	2.35	2.29	2.23	2.18	18
19	3.21	3.11	3.02	2.93	2.85	2.77	2.70	2.62	2.55	2.49	2.42	2.36	2.30	2.24	2.18	2.13	19
20	3.11	3.02	2.93	2.85	2.77	2.70	2.63	2.56	2.49	2.43	2.36	2.31	2.25	2.19	2.14	2.09	20
21	3.01	2.93	2.85	2.77	2.70	2.63	2.56	2.49	2.43	2.37	2.31	2.25	2.20	2.14	2.09	2.04	21
22	2.92	2.84	2.77	2.69	2.62	2.56	2.49	2.43	2.37	2.31	2.26	2.20	2.15	2.10	2.05	2.00	22
23	2.84	2.76	2.69	2.62	2.55	2.49	2.43	2.37	2.31	2.26	2.20	2.15	2.10	2.05	2.01	1.96	23
24	2.75	2.68	2.61	2.55	2.49	2.43	2.37	2.31	2.26	2.21	2.15	2.10	2.06	2.01	1.96	1.92	24
25	2.67	2.61	2.54	2.48	2.42	2.36	2.31	2.26	2.20	2.15	2.11	2.06	2.01	1.96	1.91	1.87	25
26	2.60	2.54	2.47	2.42	2.36	2.31	2.25	2.20	2.15	2.10	2.05	2.01	1.97	1.92	1.88	1.84	26
27	2.53	2.47	2.41	2.35	2.30	2.25	2.20	2.15	2.10	2.06	2.01	1.97	1.93	1.89	1.85	1.81	27
28	2.46	2.40	2.34	2.29	2.24	2.19	2.14	2.10	2.05	2.01	1.97	1.93	1.89	1.85	1.81	1.77	28
29	2.39	2.33	2.28	2.23	2.18	2.14	2.09	2.05	2.01	1.96	1.92	1.88	1.85	1.81	1.77	1.74	29
30	2.32	2.27	2.22	2.18	2.13	2.09	2.04	2.00	1.96	1.92	1.88	1.85	1.81	1.77	1.74	1.70	30
31	2.26	2.21	2.17	2.12	2.08	2.04	1.99	1.95	1.91	1.88	1.84	1.81	1.77	1.73	1.70	1.66	31
32	2.20	2.15	2.11	2.07	2.03	1.99	1.95	1.91	1.87	1.83	1.80	1.76	1.73	1.70	1.67	1.63	32
33	2.14	2.10	2.06	2.02	1.98	1.94	1.90	1.86	1.83	1.79	1.76	1.72	1.69	1.66	1.63	1.60	33
34	2.08	2.04	2.00	1.96	1.93	1.89	1.86	1.82	1.78	1.75	1.72	1.69	1.66	1.63	1.60	1.57	34
35	2.03	1.99	1.95	1.92	1.88	1.85	1.81	1.78	1.75	1.71	1.68	1.65	1.62	1.59	1.57	1.54	35
36	1.97	1.94	1.90	1.87	1.83	1.80	1.77	1.74	1.71	1.68	1.64	1.61	1.58	1.56	1.53	1.51	36
37	1.92	1.89	1.85	1.82	1.79	1.76	1.73	1.70	1.67	1.64	1.60	1.58	1.55	1.53	1.50	1.48	37
38	1.87	1.84	1.81	1.77	1.74	1.71	1.69	1.66	1.63	1.60	1.58	1.55	1.52	1.50	1.47	1.45	38
39	1.82	1.79	1.76	1.73	1.70	1.67	1.64	1.62	1.59	1.56	1.54	1.51	1.49	1.46	1.44	1.42	39
40	1.77	1.74	1.71	1.69	1.66	1.63	1.60	1.58	1.55	1.53	1.50	1.48	1.46	1.43	1.41	1.39	40
41	1.72	1.69	1.67	1.64	1.62	1.59	1.56	1.54	1.51	1.49	1.47	1.45	1.42	1.40	1.38	1.36	41
42	1.68	1.65	1.63	1.60	1.58	1.55	1.53	1.50	1.48	1.46	1.44	1.41	1.39	1.37	1.35	1.33	42
43	1.63	1.61	1.58	1.56	1.54	1.51	1.49	1.47	1.44	1.42	1.40	1.38	1.36	1.34	1.32	1.30	43
44	1.59	1.57	1.54	1.52	1.50	1.48	1.45	1.43	1.41	1.39	1.37	1.35	1.33	1.31	1.29	1.27	44
45	1.55	1.53	1.50	1.48	1.46	1.44	1.42	1.40	1.38	1.36	1.34	1.32	1.30	1.28	1.26	1.24	45
46	1.51	1.48	1.46	1.44	1.42	1.40	1.38	1.36	1.34	1.33	1.31	1.29	1.27	1.25	1.23	1.22	46
47	1.46	1.44	1.42	1.40	1.39	1.37	1.35	1.33	1.31	1.29	1.28	1.26	1.24	1.22	1.21	1.19	47
48	1.42	1.41	1.39	1.37	1.35	1.33	1.31	1.30	1.28	1.26	1.24	1.23	1.21	1.20	1.18	1.16	48
49	1.38	1.37	1.35	1.33	1.31	1.30	1.28	1.26	1.25	1.23	1.22	1.20	1.18	1.17	1.15	1.14	49
50	1.35	1.33	1.31	1.29	1.28	1.26	1.25	1.23	1.21	1.20	1.19	1.17	1.16	1.14	1.13	1.11	50
51	1.31	1.29	1.27	1.26	1.24	1.23	1.21	1.20	1.18	1.17	1.16	1.14	1.13	1.11	1.10	1.08	51
52	1.27	1.25	1.24	1.22	1.21	1.19	1.18	1.17	1.15	1.14	1.13	1.11	1.10	1.09	1.07	1.06	52
53	1.23	1.22	1.20	1.19	1.17	1.16	1.15	1.13	1.12	1.11	1.10	1.08	1.07	1.06	1.04	1.03	53
54	1.19	1.18	1.17	1.15	1.14	1.13	1.11	1.10	1.09	1.08	1.07	1.05	1.04	1.03	1.02	1.00	54
55	1.15	1.14	1.13	1.12	1.10	1.09	1.08	1.07	1.06	1.05	1.04	1.02	1.01	1.00	.990	.979	55
56	1.12	1.11	1.10	1.09	1.07	1.06	1.05	1.04	1.03	1.02	1.01	1.00	.986	.975	.964	.953	56
57	1.09	1.07	1.06	1.05	1.04	1.03	1.02	1.01	1.00	.989	.979	.968	.958	.948	.938		57
58	1.05	1.04	1.03	1.02	1.01	1.00	.990	.980	.970	.960	.950	.940	.931	.921			58
59	1.02	1.01	1.00	.987	.978	.968	.959	.949	.940	.931	.922	.912	.903				59
60	.982	.973	.964	.955	.946	.937	.928	.919	.910	.902	.893	.885					60
61	.948	.939	.931	.922	.914	.906	.898	.889	.881	.873	.865						61
62	.914	.906	.898	.890	.882	.875	.867	.859	.852	.844							62
63	.880	.873	.866	.858	.851	.844	.837	.830	.823								63
	15°	16°	17°	18°	19°	20°	21°	22°	23°	24°	25°	26°	27°	28°	29°	30°	

Table 21

EX-MERIDIAN Containing Values of F (Ex-Meridian Factor) Table I

LATITUDE, CONTRARY* name to declination

Dec.	30°	31°	32°	33°	34°	35°	36°	37°	38°	39°	40°	41°	42°	43°	44°	45°	Dec.
0°	3.40	3.27	3.14	3.02	2.91	2.80	2.70	2.61	2.51	2.42	2.34	2.26	2.18	2.11	2.03	1.96	0°
1	3.30	3.18	3.06	2.94	2.84	2.74	2.64	2.55	2.46	2.37	2.29	2.21	2.14	2.07	2.00	1.93	1
2	3.21	3.09	2.98	2.87	2.77	2.67	2.58	2.49	2.41	2.32	2.25	2.17	2.10	2.03	1.96	1.90	2
3	3.12	3.01	2.90	2.80	2.70	2.61	2.52	2.44	2.36	2.28	2.20	2.13	2.06	1.99	1.93	1.87	3
4	3.03	2.93	2.83	2.73	2.64	2.55	2.47	2.38	2.31	2.23	2.16	2.09	2.02	1.96	1.90	1.84	4
5	2.95	2.85	2.76	2.66	2.58	2.49	2.41	2.33	2.26	2.19	2.12	2.05	1.99	1.92	1.86	1.81	5
6	2.88	2.78	2.69	2.60	2.52	2.44	2.36	2.29	2.22	2.15	2.08	2.02	1.95	1.89	1.83	1.78	6
7	2.80	2.71	2.63	2.54	2.46	2.39	2.31	2.24	2.17	2.11	2.04	1.98	1.92	1.86	1.80	1.75	7
8	2.74	2.65	2.57	2.49	2.41	2.34	2.26	2.20	2.13	2.07	2.00	1.94	1.89	1.83	1.77	1.72	8
9	2.67	2.59	2.51	2.43	2.36	2.29	2.22	2.15	2.09	2.03	1.97	1.91	1.85	1.80	1.75	1.70	9
10	2.61	2.53	2.45	2.38	2.31	2.24	2.17	2.11	2.05	1.99	1.93	1.88	1.82	1.77	1.72	1.67	10
11	2.54	2.47	2.40	2.33	2.26	2.19	2.13	2.07	2.01	1.96	1.90	1.85	1.79	1.74	1.69	1.64	11
12	2.49	2.41	2.34	2.28	2.21	2.15	2.09	2.03	1.98	1.92	1.87	1.81	1.76	1.71	1.67	1.62	12
13	2.43	2.36	2.29	2.23	2.17	2.11	2.05	1.99	1.94	1.89	1.84	1.78	1.74	1.69	1.64	1.60	13
14	2.38	2.31	2.25	2.18	2.13	2.07	2.01	1.96	1.91	1.85	1.80	1.76	1.71	1.66	1.62	1.57	14
15	2.32	2.26	2.20	2.14	2.08	2.03	1.97	1.92	1.87	1.82	1.77	1.73	1.68	1.64	1.59	1.55	15
16	2.27	2.21	2.15	2.10	2.04	1.99	1.94	1.89	1.84	1.79	1.74	1.70	1.65	1.61	1.57	1.53	16
17	2.22	2.17	2.11	2.06	2.00	1.95	1.90	1.85	1.81	1.76	1.72	1.67	1.63	1.59	1.54	1.50	17
18	2.18	2.12	2.07	2.02	1.96	1.92	1.87	1.82	1.77	1.73	1.69	1.64	1.60	1.56	1.52	1.48	18
19	2.13	2.08	2.03	1.98	1.93	1.88	1.83	1.79	1.74	1.70	1.66	1.62	1.58	1.54	1.50	1.46	19
20	2.09	2.04	1.99	1.94	1.89	1.85	1.80	1.76	1.71	1.67	1.63	1.59	1.55	1.51	1.48	1.44	20
21	2.04	1.99	1.95	1.90	1.86	1.81	1.77	1.73	1.69	1.64	1.61	1.57	1.53	1.49	1.45	1.42	21
22	2.00	1.95	1.91	1.86	1.82	1.78	1.74	1.70	1.66	1.62	1.58	1.54	1.51	1.47	1.43	1.40	22
23	1.96	1.91	1.87	1.83	1.78	1.75	1.71	1.67	1.63	1.59	1.55	1.52	1.48	1.45	1.41	1.38	23
24	1.92	1.88	1.83	1.79	1.75	1.71	1.68	1.64	1.60	1.56	1.53	1.49	1.46	1.43	1.39	1.36	24
25	1.87	1.83	1.79	1.75	1.71	1.67	1.64	1.60	1.57	1.53	1.50	1.46	1.43	1.40	1.37	1.33	25
26	1.84	1.80	1.76	1.72	1.68	1.65	1.61	1.58	1.54	1.51	1.48	1.44	1.41	1.38	1.35	1.32	26
27	1.81	1.77	1.73	1.69	1.65	1.62	1.58	1.55	1.52	1.49	1.46	1.42	1.39	1.36	1.33	1.30	27
28	1.77	1.73	1.70	1.66	1.63	1.59	1.56	1.53	1.49	1.46	1.43	1.40	1.37	1.34	1.31	1.28	28
29	1.74	1.70	1.67	1.63	1.60	1.57	1.53	1.50	1.47	1.44	1.41	1.38	1.35	1.32	1.29	1.26	29
30	1.70	1.66	1.63	1.60	1.57	1.54	1.51	1.48	1.45	1.42	1.39	1.36	1.33	1.30	1.27	1.24	30
31	1.66	1.63	1.60	1.57	1.54	1.51	1.48	1.45	1.42	1.39	1.36	1.33	1.31	1.28	1.25	1.22	31
32	1.63	1.60	1.57	1.54	1.51	1.48	1.45	1.42	1.40	1.37	1.34	1.31	1.29	1.26	1.23	1.21	32
33	1.60	1.57	1.54	1.51	1.48	1.45	1.43	1.40	1.37	1.35	1.32	1.29	1.27	1.24	1.22	1.19	33
34	1.57	1.54	1.51	1.48	1.46	1.43	1.40	1.38	1.35	1.33	1.30	1.27	1.24	1.22	1.19	1.17	34
35	1.54	1.51	1.48	1.46	1.43	1.40	1.38	1.35	1.33	1.30	1.28	1.25	1.23	1.20	1.18	1.15	35
36	1.51	1.48	1.45	1.43	1.40	1.38	1.35	1.33	1.30	1.29	1.26	1.23	1.21	1.19	1.17	1.14	36
37	1.48	1.45	1.42	1.40	1.38	1.35	1.33	1.30	1.28	1.26	1.24	1.21	1.19	1.17	1.15	1.12	37
38	1.45	1.42	1.40	1.37	1.35	1.33	1.30	1.28	1.26	1.23	1.21	1.19	1.17	1.15	1.12	1.10	38
39	1.42	1.40	1.37	1.35	1.33	1.30	1.28	1.25	1.24	1.22	1.19	1.17	1.15	1.13	1.11	1.08	39
40	1.39	1.36	1.34	1.32	1.30	1.27	1.25	1.23	1.21	1.19	1.17	1.15	1.13	1.11	1.09	1.07	40
41	1.36	1.33	1.31	1.29	1.27	1.25	1.23	1.21	1.19	1.17	1.15	1.13	1.11	1.09	1.07	1.05	41
42	1.33	1.31	1.29	1.27	1.25	1.23	1.21	1.19	1.17	1.15	1.13	1.11	1.09	1.07	1.05		42
43	1.30	1.28	1.26	1.24	1.22	1.20	1.19	1.17	1.15	1.13	1.11	1.09	1.07	1.05			43
44	1.27	1.26	1.24	1.22	1.20	1.18	1.17	1.15	1.13	1.11	1.09	1.07	1.05				44
45	1.24	1.23	1.21	1.19	1.18	1.16	1.14	1.12	1.11	1.09	1.07	1.05					45
46	1.22	1.20	1.18	1.17	1.15	1.14	1.12	1.10	1.08	1.07	1.05						46
47	1.19	1.17	1.16	1.14	1.13	1.11	1.10	1.08	1.06	1.05							47
48	1.16	1.15	1.13	1.12	1.10	1.09	1.07	1.05	1.04								48
49	1.14	1.12	1.11	1.09	1.08	1.07	1.05	1.03								.92	49
50	1.11	1.10	1.09	1.07	1.06	1.04	1.03								.91	.90	50
51	1.08	1.07	1.06	1.05	1.03	1.02								.91	.89	.88	51
52	1.06	1.04	1.03	1.02	1.01								.90	.88	.87	.86	52
53	1.03	1.02	1.01	1.00								.90	.88	.87	.86	.84	53
54	1.00	.99	.98								.89	.88	.86	.85	.84	.83	54
55	.97	.96								.88	.87	.85	.84	.83	.82	.81	55
56	.95								.87	.86	.84	.83	.82	.81	.80	.79	56
57								.86	.84	.83	.82	.81	.80	.79	.78	.77	57
58							.84	.83	.82	.81	.80	.79	.78	.77	.76	.76	58
59						.83	.82	.81	.79	.79	.78	.78	.77	.76	.75	.74	59
60					.81	.80	.79	.79	.78	.77	.77	.76	.75	.74	.73	.72	60
61				.80	.79	.78	.77	.77	.76	.76	.75	.74	.73	.72	.71	.70	61
62			.78	.77	.76	.75	.75	.74	.74	.73	.72	.71	.70	.69	.68	.68	62
63		.76	.76	.75	.74	.74	.73	.73	.72	.71	.70	.69	.68	.67	.66	.66	63
	30°	31°	32°	33°	34°	35°	36°	37°	38°	39°	40°	41°	42°	43°	44°	45°	

*The figures in the lower portion of the table pertain to Ex-Meridians BELOW POLE, in which case Lat. and Dec. will be of SAME name, and the reduction SUBTRACTIVE to the true altitude to get the meridian altitude: but ADDITIVE to the calculated meridian altitude to get the calculated altitude at the instant the sight was taken.

Table 21

EX-MERIDIAN   Containing Values of **F** (Ex-Meridian Factor)   Table I

LATITUDE, CONTRARY* name to declination

Dec.	45°	46°	47°	48°	49°	50°	51°	52°	53°	54°	55°	56°	57°	58°	59°	60°	Dec.
0°	1.96	1.90	1.83	1.77	1.71	1.65	1.59	1.53	1.48	1.43	1.37	1.32	1.28	1.23	1.18	1.13	0°
1	1.93	1.86	1.80	1.74	1.68	1.62	1.57	1.51	1.46	1.41	1.36	1.31	1.26	1.21	1.17	1.12	1
2	1.90	1.83	1.77	1.71	1.66	1.60	1.55	1.49	1.44	1.39	1.34	1.29	1.25	1.20	1.16	1.11	2
3	1.87	1.80	1.75	1.69	1.63	1.58	1.53	1.47	1.42	1.37	1.33	1.28	1.23	1.19	1.14	1.10	3
4	1.84	1.78	1.72	1.66	1.61	1.56	1.50	1.45	1.41	1.36	1.31	1.26	1.22	1.18	1.13	1.09	4
5	1.81	1.75	1.69	1.64	1.59	1.53	1.48	1.44	1.39	1.34	1.30	1.25	1.21	1.16	1.12	1.08	5
6	1.78	1.72	1.67	1.62	1.56	1.51	1.47	1.42	1.37	1.33	1.28	1.24	1.19	1.15	1.11	1.07	6
7	1.75	1.70	1.64	1.59	1.54	1.49	1.45	1.40	1.35	1.31	1.27	1.22	1.18	1.14	1.10	1.06	7
8	1.72	1.67	1.62	1.57	1.52	1.47	1.43	1.38	1.34	1.29	1.25	1.21	1.17	1.13	1.09	1.05	8
9	1.70	1.64	1.60	1.55	1.50	1.45	1.41	1.37	1.32	1.28	1.24	1.20	1.16	1.12	1.08	1.04	9
10	1.67	1.62	1.57	1.53	1.48	1.44	1.39	1.35	1.31	1.26	1.22	1.18	1.14	1.11	1.07	1.03	10
11	1.64	1.60	1.55	1.50	1.46	1.42	1.37	1.33	1.29	1.25	1.21	1.17	1.13	1.09	1.06	1.02	11
12	1.62	1.57	1.53	1.48	1.44	1.40	1.36	1.32	1.28	1.24	1.20	1.16	1.12	1.08	1.05	1.01	12
13	1.60	1.55	1.51	1.46	1.42	1.38	1.34	1.30	1.26	1.22	1.18	1.15	1.11	1.07	1.04	1.00	13
14	1.57	1.53	1.49	1.44	1.40	1.36	1.32	1.28	1.25	1.21	1.17	1.13	1.10	1.06	1.03	.991	14
15	1.55	1.51	1.46	1.42	1.38	1.35	1.31	1.27	1.23	1.19	1.16	1.12	1.09	1.05	1.02	.982	15
16	1.53	1.48	1.44	1.41	1.37	1.33	1.29	1.25	1.22	1.18	1.14	1.11	1.07	1.04	1.01	.973	16
17	1.50	1.46	1.42	1.39	1.35	1.31	1.27	1.24	1.20	1.17	1.13	1.10	1.06	1.03	1.00	.964	17
18	1.48	1.44	1.40	1.37	1.33	1.29	1.26	1.22	1.19	1.15	1.12	1.09	1.05	1.02	.987	.955	18
19	1.46	1.42	1.39	1.35	1.31	1.28	1.24	1.21	1.17	1.14	1.11	1.07	1.04	1.01	.978	.946	19
20	1.44	1.40	1.37	1.33	1.30	1.26	1.23	1.19	1.16	1.13	1.10	1.06	1.03	1.00	.968	.937	20
21	1.42	1.38	1.35	1.31	1.28	1.25	1.21	1.18	1.15	1.12	1.08	1.05	1.02	.990	.959	.928	21
22	1.40	1.36	1.33	1.30	1.26	1.23	1.20	1.17	1.13	1.10	1.07	1.04	1.01	.980	.949	.919	22
23	1.38	1.34	1.31	1.28	1.25	1.21	1.18	1.15	1.12	1.09	1.06	1.03	1.00	.970	.940	.910	23
24	1.36	1.32	1.29	1.26	1.23	1.20	1.17	1.14	1.11	1.08	1.05	1.02	.989	.960	.931	.902	24
25	1.33	1.30	1.27	1.24	1.21	1.18	1.15	1.12	1.09	1.06	1.03	1.00	.979	.950	.922	.893	25
26	1.32	1.29	1.26	1.23	1.20	1.16	1.13	1.10	1.07	1.04	1.02	.997	.968	.940	.912	.885	26
27	1.30	1.27	1.24	1.21	1.18	1.15	1.12	1.09	1.06	1.03	1.01	.986	.958	.931	.903		27
28	1.28	1.25	1.22	1.20	1.17	1.14	1.11	1.08	1.06	1.03	1.00	.975	.948	.921			28
29	1.26	1.23	1.20	1.18	1.15	1.12	1.10	1.07	1.04	1.02	.990	.964	.938				29
30	1.24	1.21	1.19	1.16	1.13	1.11	1.08	1.05	1.03	1.00	.979	.953					30
31	1.22	1.20	1.17	1.14	1.12	1.09	1.07	1.04	1.02	.993	.968						31
32	1.21	1.18	1.16	1.13	1.11	1.08	1.06	1.03	1.01	.981							32
33	1.19	1.17	1.14	1.12	1.09	1.06	1.04	1.02	.993								33
34	1.17	1.15	1.12	1.10	1.08	1.05	1.03	1.00								.81	34
35	1.15	1.13	1.11	1.08	1.06	1.04	1.01								.83	.80	35
36	1.14	1.12	1.10	1.07	1.05	1.03								.84	.82	.79	36
37	1.12	1.10	1.08	1.05	1.03								.86	.83	.81	.79	37
38	1.10	1.08	1.06	1.04								.87	.84	.82	.80	.78	38
39	1.08	1.06	1.04								.88	.86	.83	.81	.79	.77	39
40	1.07	1.05								.89	.87	.84	.82	.80	.78	.77	40
41	1.05								.90	.88	.85	.83	.81	.79	.78	.76	41
42								.90	.88	.86	.84	.82	.80	.78	.77	.75	42
43							.91	.88	.87	.85	.83	.81	.79	.77	.76	.74	43
44						.91	.89	.87	.86	.84	.82	.80	.78	.76	.75	.73	44
45					.92	.90	.88	.86	.84	.83	.81	.79	.77	.76	.74	.72	45
46				.92	.90	.88	.86	.85	.83	.81	.79	.78	.76	.75	.73	.71	46
47			.92	.90	.88	.86	.85	.83	.82	.80	.78	.77	.75	.74	.72	.70	47
48		.92	.90	.88	.87	.85	.84	.82	.81	.79	.77	.75	.74	.73	.71	.70	48
49	.92	.90	.88	.87	.86	.84	.82	.80	.79	.78	.75	.74	.73	.72	.70	.69	49
50	.90	.88	.86	.85	.84	.82	.80	.79	.78	.76	.74	.73	.72	.71	.69	.68	50
51	.88	.86	.85	.84	.82	.80	.79	.78	.76	.75	.73	.72	.71	.70	.68	.67	51
52	.86	.85	.83	.82	.80	.79	.78	.77	.75	.74	.72	.71	.70	.69	.67	.66	52
53	.84	.83	.82	.81	.79	.78	.76	.75	.74	.72	.71	.70	.69	.67	.66	.64	53
54	.83	.81	.80	.79	.78	.76	.75	.74	.72	.71	.69	.69	.67	.66	.64	.63	54
55	.81	.79	.78	.77	.75	.74	.73	.72	.71	.69	.68	.67	.66	.65	.63	.62	55
56	.79	.78	.77	.75	.74	.73	.72	.71	.70	.69	.67	.66	.65	.63	.62	.61	56
57	.77	.76	.75	.74	.73	.72	.71	.70	.69	.67	.66	.65	.63	.62	.61	.60	57
58	.76	.75	.74	.73	.72	.71	.70	.69	.67	.66	.65	.63	.62	.61	.60	.59	58
59	.74	.73	.72	.71	.70	.69	.68	.67	.66	.64	.63	.62	.61	.60	.59	.58	59
60	.72	.71	.70	.70	.69	.68	.67	.66	.64	.63	.62	.61	.60	.59	.58	.57	60
61	.70	.69	.69	.68	.67	.66	.65	.64	.63	.62	.61	.60	.59	.58	.57	.56	61
62	.68	.67	.66	.65	.64	.64	.63	.62	.61	.60	.59	.58	.57	.57	.56	.55	62
63	.66	.65	.64	.63	.63	.62	.61	.60	.59	.58	.57	.57	.56	.55	.54	.53	63
	45°	46°	47°	48°	49°	50°	51°	52°	53°	54°	55°	56°	57°	58°	59°	60°	

*The figures in the lower portion of the table pertain to Ex-Meridians BELOW POLE, in which case Lat. and Dec. will be of SAME name, and the reduction SUBTRACTIVE to the true altitude to get the meridian altitude: but ADDITIVE to the calculated meridian altitude to get the calculated altitude at the instant the sight was taken.

225

Table 21

EX-MERIDIAN

Containing Values of F (Ex-Meridian Factor) — Table I

LATITUDE, CONTRARY* name to declination

Dec.	60°	61°	62°	63°	64°	65°	66°	67°	68°	69°	70°	71°	72°	73°	74°	75°	76°	77°	78°	79°	80°	81°	82°	Dec.
0°	1.13	1.09	1.04	1.00	.96	.92	.87	.83	.79	.75	.71	.68	.64	.60	.56	.53	.49	.45	.42	.38	.35	.31	.28	0°
1	1.12	1.08	1.03	.99	.95	.91	.87	.83	.79	.75	.71	.67	.63	.60	.56	.52	.49	.45	.42	.38	.35	.31	.28	1
2	1.11	1.07	1.02	.98	.94	.90	.86	.82	.78	.74	.71	.67	.63	.59	.56	.52	.49	.45	.41	.38	.34	.31	.27	2
3	1.10	1.06	1.02	.97	.93	.89	.85	.82	.78	.74	.70	.66	.63	.59	.55	.52	.48	.45	.41	.38	.34	.31	.27	3
4	1.09	1.05	1.01	.97	.93	.89	.85	.81	.77	.73	.70	.66	.62	.59	.55	.52	.48	.45	.41	.38	.34	.31	.27	4
5	1.08	1.04	1.00	.96	.92	.88	.84	.80	.77	.73	.69	.66	.62	.58	.55	.51	.48	.44	.41	.38	.34	.31		5
6	1.07	1.03	.99	.95	.91	.87	.84	.80	.76	.72	.69	.65	.62	.58	.55	.51	.48	.44	.41	.37	.34			6
7	1.06	1.02	.98	.94	.90	.87	.83	.79	.76	.72	.68	.65	.61	.58	.54	.51	.48	.44	.41	.37				7
8	1.05	1.01	.97	.93	.90	.86	.82	.79	.75	.72	.68	.64	.61	.58	.54	.51	.47	.44	.41					8
9	1.04	1.00	.96	.93	.89	.85	.82	.78	.75	.71	.68	.64	.61	.57	.54	.50	.47	.44						9
10	1.03	.99	.95	.92	.88	.85	.81	.78	.74	.71	.67	.64	.60	.57	.54	.50	.47							10
11	1.02	.98	.95	.91	.87	.84	.80	.77	.74	.70	.67	.63	.60	.57	.53	.50								11
12	1.01	.97	.94	.90	.87	.83	.80	.76	.73	.70	.66	.63	.60	.56	.53								.27	12
13	1.00	.96	.93	.90	.86	.83	.79	.76	.73	.69	.66	.63	.59	.56								.30	.27	13
14	.99	.96	.92	.89	.85	.82	.79	.75	.72	.69	.66	.62	.59								.33	.30	.27	14
15	.98	.95	.91	.88	.85	.81	.78	.75	.72	.68	.65	.62								.36	.33	.30	.27	15
16	.97	.94	.91	.87	.84	.81	.78	.74	.71	.68	.65								.39	.36	.33	.30	.27	16
17	.96	.93	.90	.87	.83	.80	.77	.74	.71	.67								.42	.39	.36	.33	.30	.26	17
18	.95	.92	.89	.86	.83	.80	.76	.73	.70								.45	.42	.39	.36	.33	.30	.26	18
19	.95	.91	.88	.85	.82	.79	.76	.73								.48	.45	.42	.39	.36	.33	.29	.26	19
20	.94	.91	.87	.84	.81	.78	.75								.51	.48	.45	.42	.39	.36	.33	.29	.26	20
21	.93	.90	.87	.84	.81	.78								.54	.51	.48	.45	.42	.39	.36	.32	.29	.26	21
22	.92	.89	.86	.83	.80								.56	.53	.50	.47	.44	.41	.39	.35	.32	.29	.26	22
23	.91	.88	.85	.82								.59	.56	.53	.50	.47	.44	.41	.38	.35	.32	.29	.26	23
24	.90	.87	.84								.61	.59	.56	.53	.50	.47	.44	.41	.38	.35	.32	.29	.26	24
25	.89	.86								.64	.61	.58	.55	.53	.50	.47	.44	.41	.38	.35	.32	.29	.26	25
26	.88								.66	.63	.61	.58	.55	.52	.49	.47	.44	.41	.38	.35	.32	.29	.26	26
27								.69	.66	.63	.60	.58	.55	.52	.49	.46	.43	.41	.38	.35	.32	.29	.26	27
28							.71	.68	.65	.63	.60	.57	.54	.52	.49	.46	.43	.40	.37	.35	.32	.29	.26	28
29						.73	.70	.67	.65	.62	.59	.57	.54	.51	.49	.46	.43	.40	.37	.34	.32	.29	.26	29
30				.75	.72	.70	.67	.64	.62	.59	.56	.54	.51	.48	.46	.43	.40	.37	.34	.31	.28	.26		30
31			.77	.74	.72	.69	.66	.64	.61	.59	.56	.53	.51	.48	.45	.43	.40	.37	.34	.31	.28	.25		31
32		.78	.76	.73	.71	.68	.66	.63	.61	.58	.56	.53	.50	.48	.45	.42	.40	.37	.34	.31	.28	.25		32
33		.80	.77	.75	.73	.70	.68	.65	.63	.60	.58	.55	.53	.50	.47	.45	.42	.39	.37	.34	.31	.28	.25	33
34	.81	.80	.77	.74	.72	.70	.67	.65	.62	.60	.57	.55	.52	.50	.47	.45	.42	.39	.37	.34	.31	.28	.25	34
35	.80	.78	.76	.74	.71	.69	.67	.64	.62	.59	.57	.54	.52	.49	.47	.44	.42	.39	.36	.34	.31	.28	.25	35
36	.79	.78	.75	.73	.71	.68	.66	.64	.61	.59	.57	.54	.52	.49	.47	.44	.41	.39	.36	.33	.31	.28	.25	36
37	.79	.77	.75	.72	.70	.68	.65	.63	.61	.58	.56	.54	.51	.49	.46	.44	.41	.39	.36	.33	.31	.28	.25	37
38	.78	.76	.74	.72	.69	.67	.65	.63	.60	.58	.56	.53	.51	.48	.46	.44	.41	.38	.36	.33	.30	.28	.25	38
39	.77	.75	.73	.71	.69	.66	.64	.62	.60	.57	.55	.53	.51	.48	.46	.43	.41	.38	.36	.33	.30	.28	.25	39
40	.77	.74	.72	.70	.68	.66	.64	.61	.59	.57	.55	.52	.50	.48	.45	.43	.40	.38	.35	.33	.30	.27	.25	40
41	.76	.73	.71	.69	.67	.65	.63	.61	.59	.57	.54	.52	.50	.47	.45	.43	.40	.38	.35	.33	.30	.27	.25	41
42	.75	.73	.71	.69	.67	.64	.62	.60	.58	.56	.54	.52	.49	.47	.45	.42	.40	.38	.35	.32	.30	.27	.25	42
43	.74	.72	.70	.68	.66	.64	.62	.60	.58	.56	.53	.51	.49	.47	.44	.42	.40	.37	.35	.32	.30	.27	.24	43
44	.73	.71	.69	.67	.65	.63	.61	.59	.57	.55	.53	.51	.49	.46	.44	.42	.39	.37	.35	.32	.30	.27	.24	44
45	.72	.70	.68	.66	.64	.62	.60	.59	.57	.54	.52	.50	.48	.46	.44	.41	.39	.37	.34	.32	.29	.27	.24	45
46	.71	.69	.67	.65	.64	.62	.60	.58	.56	.54	.52	.50	.48	.46	.43	.41	.39	.37	.34	.32	.29	.27	.24	46
47	.70	.68	.67	.65	.63	.61	.59	.57	.55	.53	.51	.49	.47	.45	.43	.41	.39	.36	.34	.32	.29	.27	.24	47
48	.70	.67	.66	.64	.62	.60	.58	.57	.55	.53	.51	.49	.47	.45	.43	.41	.38	.36	.34	.31	.29	.26	.24	48
49	.69	.66	.65	.63	.61	.60	.58	.56	.54	.52	.50	.48	.46	.44	.42	.40	.38	.36	.34	.31	.29	.26	.24	49
50	.68	.66	.64	.62	.61	.60	.57	.55	.54	.52	.50	.48	.46	.44	.42	.40	.38	.36	.33	.31	.29	.26	.24	50
51	.67	.65	.63	.61	.60	.58	.56	.55	.53	.51	.49	.47	.46	.44	.42	.40	.37	.35	.33	.31	.28	.26	.23	51
52	.66	.64	.62	.61	.59	.57	.56	.54	.52	.51	.49	.47	.45	.43	.41	.39	.37	.35	.33	.31	.28	.26	.23	52
53	.64	.63	.61	.60	.58	.57	.55	.53	.52	.50	.48	.46	.45	.43	.41	.39	.37	.35	.33	.30	.28	.26	.23	53
54	.63	.62	.60	.59	.57	.56	.54	.52	.51	.49	.48	.46	.44	.42	.40	.38	.36	.34	.32	.30	.28	.26	.23	54
55	.62	.61	.59	.58	.56	.55	.53	.52	.50	.49	.47	.45	.44	.42	.40	.38	.36	.34	.32	.30	.28	.25	.23	55
56	.61	.60	.58	.57	.56	.54	.53	.51	.50	.48	.46	.45	.43	.41	.40	.38	.36	.34	.32	.30	.27	.25	.23	56
57	.60	.59	.57	.56	.55	.53	.52	.50	.49	.47	.46	.44	.43	.41	.39	.37	.35	.33	.31	.29	.27	.25	.23	57
58	.59	.58	.56	.55	.54	.52	.51	.50	.48	.47	.45	.44	.42	.40	.39	.37	.35	.33	.31	.29	.27	.25	.23	58
59	.58	.57	.55	.54	.53	.52	.50	.49	.47	.46	.45	.43	.41	.40	.38	.36	.35	.33	.31	.29	.27	.25	.22	59
60	.57	.56	.54	.53	.52	.51	.49	.48	.47	.45	.44	.42	.41	.39	.38	.36	.34	.32	.31	.29	.27	.24	.22	60
61	.56	.54	.53	.52	.51	.50	.48	.47	.46	.45	.43	.42	.40	.39	.37	.35	.34	.32	.30	.28	.26	.24	.22	61
62	.55	.53	.52	.51	.50	.49	.48	.46	.45	.44	.42	.41	.40	.38	.37	.35	.33	.32	.30	.28	.26	.24	.22	62
63	.53	.52	.51	.50	.49	.48	.47	.45	.44	.43	.42	.40	.39	.38	.36	.34	.33	.31	.29	.28	.26	.24	.22	63
64	.52	.51	.50	.49	.48	.47	.46	.45	.43	.42	.41	.40	.38	.37	.35	.34	.32	.31	.29	.27	.25	.23	.21	64
68	.47	.46	.45	.44	.43	.43	.42	.41	.40	.39	.38	.37	.35	.34	.33	.32	.30	.29	.27	.26	.24	.22	.20	68
69	.45	.45	.44	.43	.42	.41	.40	.40	.39	.38	.37	.36	.35	.33	.32	.31	.30	.28	.27	.25	.24	.22	.20	69
70	.44	.43	.42	.42	.41	.40	.39	.38	.38	.37	.36	.35	.34	.33	.31	.30	.29	.28	.26	.25	.23	.22	.20	70
74	.38	.37	.37	.36	.35	.35	.34	.34	.33	.32	.31	.31	.30	.29	.28	.27	.26	.25	.24	.23	.21	.20	.19	74
75	.36	.36	.35	.34	.34	.33	.33	.32	.32	.31	.30	.30	.29	.28	.27	.26	.25	.24	.23	.22	.21	.20	.18	75
	60°	61°	62°	63°	64°	65°	66°	67°	68°	69°	70°	71°	72°	73°	74°	75°	76°	77°	78°	79°	80°	81°	82°	

*The figures in the lower portion of the table pertain to Ex-Meridians BELOW POLE, in which case Lat. and Dec. will be of SAME name and the reduction SUBTRACTIVE to the true altitude to get the meridian altitude: but ADDITIVE to the calculated meridian altitude to get the calculated altitude at the instant the sight was taken.

Table 22
EX-MERIDIAN

Table II

L. H. A.

F	0° (180°)									1° (181°)								F
	15′	20′	25′	30′	35′	40′	45′	50′	55′	0′	5′	10′	15′	20′	25′	30′	35′	
	1m	20	40	2m	20	40	3m	20	40	4m	20	40	5m	20	40	6m	20	
.2	.0	.0	.0	.0	.0	.0	.0	.0	.0	.1	.1	.1	.1	.1	.1	.1	.1	.2
.3	.0	.0	.0	.0	.0	.0	.0	.1	.1	.1	.1	.1	.1	.1	.2	.2	.2	.3
.4	.0	.0	.0	.0	.0	.0	.1	.1	.1	.1	.1	.1	.2	.2	.2	.2	.3	.4
.5	.0	.0	.0	.0	.0	.1	.1	.1	.1	.1	.2	.2	.2	.2	.3	.3	.3	.5
.6	.0	.0	.0	.0	.1	.1	.1	.1	.1	.2	.2	.2	.2	.3	.3	.4	.4	.6
.7	.0	.0	.0	.0	.1	.1	.1	.1	.2	.2	.2	.3	.3	.3	.4	.4	.5	.7
.8	.0	.0	.0	.1	.1	.1	.1	.1	.2	.2	.3	.3	.3	.4	.4	.5	.5	.8
.9	.0	.0	.0	.1	.1	.1	.1	.2	.2	.2	.3	.3	.4	.4	.5	.5	.6	.9
1.0	.0	.0	.0	.1	.1	.1	.1	.2	.2	.3	.3	.4	.4	.5	.5	.6	.7	1.0
2.0	.0	.1	.1	.1	.2	.2	.3	.4	.4	.5	.6	.7	.8	.9	1.1	1.2	1.3	2.0
3.0	.0	.1	.1	.2	.3	.4	.4	.6	.7	.8	.9	1.1	1.2	1.4	1.6	1.8	2.0	3.0
4.0	.1	.1	.2	.3	.4	.5	.6	.7	.9	1.1	1.3	1.5	1.7	1.9	2.1	2.4	2.7	4.0
5.0	.1	.1	.2	.3	.5	.6	.7	.9	1.1	1.3	1.6	1.8	2.1	2.4	2.7	3.0	3.3	5.0
6.0	.1	.2	.3	.4	.5	.7	.9	1.1	1.3	1.6	1.9	2.2	2.5	2.8	3.2	3.6	4.0	6.0
7.0	.1	.2	.3	.5	.6	.8	1.0	1.3	1.6	1.9	2.2	2.5	2.9	3.3	3.7	4.2	4.7	7.0
8.0	.1	.2	.4	.5	.7	.9	1.2	1.5	1.8	2.1	2.5	2.9	3.3	3.8	4.3	4.8	5.3	8.0
9.0	.1	.3	.4	.6	.8	1.1	1.3	1.7	2.0	2.4	2.8	3.3	3.7	4.3	4.8	5.4	6.0	9.0
10.0	.2	.3	.5	.7	.9	1.2	1.5	1.9	2.2	2.7	3.1	3.6	4.2	4.7	5.4	6.0	6.7	10.0
11.0	.2	.3	.5	.7	1.0	1.3	1.6	2.0	2.5	2.9	3.4	4.0	4.6	5.2	5.9	6.6	7.4	11.0
12.0	.2	.4	.6	.8	1.1	1.4	1.8	2.2	2.7	3.2	3.8	4.4	5.0	5.7	6.4	7.2	8.0	12.0
13.0	.2	.4	.6	.9	1.2	1.5	2.0	2.4	2.9	3.5	4.1	4.7	5.4	6.2	7.0	7.8	8.7	13.0
14.0	.2	.4	.6	.9	1.3	1.7	2.1	2.6	3.1	3.7	4.4	5.1	5.8	6.6	7.5	8.4	9.4	14.0
15.0	.2	.4	.7	1.0	1.4	1.8	2.3	2.8	3.4	4.0	4.7	5.4	6.3	7.1	8.0	9.0	10.0	15.0
16.0	.3	.5	.8	1.1	1.5	1.9	2.4	3.0	3.6	4.3	5.0	5.8	6.7	7.6	8.6	9.6	10.7	16.0
17.0	.3	.5	.8	1.1	1.5	2.0	2.6	3.1	3.8	4.5	5.3	6.2	7.1	8.1	9.1	10.2	11.4	17.0
18.0	.3	.5	.8	1.2	1.6	2.1	2.7	3.3	4.0	4.8	5.6	6.5	7.5	8.5	9.6	10.8	12.0	18.0
19.0	.3	.6	.9	1.3	1.7	2.3	2.9	3.5	4.3	5.1	5.9	6.9	7.9	9.0	10.2	11.4	12.7	19.0
20.0	.3	.6	.9	1.3	1.8	2.4	3.0	3.7	4.5	5.3	6.3	7.3	8.3	9.5	10.7	12.0	13.4	20.0
21.0	.4	.6	1.0	1.4	1.9	2.5	3.2	3.9	4.7	5.6	6.6	7.6	8.8	10.0	11.2	12.6	14.0	21.0
22.0	.4	.7	1.1	1.5	2.0	2.6	3.3	4.1	4.9	5.9	6.9	8.0	9.1	10.4	11.8	13.2	14.7	22.0
23.0	.4	.7	1.1	1.5	2.1	2.7	3.5	4.3	5.2	6.1	7.2	8.4	9.6	10.9	12.3	13.8	15.4	23.0
24.0	.4	.7	1.1	1.6	2.2	2.8	3.6	4.4	5.4	6.4	7.5	8.7	10.0	11.4	12.8	14.4	16.0	24.0
25.0	.4	.7	1.2	1.7	2.3	3.0	3.8	4.6	5.6	6.7	7.8	9.1	10.4	11.9	13.4	15.0	16.7	25.0
26.0	.4	.8	1.2	1.7	2.4	3.1	3.9	4.8	5.8	6.9	8.1	9.4	10.8	12.3	13.9	15.6	17.4	26.0
27.0	.5	.8	1.3	1.8	2.5	3.2	4.1	5.0	6.1	7.2	8.5	9.8	11.3	12.8	14.5	16.2	18.1	27.0
28.0	.5	.8	1.3	1.9	2.6	3.3	4.2	5.2	6.3	7.5	8.8	10.2	11.7	13.3	15.0	16.8	18.7	28.0
	45′	40′	35′	30′	25′	20′	15′	10′	5′	0′	55′	50′	45′	40′	35′	30′	25′	
				(179°) 359°									(178°) 358°					

Table 22

EX-MERIDIAN

Table II

F	40′	45′	50′	55′	0′	5′	10′	15′	20′	25′	30′	35′	40′	45′	50′	55′	0′	F
	1° (181°)				**2° (182°)**												**3° (183°)**	
	6m 40	7m	20	40	8m	20	40	9m	20	40	10m	20	40	11m	20	40	12m	
.1	.1	.1	.1	.1	.1	.1	.1	.1	.1	.2	.2	.2	.2	.2	.2	.2	.2	.1
.2	.2	.2	.2	.2	.2	.2	.3	.3	.3	.3	.3	.4	.4	.4	.4	.5	.5	.2
.3	.2	.2	.3	.3	.3	.3	.4	.4	.4	.5	.5	.6	.6	.6	.6	.7	.7	.3
.4	.3	.3	.4	.4	.4	.5	.5	.5	.6	.6	.7	.7	.8	.8	.9	.9	1.0	.4
.5	.4	.4	.4	.5	.5	.6	.6	.7	.7	.8	.8	.9	.9	1.0	1.1	1.1	1.2	.5
.6	.4	.5	.5	.6	.6	.7	.8	.8	.9	.9	1.0	1.1	1.1	1.2	1.3	1.4	1.4	.6
.7	.5	.6	.6	.7	.7	.8	.9	.9	1.0	1.1	1.2	1.2	1.3	1.4	1.5	1.6	1.7	.7
.8	.6	.7	.7	.8	.9	.9	1.0	1.1	1.2	1.2	1.3	1.4	1.5	1.6	1.7	1.8	1.9	.8
.9	.7	.7	.8	.9	1.0	1.0	1.1	1.2	1.3	1.4	1.5	1.6	1.7	1.8	1.9	2.0	2.2	.9
1.0	.7	.8	.9	1.0	1.1	1.2	1.3	1.4	1.5	1.6	1.7	1.8	1.9	2.0	2.1	2.3	2.4	1.0
2.0	1.5	1.6	1.8	2.0	2.1	2.3	2.5	2.7	2.9	3.1	3.3	3.6	3.8	4.0	4.3	4.5	4.8	2.0
3.0	2.2	2.5	2.7	2.9	3.2	3.5	3.8	4.1	4.4	4.7	5.0	5.3	5.7	6.1	6.4	6.8	7.2	3.0
4.0	3.0	3.3	3.6	3.9	4.3	4.6	5.0	5.4	5.8	6.2	6.7	7.1	7.6	8.1	8.6	9.1	9.6	4.0
5.0	3.7	4.1	4.5	4.9	5.3	5.8	6.3	6.8	7.3	7.8	8.3	8.9	9.5	10.1	10.7	11.4	12.0	5.0
6.0	4.4	4.9	5.4	5.9	6.4	6.9	7.5	8.1	8.7	9.3	10.0	10.7	11.4	12.1	12.9	13.6	14.4	6.0
7.0	5.2	5.7	6.3	6.9	7.5	8.1	8.8	9.5	10.2	10.9	11.7	12.5	13.3	14.1	15.0	15.9	16.8	7.0
8.0	5.9	6.5	7.2	7.8	8.5	9.3	10.0	10.8	11.6	12.5	13.3	14.2	15.2	16.1	17.2	18.2	19.2	8.0
9.0	6.7	7.4	8.1	8.8	9.6	10.4	11.3	12.2	13.1	14.0	15.0	16.0	17.1	18.2	19.3	20.4	21.6	9.0
10.0	7.4	8.2	9.0	9.8	10.7	11.6	12.5	13.5	14.5	15.6	16.7	17.8	19.0	20.2	21.4	22.7	24.0	10.0
11.0	8.2	9.0	9.9	10.8	11.7	12.7	13.8	14.9	16.0	17.1	18.3	19.6	20.8	22.2	23.6	25.0	26.4	11.0
12.0	8.9	9.8	10.8	11.8	12.8	13.9	15.0	16.2	17.4	18.7	20.0	21.4	22.8	24.2	25.7	27.2	28.8	12.0
13.0	9.6	10.6	11.7	12.8	13.9	15.0	16.3	17.6	18.9	20.2	21.7	23.1	24.6	26.2	27.8	29.5	31.2	13.0
14.0	10.4	11.4	12.6	13.7	14.9	16.2	17.5	18.9	20.3	21.8	23.3	24.9	26.5	28.2	30.0	31.8	33.6	14.0
15.0	11.1	12.3	13.4	14.7	16.0	17.4	18.8	20.3	21.8	23.4	25.0	26.7	28.4	30.3	32.1	34.0	36.0	15.0
16.0	11.9	13.1	14.3	15.7	17.1	18.5	20.1	21.6	23.2	24.9	26.7	28.5	30.3	32.3	34.2	36.3	38.4	16.0
17.0	12.6	13.9	15.2	16.7	18.1	19.7	21.3	23.0	24.7	26.5	28.3	30.2	32.2	34.3	36.4	38.6	40.8	17.0
18.0	13.3	14.7	16.1	17.6	19.2	20.8	22.5	24.3	26.1	28.0	30.0	32.0	34.1	36.3	38.6	40.8	43.2	18.0
19.0	14.1	15.5	17.0	18.6	20.3	22.0	23.8	25.7	27.6	29.6	31.7	33.8	36.0	38.3	40.7	43.1	45.6	19.0
20.0	14.8	16.3	17.9	19.6	21.3	23.1	25.0	27.0	29.0	31.1	33.3	35.6	37.9	40.3	42.8	45.4	48.0	20.0
21.0	15.6	17.2	18.8	20.6	22.4	24.3	26.3	28.4	30.5	32.7	35.0	37.4	39.8	42.4	45.0	47.7	50.4	21.0
22.0	16.3	18.0	19.7	21.6	23.5	25.4	27.6	29.7	32.0	34.2	36.7	39.2	41.7	44.4	47.1	49.9	52.8	22.0
23.0	17.0	18.8	20.6	22.6	24.5	26.6	28.8	31.1	33.4	35.8	38.3	40.9	43.6	46.4	49.2	52.2	55.2	23.0
24.0	17.8	19.6	21.5	23.6	25.6	27.8	30.1	32.4	34.9	37.4	40.0	42.8	45.5	48.4	51.3	54.5	57.6	24.0
25.0	18.5	20.4	22.4	24.5	26.7	28.9	31.3	33.8	36.3	39.0	41.7	44.5	47.4	50.4	53.5	56.8	60.0	25.0
26.0	19.3	21.2	23.3	25.4	27.7	30.1	32.6	35.1	37.8	40.5	43.3	46.3	49.3	52.4	55.7	59.0	62.4	26.0
27.0	20.0	22.1	24.2	26.4	28.8	31.2	33.8	36.5	39.2	42.1	45.0	48.1	51.2	54.5	57.8	61.3	64.8	27.0
28.0	20.7	22.9	25.1	27.4	29.9	32.4	35.1	37.8	40.7	43.7	46.7	49.8	53.1	56.5	60.0	63.6	67.2	28.0
	20′	15′	10′	5′	0′	55′	50′	45′	40′	35′	30′	25′	20′	15′	10′	5′	0′	
					(178°) 358°									(177°) 357°				

Table 22

EX-MERIDIAN

Table **II**

F	L. H. A. 3° (183°) 5′	10′	15′	20′	25′	30′	35′	40′	45′	50′	55′	4° (184°) 0′	5′	10′	15′	20′	25′	F
	12m 20	40	13m	20	40	14m	20	40	15m	20	40	16m	20	40	17m	20	40	
.02	.1	.1	.1	.1	.1	.1	.1	.1	.1	.1	.1	.1	.1	.1	.1	.1	.1	.02
.04	.1	.1	.1	.1	.1	.1	.1	.1	.1	.2	.2	.2	.2	.2	.2	.2	.2	.04
.06	.2	.2	.2	.2	.2	.2	.2	.2	.2	.2	.2	.3	.3	.3	.3	.3	.3	.06
.08	.2	.2	.2	.2	.2	.3	.3	.3	.3	.3	.3	.3	.3	.4	.4	.4	.4	.08
.1	.3	.3	.3	.3	.3	.3	.3	.4	.4	.4	.4	.4	.4	.5	.5	.5	.5	.1
.2	.5	.5	.6	.6	.6	.7	.7	.7	.7	.8	.8	.9	.9	.9	1.0	1.0	1.0	.2
.3	.8	.8	.8	.9	.9	1.0	1.0	1.1	1.1	1.2	1.2	1.3	1.3	1.4	1.4	1.5	1.6	.3
.4	1.0	1.1	1.1	1.2	1.2	1.3	1.4	1.4	1.5	1.6	1.6	1.7	1.8	1.9	1.9	2.0	2.1	.4
.5	1.3	1.3	1.4	1.5	1.6	1.6	1.7	1.8	1.9	2.0	2.0	2.1	2.2	2.3	2.4	2.5	2.6	.5
.6	1.5	1.6	1.7	1.8	1.9	2.0	2.1	2.2	2.2	2.4	2.4	2.6	2.7	2.8	2.9	3.0	3.1	.6
.7	1.8	1.9	2.0	2.1	2.2	2.3	2.4	2.5	2.6	2.7	2.7	3.0	3.1	3.2	3.4	3.5	3.6	.7
.8	2.0	2.1	2.3	2.4	2.5	2.6	2.7	2.9	3.0	3.1	3.1	3.4	3.6	3.7	3.9	4.0	4.2	.8
.9	2.3	2.4	2.5	2.7	2.8	2.9	3.1	3.2	3.4	3.5	3.5	3.8	4.0	4.2	4.3	4.5	4.7	.9
1	2.5	2.7	2.8	3.0	3.1	3.3	3.4	3.6	3.7	3.9	4.1	4.3	4.5	4.6	4.8	5.0	5.2	1
2	5.1	5.3	5.6	5.9	6.2	6.5	6.8	7.2	7.5	7.8	8.2	8.5	8.9	9.3	9.6	10.0	10.4	2
3	7.6	8.0	8.4	8.9	9.3	9.8	10.3	10.8	11.2	11.8	12.3	12.8	13.3	13.9	14.4	15.0	15.6	3
4	10.1	10.7	11.3	11.9	12.5	13.1	13.7	14.3	15.0	15.7	16.4	17.1	17.8	18.5	19.3	20.0	20.8	4
5	12.7	13.4	14.1	14.8	15.6	16.3	17.1	17.9	18.7	19.6	20.5	21.3	22.2	23.2	24.1	25.0	26.0	5
6	15.2	16.0	16.9	17.8	18.7	19.6	20.6	21.5	22.5	23.5	24.6	25.6	26.7	27.8	28.9	30.0	31.2	6
7	17.7	18.7	19.7	20.8	21.8	22.9	24.0	25.1	26.2	27.4	28.6	29.9	31.1	32.4	33.7	35.0	36.4	7
8	20.3	21.4	22.5	23.7	24.9	26.1	27.4	28.7	30.0	31.4	32.7	34.1	35.6	37.1	38.5	40.1	41.6	8
9	22.8	24.1	25.3	26.7	28.0	29.4	30.8	32.3	33.7	35.3	36.8	38.4	40.0	41.7	43.4	45.1	46.8	9
10	25.4	26.8	28.2	29.6	31.1	32.7	34.2	35.8	37.5	39.2	40.9	42.7	44.5	46.3	48.2	50.1	52.0	10
11	27.9	29.4	31.0	32.6	34.2	35.9	37.7	39.4	41.3	43.1	45.0	46.9	48.9	50.9	53.0	55.1	57.2	11
12	30.4	32.1	33.8	35.6	37.4	39.2	41.1	43.0	45.0	47.0	49.1	51.2	53.4	55.6	57.8	60.1	62.4	12
13	33.0	34.8	36.6	38.5	40.5	42.5	44.5	46.6	48.8	50.9	53.2	55.5	57.8	60.2	62.6	65.1	67.6	13
14	35.5	37.4	39.4	41.5	43.6	45.7	47.9	50.2	52.5	54.8	57.3	59.7	62.2	64.8	67.4	70.1	72.8	14
15	38.0	40.1	42.3	44.4	46.7	49.0	51.3	53.8	56.3	58.8	61.4	64.0	66.7	69.4	72.2	75.1	78.0	15
16	40.6	42.8	45.1	47.4	49.8	52.3	54.8	57.4	60.0	62.7	65.5	68.3	71.1	74.1	77.1	80.1	83.2	16
17	43.2	45.5	47.9	50.4	52.9	55.5	58.2	61.0	63.8	66.6	69.6	72.5	75.6	78.7	81.9	85.1	88.4	17
18	45.7	48.2	50.7	53.3	56.0	58.8	61.7	64.6	67.5	70.5	73.7	76.8	80.0	83.3	86.7	90.1	93.6	18
19	48.2	50.8	53.5	56.3	59.1	62.1	65.1	68.2	71.3	74.5	77.8	81.0	84.5	87.9	91.5	95.1	98.8	19
20	50.7	53.5	56.3	59.3	62.3	65.3	68.5	71.7	75.0	78.4	81.8	85.3	88.9	92.6	96.3		104.0	20
21	53.2	56.2	59.2	62.3	65.4	68.6	71.9	75.3	78.8	82.3	85.9	89.6	93.4	97.2				21
22	55.8	58.9	62.0	65.3	68.5	71.9	75.3	79.0	82.5	86.2	90.0	93.9	97.8					22
23	58.3	61.5	64.8	68.2	71.6	75.1	78.8	82.5	86.3	90.2	94.1	98.1						23
24	60.8	64.2	67.7	71.2	74.7	78.4	82.3	86.1	90.0	94.1	98.2							24
25	63.3	67.0	70.4	74.2	77.8	81.7	85.7	89.6	93.8	98.0								25
26	65.9	69.6	73.3	77.1	80.9	84.9	89.0	93.2	97.5									26
27	68.5	72.3	76.1	80.1	84.1	88.2	92.5	96.8										27
28	71.0	75.0	78.9	83.1	87.2	91.5	95.8											28
	55′	50′	45′	40′	35′	30′	25′	20′	15′	10′	5′	0′	55′	50′	45′	40′	35′	
										(176°) 356°					(175°) 355°			

Table 22

EX-MERIDIAN

Table II

L. H. A.

F	4° (184°)						5° (185°)											F
	30′	35′	40′	45′	50′	55′	0′	5′	10′	15′	20′	25′	30′	35′	40′	45′	50′	
	18m	20	40	19m	20	40	20m	20	40	21m	20	40	22m	20	40	23m	20	
.01	.1	.1	.1	.1	.1	.1	.1	.1	.1	.1	.1	.1	.1	.1	.1	.1	.1	.01
.02	.1	.1	.1	.1	.1	.1	.1	.1	.1	.1	.2	.2	.2	.2	.2	.2	.2	.02
.03	.2	.2	.2	.2	.2	.2	.2	.2	.2	.2	.2	.2	.2	.2	.3	.3	.3	.03
.04	.2	.2	.2	.2	.2	.3	.3	.3	.3	.3	.3	.3	.3	.3	.3	.4	.4	.04
.05	.3	.3	.3	.3	.3	.3	.3	.3	.4	.4	.4	.4	.4	.4	.4	.4	.5	.05
.06	.3	.3	.3	.4	.4	.4	.4	.4	.4	.4	.5	.5	.5	.5	.5	.5	.5	.06
.07	.4	.4	.4	.4	.4	.5	.5	.5	.5	.5	.5	.5	.6	.6	.6	.6	.6	.07
.08	.4	.4	.5	.5	.5	.5	.5	.6	.6	.6	.6	.6	.6	.7	.7	.7	.7	.08
.09	.5	.5	.5	.5	.6	.6	.6	.6	.7	.7	.7	.7	.7	.7	.8	.8	.8	.09
.1	.5	.6	.6	.6	.6	.6	.7	.7	.7	.7	.8	.8	.8	.8	.9	.9	.9	.1
.2	1.1	1.1	1.2	1.2	1.2	1.3	1.3	1.4	1.4	1.5	1.5	1.6	1.6	1.7	1.7	1.8	1.8	.2
.3	1.6	1.7	1.7	1.8	1.9	1.9	2.0	2.1	2.1	2.2	2.3	2.3	2.4	2.5	2.6	2.7	2.7	.3
.4	2.2	2.2	2.3	2.4	2.5	2.6	2.7	2.8	2.8	2.9	3.0	3.1	3.2	3.3	3.4	3.5	3.6	.4
.5	2.7	2.8	2.9	3.0	3.1	3.2	3.3	3.4	3.6	3.7	3.8	3.9	4.0	4.2	4.3	4.4	4.5	.5
.6	3.2	3.4	3.5	3.6	3.7	3.9	4.0	4.1	4.3	4.4	4.6	4.7	4.8	5.0	5.1	5.3	5.4	.6
.7	3.8	3.9	4.1	4.2	4.4	4.5	4.7	4.8	5.0	5.1	5.3	5.5	5.6	5.8	6.0	6.2	6.4	.7
.8	4.3	4.5	4.6	4.8	5.0	5.2	5.3	5.5	5.7	5.9	6.1	6.3	6.5	6.7	6.8	7.1	7.3	.8
.9	4.9	5.0	5.2	5.4	5.6	5.8	6.0	6.2	6.4	6.6	6.8	7.0	7.3	7.5	7.7	7.9	8.2	.9
1	5.4	5.6	5.8	6.0	6.2	6.4	6.7	6.9	7.1	7.3	7.6	7.8	8.1	8.3	8.6	8.8	9.1	1
2	10.8	11.2	11.6	12.0	12.5	12.9	13.3	13.8	14.2	14.7	15.2	15.6	16.1	16.6	17.1	17.6	18.1	2
3	16.2	16.8	17.4	18.0	18.7	19.3	20.0	20.7	21.4	22.0	22.8	23.5	24.2	24.9	25.7	26.5	27.2	3
4	21.6	22.4	23.2	24.1	24.9	25.8	26.7	27.6	28.5	29.4	30.4	31.3	32.3	33.3	34.2	35.3	36.3	4
5	27.0	28.0	29.0	30.1	31.2	32.2	33.3	34.5	35.6	36.7	37.9	39.2	40.3	41.6	42.8	44.1	45.4	5
6	32.4	33.6	34.8	36.1	37.4	38.7	40.0	41.3	42.7	44.1	45.5	47.0	48.4	49.9	51.4	52.9	54.4	6
7	37.8	39.2	40.6	42.1	43.6	45.1	46.7	48.2	49.8	51.4	53.1	54.8	56.5	58.2	59.9	61.7	63.5	7
8	43.2	44.8	46.5	48.1	49.8	51.6	53.3	55.1	56.9	58.8	60.7	62.6	64.5	66.5	68.5	70.5	72.6	8
9	48.6	50.4	52.3	54.1	56.1	58.0	60.0	62.0	64.1	66.1	68.3	70.4	72.6	74.8	77.1	79.4	81.7	9
10	54.0	56.0	58.1	60.2	62.3	64.5	66.7	68.9	71.2	73.5	75.8	78.2	80.7	83.1	85.6	88.2	90.7	10
11	59.4	61.6	63.9	66.2	68.5	70.9	73.3	75.8	78.3	80.9	83.4	86.1	88.7	91.4	94.2	97.0	99.8	11
12	64.8	67.2	69.7	72.2	74.7	77.4	80.0	82.7	85.4	88.2	91.0	93.9	96.8	99.8				12
13	70.2	72.8	75.5	78.2	81.0	83.8	86.7	89.6	92.5	95.5	98.6							13
14	75.6	78.4	81.3	84.2	87.2	90.2	93.3	96.5	99.6									14
15	81.0	84.0	87.1	90.2	93.4	96.7												15
16	86.4	89.6	92.9	96.3														16
17	91.8	95.2	98.7															17
18	97.2																	18
	30′	25′	20′	15′	10′	5′	0′	55′	50′	45′	40′	35′	30′	25′	20′	15′	10′	

(175°) 355°   (174°) 354°

Table 22
EX-MERIDIAN
Table II

L. H. A.

F	5° (185°) 55'	6° (186°) 0'	5'	10'	15'	20'	25'	30'	35'	40'	45'	50'	55'	7° (187°) 0'	5'	10'	15'	F
	23m 40	24m	20	40	25m	20	40	26m	20	40	27m	20	40	28m	20	40	29m	
.01	.1	.1	.1	.1	.1	.1	.1	.1	.1	.1	.1	.1	.1	.1	.1	.1	.1	.01
.02	.2	.2	.2	.2	.2	.2	.2	.2	.2	.2	.2	.2	.3	.3	.3	.3	.3	.02
.03	.3	.3	.3	.3	.3	.3	.3	.3	.3	.4	.4	.4	.4	.4	.4	.4	.4	.03
.04	.4	.4	.4	.4	.4	.4	.4	.5	.5	.5	.5	.5	.5	.5	.5	.5	.6	.04
.05	.5	.5	.5	.5	.5	.5	.5	.6	.6	.6	.6	.6	.6	.7	.7	.7	.7	.05
.06	.6	.6	.6	.6	.6	.6	.7	.7	.7	.7	.7	.7	.8	.8	.8	.8	.8	.06
.07	.7	.7	.7	.7	.7	.7	.8	.8	.8	.8	.9	.9	.9	.9	.9	1.0	1.0	.07
.08	.7	.8	.8	.8	.8	.9	.9	.9	.9	.9	1.0	1.0	1.0	1.0	1.1	1.1	1.1	.08
.09	.8	.9	.9	.9	.9	1.0	1.0	1.0	1.0	1.1	1.1	1.1	1.1	1.2	1.2	1.2	1.3	.09
.1	.9	1.0	1.0	1.0	1.0	1.1	1.1	1.1	1.2	1.2	1.2	1.3	1.3	1.3	1.3	1.4	1.4	.1
.2	1.9	1.9	2.0	2.0	2.1	2.1	2.2	2.3	2.3	2.4	2.4	2.5	2.6	2.6	2.7	2.7	2.8	.2
.3	2.8	2.9	3.0	3.0	3.1	3.2	3.3	3.4	3.5	3.5	3.6	3.7	3.8	3.9	4.0	4.1	4.2	.3
.4	3.7	3.8	3.9	4.1	4.2	4.3	4.4	4.5	4.6	4.7	4.9	5.0	5.1	5.2	5.4	5.5	5.6	.4
.5	4.7	4.8	4.9	5.1	5.2	5.3	5.5	5.6	5.8	5.9	6.1	6.2	6.4	6.5	6.7	6.8	7.0	.5
.6	5.6	5.8	5.9	6.1	6.2	6.4	6.6	6.8	6.9	7.1	7.3	7.5	7.6	7.8	8.0	8.2	8.4	.6
.7	6.5	6.7	6.9	7.1	7.3	7.5	7.7	7.9	8.1	8.3	8.5	8.7	8.9	9.1	9.4	9.6	9.8	.7
.8	7.5	7.7	7.9	8.1	8.3	8.6	8.8	9.0	9.2	9.5	9.7	10.0	10.2	10.5	10.7	11.0	11.2	.8
.9	8.4	8.6	8.9	9.1	9.4	9.6	9.9	10.1	10.4	10.7	10.9	11.2	11.5	11.8	12.0	12.3	12.6	.9
1	9.3	9.6	9.9	10.1	10.4	10.7	11.0	11.3	11.6	11.9	12.1	12.5	12.8	13.1	13.4	13.7	14.0	1
2	18.7	19.2	19.7	20.3	20.8	21.4	22.0	22.5	23.1	23.7	24.3	24.9	25.5	26.1	26.8	27.4	28.0	2
3	28.0	28.8	29.6	30.4	31.2	32.1	32.9	33.8	34.7	35.5	36.4	37.4	38.3	39.2	40.1	41.1	42.1	3
4	37.3	38.4	39.5	40.6	41.7	42.8	43.9	45.1	46.2	47.4	48.6	49.8	51.0	52.3	53.5	54.8	56.1	4
5	46.7	48.0	49.3	50.7	52.1	53.5	54.9	56.3	57.8	59.2	60.7	62.3	63.8	65.3	66.9	68.5	70.1	5
6	56.0	57.6	59.2	60.8	62.5	64.2	65.9	67.6	69.4	71.1	72.9	74.7	76.5	78.4	80.3	82.2	84.1	6
7	65.3	67.2	69.1	71.0	72.9	74.9	76.9	78.9	80.9	82.9	85.1	87.2	89.3	91.5	93.7	95.9	98.1	7
8	74.7	76.8	79.0	81.1	83.3	85.6	87.8	90.1	92.5	94.8	97.2	99.6						8
9	84.0	86.4	88.8	91.3	93.8	96.3	98.8											9

5' 0' (174°) 354°	55'	50'	45'	40'	35'	30'	25'	20'	15'	10'	5' 0' (173°) 353°	55' 50' 45' (172°) 352°

L. H. A.

F	7° (187°) 20'	25'	30'	35'	40'	45'	50'	55'	8° (188°) 0'	5'	10'	15'	20'	25'	30'	35'	40'	F
	29m 20	40	30m	20	40	31m	20	40	32m	20	40	33m	20	40	34m	20	40	
.01	.1	.1	.1	.2	.2	.2	.2	.2	.2	.2	.2	.2	.2	.2	.2	.2	.2	.01
.02	.3	.3	.3	.3	.3	.3	.3	.3	.3	.3	.4	.4	.4	.4	.4	.4	.4	.02
.03	.4	.4	.4	.5	.5	.5	.5	.5	.5	.5	.5	.5	.6	.6	.6	.6	.6	.03
.04	.6	.6	.6	.6	.6	.6	.7	.7	.7	.7	.7	.7	.7	.8	.8	.8	.8	.04
.05	.7	.7	.7	.8	.8	.8	.8	.8	.9	.9	.9	.9	.9	.9	1.0	1.0	1.0	.05
.06	.9	.9	.9	.9	.9	1.0	1.0	1.0	1.0	1.0	1.1	1.1	1.1	1.1	1.2	1.2	1.2	.06
.07	1.0	1.0	1.0	1.1	1.1	1.1	1.1	1.2	1.2	1.2	1.2	1.3	1.3	1.3	1.3	1.4	1.4	.07
.08	1.1	1.2	1.2	1.2	1.2	1.3	1.3	1.3	1.4	1.4	1.4	1.5	1.5	1.5	1.5	1.6	1.6	.08
.09	1.3	1.3	1.3	1.4	1.4	1.4	1.5	1.5	1.5	1.6	1.6	1.6	1.7	1.7	1.7	1.8	1.8	.09
.1	1.4	1.5	1.5	1.5	1.6	1.6	1.6	1.7	1.7	1.7	1.8	1.8	1.9	1.9	1.9	2.0	2.0	.1
.2	2.9	2.9	3.0	3.1	3.1	3.2	3.3	3.3	3.4	3.5	3.6	3.6	3.7	3.8	3.9	3.9	4.0	.2
.3	4.3	4.4	4.5	4.6	4.7	4.8	4.9	5.0	5.1	5.2	5.3	5.4	5.6	5.7	5.8	5.9	6.0	.3
.4	5.7	5.9	6.0	6.1	6.3	6.4	6.5	6.7	6.8	7.0	7.1	7.3	7.4	7.6	7.7	7.9	8.0	.4
.5	7.2	7.3	7.5	7.7	7.8	8.0	8.2	8.4	8.5	8.7	8.9	9.1	9.3	9.4	9.6	9.8	10.0	.5
.6	8.6	8.8	9.0	9.2	9.4	9.6	9.8	10.0	10.2	10.5	10.7	10.9	11.1	11.3	11.6	11.8	12.0	.6
.7	10.0	10.3	10.5	10.7	11.0	11.2	11.5	11.7	11.9	12.2	12.4	12.7	13.0	13.2	13.5	13.8	14.0	.7
.8	11.5	11.7	12.0	12.3	12.5	12.8	13.1	13.4	13.7	13.9	14.2	14.5	14.8	15.1	15.4	15.7	16.0	.8
.9	12.9	13.2	13.5	13.8	14.1	14.4	14.7	15.0	15.4	15.7	16.0	16.3	16.7	17.0	17.3	17.7	18.0	.9
1	14.3	14.7	15.0	15.3	15.7	16.0	16.4	16.7	17.1	17.4	17.8	18.1	18.5	18.9	19.3	19.6	20.0	1
2	28.7	29.3	30.0	30.7	31.3	32.0	32.7	33.4	34.1	34.8	35.6	36.3	37.0	37.8	38.5	39.3	40.1	2
3	43.0	44.0	45.0	46.0	47.0	48.0	49.1	50.1	51.2	52.3	53.4	54.4	55.6	56.7	57.8	58.9	60.1	3
4	57.4	58.7	60.0	61.3	62.7	64.1	65.4	66.8	68.3	69.7	71.1	72.6	74.1	75.6	77.1	78.6	80.1	4
5	71.7	73.3	75.0	76.7	78.4	80.1	81.8	83.6	85.3	87.1	88.9	90.7	92.6	94.4	96.3	98.2		5

40'	35'	30'	25'	20'	15'	10'	5'	0' (172°) 352°	55'	50'	45'	40'	35'	30'	25'	20' (171°) 351°

Table 22

EX-MERIDIAN

Table II

L.H.A.

F	8° (188°)			9° (189°)												10°(190°)		F
	45'	50'	55'	0'	5'	10'	15'	20'	25'	30'	35'	40'	45'	50'	55'	0'	5'	
	35m	20	40	36m	20	40	37m	20	40	38m	20	40	39m	20	40	40m	20	
.01	.2	.2	.2	.2	.2	.2	.2	.2	.2	.2	.2	.2	.3	.3	.3	.3	.3	.01
.02	.4	.4	.4	.4	.4	.4	.5	.5	.5	.5	.5	.5	.5	.5	.5	.5	.5	.02
.03	.6	.6	.6	.6	.7	.7	.7	.7	.7	.7	.7	.7	.8	.8	.8	.8	.8	.03
.04	.8	.8	.8	.9	.9	.9	.9	.9	.9	1.0	1.0	1.0	1.0	1.0	1.0	1.1	1.1	.04
.05	1.0	1.0	1.1	1.1	1.1	1.1	1.1	1.2	1.2	1.2	1.2	1.2	1.3	1.3	1.3	1.3	1.4	.05
.06	1.2	1.2	1.3	1.3	1.3	1.4	1.4	1.4	1.4	1.4	1.5	1.5	1.5	1.5	1.6	1.6	1.6	.06
.07	1.4	1.5	1.5	1.5	1.5	1.6	1.6	1.6	1.7	1.7	1.7	1.7	1.8	1.8	1.8	1.9	1.9	.07
.08	1.6	1.7	1.7	1.7	1.8	1.8	1.8	1.9	1.9	1.9	2.0	2.0	2.0	2.1	2.1	2.1	2.2	.08
.09	1.8	1.9	1.9	1.9	2.0	2.0	2.1	2.1	2.1	2.2	2.2	2.2	2.3	2.3	2.4	2.4	2.4	.09
.1	2.0	2.1	2.1	2.2	2.2	2.2	2.3	2.3	2.4	2.4	2.4	2.5	2.5	2.6	2.6	2.6	2.7	.1
.2	4.1	4.2	4.2	4.3	4.4	4.5	4.6	4.6	4.7	4.8	4.9	5.0	5.1	5.2	5.2	5.3	5.4	.2
.3	6.1	6.2	6.4	6.5	6.6	6.7	6.8	7.0	7.1	7.2	7.3	7.5	7.6	7.7	7.9	8.0	8.1	.3
.4	8.2	8.3	8.5	8.6	8.8	9.0	9.1	9.3	9.5	9.6	9.8	10.0	10.1	10.3	10.5	10.7	10.8	.4
.5	10.2	10.4	10.6	10.8	11.0	11.2	11.4	11.6	11.8	12.0	12.2	12.5	12.7	12.9	13.1	13.3	13.6	.5
.6	12.2	12.5	12.7	13.0	13.2	13.4	13.7	13.9	14.2	14.4	14.7	15.0	15.2	15.5	15.7	16.0	16.3	.6
.7	14.3	14.6	14.8	15.1	15.4	15.7	16.0	16.3	16.6	16.8	17.1	17.4	17.8	18.0	18.3	18.7	19.0	.7
.8	16.3	16.6	17.0	17.3	17.6	17.9	18.3	18.6	18.9	19.3	19.6	19.9	20.3	20.6	21.0	21.3	21.7	.8
.9	18.4	18.7	19.1	19.4	19.8	20.2	20.5	20.9	21.2	21.7	22.0	22.4	22.8	23.2	23.6	24.0	24.4	.9
1	20.4	20.8	21.2	21.6	22.0	22.4	22.8	23.2	23.6	24.1	24.5	24.9	25.3	25.8	26.2	26.7	27.1	1
2	40.8	41.6	42.4	43.2	44.0	44.8	45.6	46.4	47.3	48.1	49.0	49.8	50.7	51.6	52.4	53.3	54.2	2
3	61.2	62.4	63.6	64.8	66.0	67.2	68.4	69.7	70.9	72.2	73.5	74.8	76.0	77.4	78.6	80.0	81.3	3
4	81.6	83.2	84.8	86.4	88.0	89.6	91.2	92.9	94.6	96.3	98.0	99.7						4

L.H.A.

F	10° (190°)										11° (191°)							F
	10'	15'	20'	25'	30'	35'	40'	45'	50'	55'	0'	5'	10'	15'	20'	25'	30'	
	40m 40	41m	20	40	42m	20	40	43m	20	40	44m	20	40	45m	20	40	46m	
.01	.3	.3	.3	.3	.3	.3	.3	.3	.3	.3	.3	.3	.3	.3	.3	.3	.4	.01
.02	.6	.6	.6	.6	.6	.6	.6	.6	.6	.6	.6	.7	.7	.7	.7	.7	.7	.02
.03	.8	.8	.9	.9	.9	.9	.9	.9	.9	1.0	1.0	1.0	1.0	1.0	1.0	1.0	1.1	.03
.04	1.1	1.1	1.1	1.2	1.2	1.2	1.2	1.2	1.3	1.3	1.3	1.3	1.3	1.3	1.4	1.4	1.4	.04
.05	1.4	1.4	1.4	1.4	1.5	1.5	1.5	1.5	1.6	1.6	1.6	1.6	1.6	1.7	1.7	1.7	1.8	.05
.06	1.7	1.7	1.7	1.7	1.8	1.8	1.8	1.8	1.9	1.9	1.9	2.0	2.0	2.0	2.1	2.1	2.1	.06
.07	1.9	2.0	2.0	2.0	2.1	2.1	2.1	2.2	2.2	2.2	2.3	2.3	2.3	2.4	2.4	2.4	2.5	.07
.08	2.2	2.2	2.3	2.3	2.4	2.4	2.4	2.5	2.5	2.5	2.6	2.6	2.7	2.7	2.7	2.8	2.8	.08
.09	2.5	2.5	2.6	2.6	2.6	2.7	2.7	2.8	2.8	2.9	2.9	2.9	3.0	3.0	3.1	3.1	3.2	.09
.1	2.8	2.8	2.8	2.9	2.9	3.0	3.0	3.1	3.1	3.2	3.2	3.3	3.3	3.4	3.4	3.5	3.5	.1
.2	5.5	5.6	5.7	5.8	5.9	6.0	6.1	6.2	6.3	6.4	6.5	6.6	6.7	6.7	6.9	7.0	7.1	.2
.3	8.3	8.4	8.5	8.7	8.8	9.0	9.1	9.2	9.4	9.5	9.7	9.8	10.0	10.1	10.3	10.4	10.6	.3
.4	11.0	11.2	11.4	11.6	11.8	11.9	12.1	12.3	12.5	12.7	12.9	13.1	13.3	13.5	13.7	13.9	14.1	.4
.5	13.8	14.0	14.2	14.5	14.7	14.9	15.2	15.4	15.6	15.9	16.1	16.4	16.6	16.9	17.1	17.4	17.6	.5
.6	16.5	16.8	17.1	17.4	17.6	17.9	18.2	18.5	18.8	19.1	19.4	19.7	20.0	20.2	20.6	20.9	21.2	.6
.7	19.3	19.6	19.9	20.3	20.6	20.9	21.2	21.6	21.9	22.2	22.6	22.9	23.3	23.6	24.0	24.3	24.7	.7
.8	22.0	22.4	22.8	23.1	23.5	23.9	24.3	24.7	25.0	25.4	25.8	26.2	26.6	27.0	27.4	27.8	28.2	.8
.9	24.8	25.2	25.6	26.0	26.5	26.9	27.3	27.7	28.2	28.6	29.0	29.5	29.9	30.4	30.8	31.3	31.7	.9
1	27.6	28.0	28.5	28.9	29.4	29.9	30.3	30.8	31.3	31.8	32.3	32.8	33.3	33.7	34.3	34.8	35.3	1
2	55.1	56.0	56.9	57.9	58.8	59.7	60.7	61.6	62.6	63.6	64.5	65.5	66.5	67.5	68.5	69.5	70.5	2

Table 22

EX-MERIDIAN

Table II

L.H.A.

F	11° (191°)					12° (192°)													F
	35′	40′	45′	50′	55′	0′	5′	10′	15′	20′	25′	30′	35′	40′	45′	50′	55′	
	46m 20	40	47m	20	40	48m	20	40	49m	20	40	50m	20	40	51m	20	40	
.01	.4	.4	.4	.4	.4	.4	.4	.4	.4	.4	.4	.4	.4	.4	.4	.4	.4	.01
.02	.7	.7	.7	.7	.8	.8	.8	.8	.8	.8	.8	.8	.8	.9	.9	.9	.9	.02
.03	1.1	1.1	1.1	1.1	1.1	1.2	1.2	1.2	1.2	1.2	1.2	1.2	1.3	1.3	1.3	1.3	1.3	.03
.04	1.4	1.5	1.5	1.5	1.5	1.5	1.6	1.6	1.6	1.6	1.6	1.7	1.7	1.7	1.7	1.8	1.8	.04
.05	1.8	1.8	1.8	1.9	1.9	1.9	1.9	2.0	2.0	2.0	2.1	2.1	2.1	2.1	2.2	2.2	2.2	.05
.06	2.1	2.2	2.2	2.2	2.3	2.3	2.3	2.4	2.4	2.4	2.5	2.5	2.5	2.6	2.6	2.6	2.7	.06
.07	2.5	2.5	2.6	2.6	2.7	2.7	2.7	2.8	2.8	2.8	2.9	2.9	3.0	3.0	3.0	3.1	3.1	.07
.08	2.9	2.9	2.9	3.0	3.0	3.1	3.1	3.2	3.2	3.2	3.3	3.3	3.4	3.4	3.5	3.5	3.6	.08
.09	3.2	3.3	3.3	3.4	3.4	3.5	3.5	3.6	3.6	3.7	3.7	3.7	3.8	3.9	3.9	4.0	4.0	.09
.1	3.6	3.6	3.7	3.7	3.8	3.8	3.9	3.9	4.0	4.1	4.1	4.2	4.2	4.3	4.3	4.4	4.4	.1
.2	7.2	7.3	7.4	7.5	7.6	7.7	7.8	7.9	8.0	8.1	8.2	8.3	8.4	8.6	8.7	8.8	8.9	.2
.3	10.7	10.9	11.0	11.2	11.4	11.5	11.7	11.8	12.0	12.2	12.3	12.5	12.7	12.8	13.0	13.2	13.3	.3
.4	14.3	14.5	14.7	14.9	15.1	15.4	15.6	15.8	16.0	16.2	16.4	16.7	16.9	17.1	17.3	17.6	17.8	.4
.5	17.9	18.1	18.4	18.7	18.9	19.2	19.5	19.7	20.0	20.3	20.6	20.8	21.1	21.4	21.7	22.0	22.2	.5
.6	21.5	21.8	22.1	22.4	22.7	23.0	23.4	23.7	24.0	24.3	24.7	25.0	25.3	25.7	26.0	26.4	26.7	.6
.7	25.0	25.4	25.8	26.1	26.5	26.9	27.3	27.6	28.0	28.4	28.8	29.2	29.6	29.9	30.3	30.7	31.1	.7
.8	28.6	29.0	29.5	29.9	30.3	30.7	31.1	31.6	32.0	32.5	32.9	33.3	33.8	34.2	34.7	35.1	35.6	.8
.9	32.2	32.7	33.1	33.6	34.1	34.6	35.0	35.5	36.0	36.6	37.0	37.5	38.0	38.5	39.0	39.5	40.0	.9
1	35.8	36.3	36.8	37.3	37.9	38.4	38.9	39.5	40.0	40.6	41.1	41.7	42.2	42.8	43.3	43.9	44.5	1
2	71.6	72.6	73.6	74.7	75.7	76.8	77.9	78.9	80.0	81.1	82.2	83.3	84.4	85.6	86.7	87.8	89.0	2

25′	20′	15′	10′	5′	0′	55′	50′	45′	40′	35′	30′	25′	20′	15′	10′	5′
					(168°) 348°										(167°) 347°	

L.H.A.

F	13° (193°)												14° (194°)					F
	0′	5′	10′	15′	20′	25′	30′	35′	40′	45′	50′	55′	0′	5′	10′	15′	20′	
	52m	20	40	53m	20	40	54m	20	40	55m	20	40	56m	20	40	57m	20	
.01	.5	.5	.5	.5	.5	.5	.5	.5	.5	.5	.5	.5	.5	.5	.5	.5	.5	.01
.02	.9	.9	.9	.9	.9	1.0	1.0	1.0	1.0	1.0	1.0	1.0	1.0	1.1	1.1	1.1	1.1	.02
.03	1.4	1.4	1.4	1.4	1.4	1.4	1.5	1.5	1.5	1.5	1.5	1.5	1.6	1.6	1.6	1.6	1.6	.03
.04	1.8	1.8	1.8	1.9	1.9	1.9	1.9	2.0	2.0	2.0	2.0	2.1	2.1	2.1	2.1	2.2	2.2	.04
.05	2.3	2.3	2.3	2.3	2.4	2.4	2.4	2.5	2.5	2.5	2.6	2.6	2.6	2.6	2.7	2.7	2.7	.05
.06	2.7	2.7	2.8	2.8	2.8	2.9	2.9	3.0	3.0	3.0	3.1	3.1	3.1	3.2	3.2	3.2	3.3	.06
.07	3.2	3.2	3.2	3.3	3.3	3.4	3.4	3.4	3.5	3.5	3.6	3.6	3.7	3.7	3.7	3.8	3.8	.07
.08	3.6	3.7	3.7	3.7	3.8	3.8	3.9	3.9	4.0	4.0	4.1	4.1	4.2	4.2	4.3	4.3	4.4	.08
.09	4.1	4.1	4.2	4.2	4.3	4.3	4.4	4.4	4.5	4.5	4.6	4.6	4.7	4.8	4.8	4.9	4.9	.09
.1	4.5	4.6	4.6	4.7	4.7	4.8	4.9	4.9	5.0	5.0	5.1	5.2	5.2	5.3	5.4	5.4	5.5	.1
.2	9.0	9.1	9.2	9.4	9.5	9.6	9.7	9.8	10.0	10.1	10.2	10.3	10.5	10.6	10.7	10.8	11.0	.2
.3	13.5	13.7	13.9	14.0	14.2	14.4	14.6	14.8	14.9	15.1	15.3	15.5	15.7	15.9	16.1	16.2	16.4	.3
.4	18.0	18.3	18.5	18.7	19.0	19.2	19.4	19.7	19.9	20.2	20.4	20.7	20.9	21.2	21.4	21.7	21.9	.4
.5	22.5	22.8	23.1	23.4	23.7	24.0	24.3	24.6	24.9	25.2	25.5	25.8	26.1	26.4	26.8	27.1	27.4	.5
.6	27.0	27.4	27.7	28.1	28.4	28.8	29.2	29.5	29.9	30.2	30.6	31.0	31.4	31.7	32.1	32.5	32.9	.6
.7	31.5	32.0	32.4	32.8	33.2	33.6	34.0	34.4	34.9	35.3	35.7	36.1	36.6	37.0	37.5	37.9	38.3	.7
.8	36.1	36.5	37.0	37.5	37.9	38.4	38.9	39.4	39.8	40.3	40.8	41.3	41.8	42.3	42.8	43.3	43.8	.8
.9	40.6	41.1	41.6	42.1	42.7	43.2	43.7	44.3	44.8	45.4	45.9	46.5	47.0	47.6	48.2	48.7	49.3	.9
1	45.1	45.7	46.2	46.8	47.4	48.0	48.6	49.2	49.8	50.4	51.0	51.6	52.3	52.9	53.5	54.1	54.8	1

0′ (167°) 347°	55′	50′	45′	40′	35′	30′	25′	20′	15′	10′	5′	0′	55′	50′	45′	40′
												(166°) 346°		(165°) 345°		

233

Table 22
EX-MERIDIAN

Table II

F	14° (194°) 25'	30'	35'	40'	45'	50'	55'	15° (195°) 0'	5'	10'	15'	20'	25'	30'	35'	40'	45'	F
	57m 40	58m	20	40	59m	20	40	60m	20	40	61m	20	40	62m	20	40	63m	
.01	.6	.6	.6	.6	.6	.6	.6	.6	.6	.6	.6	.6	.6	.6	.6	.7	.7	.01
.02	1.1	1.1	1.1	1.1	1.2	1.2	1.2	1.2	1.2	1.2	1.2	1.3	1.3	1.3	1.3	1.3	1.3	.02
.03	1.7	1.7	1.7	1.7	1.7	1.8	1.8	1.8	1.8	1.8	1.9	1.9	1.9	1.9	1.9	2.0	2.0	.03
.04	2.2	2.2	2.3	2.3	2.3	2.3	2.4	2.4	2.4	2.5	2.5	2.5	2.5	2.6	2.6	2.6	2.6	.04
.05	2.8	2.8	2.8	2.9	2.9	2.9	3.0	3.0	3.0	3.1	3.1	3.1	3.2	3.2	3.2	3.3	3.3	.05
.06	3.3	3.4	3.4	3.4	3.5	3.5	3.6	3.6	3.6	3.7	3.7	3.8	3.8	3.8	3.9	3.9	4.0	.06
.07	3.9	3.9	4.0	4.0	4.1	4.1	4.2	4.2	4.2	4.3	4.3	4.4	4.4	4.5	4.5	4.6	4.6	.07
.08	4.4	4.5	4.5	4.6	4.6	4.7	4.7	4.8	4.9	4.9	5.0	5.0	5.1	5.1	5.2	5.2	5.3	.08
.09	5.0	5.0	5.1	5.2	5.2	5.3	5.3	5.4	5.5	5.5	5.6	5.6	5.7	5.8	5.8	5.9	6.0	.09
.1	5.5	5.6	5.7	5.7	5.8	5.9	5.9	6.0	6.1	6.1	6.2	6.3	6.3	6.4	6.5	6.5	6.6	.1
.2	11.1	11.2	11.3	11.5	11.6	11.7	11.9	12.0	12.1	12.3	12.4	12.5	12.7	12.8	13.0	13.1	13.2	.2
.3	16.6	16.8	17.0	17.2	17.4	17.6	17.8	18.0	18.2	18.4	18.6	18.8	19.0	19.2	19.4	19.6	19.8	.3
.4	22.2	22.4	22.7	22.9	23.2	23.5	23.7	24.0	24.3	24.5	24.8	25.1	25.4	25.6	25.9	26.2	26.5	.4
.5	27.7	28.0	28.4	28.7	29.0	29.3	29.7	30.0	30.3	30.7	31.0	31.3	31.7	32.0	32.4	32.7	33.1	.5
.6	33.3	33.6	34.0	34.4	34.8	35.2	35.6	36.0	36.4	36.8	37.2	37.6	38.0	38.4	38.9	39.3	39.7	.6
.7	38.8	39.2	39.7	40.2	40.6	41.1	41.5	42.0	42.5	42.9	43.4	43.9	44.4	44.8	45.3	45.8	46.3	.7
.8	44.3	44.9	45.4	45.9	46.4	46.9	47.5	48.0	48.5	49.1	49.6	50.2	50.7	51.3	51.8	52.4	52.9	.8
.9	49.9	50.5	51.0	51.6	52.2	52.8	53.4	54.0	54.6	55.2	55.8	56.4	57.0	57.7	58.3	58.9	59.5	.9
1	55.4	56.1	56.7	57.4	58.0	58.7	59.3	60.0	60.7	61.3	62.0	62.7	63.4	64.1	64.8	65.5	66.1	1

35'	30'	25'	20'	15'	10'	5'	0'	55'	50'	45'	40'	35'	30'	25'	20'	15'
				(165°)	345°								(164°)	344°		

Table 23
EX-MERIDIAN
SECOND CORRECTION
To be SUBTRACTED from FIRST CORRECTION

Table III

Alt.	FIRST CORRECTION 10'	20'	30'	40'	45'	50'	55'	60'	65'	70'	75'	80'	85'	90'	95'	100'	105'	110'	115'	120'
20°	.0	.0	.0	.1	.1	.1	.2	.2	.2	.3	.3	.3	.4	.4	.5	.5	.6	.6	.7	.8
30	.0	.0	.1	.1	.2	.2	.3	.3	.4	.4	.5	.5	.6	.7	.8	.8	.9	1.0	1.1	1.2
40	.0	.0	.1	.2	.2	.3	.4	.4	.5	.6	.7	.8	.9	1.0	1.1	1.2	1.3	1.5	1.6	1.8
50	.0	.1	.2	.3	.4	.4	.5	.6	.7	.9	1.0	1.1	1.3	1.4	1.6	1.7	1.9	2.1	2.3	2.4
55	.0	.1	.2	.3	.4	.5	.6	.7	.9	1.0	1.2	1.3	1.5	1.7	1.9	2.1	2.3	2.5	2.7	3.0
60	.0	.1	.2	.4	.5	.6	.8	.9	1.1	1.2	1.4	1.6	1.8	2.0	2.3	2.5	2.8	3.0	3.3	3.6
65	.0	.1	.3	.5	.6	.8	.9	1.1	1.3	1.5	1.8	2.0	2.3	2.5	2.8	3.1	3.4	3.8	4.1	4.5
68	.0	.1	.3	.6	.7	.9	1.1	1.3	1.5	1.8	2.0	2.3	2.6	2.9	3.2	3.6	4.0	4.4	4.8	5.2
70	.0	.2	.4	.6	.8	1.0	1.2	1.4	1.7	2.0	2.2	2.6	2.9	3.2	3.6	4.0	4.4	4.8	5.3	5.8
72	.0	.2	.4	.7	.9	1.1	1.4	1.6	1.9	2.2	2.5	2.9	3.2	3.6	4.0	4.5	4.9	5.4	5.9	6.4
74	.1	.2	.5	.8	1.0	1.3	1.5	1.8	2.1	2.5	2.9	3.3	3.7	4.1	4.6	5.1	5.6	6.1	6.7	7.3
75	.1	.2	.5	.9	1.1	1.4	1.6	2.0	2.3	2.7	3.1	3.5	3.9	4.4	4.9	5.4	6.0	6.6	7.2	7.8
76	.1	.2	.5	.9	1.2	1.5	1.8	2.1	2.5	2.9	3.3	3.7	4.2	4.7	5.3	5.8	6.4	7.1	7.7	8.6
77	.1	.3	.6	1.0	1.3	1.6	1.9	2.3	2.7	3.1	3.5	4.0	4.5	5.1	5.7	6.3	7.0	7.6	8.3	9.1
78	.1	.3	.6	1.1	1.4	1.7	2.1	2.5	2.9	3.4	3.8	4.4	4.9	5.5	6.2	6.8	7.5	8.3	9.0	9.9
79	.1	.3	.7	1.2	1.5	1.9	2.3	2.7	3.2	3.7	4.2	4.8	5.4	6.1	6.8	7.5	8.3	9.1	9.9	10.8
80 00	.1	.3	.7	1.3	1.7	2.1	2.5	3.0	3.5	4.0	4.6	5.3	6.0	6.7	7.4	8.2	9.1	10.0	10.9	11.9
30	.1	.3	.8	1.4	1.8	2.2	2.6	3.1	3.7	4.3	4.9	5.6	6.3	7.0	7.8	8.7	9.6	10.5	11.5	12.5
81 00	.1	.4	.8	1.5	1.9	2.3	2.8	3.3	3.9	4.5	5.2	5.9	6.6	7.4	8.3	9.2	10.1	11.1	12.1	13.2
30	.1	.4	.9	1.6	2.0	2.4	2.9	3.5	4.1	4.8	5.5	6.2	7.0	7.9	8.8	9.7	10.7	11.8	12.9	14.0
82 00	.1	.4	.9	1.7	2.1	2.6	3.1	3.7	4.4	5.1	5.8	6.6	7.5	8.4	9.3	10.3	11.4	12.5	13.7	14.9
30	.1	.4	1.0	1.8	2.2	2.8	3.3	4.0	4.7	5.4	6.2	7.1	8.0	9.0	10.0	11.0	12.2	13.4	14.7	15.9
83 00	.1	.5	1.1	1.9	2.4	3.0	3.6	4.3	5.0	5.8	6.7	7.6	8.6	9.6	10.7	11.8	13.1	14.3	15.7	17.1
20	.1	.5	1.1	2.0	2.5	3.1	3.8	4.5	5.3	6.1	7.0	8.0	9.0	10.1	11.2	12.4	13.7	15.1	16.5	17.9
40	.1	.5	1.2	2.1	2.7	3.3	4.0	4.7	5.5	6.4	7.4	8.4	9.5	10.6	11.8	13.1	14.5	15.9	17.4	18.9
84 00	.1	.6	1.2	2.2	2.8	3.5	4.2	5.0	5.8	6.8	7.8	8.9	10.0	11.2	12.5	13.8	15.3	16.8	18.3	19.9
10	.1	.6	1.3	2.3	2.9	3.6	4.3	5.1	6.0	7.0	8.0	9.1	10.3	11.5	12.8	14.2	15.7	17.2	18.8	20.5
20	.1	.6	1.3	2.3	3.0	3.7	4.4	5.3	6.2	7.2	8.2	9.4	10.6	11.9	13.2	14.7	16.2	17.7	19.4	21.1
30	.2	.6	1.4	2.4	3.1	3.8	4.6	5.4	6.4	7.4	8.5	9.7	10.9	12.2	13.6	15.1	16.7	18.3	20.0	21.8
40	.2	.6	1.4	2.5	3.2	3.9	4.7	5.6	6.6	7.6	8.8	10.0	11.3	12.6	14.1	15.6	17.2	18.9	20.6	22.4
50	.2	.6	1.4	2.6	3.3	4.0	4.9	5.8	6.8	7.9	9.1	10.3	11.6	13.0	14.5	16.1	17.7	19.4	21.3	23.2
85 00	.2	.7	1.5	2.7	3.4	4.2	5.0	6.0	7.0	8.1	9.4	10.6	12.0	13.5	15.0	16.6	18.3	20.1	22.0	23.9
10	.2	.7	1.5	2.8	3.5	4.3	5.2	6.2	7.2	8.4	9.7	11.0	12.4	13.9	15.5	17.2	18.9	20.8	22.8	24.8
20	.2	.7	1.6	2.9	3.6	4.5	5.4	6.4	7.5	8.7	10.0	11.4	12.9	14.4	16.0	17.8	19.6	21.6	23.6	25.7
30	.2	.7	1.7	3.0	3.7	4.6	5.6	6.6	7.8	9.0	10.4	11.8	13.4	15.0	16.6	18.5	20.4	22.4	24.5	26.6
40	.2	.8	1.7	3.1	3.9	4.8	5.8	6.9	8.1	9.4	10.8	12.3	13.9	15.6	17.3	19.2	21.2	23.2	25.4	27.6
50	.2	.8	1.8	3.2	4.0	5.0	6.0	7.2	8.4	9.8	11.2	12.8	14.4	16.2	18.0	20.0	22.0	24.2	26.4	28.8
86 00	.2	.8	1.9	3.3	4.2	5.2	6.3	7.5	8.8	10.2	11.7	13.3	15.0	16.8	18.8	20.8	22.9	25.2	27.5	30.0

Note.   The altitude to be used with Table III is the true altitude (not the mer. alt.).

Table 24
Approximate Limits of Hour Angle for Ex-Meridian Table
(Limits in minutes of time)

LATITUDE SAME name as declination

Dec.	0°	3°	5°	10°	15°	20°	25°	30°	35°	40°	45°	50°	55°	60°	65°	70°	75°	80°	Dec.
°	m	m	m	m	m	m	m	m	m	m	m	m	m	m	m	m	m	m	°
0	0	3	5	11	16	21	26	30	35	39	43	46	49	52	54	56	58	59	0
3	3	0	3	8	13	18	23	28	33	37	42	45	48	51	53	54	56	58	3
5	5	3	0	6	11	16	21	26	31	36	40	44	47	50	51	53	55	57	5
10	11	8	4	0	6	11	16	22	27	32	36	40	44	47	50	51	54	56	10
15	16	13	11	5	0	6	11	17	22	27	32	37	42	45	47	50	53	55	15
20	21	19	17	12	6	0	6	11	17	22	27	33	38	42	45	49	52	54	20
25	29	25	23	18	12	6	0	6	12	18	24	29	35	40	42	48	51	53	25
30	36	33	29	25	19	12	6	0	6	12	18	25	30	36	40	46	49	52	30
35	43	41	38	33	27	19	13	7	0	6	13	20	25	31	37	44	48	51	35
40	52	50	47	43	35	28	21	14	7	0	7	14	21	26	34	41	46	50	40
45	63	60	57	54	46	36	30	22	15	8	0	8	15	22	30	37	43	49	45
50	63	63	63	63	57	48	40	34	26	17	9	0	9	17	25	32	39	47	50
55	63	63	63	63	63	60	54	46	38	29	19	10	0	11	19	27	36	45	55
60	63	63	63	63	63	63	63	63	53	42	31	21	11	0	11	21	31	41	60
65	63	63	63	63	63	63	63	63	63	62	50	38	26	13	0	13	25	36	65
70	63	63	63	63	63	63	63	63	63	63	63	60	45	30	15	0	15	31	70

LATITUDE CONTRARY name to declination

Dec.	0°	3°	5°	10°	15°	20°	25°	30°	35°	40°	45°	50°	55°	60°	65°	70°	75°	80°	Dec.
°	m	m	m	m	m	m	m	m	m	m	m	m	m	m	m	m	m	m	°
0	0	3	5	11	16	21	26	30	35	39	43	46	49	52	55	57	58	59	0
3	3	6	9	14	19	24	29	34	38	43	45	48	50	53	56	58	59	60	3
5	5	9	11	16	21	26	31	36	40	44	47	49	51	54	57	59	60	61	5
10	11	14	16	21	26	31	36	41	45	48	50	52	54	56	58	60	61		10
15	16	20	22	27	32	36	41	46	49	52	54	55	58	59	60	61			15
20	22	25	27	32	37	41	46	51	54	56	58	60	62	62	62				20
25	29	31	33	38	43	47	51	56	58	60	62	63	63	63					25
30	36	38	40	45	50	52	58	61	62	63	63	63	63						30
35	43	45	47	52	57	60	62	63	63	63	63	63							35
40	52	54	56	62	63	63	63	63	63	63	63								40
45	60	63	63	63	63	63	63	63	63	63									45
50	63	63	63	63	63	63	63	63	63										50
55	63	63	63	63	63	63	63	63											55
60	63	63	63	63	63	63	63												60
65	63	63	63	63	63	63													65
70	63	63	63	63	63														70

Table 25 — ALTITUDE CHANGE in 1ᵐ of Time

LAT.	0° 180 180 360	1° 179 181 359	2° 178 182 358	3° 177 183 357	4° 176 184 356	5° 175 185 355	6° 174 186 354	7° 173 187 353	8° 172 188 352	9° 171 189 351	10° 170 190 350	11° 169 191 349	12° 168 192 348	13° 167 193 347	14° 166 194 346	15° 165 195 345	16° 164 196 344	LAT.
0°	.0	.3	.5	.8	1.0	1.3	1.6	1.8	2.1	2.3	2.6	2.9	3.1	3.4	3.6	3.9	4.1	0°
5	.0	.3	.5	.8	1.0	1.3	1.5	1.8	2.1	2.3	2.6	2.9	3.1	3.4	3.6	3.9	4.1	5
10	.0	.3	.5	.8	1.0	1.3	1.5	1.8	2.1	2.3	2.6	2.8	3.1	3.3	3.6	3.8	4.1	10
13	.0	.3	.5	.8	1.0	1.3	1.5	1.8	2.0	2.3	2.5	2.8	3.0	3.3	3.5	3.8	4.0	13
16	.0	.3	.5	.8	1.0	1.3	1.4	1.8	2.0	2.3	2.5	2.8	3.0	3.2	3.5	3.7	4.0	16
18	.0	.2	.5	.7	1.0	1.2	1.4	1.7	2.0	2.2	2.5	2.7	3.0	3.2	3.5	3.7	3.9	18
20	.0	.2	.5	.7	1.0	1.2	1.4	1.7	2.0	2.2	2.4	2.7	2.9	3.2	3.4	3.6	3.9	20
22	.0	.2	.5	.7	1.0	1.2	1.4	1.7	1.9	2.2	2.4	2.7	2.9	3.1	3.4	3.6	3.8	22
24	.0	.2	.5	.7	1.0	1.2	1.4	1.7	1.9	2.1	2.4	2.6	2.8	3.1	3.3	3.5	3.8	24
26	.0	.2	.5	.7	.9	1.2	1.4	1.6	1.9	2.1	2.3	2.6	2.8	3.0	3.3	3.5	3.7	26
27	.0	.2	.5	.7	.9	1.2	1.4	1.6	1.9	2.1	2.3	2.6	2.8	3.0	3.2	3.5	3.7	27
28	.0	.2	.5	.7	.9	1.2	1.4	1.6	1.8	2.1	2.3	2.5	2.8	3.0	3.2	3.4	3.7	28
29	.0	.2	.5	.7	.9	1.1	1.4	1.6	1.8	2.1	2.3	2.5	2.7	3.0	3.2	3.4	3.6	29
30	.0	.2	.5	.7	.9	1.1	1.4	1.6	1.8	2.0	2.3	2.5	2.7	2.9	3.1	3.4	3.6	30
31	.0	.2	.4	.7	.9	1.1	1.3	1.6	1.8	2.0	2.2	2.5	2.7	2.9	3.1	3.3	3.5	31
32	.0	.2	.4	.7	.9	1.1	1.3	1.6	1.8	2.0	2.2	2.4	2.6	2.9	3.1	3.3	3.5	32
33	.0	.2	.4	.7	.9	1.1	1.3	1.5	1.8	2.0	2.2	2.4	2.6	2.8	3.0	3.3	3.5	33
34	.0	.2	.4	.6	.9	1.1	1.3	1.5	1.7	1.9	2.2	2.4	2.6	2.8	3.0	3.2	3.4	34
35	.0	.2	.4	.6	.9	1.1	1.3	1.5	1.7	1.9	2.1	2.3	2.6	2.8	3.0	3.2	3.4	35
36	.0	.2	.4	.6	.8	1.1	1.3	1.5	1.7	1.9	2.1	2.3	2.5	2.7	2.9	3.1	3.3	36
37	.0	.2	.4	.6	.8	1.0	1.3	1.5	1.7	1.9	2.1	2.3	2.5	2.7	2.9	3.1	3.3	37
38	.0	.2	.4	.6	.8	1.0	1.2	1.4	1.6	1.8	2.1	2.3	2.5	2.7	2.9	3.1	3.3	38
39	.0	.2	.4	.6	.8	1.0	1.2	1.4	1.6	1.8	2.0	2.2	2.4	2.6	2.8	3.0	3.2	39
40	.0	.2	.4	.6	.8	1.0	1.2	1.4	1.6	1.8	2.0	2.2	2.4	2.6	2.8	3.0	3.2	40
41	.0	.2	.4	.6	.8	1.0	1.2	1.4	1.6	1.8	2.0	2.2	2.4	2.6	2.7	2.9	3.1	41
42	.0	.2	.4	.6	.8	1.0	1.2	1.4	1.6	1.7	1.9	2.1	2.3	2.5	2.7	2.9	3.1	42
43	.0	.2	.4	.6	.8	1.0	1.1	1.3	1.5	1.7	1.9	2.1	2.3	2.5	2.7	2.8	3.0	43
44	.0	.2	.4	.6	.8	.9	1.1	1.3	1.5	1.7	1.9	2.1	2.2	2.4	2.6	2.8	3.0	44
45	.0	.2	.4	.6	.7	.9	1.1	1.3	1.5	1.7	1.8	2.0	2.2	2.4	2.6	2.7	2.9	45
46	.0	.2	.4	.5	.7	.9	1.1	1.3	1.5	1.6	1.8	2.0	2.2	2.3	2.5	2.7	2.9	46
47	.0	.2	.4	.5	.7	.9	1.1	1.2	1.4	1.6	1.8	2.0	2.1	2.3	2.5	2.6	2.8	47
48	.0	.2	.4	.5	.7	.9	1.0	1.2	1.4	1.6	1.7	1.9	2.1	2.3	2.4	2.6	2.8	48
49	.0	.2	.3	.5	.7	.8	1.0	1.2	1.4	1.5	1.7	1.9	2.0	2.2	2.4	2.5	2.7	49
50	.0	.2	.3	.5	.7	.8	1.0	1.2	1.3	1.5	1.7	1.8	2.0	2.2	2.3	2.5	2.7	50
51	.0	.2	.3	.5	.7	.8	1.0	1.2	1.3	1.5	1.6	1.8	2.0	2.1	2.3	2.4	2.6	51
52	.0	.2	.3	.5	.6	.8	1.0	1.1	1.3	1.4	1.6	1.8	1.9	2.1	2.2	2.4	2.5	52
53	.0	.2	.3	.5	.6	.8	.9	1.1	1.3	1.4	1.6	1.7	1.9	2.0	2.2	2.3	2.5	53
54	.0	.2	.3	.5	.6	.8	.9	1.1	1.2	1.4	1.5	1.7	1.8	2.0	2.1	2.3	2.4	54
55	.0	.2	.3	.5	.6	.7	.9	1.0	1.2	1.3	1.5	1.6	1.8	1.9	2.1	2.2	2.4	55
56	.0	.1	.3	.4	.6	.7	.9	1.0	1.2	1.3	1.5	1.6	1.7	1.9	2.0	2.2	2.3	56
57	.0	.1	.3	.4	.6	.7	.9	1.0	1.1	1.3	1.4	1.6	1.7	1.8	2.0	2.1	2.3	57
58	.0	.1	.3	.4	.6	.7	.8	1.0	1.1	1.2	1.4	1.5	1.7	1.8	1.9	2.0	2.2	58
59	.0	.1	.3	.4	.5	.7	.8	.9	1.1	1.2	1.3	1.5	1.6	1.7	1.9	2.0	2.1	59
60	.0	.1	.3	.4	.5	.7	.8	.9	1.0	1.2	1.3	1.4	1.6	1.7	1.8	1.9	2.1	60
61	.0	.1	.3	.4	.5	.7	.8	.9	1.0	1.1	1.3	1.4	1.5	1.6	1.8	1.9	2.0	61
62	.0	.1	.2	.4	.5	.6	.7	.9	1.0	1.1	1.2	1.3	1.5	1.6	1.7	1.8	1.9	62
63	.0	.1	.2	.4	.5	.6	.7	.8	.9	1.1	1.2	1.3	1.4	1.5	1.6	1.7	1.9	63
64	.0	.1	.2	.3	.5	.6	.7	.8	.9	1.0	1.2	1.3	1.4	1.5	1.6	1.7	1.8	64
65	.0	.1	.2	.3	.4	.6	.7	.8	.9	1.0	1.1	1.2	1.3	1.4	1.5	1.6	1.7	65
66	.0	.1	.2	.3	.4	.5	.6	.7	.8	1.0	1.0	1.2	1.3	1.4	1.5	1.5	1.7	66
67	.0	.1	.2	.3	.4	.5	.6	.7	.8	.9	1.0	1.1	1.2	1.3	1.4	1.5	1.6	67
68	.0	.1	.2	.3	.4	.5	.6	.7	.8	.9	1.0	1.1	1.2	1.3	1.4	1.5	1.5	68
69	.0	.1	.2	.3	.4	.5	.6	.7	.7	.8	.9	1.0	1.1	1.2	1.3	1.4	1.5	69
70	.0	.1	.2	.3	.4	.5	.5	.6	.7	.8	.9	1.0	1.1	1.2	1.2	1.4	1.4	70
71	.0	.1	.2	.3	.3	.4	.5	.6	.7	.8	.9	.9	1.0	1.1	1.1	1.3	1.3	71
72	.0	.1	.2	.2	.3	.4	.5	.6	.6	.7	.8	.9	1.0	1.0	1.1	1.2	1.3	72
73	.0	.1	.2	.2	.3	.4	.5	.5	.6	.7	.8	.8	.9	1.0	1.1	1.1	1.2	73
74	.0	.1	.1	.2	.3	.4	.4	.5	.6	.6	.7	.8	.9	.9	1.0	1.1	1.1	74
75	.0	.1	.1	.2	.3	.3	.4	.5	.5	.6	.7	.7	.8	.9	.9	1.0	1.1	75
76	.0	.1	.1	.2	.3	.3	.4	.4	.5	.6	.6	.7	.8	.8	.9	.9	1.0	76
77	.0	.1	.1	.2	.2	.3	.4	.4	.5	.5	.6	.6	.7	.8	.8	.9	.9	77
78	.0	.1	.1	.2	.2	.3	.3	.4	.4	.5	.5	.6	.6	.7	.8	.8	.9	78
79	.0	.0	.1	.1	.2	.2	.3	.3	.4	.4	.5	.5	.6	.6	.7	.7	.8	79
80	.0	.0	.1	.1	.2	.2	.3	.3	.4	.4	.5	.5	.5	.6	.6	.7	.7	80
81	.0	.0	.1	.1	.2	.2	.2	.3	.3	.4	.4	.4	.5	.5	.6	.6	.6	81
82	.0	.0	.1	.1	.1	.2	.2	.3	.3	.3	.4	.4	.4	.5	.5	.5	.6	82
LAT.	0°	1°	2°	3°	4°	5°	6°	7°	8°	9°	10°	11°	12°	13°	14°	15°	16°	LAT.

Seconds	1	2	3	4	5	6
Minutes	.02	.03	.05	.07	.08	.1

Table 25 — ALTITUDE CHANGE in 1ᵐ of Time

AZIMUTH

LAT.	16° 164 196 344	17° 163 197 343	18° 162 198 342	19° 161 199 341	20° 160 200 340	21° 159 201 339	22° 158 202 338	23° 157 203 337	24° 156 204 336	25° 155 205 335	26° 154 206 334	27° 153 207 333	28° 152 208 332	29° 151 209 331	30° 150 210 330	31° 149 211 329	32° 148 212 328	LAT.
0°	4.1	4.4	4.6	4.9	5.1	5.4	5.6	5.9	6.1	6.3	6.6	6.8	7.0	7.3	7.5	7.7	7.9	0°
5	4.1	4.4	4.6	4.9	5.1	5.4	5.6	5.8	6.1	6.3	6.6	6.8	7.0	7.2	7.5	7.7	7.9	5
10	4.1	4.3	4.6	4.8	5.1	5.3	5.5	5.8	6.0	6.2	6.5	6.7	6.9	7.2	7.4	7.6	7.8	10
13	4.0	4.3	4.5	4.8	5.0	5.2	5.5	5.7	5.9	6.2	6.4	6.6	6.9	7.1	7.3	7.5	7.7	13
16	4.0	4.2	4.5	4.7	4.9	5.2	5.4	5.6	5.9	6.1	6.3	6.5	6.8	7.0	7.2	7.4	7.6	16
18	3.9	4.2	4.4	4.6	4.9	5.1	5.3	5.6	5.8	6.0	6.3	6.5	6.7	6.9	7.1	7.3	7.6	18
20	3.9	4.1	4.4	4.6	4.8	5.1	5.3	5.5	5.7	6.0	6.2	6.4	6.6	6.8	7.0	7.3	7.5	20
22	3.8	4.1	4.3	4.5	4.8	5.0	5.2	5.4	5.7	5.9	6.1	6.3	6.5	6.7	7.0	7.2	7.4	22
24	3.8	4.0	4.2	4.5	4.7	4.9	5.1	5.4	5.6	5.8	6.0	6.2	6.4	6.6	6.9	7.1	7.3	24
26	3.7	3.9	4.2	4.4	4.6	4.8	5.1	5.3	5.5	5.7	5.9	6.1	6.3	6.5	6.7	6.9	7.1	26
27	3.7	3.9	4.1	4.4	4.6	4.8	5.0	5.2	5.4	5.6	5.9	6.1	6.3	6.5	6.7	6.9	7.1	27
28	3.7	3.9	4.1	4.3	4.5	4.7	5.0	5.2	5.4	5.6	5.8	6.0	6.2	6.4	6.6	6.8	7.0	28
29	3.6	3.8	4.1	4.3	4.5	4.7	4.9	5.1	5.3	5.6	5.8	6.0	6.2	6.4	6.6	6.8	7.0	29
30	3.6	3.8	4.0	4.2	4.4	4.7	4.9	5.1	5.3	5.5	5.7	5.9	6.1	6.3	6.5	6.7	6.9	30
31	3.5	3.8	4.0	4.2	4.4	4.6	4.8	5.0	5.2	5.4	5.6	5.8	6.0	6.2	6.4	6.6	6.8	31
32	3.5	3.7	3.9	4.1	4.4	4.6	4.7	5.0	5.2	5.4	5.6	5.8	6.0	6.2	6.4	6.6	6.7	32
33	3.5	3.7	3.9	4.1	4.3	4.5	4.7	4.9	5.1	5.3	5.5	5.7	5.9	6.1	6.3	6.5	6.7	33
34	3.4	3.6	3.8	4.0	4.3	4.5	4.7	4.9	5.1	5.3	5.5	5.6	5.8	6.0	6.2	6.4	6.6	34
35	3.4	3.6	3.8	4.0	4.2	4.4	4.6	4.8	5.0	5.2	5.4	5.6	5.8	6.0	6.1	6.3	6.5	35
36	3.3	3.5	3.8	4.0	4.2	4.3	4.5	4.7	4.9	5.1	5.3	5.5	5.7	5.9	6.1	6.3	6.4	36
37	3.3	3.5	3.7	3.9	4.1	4.3	4.5	4.7	4.9	5.1	5.3	5.4	5.6	5.8	6.0	6.2	6.3	37
38	3.3	3.5	3.7	3.8	4.0	4.2	4.4	4.6	4.8	5.0	5.2	5.4	5.5	5.7	5.9	6.1	6.3	38
39	3.2	3.4	3.6	3.8	4.0	4.2	4.4	4.6	4.7	4.9	5.1	5.3	5.5	5.7	5.8	6.0	6.2	39
40	3.2	3.4	3.6	3.7	3.9	4.1	4.3	4.5	4.7	4.9	5.0	5.2	5.4	5.6	5.7	5.9	6.1	40
41	3.1	3.3	3.5	3.7	3.9	4.1	4.2	4.4	4.6	4.8	5.0	5.1	5.3	5.5	5.7	5.8	6.0	41
42	3.1	3.3	3.4	3.6	3.8	4.0	4.2	4.4	4.5	4.7	4.9	5.1	5.2	5.4	5.6	5.7	5.9	42
43	3.0	3.2	3.4	3.6	3.8	3.9	4.1	4.3	4.5	4.6	4.8	5.0	5.2	5.3	5.5	5.7	5.8	43
44	3.0	3.2	3.3	3.5	3.7	3.9	4.0	4.2	4.4	4.6	4.7	4.9	5.1	5.2	5.4	5.6	5.7	44
45	2.9	3.1	3.3	3.5	3.6	3.8	4.0	4.1	4.3	4.5	4.6	4.8	5.0	5.1	5.3	5.5	5.6	45
46	2.9	3.0	3.2	3.4	3.6	3.7	3.9	4.1	4.2	4.4	4.6	4.7	4.9	5.1	5.2	5.4	5.5	46
47	2.8	3.0	3.2	3.3	3.5	3.7	3.8	4.0	4.2	4.3	4.5	4.6	4.8	5.0	5.1	5.3	5.4	47
48	2.8	2.9	3.1	3.3	3.4	3.6	3.8	3.9	4.1	4.3	4.4	4.6	4.7	4.9	5.0	5.2	5.3	48
49	2.7	2.9	3.0	3.2	3.4	3.5	3.7	3.8	4.0	4.2	4.3	4.5	4.6	4.8	4.9	5.1	5.2	49
50	2.7	2.8	3.0	3.1	3.3	3.5	3.6	3.8	3.9	4.1	4.2	4.4	4.5	4.7	4.8	5.0	5.1	50
51	2.6	2.8	2.9	3.1	3.2	3.4	3.5	3.7	3.8	4.0	4.1	4.3	4.4	4.6	4.7	4.9	5.0	51
52	2.5	2.7	2.9	3.0	3.2	3.3	3.5	3.6	3.8	3.9	4.0	4.2	4.3	4.5	4.6	4.8	4.9	52
53	2.5	2.6	2.8	2.9	3.1	3.2	3.4	3.5	3.7	3.8	4.0	4.1	4.2	4.4	4.5	4.6	4.7	53
54	2.4	2.6	2.7	2.9	3.0	3.2	3.3	3.4	3.6	3.7	3.9	4.0	4.1	4.3	4.4	4.5	4.7	54
55	2.4	2.5	2.7	2.8	2.9	3.1	3.2	3.4	3.5	3.6	3.8	3.9	4.0	4.2	4.3	4.4	4.6	55
56	2.3	2.5	2.6	2.7	2.9	3.0	3.1	3.3	3.4	3.5	3.7	3.8	3.9	4.1	4.2	4.3	4.4	56
57	2.3	2.4	2.5	2.7	2.8	2.9	3.1	3.2	3.3	3.5	3.6	3.7	3.8	4.0	4.1	4.2	4.3	57
58	2.2	2.3	2.5	2.6	2.7	2.8	3.0	3.1	3.2	3.4	3.5	3.6	3.7	3.9	4.0	4.1	4.2	58
59	2.1	2.3	2.4	2.5	2.6	2.8	2.9	3.0	3.1	3.3	3.4	3.5	3.7	3.7	3.9	4.0	4.1	59
60	2.1	2.2	2.3	2.4	2.6	2.7	2.8	2.9	3.1	3.2	3.3	3.4	3.6	3.6	3.8	3.9	4.0	60
61	2.0	2.1	2.2	2.4	2.5	2.6	2.7	2.8	3.0	3.1	3.2	3.3	3.4	3.5	3.6	3.7	3.9	61
62	1.9	2.1	2.2	2.3	2.4	2.5	2.6	2.8	2.9	3.0	3.1	3.2	3.3	3.4	3.5	3.6	3.7	62
63	1.9	2.0	2.1	2.2	2.3	2.4	2.6	2.7	2.8	2.9	3.0	3.1	3.2	3.3	3.4	3.5	3.6	63
64	1.8	1.9	2.0	2.1	2.3	2.4	2.5	2.6	2.7	2.8	2.9	3.0	3.1	3.2	3.3	3.4	3.5	64
65	1.7	1.9	2.0	2.1	2.2	2.3	2.4	2.5	2.6	2.7	2.8	2.9	3.0	3.1	3.2	3.3	3.4	65
66	1.7	1.8	1.9	2.0	2.1	2.2	2.3	2.4	2.5	2.6	2.7	2.8	2.9	3.0	3.0	3.1	3.2	66
67	1.6	1.7	1.8	1.9	2.0	2.1	2.2	2.3	2.4	2.5	2.6	2.7	2.8	2.8	2.9	3.0	3.1	67
68	1.5	1.6	1.7	1.8	1.9	2.0	2.1	2.2	2.3	2.4	2.5	2.6	2.6	2.7	2.8	2.9	3.0	68
69	1.5	1.6	1.7	1.8	1.8	1.9	2.0	2.1	2.2	2.3	2.4	2.4	2.5	2.6	2.7	2.8	2.8	69
70	1.4	1.5	1.6	1.7	1.8	1.8	1.9	2.0	2.1	2.2	2.2	2.3	2.4	2.5	2.6	2.6	2.7	70
71	1.3	1.4	1.6	1.6	1.7	1.8	1.8	1.9	2.0	2.1	2.1	2.2	2.3	2.4	2.5	2.5	2.6	71
72	1.3	1.4	1.5	1.5	1.6	1.7	1.7	1.8	1.9	2.0	2.0	2.1	2.2	2.2	2.3	2.4	2.5	72
73	1.2	1.3	1.4	1.4	1.5	1.6	1.6	1.7	1.8	1.9	1.9	2.0	2.1	2.1	2.2	2.3	2.3	73
74	1.1	1.2	1.3	1.3	1.4	1.5	1.5	1.6	1.7	1.8	1.8	1.9	1.9	2.0	2.0	2.1	2.2	74
75	1.1	1.1	1.2	1.3	1.3	1.4	1.5	1.5	1.6	1.6	1.7	1.8	1.8	1.9	1.9	2.0	2.1	75
76	1.0	1.1	1.1	1.2	1.2	1.3	1.4	1.4	1.5	1.5	1.6	1.6	1.7	1.8	1.8	1.9	1.9	76
77	.9	1.0	1.0	1.1	1.2	1.2	1.3	1.3	1.4	1.4	1.5	1.5	1.6	1.6	1.7	1.7	1.8	77
78	.9	.9	1.0	1.0	1.1	1.1	1.2	1.2	1.3	1.3	1.4	1.4	1.5	1.5	1.6	1.6	1.7	78
79	.8	.8	.9	.9	1.0	1.0	1.1	1.1	1.2	1.2	1.3	1.3	1.3	1.4	1.4	1.5	1.5	79
80	.7	.8	.8	.8	.9	.9	1.0	1.0	1.1	1.1	1.1	1.2	1.2	1.3	1.3	1.3	1.4	80
81	.6	.7	.7	.8	.8	.8	.9	.9	1.0	1.0	1.0	1.1	1.1	1.1	1.2	1.2	1.2	81
82	.6	.6	.6	.7	.7	.7	.8	.8	.8	.9	.9	.9	1.0	1.0	1.0	1.1	1.1	82
LAT.	16°	17°	18°	19°	20°	21°	22°	23°	24°	25°	26°	27°	28°	29°	30°	31°	32°	LAT.

Seconds	1	2	3	4	5	6
Minutes	.02	.03	.05	.07	.08	.1

Table 25 ALTITUDE CHANGE in 1ᵐ of Time

AZIMUTH

LAT.	32° 148 212 328	33° 147 213 327	34° 146 214 326	35° 145 215 325	36° 144 216 324	37° 143 217 323	38° 142 218 322	39° 141 219 321	40° 140 220 320	41° 139 221 319	42° 138 222 318	43° 137 223 317	44° 136 224 316	45° 135 225 315	46° 134 226 314	47° 133 227 313	48° 132 228 312	LAT.
0°	7.9	8.2	8.4	8.6	8.8	9.0	9.2	9.4	9.6	9.8	10.0	10.2	10.4	10.6	10.8	11.0	11.1	0°
5	7.9	8.1	8.4	8.6	8.8	9.0	9.2	9.4	9.6	9.8	10.0	10.2	10.4	10.6	10.7	10.9	11.1	5
10	7.8	8.0	8.3	8.5	8.7	8.9	9.1	9.3	9.5	9.7	9.9	10.1	10.3	10.4	10.6	10.8	11.0	10
13	7.7	8.0	8.2	8.4	8.6	8.8	9.0	9.2	9.4	9.6	9.8	10.0	10.2	10.3	10.5	10.7	10.9	13
16	7.6	7.9	8.1	8.3	8.5	8.7	8.9	9.1	9.3	9.5	9.6	9.8	10.0	10.2	10.4	10.5	10.7	16
18	7.6	7.8	8.0	8.2	8.4	8.6	8.8	9.0	9.2	9.4	9.5	9.7	9.9	10.1	10.3	10.4	10.6	18
20	7.5	7.7	7.9	8.1	8.3	8.5	8.7	8.9	9.1	9.2	9.4	9.6	9.8	10.0	10.1	10.3	10.5	20
22	7.4	7.6	7.8	8.0	8.2	8.4	8.6	8.8	8.9	9.1	9.3	9.5	9.7	9.8	10.0	10.2	10.3	22
24	7.3	7.5	7.7	7.9	8.1	8.2	8.4	8.6	8.8	9.0	9.2	9.3	9.5	9.7	9.9	10.0	10.2	24
26	7.1	7.3	7.5	7.7	7.9	8.1	8.3	8.5	8.7	8.8	9.0	9.2	9.4	9.5	9.7	9.9	10.0	26
27	7.1	7.3	7.5	7.7	7.9	8.0	8.2	8.4	8.6	8.8	8.9	9.1	9.3	9.5	9.6	9.8	9.9	27
28	7.0	7.2	7.4	7.6	7.8	8.0	8.2	8.3	8.5	8.7	8.9	9.0	9.2	9.4	9.5	9.7	9.8	28
29	7.0	7.1	7.3	7.5	7.7	7.9	8.1	8.3	8.4	8.6	8.8	8.9	9.1	9.3	9.4	9.6	9.7	29
30	6.9	7.1	7.3	7.4	7.6	7.8	8.0	8.2	8.3	8.5	8.7	8.9	9.0	9.2	9.3	9.5	9.7	30
31	6.8	7.0	7.2	7.4	7.6	7.7	7.9	8.1	8.3	8.4	8.6	8.8	8.9	9.1	9.2	9.4	9.6	31
32	6.7	6.9	7.1	7.3	7.5	7.7	7.8	8.0	8.2	8.3	8.5	8.7	8.8	9.0	9.2	9.3	9.5	32
33	6.7	6.9	7.0	7.2	7.4	7.6	7.7	7.9	8.1	8.3	8.4	8.6	8.7	8.9	9.0	9.2	9.3	33
34	6.6	6.8	7.0	7.1	7.3	7.5	7.7	7.8	8.0	8.2	8.3	8.5	8.6	8.8	8.9	9.1	9.2	34
35	6.5	6.7	6.9	7.0	7.2	7.4	7.6	7.7	7.9	8.1	8.2	8.4	8.5	8.7	8.8	9.0	9.1	35
36	6.4	6.6	6.8	7.0	7.1	7.3	7.5	7.6	7.8	8.0	8.1	8.3	8.4	8.6	8.7	8.9	9.0	36
37	6.3	6.5	6.7	6.9	7.0	7.2	7.4	7.5	7.7	7.9	8.0	8.2	8.3	8.5	8.6	8.8	8.9	37
38	6.3	6.4	6.6	6.8	6.9	7.1	7.3	7.4	7.6	7.8	7.9	8.1	8.2	8.4	8.5	8.6	8.8	38
39	6.2	6.3	6.5	6.7	6.9	7.0	7.2	7.3	7.5	7.6	7.8	8.0	8.1	8.2	8.4	8.5	8.7	39
40	6.1	6.3	6.4	6.6	6.8	6.9	7.1	7.2	7.4	7.5	7.7	7.8	8.0	8.1	8.3	8.4	8.5	40
41	6.0	6.2	6.3	6.5	6.7	6.8	7.0	7.1	7.3	7.4	7.6	7.7	7.9	8.0	8.1	8.3	8.4	41
42	5.9	6.1	6.2	6.4	6.6	6.7	6.9	7.0	7.2	7.3	7.5	7.6	7.7	7.9	8.0	8.2	8.3	42
43	5.8	6.0	6.1	6.3	6.4	6.6	6.8	6.9	7.1	7.2	7.3	7.5	7.6	7.8	7.9	8.0	8.2	43
44	5.7	5.9	6.0	6.2	6.3	6.5	6.6	6.8	6.9	7.1	7.2	7.4	7.5	7.6	7.8	7.9	8.0	44
45	5.6	5.8	5.9	6.1	6.2	6.4	6.5	6.7	6.8	7.0	7.1	7.2	7.4	7.5	7.6	7.8	7.9	45
46	5.5	5.7	5.8	6.0	6.1	6.3	6.4	6.6	6.7	6.8	7.0	7.1	7.2	7.4	7.5	7.6	7.7	46
47	5.4	5.6	5.7	5.9	6.0	6.2	6.3	6.4	6.6	6.7	6.8	7.0	7.1	7.2	7.4	7.5	7.6	47
48	5.3	5.5	5.6	5.8	5.9	6.0	6.2	6.3	6.5	6.6	6.7	6.8	7.0	7.1	7.2	7.3	7.5	48
49	5.2	5.4	5.5	5.7	5.8	5.9	6.1	6.2	6.3	6.5	6.6	6.7	6.8	6.9	7.1	7.2	7.3	49
50	5.1	5.3	5.4	5.5	5.7	5.8	5.9	6.1	6.2	6.3	6.5	6.6	6.7	6.8	6.9	7.1	7.2	50
51	5.0	5.1	5.3	5.4	5.5	5.7	5.8	5.9	6.0	6.2	6.3	6.4	6.6	6.6	6.8	6.9	7.0	51
52	4.9	5.0	5.2	5.3	5.4	5.6	5.7	5.8	5.9	6.1	6.2	6.3	6.4	6.5	6.6	6.8	6.9	52
53	4.8	4.9	5.0	5.2	5.3	5.4	5.6	5.7	5.8	5.9	6.0	6.2	6.3	6.4	6.5	6.6	6.7	53
54	4.7	4.8	4.9	5.1	5.2	5.3	5.4	5.5	5.7	5.8	5.9	6.0	6.1	6.2	6.3	6.4	6.6	54
55	4.6	4.7	4.8	4.9	5.1	5.2	5.3	5.4	5.5	5.6	5.8	5.9	6.0	6.1	6.2	6.3	6.4	55
56	4.4	4.6	4.7	4.8	4.9	5.0	5.2	5.3	5.4	5.5	5.6	5.7	5.8	5.9	6.0	6.1	6.2	56
57	4.3	4.4	4.6	4.7	4.8	4.9	5.0	5.1	5.2	5.4	5.5	5.6	5.7	5.8	5.9	6.0	6.1	57
58	4.2	4.3	4.4	4.6	4.7	4.8	4.9	5.0	5.1	5.2	5.3	5.4	5.5	5.6	5.7	5.8	5.9	58
59	4.1	4.2	4.3	4.4	4.5	4.6	4.8	4.9	5.0	5.1	5.2	5.3	5.4	5.5	5.6	5.7	5.7	59
60	4.0	4.1	4.2	4.3	4.4	4.5	4.6	4.7	4.8	4.9	5.0	5.1	5.2	5.3	5.4	5.5	5.6	60
61	3.9	4.0	4.1	4.2	4.3	4.4	4.5	4.6	4.7	4.8	4.9	5.0	5.1	5.1	5.2	5.3	5.4	61
62	3.7	3.8	3.9	4.0	4.1	4.2	4.3	4.4	4.5	4.6	4.7	4.8	4.9	5.0	5.1	5.2	5.2	62
63	3.6	3.7	3.8	3.9	4.0	4.1	4.2	4.3	4.3	4.5	4.6	4.6	4.7	4.8	4.9	5.0	5.1	63
64	3.5	3.6	3.7	3.7	3.9	4.0	4.0	4.1	4.2	4.3	4.4	4.5	4.6	4.7	4.7	4.8	4.9	64
65	3.4	3.5	3.5	3.6	3.7	3.8	3.9	4.0	4.1	4.2	4.2	4.3	4.4	4.5	4.6	4.6	4.7	65
66	3.2	3.3	3.4	3.5	3.6	3.7	3.8	3.8	4.0	4.0	4.1	4.2	4.2	4.3	4.4	4.5	4.5	66
67	3.1	3.2	3.3	3.4	3.4	3.5	3.6	3.7	3.8	3.8	3.9	4.0	4.1	4.1	4.2	4.3	4.4	67
68	3.0	3.1	3.1	3.2	3.3	3.4	3.5	3.5	3.6	3.7	3.8	3.8	3.9	4.0	4.0	4.1	4.2	68
69	2.8	2.9	3.0	3.1	3.2	3.2	3.3	3.4	3.5	3.5	3.6	3.7	3.7	3.8	3.9	3.9	4.0	69
70	2.7	2.8	2.9	3.0	3.0	3.1	3.2	3.2	3.3	3.4	3.4	3.5	3.6	3.6	3.7	3.8	3.8	70
71	2.6	2.7	2.7	2.8	2.9	2.9	3.0	3.1	3.1	3.2	3.3	3.3	3.4	3.5	3.5	3.6	3.6	71
72	2.5	2.5	2.6	2.6	2.7	2.8	2.9	2.9	2.9	3.0	3.1	3.2	3.2	3.3	3.3	3.4	3.4	72
73	2.3	2.4	2.5	2.5	2.6	2.6	2.7	2.8	2.8	2.9	2.9	3.0	3.0	3.1	3.2	3.2	3.3	73
74	2.2	2.3	2.3	2.4	2.4	2.5	2.5	2.6	2.6	2.7	2.8	2.8	2.9	2.9	3.0	3.0	3.1	74
75	2.1	2.1	2.2	2.2	2.3	2.3	2.4	2.4	2.5	2.5	2.6	2.6	2.7	2.7	2.8	2.8	2.9	75
76	1.9	2.0	2.0	2.1	2.1	2.2	2.2	2.3	2.3	2.4	2.4	2.5	2.5	2.6	2.6	2.7	2.7	76
77	1.8	1.8	1.9	1.9	2.0	2.0	2.1	2.1	2.2	2.2	2.3	2.3	2.3	2.4	2.4	2.5	2.5	77
78	1.7	1.7	1.7	1.8	1.8	1.9	1.9	2.0	2.0	2.0	2.1	2.2	2.2	2.2	2.2	2.3	2.3	78
79	1.5	1.6	1.6	1.6	1.7	1.7	1.8	1.8	1.8	1.9	1.9	2.0	2.0	2.0	2.1	2.1	2.1	79
80	1.4	1.4	1.5	1.5	1.5	1.6	1.6	1.6	1.7	1.7	1.7	1.8	1.8	1.8	1.9	1.9	1.9	80
81	1.2	1.3	1.3	1.3	1.4	1.4	1.4	1.5	1.5	1.5	1.6	1.6	1.6	1.7	1.7	1.7	1.7	81
82	1.1	1.1	1.2	1.2	1.2	1.3	1.3	1.3	1.3	1.4	1.4	1.4	1.5	1.5	1.5	1.5	1.6	82
LAT.	32°	33°	34°	35°	36°	37°	38°	39°	40°	41°	42°	43°	44°	45°	46°	47°	48°	LAT.

Seconds	1	2	3	4	5	6
Minutes	.02	.03	.05	.07	.08	.1

Table 25 — ALTITUDE CHANGE in 1ᵐ of Time

AZIMUTH

LAT.	48° 132 228 312	49° 131 229 311	50° 130 230 310	52° 128 232 308	54° 126 234 306	56° 124 236 304	58° 122 238 302	60° 120 240 300	62° 118 242 298	64° 116 244 296	67° 113 247 293	70° 110 250 290	73° 107 253 287	76° 104 256 284	80° 100 260 280	85° 95 265 275	90° 90 270 270	LAT.
0°	11.1	11.3	11.5	11.8	12.1	12.4	12.7	13.0	13.2	13.5	13.8	14.1	14.4	14.6	14.8	14.9	15.0	0°
5	11.1	11.3	11.4	11.8	12.1	12.4	12.7	12.9	13.2	13.4	13.8	14.0	14.3	14.5	14.7	14.9	14.9	5
10	11.0	11.1	11.3	11.6	12.0	12.2	12.5	12.8	13.0	13.3	13.6	13.9	14.1	14.3	14.5	14.7	14.8	10
13	10.9	11.0	11.2	11.5	11.8	12.1	12.4	12.7	12.9	13.1	13.5	13.7	14.0	14.2	14.4	14.6	14.6	13
16	10.7	10.9	11.0	11.4	11.7	12.0	12.2	12.5	12.7	13.0	13.3	13.5	13.8	14.0	14.2	14.4	14.4	16
18	10.6	10.8	10.9	11.2	11.5	11.8	12.1	12.4	12.6	12.8	13.1	13.4	13.6	13.8	14.0	14.2	14.3	18
20	10.5	10.6	10.8	11.1	11.4	11.7	12.0	12.2	12.4	12.7	13.0	13.2	13.5	13.7	13.9	14.0	14.1	20
22	10.3	10.5	10.7	11.0	11.3	11.5	11.8	12.0	12.3	12.5	12.8	13.1	13.3	13.5	13.7	13.9	13.9	22
24	10.2	10.3	10.5	10.8	11.1	11.4	11.6	11.9	12.1	12.3	12.6	12.9	13.1	13.3	13.5	13.7	13.7	24
26	10.0	10.2	10.3	10.6	10.9	11.2	11.4	11.7	11.9	12.1	12.4	12.7	12.9	13.1	13.3	13.4	13.5	26
27	9.9	10.1	10.2	10.5	10.8	11.1	11.3	11.6	11.8	12.0	12.3	12.6	12.8	13.0	13.2	13.3	13.4	27
28	9.8	10.0	10.1	10.4	10.7	11.0	11.2	11.5	11.7	11.9	12.2	12.4	12.7	12.9	13.1	13.2	13.2	28
29	9.7	9.9	10.0	10.3	10.6	10.9	11.1	11.4	11.6	11.8	12.1	12.3	12.5	12.7	12.9	13.1	13.1	29
30	9.7	9.8	9.9	10.2	10.5	10.8	11.0	11.2	11.5	11.7	12.0	12.2	12.4	12.6	12.8	12.9	13.0	30
31	9.6	9.7	9.8	10.1	10.4	10.7	10.9	11.1	11.4	11.6	11.8	12.1	12.3	12.5	12.7	12.8	12.9	31
32	9.5	9.6	9.7	10.0	10.3	10.5	10.8	11.0	11.2	11.4	11.7	12.0	12.2	12.3	12.5	12.7	12.7	32
33	9.3	9.5	9.6	9.9	10.2	10.4	10.7	10.9	11.1	11.3	11.6	11.8	12.0	12.2	12.4	12.5	12.6	33
34	9.2	9.4	9.5	9.8	10.1	10.3	10.5	10.8	11.0	11.2	11.4	11.7	11.9	12.1	12.3	12.4	12.4	34
35	9.1	9.3	9.4	9.7	9.9	10.2	10.4	10.6	10.8	11.0	11.3	11.5	11.8	11.9	12.1	12.2	12.3	35
36	9.0	9.2	9.3	9.6	9.8	10.1	10.3	10.5	10.7	10.9	11.2	11.4	11.6	11.8	12.0	12.1	12.1	36
37	8.9	9.0	9.2	9.4	9.7	9.9	10.2	10.4	10.6	10.8	11.0	11.3	11.4	11.6	11.8	11.9	12.0	37
38	8.8	8.9	9.1	9.3	9.6	9.8	10.0	10.2	10.4	10.6	10.9	11.1	11.3	11.5	11.6	11.8	11.8	38
39	8.7	8.8	8.9	9.2	9.4	9.7	9.9	10.1	10.3	10.5	10.7	11.0	11.1	11.3	11.5	11.6	11.7	39
40	8.5	8.7	8.8	9.1	9.3	9.5	9.7	10.0	10.1	10.3	10.6	10.8	11.0	11.1	11.3	11.4	11.5	40
41	8.4	8.5	8.7	8.9	9.2	9.4	9.6	9.8	10.0	10.2	10.4	10.6	10.8	11.0	11.1	11.3	11.3	41
42	8.3	8.4	8.5	8.8	9.0	9.2	9.5	9.7	9.8	10.0	10.3	10.5	10.7	10.8	11.0	11.1	11.1	42
43	8.2	8.3	8.4	8.6	8.9	9.1	9.3	9.5	9.7	9.9	10.1	10.3	10.4	10.6	10.8	10.9	11.0	43
44	8.0	8.1	8.3	8.5	8.7	8.9	9.2	9.3	9.5	9.7	9.9	10.1	10.3	10.5	10.6	10.7	10.8	44
45	7.9	8.0	8.1	8.4	8.6	8.8	9.0	9.2	9.4	9.5	9.8	10.0	10.1	10.3	10.4	10.6	10.6	45
46	7.7	7.9	8.0	8.2	8.4	8.6	8.8	9.0	9.2	9.4	9.6	9.8	10.0	10.1	10.3	10.4	10.4	46
47	7.6	7.7	7.8	8.1	8.3	8.5	8.7	8.9	9.0	9.2	9.4	9.6	9.8	9.9	10.1	10.2	10.2	47
48	7.5	7.6	7.7	7.9	8.1	8.3	8.5	8.7	8.9	9.0	9.2	9.4	9.6	9.7	9.9	10.0	10.0	48
49	7.3	7.4	7.6	7.8	8.0	8.2	8.3	8.5	8.7	8.8	9.1	9.2	9.4	9.5	9.7	9.8	9.8	49
50	7.2	7.3	7.4	7.6	7.8	8.0	8.2	8.3	8.5	8.7	8.9	9.1	9.2	9.4	9.5	9.6	9.6	50
51	7.0	7.1	7.2	7.4	7.6	7.8	8.0	8.1	8.3	8.5	8.7	8.9	9.0	9.2	9.3	9.4	9.4	51
52	6.9	7.0	7.1	7.3	7.5	7.7	7.8	8.0	8.2	8.3	8.5	8.7	8.8	9.0	9.1	9.2	9.2	52
53	6.7	6.8	7.0	7.1	7.3	7.5	7.7	7.9	8.0	8.1	8.3	8.5	8.6	8.8	8.9	9.0	9.0	53
54	6.6	6.7	6.8	6.9	7.1	7.3	7.5	7.6	7.8	7.9	8.1	8.3	8.4	8.6	8.7	8.8	8.8	54
55	6.4	6.5	6.6	6.8	7.0	7.1	7.3	7.5	7.6	7.7	7.9	8.1	8.2	8.3	8.5	8.6	8.6	55
56	6.2	6.3	6.4	6.6	6.8	7.0	7.1	7.3	7.4	7.5	7.7	7.9	8.0	8.1	8.3	8.4	8.4	56
57	6.1	6.2	6.3	6.4	6.6	6.8	6.9	7.1	7.2	7.3	7.5	7.7	7.8	7.9	8.0	8.1	8.2	57
58	5.9	6.0	6.1	6.3	6.4	6.6	6.7	6.9	7.0	7.1	7.3	7.5	7.6	7.7	7.8	7.9	8.0	58
59	5.7	5.8	5.9	6.1	6.2	6.4	6.6	6.7	6.8	6.9	7.1	7.3	7.4	7.5	7.6	7.7	7.7	59
60	5.6	5.7	5.7	5.9	6.1	6.2	6.4	6.5	6.6	6.7	6.9	7.0	7.2	7.3	7.4	7.5	7.5	60
61	5.4	5.5	5.6	5.7	5.9	6.0	6.2	6.3	6.4	6.5	6.7	6.9	7.0	7.1	7.2	7.2	7.3	61
62	5.2	5.3	5.4	5.5	5.7	5.8	6.0	6.1	6.2	6.3	6.5	6.6	6.7	6.8	6.9	7.0	7.0	62
63	5.1	5.1	5.2	5.4	5.5	5.6	5.8	5.9	6.0	6.1	6.3	6.4	6.5	6.6	6.7	6.8	6.8	63
64	4.9	5.0	5.1	5.2	5.3	5.5	5.6	5.7	5.8	5.9	6.1	6.2	6.3	6.4	6.5	6.6	6.6	64
65	4.7	4.8	4.9	5.0	5.1	5.3	5.4	5.5	5.6	5.7	5.8	6.0	6.1	6.2	6.2	6.3	6.3	65
66	4.5	4.6	4.7	4.8	4.9	5.1	5.2	5.3	5.4	5.5	5.6	5.7	5.8	5.9	6.0	6.1	6.1	66
67	4.4	4.4	4.5	4.6	4.7	4.9	5.0	5.1	5.2	5.3	5.4	5.5	5.6	5.7	5.8	5.8	5.9	67
68	4.2	4.2	4.3	4.4	4.5	4.7	4.8	4.9	5.0	5.1	5.2	5.2	5.4	5.5	5.5	5.6	5.6	68
69	4.0	4.1	4.1	4.2	4.3	4.5	4.6	4.7	4.7	4.8	4.9	5.0	5.1	5.2	5.3	5.4	5.4	69
70	3.8	3.9	3.9	4.0	4.2	4.3	4.4	4.5	4.5	4.6	4.7	4.8	4.9	5.0	5.0	5.1	5.1	70
71	3.6	3.7	3.7	3.8	4.0	4.0	4.1	4.2	4.3	4.4	4.5	4.6	4.7	4.7	4.8	4.9	4.9	71
72	3.4	3.5	3.5	3.7	3.8	3.8	3.9	4.0	4.1	4.2	4.3	4.3	4.4	4.5	4.5	4.6	4.6	72
73	3.3	3.3	3.4	3.5	3.5	3.6	3.7	3.8	3.9	3.9	4.0	4.1	4.2	4.3	4.3	4.4	4.4	73
74	3.1	3.1	3.2	3.3	3.3	3.4	3.5	3.6	3.7	3.7	3.8	3.9	4.0	4.0	4.0	4.1	4.1	74
75	2.9	2.9	3.0	3.1	3.1	3.2	3.3	3.4	3.4	3.5	3.6	3.6	3.7	3.8	3.8	3.9	3.9	75
76	2.7	2.7	2.8	2.9	2.9	3.0	3.1	3.1	3.2	3.3	3.3	3.4	3.5	3.5	3.6	3.6	3.6	76
77	2.5	2.5	2.6	2.7	2.7	2.8	2.9	2.9	3.0	3.0	3.1	3.2	3.2	3.3	3.3	3.4	3.4	77
78	2.3	2.4	2.4	2.5	2.5	2.6	2.6	2.7	2.8	2.8	2.9	2.9	3.0	3.0	3.1	3.1	3.1	78
79	2.1	2.2	2.2	2.3	2.3	2.4	2.4	2.5	2.5	2.6	2.6	2.7	2.7	2.8	2.8	2.9	2.9	79
80	1.9	2.0	2.0	2.1	2.1	2.2	2.2	2.3	2.3	2.3	2.4	2.4	2.5	2.5	2.6	2.6	2.6	80
81	1.7	1.8	1.8	1.8	1.9	1.9	2.0	2.0	2.1	2.1	2.2	2.2	2.2	2.3	2.3	2.3	2.3	81
82	1.6	1.6	1.6	1.6	1.7	1.7	1.8	1.8	1.8	1.9	1.9	2.0	2.0	2.0	2.1	2.1	2.1	82
LAT.	48°	49°	50°	52°	54°	56°	58°	60°	62°	64°	67°	70°	73°	76°	80°	85°	90°	LAT.

Seconds	1	2	3	4	5	6
Minutes	.02	.03	.05	.07	.08	.1

239

Table 26

STARS AND THE MERIDIAN

S.H.A.M. = M.P.♈ − L.M.T.

where Mer. Pass. Aries is the time of the meridian passage of Aries given at the foot of the G.H.A. Aries column in the daily pages of the almanac, and L.M.T. is the local mean time of observing time, which, if not known, may be gauged from the (civil) twilight data also given in the daily pages of the almanac. It is recommended that Mer. Pass. Aries be always taken out for the local date.

See Note, p. xiii.

SELECTED STAR LIST

With S.H.A.s in intervals of Mean Solar Time

No.	Name	Mag.	S.H.A.		Dec.	No.	Name	Mag.	S.H.A.		Dec.
			h	m	°				h	m	°
1	Alpheratz	2.2	23	54	29 N	30	Acrux	1.1	11	38	63 S
2	Ankaa	2.4	23	36	43 S	31	Gacrux	1.6	11	33	57 S
3	Schedar	2.5	23	22	56 N	32	Alioth	1.7	11	10	56 N
4	Diphda	2.2	23	19	18 S	33	Spica	1.2	10	39	11 S
5	Achernar	0.6	22	24	57 S	34	Alkaid	1.9	10	16	50 N
6	Hamal	2.2	21	55	23 N	35	Hadar	0.9	10	01	60 S
7	Acamar	3.1	21	04	40 S	36	Menkent	2.3	9	58	36 S
8	Menkar	2.8	21	00	4 N	37	Arcturus	0.2	9	49	19 N
9	Mirfak	1.9	20	39	50 N	38	Rigil Kent.	0.1	9	25	61 S
10	Aldebaran	1.1	19	27	16 N	39	Zuben'ubi	2.9	9	14	16 S
11	Rigel	0.3	18	48	8 S	40	Kochab	2.2	9	12	74 N
12	Capella	0.2	18	47	46 N	41	Alphecca	2.3	8	30	27 N
13	Bellatrix	1.7	18	38	6 N	42	Antares	1.2	7	36	26 S
14	Elnath	1.8	18	37	29 N	43	Atria	1.9	7	18	69 S
15	Alnilam	1.8	18	27	1 S	44	Sabik	2.6	6	55	16 S
16	Betelgeuse	*	18	08	7 N	45	Shaula	1.7	6	32	37 S
17	Canopus	−0.9	17	38	53 S	46	Rasalhague	2.1	6	30	13 N
18	Sirius	−1.6	17	18	17 S	47	Eltanin	2.4	6	07	51 N
19	Adhara	1.6	17	04	29 S	48	Kaus Aust.	2.0	5	42	34 S
20	Procyon	0.5	16	24	5 N	49	Vega	0.1	5	28	39 N
21	Pollux	1.2	16	18	28 N	50	Nunki	2.1	5	10	26 S
22	Avior	1.7	15	40	59 S	51	Altair	0.9	4	14	9 N
23	Suhail	2.2	14	55	43 S	52	Peacock	2.1	3	41	57 S
24	Miaplacidus	1.8	14	49	70 S	53	Deneb	1.3	3	23	45 N
25	Alphard	2.2	14	36	8 S	54	Enif	2.5	2	21	10 N
26	Regulus	1.3	13	55	12 N	55	Al Na'ir	2.2	1	58	47 S
27	Dubhe	2.0	13	01	62 N	56	Fomalhaut	1.3	1	08	30 S
28	Denebola	2.2	12	15	15 N	57	Markab	2.6	1	01	15 N
29	Gienah	2.8	11	48	17 S						

* Varies 0 to 1.3

Correction to S.H.A.M. for Longitude, EAST +, WEST −		
0° to 45°	45° to 135°	135° to 180°
Nil	1m	2m

Table 27 — HOUR ANGLE CHANGE per 1′ of Altitude

AZIMUTH

LAT.	10° 170 190 350	15° 165 195 345	20° 160 200 340	25° 155 205 335	30° 150 210 330	35° 145 215 325	40° 140 220 320	45° 135 225 315	50° 130 230 310	55° 125 235 305	60° 120 240 300	65° 115 245 295	70° 110 250 290	75° 105 255 285	80° 100 260 280	90° 90 270 270	LAT.
	s	s	s	s	s	s	s	s	s	s	s	s	s	s	s	s	
0°	23.0	15.5	11.7	9.5	8.0	7.0	6.2	5.7	5.2	4.9	4.6	4.4	4.3	4.1	4.1	4.0	0°
10	23.4	15.7	11.9	9.6	8.1	7.1	6.3	5.7	5.3	5.0	4.7	4.5	4.3	4.2	4.1	4.1	10
15	23.8	16.0	12.1	9.8	8.3	7.2	6.4	5.9	5.4	5.1	4.8	4.6	4.4	4.3	4.2	4.1	15
20	24.5	16.4	12.4	10.1	8.5	7.4	6.6	6.0	5.6	5.2	4.9	4.7	4.5	4.4	4.3	4.3	20
22	24.8	16.7	12.6	10.2	8.6	7.5	6.7	6.1	5.6	5.3	5.0	4.8	4.6	4.5	4.4	4.3	22
24	25.2	16.9	12.8	10.4	8.8	7.6	6.8	6.2	5.7	5.3	5.1	4.8	4.7	4.5	4.4	4.4	24
26	25.6	17.2	13.0	10.5	8.9	7.8	6.9	6.3	5.8	5.4	5.1	4.9	4.7	4.6	4.5	4.5	26
28	26.1	17.5	13.2	10.7	9.1	7.9	7.0	6.4	5.9	5.5	5.2	5.0	4.8	4.7	4.6	4.5	28
30	26.6	17.8	13.5	10.9	9.2	8.1	7.2	6.5	6.0	5.6	5.3	5.1	4.9	4.8	4.7	4.6	30
32	27.2	18.2	13.8	11.2	9.4	8.2	7.3	6.7	6.2	5.8	5.4	5.2	5.0	4.9	4.8	4.7	32
34	27.8	18.6	14.1	11.4	9.6	8.4	7.5	6.8	6.3	5.9	5.6	5.3	5.1	5.0	4.9	4.8	34
36	28.5	19.1	14.5	11.7	9.9	8.6	7.7	7.0	6.5	6.0	5.7	5.5	5.3	5.1	5.0	4.9	36
38	29.2	19.6	14.8	12.0	10.2	8.8	7.9	7.2	6.6	6.2	5.9	5.6	5.4	5.3	5.2	5.1	38
40	30.1	20.2	15.3	12.4	10.4	9.1	8.1	7.4	6.8	6.4	6.0	5.8	5.6	5.4	5.3	5.2	40
42	31.0	20.8	15.7	12.7	10.8	9.4	8.4	7.6	7.0	6.6	6.2	5.9	5.7	5.6	5.5	5.4	42
44	32.0	21.5	16.3	13.2	11.1	9.7	8.7	7.9	7.3	6.8	6.4	6.1	5.9	5.8	5.6	5.6	44
46	33.2	22.2	16.8	13.6	11.5	10.0	9.0	8.1	7.5	7.0	6.6	6.4	6.1	6.0	5.8	5.8	46
48	34.4	23.1	17.5	14.1	12.0	10.4	9.3	8.5	7.8	7.3	6.9	6.6	6.4	6.2	6.1	6.0	48
50	35.8	24.0	18.2	14.7	12.5	10.8	9.7	8.8	8.1	7.6	7.2	6.9	6.6	6.4	6.3	6.2	50
51	36.6	24.6	18.6	15.0	12.7	11.1	9.9	9.0	8.3	7.8	7.3	7.0	6.8	6.6	6.5	6.4	51
52	37.4	25.1	19.0	15.4	13.0	11.3	10.1	9.2	8.5	7.9	7.5	7.2	6.9	6.7	6.6	6.5	52
53	38.3	25.7	19.4	15.7	13.3	11.6	10.3	9.4	8.7	8.1	7.7	7.3	7.1	6.9	6.7	6.6	53
54	39.2	26.3	19.9	16.1	13.6	11.9	10.6	9.6	8.9	8.3	7.9	7.5	7.2	7.0	6.9	6.8	54
55	40.2	26.9	20.4	16.5	13.9	12.2	10.8	9.9	9.1	8.5	8.1	7.7	7.4	7.2	7.1	7.0	55
56	41.2	27.6	20.9	16.9	14.3	12.5	11.1	10.1	9.3	8.7	8.3	7.9	7.6	7.4	7.3	7.2	56
57	42.3	28.4	21.5	17.4	14.7	12.8	11.4	10.4	9.6	9.0	8.5	8.1	7.8	7.6	7.5	7.3	57
58	43.5	29.2	22.1	17.9	15.1	13.2	11.7	10.7	9.9	9.2	8.7	8.3	8.0	7.8	7.7	7.5	58
59	44.7	30.0	22.7	18.4	15.5	13.5	12.1	11.0	10.1	9.5	9.0	8.6	8.3	8.0	7.9	7.9	59
60	46.1	30.9	23.4	18.9	16.0	13.9	12.4	11.3	10.4	9.8	9.2	8.8	8.5	8.3	8.1	8.0	60
61	47.5	31.9	24.1	19.5	16.5	14.4	12.8	11.7	10.8	10.1	9.5	9.1	8.8	8.5	8.4	8.3	61
62	49.1	32.9	24.9	20.2	17.0	14.9	13.3	12.0	11.1	10.4	9.8	9.4	9.1	8.8	8.7	8.5	62
63	50.7	34.0	25.8	20.8	17.6	15.4	13.7	12.5	11.5	10.8	10.2	9.7	9.4	9.1	8.9	8.8	63
64	52.5	35.3	26.7	21.6	18.2	15.9	14.2	12.9	11.9	11.1	10.5	10.1	9.7	9.4	9.3	9.1	64
65	54.5	36.6	27.7	22.4	18.9	16.5	14.7	13.4	12.4	11.5	10.9	10.4	10.1	9.8	9.6	9.5	65
66	56.6	38.0	28.8	23.3	19.7	17.1	15.3	13.9	12.8	12.0	11.4	10.9	10.5	10.2	10.0	9.8	66
67	59.0	39.6	29.9	24.2	20.5	17.8	15.9	14.5	13.4	12.5	11.8	11.3	10.9	10.6	10.4	10.2	67
68	61.5	41.3	31.2	25.3	21.4	18.6	16.6	15.1	13.9	13.0	12.3	11.8	11.4	11.1	10.8	10.7	68
69	64.3	43.1	32.6	26.4	22.3	19.5	17.4	15.8	14.6	13.6	12.9	12.3	11.9	11.6	11.3	11.2	69
70	67.3	45.2	34.2	27.7	23.4	20.4	18.2	16.5	15.3	14.3	13.5	12.9	12.4	12.1	11.9	11.7	70
71	70.8	47.5	35.9	29.1	24.6	21.4	19.1	17.4	16.0	15.0	14.2	13.6	13.1	12.7	12.5	12.3	71
72	74.5	50.0	37.8	30.6	25.9	22.6	20.1	18.3	16.9	15.8	14.9	14.3	13.8	13.4	13.1	12.9	72
73	78.8	52.9	40.0	32.4	27.4	23.9	21.3	19.3	17.9	16.7	15.8	15.1	14.6	14.2	13.9	13.7	73
74	83.6	56.1	42.4	34.3	29.0	25.3	22.6	20.5	18.9	17.7	16.8	16.0	15.4	15.0	14.7	14.5	74
75	89.0	59.7	45.2	36.6	30.9	26.9	24.0	21.9	20.2	18.9	17.8	17.1	16.4	16.0	15.7	15.5	75
76	95.2	63.9	48.3	39.1	33.1	28.8	25.7	23.4	21.6	20.2	19.1	18.2	17.6	17.1	16.8	16.5	76
77	102.	68.7	52.0	42.1	35.6	31.0	27.7	25.1	23.2	21.7	20.5	19.6	18.9	18.4	18.1	17.8	77
78	111.	74.3	56.3	45.5	38.5	33.5	29.9	27.2	25.1	23.5	22.2	21.2	20.5	19.9	19.5	19.2	78
79	121.	81.0	61.3	49.6	41.9	36.5	32.6	29.6	27.4	25.6	24.2	23.1	22.3	21.7	21.3	21.0	79
80	133.	89.0	67.4	54.5	46.1	40.2	35.8	32.6	30.1	28.1	26.6	25.4	24.5	23.8	23.4	23.0	80
81	147.	98.8	74.8	60.5	51.1	44.6	39.8	36.2	33.4	31.2	29.5	28.2	27.2	26.5	26.0	25.6	81
82	166.	111.	84.0	68.0	57.5	50.1	44.7	40.6	37.5	35.1	33.2	31.7	30.6	29.8	29.2	28.7	82

Table 28 — TRUE AMPLITUDES

DECLINATION

LAT.	1° Time	1° Arc	2° Time	2° Arc	3° Time	3° Arc	4° Time	4° Arc	5° Time	5° Arc	6° Time	6° Arc	7° Time	7° Arc	8° Time	8° Arc	9° Time	9° Arc	LAT.
	h m	°	h m	°	h m	°	h m	°	h m	°	h m	°	h m	°	h m	°	h m	°	
5°	0 0	1.0	0 1	2.0	0 1	3.0	0 1	4.0	0 2	5.0	0 2	6.0	0 2	7.0	0 3	8.0	0 3	9.0	5°
10	0 1	1.0	0 1	2.0	0 2	3.1	0 3	4.1	0 4	5.1	0 4	6.1	0 5	7.1	0 6	8.1	0 6	9.2	10
14	0 1	1.0	0 2	2.1	0 3	3.1	0 4	4.1	0 5	5.2	0 6	6.2	0 7	7.2	0 8	8.3	0 9	9.3	14
17	0 1	1.1	0 2	2.1	0 4	3.1	0 5	4.2	0 6	5.2	0 7	6.3	0 9	7.3	0 10	8.4	0 11	9.4	17
20	0 1	1.1	0 3	2.1	0 4	3.2	0 6	4.3	0 7	5.3	0 9	6.4	0 10	7.5	0 12	8.5	0 13	9.6	20
22	0 2	1.1	0 3	2.2	0 5	3.2	0 6	4.3	0 8	5.4	0 10	6.5	0 11	7.6	0 13	8.6	0 15	9.7	22
24	0 2	1.1	0 4	2.2	0 5	3.3	0 7	4.4	0 9	5.5	0 11	6.6	0 13	7.7	0 14	8.8	0 16	9.9	24
26	0 2	1.1	0 4	2.2	0 6	3.4	0 8	4.5	0 10	5.6	0 12	6.7	0 14	7.8	0 16	8.9	0 18	10.0	26
28	0 2	1.1	0 4	2.3	0 6	3.4	0 9	4.5	0 11	5.7	0 13	6.8	0 15	7.9	0 17	9.1	0 19	10.2	28
30	0 2	1.2	0 5	2.3	0 7	3.5	0 9	4.6	0 12	5.8	0 14	6.9	0 16	8.1	0 19	9.3	0 21	10.4	30
31	0 2	1.2	0 5	2.3	0 7	3.5	0 10	4.7	0 12	5.8	0 14	7.0	0 17	8.2	0 19	9.4	0 22	10.5	31
32	0 2	1.2	0 5	2.4	0 7	3.5	0 10	4.7	0 13	5.9	0 15	7.1	0 18	8.3	0 20	9.5	0 23	10.6	32
33	0 3	1.2	0 5	2.4	0 8	3.6	0 11	4.8	0 13	6.0	0 16	7.2	0 18	8.4	0 21	9.6	0 24	10.8	33
34	0 3	1.2	0 5	2.4	0 8	3.6	0 11	4.8	0 14	6.0	0 16	7.3	0 19	8.4	0 22	9.7	0 25	10.9	34
35	0 3	1.2	0 6	2.4	0 8	3.7	0 11	4.9	0 14	6.1	0 17	7.3	0 20	8.5	0 23	9.8	0 25	11.0	35
36	0 3	1.2	0 6	2.5	0 9	3.7	0 12	4.9	0 15	6.2	0 18	7.4	0 20	8.7	0 23	9.9	0 26	11.2	36
37	0 3	1.3	0 6	2.5	0 9	3.8	0 12	5.0	0 15	6.3	0 18	7.5	0 21	8.8	0 24	10.0	0 27	11.3	37
38	0 3	1.3	0 6	2.5	0 9	3.8	0 13	5.1	0 16	6.3	0 19	7.6	0 22	8.9	0 25	10.2	0 28	11.4	38
39	0 3	1.3	0 6	2.6	0 10	3.9	0 13	5.2	0 16	6.4	0 20	7.7	0 23	9.0	0 26	10.3	0 29	11.6	39
40	0 3	1.3	0 7	2.6	0 10	3.9	0 13	5.2	0 17	6.5	0 20	7.9	0 24	9.2	0 27	10.5	0 31	11.8	40
41	0 3	1.3	0 7	2.6	0 10	4.0	0 14	5.3	0 17	6.6	0 21	8.0	0 25	9.3	0 28	10.6	0 32	12.0	41
42	0 4	1.4	0 7	2.7	0 11	4.0	0 14	5.4	0 18	6.7	0 22	8.1	0 25	9.4	0 29	10.8	0 33	12.2	42
43	0 4	1.4	0 7	2.7	0 11	4.1	0 15	5.5	0 19	6.9	0 22	8.2	0 26	9.6	0 30	11.0	0 34	12.4	43
44	0 4	1.4	0 8	2.8	0 12	4.2	0 15	5.6	0 19	7.0	0 23	8.4	0 27	9.8	0 31	11.2	0 35	12.6	44
45	0 4	1.4	0 8	2.8	0 12	4.3	0 16	5.7	0 20	7.1	0 24	8.5	0 28	9.9	0 32	11.4	0 36	12.8	45
46	0 4	1.4	0 8	2.9	0 12	4.3	0 17	5.8	0 21	7.2	0 25	8.7	0 29	10.1	0 33	11.6	0 38	13.0	46
47	0 4	1.5	0 9	2.9	0 13	4.4	0 17	5.9	0 22	7.4	0 26	8.8	0 30	10.3	0 35	11.8	0 39	13.3	47
48	0 4	1.5	0 9	3.0	0 13	4.5	0 18	6.0	0 22	7.5	0 27	9.0	0 31	10.5	0 36	12.0	0 41	13.5	48
½	0 5	1.5	0 9	3.0	0 14	4.5	0 18	6.0	0 23	7.6	0 27	9.1	0 32	10.6	0 37	12.1	0 41	13.7	½
49	0 5	1.5	0 9	3.0	0 14	4.6	0 18	6.1	0 23	7.6	0 28	9.2	0 32	10.7	0 37	12.3	0 42	13.8	49
½	0 5	1.5	0 9	3.1	0 14	4.6	0 19	6.2	0 24	7.7	0 28	9.3	0 33	10.8	0 38	12.4	0 43	13.9	½
50	0 5	1.5	0 10	3.1	0 14	4.7	0 19	6.2	0 24	7.8	0 29	9.4	0 34	10.9	0 39	12.5	0 44	14.1	50
½	0 5	1.5	0 10	3.1	0 15	4.7	0 19	6.3	0 24	7.9	0 29	9.5	0 34	11.0	0 39	12.6	0 44	14.2	½
51	0 5	1.6	0 10	3.2	0 15	4.8	0 20	6.4	0 25	8.0	0 30	9.6	0 35	11.2	0 40	12.8	0 45	14.4	51
½	0 5	1.6	0 10	3.2	0 15	4.8	0 20	6.4	0 25	8.0	0 30	9.7	0 36	11.3	0 41	12.9	0 46	14.6	½
52	0 5	1.6	0 10	3.3	0 15	4.9	0 21	6.5	0 26	8.1	0 31	9.8	0 36	11.4	0 41	13.1	0 47	14.7	52
½	0 5	1.6	0 10	3.3	0 16	4.9	0 21	6.6	0 26	8.2	0 31	9.9	0 37	11.6	0 42	13.2	0 48	14.9	½
53	0 5	1.6	0 11	3.3	0 16	5.0	0 21	6.7	0 27	8.3	0 32	10.0	0 38	11.7	0 43	13.4	0 49	15.1	53
½	0 5	1.7	0 11	3.4	0 16	5.0	0 22	6.7	0 27	8.4	0 33	10.1	0 38	11.8	0 44	13.5	0 49	15.2	½
54	0 5	1.7	0 11	3.4	0 16	5.1	0 22	6.8	0 28	8.5	0 33	10.3	0 39	12.0	0 45	13.7	0 50	15.4	54
½	0 6	1.7	0 11	3.5	0 17	5.2	0 23	6.9	0 28	8.6	0 34	10.4	0 40	12.1	0 45	13.8	0 51	15.6	½
55	0 6	1.7	0 11	3.5	0 17	5.2	0 23	7.0	0 29	8.7	0 35	10.5	0 40	12.3	0 46	14.1	0 52	15.8	55
½	0 6	1.8	0 12	3.6	0 17	5.3	0 23	7.1	0 29	8.9	0 35	10.6	0 41	12.4	0 47	14.2	0 53	16.0	½
56	0 6	1.8	0 12	3.6	0 18	5.4	0 24	7.2	0 30	9.0	0 36	10.7	0 42	12.6	0 48	14.4	0 54	16.3	56
½	0 6	1.8	0 12	3.7	0 18	5.5	0 24	7.3	0 30	9.1	0 37	10.9	0 43	12.8	0 49	14.6	0 55	16.5	½
57	0 6	1.8	0 12	3.7	0 18	5.5	0 25	7.4	0 31	9.2	0 37	11.1	0 44	12.9	0 50	14.8	0 56	16.7	57
½	0 6	1.9	0 13	3.7	0 19	5.6	0 25	7.5	0 32	9.3	0 38	11.2	0 44	13.1	0 51	15.0	0 58	16.9	½
58	0 6	1.9	0 13	3.8	0 19	5.7	0 26	7.6	0 32	9.5	0 39	11.4	0 45	13.3	0 52	15.2	0 59	17.2	58
½	0 7	1.9	0 13	3.8	0 20	5.7	0 26	7.7	0 33	9.6	0 40	11.5	0 46	13.5	0 53	15.4	1 00	17.4	½
59	0 7	1.9	0 13	3.9	0 20	5.8	0 27	7.8	0 33	9.8	0 40	11.7	0 47	13.7	0 54	15.7	1 01	17.7	59
½	0 7	2.0	0 14	3.9	0 20	5.9	0 27	7.9	0 34	9.9	0 41	11.9	0 48	13.9	0 55	15.9	1 02	18.0	½
60	0 7	2.0	0 14	4.0	0 21	6.0	0 28	8.0	0 35	10.0	0 42	12.1	0 49	14.1	0 56	16.2	1 04	18.2	60
LAT.	1°		2°		3°		4°		5°		6°		7°		8°		9°		LAT.

Note.—Owing to refraction the moment of TRUE Amplitude occurs when the sun's lower limb appears to be about half a diameter above the horizon. In moderate latitudes it is sufficient to judge this moment and observe accordingly. In the case of the higher latitudes, however, observations should either be timed, or the APPARENT Amplitude observed and corrected by means of the supplementary table.

Table 28

TRUE AMPLITUDES

DECLINATION

LAT.	10° Time	10° Arc	11° Time	11° Arc	12° Time	12° Arc	13° Time	13° Arc	14° Time	14° Arc	15° Time	15° Arc	16° Time	16° Arc	17° Time	17° Arc	18° Time	18° Arc	LAT.
	h m	°	h m	°	h m	°	h m	°	h m	°	h m	°	h m	°	h m	°	h m	°	
0°	0 0	10.0	0 0	11.0	0 0	12.0	0 0	13.0	0 0	14.0	0 0	15.0	0 0	16.0	0 0	17.0	0 0	18.0	0°
5	0 4	10.1	0 4	11.1	0 4	12.1	0 5	13.1	0 5	14.1	0 5	15.1	0 6	16.1	0 6	17.1	0 7	18.1	5
10	0 7	10.1	0 8	11.2	0 9	12.2	0 9	13.2	0 10	14.2	0 11	15.2	0 12	16.2	0 12	17.3	0 13	18.3	10
14	0 10	10.3	0 11	11.3	0 12	12.4	0 13	13.4	0 14	14.4	0 15	15.5	0 16	16.5	0 17	17.5	0 19	18.6	14
17	0 12	10.5	0 14	11.5	0 15	12.6	0 16	13.6	0 17	14.7	0 19	15.7	0 20	16.8	0 21	17.8	0 23	18.9	17
20	0 15	10.6	0 16	11.7	0 18	12.8	0 19	13.8	0 21	14.9	0 22	16.0	0 24	17.1	0 26	18.1	0 27	19.2	20
22	0 16	10.8	0 18	11.9	0 20	13.0	0 21	14.1	0 23	15.1	0 25	16.2	0 27	17.3	0 28	18.4	0 30	19.5	22
24	0 18	11.0	0 20	12.1	0 22	13.2	0 24	14.3	0 26	15.4	0 27	16.5	0 29	17.6	0 31	18.7	0 33	19.8	24
26	0 20	11.2	0 22	12.3	0 24	13.4	0 26	14.5	0 28	15.6	0 30	16.8	0 32	17.9	0 34	19.0	0 36	20.1	26
28	0 22	11.4	0 24	12.5	0 26	13.6	0 28	14.8	0 30	15.9	0 33	17.1	0 35	18.2	0 37	19.3	0 40	20.5	28
30	0 23	11.6	0 26	12.7	0 28	13.9	0 31	15.0	0 33	16.2	0 36	17.4	0 38	18.6	0 41	19.7	0 43	20.9	30
31	0 24	11.7	0 27	12.9	0 29	14.0	0 32	15.2	0 34	16.4	0 37	17.6	0 40	18.8	0 42	20.0	0 45	21.1	31
32	0 25	11.8	0 28	13.0	0 31	14.2	0 33	15.4	0 36	16.6	0 39	17.8	0 41	19.0	0 44	20.2	0 47	21.4	32
33	0 26	12.0	0 29	13.2	0 32	14.4	0 34	15.6	0 37	16.8	0 40	18.0	0 43	19.2	0 46	20.4	0 49	21.6	33
34	0 27	12.1	0 30	13.3	0 33	14.5	0 36	15.7	0 39	17.0	0 42	18.2	0 45	19.4	0 48	20.6	0 51	21.9	34
35	0 28	12.2	0 31	13.5	0 34	14.7	0 37	15.9	0 40	17.2	0 43	18.4	0 46	19.6	0 49	20.9	0 53	22.2	35
36	0 29	12.4	0 32	13.6	0 36	14.9	0 39	16.1	0 42	17.4	0 45	18.7	0 48	19.9	0 51	21.2	0 55	22.4	36
37	0 31	12.6	0 34	13.8	0 37	15.1	0 40	16.4	0 43	17.6	0 47	18.9	0 50	20.2	0 53	21.5	0 57	22.8	37
38	0 32	12.7	0 35	14.0	0 38	15.3	0 42	16.6	0 45	17.9	0 48	19.2	0 52	20.5	0 55	21.8	0 59	23.1	38
39	0 33	12.9	0 36	14.2	0 40	15.5	0 43	16.8	0 47	18.1	0 50	19.4	0 54	20.8	0 57	22.1	1 01	23.4	39
40	0 34	13.1	0 38	14.4	0 41	15.7	0 45	17.1	0 48	18.4	0 52	19.7	0 56	21.1	0 59	22.4	1 03	23.8	40
41	0 35	13.3	0 39	14.6	0 43	16.0	0 46	17.3	0 50	18.7	0 54	20.0	0 58	21.4	1 02	22.8	1 06	24.2	41
42	0 37	13.5	0 40	14.8	0 44	16.2	0 48	17.6	0 52	19.0	0 56	20.4	1 00	21.8	1 04	23.2	1 08	24.6	42
43	0 38	13.7	0 42	15.1	0 46	16.5	0 50	17.9	0 54	19.3	0 58	20.7	1 02	22.1	1 06	23.6	1 11	25.0	43
44	0 39	14.0	0 43	15.4	0 47	16.8	0 52	18.2	0 56	19.6	1 00	21.1	1 04	22.5	1 09	24.0	1 13	25.4	44
45	0 41	14.2	0 45	15.6	0 49	17.1	0 53	18.5	0 58	20.0	1 02	21.5	1 07	22.9	1 11	24.4	1 16	25.9	45
46	0 42	14.5	0 46	15.9	0 51	17.4	0 55	18.9	1 00	20.4	1 04	21.9	1 09	23.4	1 14	24.9	1 19	26.4	46
47	0 44	14.7	0 48	16.2	0 53	17.7	0 57	19.3	1 02	20.8	1 07	22.3	1 12	23.8	1 17	25.4	1 22	26.9	47
48	0 45	15.0	0 50	16.6	0 55	18.1	0 59	19.6	1 04	21.2	1 09	22.8	1 14	24.3	1 19	25.9	1 25	27.5	48
48½	0 46	15.2	0 51	16.7	0 56	18.3	1 00	19.8	1 05	21.4	1 11	23.0	1 16	24.6	1 21	26.2	1 26	27.8	48½
49	0 47	15.3	0 52	16.9	0 57	18.5	1 02	20.0	1 07	21.6	1 12	23.2	1 17	24.8	1 22	26.5	1 28	28.1	49
49½	0 48	15.5	0 53	17.1	0 58	18.7	1 03	20.3	1 08	21.9	1 13	23.5	1 18	25.1	1 24	26.8	1 29	28.4	49½
50	0 49	15.7	0 54	17.3	0 59	18.9	1 04	20.5	1 09	22.1	1 15	23.7	1 20	25.4	1 25	27.0	1 31	28.7	50
50½	0 49	15.8	0 55	17.5	1 00	19.1	1 05	20.7	1 10	22.4	1 16	24.0	1 21	25.7	1 27	27.4	1 33	29.1	50½
51	0 50	16.0	0 56	17.6	1 01	19.3	1 06	20.9	1 12	22.6	1 17	24.3	1 23	26.0	1 29	27.7	1 35	29.4	51
51½	0 51	16.2	0 57	17.8	1 02	19.5	1 07	21.2	1 13	22.9	1 19	24.6	1 25	26.3	1 30	28.0	1 36	29.8	51½
52	0 52	16.4	0 58	18.0	1 03	19.7	1 09	21.4	1 14	23.1	1 20	24.9	1 26	26.6	1 32	28.3	1 38	30.1	52
52½	0 53	16.6	0 59	18.3	1 04	20.0	1 10	21.7	1 16	23.4	1 22	25.2	1 28	26.9	1 34	28.7	1 40	30.5	52½
53	0 54	16.8	1 00	18.5	1 06	20.2	1 11	21.9	1 17	23.7	1 23	25.5	1 29	27.3	1 36	29.1	1 42	30.9	53
53½	0 55	17.0	1 01	18.7	1 07	20.5	1 13	22.2	1 19	24.0	1 25	25.8	1 31	27.6	1 38	29.4	1 44	31.3	53½
54	0 56	17.2	1 02	18.9	1 08	20.7	1 14	22.5	1 20	24.3	1 27	26.1	1 33	28.0	1 40	29.8	1 46	31.7	54
54½	0 57	17.4	1 03	19.2	1 09	21.0	1 16	22.8	1 22	24.6	1 28	26.5	1 35	28.3	1 42	30.2	1 48	32.2	54½
55	0 58	17.6	1 04	19.4	1 11	21.2	1 17	23.1	1 23	24.9	1 30	26.8	1 37	28.7	1 44	30.6	1 51	32.6	55
55½	0 59	17.9	1 06	19.7	1 12	21.5	1 19	23.4	1 25	25.3	1 32	27.2	1 39	29.1	1 46	31.1	1 53	33.1	55½
56	1 01	18.1	1 07	19.9	1 13	21.8	1 20	23.7	1 27	25.6	1 34	27.6	1 41	29.5	1 48	31.5	1 55	33.5	56
56½	1 02	18.3	1 08	20.2	1 15	22.1	1 22	24.1	1 29	26.0	1 36	28.0	1 43	30.0	1 50	32.0	1 58	34.0	56½
57	1 03	18.6	1 10	20.5	1 16	22.4	1 23	24.4	1 30	26.4	1 37	28.4	1 45	30.4	1 52	32.5	2 00	34.5	57
57½	1 04	18.9	1 11	20.8	1 18	22.8	1 25	24.8	1 32	26.8	1 39	28.8	1 47	30.9	1 55	33.0	2 03	35.1	57½
58	1 06	19.1	1 12	21.1	1 19	23.1	1 27	25.1	1 34	27.2	1 42	29.2	1 49	31.3	1 57	33.5	2 05	35.7	58
58½	1 07	19.4	1 14	21.4	1 21	23.5	1 29	25.5	1 36	27.6	1 44	29.7	1 52	31.8	2 00	34.0	2 08	36.3	58½
59	1 08	19.7	1 16	21.7	1 23	23.8	1 30	25.9	1 38	28.0	1 46	30.2	1 54	32.3	2 02	34.6	2 11	36.8	59
59½	1 10	20.0	1 17	22.1	1 25	24.2	1 32	26.3	1 40	28.5	1 48	30.7	1 57	32.9	2 05	35.2	2 14	37.5	59½
60	1 11	20.3	1 19	22.4	1 26	24.6	1 34	26.7	1 42	28.9	1 51	31.2	1 59	33.4	2 08	35.8	2 17	38.2	60
LAT.	10°		11°		12°		13°		14°		15°		16°		17°		18°		LAT.

Table 28A
Corr. for APPARENT AMPLITUDE
ADD to AZIMUTH reckoned from elevated Pole when sun observed with centre on horizon

Dec.	LAT.					
	0°	20°	40°	50°	55°	60°
°	°	°	°	°	°	°
0	.0	.2	.6	.8	1.0	1.2
15	.0	.2	.6	.9	1.1	1.4
24	.0	.3	.7	1.1	1.4	2.0

Table 28 — TRUE AMPLITUDES

DECLINATION

LAT.	19° Time	19° Arc	20° Time	20° Arc	½ Time	½ Arc	21° Time	21° Arc	½ Time	½ Arc	22° Time	22° Arc	½ Time	½ Arc	23° Time	23° Arc	½ Time	½ Arc	LAT.
0°	0 00	19.0	0 00	20.0	0 00	20.5	0 00	21.0	0 00	21.5	0 00	22.0	0 00	22.5	0 00	23.0	0 00	23.5	0°
5	0 07	19.1	0 07	20.1	0 07	20.6	0 08	21.1	0 08	21.6	0 08	22.1	0 08	22.6	0 09	23.1	0 09	23.6	5
10	0 14	19.3	0 15	20.3	0 15	20.8	0 16	21.3	0 16	21.8	0 16	22.3	0 17	22.9	0 17	23.4	0 18	23.9	10
14	0 20	19.6	0 21	20.6	0 21	21.2	0 22	21.7	0 23	22.2	0 23	22.7	0 24	23.2	0 24	23.8	0 25	24.3	14
17	0 24	19.9	0 26	21.0	0 26	21.5	0 27	22.0	0 28	22.5	0 28	23.1	0 29	23.6	0 30	24.1	0 31	24.6	17
20	0 29	20.3	0 30	21.3	0 31	21.9	0 32	22.4	0 33	22.9	0 34	23.5	0 35	24.0	0 36	24.6	0 36	25.1	20
22	0 32	20.6	0 34	21.7	0 35	22.2	0 36	22.7	0 37	23.3	0 38	23.8	0 39	24.4	0 40	24.9	0 41	25.5	22
24	0 35	20.9	0 37	22.0	0 38	22.5	0 39	23.1	0 40	23.7	0 41	24.2	0 43	24.8	0 44	25.3	0 45	25.9	24
26	0 39	21.2	0 41	22.4	0 42	22.9	0 43	23.5	0 44	24.1	0 45	24.6	0 47	25.2	0 48	25.8	0 49	26.3	26
28	0 42	21.6	0 45	22.8	0 46	23.4	0 47	24.0	0 48	24.5	0 50	25.1	0 51	25.7	0 52	26.3	0 54	26.8	28
30	0 46	22.1	0 49	23.3	0 50	23.8	0 51	24.4	0 53	25.0	0 54	25.6	0 55	26.2	0 57	26.8	0 58	27.4	30
31	0 48	22.3	0 51	23.5	0 52	24.1	0 53	24.7	0 55	25.3	0 56	25.9	0 58	26.5	0 59	27.1	1 01	27.7	31
32	0 50	22.6	0 53	23.8	0 54	24.4	0 56	25.0	0 57	25.6	0 58	26.2	1 00	26.8	1 02	27.4	1 03	28.0	32
33	0 52	22.9	0 55	24.1	0 56	24.7	0 58	25.3	0 59	25.9	1 01	26.5	1 02	27.1	1 04	27.8	1 06	28.4	33
34	0 54	23.1	0 57	24.4	0 58	25.0	1 00	25.6	1 02	26.2	1 03	26.8	1 05	27.5	1 07	28.1	1 08	28.7	34
35	0 56	23.4	0 59	24.7	1 01	25.3	1 02	25.9	1 04	26.6	1 06	27.2	1 07	27.8	1 09	28.5	1 11	29.1	35
36	0 58	23.7	1 01	25.0	1 03	25.6	1 05	26.3	1 07	26.9	1 08	27.6	1 10	28.2	1 12	28.9	1 14	29.5	36
37	1 00	24.0	1 04	25.3	1 05	26.0	1 07	26.7	1 09	27.3	1 11	28.0	1 13	28.6	1 15	29.3	1 16	29.9	37
38	1 02	24.4	1 06	25.7	1 08	26.4	1 10	27.1	1 12	27.7	1 14	28.4	1 16	29.0	1 17	29.7	1 19	30.3	38
39	1 05	24.8	1 09	26.1	1 10	26.8	1 12	27.5	1 14	28.1	1 16	28.8	1 18	29.5	1 20	30.2	1 22	30.8	39
40	1 07	25.1	1 11	26.5	1 13	27.2	1 15	27.9	1 17	28.6	1 19	29.3	1 21	30.0	1 23	30.7	1 26	31.3	40
41	1 10	25.5	1 14	26.9	1 16	27.6	1 18	28.3	1 20	29.0	1 22	29.8	1 24	30.5	1 27	31.2	1 29	31.8	41
42	1 12	26.0	1 17	27.4	1 19	28.1	1 21	28.8	1 23	29.5	1 25	30.3	1 28	31.0	1 30	31.7	1 32	32.4	42
43	1 15	26.4	1 19	27.8	1 22	28.6	1 24	29.3	1 26	30.1	1 29	30.8	1 31	31.5	1 33	32.3	1 36	33.0	43
44	1 18	26.9	1 22	28.4	1 25	29.1	1 27	29.9	1 29	30.6	1 32	31.4	1 34	32.1	1 37	32.9	1 39	33.6	44
45	1 21	27.4	1 25	28.9	1 28	29.7	1 30	30.4	1 33	31.2	1 35	32.0	1 38	32.8	1 40	33.5	1 43	34.3	45
46	1 24	27.9	1 29	29.5	1 31	30.3	1 34	31.0	1 36	31.8	1 39	32.6	1 42	33.3	1 44	34.2	1 47	35.0	46
47	1 27	28.5	1 32	30.1	1 35	30.9	1 37	31.7	1 40	32.5	1 43	33.3	1 45	34.1	1 48	34.9	1 51	35.7	47
48	1 30	29.1	1 35	30.7	1 38	31.6	1 41	32.4	1 44	33.2	1 47	34.0	1 50	34.8	1 53	35.7	1 56	36.5	48
½	1 32	29.4	1 37	31.1	1 40	31.9	1 43	32.8	1 46	33.6	1 49	34.4	1 52	35.3	1 55	36.1	1 58	37.0	½
49	1 33	29.7	1 39	31.4	1 42	32.3	1 45	33.1	1 48	33.9	1 51	34.8	1 54	35.7	1 57	36.5	2 00	37.4	49
½	1 35	30.1	1 41	31.8	1 44	32.6	1 47	33.5	1 50	34.4	1 53	35.2	1 56	36.1	1 59	37.0	2.02	37.9	½
50	1 37	30.4	1 43	32.1	1 46	33.0	1 49	33.9	1 52	34.8	1 55	35.6	1 58	36.5	2 02	37.4	2 05	38.3	50
½	1 39	30.8	1 45	32.5	1 48	33.4	1 51	34.3	1 54	35.2	1 57	36.1	2 01	37.0	2 04	37.9	2 07	38.8	½
51	1 41	31.1	1 47	32.9	1 50	33.8	1 53	34.7	1 56	35.6	2 00	36.5	2 03	37.5	2 06	38.4	2 10	39.3	51
½	1 43	31.5	1 49	33.3	1 52	34.2	1 55	35.1	1 59	36.1	2 02	37.0	2 06	37.9	2 09	38.9	2 13	39.8	½
52	1 45	31.9	1 51	33.7	1 54	34.7	1 58	35.6	2 01	36.5	2 05	37.5	2 08	38.4	2 12	39.4	2 15	40.3	52
½	1 47	32.3	1 53	34.2	1 57	35.1	2 00	36.1	2 04	37.0	2 07	38.0	2 11	38.9	2 14	39.9	2 18	40.9	½
53	1 49	32.7	1 56	34.6	1 59	35.6	2 02	36.5	2 06	37.5	2 10	38.5	2 13	39.5	2 17	40.5	2 21	41.4	53
½	1 51	33.2	1 58	35.1	2 01	36.1	2 05	37.1	2 09	38.0	2 12	39.0	2 16	40.0	2 20	41.1	2 24	42.0	½
54	1 53	33.6	2 00	35.6	2 04	36.6	2 08	37.6	2 11	38.6	2 15	39.6	2 19	40.6	2 23	41.7	2 27	42.6	54
½	1 55	34.1	2 03	36.1	2 06	37.1	2 10	38.1	2 14	39.1	2 18	40.2	2 22	41.2	2 26	42.3	2 30	43.3	½
55	1 58	34.6	2 05	36.6	2 09	37.6	2 13	38.7	2 17	39.7	2 21	40.8	2 25	41.8	2 29	42.9	2 34	44.0	55
½	2 00	35.1	2 08	37.1	2 12	38.2	2 16	39.2	2 20	40.3	2 24	41.4	2 28	42.5	2 33	43.6	2 37	44.7	½
56	2 03	35.6	2 11	37.7	2 15	38.8	2 19	39.8	2 23	40.9	2 27	42.1	2 32	43.2	2 36	44.3	2 41	45.4	56
½	2 05	36.1	2 13	38.3	2 18	39.4	2 22	40.5	2 26	41.6	2 31	42.7	2 35	43.9	2 40	45.0	2 44	46.2	½
57	2 08	36.7	2 16	38.9	2 21	40.0	2 25	41.1	2 29	42.3	2 34	43.4	2 39	44.6	2 43	45.8	2 48	47.0	57
½	2 11	37.3	2 19	39.5	2 24	40.7	2 28	41.8	2 33	43.0	2 37	44.2	2 42	45.4	2 47	46.6	2 52	47.9	½
58	2 14	37.9	2 22	40.2	2 27	41.4	2 32	42.5	2 36	43.8	2 41	45.0	2 46	46.2	2 51	47.5	2 56	48.7	58
½	2 17	38.5	2 26	40.9	2 30	42.1	2 35	43.3	2 40	44.6	2 45	45.8	2 50	47.1	2 55	48.4	3 01	49.7	½
59	2 20	39.2	2 29	41.6	2 34	42.8	2 39	44.1	2 44	45.4	2 49	46.7	2 54	48.0	3 00	49.3	3 05	50.6	59
½	2 23	39.9	2 33	42.4	2 38	43.6	2 43	44.9	2 48	46.2	2 53	47.6	2 59	48.9	3 04	50.3	3 10	51.7	½
60	2 26	40.6	2 36	43.2	2 41	44.5	2 47	45.8	2 52	47.1	2 58	48.5	3 03	49.9	3 09	51.4	3 15	52.9	60
LAT.	19°		20°		½		21°		½		22°		½		23°		½		LAT.

Note.—Owing to refraction the moment of TRUE Amplitude occurs when the sun's lower limb appears to be about half a diameter above the horizon. In moderate latitudes it is sufficient to judge this moment and observe accordingly. In the case of the higher latitudes, however, observations should either be timed, or the APPARENT Amplitude observed and corrected by means of the supplementary table.

Table 28 — TRUE AMPLITUDES

DECLINATION

LAT.	24° Time	24° Arc	½ Time	½ Arc	25° Time	25° Arc	½ Time	½ Arc	26° Time	26° Arc	½ Time	½ Arc	27° Time	27° Arc	½ Time	½ Arc	28° Time	28° Arc	LAT.
	h m	°	h m	°	h m	°	h m	°	h m	°	h m	°	h m	°	h m	°	h m	°	
0°	0 00	24.0	0 00	24.5	0 00	25.0	0 00	25.5	0 00	26.0	0 00	26.5	0 00	27.0	0 00	27.5	0 00	28.0	0°
5	0 09	24.1	0 09	24.6	0 09	25.1	0 10	25.6	0 10	26.1	0 10	26.6	0 10	27.1	0 10	27.6	0 11	28.1	5
10	0 18	24.4	0 18	24.9	0 19	25.4	0 19	25.9	0 20	26.4	0 20	27.0	0 21	27.5	0 21	28.0	0 21	28.5	10
14	0 25	24.8	0 26	25.3	0 26	25.8	0 27	26.3	0 28	26.9	0 29	27.4	0 29	27.9	0 30	28.4	0 30	28.9	14
17	0 31	25.2	0 32	25.7	0 32	26.2	0 33	26.8	0 34	27.3	0 35	27.8	0 35	28.4	0 36	28.9	0 37	29.4	17
20	0 37	25.7	0 38	26.2	0 39	26.7	0 40	27.3	0 41	27.8	0 42	28.3	0 43	28.9	0 44	29.4	0 45	30.0	20
22	0 41	26.0	0 42	26.6	0 43	27.1	0 44	27.7	0 45	28.2	0 46	28.8	0 48	29.3	0 49	29.9	0 50	30.4	22
24	0 46	26.4	0 47	27.0	0 48	27.6	0 49	28.1	0 50	28.7	0 51	29.2	0 52	29.8	0 54	30.4	0 55	30.9	24
26	0 50	26.9	0 51	27.5	0 52	28.0	0 54	28.6	0 55	29.2	0 56	29.8	0 58	30.3	0 59	30.9	1 00	31.5	26
28	0 55	27.4	0 56	28.0	0 57	28.6	0 59	29.2	1 00	29.8	1 01	30.4	1 03	30.9	1 04	31.5	1 06	32.1	28
30	1 00	28.0	1 01	28.6	1 02	29.2	1 04	29.8	1 05	30.4	1 07	31 0	1 08	31.6	1 10	32.2	1 12	32.8	30
31	1 02	28.3	1 04	28.9	1 05	29.5	1 07	30.1	1 08	30.8	1 10	31.4	1 11	32.0	1 13	32.6	1 15	33.2	31
32	1 05	28.7	1 06	29.3	1 08	29.9	1 09	30.5	1 11	31.1	1 13	31.7	1 14	32.4	1 16	33.0	1 18	33.6	32
33	1 07	29.0	1 09	29.6	1 10	30.3	1 12	30.9	1 14	31.5	1 16	32.1	1 17	32.8	1 19	33.4	1 21	34.0	33
34	1 10	29.4	1 12	30.0	1 13	30.7	1 15	31.3	1 17	31.9	1 19	32.5	1 20	33.2	1 22	33.8	1 24	34.5	34
35	1 13	29.8	1 14	30.4	1 16	31.1	1 18	31.7	1 20	32.4	1 22	33.0	1 23	33.7	1 26	34.3	1 27	35.0	35
36	1 16	30.2	1 17	30.8	1 19	31.5	1 21	32.1	1 23	32.8	1 25	33.5	1 27	34.1	1 29	34.8	1 31	35.5	36
37	1 18	30.6	1 20	31.3	1 22	31.9	1 24	32.6	1 26	33.3	1 28	34.0	1 30	34.6	1 32	35.3	1 34	36.0	37
38	1 21	31.1	1 23	31.8	1 25	32.4	1 28	33.1	1 30	33.8	1 32	34.5	1 34	35.2	1 36	35.9	1 38	36 6	38
39	1 25	31.6	1 27	32.3	1 29	32.9	1 31	33.6	1 33	34.3	1 35	35.0	1 37	35.8	1 40	36.5	1 42	37.2	39
40	1 28	32.1	1 30	32.8	1 32	33.5	1 34	34.2	1 37	34.9	1 39	35.6	1 41	36.4	1 44	37.1	1 46	37.8	40
41	1 31	32.6	1 33	33.3	1 36	34.1	1 38	34.8	1 40	35.5	1 43	36.2	1 45	37.0	1 48	37.7	1 50	38.5	41
42	1 35	33.2	1 37	33.9	1 39	34.7	1 42	35.4	1 44	36.2	1 47	36.9	1 49	37.7	1 52	38.4	1 54	39.2	42
43	1 38	33.8	1 41	34.6	1 43	35.3	1 46	36.1	1 48	36.8	1 51	37.6	1 53	38.4	1 56	39.1	1 59	39.9	43
44	1 42	34.4	1 44	35.2	1 47	36.0	1 50	36.8	1 52	37.5	1 55	38.3	1 58	39.2	2 01	39.9	2 04	40.7	44
45	1 46	35.1	1 49	35.9	1 51	36.7	1 54	37.5	1 57	38.3	2 00	39.1	2 03	39.9	2 06	40.8	2 08	41.6	45
46	1 50	35.8	1 53	36.7	1 55	37.5	1 58	38.3	2 01	39.1	2 04	40.0	2 07	40.8	2 11	41.7	2 14	42.5	46
47	1 54	36.6	1 57	37.5	2 00	38.3	2 03	39.1	2 06	40.0	2 09	40.9	2 12	41.7	2 16	42.6	2 19	43.5	47
48	1 59	37.4	2 02	38.3	2 05	39.2	2 08	40.0	2 11	40.9	2 14	41.8	2 18	42.7	2 20	43.6	2 25	44.5	48
½	2 01	37.8	2 04	38.7	2 07	39.6	2 11	40.5	2 14	41.4	2 17	42.3	2 21	43.2	2 24	44.2	2 28	45.1	½
49	2 03	38.3	2 06	39.2	2 10	40.1	2 13	41.0	2 17	41.9	2 20	42.8	2 24	43.8	2 27	44.7	2 31	45.7	49
½	2 06	38.8	2 09	39.7	2 12	40.6	2 16	41.5	2 19	42.4	2 23	43.4	2 27	44.3	2 30	45.3	2 34	46.3	½
50	2 08	39.3	2 12	40.2	2 15	41.1	2 19	42.0	2 22	43.0	2 26	43.9	2 29	44.9	2 33	45.9	2 37	46.9	50
½	2 11	39.8	2 14	40.7	2 18	41.6	2 21	42.6	2 25	43.6	2 29	44.5	2 33	45.5	2 37	46.5	2 41	47.6	½
51	2 13	40.3	2 17	41.2	2 20	42.2	2 24	43.2	2 28	44.2	2 32	45.2	2 36	46.2	2 40	47.2	2 44	48.2	51
½	2 16	40.8	2 20	41.8	2 24	42.8	2 28	43.8	2 31	44.8	2 35	45.8	2 39	46.8	2 44	47.9	2 48	49.0	½
52	2 19	41.4	2 23	42.4	2 27	43.4	2 31	44.4	2 35	45.4	2 39	46.4	2 43	47.5	2 47	48.6	2 52	49.7	52
½	2 22	41.9	2 26	42.9	2 30	44.0	2 34	45.0	2 38	46.0	2 42	47.1	2 46	48.2	2 51	49.3	2 56	50.5	½
53	2 25	42.5	2 29	43.6	2 33	44.6	2 37	45.7	2 41	46.7	2 46	47.8	2 50	49.0	2 55	50.1	3 00	51.3	53
½	2 28	43.1	2 32	44.2	2 36	45.3	2 41	46.4	2 45	47.5	2 49	48.6	2 54	49.8	2 59	50.9	3 04	52.1	½
54	2 31	43.8	2 35	44.9	2 40	46.0	2 44	47.1	2 49	48.2	2 53	49.4	2 58	50.6	3 03	51.8	3 08	53.0	54
½	2 34	44.5	2 39	45.7	2 43	46.7	2 48	47.9	2 53	49.0	2 57	50.2	3 02	51.4	3 07	52.7	3 13	54.0	½
55	2 38	45.2	2 42	46.3	2 47	47.5	2 52	48.7	2 57	49.8	3 02	51.1	3 07	52.3	3 12	53.6	3 18	54.9	55
½	2 42	45.9	2 46	47.1	2 51	48.3	2 56	49.5	3 01	50.7	3 06	52.0	3 11	53.3	3 17	54.6	3 23	56.0	½
56	2 46	46.7	2 50	47.9	2 55	49.1	3 00	50.4	3 05	51.6	3 11	53.0	3 16	54.3	3 22	55.7	3 28	57.1	56
½	2 49	47.5	2 54	48.7	2 59	50.0	3 04	51.3	3 10	52.6	3 15	54.0	3 21	55.4	3 27	56.8	3 34	58.3	½
57	2 53	48.3	2 58	49.6	3 04	50.9	3 09	52.2	3 15	53.6	3 21	55.0	3 27	56.5	3 33	58.0	3 40	59.6	57
½	2 57	49.2	3 03	50.5	3 08	51.9	3 14	53.2	3 20	54.7	3 26	56.1	3 33	57.7	3 39	59.3	3 46	60.9	½
58	3 02	50.1	3 07	51.5	3 13	52.9	3 19	54.3	3 25	55.8	3 32	57.3	3 39	58.9	3 46	60.7	3 53	62.4	58
½	3 06	51.1	3 12	52.5	3 18	54.0	3 25	55.5	3 31	57.0	3 38	58.6	3 45	60.3	3 53	62.1	4 01	64.0	½
59	3 11	52.2	3 17	53.6	3 24	55.1	3 30	56.7	3 37	58.3	3 44	60.0	3 52	61.8	4 00	63.7	4 09	65.7	59
½	3 16	53.3	3 23	54.8	3 30	56.4	3 36	58.0	3 44	59.7	3 51	61.5	4 00	63.4	4 08	65.5	4 18	67.7	½
60	3 22	54.4	3 29	56.0	3 36	57.7	3 43	59.4	3 51	61.2	3 59	63.2	4 08	65.2	4 18	67.4	4 29	69.9	60
LAT.	24°		½		25°		½		26°		½		27°		½		28°		LAT.

Table 28A
Corr. for APPARENT AMPLITUDE
ADD to AZIMUTH reckoned from elevated Pole when sun observed with centre on horizon

Dec.	LAT. 0°	20°	40°	50°	55°	60°
°	°	°	°	°	°	°
0	.0	.2	.6	.8	1.0	1.2
15	.0	.2	.6	.9	1.1	1.4
24	.0	.3	.7	1.1	1.4	2.0

Table 29

A

If entered with H.A. at **top**, Sign **+**

„ „ „ „ **foot**, „ **−**

0 hrs.

HOUR ANGLE or DIFF. LONG.

LAT.	01m	02m	03m	04m	05m	06m	07m	08m	09m	10m	11m	12m	13m	14m	15m	LAT.
	$\frac{1}{4}°$ 359¾	$\frac{1}{2}°$ 359½	$\frac{3}{4}°$ 359¼	**1°** **359**	1¼° 358¾	1½° 358½	1¾° 358¼	**2°** **358**	2¼° 357¾	2½° 357½	2¾° 357¼	**3°** **357**	3¼° 356¾	3½° 356½	3¾° 356¼	
0°	.000	.000	.000	.000	.000	.000	.000	.000	.000	.000	.000	.000	.000	.000	.000	0°
1	4.00	2.00	1.33	1.00	.800	.667	.571	.500	.444	.400	.363	.333	.307	.285	.266	1
2	8.00	4.00	2.67	2.00	1.60	1.33	1.14	1.00	.889	.800	.727	.666	.615	.571	.533	2
3	12.0	6.01	4.00	3.00	2.40	2.00	1.72	1.50	1.33	1.20	1.09	1.00	.923	.857	.800	3
4	16.0	8.01	5.34	4.01	3.21	2.67	2.29	2.00	1.78	1.60	1.46	1.33	1.23	1.14	1.07	4
5	20.1	10.0	6.68	5.01	4.01	3.34	2.86	2.51	2.23	2.00	1.82	1.67	1.54	1.43	1.34	5
6	24.1	12.0	8.03	6.02	4.82	4.01	3.44	3.01	2.68	2.41	2.19	2.01	1.85	1.72	1.60	6
7	28.1	14.1	9.38	7.03	5.63	4.69	4.02	3.52	3.13	2.81	2.56	2.34	2.16	2.01	1.87	7
8	32.2	16.1	10.7	8.05	6.44	5.37	4.60	4.02	3.58	3.22	2.93	2.68	2.48	2.30	2.14	8
9	36.3	18.1	12.1	9.07	7.26	6.05	5.18	4.54	4.03	3.63	3.30	3.02	2.79	2.59	2.42	9
10	40.4	20.2	13.5	10.1	8.08	6.73	5.77	5.05	4.49	4.04	3.67	3.36	3.11	2.88	2.69	10
11	44.6	22.3	14.9	11.1	8.91	7.42	6.36	5.57	4.95	4.45	4.05	3.71	3.42	3.18	2.97	11
12	48.7	24.4	16.2	12.2	9.74	8.12	6.96	6.09	5.41	4.87	4.43	4.06	3.74	3.48	3.24	12
13	52.9	26.5	17.6	13.2	10.6	8.82	7.56	6.61	5.88	5.29	4.81	4.41	4.07	3.78	3.52	13
14	57.1	28.6	19.1	14.3	11.4	9.52	8.16	7.14	6.35	5.71	5.19	4.76	4.39	4.08	3.80	14
15	61.4	30.7	20.5	15.4	12.3	10.2	8.77	7.67	6.82	6.14	5.58	5.11	4.72	4.38	4.09	15
16	65.7	32.9	21.9	16.4	13.1	11.0	9.39	8.21	7.30	6.57	5.97	5.47	5.05	4.69	4.38	16
17	70.1	35.0	23.4	17.5	14.0	11.7	10.0	8.76	7.78	7.00	6.37	5.83	5.38	5.00	4.67	17
18	74.5	37.2	24.8	18.6	14.9	12.4	10.6	9.30	8.27	7.44	6.76	6.20	5.72	5.31	4.96	18
19	78.9	39.5	26.3	19.7	15.8	13.2	11.3	9.86	8.76	7.89	7.17	6.57	6.06	5.63	5.25	19
20	83.4	41.7	27.8	20.9	16.7	13.9	11.9	10.4	9.26	8.34	7.58	6.95	6.41	5.95	5.55	20
21	88.0	44.0	29.3	22.0	17.6	14.7	12.6	11.0	9.77	8.79	8.00	7.32	6.76	6.28	5.86	21
22	92.6	46.3	30.9	23.1	18.5	15.4	13.2	11.6	10.3	9.25	8.41	7.71	7.12	6.61	6.16	22
23	97.3	48.6	32.4	24.3	19.5	16.2	13.9	12.2	10.8	9.72	8.84	8.10	7.48	6.94	6.48	23
24	102.	51.0	34.0	25.5	20.4	17.0	14.6	12.8	11.3	10.2	9.27	8.50	7.84	7.28	6.79	24
25	107.	53.4	35.6	26.7	21.4	17.8	15.3	13.4	11.9	10.7	9.71	8.90	8.21	7.62	7.12	25
26	112.	55.9	37.3	27.9	22.4	18.6	16.0	14.0	12.4	11.2	10.2	9.31	8.59	7.97	7.44	26
27	117.	58.4	38.9	29.2	23.4	19.5	16.7	14.6	13.0	11.7	10.6	9.72	8.97	8.33	7.77	27
28	122.	60.9	40.6	30.5	24.4	20.3	17.4	15.2	13.5	12.2	11.1	10.1	9.36	8.69	8.11	28
29	127.	63.5	42.3	31.8	25.4	21.2	18.1	15.9	14.1	12.7	11.5	10.6	9.76	9.06	8.46	29
30	132.	66.2	44.1	33.1	26.5	22.0	18.9	16.5	14.7	13.2	12.0	11.0	10.2	9.44	8.81	30
31	138.	68.9	45.9	34.4	27.5	23.0	19.7	17.2	15.3	13.8	12.5	11.5	10.6	9.82	9.17	31
32	143.	71.6	47.7	35.8	28.6	23.9	20.5	17.9	15.9	14.3	13.0	11.9	11.0	10.2	9.53	32
33	149.	74.4	49.6	37.2	29.8	24.8	21.3	18.6	16.5	14.9	13.5	12.4	11.4	10.6	9.91	33
34	155.	77.3	51.5	38.6	30.9	25.8	22.1	19.3	17.2	15.4	14.0	12.9	11.9	11.0	10.3	34
35	161.	80.2	53.5	40.1	32.1	26.7	22.9	20.1	17.8	16.0	14.6	13.4	12.3	11.4	10.7	35
36	167.	83.3	55.5	41.6	33.3	27.8	23.8	20.8	18.5	16.6	15.1	13.9	12.8	11.9	11.1	36
37	173.	86.3	57.6	43.2	34.5	28.8	24.7	21.6	19.2	17.3	15.7	14.4	13.3	12.3	11.5	37
38	179.	89.5	59.7	44.8	35.8	29.8	25.6	22.4	19.9	17.9	16.3	14.9	13.8	12.8	11.9	38
39	186.	92.8	61.9	46.4	37.1	30.9	26.5	23.2	20.6	18.5	16.9	15.5	14.3	13.2	12.4	39
40	192.	96.2	64.1	48.1	38.5	32.0	27.5	24.0	21.4	19.2	17.5	16.0	14.8	13.7	12.8	40
41	199.	99.6	66.4	49.8	39.8	33.2	28.5	24.9	22.1	19.9	18.1	16.6	15.3	14.2	13.3	41
42	206.	103.	68.8	51.6	41.3	34.4	29.5	25.8	22.9	20.6	18.8	17.2	15.9	14.7	13.7	42
43	214.	107.	71.2	53.4	42.7	35.6	30.5	26.7	23.7	21.4	19.4	17.8	16.4	15.3	14.2	43
44	221.	111.	73.8	55.3	44.3	36.9	31.6	27.7	24.6	22.1	20.1	18.4	17.0	15.8	14.7	44
45	229.	115.	76.4	57.3	45.8	38.2	32.7	28.6	25.5	22.9	20.8	19.1	17.6	16.4	15.3	45
46	237.	119.	79.1	59.3	47.5	39.6	33.9	29.7	26.4	23.7	21.6	19.8	18.2	16.9	15.8	46
47	246.	123.	81.9	61.4	49.2	41.1	35.1	30.7	27.3	24.6	22.3	20.5	18.9	17.5	16.4	47
48	255.	127.	84.8	63.6	50.9	42.4	36.4	31.8	28.3	25.4	23.1	21.2	19.6	18.2	17.0	48
49	264.	132.	87.9	65.9	52.7	43.9	37.7	32.9	29.3	26.3	24.0	22.0	20.3	18.8	17.6	49
50	273.	137.	91.0	68.3	54.6	45.5	39.0	34.1	30.3	27.3	24.8	22.7	21.0	19.5	18.2	50
51	283.	142.	94.2	70.7	56.6	47.2	40.4	35.4	31.4	28.3	25.7	23.6	21.8	20.2	18.8	51
52	293.	147.	97.8	73.3	58.7	48.9	41.9	36.7	32.6	29.3	26.7	24.4	22.5	20.9	19.5	52
53	304.	152.	101.	76.0	60.8	50.7	43.4	38.0	33.8	30.4	27.6	25.3	23.4	21.7	20.3	53
54	315.	158.	105.	78.9	63.1	52.6	45.1	39.4	35.0	31.5	28.7	26.3	24.2	22.5	21.0	54
55	327.	164.	109.	81.8	65.5	54.5	46.7	40.9	36.4	32.7	29.7	27.3	25.2	23.4	21.8	55
56	340.	170.	113.	84.9	67.9	56.6	48.5	42.5	37.7	34.0	30.9	28.3	26.1	24.2	22.6	56
57	353.	176.	118.	88.2	70.6	58.8	50.4	44.1	39.2	35.3	32.1	29.4	27.1	25.2	23.5	57
58	367.	183.	122.	91.7	73.3	61.1	52.4	45.8	40.7	36.7	33.3	30.5	28.2	26.2	24.4	58
59	381.	191.	127.	95.3	76.3	63.6	54.5	47.7	42.4	38.1	34.7	31.8	29.3	27.2	25.4	59
60	397.	198.	132.	99.2	79.4	66.1	56.7	49.6	44.1	39.7	36.1	33.0	30.5	28.3	26.4	60
LAT.	179¾ 180¼	179½ 180½	179¼ 180¾	**179°** **181**	178¾ 181¼	178½ 181½	178¼ 181¾	**178°** **182**	177¾ 182¼	177½ 182½	177¼ 182¾	**177°** **183**	176¾ 183¼	176½ 183½	176¼ 183¾	LAT.

Table 29　**B**　Lat. and Dec. SAME name, Sign −

0 hrs.　　　　Lat. and Dec. CONTRARY names, Sign +

HOUR ANGLE or DIFF. LONG.

DEC.	01m	02m	03m	04m	05m	06m	07m	08m	09m	10m	11m	12m	13m	14m	15m	DEC.
	¼°	½°	¾°	1°	1¼°	1½°	1¾°	2°	2¼°	2½°	2¾°	3°	3¼°	3½°	3¾°	
	359¾	359½	359¼	359	358¾	358½	358¼	358	357¾	357½	357¼	357	356¾	356½	356¼	
0°	.000	.000	.000	.000	.000	.000	.000	.000	.000	.000	.000	.000	.000	.000	.000	0°
1	4.00	2.00	1.33	1.00	.800	.667	.572	.500	.445	.400	.364	.334	.308	.286	.267	1
2	8.00	4.00	2.67	2.00	1.60	1.33	1.14	1.00	.889	.801	.728	.667	.616	.572	.534	2
3	12.0	6.01	4.00	3.00	2.40	2.00	1.72	1.50	1.34	1.20	1.09	1.00	.924	.858	.801	3
4	16.0	8.01	5.34	4.01	3.21	2.67	2.29	2.00	1.78	1.60	1.46	1.34	1.23	1.15	1.07	4
5	20.1	10.0	6.68	5.01	4.01	3.34	2.87	2.51	2.23	2.01	1.82	1.67	1.54	1.43	1.34	5
6	24.1	12.0	8.03	6.02	4.82	4.02	3.44	3.01	2.68	2.41	2.19	2.01	1.85	1.72	1.61	6
7	28.1	14.1	9.38	7.04	5.63	4.69	4.02	3.52	3.13	2.81	2.56	2.35	2.17	2.01	1.88	7
8	32.2	16.1	10.7	8.05	6.44	5.37	4.60	4.03	3.58	3.22	2.93	2.69	2.48	2.30	2.15	8
9	36.3	18.2	12.1	9.08	7.26	6.05	5.19	4.54	4.03	3.63	3.30	3.03	2.79	2.59	2.42	9
10	40.4	20.2	13.5	10.1	8.08	6.74	5.77	5.05	4.49	4.04	3.68	3.37	3.11	2.89	2.70	10
11	44.6	22.3	14.9	11.1	8.91	7.43	6.37	5.57	4.95	4.46	4.05	3.71	3.43	3.18	2.97	11
12	48.7	24.4	16.2	12.2	9.74	8.12	6.96	6.09	5.41	4.87	4.43	4.06	3.75	3.48	3.25	12
13	52.9	26.5	17.6	13.2	10.6	8.82	7.56	6.62	5.88	5.29	4.81	4.41	4.07	3.78	3.53	13
14	57.1	28.6	19.1	14.3	11.4	9.52	8.16	7.14	6.35	5.72	5.20	4.76	4.40	4.08	3.81	14
15	61.4	30.7	20.5	15.4	12.3	10.2	8.77	7.68	6.83	6.14	5.59	5.12	4.73	4.39	4.10	15
16	65.7	32.9	21.9	16.4	13.1	11.0	9.39	8.22	7.30	6.57	5.98	5.48	5.06	4.70	4.38	16
17	70.1	35.0	23.4	17.5	14.0	11.7	10.0	8.76	7.79	7.01	6.37	5.84	5.39	5.01	4.68	17
18	74.5	37.2	24.8	18.6	14.9	12.4	10.6	9.31	8.28	7.45	6.77	6.21	5.73	5.32	4.97	18
19	78.9	39.5	26.3	19.7	15.8	13.2	11.3	9.87	8.77	7.89	7.18	6.58	6.07	5.64	5.27	19
20	83.4	41.7	27.8	20.9	16.7	13.9	11.9	10.4	9.27	8.34	7.59	6.95	6.42	5.96	5.57	20
21	88.0	44.0	29.3	22.0	17.6	14.7	12.6	11.0	9.78	8.80	8.00	7.34	6.77	6.29	5.87	21
22	92.6	46.3	30.9	23.2	18.5	15.4	13.2	11.6	10.3	9.26	8.42	7.72	7.13	6.62	6.18	22
23	97.3	48.6	32.4	24.3	19.5	16.2	13.9	12.2	10.8	9.73	8.85	8.11	7.49	6.95	6.49	23
24	102.	51.0	34.0	25.5	20.4	17.0	14.6	12.8	11.3	10.2	9.28	8.51	7.85	7.29	6.81	24
25	107.	53.4	35.6	26.7	21.4	17.8	15.3	13.4	11.9	10.7	9.72	8.91	8.23	7.64	7.13	25
26	112.	55.9	37.3	27.9	22.4	18.6	16.0	14.0	12.4	11.2	10.2	9.32	8.60	7.99	7.46	26
27	117.	58.4	38.9	29.2	23.4	19.5	16.7	14.6	13.0	11.7	10.6	9.74	8.99	8.35	7.79	27
28	122.	60.9	40.6	30.5	24.4	20.3	17.4	15.2	13.5	12.2	11.1	10.2	9.38	8.71	8.13	28
29	127.	63.5	42.4	31.8	25.4	21.2	18.2	15.9	14.1	12.7	11.6	10.6	9.78	9.08	8.48	29
30	132.	66.2	44.1	33.1	26.5	22.1	18.9	16.5	14.7	13.2	12.0	11.0	10.2	9.46	8.83	30
31	138.	68.9	45.9	34.4	27.5	23.0	19.7	17.2	15.3	13.8	12.5	11.5	10.6	9.84	9.19	31
32	143.	71.6	47.7	35.8	28.6	23.9	20.5	17.9	15.9	14.3	13.0	11.9	11.0	10.2	9.55	32
33	149.	74.4	49.6	37.2	29.8	24.8	21.3	18.6	16.5	14.9	13.5	12.4	11.5	10.6	9.93	33
34	155.	77.3	51.5	38.6	30.9	25.8	22.1	19.3	17.2	15.5	14.1	12.9	11.9	11.0	10.3	34
35	161.	80.2	53.5	40.1	32.1	26.7	22.9	20.1	17.8	16.1	14.6	13.4	12.4	11.5	10.7	35
36	167.	83.3	55.5	41.6	33.3	27.8	23.8	20.8	18.5	16.7	15.1	13.9	12.8	11.9	11.1	36
37	173.	86.4	57.6	43.2	34.5	28.8	24.7	21.6	19.2	17.3	15.7	14.4	13.3	12.3	11.5	37
38	179.	89.5	59.7	44.8	35.8	29.8	25.6	22.4	19.9	17.9	16.3	14.9	13.8	12.8	12.0	38
39	186.	92.8	61.9	46.4	37.1	30.9	26.5	23.2	20.6	18.6	16.9	15.5	14.3	13.3	12.4	39
40	192.	96.2	64.1	48.1	38.5	32.1	27.5	24.0	21.4	19.2	17.5	16.0	14.8	13.7	12.8	40
41	199.	99.6	66.4	49.8	39.9	33.2	28.5	24.9	22.1	19.9	18.1	16.6	15.3	14.2	13.3	41
42	206.	103.	68.8	51.6	41.3	34.4	29.5	25.8	22.9	20.6	18.8	17.2	15.9	14.7	13.8	42
43	214.	107.	71.2	53.4	42.8	35.6	30.5	26.7	23.8	21.4	19.4	17.8	16.5	15.3	14.3	43
44	221.	111.	73.8	55.3	44.3	36.9	31.6	27.7	24.6	22.1	20.1	18.5	17.0	15.8	14.8	44
45	229.	115.	76.4	57.3	45.8	38.2	32.8	28.7	25.5	22.9	20.8	19.1	17.6	16.4	15.3	45
46	237.	119.	79.1	59.3	47.5	39.6	33.9	29.7	26.4	23.7	21.6	19.8	18.3	17.0	15.8	46
47	246.	123.	81.9	61.5	49.2	41.0	35.1	30.7	27.3	24.6	22.4	20.5	18.9	17.6	16.4	47
48	255.	127.	84.9	63.6	50.9	42.4	36.4	31.8	28.3	25.5	23.2	21.2	19.6	18.2	17.0	48
49	264.	132.	87.9	65.9	52.7	43.9	37.7	33.0	29.3	26.4	24.0	22.0	20.3	18.8	17.6	49
50	273.	137.	91.1	68.3	54.6	45.5	39.0	34.1	30.4	27.3	24.8	22.8	21.0	19.5	18.2	50
51	283.	142.	94.3	70.8	56.6	47.2	40.4	35.4	31.5	28.3	25.7	23.6	21.8	20.2	18.9	51
52	293.	147.	97.8	73.3	58.7	48.9	41.9	36.7	32.6	29.3	26.7	24.5	22.6	21.0	19.6	52
53	304.	152.	101.	76.0	60.8	50.7	43.5	38.0	33.8	30.4	27.7	25.4	23.4	21.7	20.3	53
54	315.	158.	105.	78.9	63.1	52.6	45.1	39.4	35.1	31.6	28.7	26.3	24.3	22.5	21.0	54
55	327.	164.	109.	81.8	65.5	54.6	46.8	40.9	36.4	32.7	29.8	27.3	25.2	23.4	21.8	55
56	340.	170.	113.	84.9	68.0	56.6	48.6	42.5	37.8	34.0	30.9	28.3	26.2	24.3	22.7	56
57	353.	176.	118.	88.2	70.6	58.8	50.4	44.1	39.2	35.3	32.1	29.4	27.2	25.2	23.5	57
58	367.	183.	122.	91.7	73.4	61.1	52.4	45.9	40.8	36.7	33.4	30.6	28.2	26.2	24.5	58
59	381.	191.	127.	95.4	76.3	63.6	54.5	47.7	42.4	38.2	34.7	31.8	29.4	27.3	25.5	59
60	397.	198.	132.	99.2	79.4	66.2	56.7	49.6	44.1	39.7	36.1	33.1	30.6	28.4	26.5	60
61	414.	207.	138.	103.	82.7	68.9	59.1	51.7	46.0	41.4	37.6	34.5	31.8	29.6	27.6	61
62	431.	216.	144.	108.	86.2	71.9	61.6	53.9	47.9	43.1	39.2	35.9	33.2	30.8	28.8	62
63	450.	225.	150.	112.	90.0	75.0	64.3	56.2	50.0	45.0	40.9	37.5	34.6	32.1	30.0	63
DEC.	179¾ 180¼	179½ 180½	179¼ 180¾	179° 181	178¾ 181¼	178½ 181½	178¼ 181¾	178° 182	177¾ 182¼	177½ 182½	177¼ 182¾	177° 183	176¾ 183¼	176½ 183½	176¼ 183¾	DEC.

Table 29

A

If entered with H.A. at **top**, Sign **+**

„ „ „ „ **foot**, „ **—**

0 hrs.

HOUR ANGLE or DIFF. LONG.

LAT.	15m	16m	17m	18m	19m	20m	21m	22m	23m	24m	25m	26m	27m	28m	29m	30m	LAT.
	3¾° 356¼	4° 356	4¼° 355¾	4½° 355½	4¾° 355¼	5° 355	5¼° 354¾	5½° 354½	5¾° 354¼	6° 354	6¼° 353¾	6½° 353½	6¾° 353¼	7° 353	7¼° 352¾	7½° 352½	
0°	·000	·000	·000	·000	·000	·000	·000	·000	·000	·000	·000	·000	·000	·000	·000	·000	0°
1	·266	·250	·235	·222	·210	·200	·190	·181	·173	·166	·159	·153	·148	·142	·137	·133	1
2	·533	·499	·470	·444	·420	·399	·380	·363	·347	·332	·319	·307	·295	·284	·275	·265	2
3	·800	·749	·705	·666	·631	·599	·570	·544	·521	·499	·479	·460	·443	·427	·412	·398	3
4	1·07	1·00	·941	·889	·842	·799	·761	·726	·694	·665	·639	·614	·591	·570	·550	·531	4
5	1·34	1·25	1·18	1·11	1·05	1·00	·952	·909	·869	·832	·799	·768	·739	·713	·688	·665	5
6	1·60	1·50	1·41	1·34	1·27	1·20	1·14	1·09	1·04	1·00	·960	·923	·888	·856	·826	·798	6
7	1·87	1·76	1·65	1·56	1·48	1·40	1·34	1·28	1·22	1·17	1·12	1·08	1·04	1·00	·965	·933	7
8	2·14	2·01	1·89	1·79	1·69	1·61	1·53	1·46	1·40	1·34	1·28	1·23	1·19	1·14	1·11	1·07	8
9	2·42	2·27	2·13	2·01	1·91	1·81	1·72	1·65	1·57	1·51	1·45	1·39	1·34	1·29	1·25	1·20	9
10	2·69	2·52	2·37	2·24	2·12	2·02	1·92	1·83	1·75	1·68	1·61	1·55	1·49	1·44	1·39	1·34	10
11	2·97	2·78	2·62	2·47	2·34	2·22	2·12	2·02	1·93	1·85	1·78	1·71	1·64	1·58	1·53	1·48	11
12	3·24	3·04	2·86	2·70	2·56	2·43	2·31	2·21	2·11	2·02	1·94	1·87	1·80	1·73	1·67	1·62	12
13	3·52	3·30	3·11	2·93	2·78	2·64	2·51	2·40	2·29	2·20	2·11	2·03	1·95	1·88	1·82	1·75	13
14	3·80	3·57	3·36	3·17	3·00	2·85	2·71	2·59	2·48	2·37	2·28	2·19	2·11	2·03	1·96	1·89	14
15	4·09	3·83	3·61	3·41	3·23	3·06	2·92	2·78	2·66	2·55	2·45	2·35	2·26	2·18	2·11	2·04	15
16	4·38	4·10	3·86	3·64	3·45	3·28	3·12	2·98	2·85	2·73	2·62	2·52	2·42	2·34	2·25	2·18	16
17	4·67	4·37	4·11	3·88	3·68	3·49	3·33	3·18	3·04	2·91	2·79	2·68	2·58	2·49	2·40	2·32	17
18	4·96	4·65	4·37	4·13	3·91	3·71	3·54	3·37	3·23	3·09	2·97	2·85	2·75	2·65	2·55	2·47	18
19	5·25	4·92	4·63	4·38	4·14	3·94	3·75	3·58	3·42	3·28	3·14	3·02	2·91	2·80	2·71	2·62	19
20	5·55	5·21	4·90	4·62	4·38	4·16	3·96	3·78	3·62	3·46	3·32	3·19	3·08	2·96	2·86	2·77	20
21	5·86	5·49	5·17	4·88	4·62	4·39	4·18	3·99	3·81	3·65	3·51	3·37	3·24	3·13	3·02	2·92	21
22	6·16	5·78	5·44	5·13	4·86	4·62	4·40	4·20	4·01	3·84	3·69	3·55	3·41	3·29	3·18	3·07	22
23	6·48	6·07	5·71	5·39	5·11	4·85	4·62	4·41	4·22	4·04	3·88	3·73	3·59	3·46	3·34	3·22	23
24	6·79	6·37	5·99	5·66	5·36	5·09	4·85	4·62	4·42	4·24	4·07	3·91	3·76	3·63	3·50	3·38	24
25	7·12	6·67	6·28	5·93	5·61	5·33	5·08	4·84	4·63	4·44	4·26	4·09	3·94	3·80	3·67	3·54	25
26	7·44	6·98	6·56	6·20	5·87	5·57	5·31	5·07	4·84	4·64	4·45	4·28	4·12	3·97	3·83	3·70	26
27	7·77	7·29	6·86	6·47	6·13	5·82	5·55	5·29	5·06	4·85	4·65	4·47	4·31	4·15	4·01	3·87	27
28	8·11	7·60	7·16	6·76	6·40	6·08	5·79	5·52	5·28	5·06	4·86	4·67	4·49	4·33	4·18	4·04	28
29	8·46	7·93	7·46	7·04	6·67	6·34	6·03	5·76	5·51	5·27	5·06	4·87	4·68	4·51	4·36	4·21	29
30	8·81	8·26	7·77	7·34	6·95	6·60	6·28	6·00	5·73	5·49	5·27	5·07	4·88	4·70	4·54	4·39	30
31	9·17	8·59	8·09	7·63	7·23	6·87	6·54	6·24	5·97	5·72	5·49	5·27	5·08	4·89	4·72	4·56	31
32	9·53	8·94	8·41	7·94	7·52	7·14	6·80	6·49	6·21	5·95	5·71	5·48	5·28	5·09	4·91	4·75	32
33	9·91	9·29	8·74	8·25	7·82	7·42	7·07	6·74	6·45	6·18	5·93	5·70	5·49	5·29	5·11	4·93	33
34	10·3	9·65	9·08	8·57	8·12	7·71	7·34	7·01	6·70	6·42	6·16	5·92	5·70	5·49	5·30	5·12	34
35	10·7	10·0	9·42	8·90	8·43	8·00	7·62	7·27	6·95	6·66	6·39	6·15	5·92	5·70	5·50	5·32	35
36	11·1	10·4	9·78	9·23	8·74	8·30	7·91	7·55	7·22	6·91	6·63	6·38	6·14	5·92	5·71	5·52	36
37	11·5	10·8	10·1	9·57	9·07	8·61	8·20	7·83	7·48	7·17	6·88	6·61	6·37	6·14	5·92	5·72	37
38	11·9	11·2	10·5	9·93	9·40	8·93	8·50	8·11	7·76	7·43	7·13	6·86	6·60	6·36	6·14	5·93	38
39	12·4	11·6	10·9	10·3	9·75	9·26	8·81	8·41	8·04	7·70	7·39	7·11	6·84	6·60	6·37	6·15	39
40	12·8	12·0	11·3	10·7	10·1	9·59	9·13	8·71	8·33	7·98	7·66	7·36	7·09	6·83	6·60	6·37	40
41	13·3	12·4	11·7	11·1	10·5	9·94	9·46	9·03	8·63	8·27	7·94	7·63	7·35	7·08	6·83	6·60	41
42	13·7	12·9	12·1	11·4	10·8	10·3	9·80	9·35	8·94	8·57	8·22	7·90	7·61	7·33	7·08	6·84	42
43	14·2	13·3	12·6	11·8	11·2	10·7	10·2	9·68	9·26	8·87	8·52	8·18	7·88	7·60	7·33	7·08	43
44	14·7	13·8	13·0	12·3	11·6	11·0	10·5	10·0	9·59	9·19	8·82	8·48	8·16	7·87	7·59	7·34	44
45	15·3	14·3	13·5	12·7	12·0	11·4	10·9	10·4	9·93	9·51	9·13	8·78	8·45	8·14	7·86	7·60	45
46	15·8	14·8	13·9	13·2	12·5	11·8	11·3	10·8	10·3	9·85	9·46	9·09	8·75	8·43	8·14	7·87	46
47	16·4	15·3	14·4	13·6	12·9	12·3	11·7	11·1	10·7	10·2	9·79	9·41	9·06	8·73	8·43	8·15	47
48	17·0	15·9	15·0	14·1	13·4	12·7	12·1	11·5	11·0	10·6	10·1	9·75	9·38	9·05	8·73	8·44	48
49	17·6	16·5	15·5	14·6	13·8	13·2	12·5	12·0	11·4	10·9	10·5	10·1	9·72	9·37	9·04	8·74	49
50	18·2	17·0	16·0	15·1	14·3	13·6	13·0	12·4	11·8	11·3	10·9	10·5	10·1	9·71	9·37	9·05	50
51	18·8	17·7	16·6	15·7	14·9	14·1	13·4	12·8	12·3	11·8	11·3	10·8	10·4	10·1	9·71	9·38	51
52	19·5	18·3	17·2	16·3	15·4	14·6	13·9	13·3	12·7	12·2	11·7	11·2	10·8	10·4	10·1	9·72	52
53	20·3	19·0	17·9	16·9	16·0	15·2	14·4	13·8	13·2	12·6	12·1	11·7	11·2	10·8	10·4	10·1	53
54	21·0	19·7	18·5	17·5	16·6	15·7	15·0	14·3	13·7	13·1	12·6	12·1	11·6	11·2	10·8	10·5	54
55	21·8	20·4	19·2	18·1	17·2	16·3	15·5	14·8	14·2	13·6	13·0	12·5	12·1	11·6	11·2	10·8	55
56	22·6	21·2	20·0	18·8	17·8	17·0	16·1	15·4	14·7	14·1	13·5	13·0	12·5	12·1	11·7	11·3	56
57	23·5	22·0	20·7	19·6	18·5	17·6	16·8	16·0	15·3	14·7	14·1	13·5	13·0	12·5	12·1	11·7	57
58	24·4	22·9	21·5	20·3	19·3	18·3	17·4	16·6	15·9	15·2	14·6	14·0	13·5	13·0	12·6	12·2	58
59	25·4	23·8	22·4	21·2	20·0	19·0	18·1	17·3	16·5	15·8	15·2	14·6	14·1	13·6	13·1	12·6	59
60	26·4	24·8	23·3	22·0	20·8	19·8	18·9	18·0	17·2	16·5	15·8	15·2	14·6	14·1	13·6	13·2	60
LAT.	176¼ 183¾	176° 184	175¾ 184¼	175½ 184½	175¼ 184¾	175° 185	174¾ 185¼	174½ 185½	174¼ 185¾	174° 186	173¾ 186¼	173½ 186½	173¼ 186¾	173° 187	172¾ 187¼	172½ 187½	LAT.

Subscription Order Form

The Nautical Magazine

20p Monthly (per post 25p)

Annual Subscription £3.00   3 years £8.60   Postage Included

Please supply the "*NAUTICAL MAGAZINE*" *each month from* .... 19......

to .... 19 ......for which I enclose remittance of .... for .... year ......

Name..................
(IN BLOCK LETTERS)

Address (in full)..................
(IN BLOCK LETTERS)

To

The "Nautical Magazine"
BROWN, SON & FERGUSON, LTD.
52 Darnley St., GLASGOW, G41 2SG
SCOTLAND

PAYMENT of Subscription can be made by either Bank Cheque or Money Order. Cheques should be made out to "Brown Son & Ferguson, Ltd." Money Orders made out payable to "Brown Son & Ferguson, Ltd.," at "Glasgow". Subscriptions can be paid for three years in advance if desired, for £8·60, thereby saving trouble of remitting each year, and ensuring that the *Nautical Magazine* will be sent for three years.

Table 29 B   0 hrs.

Lat. and Dec. SAME name, Sign —
Lat. and Dec. CONTRARY names, Sign +

OUR ANGLE or DIFF. LONG.

DEC.	15m	16m	17m	18m	19m	20m	21m	22m	23m	24m	25m	26m	27m	28m	29m	30m	DEC.
	3¾°	4°	4¼°	4½°	4¾°	5°	5¼°	5½°	5¾°	6°	6¼°	6½°	6¾°	7°	7¼°	7½°	
	356¼	356	355¾	355½	355¼	355	354¾	354½	354¼	354	353¾	353½	353¼	353	352¾	352½	
0°	·000	·000	·000	·000	·000	·000	·000	·000	·000	·000	·000	·000	·000	·000	·000	·000	0°
1	·267	·250	·236	·222	·211	·200	·191	·182	·174	·167	·160	·154	·149	·143	·138	·134	1
2	·534	·501	·471	·445	·422	·401	·382	·364	·349	·334	·321	·308	·297	·287	·277	·268	2
3	·801	·751	·707	·668	·633	·601	·573	·547	·523	·501	·481	·463	·446	·430	·415	·402	3
4	1·07	1·00	·944	·891	·844	·802	·764	·730	·698	·669	·642	·618	·595	·574	·554	·536	4
5	1·34	1·25	1·18	1·12	1·06	1·00	·956	·913	·873	·837	·804	·773	·744	·718	·693	·670	5
6	1·61	1·51	1·42	1·34	1·27	1·21	1·15	1·10	1·05	1·01	·965	·928	·894	·862	·833	·805	6
7	1·88	1·76	1·66	1·57	1·48	1·41	1·34	1·28	1·23	1·17	1·13	1·08	1·05	1·01	·973	·941	7
8	2·15	2·01	1·90	1·79	1·70	1·61	1·54	1·47	1·40	1·34	1·29	1·24	1·20	1·15	1·11	1·08	8
9	2·42	2·27	2·14	2·02	1·91	1·82	1·73	1·65	1·58	1·52	1·46	1·40	1·35	1·30	1·26	1·21	9
10	2·70	2·53	2·38	2·25	2·13	2·02	1·93	1·84	1·76	1·69	1·62	1·56	1·50	1·45	1·40	1·35	10
11	2·97	2·79	2·62	2·48	2·35	2·23	2·12	2·03	1·94	1·86	1·79	1·72	1·65	1·60	1·54	1·49	11
12	3·25	3·05	2·87	2·71	2·57	2·44	2·32	2·22	2·12	2·03	1·95	1·88	1·81	1·74	1·68	1·63	12
13	3·53	3·31	3·12	2·94	2·79	2·65	2·52	2·41	2·30	2·21	2·12	2·04	1·96	1·89	1·83	1·77	13
14	3·81	3·57	3·36	3·18	3·01	2·86	2·73	2·60	2·49	2·39	2·29	2·20	2·12	2·05	1·98	1·91	14
15	4·10	3·84	3·62	3·42	3·24	3·07	2·93	2·80	2·67	2·56	2·46	2·37	2·28	2·20	2·12	2·05	15
16	4·38	4·11	3·87	3·65	3·46	3·29	3·13	2·99	2·86	2·74	2·63	2·53	2·44	2·35	2·27	2·20	16
17	4·68	4·38	4·13	3·90	3·69	3·51	3·34	3·19	3·05	2·92	2·81	2·70	2·60	2·51	2·42	2·34	17
18	4·97	4·66	4·38	4·14	3·92	3·73	3·55	3·39	3·24	3·11	2·99	2·87	2·76	2·67	2·58	2·49	18
19	5·27	4·94	4·65	4·39	4·16	3·95	3·76	3·59	3·44	3·29	3·16	3·04	2·93	2·83	2·73	2·64	19
20	5·57	5·22	4·91	4·64	4·40	4·18	3·98	3·80	3·63	3·48	3·34	3·22	3·10	2·99	2·88	2·79	20
21	5·87	5·50	5·18	4·89	4·64	4·40	4·20	4·01	3·83	3·67	3·53	3·39	3·27	3·15	3·04	2·94	21
22	6·18	5·79	5·45	5·15	4·88	4·64	4·42	4·22	4·03	3·87	3·71	3·57	3·44	3·32	3·20	3·10	22
23	6·49	6·09	5·73	5·41	5·13	4·87	4·64	4·43	4·24	4·06	3·90	3·75	3·61	3·48	3·36	3·25	23
24	6·81	6·38	6·01	5·67	5·38	5·11	4·87	4·65	4·44	4·26	4·09	3·93	3·79	3·65	3·53	3·41	24
25	7·13	6·68	6·29	5·94	5·63	5·35	5·10	4·87	4·65	4·46	4·28	4·12	3·97	3·83	3·70	3·57	25
26	7·46	6·99	6·58	6·22	5·89	5·60	5·33	5·09	4·87	4·67	4·48	4·31	4·15	4·00	3·87	3·74	26
27	7·79	7·30	6·88	6·49	6·15	5·85	5·57	5·32	5·09	4·87	4·68	4·50	4·34	4·18	4·04	3·90	27
28	8·13	7·62	7·18	6·78	6·42	6·10	5·81	5·55	5·31	5·09	4·88	4·70	4·52	4·36	4·21	4·07	28
29	8·48	7·95	7·48	7·06	6·69	6·36	6·06	5·78	5·53	5·30	5·09	4·90	4·72	4·55	4·39	4·25	29
30	8·83	8·28	7·79	7·36	6·97	6·62	6·31	6·02	5·76	5·52	5·30	5·10	4·91	4·74	4·58	4·42	30
31	9·19	8·61	8·11	7·66	7·26	6·89	6·57	6·27	6·00	5·75	5·52	5·31	5·11	4·93	4·76	4·60	31
32	9·55	8·96	8·43	7·96	7·55	7·17	6·83	6·52	6·24	5·98	5·74	5·52	5·32	5·13	4·95	4·79	32
33	9·93	9·31	8·76	8·28	7·84	7·45	7·10	6·78	6·48	6·21	5·97	5·74	5·53	5·33	5·15	4·98	33
34	10·3	9·67	9·10	8·60	8·15	7·74	7·37	7·04	6·73	6·45	6·20	5·96	5·74	5·53	5·35	5·17	34
35	10·7	10·0	9·45	8·92	8·46	8·03	7·65	7·31	6·99	6·70	6·43	6·19	5·96	5·75	5·55	5·36	35
36	11·1	10·4	9·80	9·26	8·77	8·34	7·94	7·58	7·25	6·95	6·67	6·42	6·18	5·96	5·76	5·57	36
37	11·5	10·8	10·2	9·60	9·10	8·65	8·24	7·86	7·52	7·21	6·92	6·66	6·41	6·18	5·97	5·77	37
38	12·0	11·2	10·5	9·96	9·44	8·96	8·54	8·15	7·80	7·47	7·18	6·90	6·65	6·41	6·19	5·97	38
39	12·4	11·6	10·9	10·3	9·78	9·29	8·85	8·45	8·08	7·75	7·44	7·15	6·89	6·64	6·42	6·20	39
40	12·8	12·0	11·3	10·7	10·1	9·63	9·17	8·75	8·38	8·03	7·71	7·41	7·14	6·89	6·65	6·43	40
41	13·3	12·5	11·7	11·1	10·5	9·97	9·50	9·07	8·68	8·32	7·99	7·68	7·40	7·13	6·89	6·66	41
42	13·8	12·9	12·2	11·5	10·9	10·3	9·84	9·39	8·99	8·61	8·27	7·95	7·66	7·39	7·14	6·90	42
43	14·3	13·4	12·6	11·9	11·3	10·7	10·2	9·73	9·31	8·92	8·57	8·24	7·93	7·65	7·39	7·14	43
44	14·8	13·8	13·0	12·3	11·7	11·1	10·6	10·1	9·64	9·24	8·87	8·53	8·22	7·92	7·65	7·40	44
45	15·3	14·3	13·5	12·7	12·1	11·5	10·9	10·4	9·98	9·57	9·19	8·83	8·51	8·21	7·92	7·66	45
46	15·8	14·8	14·0	13·2	12·5	11·9	11·3	10·8	10·3	9·91	9·51	9·15	8·81	8·50	8·21	7·93	46
47	16·4	15·4	14·5	13·7	13·0	12·3	11·7	11·2	10·7	10·3	9·85	9·47	9·12	8·80	8·50	8·22	47
48	17·0	15·9	15·0	14·2	13·4	12·7	12·1	11·6	11·1	10·6	10·2	9·81	9·45	9·11	8·80	8·51	48
49	17·6	16·5	15·5	14·7	13·9	13·2	12·6	12·0	11·5	11·0	10·6	10·2	9·79	9·44	9·12	8·81	49
50	18·2	17·1	16·1	15·2	14·4	13·7	13·0	12·4	11·9	11·4	11·0	10·5	10·1	9·78	9·44	9·13	50
51	18·9	17·7	16·7	15·7	14·9	14·2	13·5	12·9	12·3	11·8	11·3	10·9	10·5	10·1	9·79	9·46	51
52	19·6	18·3	17·3	16·3	15·5	14·7	14·0	13·4	12·8	12·2	11·8	11·3	10·9	10·5	10·1	9·81	52
53	20·3	19·0	17·9	16·9	16·0	15·2	14·5	13·9	13·3	12·7	12·2	11·7	11·3	10·9	10·5	10·2	53
54	21·0	19·7	18·6	17·5	16·6	15·8	15·0	14·4	13·7	13·2	12·6	12·2	11·7	11·3	10·9	10·5	54
55	21·8	20·5	19·3	18·2	17·3	16·4	15·6	14·9	14·3	13·7	13·1	12·6	12·2	11·7	11·3	10·9	55
56	22·7	21·3	20·0	18·9	17·9	17·0	16·2	15·5	14·8	14·2	13·6	13·1	12·6	12·2	11·8	11·4	56
57	23·5	22·1	20·8	19·6	18·6	17·7	16·8	16·1	15·4	14·7	14·1	13·6	13·1	12·6	12·2	11·8	57
58	24·5	22·9	21·6	20·4	19·3	18·4	17·5	16·7	16·0	15·3	14·7	14·1	13·6	13·1	12·7	12·3	58
59	25·5	23·9	22·5	21·2	20·1	19·1	18·2	17·4	16·6	15·9	15·3	14·7	14·2	13·7	13·2	12·8	59
60	26·5	24·8	23·4	22·1	20·9	19·9	18·9	18·1	17·3	16·6	15·9	15·3	14·7	14·2	13·7	13·3	60
61	27·6	25·9	24·3	23·0	21·8	20·7	19·7	18·8	18·0	17·3	16·6	15·9	15·4	14·8	14·3	13·8	61
62	28·8	27·0	25·4	24·0	22·7	21·6	20·6	19·6	18·8	18·0	17·3	16·6	16·0	15·4	14·9	14·4	62
63	30·0	28·1	26·5	25·0	23·7	22·5	21·5	20·5	19·6	18·8	18·0	17·3	16·7	16·1	15·6	15·0	63
DEC.	176¼	176°	175¾	175½	175¼	175°	174¾	174½	174¼	174°	173¾	173½	173¼	173°	172¾	172½	DEC.
	183¾	184	184¼	184½	184¾	185	185¼	185½	185¾	186	186¼	186½	186¾	187	187¼	187½	

Table 29

A

0 hrs.

If entered with H.A. at **top**, Sign **+**
„   „   „   „ **foot**, „ **—**

HOUR ANGLE or DIFF. LONG.

LAT.	30m	31m	32m	33m	34m	35m	36m	37m	38m	39m	40m	41m	42m	43m	44m	45m	LAT.
	7½° 352½	7¾° 352¼	8° 352	8¼° 351¾	8½° 351½	8¾° 351¼	9° 351	9¼° 350¾	9½° 350½	9¾° 350¼	10° 350	10¼° 349¾	10½° 349½	10¾° 349¼	11° 349	11¼° 348¾	
0°	.000	.000	.000	.000	.000	.000	.000	.000	.000	.000	.000	.000	.000	.000	.000	.000	0°
1	.133	.128	.124	.120	.117	.113	.110	.107	.104	.102	.099	.097	.094	.092	.090	.088	1
2	.265	.257	.248	.241	.234	.227	.220	.214	.209	.203	.198	.193	.188	.184	.180	.176	2
3	.398	.385	.373	.361	.351	.340	.331	.322	.313	.305	.297	.290	.283	.276	.270	.263	3
4	.531	.514	.498	.482	.468	.454	.442	.429	.418	.407	.397	.387	.377	.368	.360	.352	4
5	.665	.643	.623	.603	.585	.568	.552	.537	.523	.509	.496	.484	.472	.461	.450	.440	5
6	.798	.772	.748	.725	.703	.683	.664	.645	.628	.612	.596	.581	.567	.554	.541	.528	6
7	.933	.902	.874	.847	.822	.798	.775	.754	.734	.715	.696	.679	.662	.647	.632	.617	7
8	1.07	1.03	1.00	.969	.940	.913	.887	.863	.840	.818	.797	.777	.758	.740	.723	.707	8
9	1.20	1.16	1.13	1.09	1.06	1.03	1.00	.973	.946	.923	.898	.876	.855	.834	.815	.796	9
10	1.34	1.30	1.26	1.22	1.18	1.15	1.11	1.08	1.05	1.03	1.00	.975	.951	.929	.907	.886	10
11	1.48	1.43	1.38	1.34	1.30	1.26	1.23	1.19	1.16	1.13	1.10	1.08	1.05	1.02	1.00	.977	11
12	1.62	1.56	1.51	1.47	1.42	1.38	1.34	1.31	1.27	1.24	1.21	1.18	1.15	1.12	1.09	1.07	12
13	1.75	1.70	1.64	1.59	1.54	1.50	1.46	1.42	1.38	1.34	1.31	1.28	1.25	1.22	1.19	1.16	13
14	1.89	1.83	1.77	1.72	1.67	1.62	1.57	1.53	1.49	1.45	1.41	1.38	1.35	1.31	1.28	1.25	14
15	2.04	1.97	1.91	1.85	1.79	1.74	1.69	1.65	1.60	1.56	1.52	1.49	1.45	1.41	1.38	1.35	15
16	2.18	2.11	2.04	1.98	1.92	1.86	1.81	1.76	1.71	1.67	1.62	1.59	1.55	1.51	1.48	1.44	16
17	2.32	2.25	2.18	2.11	2.05	1.99	1.93	1.88	1.83	1.78	1.73	1.69	1.65	1.61	1.57	1.54	17
18	2.47	2.39	2.31	2.24	2.17	2.11	2.05	2.00	1.94	1.89	1.84	1.80	1.75	1.71	1.67	1.63	18
19	2.62	2.53	2.45	2.38	2.30	2.24	2.17	2.11	2.06	2.00	1.95	1.90	1.86	1.81	1.77	1.73	19
20	2.77	2.67	2.59	2.51	2.44	2.37	2.30	2.24	2.18	2.12	2.06	2.01	1.96	1.92	1.87	1.83	20
21	2.92	2.82	2.73	2.65	2.57	2.49	2.42	2.36	2.29	2.23	2.18	2.12	2.07	2.02	1.97	1.93	21
22	3.07	2.97	2.87	2.79	2.70	2.63	2.55	2.48	2.41	2.35	2.29	2.23	2.18	2.13	2.08	2.03	22
23	3.22	3.12	3.02	2.93	2.84	2.76	2.68	2.61	2.54	2.47	2.41	2.35	2.29	2.24	2.18	2.13	23
24	3.38	3.27	3.17	3.07	2.98	2.89	2.81	2.73	2.66	2.59	2.53	2.46	2.40	2.35	2.29	2.24	24
25	3.54	3.43	3.32	3.22	3.12	3.03	2.94	2.86	2.79	2.71	2.65	2.58	2.52	2.46	2.40	2.34	25
26	3.70	3.58	3.47	3.36	3.26	3.17	3.08	3.00	2.91	2.84	2.77	2.70	2.63	2.57	2.51	2.45	26
27	3.87	3.74	3.63	3.51	3.41	3.31	3.22	3.13	3.04	2.97	2.89	2.82	2.75	2.68	2.62	2.56	27
28	4.04	3.91	3.78	3.67	3.56	3.46	3.36	3.27	3.18	3.09	3.02	2.94	2.87	2.80	2.74	2.67	28
29	4.21	4.07	3.94	3.82	3.71	3.60	3.50	3.40	3.31	3.23	3.14	3.07	2.99	2.92	2.85	2.79	29
30	4.39	4.24	4.11	3.98	3.86	3.75	3.65	3.55	3.45	3.36	3.27	3.19	3.12	3.04	2.97	2.90	30
31	4.56	4.42	4.28	4.14	4.02	3.90	3.79	3.69	3.59	3.50	3.41	3.32	3.24	3.17	3.09	3.02	31
32	4.75	4.59	4.45	4.31	4.18	4.06	3.95	3.84	3.73	3.64	3.54	3.46	3.37	3.29	3.21	3.14	32
33	4.93	4.77	4.62	4.48	4.35	4.22	4.10	3.99	3.88	3.78	3.68	3.59	3.50	3.42	3.34	3.27	33
34	5.12	4.96	4.80	4.65	4.51	4.38	4.26	4.14	4.03	3.93	3.83	3.73	3.64	3.55	3.47	3.39	34
35	5.32	5.15	4.98	4.83	4.69	4.55	4.42	4.30	4.18	4.08	3.97	3.87	3.78	3.69	3.60	3.52	35
36	5.52	5.34	5.17	5.01	4.86	4.73	4.59	4.46	4.34	4.23	4.12	4.02	3.92	3.83	3.74	3.65	36
37	5.72	5.54	5.36	5.20	5.04	4.90	4.76	4.63	4.50	4.39	4.27	4.17	4.07	3.97	3.88	3.79	37
38	5.93	5.74	5.56	5.39	5.23	5.08	4.93	4.80	4.67	4.55	4.43	4.32	4.22	4.12	4.02	3.93	38
39	6.15	5.95	5.76	5.59	5.42	5.26	5.11	4.97	4.84	4.71	4.59	4.48	4.37	4.27	4.17	4.07	39
40	6.37	6.17	5.97	5.79	5.61	5.45	5.30	5.15	5.01	4.88	4.76	4.64	4.53	4.42	4.32	4.22	40
41	6.60	6.39	6.19	6.00	5.82	5.65	5.49	5.34	5.20	5.06	4.93	4.81	4.69	4.58	4.47	4.37	41
42	6.84	6.62	6.41	6.21	6.02	5.85	5.69	5.53	5.38	5.24	5.11	4.98	4.86	4.74	4.63	4.53	42
43	7.08	6.85	6.64	6.43	6.24	6.06	5.89	5.73	5.57	5.43	5.29	5.16	5.03	4.91	4.80	4.69	43
44	7.34	7.10	6.87	6.66	6.46	6.27	6.10	5.93	5.77	5.62	5.48	5.34	5.21	5.09	4.97	4.86	44
45	7.60	7.35	7.12	6.90	6.69	6.50	6.31	6.14	5.98	5.82	5.67	5.53	5.40	5.27	5.15	5.03	45
46	7.87	7.61	7.37	7.14	6.93	6.73	6.54	6.36	6.19	6.03	5.87	5.73	5.59	5.45	5.33	5.21	46
47	8.15	7.88	7.63	7.40	7.18	6.97	6.77	6.59	6.41	6.24	6.08	5.93	5.79	5.65	5.52	5.39	47
48	8.44	8.16	7.90	7.66	7.43	7.22	7.01	6.82	6.64	6.46	6.30	6.14	5.99	5.85	5.71	5.58	48
49	8.74	8.45	8.19	7.93	7.70	7.47	7.26	7.06	6.87	6.70	6.52	6.36	6.21	6.06	5.92	5.78	49
50	9.05	8.76	8.48	8.22	7.97	7.74	7.52	7.32	7.12	6.94	6.76	6.59	6.43	6.28	6.13	5.99	50
51	9.38	9.07	8.79	8.52	8.26	8.02	7.80	7.58	7.38	7.19	7.00	6.83	6.66	6.50	6.35	6.21	51
52	9.72	9.41	9.11	8.83	8.56	8.32	8.08	7.86	7.65	7.45	7.26	7.08	6.91	6.74	6.58	6.44	52
53	10.1	9.75	9.44	9.15	8.88	8.62	8.38	8.15	7.93	7.72	7.53	7.34	7.16	6.99	6.83	6.67	53
54	10.5	10.1	9.79	9.49	9.21	8.94	8.69	8.45	8.23	8.01	7.81	7.61	7.43	7.25	7.08	6.92	54
55	10.8	10.5	10.2	9.85	9.56	9.28	9.02	8.77	8.53	8.31	8.10	7.90	7.71	7.52	7.35	7.18	55
56	11.3	10.9	10.6	10.2	9.92	9.63	9.36	9.10	8.86	8.63	8.41	8.20	8.00	7.81	7.63	7.45	56
57	11.7	11.3	11.0	10.6	10.3	10.0	9.72	9.46	9.20	8.96	8.73	8.52	8.31	8.11	7.92	7.74	57
58	12.2	11.8	11.4	11.0	10.7	10.4	10.1	9.83	9.56	9.31	9.08	8.85	8.64	8.43	8.23	8.05	58
59	12.6	12.2	11.8	11.5	11.1	10.8	10.5	10.2	9.95	9.69	9.44	9.20	8.98	8.77	8.56	8.37	59
60	13.2	12.7	12.3	12.0	11.6	11.3	10.9	10.6	10.4	10.1	9.82	9.58	9.35	9.12	8.91	8.71	60
LAT.	172½ 187½	172¼ 187¾	172° 188	171¾ 188¼	171½ 188½	171¼ 188¾	171° 189	170¾ 189¼	170½ 189½	170¼ 189¾	170° 190	169¾ 190¼	169½ 190½	169¼ 190¾	169° 191	168¾ 191¼	LAT.

Table 29 — B — 0 hrs.

Lat. and Dec. SAME name, Sign —
Lat. and Dec. CONTRARY names, Sign +

HOUR ANGLE or DIFF. LONG.

DEC.	30m	31m	32m	33m	34m	35m	36m	37m	38m	39m	40m	41m	42m	43m	44m	45m	DEC.
	7½° 352½	7¾° 352¼	8° 352	8¼° 351¾	8½° 351½	8¾° 351¼	9° 351	9¼° 350¾	9½° 350½	9¾° 350¼	10° 350	10¼° 349¾	10½° 349½	10¾° 349¼	11° 349	11¼° 348¾	
0°	.000	.000	.000	.000	.000	.000	.000	.000	.000	.000	.000	.000	.000	.000	.000	.000	0°
1	.134	.129	.125	.122	.118	.115	.112	.109	.106	.103	.101	.098	.096	.094	.091	.089	1
2	.268	.259	.251	.243	.236	.230	.223	.217	.212	.206	.201	.196	.192	.187	.183	.179	2
3	.402	.389	.377	.365	.355	.345	.335	.326	.318	.309	.302	.295	.288	.281	.275	.269	3
4	.536	.519	.502	.487	.473	.460	.447	.435	.424	.413	.403	.393	.384	.375	.366	.358	4
5	.670	.649	.629	.610	.592	.575	.559	.544	.530	.517	.504	.492	.480	.469	.459	.448	5
6	.805	.779	.755	.732	.711	.691	.672	.654	.637	.621	.605	.591	.577	.563	.551	.539	6
7	.941	.911	.882	.856	.831	.807	.785	.764	.744	.725	.707	.690	.674	.658	.643	.629	7
8	1.08	1.04	1.01	.979	.951	.924	.898	.874	.852	.830	.809	.790	.771	.753	.737	.720	8
9	1.21	1.18	1.14	1.10	1.07	1.04	1.01	.985	.960	.935	.912	.890	.869	.849	.830	.812	9
10	1.35	1.31	1.27	1.23	1.19	1.16	1.13	1.10	1.07	1.04	1.02	.991	.968	.945	.924	.904	10
11	1.49	1.44	1.40	1.36	1.32	1.28	1.24	1.21	1.18	1.15	1.12	1.09	1.07	1.04	1.02	.996	11
12	1.63	1.58	1.53	1.48	1.44	1.40	1.36	1.32	1.29	1.26	1.22	1.20	1.17	1.14	1.11	1.09	12
13	1.77	1.71	1.66	1.61	1.56	1.52	1.48	1.44	1.40	1.36	1.33	1.30	1.27	1.24	1.21	1.18	13
14	1.91	1.85	1.79	1.74	1.69	1.64	1.59	1.55	1.51	1.47	1.44	1.40	1.37	1.34	1.31	1.28	14
15	2.05	1.99	1.93	1.87	1.81	1.76	1.71	1.67	1.62	1.58	1.54	1.51	1.47	1.44	1.40	1.37	15
16	2.20	2.13	2.06	2.00	1.94	1.89	1.83	1.78	1.74	1.69	1.65	1.61	1.57	1.54	1.50	1.47	16
17	2.34	2.27	2.20	2.13	2.07	2.01	1.95	1.90	1.85	1.81	1.76	1.72	1.68	1.64	1.60	1.57	17
18	2.49	2.41	2.33	2.26	2.20	2.14	2.08	2.02	1.97	1.92	1.87	1.83	1.78	1.74	1.70	1.67	18
19	2.64	2.55	2.47	2.40	2.33	2.26	2.20	2.14	2.09	2.03	1.98	1.94	1.89	1.85	1.80	1.77	19
20	2.79	2.70	2.62	2.54	2.46	2.39	2.33	2.26	2.21	2.15	2.10	2.05	2.00	1.95	1.91	1.87	20
21	2.94	2.85	2.76	2.68	2.60	2.52	2.45	2.39	2.33	2.27	2.21	2.16	2.11	2.06	2.01	1.97	21
22	3.10	3.00	2.90	2.82	2.73	2.66	2.58	2.51	2.45	2.39	2.33	2.27	2.22	2.17	2.12	2.07	22
23	3.25	3.15	3.05	2.96	2.87	2.79	2.71	2.64	2.57	2.51	2.44	2.39	2.33	2.28	2.22	2.18	23
24	3.41	3.30	3.20	3.10	3.01	2.93	2.85	2.77	2.70	2.63	2.56	2.50	2.44	2.39	2.33	2.28	24
25	3.57	3.46	3.35	3.25	3.15	3.07	2.98	2.90	2.83	2.75	2.69	2.62	2.56	2.50	2.44	2.39	25
26	3.74	3.62	3.50	3.40	3.30	3.21	3.12	3.03	2.96	2.88	2.81	2.74	2.68	2.62	2.56	2.50	26
27	3.90	3.78	3.66	3.55	3.45	3.35	3.26	3.17	3.09	3.01	2.93	2.86	2.80	2.73	2.67	2.61	27
28	4.07	3.94	3.82	3.71	3.60	3.50	3.40	3.31	3.22	3.14	3.06	2.99	2.92	2.85	2.79	2.73	28
29	4.25	4.11	3.98	3.86	3.75	3.64	3.54	3.45	3.36	3.27	3.19	3.12	3.04	2.97	2.91	2.84	29
30	4.42	4.28	4.15	4.02	3.91	3.80	3.69	3.59	3.50	3.41	3.32	3.25	3.17	3.10	3.03	2.96	30
31	4.60	4.46	4.32	4.19	4.07	3.95	3.84	3.74	3.64	3.55	3.46	3.38	3.30	3.22	3.15	3.08	31
32	4.79	4.63	4.49	4.36	4.23	4.11	3.99	3.89	3.79	3.69	3.60	3.51	3.43	3.35	3.27	3.20	32
33	4.98	4.82	4.67	4.53	4.39	4.27	4.15	4.04	3.93	3.84	3.74	3.65	3.56	3.48	3.40	3.33	33
34	5.17	5.00	4.85	4.70	4.56	4.43	4.31	4.20	4.09	3.98	3.88	3.79	3.70	3.62	3.54	3.46	34
35	5.36	5.19	5.03	4.88	4.74	4.60	4.48	4.36	4.24	4.14	4.03	3.94	3.84	3.75	3.67	3.59	35
36	5.57	5.39	5.22	5.06	4.92	4.78	4.64	4.52	4.40	4.29	4.18	4.08	3.99	3.90	3.81	3.72	36
37	5.77	5.59	5.41	5.25	5.10	4.95	4.82	4.69	4.57	4.45	4.34	4.24	4.14	4.04	3.95	3.86	37
38	5.99	5.79	5.61	5.45	5.29	5.14	4.99	4.86	4.73	4.61	4.50	4.39	4.29	4.19	4.10	4.01	38
39	6.20	6.01	5.82	5.64	5.48	5.32	5.18	5.04	4.91	4.78	4.66	4.55	4.44	4.34	4.24	4.15	39
40	6.43	6.22	6.03	5.85	5.68	5.52	5.36	5.22	5.08	4.96	4.83	4.72	4.60	4.50	4.40	4.30	40
41	6.66	6.45	6.25	6.06	5.88	5.71	5.56	5.41	5.27	5.13	5.01	4.89	4.77	4.66	4.56	4.46	41
42	6.90	6.68	6.47	6.28	6.09	5.92	5.76	5.60	5.46	5.32	5.19	5.06	4.94	4.83	4.72	4.62	42
43	7.14	6.92	6.70	6.50	6.31	6.13	5.96	5.80	5.65	5.51	5.37	5.24	5.12	5.00	4.89	4.78	43
44	7.40	7.16	6.94	6.73	6.53	6.35	6.17	6.01	5.85	5.70	5.56	5.43	5.30	5.18	5.06	4.95	44
45	7.66	7.42	7.19	6.97	6.77	6.57	6.39	6.22	6.06	5.91	5.76	5.62	5.49	5.36	5.24	5.13	45
46	7.93	7.68	7.44	7.22	7.01	6.81	6.62	6.44	6.27	6.12	5.96	5.82	5.68	5.55	5.43	5.31	46
47	8.22	7.95	7.71	7.47	7.26	7.05	6.86	6.67	6.50	6.33	6.18	6.03	5.89	5.75	5.62	5.50	47
48	8.51	8.24	7.98	7.74	7.51	7.30	7.10	6.91	6.73	6.56	6.40	6.24	6.09	5.95	5.82	5.69	48
49	8.81	8.53	8.27	8.02	7.78	7.56	7.35	7.16	6.97	6.79	6.62	6.47	6.31	6.17	6.03	5.90	49
50	9.13	8.84	8.56	8.31	8.06	7.83	7.62	7.41	7.22	7.04	6.86	6.70	6.54	6.39	6.25	6.11	50
51	9.46	9.16	8.87	8.61	8.35	8.12	7.89	7.68	7.48	7.29	7.11	6.94	6.78	6.62	6.47	6.33	51
52	9.81	9.49	9.20	8.92	8.66	8.41	8.18	7.96	7.76	7.56	7.37	7.19	7.02	6.86	6.71	6.56	52
53	10.2	9.84	9.54	9.25	8.98	8.72	8.48	8.26	8.04	7.84	7.64	7.46	7.28	7.12	6.95	6.80	53
54	10.5	10.2	9.89	9.59	9.31	9.05	8.80	8.56	8.34	8.13	7.93	7.74	7.55	7.38	7.21	7.06	54
55	10.9	10.6	10.3	9.95	9.66	9.39	9.13	8.89	8.65	8.43	8.22	8.03	7.84	7.66	7.48	7.32	55
56	11.4	11.0	10.7	10.3	10.0	9.75	9.48	9.22	8.98	8.75	8.54	8.33	8.14	7.95	7.77	7.60	56
57	11.8	11.4	11.1	10.7	10.4	10.1	9.84	9.58	9.33	9.09	8.87	8.65	8.45	8.26	8.07	7.89	57
58	12.3	11.9	11.5	11.2	10.8	10.5	10.2	9.96	9.70	9.45	9.22	8.99	8.78	8.58	8.39	8.20	58
59	12.8	12.3	12.0	11.6	11.3	10.9	10.6	10.4	10.1	9.83	9.58	9.35	9.13	8.92	8.72	8.53	59
60	13.3	12.8	12.5	12.1	11.7	11.4	11.1	10.8	10.5	10.2	9.97	9.73	9.50	9.29	9.08	8.88	60
61	13.8	13.4	13.0	12.6	12.2	11.9	11.5	11.2	10.9	10.7	10.4	10.1	9.90	9.67	9.45	9.25	61
62	14.4	14.0	13.5	13.1	12.7	12.4	12.0	11.7	11.4	11.1	10.8	10.6	10.3	10.1	9.86	9.64	62
63	15.0	14.6	14.1	13.7	13.3	12.9	12.5	12.2	11.9	11.6	11.3	11.0	10.8	10.5	10.3	10.1	63
DEC.	172½° 187½	172¼° 187¾	172° 188	171¾° 188¼	171½° 188½	171¼° 188¾	171° 189	170¾° 189¼	170½° 189½	170¼° 189¾	170° 190	169¾° 190¼	169½° 190½	169¼° 190¾	169° 191	168¾° 191¼	DEC.

Table 29

A

If entered with H.A. at **top**, Sign **+**

„   „   „   „ **foot**, „ **−**

0 hrs.

HOUR ANGLE or DIFF. LONG.

LAT.	45m	46m	47m	48m	49m	50m	51m	52m	53m	54m	55m	56m	57m	58m	59m	60m	LAT.
	11¼°	11½°	11¾°	12°	12¼°	12½°	12¾°	13°	13¼°	13½°	13¾°	14°	14¼°	14½°	14¾°	15°	
	348¾	348½	348¼	348	347¾	347½	347¼	347	346¾	346½	346¼	346	345¾	345½	345¼	345	
0°	.000	.000	.000	.000	.000	.000	.000	.000	.000	.000	.000	.000	.000	.000	.000	.000	0°
1	.088	.086	.084	.082	.080	.079	.077	.076	.074	.073	.071	.070	.069	.067	.066	.065	1
2	.176	.172	.168	.164	.161	.158	.154	.151	.148	.145	.143	.140	.138	.135	.133	.130	2
3	.263	.258	.252	.247	.241	.236	.232	.227	.223	.218	.214	.210	.206	.203	.199	.196	3
4	.352	.344	.336	.329	.322	.315	.309	.303	.297	.291	.286	.280	.275	.270	.266	.261	4
5	.440	.430	.421	.412	.403	.395	.387	.379	.372	.364	.358	.351	.344	.338	.332	.327	5
6	.528	.517	.505	.494	.484	.474	.464	.455	.446	.438	.430	.422	.414	.406	.399	.392	6
7	.617	.604	.590	.578	.566	.554	.543	.532	.521	.511	.502	.492	.483	.475	.466	.458	7
8	.707	.691	.676	.661	.647	.634	.621	.609	.597	.585	.574	.564	.553	.543	.534	.525	8
9	.796	.778	.761	.745	.729	.714	.700	.686	.673	.660	.647	.635	.624	.612	.602	.591	9
10	.886	.867	.848	.830	.812	.795	.779	.764	.749	.734	.721	.707	.694	.682	.670	.658	10
11	.977	.955	.935	.914	.895	.877	.859	.842	.826	.810	.794	.780	.765	.752	.738	.725	11
12	1.07	1.05	1.02	1.00	.979	.959	.939	.921	.903	.885	.869	.853	.837	.822	.807	.793	12
13	1.16	1.13	1.11	1.09	1.06	1.04	1.02	1.00	.980	.962	.943	.926	.909	.893	.877	.862	13
14	1.25	1.23	1.20	1.17	1.15	1.13	1.10	1.08	1.06	1.04	1.02	1.00	.982	.964	.947	.931	14
15	1.35	1.32	1.29	1.26	1.23	1.21	1.18	1.16	1.14	1.12	1.10	1.07	1.06	1.04	1.02	1.00	15
16	1.44	1.41	1.38	1.35	1.32	1.29	1.27	1.24	1.22	1.19	1.17	1.15	1.13	1.11	1.09	1.07	16
17	1.54	1.50	1.47	1.44	1.41	1.38	1.35	1.32	1.30	1.27	1.25	1.23	1.20	1.18	1.16	1.14	17
18	1.63	1.60	1.56	1.53	1.50	1.47	1.44	1.41	1.38	1.35	1.33	1.30	1.28	1.26	1.23	1.21	18
19	1.73	1.69	1.66	1.62	1.59	1.55	1.52	1.49	1.46	1.43	1.41	1.38	1.36	1.33	1.31	1.29	19
20	1.83	1.79	1.75	1.71	1.68	1.64	1.61	1.58	1.55	1.52	1.49	1.46	1.43	1.41	1.38	1.36	20
21	1.93	1.89	1.85	1.81	1.77	1.73	1.70	1.66	1.63	1.60	1.57	1.54	1.51	1.48	1.46	1.43	21
22	2.03	1.99	1.94	1.90	1.86	1.82	1.79	1.75	1.72	1.68	1.65	1.62	1.59	1.56	1.54	1.51	22
23	2.13	2.09	2.04	2.00	1.96	1.92	1.88	1.84	1.80	1.77	1.73	1.70	1.67	1.64	1.61	1.58	23
24	2.24	2.19	2.14	2.10	2.05	2.01	1.97	1.93	1.89	1.85	1.82	1.79	1.75	1.72	1.69	1.66	24
25	2.34	2.29	2.24	2.19	2.15	2.10	2.06	2.02	1.98	1.94	1.91	1.87	1.84	1.80	1.77	1.74	25
26	2.45	2.40	2.35	2.29	2.25	2.20	2.16	2.11	2.07	2.03	1.99	1.96	1.92	1.89	1.85	1.82	26
27	2.56	2.50	2.45	2.40	2.35	2.30	2.25	2.21	2.16	2.12	2.08	2.04	2.01	1.97	1.94	1.90	27
28	2.67	2.61	2.56	2.50	2.45	2.40	2.35	2.30	2.26	2.21	2.17	2.13	2.09	2.06	2.02	1.98	28
29	2.79	2.73	2.66	2.61	2.55	2.50	2.45	2.40	2.35	2.31	2.27	2.22	2.18	2.14	2.11	2.07	29
30	2.90	2.84	2.78	2.72	2.66	2.60	2.55	2.50	2.45	2.41	2.36	2.32	2.27	2.23	2.19	2.15	30
31	3.02	2.95	2.89	2.83	2.77	2.71	2.66	2.60	2.55	2.50	2.46	2.41	2.37	2.32	2.28	2.24	31
32	3.14	3.07	3.00	2.94	2.88	2.82	2.76	2.71	2.65	2.60	2.55	2.51	2.46	2.42	2.37	2.33	32
33	3.26	3.19	3.12	3.06	2.99	2.93	2.87	2.81	2.76	2.71	2.65	2.61	2.56	2.51	2.47	2.42	33
34	3.39	3.32	3.24	3.17	3.11	3.04	2.98	2.92	2.87	2.81	2.76	2.71	2.66	2.61	2.56	2.52	34
35	3.52	3.44	3.37	3.29	3.23	3.16	3.09	3.03	2.97	2.92	2.86	2.81	2.76	2.71	2.66	2.61	35
36	3.65	3.57	3.49	3.42	3.35	3.28	3.21	3.15	3.09	3.03	2.97	2.91	2.86	2.81	2.76	2.71	36
37	3.79	3.70	3.62	3.55	3.47	3.40	3.33	3.26	3.20	3.14	3.08	3.02	2.97	2.91	2.86	2.81	37
38	3.93	3.84	3.76	3.68	3.60	3.52	3.45	3.38	3.32	3.25	3.19	3.13	3.08	3.02	2.97	2.92	38
39	4.07	3.98	3.89	3.81	3.73	3.65	3.58	3.51	3.44	3.37	3.31	3.25	3.19	3.13	3.08	3.02	39
40	4.22	4.12	4.03	3.95	3.86	3.79	3.71	3.64	3.56	3.50	3.43	3.37	3.30	3.24	3.19	3.13	40
41	4.37	4.27	4.18	4.09	4.00	3.92	3.84	3.77	3.69	3.62	3.55	3.49	3.42	3.36	3.30	3.24	41
42	4.53	4.43	4.33	4.24	4.15	4.06	3.98	3.90	3.82	3.75	3.68	3.61	3.55	3.48	3.42	3.36	42
43	4.69	4.58	4.48	4.39	4.30	4.21	4.12	4.04	3.96	3.88	3.81	3.74	3.67	3.61	3.54	3.48	43
44	4.86	4.75	4.64	4.54	4.45	4.36	4.27	4.18	4.10	4.02	3.95	3.87	3.80	3.73	3.67	3.60	44
45	5.03	4.92	4.81	4.70	4.61	4.51	4.42	4.33	4.25	4.17	4.09	4.01	3.94	3.87	3.80	3.73	45
46	5.21	5.09	4.98	4.87	4.77	4.67	4.58	4.49	4.40	4.31	4.23	4.15	4.08	4.00	3.93	3.87	46
47	5.39	5.27	5.16	5.05	4.94	4.84	4.74	4.65	4.55	4.47	4.38	4.30	4.22	4.15	4.07	4.00	47
48	5.58	5.46	5.34	5.23	5.12	5.01	4.91	4.81	4.72	4.63	4.54	4.45	4.37	4.29	4.22	4.14	48
49	5.78	5.65	5.53	5.41	5.30	5.19	5.08	4.98	4.89	4.79	4.70	4.61	4.53	4.45	4.37	4.29	49
50	5.99	5.86	5.73	5.61	5.49	5.38	5.27	5.16	5.06	4.96	4.87	4.78	4.69	4.61	4.53	4.45	50
51	6.21	6.07	5.94	5.81	5.69	5.57	5.46	5.35	5.24	5.14	5.05	4.95	4.86	4.78	4.69	4.61	51
52	6.43	6.29	6.15	6.02	5.90	5.77	5.66	5.54	5.44	5.33	5.23	5.13	5.04	4.95	4.86	4.78	52
53	6.67	6.52	6.38	6.25	6.11	5.99	5.86	5.75	5.64	5.53	5.42	5.32	5.23	5.13	5.04	4.95	53
54	6.92	6.77	6.62	6.48	6.34	6.21	6.08	5.96	5.85	5.73	5.62	5.52	5.42	5.32	5.23	5.14	54
55	7.18	7.02	6.87	6.72	6.58	6.44	6.31	6.19	6.07	5.95	5.84	5.73	5.62	5.52	5.42	5.33	55
56	7.45	7.29	7.13	6.97	6.83	6.69	6.55	6.42	6.30	6.18	6.06	5.95	5.84	5.73	5.63	5.53	56
57	7.74	7.57	7.40	7.24	7.09	6.95	6.81	6.67	6.54	6.41	6.29	6.18	6.06	5.95	5.85	5.75	57
58	8.05	7.87	7.69	7.53	7.37	7.22	7.07	6.93	6.80	6.67	6.54	6.42	6.30	6.19	6.08	5.97	58
59	8.37	8.18	8.00	7.83	7.67	7.51	7.36	7.21	7.07	6.93	6.80	6.68	6.55	6.44	6.32	6.21	59
60	8.71	8.51	8.33	8.15	7.98	7.81	7.66	7.50	7.36	7.22	7.08	6.95	6.82	6.70	6.58	6.46	60
LAT.	168¾ 191¼	168½ 191½	168¼ 191¾	168° 192	167¾ 192¼	167½ 192½	167¼ 192¾	167° 193	166¾ 1 3¼	166½ 193½	166¼ 193¾	166° 194	165¾ 194¼	165½ 194½	165¼ 194¾	165° 195	LAT.

Table 29	**B**	Lat. and Dec. SAME name, Sign —
0 hrs.		Lat. and Dec. CONTRARY names, Sign **+**

HOUR ANGLE or DIFF. LONG.

DEC.	45m	46m	47m	48m	49m	50m	51m	52m	53m	54m	55m	56m	57m	58m	59m	60m	DEC.
	11¼° 348¾	11½° 348½	11¾° 348¼	**12°** **348**	12¼° 347¾	12½° 347½	12¾° 347¼	**13°** **347**	13¼° 346¾	13½° 346½	13¾° 346¼	**14°** **346**	14¼° 345¾	14½° 345½	14¾° 345¼	**15°** **345**	
0°	.000	.000	.000	.000	.000	.000	.000	.000	.000	.000	.000	.000	.000	.000	.000	.000	0°
1	.089	.088	.086	.084	.082	.081	.079	.078	.076	.075	.073	.072	.071	.070	.069	.067	1
2	.179	.175	.171	.168	.165	.161	.158	.155	.152	.150	.147	.144	.142	.140	.137	.135	2
3	.269	.263	.257	.252	.247	.242	.237	.233	.229	.224	.220	.217	.213	.209	.206	.202	3
4	.358	.351	.343	.336	.330	.323	.317	.311	.305	.300	.294	.289	.284	.279	.275	.270	4
5	.448	.439	.430	.421	.412	.404	.396	.389	.382	.375	.368	.362	.355	.349	.344	.338	5
6	.539	.527	.516	.506	.495	.486	.476	.467	.459	.450	.442	.434	.427	.420	.413	.406	6
7	.629	.616	.603	.591	.579	.567	.556	.546	.536	.526	.517	.508	.499	.490	.482	.474	7
8	.720	.705	.690	.676	.662	.649	.637	.625	.613	.602	.591	.581	.571	.561	.552	.543	8
9	.812	.794	.778	.762	.746	.732	.718	.704	.691	.678	.666	.655	.643	.633	.622	.612	9
10	.904	.884	.866	.848	.831	.815	.799	.784	.769	.755	.742	.729	.716	.704	.693	.681	10
11	.996	.975	.955	.935	.916	.898	.881	.864	.848	.833	.818	.803	.790	.776	.763	.751	11
12	1.09	1.07	1.04	1.02	1.00	.982	.963	.945	.927	.911	.894	.879	.864	.849	.835	.821	12
13	1.18	1.16	1.13	1.11	1.09	1.07	1.05	1.03	1.01	.989	.971	.954	.938	.922	.907	.892	13
14	1.28	1.25	1.22	1.20	1.18	1.15	1.13	1.11	1.09	1.07	1.05	1.03	1.01	.996	.979	.963	14
15	1.37	1.34	1.32	1.29	1.26	1.24	1.21	1.19	1.17	1.15	1.13	1.11	1.09	1.07	1.05	1.04	15
16	1.47	1.44	1.41	1.38	1.35	1.32	1.30	1.27	1.25	1.23	1.21	1.19	1.17	1.15	1.13	1.11	16
17	1.57	1.53	1.50	1.47	1.44	1.41	1.39	1.36	1.33	1.31	1.29	1.26	1.24	1.22	1.20	1.18	17
18	1.67	1.63	1.60	1.56	1.53	1.50	1.47	1.44	1.42	1.39	1.37	1.34	1.32	1.30	1.28	1.26	18
19	1.77	1.73	1.69	1.66	1.62	1.59	1.56	1.53	1.50	1.48	1.45	1.42	1.40	1.38	1.35	1.33	19
20	1.87	1.83	1.79	1.75	1.72	1.68	1.65	1.62	1.59	1.56	1.53	1.50	1.48	1.45	1.43	1.41	20
21	1.97	1.93	1.89	1.85	1.81	1.77	1.74	1.71	1.68	1.64	1.62	1.59	1.56	1.53	1.51	1.48	21
22	2.07	2.03	1.98	1.94	1.90	1.87	1.83	1.80	1.76	1.73	1.70	1.67	1.64	1.61	1.59	1.56	22
23	2.18	2.13	2.08	2.04	2.00	1.96	1.92	1.89	1.85	1.82	1.79	1.75	1.72	1.70	1.67	1.64	23
24	2.28	2.23	2.19	2.14	2.10	2.06	2.02	1.98	1.94	1.91	1.87	1.84	1.81	1.78	1.75	1.72	24
25	2.39	2.34	2.29	2.24	2.20	2.15	2.11	2.07	2.03	2.00	1.96	1.93	1.89	1.86	1.83	1.80	25
26	2.50	2.45	2.40	2.35	2.30	2.25	2.21	2.17	2.13	2.09	2.05	2.02	1.98	1.95	1.92	1.88	26
27	2.61	2.56	2.50	2.45	2.40	2.35	2.31	2.27	2.22	2.18	2.14	2.11	2.07	2.04	2.00	1.97	27
28	2.73	2.67	2.61	2.56	2.51	2.46	2.41	2.36	2.32	2.28	2.24	2.20	2.16	2.12	2.09	2.05	28
29	2.84	2.78	2.72	2.67	2.61	2.56	2.51	2.46	2.42	2.37	2.33	2.29	2.25	2.21	2.18	2.14	29
30	2.96	2.90	2.84	2.78	2.72	2.67	2.62	2.57	2.52	2.47	2.43	2.39	2.35	2.31	2.27	2.23	30
31	3.08	3.01	2.95	2.89	2.83	2.78	2.72	2.67	2.62	2.57	2.53	2.48	2.44	2.40	2.36	2.32	31
32	3.20	3.13	3.07	3.01	2.95	2.89	2.83	2.78	2.73	2.68	2.63	2.58	2.54	2.50	2.45	2.41	32
33	3.33	3.26	3.19	3.12	3.06	3.00	2.94	2.89	2.83	2.78	2.73	2.68	2.64	2.59	2.55	2.51	33
34	3.46	3.38	3.31	3.24	3.18	3.12	3.06	3.00	2.94	2.89	2.84	2.79	2.74	2.69	2.65	2.61	34
35	3.59	3.51	3.44	3.37	3.30	3.24	3.17	3.11	3.06	3.00	2.95	2.89	2.85	2.80	2.75	2.71	35
36	3.72	3.64	3.57	3.49	3.42	3.36	3.29	3.23	3.17	3.11	3.06	3.00	2.95	2.90	2.85	2.81	36
37	3.86	3.78	3.70	3.62	3.55	3.48	3.41	3.35	3.29	3.23	3.17	3.11	3.06	3.01	2.96	2.91	37
38	4.01	3.92	3.84	3.76	3.68	3.61	3.54	3.47	3.41	3.35	3.29	3.23	3.17	3.12	3.07	3.02	38
39	4.15	4.06	3.98	3.89	3.82	3.74	3.67	3.60	3.53	3.47	3.41	3.35	3.29	3.23	3.18	3.13	39
40	4.30	4.21	4.12	4.04	3.96	3.88	3.80	3.73	3.66	3.59	3.53	3.47	3.41	3.35	3.30	3.24	40
41	4.46	4.36	4.27	4.18	4.10	4.02	3.94	3.86	3.79	3.72	3.66	3.59	3.53	3.47	3.41	3.36	41
42	4.62	4.52	4.42	4.33	4.24	4.16	4.08	4.00	3.93	3.86	3.79	3.72	3.66	3.60	3.54	3.48	42
43	4.78	4.68	4.58	4.49	4.40	4.31	4.23	4.15	4.07	3.99	3.92	3.85	3.79	3.72	3.66	3.60	43
44	4.95	4.84	4.74	4.64	4.55	4.46	4.38	4.29	4.21	4.14	4.06	3.99	3.92	3.86	3.79	3.73	44
45	5.13	5.02	4.91	4.81	4.71	4.62	4.53	4.45	4.36	4.28	4.21	4.13	4.06	3.99	3.93	3.86	45
46	5.31	5.19	5.09	4.98	4.88	4.78	4.69	4.60	4.52	4.44	4.36	4.28	4.21	4.14	4.07	4.00	46
47	5.50	5.38	5.27	5.16	5.05	4.95	4.86	4.77	4.68	4.59	4.51	4.43	4.36	4.28	4.21	4.14	47
48	5.69	5.57	5.45	5.34	5.23	5.13	5.03	4.94	4.85	4.76	4.67	4.59	4.51	4.44	4.36	4.29	48
49	5.90	5.77	5.65	5.53	5.42	5.32	5.21	5.11	5.02	4.93	4.84	4.76	4.67	4.59	4.52	4.44	49
50	6.11	5.98	5.85	5.73	5.62	5.51	5.40	5.30	5.20	5.11	5.01	4.93	4.84	4.76	4.68	4.60	50
51	6.33	6.19	6.06	5.94	5.82	5.71	5.60	5.49	5.39	5.29	5.20	5.10	5.02	4.93	4.85	4.77	51
52	6.56	6.42	6.29	6.16	6.03	5.91	5.80	5.69	5.58	5.48	5.39	5.29	5.20	5.11	5.03	4.95	52
53	6.80	6.66	6.52	6.38	6.25	6.13	6.01	5.90	5.79	5.68	5.58	5.49	5.39	5.30	5.21	5.13	53
54	7.06	6.90	6.76	6.62	6.49	6.36	6.24	6.12	6.01	5.90	5.79	5.69	5.59	5.50	5.41	5.32	54
55	7.32	7.16	7.01	6.87	6.73	6.60	6.47	6.35	6.23	6.12	6.01	5.90	5.80	5.70	5.61	5.52	55
56	7.60	7.44	7.28	7.13	6.99	6.85	6.72	6.59	6.47	6.35	6.24	6.13	6.02	5.92	5.82	5.73	56
57	7.89	7.72	7.56	7.41	7.26	7.11	6.98	6.85	6.72	6.60	6.48	6.37	6.26	6.15	6.05	5.95	57
58	8.20	8.03	7.86	7.70	7.54	7.39	7.25	7.11	6.98	6.86	6.73	6.62	6.50	6.39	6.29	6.18	58
59	8.53	8.35	8.17	8.00	7.84	7.69	7.54	7.40	7.26	7.13	7.00	6.88	6.76	6.65	6.54	6.43	59
60	8.88	8.69	8.51	8.33	8.16	8.00	7.85	7.70	7.56	7.42	7.29	7.16	7.04	6.92	6.80	6.69	60
61	9.25	9.05	8.86	8.68	8.50	8.34	8.17	8.02	7.87	7.73	7.59	7.46	7.33	7.21	7.09	6.97	61
62	9.64	9.43	9.24	9.05	8.86	8.69	8.52	8.36	8.21	8.06	7.91	7.77	7.64	7.51	7.39	7.27	62
63	10.1	9.84	9.64	9.44	9.25	9.07	8.89	8.72	8.56	8.41	8.26	8.11	7.97	7.84	7.71	7.58	63
DEC.	168¾ 191¼	168½ 191½	168¼ 191¾	**168°** **192**	167¾ 192¼	167½ 192½	167¼ 192¾	**167°** **193**	166¾ 193¼	166½ 193½	166¼ 193¾	**166°** **194**	165¾ 194¼	165½ 194½	165¼ 194¾	**165°** **195**	DEC.

Table 29

A   If entered with H.A. at **top**, Sign **+**

„   „   „   „   **foot**, „   **—**

I hr.

HOUR ANGLE or DIFF. LONG.

LAT.	00m	01m	02m	03m	04m	05m	06m	07m	08m	09m	10m	11m	12m	13m	14m	15m	LAT.
	15° 345	15¼° 344¾	15½° 344½	15¾° 344¼	**16°** 344	16¼° 343¾	16½° 343½	16¾° 343¼	**17°** 343	17¼° 342¾	17½° 342½	17¾° 342¼	**18°** 342	18¼° 341¾	18½° 341½	18¾° 341¼	
0°	.000	.000	.000	.000	.000	.000	.000	.000	.000	.000	.000	.000	.000	.000	.000	.000	0°
1	.065	.064	.063	.062	.061	.060	.059	.058	.057	.056	.055	.055	.054	.053	.052	.051	1
2	.130	.128	.126	.124	.122	.120	.118	.116	.114	.113	.111	.109	.108	.106	.104	.103	2
3	.196	.192	.189	.186	.183	.180	.177	.174	.171	.169	.166	.164	.161	.159	.157	.154	3
4	.261	.257	.252	.248	.244	.240	.236	.232	.229	.225	.222	.218	.215	.212	.209	.206	4
5	.327	.321	.315	.310	.305	.300	.295	.291	.286	.282	.277	.273	.269	.265	.262	.258	5
6	.392	.386	.379	.373	.367	.361	.355	.349	.344	.338	.333	.328	.323	.319	.314	.310	6
7	.458	.450	.443	.435	.428	.421	.415	.408	.402	.395	.389	.384	.378	.372	.367	.362	7
8	.525	.515	.507	.498	.490	.482	.474	.467	.460	.453	.446	.439	.433	.426	.420	.414	8
9	.591	.581	.571	.562	.552	.543	.535	.526	.518	.510	.502	.495	.487	.480	.473	.467	9
10	.658	.647	.636	.625	.615	.605	.595	.586	.577	.568	.559	.551	.543	.535	.527	.519	10
11	.725	.713	.701	.689	.678	.667	.656	.646	.636	.626	.616	.607	.598	.589	.581	.573	11
12	.793	.780	.766	.754	.741	.729	.718	.706	.695	.685	.674	.664	.654	.645	.635	.626	12
13	.862	.847	.832	.819	.805	.792	.779	.767	.755	.744	.732	.721	.711	.700	.690	.680	13
14	.931	.915	.899	.884	.870	.855	.842	.828	.816	.803	.791	.779	.767	.756	.745	.734	14
15	1.00	.983	.966	.950	.934	.919	.905	.890	.876	.863	.850	.837	.825	.813	.801	.789	15
16	1.07	1.05	1.03	1.02	1.00	.984	.968	.953	.938	.923	.909	.896	.883	.870	.857	.845	16
17	1.14	1.12	1.10	1.08	1.07	1.05	1.03	1.02	1.00	.985	.970	.955	.941	.927	.914	.901	17
18	1.21	1.19	1.17	1.15	1.13	1.12	1.10	1.08	1.06	1.05	1.03	1.02	1.00	.985	.971	.957	18
19	1.29	1.26	1.24	1.22	1.20	1.18	1.16	1.14	1.13	1.11	1.09	1.08	1.06	1.04	1.03	1.01	19
20	1.36	1.34	1.31	1.29	1.27	1.25	1.23	1.21	1.19	1.17	1.15	1.14	1.12	1.10	1.09	1.07	20
21	1.43	1.41	1.38	1.36	1.34	1.32	1.30	1.28	1.26	1.24	1.22	1.20	1.18	1.16	1.15	1.13	21
22	1.51	1.48	1.46	1.43	1.41	1.39	1.36	1.34	1.32	1.30	1.28	1.26	1.24	1.23	1.21	1.19	22
23	1.58	1.56	1.53	1.51	1.48	1.46	1.43	1.41	1.39	1.37	1.35	1.33	1.31	1.29	1.27	1.25	23
24	1.66	1.63	1.61	1.58	1.55	1.53	1.50	1.48	1.46	1.43	1.41	1.39	1.37	1.35	1.33	1.31	24
25	1.74	1.71	1.68	1.65	1.63	1.60	1.57	1.55	1.53	1.50	1.48	1.46	1.44	1.41	1.39	1.37	25
26	1.82	1.79	1.76	1.73	1.70	1.67	1.65	1.62	1.60	1.57	1.55	1.52	1.50	1.48	1.46	1.44	26
27	1.90	1.87	1.84	1.81	1.78	1.75	1.72	1.69	1.67	1.64	1.62	1.59	1.57	1.55	1.52	1.50	27
28	1.98	1.95	1.92	1.89	1.85	1.82	1.80	1.77	1.74	1.71	1.69	1.66	1.64	1.61	1.59	1.57	28
29	2.07	2.03	2.00	1.97	1.93	1.90	1.87	1.84	1.81	1.79	1.76	1.73	1.71	1.68	1.66	1.64	29
30	2.15	2.12	2.08	2.05	2.01	1.98	1.95	1.92	1.89	1.86	1.83	1.80	1.78	1.75	1.73	1.70	30
31	2.24	2.20	2.17	2.13	2.10	2.06	2.03	2.00	1.97	1.94	1.91	1.88	1.85	1.82	1.80	1.77	31
32	2.33	2.29	2.25	2.22	2.18	2.14	2.11	2.08	2.04	2.01	1.98	1.95	1.92	1.90	1.87	1.84	32
33	2.42	2.38	2.34	2.30	2.26	2.23	2.19	2.16	2.12	2.09	2.06	2.03	2.00	1.97	1.94	1.91	33
34	2.52	2.47	2.43	2.39	2.35	2.31	2.28	2.24	2.21	2.17	2.14	2.11	2.08	2.05	2.02	1.99	34
35	2.61	2.57	2.52	2.48	2.44	2.40	2.36	2.33	2.29	2.26	2.22	2.19	2.16	2.12	2.09	2.06	35
36	2.71	2.66	2.62	2.58	2.53	2.49	2.45	2.41	2.38	2.34	2.30	2.27	2.24	2.20	2.17	2.14	36
37	2.81	2.76	2.72	2.67	2.63	2.59	2.54	2.50	2.46	2.43	2.39	2.35	2.32	2.29	2.25	2.22	37
38	2.92	2.87	2.82	2.77	2.72	2.68	2.64	2.60	2.56	2.52	2.48	2.44	2.40	2.37	2.34	2.30	38
39	3.02	2.97	2.92	2.87	2.82	2.78	2.73	2.69	2.65	2.61	2.57	2.53	2.49	2.46	2.42	2.39	39
40	3.13	3.08	3.03	2.98	2.93	2.88	2.83	2.79	2.74	2.70	2.66	2.62	2.58	2.54	2.51	2.47	40
41	3.24	3.19	3.13	3.08	3.03	2.98	2.93	2.89	2.84	2.80	2.76	2.72	2.68	2.64	2.60	2.56	41
42	3.36	3.30	3.25	3.19	3.14	3.09	3.04	2.99	2.95	2.90	2.86	2.81	2.77	2.73	2.69	2.65	42
43	3.48	3.42	3.36	3.31	3.25	3.20	3.15	3.10	3.05	3.00	2.96	2.91	2.87	2.83	2.79	2.75	43
44	3.60	3.54	3.48	3.42	3.37	3.31	3.26	3.21	3.16	3.11	3.06	3.02	2.97	2.93	2.89	2.85	44
45	3.73	3.67	3.61	3.55	3.49	3.43	3.38	3.32	3.27	3.22	3.17	3.12	3.08	3.03	2.99	2.95	45
46	3.87	3.80	3.73	3.67	3.61	3.55	3.50	3.44	3.39	3.34	3.28	3.24	3.19	3.14	3.09	3.05	46
47	4.00	3.93	3.87	3.80	3.74	3.68	3.62	3.56	3.51	3.45	3.40	3.35	3.30	3.25	3.21	3.16	47
48	4.14	4.07	4.00	3.94	3.87	3.81	3.75	3.69	3.63	3.58	3.52	3.47	3.42	3.37	3.32	3.27	48
49	4.29	4.22	4.15	4.08	4.01	3.95	3.88	3.82	3.76	3.70	3.65	3.59	3.54	3.49	3.44	3.39	49
50	4.45	4.37	4.30	4.23	4.16	4.09	4.02	3.96	3.90	3.84	3.78	3.72	3.67	3.62	3.56	3.51	50
51	4.61	4.53	4.45	4.38	4.31	4.24	4.17	4.10	4.04	3.98	3.92	3.86	3.80	3.74	3.69	3.64	51
52	4.78	4.69	4.62	4.54	4.46	4.39	4.32	4.25	4.19	4.12	4.06	4.00	3.94	3.88	3.83	3.77	52
53	4.95	4.87	4.79	4.71	4.63	4.55	4.48	4.41	4.34	4.27	4.21	4.15	4.08	4.02	3.97	3.91	53
54	5.14	5.05	4.96	4.88	4.80	4.72	4.65	4.57	4.50	4.43	4.37	4.30	4.24	4.17	4.11	4.05	54
55	5.33	5.24	5.15	5.06	4.98	4.90	4.82	4.75	4.67	4.60	4.53	4.46	4.40	4.33	4.27	4.21	55
56	5.53	5.44	5.35	5.26	5.17	5.09	5.01	4.93	4.85	4.77	4.70	4.63	4.56	4.50	4.43	4.37	56
57	5.75	5.65	5.55	5.46	5.37	5.28	5.20	5.12	5.04	4.96	4.88	4.81	4.74	4.67	4.60	4.54	57
58	5.97	5.87	5.77	5.67	5.58	5.49	5.40	5.32	5.23	5.15	5.08	5.00	4.93	4.85	4.78	4.71	58
59	6.21	6.10	6.00	5.90	5.80	5.71	5.62	5.53	5.44	5.36	5.28	5.20	5.12	5.05	4.97	4.90	59
60	6.46	6.35	6.25	6.15	6.04	5.94	5.85	5.76	5.67	5.58	5.49	5.41	5.33	5.25	5.18	5.10	60
LAT.	**165°** 195	164¾ 195¼	164½ 195½	164¼ 195¾	**164°** 196	163¾ 196¼	163½ 196½	163¼ 196¾	**163°** 197	162¾ 197¼	162½ 197½	162¼ 197¾	**162°** 198	161¾ 198¼	161½ 198½	161¼ 198¾	LAT.

Table 29 — 1 hr. — B

Lat. and Dec. SAME name, Sign —
Lat. and Dec. CONTRARY names, Sign +

HOUR ANGLE or DIFF. LONG.

DEC.	00m 15° 345	01m 15¼° 344¾	02m 15½° 344½	03m 15¾° 344¼	04m 16° 344	05m 16¼° 343¾	06m 16½° 343½	07m 16¾° 343¼	08m 17° 343	09m 17¼° 342¾	10m 17½° 342½	11m 17¾° 342¼	12m 18° 342	13m 18¼° 341¾	14m 18½° 341½	15m 18¾° 341¼	DEC.
0°	.000	.000	.000	.000	.000	.000	.000	.000	.000	.000	.000	.000	.000	.000	.000	.000	0°
1	.067	.066	.065	.064	.063	.062	.061	.061	.060	.059	.058	.057	.057	.056	.055	.054	1
2	.135	.133	.131	.129	.127	.125	.123	.121	.119	.118	.116	.115	.113	.112	.110	.109	2
3	.202	.199	.196	.193	.190	.187	.185	.182	.179	.177	.174	.172	.170	.167	.165	.163	3
4	.270	.266	.262	.258	.254	.250	.246	.243	.239	.236	.233	.229	.226	.223	.220	.218	4
5	.338	.333	.327	.322	.317	.313	.308	.304	.299	.295	.291	.287	.283	.279	.276	.272	5
6	.406	.400	.393	.387	.381	.376	.370	.365	.359	.354	.350	.345	.340	.336	.331	.327	6
7	.474	.467	.459	.452	.445	.439	.432	.426	.420	.414	.408	.403	.397	.392	.387	.382	7
8	.543	.534	.526	.518	.510	.502	.495	.488	.481	.474	.467	.461	.455	.449	.443	.437	8
9	.612	.602	.593	.584	.575	.566	.558	.550	.542	.534	.527	.520	.513	.506	.499	.493	9
10	.681	.670	.660	.650	.640	.630	.621	.612	.603	.595	.586	.578	.571	.563	.556	.549	10
11	.751	.739	.727	.716	.705	.694	.684	.675	.665	.656	.646	.638	.629	.621	.613	.605	11
12	.821	.808	.795	.783	.771	.760	.748	.738	.727	.717	.707	.697	.688	.679	.670	.661	12
13	.892	.878	.864	.851	.838	.825	.813	.801	.790	.779	.768	.757	.747	.737	.728	.718	13
14	.963	.948	.933	.919	.905	.891	.878	.865	.853	.841	.829	.818	.807	.796	.786	.776	14
15	1.04	1.02	1.00	.987	.972	.958	.943	.930	.916	.904	.891	.879	.867	.856	.844	.834	15
16	1.11	1.09	1.07	1.06	1.04	1.02	1.01	.995	.981	.967	.954	.941	.928	.916	.904	.892	16
17	1.18	1.16	1.14	1.13	1.11	1.09	1.08	1.06	1.05	1.03	1.02	1.00	.989	.976	.964	.951	17
18	1.26	1.24	1.22	1.20	1.18	1.16	1.14	1.13	1.11	1.10	1.08	1.07	1.05	1.04	1.02	1.01	18
19	1.33	1.31	1.29	1.27	1.25	1.23	1.21	1.19	1.18	1.16	1.15	1.13	1.11	1.10	1.09	1.07	19
20	1.41	1.38	1.36	1.34	1.32	1.30	1.28	1.26	1.24	1.23	1.21	1.19	1.18	1.16	1.15	1.13	20
21	1.48	1.46	1.44	1.41	1.39	1.37	1.35	1.33	1.31	1.29	1.28	1.26	1.24	1.23	1.21	1.19	21
22	1.56	1.54	1.51	1.49	1.47	1.44	1.42	1.40	1.38	1.36	1.34	1.33	1.31	1.29	1.27	1.26	22
23	1.64	1.61	1.59	1.56	1.54	1.52	1.49	1.47	1.45	1.43	1.41	1.39	1.37	1.36	1.34	1.32	23
24	1.72	1.69	1:67	1.64	1.62	1.59	1.57	1.55	1.52	1.50	1.48	1.46	1.44	1.42	1.40	1.39	24
25	1.80	1.77	1.74	1.72	1.69	1.67	1.64	1.62	1.59	1.57	1.55	1.53	1.51	1.49	1.47	1.45	25
26	1.88	1.85	1.83	1.80	1.77	1.74	1.72	1.69	1.67	1.64	1.62	1.60	1.58	1.56	1.54	1.52	26
27	1.97	1.94	1.91	1.88	1.85	1.82	1.79	1.77	1.74	1.72	1.69	1.67	1.65	1.63	1.61	1.59	27
28	2.05	2.02	1.99	1.96	1.93	1.90	1.87	1.85	1.82	1.79	1.77	1.74	1.72	1.70	1.68	1.65	28
29	2.14	2.10	2.07	2.04	2.01	1.98	1.95	1.92	1.90	1.87	1.84	1.82	1.79	1.77	1.75	1.72	29
30	2.23	2.20	2.16	2.13	2.09	2.06	2.03	2.00	1.97	1.95	1.92	1.89	1.87	1.84	1.82	1.80	30
31	2.32	2.28	2.25	2.21	2.18	2.15	2.12	2.09	2.06	2.03	2.00	1.97	1.94	1.92	1.89	1.87	31
32	2.41	2.38	2.34	2.30	2.27	2.23	2.20	2.17	2.14	2.11	2.08	2.05	2.02	2.00	1.97	1.94	32
33	2.51	2.47	2.43	2.39	2.36	2.32	2.29	2.25	2.22	2.19	2.16	2.13	2.10	2.07	2.05	2.02	33
34	2.61	2.56	2.52	2.49	2.45	2.41	2.37	2.34	2.31	2.27	2.24	2.21	2.18	2.15	2.13	2.10	34
35	2.71	2.66	2.62	2.58	2.54	2.50	2.47	2.43	2.39	2.36	2.33	2.30	2.27	2.24	2.21	2.18	35
36	2.81	2.76	2.72	2.68	2.64	2.60	2.56	2.52	2.48	2.45	2.42	2.38	2.35	2.32	2.29	2.26	36
37	2.91	2.87	2.82	2.78	2.73	2.69	2.65	2.61	2.58	2.54	2.51	2.47	2.44	2.41	2.37	2.34	37
38	3.02	2.97	2.92	2.88	2.83	2.79	2.75	2.71	2.67	2.63	2.60	2.56	2.53	2.49	2.46	2.43	38
39	3.13	3.08	3.03	2.98	2.94	2.89	2.85	2.81	2.77	2.73	2.69	2.66	2.62	2.59	2.55	2.52	39
40	3.24	3.19	3.14	3.09	3.04	3.00	2.95	2.91	2.87	2.83	2.79	2.75	2.72	2.68	2.64	2.61	40
41	3.36	3.31	3.25	3.20	3.15	3.11	3.06	3.02	2.97	2.93	2.89	2.85	2.81	2.78	2.74	2.70	41
42	3.48	3.42	3.37	3.32	3.27	3.22	3.17	3.12	3.08	3.04	2.99	2.95	2.91	2.88	2.84	2.80	42
43	3.60	3.55	3.49	3.44	3.38	3.33	3.28	3.24	3.19	3.15	3.10	3.06	3.02	2.98	2.94	2.90	43
44	3.73	3.67	3.61	3.56	3.50	3.45	3.40	3.35	3.30	3.26	3.21	3.17	3.13	3.08	3.04	3.00	44
45	3.86	3.80	3.74	3.68	3.63	3.57	3.52	3.47	3.42	3.37	3.33	3.28	3.24	3.19	3.15	3.11	45
46	4.00	3.94	3.87	3.82	3.76	3.70	3.65	3.59	3.54	3.49	3.44	3.40	3.35	3.31	3.26	3.22	46
47	4.14	4.08	4.01	3.95	3.89	3.83	3.78	3.72	3.67	3.62	3.57	3.52	3.47	3.42	3.38	3.34	47
48	4.29	4.22	4.16	4.09	4.03	3.97	3.91	3.85	3.80	3.75	3.69	3.64	3.59	3.55	3.50	3.46	48
49	4.44	4.37	4.30	4.24	4.17	4.11	4.05	3.99	3.93	3.88	3.83	3.77	3.72	3.67	3.63	3.58	49
50	4.60	4.53	4.46	4.39	4.32	4.26	4.20	4.14	4.08	4.02	3.96	3.91	3.86	3.81	3.76	3.71	50
51	4.77	4.70	4.62	4.55	4.48	4.41	4.35	4.28	4.22	4.16	4.11	4.05	4.00	3.94	3.89	3.84	51
52	4.95	4.87	4.79	4.72	4.64	4.57	4.51	4.44	4.38	4.32	4.26	4.20	4.14	4.09	4.03	3.98	52
53	5.13	5.05	4.97	4.89	4.81	4.74	4.67	4.61	4.54	4.48	4.41	4.35	4.29	4.24	4.18	4.13	53
54	5.32	5.23	5.15	5.07	4.99	4.92	4.85	4.78	4.71	4.64	4.58	4.51	4.45	4.39	4.34	4.28	54
55	5.52	5.43	5.34	5.26	5.18	5.10	5.03	4.96	4.88	4.82	4.75	4.69	4.62	4.56	4.50	4.44	55
56	5.73	5.64	5.55	5.46	5.38	5.30	5.22	5.14	5.07	5.00	4.93	4.86	4.80	4.73	4.67	4.61	56
57	5.95	5.86	5.76	5.67	5.59	5.50	5.42	5.34	5.27	5.19	5.12	5.05	4.98	4.92	4.85	4.79	57
58	6.18	6.08	5.99	5.90	5.81	5.72	5.63	5.55	5.47	5.40	5.32	5.25	5.18	5.11	5.04	4.98	58
59	6.43	6.33	6.23	6.13	6.04	5.95	5.86	5.77	5.69	5.61	5.53	5.46	5.39	5.31	5.25	5.18	59
60	6.69	6.59	6.48	6.38	6.28	6.19	6.10	6.01	5.92	5.84	5.76	5.68	5.61	5.53	5.46	5.39	60
61	6.97	6.86	6.75	6.65	6.55	6.45	6.35	6.26	6.17	6.08	6.00	5.92	5.84	5.76	5.69	5.61	61
62	7.27	7.15	7.04	6.93	6.82	6.72	6.62	6.53	6.43	6.34	6.25	6.17	6.09	6.01	5.93	5.85	62
63	7.58	7.46	7.34	7.23	7.12	7.01	6.91	6.81	6.71	6.62	6.53	6.44	6.35	6.27	6.19	6.11	63
DEC.	165° 195	164¾ 195¼	164½ 195½	164¼ 195¾	164° 196	163¾ 196¼	163½ 196½	163¼ 196¾	163° 197	162¾ 197¼	162½ 197½	162¼ 197¾	162° 198	161¾ 198¼	161½ 198½	161¼ 198¾	DEC.

Table 29

A   If entered with H.A. at **top**, Sign **+**

,, ,, ,, ,, **foot**, ,, **−**

I hr.

HOUR ANGLE or DIFF. LONG.

LAT.	15m	16m	17m	18m	19m	20m	21m	22m	23m	24m	25m	26m	27m	28m	29m	30m	LAT.
	18¾° 341¼	19° 341	19¼° 340¾	19½° 340½	19¾° 340¼	20° 340	20¼° 339¾	20½° 339½	20¾° 339¼	21° 339	21¼° 338¾	21½° 338½	21¾° 338¼	22° 338	22¼° 337¾	22½° 337½	
0°	.000	.000	.000	.000	.000	.000	.000	.000	.000	.000	.000	.000	.000	.000	.000	.000	0°
1	.051	.051	.050	.049	.049	.048	.047	.047	.046	.046	.045	.044	.044	.043	.043	.042	1
2	.103	.101	.100	.099	.097	.096	.095	.093	.092	.091	.090	.089	.088	.086	.085	.084	2
3	.154	.152	.150	.148	.146	.144	.142	.140	.138	.137	.135	.133	.131	.130	.128	.127	3
4	.206	.203	.200	.198	.195	.192	.190	.187	.185	.182	.180	.178	.175	.173	.171	.169	4
5	.258	.254	.251	.247	.244	.240	.237	.234	.231	.228	.225	.222	.219	.217	.214	.211	5
6	.310	.305	.301	.297	.293	.289	.285	.281	.277	.274	.270	.267	.263	.260	.257	.254	6
7	.362	.357	.352	.347	.342	.337	.333	.328	.324	.320	.316	.312	.308	.304	.300	.296	7
8	.414	.408	.402	.397	.391	.386	.381	.376	.371	.366	.361	.357	.352	.348	.344	.339	8
9	.467	.460	.454	.447	.441	.435	.429	.424	.418	.413	.407	.402	.397	.392	.387	.382	9
10	.519	.512	.505	.498	.491	.484	.478	.472	.465	.459	.453	.448	.442	.436	.431	.426	10
11	.573	.565	.557	.549	.541	.534	.527	.520	.513	.506	.500	.493	.487	.481	.475	.469	11
12	.626	.617	.609	.600	.592	.584	.576	.569	.561	.554	.547	.540	.533	.526	.520	.513	12
13	.680	.670	.661	.652	.643	.634	.626	.618	.609	.601	.594	.586	.579	.571	.564	.557	13
14	.734	.724	.714	.704	.694	.685	.676	.667	.658	.650	.641	.633	.625	.617	.609	.602	14
15	.789	.778	.767	.757	.746	.736	.726	.717	.707	.698	.689	.680	.672	.663	.655	.647	15
16	.845	.833	.821	.810	.799	.788	.777	.767	.757	.747	.737	.728	.719	.710	.701	.692	16
17	.901	.888	.875	.863	.852	.840	.829	.818	.807	.796	.786	.776	.766	.757	.747	.738	17
18	.957	.944	.930	.918	.905	.893	.881	.869	.858	.846	.836	.825	.814	.804	.794	.784	18
19	1.01	1.00	.986	.972	.959	.946	.933	.921	.909	.897	.885	.874	.863	.852	.842	.831	19
20	1.07	1.06	1.04	1.03	1.01	1.00	.987	.973	.961	.948	.936	.924	.912	.901	.890	.879	20
21	1.13	1.11	1.10	1.08	1.07	1.05	1.04	1.03	1.01	1.00	.987	.974	.962	.950	.938	.927	21
22	1.19	1.17	1.16	1.14	1.13	1.11	1.10	1.08	1.07	1.05	1.04	1.03	1.01	1.00	.988	.975	22
23	1.25	1.23	1.22	1.20	1.18	1.17	1.15	1.14	1.12	1.11	1.09	1.08	1.06	1.05	1.04	1.02	23
24	1.31	1.29	1.27	1.26	1.24	1.22	1.21	1.19	1.18	1.16	1.14	1.13	1.12	1.10	1.09	1.07	24
25	1.37	1.35	1.34	1.32	1.30	1.28	1.26	1.25	1.23	1.21	1.20	1.18	1.17	1.15	1.14	1.13	25
26	1.44	1.42	1.40	1.38	1.36	1.34	1.32	1.30	1.29	1.27	1.25	1.24	1.22	1.21	1.19	1.18	26
27	1.50	1.48	1.46	1.44	1.42	1.40	1.38	1.36	1.34	1.33	1.31	1.29	1.28	1.26	1.24	1.23	27
28	1.57	1.54	1.52	1.50	1.48	1.46	1.44	1.42	1.40	1.39	1.37	1.35	1.33	1.32	1.30	1.28	28
29	1.64	1.61	1.59	1.57	1.54	1.52	1.50	1.48	1.46	1.44	1.43	1.41	1.39	1.37	1.35	1.34	29
30	1.70	1.68	1.65	1.63	1.61	1.59	1.57	1.54	1.52	1.50	1.48	1.47	1.45	1.43	1.41	1.39	30
31	1.77	1.75	1.72	1.70	1.67	1.65	1.63	1.61	1.59	1.57	1.55	1.53	1.51	1.49	1.47	1.45	31
32	1.84	1.81	1.79	1.76	1.74	1.72	1.69	1.67	1.65	1.63	1.61	1.59	1.57	1.55	1.53	1.51	32
33	1.91	1.89	1.86	1.83	1.81	1.78	1.76	1.74	1.71	1.69	1.67	1.65	1.63	1.61	1.59	1.57	33
34	1.99	1.96	1.93	1.90	1.88	1.85	1.83	1.80	1.78	1.76	1.73	1.71	1.69	1.67	1.65	1.63	34
35	2.06	2.03	2.01	1.98	1.95	1.92	1.90	1.87	1.85	1.82	1.80	1.78	1.76	1.73	1.71	1.69	35
36	2.14	2.11	2.08	2.05	2.02	2.00	1.97	1.94	1.92	1.89	1.87	1.84	1.82	1.80	1.78	1.75	36
37	2.22	2.19	2.16	2.13	2.10	2.07	2.04	2.02	1.99	1.96	1.94	1.91	1.89	1.87	1.84	1.82	37
38	2.30	2.27	2.24	2.21	2.18	2.15	2.12	2.09	2.06	2.04	2.01	1.98	1.96	1.93	1.91	1.89	38
39	2.39	2.35	2.32	2.29	2.26	2.23	2.20	2.17	2.14	2.11	2.08	2.06	2.03	2.00	1.98	1.95	39
40	2.47	2.44	2.40	2.37	2.34	2.31	2.27	2.24	2.21	2.19	2.16	2.13	2.10	2.08	2.05	2.03	40
41	2.56	2.52	2.49	2.45	2.42	2.39	2.36	2.33	2.29	2.27	2.24	2.21	2.18	2.15	2.12	2.10	41
42	2.65	2.61	2.58	2.54	2.51	2.47	2.44	2.41	2.38	2.35	2.32	2.29	2.26	2.23	2.20	2.17	42
43	2.75	2.71	2.67	2.63	2.60	2.56	2.53	2.49	2.46	2.43	2.40	2.37	2.34	2.31	2.28	2.25	43
44	2.85	2.80	2.77	2.73	2.69	2.65	2.62	2.58	2.55	2.52	2.48	2.45	2.42	2.39	2.36	2.33	44
45	2.95	2.90	2.86	2.82	2.79	2.75	2.71	2.67	2.64	2.61	2.57	2.54	2.51	2.48	2.44	2.41	45
46	3.05	3.01	2.97	2.92	2.89	2.85	2.81	2.77	2.73	2.70	2.66	2.63	2.60	2.56	2.53	2.50	46
47	3.16	3.11	3.07	3.03	2.99	2.95	2.91	2.87	2.83	2.79	2.76	2.72	2.69	2.65	2.62	2.59	47
48	3.27	3.23	3.18	3.14	3.09	3.05	3.01	2.97	2.93	2.89	2.86	2.82	2.78	2.75	2.71	2.68	48
49	3.39	3.34	3.29	3.25	3.20	3.16	3.12	3.08	3.04	3.00	2.96	2.92	2.88	2.85	2.81	2.78	49
50	3.51	3.46	3.41	3.37	3.32	3.27	3.23	3.19	3.15	3.10	3.06	3.03	2.99	2.95	2.91	2.88	50
51	3.64	3.59	3.54	3.49	3.44	3.39	3.35	3.30	3.26	3.22	3.18	3.14	3.10	3.06	3.02	2.98	51
52	3.77	3.72	3.67	3.62	3.57	3.52	3.47	3.42	3.38	3.33	3.29	3.25	3.21	3.17	3.13	3.09	52
53	3.91	3.86	3.80	3.75	3.70	3.65	3.60	3.55	3.50	3.46	3.41	3.37	3.33	3.28	3.24	3.20	53
54	4.05	4.00	3.94	3.89	3.83	3.78	3.73	3.68	3.63	3.59	3.54	3.49	3.45	3.41	3.36	3.32	54
55	4.21	4.15	4.09	4.03	3.98	3.92	3.87	3.82	3.77	3.72	3.67	3.63	3.58	3.53	3.49	3.45	55
56	4.37	4.31	4.25	4.19	4.13	4.07	4.02	3.97	3.91	3.86	3.81	3.76	3.72	3.67	3.62	3.58	56
57	4.54	4.47	4.41	4.35	4.29	4.23	4.17	4.12	4.06	4.01	3.96	3.91	3.86	3.81	3.76	3.72	57
58	4.71	4.65	4.58	4.52	4.46	4.40	4.34	4.28	4.22	4.17	4.12	4.06	4.01	3.96	3.91	3.86	58
59	4.90	4.83	4.77	4.70	4.64	4.57	4.51	4.45	4.39	4.34	4.28	4.23	4.17	4.12	4.07	4.02	59
60	5.10	5.03	4.96	4.89	4.82	4.76	4.69	4.63	4.57	4.51	4.45	4.40	4.34	4.29	4.23	4.18	60
LAT.	161¼ 198¾	161° 199	160¾ 199¼	160½ 199½	160¼ 199¾	160° 200	159¾ 200¼	159½ 200½	159¼ 200¾	159° 201	158¾ 201¼	158½ 201½	158¼ 201¾	158° 202	157¾ 202¼	157½ 202½	LAT.

Table 29　B　1 hr.

Lat. and Dec. SAME name, Sign −
Lat. and Dec. CONTRARY names, Sign +

HOUR ANGLE or DIFF. LONG.

DEC.	15m	16m	17m	18m	19m	20m	21m	22m	23m	24m	25m	26m	27m	28m	29m	30m	DEC.
	18¾°	19°	19¼°	19½°	19¾°	20°	20¼°	20½°	20¾°	21°	21¼°	21½°	21¾°	22°	22¼°	22½°	
	341¼	341	340¾	340½	340¼	340	339¾	339½	339¼	339	338¾	338½	338¼	338	337¾	337½	
0°	.000	.000	.000	.000	.000	.000	.000	.000	.000	.000	.000	.000	.000	.000	.000	.000	0°
1	.054	.054	.053	.052	.052	.051	.050	.050	.049	.049	.048	.048	.047	.047	.046	.046	1
2	.109	.107	.106	.105	.103	.102	.101	.100	.099	.097	.096	.095	.094	.093	.092	.091	2
3	.163	.161	.159	.157	.155	.153	.151	.150	.148	.146	.145	.143	.141	.140	.138	.137	3
4	.218	.215	.212	.209	.207	.204	.202	.200	.197	.195	.193	.191	.189	.187	.185	.183	4
5	.272	.269	.265	.262	.259	.256	.253	.250	.247	.244	.241	.239	.236	.234	.231	.229	5
6	.327	.323	.319	.315	.311	.307	.304	.300	.297	.293	.290	.287	.284	.281	.278	.275	6
7	.382	.377	.372	.368	.363	.359	.355	.351	.347	.343	.339	.335	.331	.328	.324	.321	7
8	.437	.432	.426	.421	.416	.411	.406	.401	.397	.392	.388	.383	.379	.375	.371	.367	8
9	.493	.486	.480	.474	.469	.463	.458	.452	.447	.442	.437	.432	.427	.423	.418	.414	9
10	.549	.542	.535	.528	.522	.516	.510	.504	.498	.492	.487	.481	.476	.471	.466	.461	10
11	.605	.597	.590	.582	.575	.568	.561	.555	.549	.542	.536	.530	.525	.519	.514	.508	11
12	.661	.653	.645	.637	.629	.621	.614	.607	.600	.593	.587	.580	.574	.567	.561	.555	12
13	.718	.709	.700	.692	.683	.675	.667	.659	.652	.644	.637	.630	.623	.616	.610	.603	13
14	.776	.766	.756	.747	.738	.729	.721	.712	.704	.696	.688	.680	.673	.666	.659	.652	14
15	.834	.823	.813	.803	.793	.783	.774	.765	.756	.748	.740	.731	.723	.715	.708	.700	15
16	.892	.881	.870	.859	.849	.838	.829	.819	.809	.800	.791	.782	.774	.765	.757	.749	16
17	.951	.939	.927	.916	.905	.894	.883	.873	.863	.853	.844	.834	.825	.816	.808	.799	17
18	1.01	.998	.986	.973	.962	.950	.939	.928	.917	.907	.897	.887	.877	.867	.858	.849	18
19	1.07	1.06	1.04	1.03	1.02	1.01	.995	.983	.972	.961	.950	.939	.929	.919	.910	.900	19
20	1.13	1.12	1.10	1.09	1.08	1.06	1.05	1.04	1.03	1.02	1.00	.993	.982	.972	.962	.951	20
21	1.19	1.18	1.16	1.15	1.14	1.12	1.11	1.10	1.08	1.07	1.06	1.05	1.04	1.02	1.01	1.00	21
22	1.26	1.24	1.23	1.21	1.20	1.18	1.17	1.15	1.14	1.13	1.11	1.10	1.09	1.08	1.07	1.06	22
23	1.32	1.30	1.29	1.27	1.26	1.24	1.23	1.21	1.20	1.18	1.17	1.16	1.15	1.13	1.12	1.11	23
24	1.39	1.37	1.35	1.33	1.32	1.30	1.29	1.27	1.26	1.24	1.23	1.21	1.20	1.19	1.18	1.16	24
25	1.45	1.43	1.41	1.40	1.38	1.36	1.35	1.33	1.32	1.30	1.29	1.27	1.26	1.24	1.23	1.22	25
26	1.52	1.50	1.48	1.46	1.44	1.43	1.41	1.39	1.38	1.36	1.35	1.33	1.32	1.30	1.29	1.27	26
27	1.59	1.57	1.55	1.53	1.51	1.49	1.47	1.45	1.44	1.42	1.41	1.39	1.38	1.36	1.35	1.33	27
28	1.65	1.63	1.61	1.59	1.57	1.55	1.54	1.52	1.50	1.48	1.47	1.45	1.43	1.42	1.40	1.39	28
29	1.72	1.70	1.68	1.66	1.64	1.62	1.60	1.58	1.56	1.55	1.53	1.51	1.50	1.48	1.46	1.45	29
30	1.80	1.77	1.75	1.73	1.71	1.69	1.67	1.65	1.63	1.61	1.59	1.58	1.56	1.54	1.52	1.51	30
31	1.87	1.85	1.82	1.80	1.78	1.76	1.74	1.72	1.70	1.68	1.66	1.64	1.62	1.60	1.59	1.57	31
32	1.94	1.92	1.90	1.87	1.85	1.83	1.81	1.78	1.76	1.74	1.72	1.71	1.69	1.67	1.65	1.63	32
33	2.02	1.99	1.97	1.95	1.92	1.90	1.88	1.85	1.83	1.81	1.79	1.77	1.75	1.73	1.72	1.70	33
34	2.10	2.07	2.05	2.02	2.00	1.97	1.95	1.93	1.90	1.88	1.86	1.84	1.82	1.80	1.78	1.76	34
35	2.18	2.15	2.12	2.10	2.07	2.05	2.02	2.00	1.98	1.95	1.93	1.91	1.89	1.87	1.85	1.83	35
36	2.26	2.23	2.20	2.18	2.15	2.12	2.10	2.08	2.05	2.03	2.01	1.98	1.96	1.94	1.92	1.90	36
37	2.34	2.31	2.29	2.26	2.23	2.20	2.18	2.15	2.13	2.10	2.08	2.06	2.03	2.01	1.99	1.97	37
38	2.43	2.40	2.37	2.34	2.31	2.28	2.26	2.23	2.21	2.18	2.16	2.13	2.11	2.09	2.06	2.04	38
39	2.52	2.49	2.46	2.43	2.40	2.37	2.34	2.31	2.29	2.26	2.23	2.21	2.19	2.16	2.14	2.12	39
40	2.61	2.58	2.55	2.51	2.48	2.45	2.42	2.40	2.37	2.34	2.32	2.29	2.26	2.24	2.22	2.19	40
41	2.70	2.67	2.64	2.60	2.57	2.54	2.51	2.48	2.45	2.43	2.40	2.37	2.35	2.32	2.30	2.27	41
42	2.80	2.77	2.73	2.70	2.66	2.63	2.60	2.57	2.54	2.51	2.48	2.46	2.43	2.40	2.38	2.35	42
43	2.90	2.86	2.83	2.79	2.76	2.73	2.69	2.66	2.63	2.60	2.57	2.54	2.52	2.49	2.46	2.44	43
44	3.00	2.97	2.93	2.89	2.86	2.82	2.79	2.76	2.73	2.69	2.66	2.64	2.61	2.58	2.55	2.52	44
45	3.11	3.07	3.03	3.00	2.96	2.92	2.89	2.86	2.82	2.79	2.76	2.73	2.70	2.67	2.64	2.61	45
46	3.22	3.18	3.14	3.10	3.07	3.03	2.99	2.96	2.92	2.89	2.86	2.83	2.79	2.76	2.74	2.71	46
47	3.34	3.29	3.25	3.21	3.17	3.14	3.10	3.06	3.03	2.99	2.96	2.93	2.89	2.86	2.83	2.80	47
48	3.46	3.41	3.37	3.33	3.29	3.25	3.21	3.17	3.14	3.10	3.07	3.03	3.00	2.97	2.93	2.90	48
49	3.58	3.53	3.49	3.45	3.40	3.36	3.32	3.28	3.25	3.21	3.17	3.14	3.10	3.07	3.04	3.01	49
50	3.71	3.66	3.62	3.57	3.53	3.48	3.44	3.40	3.36	3.33	3.29	3.25	3.22	3.18	3.15	3.11	50
51	3.84	3.79	3.75	3.70	3.65	3.61	3.57	3.53	3.49	3.45	3.41	3.37	3.33	3.30	3.26	3.23	51
52	3.98	3.93	3.88	3.83	3.79	3.74	3.70	3.65	3.61	3.57	3.53	3.49	3.45	3.42	3.38	3.34	52
53	4.13	4.08	4.03	3.98	3.93	3.88	3.83	3.79	3.75	3.70	3.66	3.62	3.58	3.54	3.51	3.47	53
54	4.28	4.23	4.17	4.12	4.07	4.02	3.98	3.93	3.88	3.84	3.80	3.76	3.71	3.67	3.64	3.60	54
55	4.44	4.39	4.33	4.28	4.23	4.18	4.13	4.08	4.03	3.99	3.94	3.90	3.85	3.81	3.77	3.73	55
56	4.61	4.55	4.50	4.44	4.39	4.33	4.28	4.23	4.18	4.14	4.09	4.05	4.00	3.96	3.92	3.87	56
57	4.79	4.73	4.67	4.61	4.56	4.50	4.45	4.40	4.35	4.30	4.25	4.20	4.16	4.11	4.07	4.02	57
58	4.98	4.92	4.85	4.79	4.74	4.68	4.62	4.57	4.52	4.47	4.42	4.37	4.32	4.27	4.23	4.18	58
59	5.18	5.11	5.05	4.99	4.93	4.87	4.81	4.75	4.70	4.64	4.59	4.54	4.49	4.44	4.40	4.35	59
60	5.39	5.32	5.25	5.19	5.13	5.06	5.01	4.95	4.89	4.83	4.78	4.73	4.67	4.62	4.58	4.53	60
61	5.61	5.54	5.47	5.40	5.34	5.27	5.21	5.15	5.09	5.03	4.98	4.92	4.87	4.82	4.76	4.71	61
62	5.85	5.78	5.70	5.63	5.57	5.50	5.43	5.37	5.31	5.25	5.19	5.13	5.08	5.02	4.97	4.91	62
63	6.11	6.03	5.95	5.88	5.81	5.74	5.67	5.60	5.54	5.48	5.42	5.36	5.30	5.24	5.18	5.13	63
DEC.	161¼°	161°	160¾°	160½°	160¼°	160°	159¾°	159½°	159¼°	159°	158¾°	158½°	158¼°	158°	157¾°	157½°	DEC.
	198¾	199	199¼	199½	199¾	200	200¼	200½	200¾	201	201¼	201½	201¾	202	202¼	202½	

Table 29

A

If entered with H.A. at **top**, Sign **+**
" " " " **foot**, " **−**

I hr.

LAT.	30m	31m	32m	33m	34m	35m	36m	37m	38m	39m	40m	41m	42m	43m	44m	45m	LAT.
	HOUR ANGLE or DIFF. LONG.																
	22½° 337½	22¾° 337¼	**23**° **337**	23¼° 336¾	23½° 336½	23¾° 336¼	**24**° **336**	24¼° 335¾	24½° 335½	24¾° 335¼	**25**° **335**	25¼° 334¾	25½° 334½	25¾° 334¼	**26**° **334**	26¼° 333¾	
0°	.000	.000	.000	.000	.000	.000	.000	.000	.000	.000	.000	.000	.000	.000	.000	.000	**0°**
1	.042	.042	.041	.041	.040	.040	.039	.039	.038	.038	.037	.037	.037	.036	.036	.035	**1**
2	.084	.083	.082	.081	.080	.079	.078	.078	.077	.076	.075	.074	.073	.072	.072	.071	**2**
3	.127	.125	.123	.122	.121	.119	.118	.116	.115	.114	.112	.111	.110	.109	.107	.106	**3**
4	.169	.167	.165	.163	.161	.159	.157	.155	.153	.152	.150	.148	.147	.145	.143	.142	**4**
5	.211	.209	.206	.204	.201	.199	.197	.194	.192	.190	.188	.186	.183	.181	.179	.177	**5**
6	.254	.251	.248	.245	.242	.239	.236	.233	.231	.228	.225	.223	.220	.218	.215	.213	**6**
7	.296	.293	.289	.286	.282	.279	.276	.273	.269	.266	.263	.260	.257	.255	.252	.249	**7**
8	.339	.335	.331	.327	.323	.319	.316	.312	.308	.305	.301	.298	.295	.291	.288	.285	**8**
9	.382	.378	.373	.369	.364	.360	.356	.352	.348	.344	.340	.336	.332	.328	.325	.321	**9**
10	.426	.420	.415	.410	.406	.401	.396	.391	.387	.382	.378	.374	.370	.366	.362	.358	**10**
11	.469	.464	.458	.452	.447	.442	.437	.432	.427	.422	.417	.412	.408	.403	.399	.394	**11**
12	.513	.507	.501	.495	.489	.483	.477	.472	.466	.461	.456	.451	.446	.441	.436	.431	**12**
13	.557	.551	.544	.537	.531	.525	.519	.513	.507	.501	.495	.490	.484	.479	.473	.468	**13**
14	.602	.595	.587	.580	.573	.567	.560	.553	.547	.541	.535	.529	.523	.517	.511	.506	**14**
15	.647	.639	.631	.624	.616	.609	.602	.595	.588	.581	.575	.568	.562	.556	.549	.543	**15**
16	.692	.684	.676	.667	.659	.652	.644	.637	.629	.622	.615	.608	.601	.594	.588	.581	**16**
17	.738	.729	.720	.712	.703	.695	.687	.679	.671	.663	.656	.648	.641	.634	.627	.620	**17**
18	.784	.775	.765	.756	.747	.738	.730	.721	.713	.705	.697	.689	.681	.674	.666	.659	**18**
19	.831	.821	.811	.801	.792	.783	.773	.764	.756	.747	.738	.730	.722	.714	.706	.698	**19**
20	.879	.868	.858	.847	.837	.827	.817	.808	.799	.790	.781	.772	.763	.755	.746	.738	**20**
21	.927	.915	.904	.893	.883	.872	.862	.852	.842	.833	.823	.814	.805	.796	.787	.778	**21**
22	.975	.963	.952	.940	.929	.918	.907	.897	.887	.876	.866	.857	.847	.838	.828	.819	**22**
23	1.02	1.01	1.00	.988	.976	.965	.953	.942	.931	.921	.910	.900	.890	.880	.870	.861	**23**
24	1.07	1.06	1.05	1.04	1.02	1.01	1.00	.988	.977	.966	.955	.944	.933	.923	.913	.903	**24**
25	1.13	1.11	1.10	1.09	1.07	1.06	1.05	1.04	1.02	1.01	1.00	.989	.978	.967	.956	.946	**25**
26	1.18	1.16	1.15	1.14	1.12	1.11	1.10	1.08	1.07	1.06	1.05	1.03	1.02	1.01	1.00	.989	**26**
27	1.23	1.22	1.20	1.19	1.17	1.16	1.14	1.13	1.12	1.11	1.09	1.08	1.07	1.06	1.04	1.03	**27**
28	1.28	1.27	1.25	1.24	1.22	1.21	1.19	1.18	1.17	1.15	1.14	1.13	1.11	1.10	1.09	1.08	**28**
29	1.34	1.32	1.31	1.29	1.27	1.26	1.25	1.23	1.22	1.20	1.19	1.18	1.16	1.15	1.14	1.12	**29**
30	1.39	1.38	1.36	1.34	1.33	1.31	1.30	1.28	1.27	1.25	1.24	1.22	1.21	1.20	1.18	1.17	**30**
31	1.45	1.43	1.42	1.40	1.38	1.37	1.35	1.33	1.32	1.30	1.29	1.27	1.26	1.25	1.23	1.22	**31**
32	1.51	1.49	1.47	1.46	1.44	1.42	1.40	1.39	1.37	1.36	1.34	1.33	1.31	1.30	1.28	1.27	**32**
33	1.57	1.55	1.53	1.51	1.49	1.48	1.46	1.44	1.42	1.41	1.39	1.38	1.36	1.35	1.33	1.32	**33**
34	1.63	1.61	1.59	1.57	1.55	1.53	1.51	1.50	1.48	1.46	1.45	1.43	1.41	1.40	1.38	1.37	**34**
35	1.69	1.67	1.65	1.63	1.61	1.59	1.57	1.55	1.54	1.52	1.50	1.48	1.47	1.45	1.44	1.42	**35**
36	1.75	1.73	1.71	1.69	1.67	1.65	1.63	1.61	1.59	1.58	1.56	1.54	1.52	1.51	1.49	1.47	**36**
37	1.82	1.80	1.78	1.75	1.73	1.71	1.69	1.67	1.65	1.63	1.62	1.60	1.58	1.56	1.55	1.53	**37**
38	1.89	1.86	1.84	1.82	1.80	1.78	1.75	1.73	1.71	1.70	1.68	1.66	1.64	1.62	1.60	1.58	**38**
39	1.95	1.93	1.91	1.88	1.86	1.84	1.82	1.80	1.78	1.76	1.74	1.72	1.70	1.68	1.66	1.64	**39**
40	2.03	2.00	1.98	1.95	1.93	1.91	1.88	1.86	1.84	1.82	1.80	1.78	1.76	1.74	1.72	1.70	**40**
41	2.10	2.07	2.05	2.02	2.00	1.98	1.95	1.93	1.91	1.89	1.86	1.84	1.82	1.80	1.78	1.76	**41**
42	2.17	2.15	2.12	2.10	2.07	2.05	2.02	2.00	1.98	1.95	1.93	1.91	1.89	1.87	1.85	1.83	**42**
43	2.25	2.22	2.20	2.17	2.14	2.12	2.09	2.07	2.05	2.02	2.00	1.98	1.96	1.93	1.91	1.89	**43**
44	2.33	2.30	2.28	2.25	2.22	2.19	2.17	2.14	2.12	2.10	2.07	2.05	2.02	2.00	1.98	1.96	**44**
45	2.41	2.38	2.36	2.33	2.30	2.27	2.25	2.22	2.19	2.17	2.14	2.12	2.10	2.07	2.05	2.03	**45**
46	2.50	2.47	2.44	2.41	2.38	2.35	2.33	2.30	2.27	2.25	2.22	2.20	2.17	2.15	2.12	2.10	**46**
47	2.59	2.56	2.53	2.50	2.47	2.44	2.41	2.38	2.35	2.33	2.30	2.27	2.25	2.22	2.20	2.17	**47**
48	2.68	2.65	2.62	2.59	2.55	2.52	2.49	2.47	2.44	2.41	2.38	2.35	2.33	2.30	2.28	2.25	**48**
49	2.78	2.74	2.71	2.68	2.65	2.61	2.58	2.55	2.52	2.50	2.47	2.44	2.41	2.39	2.36	2.33	**49**
50	2.88	2.84	2.81	2.77	2.74	2.71	2.68	2.65	2.62	2.59	2.56	2.53	2.50	2.47	2.44	2.42	**50**
51	2.98	2.95	2.91	2.87	2.84	2.81	2.77	2.74	2.71	2.68	2.65	2.62	2.59	2.56	2.53	2.50	**51**
52	3.09	3.05	3.02	2.98	2.94	2.91	2.87	2.84	2.81	2.78	2.74	2.71	2.68	2.65	2.62	2.60	**52**
53	3.20	3.16	3.13	3.09	3.05	3.02	2.98	2.95	2.91	2.88	2.85	2.81	2.78	2.75	2.72	2.69	**53**
54	3.32	3.28	3.24	3.20	3.17	3.13	3.09	3.06	3.02	2.99	2.95	2.92	2.89	2.85	2.82	2.79	**54**
55	3.45	3.41	3.36	3.32	3.28	3.25	3.21	3.17	3.13	3.10	3.06	3.03	2.99	2.96	2.93	2.90	**55**
56	3.58	3.54	3.49	3.45	3.41	3.37	3.33	3.29	3.25	3.22	3.18	3.14	3.11	3.07	3.04	3.01	**56**
57	3.72	3.67	3.63	3.58	3.54	3.50	3.46	3.42	3.38	3.34	3.30	3.27	3.23	3.19	3.16	3.12	**57**
58	3.86	3.82	3.77	3.72	3.68	3.64	3.59	3.55	3.51	3.47	3.43	3.39	3.36	3.32	3.28	3.25	**58**
59	4.02	3.97	3.92	3.87	3.83	3.78	3.74	3.69	3.65	3.61	3.57	3.53	3.49	3.45	3.41	3.37	**59**
60	4.18	4.13	4.08	4.03	3.98	3.94	3.89	3.85	3.80	3.76	3.71	3.67	3.63	3.59	3.55	3.51	**60**
LAT.	157½ 202½	157¼ 202¾	**157**° **203**	156¾ 203¼	156½ 203½	156¼ 203¾	**156**° **204**	155¾ 204¼	155½ 204½	155¼ 204¾	**155**° **205**	154¾ 205¼	154½ 205½	154¼ 205¾	**154**° **206**	153¾ 206¼	LAT.

Table 29	**B**	1 hr.

Lat. and Dec. SAME name, Sign **—**
Lat. and Dec. CONTRARY names, Sign **+**

HOUR ANGLE or DIFF. LONG.

DEC.	30m 22½° 337½	31m 22¾° 337¼	32m 23° 337	33m 23¼° 336¾	34m 23½° 336½	35m 23¾° 336¼	36m 24° 336	37m 24¼° 335¾	38m 24½° 335½	39m 24¾° 335¼	40m 25° 335	41m 25¼° 334¾	42m 25½° 334½	43m 25¾° 334¼	44m 26° 334	45m 26¼° 333¾	DEC.
0°	.000	.000	.000	.000	.000	.000	.000	.000	.000	.000	.000	.000	.000	.000	.000	.000	0°
1	.046	.045	.045	.044	.044	.043	.043	.043	.042	.042	.041	.041	.041	.040	.040	.040	1
2	.091	.090	.089	.089	.088	.087	.086	.085	.084	.083	.083	.082	.081	.080	.080	.079	2
3	.137	.136	.134	.133	.131	.130	.129	.128	.126	.125	.124	.123	.122	.121	.120	.119	3
4	.183	.181	.179	.177	.175	.174	.172	.170	.169	.167	.165	.164	.162	.161	.160	.158	4
5	.229	.226	.224	.222	.219	.217	.215	.213	.211	.209	.207	.205	.203	.201	.200	.198	5
6	.275	.272	.269	.266	.264	.261	.258	.256	.253	.251	.249	.246	.244	.242	.240	.238	6
7	.321	.318	.314	.311	.308	.305	.302	.299	.296	.293	.291	.288	.285	.283	.280	.278	7
8	.367	.363	.360	.356	.352	.349	.346	.342	.339	.336	.333	.329	.326	.324	.321	.318	8
9	.414	.410	.405	.401	.397	.393	.389	.386	.382	.378	.375	.371	.368	.365	.361	.358	9
10	.461	.456	.451	.447	.442	.438	.434	.429	.425	.421	.417	.413	.410	.406	.402	.399	10
11	.508	.503	.497	.492	.487	.483	.478	.473	.469	.464	.460	.456	.452	.448	.443	.439	11
12	.555	.550	.544	.539	.533	.528	.523	.518	.513	.508	.503	.498	.494	.489	.485	.481	12
13	.603	.597	.591	.585	.579	.573	.568	.562	.557	.552	.546	.541	.536	.532	.527	.522	13
14	.652	.645	.638	.632	.625	.619	.613	.607	.601	.596	.590	.585	.579	.574	.569	.564	14
15	.700	.693	.686	.679	.672	.666	.659	.653	.646	.640	.634	.628	.622	.617	.611	.606	15
16	.749	.742	.734	.727	.719	.712	.705	.698	.691	.685	.678	.672	.666	.660	.654	.648	16
17	.799	.791	.782	.775	.767	.759	.752	.744	.737	.730	.723	.717	.710	.704	.697	.691	17
18	.849	.840	.832	.823	.815	.807	.799	.791	.784	.776	.769	.762	.755	.748	.741	.735	18
19	.900	.891	.881	.872	.864	.855	.847	.839	.830	.823	.815	.807	.800	.793	.785	.779	19
20	.951	.941	.932	.922	.913	.904	.895	.886	.878	.869	.861	.853	.845	.838	.830	.823	20
21	1.00	.993	.982	.973	.963	.953	.944	.935	.926	.917	.908	.900	.892	.884	.876	.868	21
22	1.06	1.04	1.03	1.02	1.01	1.00	.993	.984	.974	.965	.956	.947	.938	.930	.922	.914	22
23	1.11	1.10	1.09	1.08	1.06	1.05	1.04	1.03	1.02	1.01	1.00	.995	.986	.977	.968	.960	23
24	1.16	1.15	1.14	1.13	1.12	1.11	1.09	1.08	1.07	1.06	1.05	1.04	1.03	1.03	1.02	1.01	24
25	1.22	1.21	1.19	1.18	1.17	1.16	1.15	1.14	1.12	1.11	1.10	1.09	1.08	1.07	1.06	1.05	25
26	1.27	1.26	1.25	1.24	1.22	1.21	1.20	1.19	1.18	1.17	1.15	1.14	1.13	1.12	1.11	1.10	26
27	1.33	1.32	1.30	1.29	1.28	1.27	1.25	1.24	1.23	1.22	1.21	1.19	1.18	1.17	1.16	1.15	27
28	1.39	1.38	1.36	1.35	1.33	1.32	1.31	1.29	1.28	1.27	1.26	1.25	1.24	1.22	1.21	1.20	28
29	1.45	1.43	1.42	1.40	1.39	1.38	1.36	1.35	1.34	1.32	1.31	1.30	1.29	1.28	1.26	1.25	29
30	1.51	1.49	1.48	1.46	1.45	1.43	1.42	1.41	1.39	1.38	1.37	1.35	1.34	1.33	1.32	1.31	30
31	1.57	1.55	1.54	1.52	1.51	1.49	1.48	1.46	1.45	1.44	1.42	1.41	1.40	1.38	1.37	1.36	31
32	1.63	1.62	1.60	1.58	1.57	1.55	1.54	1.52	1.51	1.49	1.48	1.47	1.45	1.44	1.43	1.41	32
33	1.70	1.68	1.66	1.65	1.63	1.61	1.60	1.58	1.57	1.55	1.54	1.52	1.51	1.50	1.48	1.47	33
34	1.76	1.74	1.73	1.71	1.69	1.68	1.66	1.64	1.63	1.61	1.60	1.58	1.57	1.55	1.54	1.53	34
35	1.83	1.81	1.79	1.77	1.76	1.74	1.72	1.71	1.69	1.67	1.66	1.64	1.63	1.61	1.60	1.58	35
36	1.90	1.88	1.86	1.84	1.82	1.80	1.79	1.77	1.75	1.74	1.72	1.70	1.69	1.67	1.66	1.64	36
37	1.97	1.95	1.93	1.91	1.89	1.87	1.85	1.84	1.82	1.80	1.78	1.77	1.75	1.73	1.72	1.70	37
38	2.04	2.02	2.00	1.98	1.96	1.94	1.92	1.90	1.88	1.87	1.85	1.83	1.81	1.80	1.78	1.77	38
39	2.12	2.09	2.07	2.05	2.03	2.01	1.99	1.97	1.95	1.93	1.92	1.90	1.88	1.86	1.85	1.83	39
40	2.19	2.17	2.15	2.13	2.10	2.08	2.06	2.04	2.02	2.00	1.99	1.97	1.95	1.93	1.91	1.90	40
41	2.27	2.25	2.22	2.20	2.18	2.16	2.14	2.12	2.10	2.08	2.06	2.04	2.02	2.00	1.98	1.97	41
42	2.35	2.33	2.30	2.28	2.26	2.24	2.21	2.19	2.17	2.15	2.13	2.11	2.09	2.07	2.05	2.04	42
43	2.44	2.41	2.39	2.36	2.34	2.32	2.29	2.27	2.25	2.23	2.21	2.19	2.17	2.15	2.13	2.11	43
44	2.52	2.50	2.47	2.45	2.42	2.40	2.37	2.35	2.33	2.31	2.29	2.26	2.24	2.22	2.20	2.18	44
45	2.61	2.59	2.56	2.53	2.51	2.48	2.46	2.44	2.41	2.39	2.37	2.34	2.32	2.30	2.28	2.26	45
46	2.71	2.68	2.65	2.62	2.60	2.57	2.55	2.52	2.50	2.47	2.45	2.43	2.41	2.38	2.36	2.34	46
47	2.80	2.77	2.74	2.72	2.69	2.66	2.64	2.61	2.59	2.56	2.54	2.51	2.49	2.47	2.45	2.42	47
48	2.90	2.87	2.84	2.81	2.79	2.76	2.73	2.70	2.68	2.65	2.63	2.60	2.58	2.56	2.53	2.51	48
49	3.01	2.97	2.94	2.91	2.88	2.86	2.83	2.80	2.77	2.75	2.72	2.70	2.67	2.65	2.62	2.60	49
50	3.11	3.08	3.05	3.02	2.99	2.96	2.93	2.90	2.87	2.85	2.82	2.79	2.77	2.74	2.72	2.69	50
51	3.23	3.19	3.16	3.13	3.10	3.07	3.04	3.01	2.98	2.95	2.92	2.90	2.87	2.84	2.82	2.79	51
52	3.34	3.31	3.28	3.24	3.21	3.18	3.15	3.12	3.09	3.06	3.03	3.00	2.97	2.95	2.92	2.89	52
53	3.47	3.43	3.40	3.36	3.33	3.30	3.26	3.23	3.20	3.17	3.14	3.11	3.08	3.06	3.03	3.00	53
54	3.60	3.56	3.52	3.49	3.45	3.42	3.38	3.35	3.32	3.29	3.26	3.23	3.20	3.17	3.14	3.11	54
55	3.73	3.69	3.66	3.62	3.58	3.55	3.51	3.48	3.44	3.41	3.38	3.35	3.32	3.29	3.26	3.23	55
56	3.87	3.83	3.79	3.76	3.72	3.68	3.65	3.61	3.58	3.54	3.51	3.48	3.44	3.41	3.38	3.35	56
57	4.02	3.98	3.94	3.90	3.86	3.82	3.79	3.75	3.71	3.68	3.64	3.61	3.58	3.55	3.51	3.48	57
58	4.18	4.14	4.10	4.05	4.01	3.97	3.93	3.90	3.86	3.82	3.79	3.75	3.72	3.68	3.65	3.62	58
59	4.35	4.30	4.26	4.22	4.17	4.13	4.09	4.05	4.01	3.98	3.94	3.90	3.87	3.83	3.80	3.76	59
60	4.53	4.48	4.43	4.39	4.34	4.30	4.26	4.22	4.18	4.14	4.10	4.06	4.02	3.99	3.95	3.92	60
61	4.71	4.67	4.62	4.57	4.52	4.48	4.44	4.39	4.35	4.31	4.27	4.23	4.19	4.15	4.12	4.08	61
62	4.91	4.86	4.81	4.76	4.72	4.67	4.62	4.58	4.54	4.49	4.45	4.41	4.37	4.33	4.29	4.25	62
63	5.13	5.08	5.02	4.97	4.92	4.87	4.83	4.78	4.73	4.69	4.64	4.60	4.56	4.52	4.48	4.44	63
DEC.	157½ 202½	157¼ 202¼	157° 203	156¾ 203¼	156½ 203½	156¼ 203¾	156° 204	155¾ 204¼	155½ 204½	155¼ 204¾	155° 205	154¾ 205¼	154½ 205½	154¼ 205¾	154° 206	153¾ 206¼	DEC.

Table 29

A

If entered with H.A. at **top**, Sign **+**

     „   „   „   „   **foot**,   „   **—**

1 hr.

HOUR ANGLE or DIFF. LONG.

LAT.	45m	46m	47m	48m	49m	50m	51m	52m	53m	54m	55m	56m	57m	58m	59m	60m	LAT.
	26¼° 333¾	26½° 333½	26¾° 333¼	27° 333	27¼° 332¾	27½° 332½	27¾° 332¼	28° 332	28¼° 331¾	28½° 331½	28¾° 331¼	29° 331	29¼° 330¾	29½° 330½	29¾° 330¼	30° 330	
0°	.000	.000	.000	.000	.000	.000	.000	.000	.000	.000	.000	.000	.000	.000	.000	.000	0°
1	.035	.035	.035	.034	.034	.034	.033	.033	.032	.032	.032	.031	.031	.031	.031	.030	1
2	.071	.070	.069	.068	.068	.067	.066	.066	.065	.064	.064	.063	.062	.062	.061	.060	2
3	.106	.105	.104	.103	.102	.101	.100	.099	.098	.097	.096	.095	.094	.093	.092	.091	3
4	.142	.140	.139	.137	.136	.134	.133	.132	.130	.129	.127	.126	.125	.124	.122	.121	4
5	.177	.175	.174	.172	.170	.168	.166	.165	.163	.161	.159	.158	.156	.155	.153	.152	5
6	.213	.211	.209	.206	.204	.202	.200	.198	.196	.194	.192	.190	.188	.186	.184	.182	6
7	.249	.246	.244	.241	.238	.236	.233	.231	.229	.226	.224	.222	.219	.217	.215	.213	7
8	.285	.282	.279	.276	.273	.270	.267	.264	.262	.259	.256	.254	.251	.248	.246	.243	8
9	.321	.318	.314	.311	.308	.304	.301	.298	.295	.292	.289	.286	.283	.280	.277	.274	9
10	.358	.354	.350	.346	.342	.339	.335	.332	.328	.325	.321	.318	.315	.312	.309	.305	10
11	.394	.390	.386	.381	.377	.373	.369	.366	.362	.358	.354	.351	.347	.344	.340	.337	11
12	.431	.426	.422	.417	.413	.408	.404	.400	.396	.391	.387	.383	.380	.376	.372	.368	12
13	.468	.463	.458	.453	.448	.443	.439	.434	.430	.425	.421	.416	.412	.408	.404	.400	13
14	.506	.500	.495	.489	.484	.479	.474	.469	.464	.459	.454	.450	.445	.441	.436	.432	14
15	.543	.537	.532	.526	.520	.515	.509	.504	.499	.494	.488	.483	.478	.474	.469	.464	15
16	.581	.575	.569	.563	.557	.551	.545	.539	.534	.528	.523	.517	.512	.507	.502	.497	16
17	.620	.613	.607	.600	.594	.587	.581	.575	.569	.563	.557	.552	.546	.540	.535	.530	17
18	.659	.652	.645	.638	.631	.624	.618	.611	.605	.598	.592	.586	.580	.574	.568	.563	18
19	.698	.691	.683	.676	.669	.661	.654	.648	.641	.634	.628	.621	.615	.609	.602	.596	19
20	.738	.730	.722	.714	.707	.699	.692	.685	.677	.670	.663	.657	.650	.643	.637	.630	20
21	.778	.770	.762	.753	.745	.737	.730	.722	.714	.707	.700	.693	.685	.678	.672	.665	21
22	.819	.810	.802	.793	.784	.776	.768	.760	.752	.744	.736	.729	.721	.714	.707	.700	22
23	.861	.851	.842	.833	.824	.815	.807	.798	.790	.782	.774	.766	.758	.750	.743	.735	23
24	.903	.893	.883	.874	.864	.855	.846	.837	.829	.820	.812	.803	.795	.787	.779	.771	24
25	.946	.935	.925	.915	.905	.896	.886	.877	.868	.859	.850	.841	.833	.824	.816	.808	25
26	.989	.978	.968	.957	.947	.937	.927	.917	.908	.898	.889	.880	.871	.862	.853	.845	26
27	1.03	1.02	1.01	1.00	.989	.979	.968	.958	.948	.938	.929	.919	.910	.901	.891	.883	27
28	1.08	1.07	1.06	1.04	1.03	1.02	1.01	1.00	.990	.979	.969	.959	.949	.940	.930	.921	28
29	1.12	1.11	1.10	1.09	1.08	1.06	1.05	1.04	1.03	1.02	1.01	1.00	.990	.980	.970	.960	29
30	1.17	1.16	1.15	1.13	1.12	1.11	1.10	1.09	1.07	1.06	1.05	1.04	1.03	1.02	1.01	1.00	30
31	1.22	1.21	1.19	1.18	1.17	1.15	1.14	1.13	1.12	1.11	1.10	1.08	1.07	1.06	1.05	1.04	31
32	1.27	1.25	1.24	1.23	1.21	1.20	1.19	1.18	1.16	1.15	1.14	1.13	1.12	1.10	1.09	1.08	32
33	1.32	1.30	1.29	1.27	1.26	1.25	1.23	1.22	1.21	1.20	1.18	1.17	1.16	1.15	1.14	1.12	33
34	1.37	1.35	1.34	1.32	1.31	1.30	1.28	1.27	1.26	1.24	1.23	1.22	1.20	1.19	1.18	1.17	34
35	1.42	1.40	1.39	1.37	1.36	1.35	1.33	1.32	1.30	1.29	1.28	1.26	1.25	1.24	1.23	1.21	35
36	1.47	1.46	1.44	1.43	1.41	1.40	1.38	1.37	1.35	1.34	1.32	1.31	1.30	1.28	1.27	1.26	36
37	1.53	1.51	1.50	1.48	1.46	1.45	1.43	1.42	1.40	1.39	1.37	1.36	1.35	1.33	1.32	1.31	37
38	1.58	1.57	1.55	1.53	1.52	1.50	1.48	1.47	1.45	1.44	1.42	1.41	1.40	1.38	1.37	1.35	38
39	1.64	1.62	1.61	1.59	1.57	1.56	1.54	1.52	1.51	1.49	1.48	1.46	1.45	1.43	1.42	1.40	39
40	1.70	1.68	1.66	1.65	1.63	1.61	1.59	1.58	1.56	1.55	1.53	1.51	1.50	1.48	1.47	1.45	40
41	1.76	1.74	1.72	1.71	1.69	1.67	1.65	1.63	1.62	1.60	1.58	1.57	1.55	1.54	1.52	1.51	41
42	1.83	1.81	1.79	1.77	1.75	1.73	1.71	1.69	1.68	1.66	1.64	1.62	1.61	1.59	1.58	1.56	42
43	1.89	1.87	1.85	1.83	1.81	1.79	1.77	1.75	1.74	1.72	1.70	1.68	1.67	1.65	1.63	1.62	43
44	1.96	1.94	1.92	1.90	1.88	1.86	1.84	1.82	1.80	1.78	1.76	1.74	1.72	1.71	1.69	1.67	44
45	2.03	2.01	1.98	1.96	1.94	1.92	1.90	1.88	1.86	1.84	1.82	1.80	1.79	1.77	1.75	1.73	45
46	2.10	2.08	2.05	2.03	2.01	1.99	1.97	1.95	1.93	1.91	1.89	1.87	1.85	1.83	1.81	1.79	46
47	2.17	2.15	2.13	2.10	2.08	2.06	2.04	2.02	2.00	1.98	1.96	1.93	1.92	1.90	1.88	1.86	47
48	2.25	2.23	2.20	2.18	2.16	2.13	2.11	2.09	2.07	2.05	2.02	2.00	1.98	1.96	1.94	1.92	48
49	2.33	2.31	2.28	2.26	2.23	2.21	2.19	2.16	2.14	2.12	2.10	2.08	2.05	2.03	2.01	1.99	49
50	2.42	2.39	2.36	2.34	2.31	2.29	2.27	2.24	2.22	2.19	2.17	2.15	2.13	2.11	2.09	2.06	50
51	2.50	2.48	2.45	2.42	2.40	2.37	2.35	2.32	2.30	2.27	2.25	2.23	2.21	2.18	2.16	2.14	51
52	2.60	2.57	2.54	2.51	2.49	2.46	2.43	2.41	2.38	2.36	2.33	2.31	2.29	2.26	2.24	2.22	52
53	2.69	2.66	2.63	2.60	2.58	2.55	2.52	2.50	2.47	2.44	2.42	2.39	2.37	2.35	2.32	2.30	53
54	2.79	2.76	2.73	2.70	2.67	2.64	2.62	2.59	2.56	2.53	2.51	2.48	2.46	2.43	2.41	2.38	54
55	2.90	2.86	2.83	2.80	2.77	2.74	2.71	2.69	2.66	2.63	2.60	2.58	2.55	2.52	2.50	2.47	55
56	3.01	2.97	2.94	2.91	2.88	2.85	2.82	2.79	2.76	2.73	2.70	2.67	2.65	2.62	2.59	2.57	56
57	3.12	3.09	3.06	3.02	2.99	2.96	2.93	2.90	2.87	2.84	2.81	2.78	2.75	2.72	2.69	2.67	57
58	3.25	3.21	3.18	3.14	3.11	3.07	3.04	3.01	2.98	2.95	2.92	2.89	2.86	2.83	2.80	2.77	58
59	3.37	3.34	3.30	3.27	3.23	3.20	3.16	3.13	3.10	3.07	3.03	3.00	2.97	2.94	2.91	2.88	59
60	3.51	3.47	3.44	3.40	3.36	3.33	3.29	3.26	3.22	3.19	3.16	3.12	3.09	3.06	3.03	3.00	60
LAT.	153¾ 206¼	153½ 206½	153¼ 206¾	153° 207	152¾ 207¼	152½ 207½	152¼ 207¾	152° 208	151¾ 208¼	151½ 208½	151¼ 208¾	151° 209	150¾ 209¼	150½ 209½	150¼ 209¾	150° 210	LAT.

Table 29 **B** 1 hr.

Lat. and Dec. SAME name, Sign —
Lat. and Dec. CONTRARY names, Sign +

HOUR ANGLE or DIFF. LONG.

DEC.	45m	46m	47m	48m	49m	50m	51m	52m	53m	54m	55m	56m	57m	58m	59m	60m	DEC.
	26¼° 333¾	26½° 333½	26¾° 333¼	27° 333	27¼° 332¾	27½° 332½	27¾° 332¼	28° 332	28¼° 331¾	28½° 331½	28¾° 331¼	29° 331	29¼° 330¾	29½° 330½	29¾° 330¼	30° 330	
0	.000	.000	.000	.000	.000	.000	.000	.000	.000	.000	.000	.000	.000	.000	.000	.000	0
1	.040	.039	.039	.038	.038	.038	.038	.037	.037	.037	.036	.036	.036	.035	.035	.035	1
2	.079	.078	.078	.077	.076	.076	.075	.074	.074	.073	.073	.072	.071	.070	.070	.070	2
3	.119	.117	.116	.115	.114	.113	.113	.112	.111	.110	.109	.108	.107	.106	.106	.105	3
4	.158	.157	.155	.154	.152	.151	.150	.149	.148	.147	.145	.144	.143	.142	.141	.140	4
5	.198	.196	.194	.193	.191	.189	.188	.186	.185	.183	.182	.180	.179	.178	.176	.175	5
6	.238	.236	.234	.232	.230	.228	.226	.224	.222	.220	.219	.217	.215	.213	.212	.210	6
7	.278	.275	.273	.270	.268	.266	.264	.262	.259	.257	.255	.253	.251	.249	.247	.246	7
8	.318	.315	.312	.310	.307	.304	.302	.299	.297	.295	.292	.290	.288	.285	.283	.281	8
9	.358	.355	.352	.349	.346	.343	.340	.337	.335	.332	.329	.327	.324	.322	.319	.317	9
10	.399	.395	.392	.388	.385	.382	.379	.376	.373	.370	.367	.364	.361	.358	.355	.353	10
11	.439	.436	.432	.428	.425	.421	.418	.414	.411	.407	.404	.401	.398	.395	.392	.389	11
12	.481	.476	.472	.468	.464	.460	.457	.453	.449	.445	.442	.438	.435	.432	.428	.425	12
13	.522	.517	.513	.509	.504	.500	.496	.492	.488	.484	.480	.476	.473	.469	.465	.462	13
14	.564	.559	.554	.549	.545	.540	.536	.531	.527	.523	.519	.514	.510	.506	.503	.499	14
15	.606	.601	.595	.590	.585	.580	.576	.571	.566	.562	.557	.553	.548	.544	.540	.536	15
16	.648	.643	.637	.632	.626	.621	.616	.611	.606	.601	.596	.591	.587	.582	.578	.573	16
17	.691	.685	.679	.673	.668	.662	.657	.651	.646	.641	.636	.631	.626	.621	.616	.611	17
18	.735	.728	.722	.716	.710	.704	.698	.692	.687	.681	.676	.670	.665	.660	.655	.650	18
19	.779	.772	.765	.758	.752	.746	.740	.733	.728	.722	.716	.710	.705	.699	.694	.689	19
20	.823	.816	.809	.802	.795	.788	.782	.775	.769	.763	.757	.751	.745	.739	.734	.728	20
21	.868	.860	.853	.846	.839	.831	.825	.818	.811	.804	.798	.792	.786	.780	.774	.768	21
22	.914	.905	.898	.890	.883	.875	.868	.861	.854	.847	.840	.833	.827	.820	.814	.808	22
23	.960	.951	.943	.935	.927	.919	.912	.904	.897	.890	.883	.876	.869	.862	.856	.849	23
24	1.01	.998	.989	.981	.973	.964	.956	.948	.941	.933	.926	.918	.911	.904	.897	.890	24
25	1.05	1.05	1.04	1.03	1.02	1.01	1.00	.993	.985	.977	.970	.962	.954	.947	.940	.933	25
26	1.10	1.09	1.08	1.07	1.07	1.06	1.05	1.04	1.03	1.02	1.01	1.01	.998	.990	.983	.975	26
27	1.15	1.14	1.13	1.12	1.11	1.10	1.09	1.09	1.08	1.07	1.06	1.05	1.04	1.03	1.02	1.02	27
28	1.20	1.19	1.18	1.17	1.16	1.15	1.14	1.13	1.12	1.11	1.11	1.10	1.09	1.08	1.07	1.06	28
29	1.25	1.24	1.23	1.22	1.21	1.20	1.19	1.18	1.17	1.16	1.15	1.14	1.13	1.13	1.12	1.11	29
30	1.31	1.29	1.28	1.27	1.26	1.25	1.24	1.23	1.22	1.21	1.20	1.19	1.18	1.17	1.16	1.15	30
31	1.36	1.35	1.34	1.32	1.31	1.30	1.29	1.28	1.27	1.26	1.25	1.24	1.23	1.22	1.21	1.20	31
32	1.41	1.40	1.39	1.38	1.37	1.35	1.34	1.33	1.32	1.31	1.30	1.29	1.28	1.27	1.26	1.25	32
33	1.47	1.46	1.44	1.43	1.42	1.41	1.39	1.38	1.37	1.36	1.35	1.34	1.33	1.32	1.31	1.30	33
34	1.53	1.51	1.50	1.49	1.48	1.46	1.45	1.44	1.43	1.41	1.40	1.39	1.38	1.37	1.36	1.35	34
35	1.58	1.57	1.56	1.54	1.53	1.52	1.50	1.49	1.48	1.47	1.46	1.44	1.43	1.42	1.41	1.40	35
36	1.64	1.63	1.61	1.60	1.59	1.57	1.56	1.55	1.54	1.52	1.51	1.50	1.49	1.48	1.46	1.45	36
37	1.70	1.69	1.67	1.66	1.65	1.63	1.62	1.61	1.59	1.58	1.57	1.55	1.54	1.53	1.52	1.51	37
38	1.77	1.75	1.74	1.72	1.71	1.69	1.68	1.66	1.65	1.64	1.62	1.61	1.60	1.59	1.57	1.56	38
39	1.83	1.81	1.80	1.78	1.77	1.75	1.74	1.72	1.71	1.70	1.68	1.67	1.66	1.64	1.63	1.62	39
40	1.90	1.88	1.86	1.85	1.83	1.82	1.80	1.79	1.77	1.76	1.74	1.73	1.72	1.70	1.69	1.68	40
41	1.97	1.95	1.93	1.91	1.90	1.88	1.87	1.85	1.84	1.82	1.81	1.79	1.78	1.77	1.75	1.74	41
42	2.04	2.02	2.00	1.98	1.97	1.95	1.93	1.92	1.90	1.89	1.87	1.86	1.84	1.83	1.81	1.80	42
43	2.11	2.09	2.07	2.05	2.04	2.02	2.00	1.99	1.97	1.95	1.94	1.92	1.91	1.89	1.88	1.87	43
44	2.18	2.16	2.15	2.13	2.11	2.09	2.07	2.06	2.04	2.02	2.01	1.99	1.98	1.96	1.95	1.93	44
45	2.26	2.24	2.22	2.20	2.18	2.17	2.15	2.13	2.11	2.10	2.08	2.06	2.05	2.03	2.02	2.00	45
46	2.34	2.32	2.30	2.28	2.26	2.24	2.22	2.21	2.19	2.17	2.15	2.14	2.12	2.10	2.09	2.07	46
47	2.42	2.40	2.38	2.36	2.34	2.32	2.30	2.28	2.27	2.25	2.23	2.21	2.19	2.18	2.16	2.14	47
48	2.51	2.49	2.47	2.45	2.43	2.41	2.39	2.37	2.35	2.33	2.31	2.29	2.27	2.26	2.24	2.22	48
49	2.60	2.58	2.56	2.53	2.51	2.49	2.47	2.45	2.43	2.41	2.39	2.37	2.35	2.34	2.32	2.30	49
50	2.69	2.67	2.65	2.63	2.60	2.58	2.56	2.54	2.52	2.50	2.48	2.46	2.44	2.42	2.40	2.38	50
51	2.79	2.77	2.74	2.72	2.70	2.67	2.65	2.63	2.61	2.59	2.57	2.55	2.53	2.51	2.49	2.47	51
52	2.89	2.87	2.84	2.82	2.80	2.77	2.75	2.73	2.70	2.68	2.66	2.64	2.62	2.60	2.58	2.56	52
53	3.00	2.97	2.95	2.92	2.90	2.87	2.85	2.83	2.80	2.78	2.76	2.74	2.72	2.69	2.67	2.65	53
54	3.11	3.08	3.06	3.03	3.01	2.98	2.96	2.93	2.91	2.89	2.86	2.84	2.82	2.80	2.77	2.75	54
55	3.23	3.20	3.17	3.15	3.12	3.09	3.07	3.04	3.02	2.99	2.97	2.95	2.92	2.90	2.88	2.86	55
56	3.35	3.32	3.29	3.27	3.24	3.21	3.18	3.16	3.13	3.11	3.08	3.06	3.03	3.01	2.99	2.97	56
57	3.48	3.45	3.42	3.39	3.36	3.33	3.31	3.28	3.25	3.23	3.20	3.18	3.15	3.13	3.10	3.08	57
58	3.62	3.59	3.56	3.53	3.50	3.47	3.44	3.41	3.38	3.35	3.33	3.30	3.28	3.25	3.23	3.20	58
59	3.76	3.73	3.70	3.67	3.64	3.60	3.57	3.55	3.52	3.49	3.46	3.43	3.40	3.38	3.35	3.33	59
60	3.92	3.88	3.85	3.82	3.78	3.75	3.72	3.69	3.66	3.63	3.60	3.57	3.55	3.52	3.49	3.46	60
61	4.08	4.04	4.01	3.97	3.94	3.91	3.87	3.84	3.81	3.78	3.75	3.72	3.69	3.66	3.64	3.61	61
62	4.25	4.22	4.18	4.14	4.11	4.07	4.04	4.01	3.97	3.94	3.91	3.88	3.85	3.82	3.79	3.76	62
63	4.44	4.40	4.36	4.32	4.29	4.25	4.22	4.18	4.15	4.11	4.08	4.05	4.02	3.99	3.96	3.93	63
DEC.	153¾ 206¼	153½ 206½	153¼ 206¾	153° 207	152¾ 207¼	152½ 207½	152¼ 207¾	152° 208	151¾ 208¼	151½ 208½	151¼ 208¾	151° 209	150¾ 209¼	150½ 209½	150¼ 209¾	150° 210	DEC.

Table 29

A

If entered with H.A. at **top**, Sign **+**

„　„　„　„ **foot,** „ **−**

2 hrs.

HOUR ANGLE or DIFF. LONG.

LAT.	00m	02m	04m	06m	08m	10m	12m	14m	16m	18m	20m	22m	24m	26m	28m	30m	LAT.
	30° / 330	30½° / 329½	31° / 329	31½° / 328½	32° / 328	32½° / 327½	33° / 327	33½° / 326½	34° / 326	34½° / 325½	35° / 325	35½° / 324½	36° / 324	36½° / 323½	37° / 323	37½° / 322½	
0°	.000	.000	.000	.000	.000	.000	.000	.000	.000	.000	.000	.000	.000	.000	.000	.000	0°
1	.030	.030	.029	.028	.028	.027	.027	.026	.026	.025	.025	.024	.024	.024	.023	.023	1
2	.060	.059	.058	.057	.056	.055	.054	.053	.052	.051	.050	.049	.048	.047	.046	.046	2
3	.091	.089	.087	.086	.084	.082	.081	.079	.078	.076	.075	.073	.072	.071	.070	.068	3
4	.121	.119	.116	.114	.112	.110	.108	.106	.104	.102	.100	.098	.096	.095	.093	.091	4
5	.152	.149	.146	.143	.140	.137	.135	.132	.130	.127	.125	.123	.120	.118	.116	.114	5
6	.182	.178	.175	.172	.168	.165	.162	.159	.156	.153	.150	.147	.145	.142	.139	.137	6
7	.213	.208	.204	.200	.196	.193	.189	.186	.182	.179	.175	.172	.169	.166	.163	.160	7
8	.243	.239	.234	.229	.225	.221	.216	.212	.208	.204	.201	.197	.193	.190	.187	.183	8
9	.274	.269	.264	.258	.253	.249	.244	.239	.235	.230	.226	.222	.218	.214	.210	.206	9
10	.305	.299	.294	.288	.282	.277	.272	.266	.261	.257	.252	.247	.243	.238	.234	.230	10
11	.337	.330	.324	.317	.311	.305	.299	.294	.288	.283	.278	.273	.268	.263	.258	.253	11
12	.368	.361	.354	.347	.340	.334	.327	.321	.315	.309	.304	.298	.293	.287	.282	.277	12
13	.400	.392	.384	.377	.369	.362	.356	.349	.342	.336	.330	.324	.318	.312	.306	.301	13
14	.432	.423	.415	.407	.399	.391	.384	.377	.370	.363	.356	.350	.343	.337	.331	.325	14
15	.464	.455	.446	.437	.429	.421	.413	.405	.397	.390	.383	.376	.369	.362	.356	.349	15
16	.497	.487	.477	.468	.459	.450	.442	.433	.425	.417	.410	.402	.395	.388	.381	.374	16
17	.530	.519	.509	.499	.489	.480	.471	.462	.453	.445	.437	.429	.421	.413	.406	.398	17
18	.563	.552	.541	.530	.520	.510	.500	.491	.482	.473	.464	.456	.447	.439	.431	.423	18
19	.596	.585	.573	.562	.551	.540	.530	.520	.510	.501	.492	.483	.474	.465	.457	.449	19
20	.630	.618	.606	.594	.582	.571	.560	.550	.540	.530	.520	.510	.501	.492	.483	.474	20
21	.665	.652	.639	.626	.614	.603	.591	.580	.569	.559	.548	.538	.528	.519	.509	.500	21
22	.700	.686	.672	.659	.647	.634	.622	.610	.599	.588	.577	.566	.556	.546	.536	.527	22
23	.735	.721	.706	.693	.679	.666	.654	.641	.629	.618	.606	.595	.584	.574	.563	.553	23
24	.771	.756	.741	.727	.713	.699	.686	.673	.660	.648	.636	.624	.613	.602	.591	.580	24
25	.808	.792	.776	.761	.746	.732	.718	.705	.691	.678	.666	.654	.642	.630	.619	.608	25
26	.845	.828	.812	.796	.781	.766	.751	.737	.723	.710	.697	.684	.671	.659	.647	.636	26
27	.883	.865	.848	.831	.815	.800	.785	.770	.755	.741	.728	.714	.701	.689	.676	.664	27
28	.921	.903	.885	.868	.851	.835	.819	.803	.788	.774	.759	.745	.732	.719	.706	.693	28
29	.960	.941	.922	.905	.887	.870	.854	.837	.822	.807	.792	.777	.763	.749	.736	.722	29
30	1.00	.980	.961	.942	.924	.906	.889	.872	.856	.840	.825	.809	.795	.780	.766	.752	30
31	1.04	1.02	1.00	.981	.962	.943	.925	.908	.891	.874	.858	.842	.827	.812	.797	.783	31
32	1.08	1.06	1.04	1.02	1.00	.981	.962	.944	.926	.909	.892	.876	.860	.844	.829	.814	32
33	1.12	1.10	1.08	1.06	1.04	1.02	1.00	.981	.963	.945	.927	.910	.894	.878	.862	.846	33
34	1.17	1.15	1.12	1.10	1.08	1.06	1.04	1.02	1.00	.981	.963	.946	.928	.912	.895	.879	34
35	1.21	1.19	1.17	1.14	1.12	1.10	1.08	1.06	1.04	1.02	1.00	.982	.964	.946	.929	.913	35
36	1.26	1.23	1.21	1.19	1.16	1.14	1.12	1.10	1.08	1.06	1.04	1.02	1.00	.982	.964	.947	36
37	1.31	1.28	1.25	1.23	1.21	1.18	1.16	1.14	1.12	1.10	1.08	1.06	1.04	1.02	1.00	.982	37
38	1.35	1.33	1.30	1.28	1.25	1.23	1.20	1.18	1.16	1.14	1.12	1.10	1.08	1.06	1.04	1.02	38
39	1.40	1.38	1.35	1.32	1.30	1.27	1.25	1.22	1.20	1.18	1.16	1.14	1.11	1.09	1.07	1.06	39
40	1.45	1.43	1.40	1.37	1.34	1.32	1.29	1.27	1.24	1.22	1.20	1.18	1.15	1.13	1.11	1.09	40
41	1.51	1.48	1.45	1.42	1.39	1.37	1.34	1.31	1.29	1.27	1.24	1.22	1.20	1.18	1.15	1.13	41
42	1.56	1.53	1.50	1.47	1.44	1.41	1.39	1.36	1.33	1.31	1.29	1.26	1.24	1.22	1.20	1.17	42
43	1.62	1.58	1.55	1.52	1.49	1.46	1.44	1.41	1.38	1.36	1.33	1.31	1.28	1.26	1.24	1.22	43
44	1.67	1.64	1.61	1.58	1.55	1.52	1.49	1.46	1.43	1.41	1.38	1.35	1.33	1.31	1.28	1.26	44
45	1.73	1.70	1.66	1.63	1.60	1.57	1.54	1.51	1.48	1.46	1.43	1.40	1.38	1.35	1.33	1.30	45
46	1.79	1.76	1.72	1.69	1.66	1.62	1.59	1.57	1.54	1.51	1.48	1.45	1.43	1.40	1.37	1.35	46
47	1.86	1.82	1.78	1.75	1.72	1.68	1.65	1.62	1.59	1.56	1.53	1.50	1.48	1.45	1.42	1.40	47
48	1.92	1.89	1.85	1.81	1.78	1.74	1.71	1.68	1.65	1.62	1.59	1.56	1.53	1.50	1.47	1.45	48
49	1.99	1.95	1.92	1.88	1.84	1.81	1.77	1.74	1.71	1.67	1.64	1.61	1.58	1.56	1.53	1.50	49
50	2.06	2.02	1.98	1.95	1.91	1.87	1.84	1.80	1.77	1.73	1.70	1.67	1.64	1.61	1.58	1.55	50
51	2.14	2.10	2.06	2.02	1.98	1.94	1.90	1.87	1.83	1.80	1.76	1.73	1.70	1.67	1.64	1.61	51
52	2.22	2.17	2.13	2.09	2.05	2.01	1.97	1.93	1.90	1.86	1.83	1.79	1.76	1.73	1.70	1.67	52
53	2.30	2.25	2.21	2.17	2.12	2.08	2.04	2.01	1.97	1.93	1.90	1.86	1.83	1.79	1.76	1.73	53
54	2.38	2.34	2.29	2.25	2.20	2.16	2.12	2.08	2.04	2.00	1.97	1.93	1.89	1.86	1.83	1.79	54
55	2.47	2.43	2.38	2.33	2.29	2.24	2.20	2.16	2.12	2.08	2.04	2.00	1.97	1.93	1.90	1.86	55
56	2.57	2.52	2.47	2.42	2.37	2.33	2.28	2.24	2.20	2.16	2.12	2.08	2.04	2.00	1.97	1.93	56
57	2.67	2.61	2.56	2.51	2.46	2.42	2.37	2.33	2.28	2.24	2.20	2.16	2.12	2.08	2.04	2.01	57
58	2.77	2.72	2.66	2.61	2.56	2.51	2.46	2.42	2.37	2.33	2.29	2.24	2.20	2.16	2.12	2.09	58
59	2.88	2.83	2.77	2.72	2.66	2.61	2.56	2.51	2.47	2.42	2.38	2.33	2.29	2.25	2.21	2.17	59
60	3.00	2.94	2.88	2.83	2.77	2.72	2.67	2.62	2.57	2.52	2.47	2.43	2.38	2.34	2.30	2.26	60
LAT.	150° / 210	149½ / 210½	149° / 211	148½ / 211½	148° / 212	147½ / 212½	147° / 213	146½ / 213½	146° / 214	145½ / 214½	145° / 215	144½ / 215½	144° / 216	143½ / 216½	143° / 217	142½ / 217½	LAT.

Table 29	**B**	Lat. and Dec. SAME name, Sign **—**
2 hrs.		Lat. and Dec. CONTRARY names, Sign **+**

HOUR ANGLE or DIFF. LONG.

DEC.	00m	02m	04m	06m	08m	10m	12m	14m	16m	18m	20m	22m	24m	26m	28m	30m	DEC.
	30° 330	**30½°** 329½	**31°** 329	**31½°** 328½	**32°** 328	**32½°** 327½	**33°** 327	**33½°** 326½	**34°** 326	**34½°** 325½	**35°** 325	**35½°** 324½	**36°** 324	**36½°** 323½	**37°** 323	**37½°** 322½	
0°	.000	.000	.000	.000	.000	.000	.000	.000	.000	.000	.000	.000	.000	.000	.000	.000	0°
1	.035	.034	.034	.033	.033	.032	.032	.032	.031	.031	.030	.030	.030	.029	.029	.029	1
2	.070	.069	.068	.067	.066	.065	.064	.063	.062	.062	.061	.060	.059	.059	.058	.057	2
3	.105	.103	.102	.100	.099	.098	.096	.095	.094	.093	.091	.090	.089	.088	.087	.086	3
4	.140	.138	.136	.134	.132	.130	.128	.127	.125	.123	.122	.120	.119	.118	.116	.115	4
5	.175	.172	.170	.167	.165	.163	.161	.159	.157	.154	.153	.151	.149	.147	.145	.144	5
6	.210	.207	.204	.201	.198	.196	.193	.190	.188	.186	.183	.181	.179	.177	.175	.173	6
7	.246	.242	.238	.235	.232	.229	.225	.222	.220	.217	.214	.211	.209	.206	.204	.202	7
8	.281	.277	.273	.269	.265	.262	.258	.255	.251	.248	.245	.242	.239	.236	.234	.231	8
9	.317	.312	.308	.303	.299	.295	.291	.287	.283	.280	.276	.273	.269	.266	.263	.260	9
10	.353	.347	.342	.337	.333	.328	.324	.319	.315	.311	.307	.304	.300	.296	.293	.290	10
11	.389	.383	.377	.372	.367	.362	.357	.352	.348	.343	.339	.335	.331	.327	.323	.319	11
12	.425	.419	.413	.407	.401	.396	.390	.385	.380	.375	.371	.366	.362	.357	.353	.349	12
13	.462	.455	.448	.442	.436	.430	.424	.418	.413	.408	.403	.398	.393	.388	.384	.379	13
14	.499	.491	.484	.477	.471	.464	.458	.452	.446	.440	.435	.429	.424	.419	.414	.410	14
15	.536	.528	.520	.513	.506	.499	.492	.485	.479	.473	.467	.461	.456	.450	.445	.440	15
16	.573	.565	.557	.549	.541	.534	.527	.520	.513	.506	.500	.494	.488	.482	.476	.471	16
17	.611	.602	.594	.585	.577	.569	.561	.554	.547	.540	.533	.526	.520	.514	.508	.502	17
18	.650	.640	.631	.622	.613	.605	.597	.589	.581	.574	.566	.560	.553	.546	.540	.534	18
19	.689	.678	.669	.659	.650	.641	.632	.624	.616	.608	.600	.593	.586	.579	.572	.566	19
20	.728	.717	.707	.697	.687	.677	.668	.659	.651	.643	.635	.627	.619	.612	.605	.598	20
21	.768	.756	.745	.735	.724	.714	.705	.695	.686	.678	.669	.661	.653	.645	.638	.631	21
22	.808	.796	.784	.773	.762	.752	.742	.732	.723	.713	.704	.696	.687	.679	.671	.664	22
23	.849	.836	.824	.812	.801	.790	.779	.769	.759	.749	.740	.731	.722	.714	.705	.697	23
24	.890	.877	.864	.852	.840	.829	.817	.807	.796	.786	.776	.767	.757	.749	.740	.731	24
25	.933	.919	.905	.892	.880	.868	.856	.845	.834	.823	.813	.803	.793	.784	.775	.766	25
26	.975	.961	.947	.933	.920	.908	.896	.884	.872	.861	.850	.840	.830	.820	.810	.801	26
27	1.02	1.00	.989	.975	.962	.948	.936	.923	.911	.900	.888	.877	.867	.857	.847	.837	27
28	1.06	1.05	1.03	1.02	1.00	.990	.976	.963	.951	.939	.927	.916	.905	.894	.884	.873	28
29	1.11	1.09	1.08	1.06	1.05	1.03	1.02	1.00	.991	.979	.966	.955	.943	.932	.921	.911	29
30	1.15	1.14	1.12	1.11	1.09	1.08	1.06	1.05	1.03	1.02	1.01	.994	.982	.971	.959	.948	30
31	1.20	1.18	1.17	1.15	1.13	1.12	1.10	1.09	1.07	1.06	1.05	1.04	1.02	1.01	.998	.987	31
32	1.25	1.23	1.21	1.20	1.18	1.16	1.15	1.13	1.12	1.10	1.09	1.08	1.06	1.05	1.04	1.03	32
33	1.30	1.28	1.26	1.24	1.23	1.21	1.19	1.18	1.16	1.15	1.13	1.12	1.10	1.09	1.08	1.07	33
34	1.35	1.33	1.31	1.29	1.27	1.26	1.24	1.22	1.21	1.19	1.18	1.16	1.15	1.13	1.12	1.11	34
35	1.40	1.38	1.36	1.34	1.32	1.30	1.29	1.27	1.25	1.24	1.22	1.21	1.19	1.18	1.16	1.15	35
36	1.45	1.43	1.41	1.39	1.37	1.35	1.33	1.32	1.30	1.28	1.27	1.25	1.24	1.22	1.21	1.19	36
37	1.51	1.49	1.46	1.44	1.42	1.40	1.38	1.37	1.35	1.33	1.31	1.30	1.28	1.27	1.25	1.24	37
38	1.56	1.54	1.52	1.50	1.47	1.45	1.43	1.42	1.40	1.38	1.36	1.35	1.33	1.31	1.30	1.28	38
39	1.62	1.60	1.57	1.55	1.53	1.51	1.49	1.47	1.45	1.43	1.41	1.39	1.38	1.36	1.35	1.33	39
40	1.68	1.65	1.63	1.61	1.58	1.56	1.54	1.52	1.50	1.48	1.46	1.45	1.43	1.41	1.39	1.38	40
41	1.74	1.71	1.69	1.66	1.64	1.62	1.60	1.58	1.55	1.54	1.52	1.50	1.48	1.46	1.44	1.43	41
42	1.80	1.77	1.75	1.72	1.70	1.68	1.65	1.63	1.61	1.59	1.57	1.55	1.53	1.51	1.50	1.48	42
43	1.87	1.84	1.81	1.79	1.76	1.74	1.71	1.69	1.67	1.65	1.63	1.61	1.59	1.57	1.55	1.53	43
44	1.93	1.90	1.88	1.85	1.82	1.80	1.77	1.75	1.73	1.71	1.68	1.66	1.64	1.62	1.60	1.59	44
45	2.00	1.97	1.94	1.91	1.89	1.86	1.84	1.81	1.79	1.77	1.74	1.72	1.70	1.68	1.66	1.64	45
46	2.07	2.04	2.01	1.98	1.95	1.93	1.90	1.88	1.85	1.83	1.81	1.78	1.76	1.74	1.72	1.70	46
47	2.14	2.11	2.08	2.05	2.02	2.00	1.97	1.94	1.92	1.89	1.87	1.85	1.82	1.80	1.78	1.76	47
48	2.22	2.19	2.16	2.13	2.10	2.07	2.04	2.01	1.99	1.96	1.94	1.91	1.89	1.87	1.85	1.82	48
49	2.30	2.27	2.23	2.20	2.17	2.14	2.11	2.08	2.06	2.03	2.01	1.98	1.96	1.93	1.91	1.89	49
50	2.38	2.35	2.31	2.28	2.25	2.22	2.19	2.16	2.13	2.10	2.08	2.05	2.03	2.00	1.98	1.96	50
51	2.47	2.43	2.40	2.36	2.33	2.30	2.27	2.24	2.21	2.18	2.15	2.13	2.10	2.08	2.05	2.03	51
52	2.56	2.52	2.49	2.45	2.42	2.38	2.35	2.32	2.29	2.26	2.23	2.20	2.18	2.15	2.13	2.10	52
53	2.65	2.62	2.58	2.54	2.50	2.47	2.44	2.40	2.37	2.34	2.31	2.29	2.26	2.23	2.21	2.18	53
54	2.75	2.71	2.67	2.63	2.60	2.56	2.53	2.49	2.46	2.43	2.40	2.37	2.34	2.31	2.29	2.26	54
55	2.86	2.81	2.77	2.73	2.70	2.66	2.62	2.59	2.55	2.52	2.49	2.46	2.43	2.40	2.37	2.35	55
56	2.97	2.92	2.88	2.84	2.80	2.76	2.72	2.69	2.65	2.62	2.58	2.55	2.52	2.49	2.46	2.44	56
57	3.08	3.03	2.99	2.95	2.91	2.87	2.83	2.79	2.75	2.72	2.68	2.65	2.62	2.59	2.56	2.53	57
58	3.20	3.15	3.11	3.06	3.02	2.98	2.94	2.90	2.86	2.83	2.79	2.76	2.72	2.69	2.66	2.63	58
59	3.33	3.28	3.23	3.19	3.14	3.10	3.06	3.02	2.98	2.94	2.90	2.87	2.83	2.80	2.77	2.73	59
60	3.46	3.41	3.36	3.32	3.27	3.22	3.18	3.14	3.10	3.06	3.02	2.98	2.95	2.91	2.88	2.85	60
61	3.61	3.56	3.50	3.45	3.40	3.36	3.31	3.27	3.23	3.19	3.15	3.11	3.07	3.03	3.00	2.96	61
62	3.76	3.71	3.65	3.60	3.55	3.50	3.45	3.41	3.36	3.32	3.28	3.24	3.20	3.16	3.13	3.09	62
63	3.93	3.87	3.81	3.76	3.70	3.65	3.60	3.56	3.51	3.47	3.42	3.38	3.34	3.30	3.26	3.22	63
DEC.	**150°** 210	149½ 210½	**149°** 211	148½ 211½	**148°** 212	147½ 212½	**147°** 213	146½ 213½	**146°** 214	145½ 214½	**145°** 215	144½ 215½	**144°** 216	143½ 216½	**143°** 217	142½ 217½	DEC.

Table 29

A

2 hrs.

If entered with H.A. at **top**, Sign **+**
    „   „   „   „   **foot**,   „   **−**

HOUR ANGLE or DIFF. LONG.

LAT.	30m	32m	34m	36m	38m	40m	42m	44m	46m	48m	50m	52m	54m	56m	58m	60m	LAT.
	37½° 322½	38° 322	38½° 321½	39° 321	39½° 320½	40° 320	40½° 319½	41° 319	41½° 318½	42° 318	42½° 317½	43° 317	43½° 316½	44° 316	44½° 315½	45° 315	
0°	.000	.000	.000	.000	.000	.000	.000	.000	.000	.000	.000	.000	.000	.000	.000	.000	0°
1	.023	.022	.022	.022	.021	.021	.020	.020	.020	.019	.019	.019	.018	.018	.018	.017	1
2	.046	.045	.044	.043	.042	.042	.041	.040	.039	.039	.038	.037	.037	.036	.036	.035	2
3	.068	.067	.066	.065	.064	.062	.061	.060	.059	.058	.057	.056	.055	.054	.053	.052	3
4	.091	.090	.088	.086	.085	.083	.082	.080	.079	.078	.076	.075	.074	.072	.071	.070	4
5	.114	.112	.110	.108	.106	.104	.102	.101	.099	.097	.095	.094	.092	.091	.089	.087	5
6	.137	.135	.132	.130	.128	.125	.123	.121	.119	.117	.115	.113	.111	.109	.107	.105	6
7	.160	.157	.154	.152	.149	.146	.144	.141	.139	.136	.134	.132	.129	.127	.125	.123	7
8	.183	.180	.177	.174	.170	.167	.165	.162	.159	.156	.153	.151	.148	.146	.143	.141	8
9	.206	.203	.199	.196	.192	.189	.185	.182	.179	.176	.173	.170	.167	.164	.161	.158	9
10	.230	.226	.222	.218	.214	.210	.206	.203	.199	.196	.192	.189	.186	.183	.179	.176	10
11	.253	.249	.244	.240	.236	.232	.228	.224	.220	.216	.212	.208	.205	.201	.198	.194	11
12	.277	.272	.267	.262	.258	.253	.249	.245	.240	.236	.232	.228	.224	.220	.216	.213	12
13	.301	.295	.290	.285	.280	.275	.270	.266	.261	.256	.252	.248	.243	.239	.235	.231	13
14	.325	.319	.313	.308	.302	.297	.292	.287	.282	.277	.272	.267	.263	.258	.254	.249	14
15	.349	.343	.337	.331	.325	.319	.314	.308	.303	.298	.292	.287	.282	.277	.273	.268	15
16	.374	.367	.360	.354	.348	.342	.336	.330	.324	.318	.313	.307	.302	.297	.292	.287	16
17	.398	.391	.384	.378	.371	.364	.358	.352	.346	.340	.334	.328	.322	.317	.311	.306	17
18	.423	.416	.408	.401	.394	.387	.380	.374	.367	.361	.355	.348	.342	.336	.331	.325	18
19	.449	.441	.433	.425	.418	.410	.403	.396	.389	.382	.376	.369	.363	.357	.350	.344	19
20	.474	.466	.458	.449	.442	.434	.426	.419	.411	.404	.397	.390	.384	.377	.370	.364	20
21	.500	.491	.483	.474	.466	.457	.449	.442	.434	.426	.419	.412	.405	.398	.391	.384	21
22	.527	.517	.508	.499	.490	.481	.473	.465	.457	.449	.441	.433	.426	.418	.411	.404	22
23	.553	.543	.534	.524	.515	.506	.497	.488	.480	.471	.463	.455	.447	.440	.432	.424	23
24	.580	.570	.560	.550	.540	.531	.521	.512	.503	.494	.486	.477	.469	.461	.453	.445	24
25	.608	.597	.586	.576	.566	.556	.546	.536	.527	.518	.509	.500	.491	.483	.475	.466	25
26	.636	.624	.613	.602	.592	.581	.571	.561	.551	.542	.532	.523	.514	.505	.496	.488	26
27	.664	.652	.641	.629	.618	.607	.597	.586	.576	.566	.556	.546	.537	.528	.518	.510	27
28	.693	.681	.668	.657	.645	.634	.623	.612	.601	.591	.580	.570	.560	.551	.541	.532	28
29	.722	.709	.697	.685	.672	.661	.649	.638	.627	.616	.605	.594	.584	.574	.564	.554	29
30	.752	.739	.726	.713	.700	.688	.676	.664	.653	.641	.630	.619	.608	.598	.588	.577	30
31	.783	.769	.755	.742	.729	.716	.704	.691	.679	.667	.656	.644	.633	.622	.611	.601	31
32	.814	.800	.786	.772	.758	.745	.732	.719	.706	.694	.682	.670	.658	.647	.636	.625	32
33	.846	.831	.816	.802	.788	.774	.760	.747	.734	.721	.709	.696	.684	.672	.661	.649	33
34	.879	.863	.848	.833	.818	.804	.790	.776	.762	.749	.736	.723	.711	.698	.686	.675	34
35	.913	.896	.880	.865	.849	.834	.820	.805	.791	.778	.764	.751	.738	.725	.713	.700	35
36	.947	.930	.913	.897	.881	.866	.851	.836	.821	.807	.793	.779	.766	.752	.739	.727	36
37	.982	.965	.947	.931	.914	.898	.882	.867	.852	.837	.822	.808	.794	.780	.767	.754	37
38	1.02	1.00	.982	.965	.948	.931	.915	.899	.883	.868	.853	.838	.823	.809	.795	.781	38
39	1.06	1.04	1.02	1.00	.982	.965	.948	.932	.915	.899	.884	.868	.853	.839	.824	.810	39
40	1.09	1.07	1.06	1.04	1.02	1.00	.982	.965	.948	.932	.916	.900	.884	.869	.854	.839	40
41	1.13	1.11	1.09	1.07	1.06	1.04	1.02	1.00	.983	.965	.949	.932	.916	.900	.885	.869	41
42	1.17	1.15	1.13	1.11	1.09	1.07	1.05	1.04	1.02	1.00	.983	.966	.949	.932	.916	.900	42
43	1.22	1.19	1.17	1.15	1.13	1.11	1.09	1.07	1.05	1.04	1.02	1.00	.983	.966	.949	.933	43
44	1.26	1.24	1.21	1.19	1.17	1.15	1.13	1.11	1.09	1.07	1.05	1.04	1.02	1.00	.983	.966	44
45	1.30	1.28	1.26	1.23	1.21	1.19	1.17	1.15	1.13	1.11	1.09	1.07	1.05	1.04	1.02	1.00	45
46	1.35	1.33	1.30	1.28	1.26	1.23	1.21	1.19	1.17	1.15	1.13	1.11	1.09	1.07	1.05	1.04	46
47	1.40	1.37	1.35	1.32	1.30	1.28	1.26	1.23	1.21	1.19	1.17	1.15	1.13	1.11	1.09	1.07	47
48	1.45	1.42	1.40	1.37	1.35	1.32	1.30	1.28	1.26	1.23	1.21	1.19	1.17	1.15	1.13	1.11	48
49	1.50	1.47	1.45	1.42	1.40	1.37	1.35	1.32	1.30	1.28	1.26	1.23	1.21	1.19	1.17	1.15	49
50	1.55	1.53	1.50	1.47	1.45	1.42	1.40	1.37	1.35	1.32	1.30	1.28	1.26	1.23	1.21	1.19	50
51	1.61	1.58	1.55	1.53	1.50	1.47	1.45	1.42	1.40	1.37	1.35	1.32	1.30	1.28	1.26	1.23	51
52	1.67	1.64	1.61	1.58	1.55	1.53	1.50	1.47	1.45	1.42	1.40	1.37	1.35	1.33	1.30	1.28	52
53	1.73	1.70	1.67	1.64	1.61	1.58	1.55	1.53	1.50	1.47	1.45	1.42	1.40	1.37	1.35	1.33	53
54	1.79	1.76	1.73	1.70	1.67	1.64	1.61	1.58	1.56	1.53	1.50	1.48	1.45	1.43	1.40	1.38	54
55	1.86	1.83	1.80	1.76	1.73	1.70	1.67	1.64	1.61	1.59	1.56	1.53	1.51	1.48	1.45	1.43	55
56	1.93	1.90	1.86	1.83	1.80	1.77	1.74	1.71	1.68	1.65	1.62	1.59	1.56	1.54	1.51	1.48	56
57	2.01	1.97	1.94	1.90	1.87	1.84	1.80	1.77	1.74	1.71	1.68	1.65	1.62	1.59	1.57	1.54	57
58	2.09	2.05	2.01	1.98	1.94	1.91	1.87	1.84	1.81	1.78	1.75	1.72	1.69	1.66	1.63	1.60	58
59	2.17	2.13	2.09	2.06	2.02	1.98	1.95	1.91	1.88	1.85	1.82	1.78	1.75	1.72	1.69	1.66	59
60	2.26	2.22	2.18	2.14	2.10	2.07	2.03	1.99	1.96	1.92	1.89	1.86	1.83	1.79	1.76	1.73	60
LAT.	142½ 217½	142° 218	141½° 218½	141° 219	140½° 219½	140° 220	139½ 220½	139° 221	138½ 221½	138° 222	137½ 222½	137° 223	136½ 223½	136° 224	135½ 224½	135° 225	LAT.

Table 29 **B**	Lat. and Dec. SAME name, Sign —
2 hrs.	Lat. and Dec. CONTRARY names, Sign **+**

HOUR ANGLE or DIFF. LONG.

DEC.	30m	32m	34m	36m	38m	40m	42m	44m	46m	48m	50m	52m	54m	56m	58m	60m	DEC.
	37½°322½	38°322	38½°321½	39°321	39½°320½	40°320	40½°319½	41°319	41½°318½	42°318	42½°317½	43°317	43½°316½	44°316	44½°315½	45°315	
0°	.000	.000	.000	.000	.000	.000	.000	.000	.000	.000	.000	.000	.000	.000	.000	.000	0°
1	.029	.028	.028	.028	.027	.027	.027	.027	.026	.026	.026	.026	.025	.025	.025	.025	1
2	.057	.057	.056	.055	.055	.054	.054	.053	.053	.052	.052	.051	.051	.050	.050	.049	2
3	.086	.085	.084	.083	.082	.082	.081	.080	.079	.078	.078	.077	.076	.075	.075	.074	3
4	.115	.114	.112	.111	.110	.109	.108	.107	.106	.105	.104	.103	.102	.101	.100	.099	4
5	.144	.142	.141	.139	.138	.136	.135	.133	.132	.131	.129	.128	.127	.126	.125	.124	5
6	.173	.171	.169	.167	.165	.164	.162	.160	.159	.157	.156	.154	.153	.151	.150	.149	6
7	.202	.199	.197	.195	.193	.191	.189	.187	.185	.183	.182	.180	.178	.177	.175	.174	7
8	.231	.228	.226	.223	.221	.219	.216	.214	.212	.210	.208	.206	.204	.202	.201	.199	8
9	.260	.257	.254	.252	.249	.246	.244	.241	.239	.237	.234	.232	.230	.228	.226	.224	9
10	.290	.286	.283	.280	.277	.274	.272	.269	.266	.264	.261	.259	.256	.254	.252	.249	10
11	.319	.316	.312	.309	.306	.302	.299	.296	.293	.290	.288	.285	.282	.280	.277	.275	11
12	.349	.345	.341	.338	.334	.331	.327	.324	.321	.318	.315	.312	.309	.306	.303	.301	12
13	.379	.375	.371	.367	.363	.359	.355	.352	.348	.345	.342	.339	.335	.332	.329	.326	13
14	.410	.405	.401	.396	.392	.388	.384	.380	.376	.373	.369	.366	.362	.359	.356	.353	14
15	.440	.435	.430	.426	.421	.417	.413	.408	.404	.400	.397	.393	.389	.386	.382	.379	15
16	.471	.466	.461	.456	.451	.446	.442	.437	.433	.429	.424	.420	.417	.413	.409	.406	16
17	.502	.497	.491	.486	.481	.476	.471	.466	.461	.457	.453	.448	.444	.440	.436	.432	17
18	.534	.528	.522	.516	.511	.505	.500	.495	.490	.486	.481	.476	.472	.468	.464	.460	18
19	.566	.559	.553	.547	.541	.536	.530	.525	.520	.515	.510	.505	.500	.496	.491	.487	19
20	.598	.591	.585	.578	.572	.566	.560	.555	.549	.544	.539	.534	.529	.524	.519	.515	20
21	.631	.623	.617	.610	.603	.597	.591	.585	.579	.574	.568	.563	.558	.553	.548	.543	21
22	.664	.656	.649	.642	.635	.629	.622	.616	.610	.604	.598	.592	.587	.582	.576	.571	22
23	.697	.689	.682	.674	.667	.660	.654	.647	.641	.634	.628	.622	.617	.611	.606	.600	23
24	.731	.723	.715	.707	.700	.693	.686	.679	.672	.665	.659	.653	.647	.641	.635	.630	24
25	.766	.757	.749	.741	.733	.725	.718	.711	.704	.697	.690	.684	.677	.671	.665	.659	25
26	.801	.792	.783	.775	.767	.759	.751	.743	.736	.729	.722	.715	.709	.702	.696	.690	26
27	.837	.828	.818	.810	.801	.793	.785	.777	.769	.761	.754	.747	.740	.733	.727	.721	27
28	.873	.864	.854	.845	.836	.827	.819	.810	.802	.795	.787	.780	.772	.765	.759	.752	28
29	.911	.900	.890	.881	.871	.862	.854	.845	.837	.828	.820	.813	.805	.798	.791	.784	29
30	.948	.938	.927	.917	.908	.898	.889	.880	.871	.863	.855	.847	.839	.831	.824	.816	30
31	.987	.976	.965	.955	.945	.935	.925	.916	.907	.898	.889	.881	.873	.865	.857	.850	31
32	1.03	1.02	1.00	.993	.982	.972	.962	.952	.943	.934	.925	.916	.908	.900	.892	.884	32
33	1.07	1.06	1.04	1.03	1.02	1.01	1.00	.990	.980	.971	.961	.952	.943	.935	.927	.918	33
34	1.11	1.10	1.08	1.07	1.06	1.05	1.04	1.03	1.02	1.01	.998	.989	.980	.971	.962	.954	34
35	1.15	1.14	1.13	1.11	1.10	1.09	1.08	1.07	1.06	1.05	1.04	1.03	1.02	1.01	.999	.990	35
36	1.19	1.18	1.17	1.15	1.14	1.13	1.12	1.11	1.10	1.09	1.08	1.07	1.06	1.05	1.04	1.03	36
37	1.24	1.22	1.21	1.20	1.19	1.17	1.16	1.15	1.14	1.13	1.12	1.11	1.10	1.09	1.08	1.07	37
38	1.28	1.27	1.26	1.24	1.23	1.22	1.20	1.19	1.18	1.17	1.16	1.15	1.14	1.13	1.12	1.11	38
39	1.33	1.32	1.30	1.29	1.27	1.26	1.25	1.23	1.22	1.21	1.20	1.19	1.18	1.17	1.16	1.15	39
40	1.38	1.36	1.35	1.33	1.32	1.31	1.29	1.28	1.27	1.25	1.24	1.23	1.22	1.21	1.20	1.19	40
41	1.43	1.41	1.40	1.38	1.37	1.35	1.34	1.33	1.31	1.30	1.29	1.27	1.26	1.25	1.24	1.23	41
42	1.48	1.46	1.45	1.43	1.42	1.40	1.39	1.37	1.36	1.35	1.33	1.32	1.31	1.30	1.29	1.27	42
43	1.53	1.51	1.50	1.48	1.47	1.45	1.44	1.42	1.41	1.39	1.38	1.37	1.36	1.34	1.33	1.32	43
44	1.59	1.57	1.55	1.53	1.52	1.50	1.49	1.47	1.46	1.44	1.43	1.42	1.40	1.39	1.38	1.37	44
45	1.64	1.62	1.61	1.59	1.57	1.56	1.54	1.52	1.51	1.49	1.48	1.47	1.45	1.44	1.43	1.41	45
46	1.70	1.68	1.66	1.65	1.63	1.61	1.59	1.58	1.56	1.55	1.53	1.52	1.50	1.49	1.48	1.46	46
47	1.76	1.74	1.72	1.70	1.69	1.67	1.65	1.63	1.62	1.60	1.59	1.57	1.56	1.54	1.53	1.52	47
48	1.82	1.80	1.78	1.77	1.75	1.73	1.71	1.69	1.68	1.66	1.64	1.63	1.61	1.60	1.59	1.57	48
49	1.89	1.87	1.85	1.83	1.81	1.79	1.77	1.75	1.74	1.72	1.70	1.69	1.67	1.66	1.64	1.63	49
50	1.96	1.94	1.91	1.89	1.87	1.85	1.84	1.82	1.80	1.78	1.76	1.75	1.73	1.72	1.70	1.69	50
51	2.03	2.01	1.98	1.96	1.94	1.92	1.90	1.88	1.86	1.85	1.83	1.81	1.79	1.78	1.76	1.75	51
52	2.10	2.08	2.06	2.03	2.01	1.99	1.97	1.95	1.93	1.91	1.90	1.88	1.86	1.84	1.83	1.81	52
53	2.18	2.16	2.13	2.11	2.09	2.06	2.04	2.02	2.00	1.98	1.96	1.95	1.93	1.91	1.89	1.88	53
54	2.26	2.24	2.21	2.19	2.16	2.14	2.12	2.10	2.08	2.06	2.04	2.02	2.00	1.98	1.96	1.95	54
55	2.35	2.32	2.29	2.27	2.25	2.22	2.20	2.18	2.16	2.13	2.11	2.09	2.08	2.06	2.04	2.02	55
56	2.44	2.41	2.38	2.36	2.33	2.31	2.28	2.26	2.24	2.22	2.19	2.17	2.15	2.13	2.12	2.10	56
57	2.53	2.50	2.47	2.45	2.42	2.40	2.37	2.35	2.32	2.30	2.28	2.26	2.24	2.22	2.20	2.18	57
58	2.63	2.60	2.57	2.54	2.52	2.49	2.46	2.44	2.42	2.39	2.37	2.35	2.33	2.30	2.28	2.26	58
59	2.73	2.70	2.67	2.65	2.62	2.59	2.56	2.54	2.51	2.49	2.46	2.44	2.42	2.40	2.37	2.35	59
60	2.85	2.81	2.78	2.75	2.72	2.69	2.67	2.64	2.61	2.59	2.56	2.54	2.52	2.49	2.47	2.45	60
61	2.96	2.93	2.90	2.87	2.84	2.81	2.78	2.75	2.72	2.70	2.67	2.65	2.62	2.60	2.57	2.55	61
62	3.09	3.05	3.02	2.99	2.96	2.93	2.90	2.87	2.84	2.81	2.78	2.76	2.73	2.71	2.68	2.66	62
63	3.22	3.19	3.15	3.12	3.09	3.05	3.02	2.99	2.96	2.93	2.91	2.88	2.85	2.83	2.80	2.78	63
DEC.	142½217½	142°218	141½°218½	141°219	140½°219½	140°220	139½220½	139°221	138½°221½	138°222	137½°222½	137°223	136½°223½	136°224	135½°224½	135°225	DEC.

Table 29

A

3 hrs.

If entered with H.A. at **top**, Sign **+**

„ „ „ „ **foot**, „ **—**

HOUR ANGLE or DIFF. LONG.

LAT.	00m 45° 315	02m 45½° 314½	04m 46° 314	06m 46½° 313½	08m 47° 313	10m 47½° 312½	12m 48° 312	14m 48½° 311½	16m 49° 311	18m 49½° 310½	20m 50° 310	22m 50½° 309½	24m 51° 309	26m 51½° 308½	28m 52° 308	30m 52½° 307½	LAT.
0	.000	.000	.000	.000	.000	.000	.000	.000	.000	.000	.000	.000	.000	.000	.000	.000	0
1	.017	.017	.017	.017	.016	.016	.016	.015	.015	.015	.015	.014	.014	.014	.014	.013	1
2	.035	.034	.034	.033	.033	.032	.031	.031	.030	.030	.029	.029	.028	.028	.027	.026	2
3	.052	.052	.051	.050	.049	.048	.047	.046	.046	.045	.044	.043	.042	.042	.041	.040	3
4	.070	.069	.068	.066	.065	.064	.063	.062	.061	.060	.059	.058	.057	.056	.055	.054	4
5	.087	.086	.084	.083	.082	.080	.079	.077	.076	.075	.073	.072	.071	.070	.068	.067	5
6	.105	.103	.101	.100	.098	.096	.095	.093	.091	.090	.088	.087	.085	.084	.082	.081	6
7	.123	.121	.119	.117	.114	.113	.111	.109	.107	.105	.103	.101	.099	.098	.096	.094	7
8	.141	.138	.136	.133	.131	.129	.127	.124	.122	.120	.118	.116	.114	.112	.110	.108	8
9	.158	.156	.153	.150	.148	.145	.143	.140	.138	.135	.133	.131	.128	.126	.124	.122	9
10	.176	.173	.170	.167	.164	.162	.159	.156	.153	.151	.148	.145	.143	.140	.138	.135	10
11	.194	.191	.188	.184	.181	.178	.175	.172	.169	.166	.163	.160	.157	.155	.152	.149	11
12	.213	.209	.205	.202	.198	.195	.191	.188	.185	.182	.178	.175	.172	.169	.166	.163	12
13	.231	.227	.223	.219	.215	.212	.208	.204	.201	.197	.194	.190	.187	.184	.180	.177	13
14	.249	.245	.241	.237	.233	.228	.224	.221	.217	.213	.209	.206	.202	.198	.195	.191	14
15	.268	.263	.259	.254	.250	.246	.241	.237	.233	.229	.225	.221	.217	.213	.209	.206	15
16	.287	.282	.277	.272	.267	.263	.258	.254	.249	.245	.241	.236	.232	.228	.224	.220	16
17	.306	.300	.295	.290	.285	.280	.275	.270	.266	.261	.257	.252	.248	.243	.239	.235	17
18	.325	.319	.314	.308	.303	.298	.293	.287	.282	.278	.273	.268	.263	.258	.254	.249	18
19	.344	.338	.333	.327	.321	.316	.310	.305	.299	.294	.289	.284	.279	.274	.269	.264	19
20	.364	.358	.351	.345	.339	.334	.328	.322	.316	.311	.305	.300	.295	.290	.284	.279	20
21	.384	.377	.371	.364	.358	.352	.346	.340	.334	.328	.322	.316	.311	.305	.300	.295	21
22	.404	.397	.390	.383	.377	.370	.364	.357	.351	.345	.339	.333	.327	.321	.316	.310	22
23	.424	.417	.410	.403	.396	.389	.382	.376	.369	.363	.356	.350	.344	.338	.332	.326	23
24	.445	.438	.430	.423	.415	.408	.401	.394	.387	.380	.374	.367	.361	.354	.348	.342	24
25	.466	.458	.450	.443	.435	.427	.420	.413	.405	.398	.391	.384	.378	.371	.364	.358	25
26	.488	.479	.471	.463	.455	.447	.439	.432	.424	.417	.409	.402	.395	.388	.381	.374	26
27	.510	.501	.492	.484	.475	.467	.459	.451	.443	.435	.428	.420	.413	.405	.398	.391	27
28	.532	.523	.513	.505	.496	.487	.479	.470	.462	.454	.446	.438	.431	.423	.415	.408	28
29	.554	.545	.535	.526	.517	.508	.499	.490	.482	.473	.465	.457	.449	.441	.433	.425	29
30	.577	.567	.558	.548	.538	.529	.520	.511	.502	.493	.484	.476	.468	.459	.451	.443	30
31	.601	.590	.580	.570	.560	.551	.541	.532	.522	.513	.504	.495	.487	.478	.469	.461	31
32	.625	.614	.603	.593	.583	.573	.563	.553	.543	.534	.524	.515	.506	.497	.488	.479	32
33	.649	.638	.627	.616	.606	.595	.585	.575	.565	.555	.545	.535	.526	.517	.507	.498	33
34	.675	.663	.651	.640	.629	.618	.607	.597	.586	.576	.566	.556	.546	.537	.527	.518	34
35	.700	.688	.676	.664	.653	.642	.630	.619	.609	.598	.588	.577	.567	.557	.547	.537	35
36	.727	.714	.702	.689	.678	.666	.654	.643	.632	.621	.610	.599	.588	.578	.568	.557	36
37	.754	.741	.728	.715	.703	.691	.679	.667	.655	.644	.632	.621	.610	.599	.589	.578	37
38	.781	.768	.754	.741	.729	.716	.703	.691	.679	.667	.656	.644	.633	.621	.610	.600	38
39	.810	.796	.782	.768	.755	.742	.729	.716	.704	.692	.679	.668	.656	.644	.633	.621	39
40	.839	.825	.810	.796	.782	.769	.756	.742	.729	.717	.704	.692	.679	.667	.656	.644	40
41	.869	.854	.839	.825	.811	.797	.783	.769	.756	.742	.729	.717	.704	.691	.679	.667	41
42	.900	.885	.870	.854	.840	.825	.811	.797	.783	.769	.756	.742	.729	.716	.703	.691	42
43	.933	.916	.901	.885	.870	.854	.840	.825	.811	.796	.782	.769	.755	.742	.729	.716	43
44	.966	.949	.933	.916	.901	.885	.870	.854	.839	.825	.810	.796	.782	.768	.754	.741	44
45	1.00	.983	.966	.949	.933	.916	.900	.885	.869	.854	.839	.824	.810	.795	.781	.767	45
46	1.04	1.02	1.00	.983	.966	.949	.932	.916	.900	.884	.869	.854	.839	.824	.809	.795	46
47	1.07	1.05	1.04	1.02	1.00	.983	.966	.949	.932	.916	.900	.884	.868	.853	.838	.823	47
48	1.11	1.09	1.07	1.05	1.04	1.02	1.00	.983	.965	.949	.932	.916	.899	.883	.868	.852	48
49	1.15	1.13	1.11	1.09	1.07	1.05	1.04	1.02	1.00	.983	.965	.948	.932	.915	.899	.883	49
50	1.19	1.17	1.15	1.13	1.11	1.09	1.07	1.05	1.04	1.02	1.00	.982	.965	.948	.931	.914	50
51	1.23	1.21	1.19	1.17	1.15	1.13	1.11	1.09	1.07	1.06	1.04	1.02	1.00	.982	.965	.948	51
52	1.28	1.26	1.24	1.22	1.19	1.17	1.15	1.13	1.11	1.09	1.07	1.06	1.04	1.02	1.00	.982	52
53	1.33	1.30	1.28	1.26	1.24	1.22	1.19	1.17	1.15	1.13	1.11	1.09	1.07	1.06	1.04	1.02	53
54	1.38	1.35	1.33	1.31	1.28	1.26	1.24	1.22	1.20	1.18	1.15	1.14	1.11	1.10	1.08	1.06	54
55	1.43	1.40	1.38	1.36	1.33	1.31	1.29	1.26	1.24	1.22	1.20	1.18	1.16	1.14	1.12	1.10	55
56	1.48	1.46	1.43	1.41	1.38	1.36	1.33	1.31	1.29	1.27	1.24	1.22	1.20	1.18	1.16	1.14	56
57	1.54	1.51	1.49	1.46	1.44	1.41	1.39	1.36	1.34	1.32	1.29	1.27	1.25	1.23	1.20	1.18	57
58	1.60	1.57	1.55	1.52	1.49	1.47	1.44	1.42	1.39	1.37	1.34	1.32	1.30	1.27	1.25	1.23	58
59	1.66	1.64	1.61	1.58	1.55	1.53	1.50	1.47	1.45	1.42	1.40	1.37	1.35	1.32	1.30	1.28	59
60	1.73	1.70	1.67	1.64	1.62	1.59	1.56	1.53	1.51	1.48	1.45	1.43	1.40	1.38	1.35	1.33	60

LAT.	135° 225	134½ 225½	134° 226	133½ 226½	133° 227	132½ 227½	132° 228	131½ 228½	131° 229	130½ 229½	130° 230	129½ 230½	129° 231	128½ 231½	128° 232	127½ 232½	LAT.

Table 29 — B — 3 hrs.

Lat. and Dec. SAME name, Sign —
Lat. and Dec. CONTRARY names, Sign +

HOUR ANGLE or DIFF. LONG.

DEC.	00m	02m	04m	06m	08m	10m	12m	14m	16m	18m	20m	22m	24m	26m	28m	30m	DEC.
	45°	45½°	46°	46½°	47°	47½°	48°	48½°	49°	49½°	50°	50½°	51°	51½°	52°	52½°	
	315	314½	314	313½	313	312½	312	311½	311	310½	310	309½	309	308½	308	307½	
0°	.000	.000	.000	.000	.000	.000	.000	.000	.000	.000	.000	.000	.000	.000	.000	.000	0°
1	.025	.024	.024	.024	.024	.024	.023	.023	.023	.023	.023	.023	.023	.022	.022	.022	1
2	.049	.049	.049	.048	.048	.047	.047	.047	.046	.046	.046	.045	.045	.045	.044	.044	2
3	.074	.073	.073	.072	.072	.071	.071	.070	.069	.069	.068	.068	.067	.067	.067	.066	3
4	.099	.098	.097	.096	.096	.095	.094	.093	.093	.092	.091	.091	.090	.089	.089	.088	4
5	.124	.123	.122	.121	.120	.119	.118	.117	.116	.115	.114	.113	.113	.112	.111	.110	5
6	.149	.147	.146	.145	.144	.143	.141	.140	.139	.138	.137	.136	.135	.134	.133	.132	6
7	.174	.172	.171	.169	.168	.167	.165	.164	.163	.161	.160	.159	.158	.157	.156	.155	7
8	.199	.197	.195	.194	.192	.191	.189	.188	.186	.185	.183	.182	.181	.180	.178	.177	8
9	.224	.222	.220	.218	.217	.215	.213	.211	.210	.208	.207	.205	.204	.202	.201	.200	9
10	.249	.247	.245	.243	.241	.239	.237	.235	.234	.232	.230	.229	.227	.225	.224	.222	10
11	.275	.273	.270	.268	.266	.264	.262	.260	.258	.256	.254	.252	.250	.248	.247	.245	11
12	.301	.298	.295	.293	.291	.288	.286	.284	.282	.280	.277	.275	.274	.272	.270	.268	12
13	.326	.324	.321	.318	.316	.313	.311	.308	.306	.304	.301	.299	.297	.295	.293	.291	13
14	.353	.350	.347	.344	.341	.338	.336	.333	.330	.328	.325	.323	.321	.319	.316	.314	14
15	.379	.376	.372	.369	.366	.363	.361	.358	.355	.352	.350	.347	.345	.342	.340	.338	15
16	.406	.402	.399	.395	.392	.389	.386	.383	.380	.377	.374	.372	.369	.366	.364	.361	16
17	.432	.429	.425	.421	.418	.415	.411	.408	.405	.402	.399	.396	.393	.391	.388	.385	17
18	.460	.456	.452	.448	.444	.441	.437	.434	.431	.427	.424	.421	.418	.415	.412	.410	18
19	.487	.483	.479	.475	.471	.467	.463	.460	.456	.453	.449	.446	.443	.440	.437	.434	19
20	.515	.510	.506	.502	.498	.494	.490	.486	.482	.479	.475	.472	.468	.465	.462	.459	20
21	.543	.538	.534	.529	.525	.521	.517	.513	.509	.505	.501	.497	.494	.490	.487	.484	21
22	.571	.566	.562	.557	.552	.548	.544	.539	.535	.531	.527	.524	.520	.516	.513	.509	22
23	.600	.595	.590	.585	.580	.576	.571	.567	.562	.558	.554	.550	.546	.542	.539	.535	23
24	.630	.624	.619	.614	.609	.604	.599	.594	.590	.586	.581	.577	.573	.569	.565	.561	24
25	.659	.654	.648	.643	.638	.632	.627	.623	.618	.613	.609	.604	.600	.596	.592	.588	25
26	.690	.684	.678	.672	.667	.662	.656	.651	.646	.641	.637	.632	.628	.623	.619	.615	26
27	.721	.714	.708	.702	.697	.691	.686	.680	.675	.670	.665	.660	.656	.651	.647	.642	27
28	.752	.745	.739	.733	.727	.721	.715	.710	.705	.699	.694	.689	.684	.679	.675	.670	28
29	.784	.777	.771	.764	.758	.752	.746	.740	.734	.729	.724	.718	.713	.708	.703	.699	29
30	.816	.809	.803	.796	.789	.783	.777	.771	.765	.759	.754	.748	.743	.738	.733	.728	30
31	.850	.842	.835	.828	.822	.815	.809	.802	.796	.790	.784	.779	.773	.768	.763	.757	31
32	.884	.876	.869	.861	.854	.848	.841	.834	.828	.822	.816	.810	.804	.798	.793	.788	32
33	.918	.910	.903	.895	.888	.881	.874	.867	.860	.854	.848	.842	.836	.830	.824	.819	33
34	.954	.946	.938	.930	.922	.915	.908	.901	.894	.887	.881	.874	.868	.862	.856	.850	34
35	.990	.982	.973	.965	.957	.950	.942	.935	.928	.921	.914	.907	.901	.895	.889	.883	35
36	1.03	1.02	1.01	1.00	.993	.985	.978	.970	.963	.955	.948	.942	.935	.928	.922	.916	36
37	1.07	1.06	1.05	1.04	1.03	1.02	1.01	1.01	.998	.991	.984	.977	.970	.963	.956	.950	37
38	1.11	1.10	1.09	1.08	1.07	1.06	1.05	1.04	1.04	1.03	1.02	1.01	1.01	.998	.991	.985	38
39	1.15	1.14	1.13	1.12	1.11	1.10	1.09	1.08	1.07	1.07	1.06	1.05	1.04	1.04	1.03	1.02	39
40	1.19	1.18	1.17	1.16	1.15	1.14	1.13	1.12	1.11	1.10	1.10	1.09	1.08	1.07	1.06	1.06	40
41	1.23	1.22	1.21	1.20	1.19	1.18	1.17	1.16	1.15	1.14	1.13	1.13	1.12	1.11	1.10	1.10	41
42	1.27	1.26	1.25	1.24	1.23	1.22	1.21	1.20	1.19	1.18	1.18	1.17	1.16	1.15	1.14	1.14	42
43	1.32	1.31	1.30	1.29	1.28	1.27	1.26	1.25	1.24	1.23	1.22	1.21	1.20	1.19	1.18	1.18	43
44	1.37	1.35	1.34	1.33	1.32	1.31	1.30	1.29	1.28	1.27	1.26	1.25	1.24	1.23	1.23	1.22	44
45	1.41	1.40	1.39	1.38	1.37	1.36	1.35	1.34	1.33	1.32	1.31	1.30	1.29	1.28	1.27	1.26	45
46	1.46	1.45	1.44	1.43	1.42	1.41	1.39	1.38	1.37	1.36	1.35	1.34	1.33	1.32	1.31	1.31	46
47	1.52	1.50	1.49	1.48	1.47	1.45	1.44	1.43	1.42	1.41	1.40	1.39	1.38	1.37	1.36	1.35	47
48	1.57	1.56	1.54	1.53	1.52	1.51	1.49	1.48	1.47	1.46	1.45	1.44	1.43	1.42	1.41	1.40	48
49	1.63	1.61	1.60	1.59	1.57	1.56	1.55	1.54	1.52	1.51	1.50	1.49	1.48	1.47	1.46	1.45	49
50	1.69	1.67	1.66	1.64	1.63	1.62	1.60	1.59	1.58	1.57	1.56	1.54	1.53	1.52	1.51	1.50	50
51	1.75	1.73	1.72	1.70	1.69	1.68	1.66	1.65	1.64	1.62	1.61	1.60	1.59	1.58	1.57	1.56	51
52	1.81	1.80	1.78	1.77	1.75	1.74	1.72	1.71	1.70	1.68	1.67	1.66	1.65	1.64	1.62	1.61	52
53	1.88	1.86	1.84	1.83	1.81	1.80	1.79	1.77	1.76	1.75	1.73	1.72	1.71	1.70	1.68	1.67	53
54	1.95	1.93	1.91	1.90	1.88	1.87	1.85	1.84	1.82	1.81	1.80	1.78	1.77	1.76	1.75	1.74	54
55	2.02	2.00	1.99	1.97	1.95	1.94	1.92	1.91	1.89	1.88	1.86	1.85	1.84	1.83	1.81	1.80	55
56	2.10	2.08	2.06	2.04	2.03	2.01	2.00	1.98	1.96	1.95	1.94	1.92	1.91	1.89	1.88	1.87	56
57	2.18	2.16	2.14	2.12	2.11	2.09	2.07	2.06	2.04	2.03	2.01	2.00	1.98	1.97	1.95	1.94	57
58	2.26	2.24	2.22	2.21	2.19	2.17	2.15	2.14	2.12	2.11	2.09	2.07	2.06	2.05	2.03	2.02	58
59	2.35	2.33	2.31	2.29	2.28	2.26	2.24	2.22	2.21	2.19	2.17	2.16	2.14	2.13	2.11	2.10	59
60	2.45	2.43	2.41	2.39	2.37	2.35	2.33	2.31	2.29	2.28	2.26	2.25	2.23	2.21	2.20	2.18	60
61	2.55	2.53	2.51	2.49	2.47	2.45	2.43	2.41	2.39	2.37	2.36	2.34	2.32	2.31	2.29	2.27	61
62	2.66	2.64	2.62	2.59	2.57	2.55	2.53	2.51	2.49	2.47	2.46	2.44	2.42	2.40	2.39	2.37	62
63	2.78	2.75	2.73	2.71	2.68	2.66	2.64	2.62	2.60	2.58	2.56	2.54	2.53	2.51	2.49	2.47	63
DEC.	135°	134½°	134°	133½°	133°	132½°	132°	131½°	131°	130½°	130°	129½°	129°	128½°	128°	127½°	DEC.
	225	225½	226	226½	227	227½	228	228½	229	229½	230	230½	231	231½	232	232½	

Table 29

A

3 hrs.

If entered with H.A. at **top**, Sign **+**

„ „ „ „ **foot**, „ **−**

HOUR ANGLE or DIFF. LONG.

LAT.	30m	32m	34m	36m	38m	40m	42m	44m	46m	48m	50m	52m	54m	56m	58m	60m	LAT.
	52½° 307½	53° 307	53½° 306½	54° 306	54½° 305½	55° 305	55½° 304½	56° 304	56½° 303½	57° 303	57½° 302½	58° 302	58½° 301½	59° 301	59½° 300½	60° 300	
0°	.000	.000	.000	.000	.000	.000	.000	.000	.000	.000	.000	.000	.000	.000	.000	.000	0°
1	.013	.013	.013	.013	.012	.012	.012	.012	.012	.011	.011	.011	.011	.010	.010	.010	1
2	.026	.026	.026	.025	.025	.025	.024	.024	.023	.023	.022	.022	.021	.021	.021	.020	2
3	.040	.039	.039	.038	.037	.037	.036	.035	.035	.034	.033	.033	.032	.031	.031	.030	3
4	.054	.053	.052	.051	.050	.049	.048	.047	.046	.045	.045	.044	.043	.042	.041	.040	4
5	.067	.066	.065	.064	.062	.061	.060	.059	.058	.057	.056	.055	.054	.053	.052	.051	5
6	.081	.079	.078	.076	.075	.074	.072	.071	.070	.068	.067	.066	.064	.063	.062	.061	6
7	.094	.093	.091	.089	.088	.086	.084	.083	.081	.080	.078	.077	.075	.074	.072	.071	7
8	.108	.106	.104	.102	.100	.098	.097	.095	.093	.091	.090	.088	.086	.084	.083	.081	8
9	.122	.119	.117	.115	.113	.111	.109	.107	.105	.103	.101	.099	.097	.095	.093	.091	9
10	.135	.133	.130	.128	.126	.123	.121	.119	.117	.115	.112	.110	.108	.106	.104	.102	10
11	.149	.146	.144	.141	.139	.136	.134	.131	.129	.126	.124	.121	.119	.117	.114	.112	11
12	.163	.160	.157	.154	.152	.149	.146	.143	.141	.138	.135	.133	.130	.128	.125	.123	12
13	.177	.174	.171	.168	.165	.162	.159	.156	.153	.150	.147	.144	.141	.139	.136	.133	13
14	.191	.188	.184	.181	.178	.175	.171	.168	.165	.162	.159	.156	.153	.150	.147	.144	14
15	.206	.202	.198	.195	.191	.188	.184	.181	.177	.174	.171	.167	.164	.161	.158	.155	15
16	.220	.216	.212	.208	.205	.201	.197	.193	.190	.186	.183	.179	.176	.172	.169	.166	16
17	.235	.230	.226	.222	.218	.214	.210	.206	.202	.199	.195	.191	.187	.184	.180	.177	17
18	.249	.245	.240	.236	.232	.228	.223	.219	.215	.211	.207	.203	.199	.195	.191	.188	18
19	.264	.259	.255	.250	.246	.241	.237	.232	.228	.224	.219	.215	.211	.207	.203	.199	19
20	.279	.274	.269	.264	.260	.255	.250	.246	.241	.236	.232	.227	.223	.219	.214	.210	20
21	.295	.289	.284	.279	.274	.269	.264	.259	.254	.249	.245	.240	.235	.231	.226	.222	21
22	.310	.304	.299	.294	.288	.283	.278	.273	.267	.262	.257	.252	.248	.243	.238	.233	22
23	.326	.320	.314	.308	.303	.297	.292	.286	.281	.276	.270	.265	.260	.255	.250	.245	23
24	.342	.336	.329	.323	.318	.312	.306	.300	.295	.289	.284	.278	.273	.268	.262	.257	24
25	.358	.351	.345	.339	.333	.327	.320	.315	.309	.303	.297	.291	.286	.280	.275	.269	25
26	.374	.368	.361	.354	.348	.342	.335	.329	.323	.317	.311	.305	.299	.293	.287	.282	26
27	.391	.384	.377	.370	.363	.357	.350	.344	.337	.331	.325	.318	.312	.306	.300	.294	27
28	.408	.401	.393	.386	.379	.372	.365	.359	.352	.345	.339	.332	.326	.319	.313	.307	28
29	.425	.418	.410	.403	.395	.388	.381	.374	.367	.360	.353	.346	.340	.333	.327	.320	29
30	.443	.435	.427	.419	.412	.404	.397	.389	.382	.375	.368	.361	.354	.347	.340	.333	30
31	.461	.453	.445	.437	.429	.421	.413	.405	.398	.390	.383	.375	.368	.361	.354	.347	31
32	.479	.471	.462	.454	.446	.438	.429	.421	.414	.406	.398	.390	.383	.375	.368	.361	32
33	.498	.489	.481	.472	.463	.455	.446	.438	.430	.422	.414	.406	.398	.390	.383	.375	33
34	.518	.508	.499	.490	.481	.472	.464	.455	.446	.438	.430	.421	.413	.405	.397	.389	34
35	.537	.528	.518	.509	.499	.490	.481	.472	.463	.455	.446	.438	.429	.421	.412	.404	35
36	.557	.547	.538	.528	.518	.509	.499	.490	.481	.472	.463	.454	.445	.437	.428	.419	36
37	.578	.568	.558	.547	.538	.528	.518	.508	.499	.489	.480	.471	.462	.453	.444	.435	37
38	.600	.589	.578	.568	.557	.547	.537	.527	.517	.507	.498	.488	.479	.469	.460	.451	38
39	.621	.610	.599	.588	.578	.567	.557	.546	.536	.526	.516	.506	.496	.487	.477	.468	39
40	.644	.632	.621	.610	.599	.588	.577	.566	.555	.545	.535	.524	.514	.504	.494	.484	40
41	.667	.655	.643	.632	.620	.609	.597	.586	.575	.565	.554	.543	.533	.522	.512	.502	41
42	.691	.679	.666	.654	.642	.630	.619	.607	.596	.585	.574	.563	.552	.541	.530	.520	42
43	.716	.703	.690	.678	.665	.653	.641	.629	.617	.606	.594	.583	.571	.560	.549	.538	43
44	.741	.728	.715	.702	.689	.676	.664	.651	.639	.627	.615	.603	.592	.580	.569	.558	44
45	.767	.754	.740	.727	.713	.700	.687	.675	.662	.649	.637	.625	.613	.601	.589	.577	45
46	.795	.780	.766	.752	.739	.725	.712	.698	.685	.672	.660	.647	.635	.622	.610	.598	46
47	.823	.808	.794	.779	.765	.751	.737	.723	.710	.696	.683	.670	.657	.644	.632	.619	47
48	.852	.837	.822	.807	.792	.778	.763	.749	.735	.721	.708	.694	.681	.667	.654	.641	48
49	.883	.867	.851	.836	.821	.805	.791	.776	.761	.747	.733	.719	.705	.691	.678	.664	49
50	.914	.898	.882	.866	.850	.834	.819	.804	.789	.774	.759	.745	.730	.716	.702	.688	50
51	.948	.931	.914	.897	.881	.865	.849	.833	.817	.802	.787	.772	.757	.742	.727	.713	51
52	.982	.965	.947	.930	.913	.896	.880	.863	.847	.831	.815	.800	.784	.769	.754	.739	52
53	1.02	1.00	.982	.964	.947	.929	.912	.895	.878	.862	.845	.829	.813	.797	.782	.766	53
54	1.06	1.04	1.02	1.00	.982	.964	.946	.928	.911	.894	.877	.860	.843	.827	.811	.795	54
55	1.10	1.08	1.06	1.04	1.02	1.00	.982	.963	.945	.927	.910	.892	.875	.858	.841	.825	55
56	1.14	1.12	1.10	1.08	1.06	1.04	1.02	1.00	.981	.963	.944	.926	.909	.891	.873	.856	56
57	1.18	1.16	1.14	1.12	1.10	1.08	1.06	1.04	1.02	1.00	.981	.962	.944	.925	.907	.889	57
58	1.23	1.21	1.18	1.16	1.14	1.12	1.10	1.08	1.06	1.04	1.02	1.00	.981	.962	.943	.924	58
59	1.28	1.25	1.23	1.21	1.19	1.17	1.14	1.12	1.10	1.08	1.06	1.04	1.02	1.00	.980	.961	59
60	1.33	1.31	1.28	1.26	1.24	1.21	1.19	1.17	1.15	1.12	1.10	1.08	1.06	1.04	1.02	1.00	60
LAT.	127½° 232½	127° 233	126½° 233½	126° 234	125½° 234½	125° 235	124½° 235½	124° 236	123½° 236½	123° 237	122½° 237½	122° 238	121½° 238½	121° 239	120½° 239½	120° 240	LAT.

Table 29 — B — 3 hrs.

Lat. and Dec. SAME name, Sign —
Lat. and Dec. CONTRARY names, Sign +

HOUR ANGLE or DIFF. LONG.

DEC.	30m	32m	34m	36m	38m	40m	42m	44m	46m	48m	50m	52m	54m	56m	58m	60m	DEC.
	52½° 307½	53° 307	53½° 306½	54° 306	54½° 305½	55° 305	55½° 304½	56° 304	56½° 303½	57° 303	57½° 302½	58° 302	58½° 301½	59° 301	59½° 300½	60° 300	
0°	.000	.000	.000	.000	.000	.000	.000	.000	.000	.000	.000	.000	.000	.000	.000	.000	0°
1	.022	.022	.022	.022	.021	.021	.021	.021	.021	.021	.021	.021	.020	.020	.020	.020	1
2	.044	.044	.043	.043	.043	.043	.042	.042	.042	.042	.041	.041	.041	.041	.041	.040	2
3	.066	.066	.065	.065	.064	.064	.064	.063	.063	.062	.062	.062	.061	.061	.061	.061	3
4	.088	.088	.087	.086	.086	.085	.085	.084	.084	.083	.083	.083	.082	.082	.081	.081	4
5	.110	.110	.109	.108	.107	.107	.106	.106	.105	.104	.104	.103	.103	.102	.102	.101	5
6	.132	.132	.131	.130	.129	.128	.128	.127	.126	.125	.125	.124	.123	.123	.122	.121	6
7	.155	.154	.153	.152	.151	.150	.149	.148	.147	.146	.146	.145	.144	.143	.143	.142	7
8	.177	.176	.175	.174	.173	.172	.171	.170	.169	.168	.167	.166	.165	.164	.163	.162	8
9	.200	.198	.197	.196	.195	.193	.192	.191	.190	.189	.188	.187	.186	.185	.184	.183	9
10	.222	.221	.219	.218	.217	.215	.214	.213	.211	.210	.209	.208	.207	.206	.205	.204	10
11	.245	.243	.242	.240	.239	.237	.236	.234	.233	.232	.230	.229	.228	.227	.226	.224	11
12	.268	.266	.264	.263	.261	.259	.258	.256	.255	.253	.252	.251	.249	.248	.247	.245	12
13	.291	.289	.287	.285	.284	.282	.280	.278	.277	.275	.274	.272	.271	.269	.268	.267	13
14	.314	.312	.310	.308	.306	.304	.303	.301	.299	.297	.296	.294	.292	.291	.289	.288	14
15	.338	.336	.333	.331	.329	.327	.325	.323	.321	.319	.318	.316	.314	.313	.311	.309	15
16	.361	.359	.357	.354	.352	.350	.348	.346	.344	.342	.340	.338	.336	.335	.333	.331	16
17	.385	.383	.380	.378	.376	.373	.371	.369	.367	.365	.363	.361	.359	.357	.355	.353	17
18	.410	.407	.404	.402	.399	.397	.394	.392	.390	.387	.385	.383	.381	.379	.377	.375	18
19	.434	.431	.428	.426	.423	.420	.418	.415	.413	.411	.408	.406	.404	.402	.400	.398	19
20	.459	.456	.453	.450	.447	.444	.442	.439	.436	.434	.432	.429	.427	.425	.422	.420	20
21	.484	.481	.478	.474	.472	.469	.466	.463	.460	.458	.455	.453	.450	.448	.446	.443	21
22	.509	.506	.503	.499	.496	.493	.490	.487	.485	.482	.479	.476	.474	.471	.469	.467	22
23	.535	.532	.528	.525	.521	.518	.515	.512	.509	.506	.503	.501	.498	.495	.493	.490	23
24	.561	.557	.554	.550	.547	.544	.540	.537	.534	.531	.528	.525	.522	.519	.517	.514	24
25	.588	.584	.580	.576	.573	.569	.566	.562	.559	.556	.553	.550	.547	.544	.541	.538	25
26	.615	.611	.607	.603	.599	.595	.592	.588	.585	.582	.578	.575	.572	.569	.566	.563	26
27	.642	.638	.634	.630	.626	.622	.618	.615	.611	.608	.604	.601	.598	.594	.591	.588	27
28	.670	.666	.661	.657	.653	.649	.645	.641	.638	.634	.630	.627	.624	.620	.617	.614	28
29	.699	.694	.690	.685	.681	.677	.673	.669	.665	.661	.657	.654	.650	.647	.643	.640	29
30	.728	.723	.718	.714	.709	.705	.701	.696	.692	.688	.685	.681	.677	.674	.670	.667	30
31	.757	.752	.747	.743	.738	.734	.729	.725	.721	.716	.712	.709	.705	.701	.697	.694	31
32	.788	.782	.777	.772	.768	.763	.758	.754	.749	.745	.741	.737	.733	.729	.725	.722	32
33	.819	.813	.808	.803	.798	.793	.788	.783	.779	.774	.770	.766	.762	.758	.754	.750	33
34	.850	.845	.839	.834	.829	.823	.818	.814	.809	.804	.800	.795	.791	.787	.783	.779	34
35	.883	.877	.871	.866	.860	.855	.850	.845	.840	.835	.830	.826	.821	.817	.813	.809	35
36	.916	.910	.904	.898	.892	.887	.882	.876	.871	.866	.861	.857	.852	.848	.843	.839	36
37	.950	.944	.937	.931	.926	.920	.914	.909	.904	.899	.893	.889	.884	.879	.875	.870	37
38	.985	.978	.972	.966	.960	.954	.948	.942	.937	.932	.926	.921	.916	.911	.907	.902	38
39	1.02	1.01	1.01	1.00	.995	.989	.983	.977	.971	.966	.960	.955	.950	.945	.940	.935	39
40	1.06	1.05	1.04	1.04	1.03	1.02	1.02	1.01	1.01	1.00	.995	.989	.984	.979	.974	.969	40
41	1.10	1.09	1.08	1.07	1.07	1.06	1.06	1.05	1.04	1.04	1.03	1.03	1.02	1.01	1.01	1.00	41
42	1.14	1.13	1.12	1.11	1.11	1.10	1.09	1.09	1.08	1.07	1.07	1.06	1.06	1.05	1.05	1.04	42
43	1.18	1.17	1.16	1.15	1.15	1.14	1.13	1.12	1.12	1.11	1.11	1.10	1.09	1.09	1.08	1.08	43
44	1.22	1.21	1.20	1.19	1.19	1.18	1.17	1.16	1.16	1.15	1.15	1.14	1.13	1.13	1.12	1.12	44
45	1.26	1.25	1.24	1.24	1.23	1.22	1.21	1.21	1.20	1.19	1.19	1.18	1.17	1.17	1.16	1.15	45
46	1.31	1.30	1.29	1.28	1.27	1.26	1.26	1.25	1.24	1.23	1.23	1.22	1.21	1.21	1.20	1.20	46
47	1.35	1.34	1.33	1.33	1.32	1.31	1.30	1.29	1.29	1.28	1.27	1.26	1.26	1.25	1.25	1.24	47
48	1.40	1.39	1.38	1.37	1.36	1.36	1.35	1.34	1.33	1.32	1.32	1.31	1.30	1.30	1.29	1.28	48
49	1.45	1.44	1.43	1.42	1.41	1.40	1.40	1.39	1.38	1.37	1.36	1.36	1.35	1.34	1.34	1.33	49
50	1.50	1.49	1.48	1.47	1.46	1.46	1.45	1.44	1.43	1.42	1.41	1.41	1.40	1.39	1.38	1.38	50
51	1.56	1.55	1.54	1.53	1.52	1.51	1.50	1.49	1.48	1.47	1.46	1.46	1.45	1.44	1.43	1.43	51
52	1.61	1.60	1.59	1.58	1.57	1.56	1.55	1.54	1.54	1.53	1.52	1.51	1.50	1.49	1.49	1.48	52
53	1.67	1.66	1.65	1.64	1.63	1.62	1.61	1.60	1.59	1.58	1.57	1.56	1.56	1.55	1.54	1.53	53
54	1.74	1.72	1.71	1.70	1.69	1.68	1.67	1.66	1.65	1.64	1.63	1.62	1.61	1.61	1.60	1.59	54
55	1.80	1.79	1.78	1.77	1.75	1.74	1.73	1.72	1.71	1.70	1.69	1.68	1.68	1.67	1.66	1.65	55
56	1.87	1.86	1.84	1.83	1.82	1.81	1.80	1.79	1.78	1.77	1.76	1.75	1.74	1.73	1.72	1.71	56
57	1.94	1.93	1.92	1.90	1.89	1.88	1.87	1.86	1.85	1.84	1.83	1.82	1.81	1.80	1.79	1.78	57
58	2.02	2.00	1.99	1.98	1.97	1.95	1.94	1.93	1.92	1.91	1.90	1.89	1.88	1.87	1.86	1.85	58
59	2.10	2.08	2.07	2.06	2.04	2.03	2.02	2.01	2.00	1.98	1.97	1.96	1.95	1.94	1.93	1.92	59
60	2.18	2.17	2.16	2.14	2.13	2.11	2.10	2.09	2.08	2.07	2.05	2.04	2.03	2.02	2.01	2.00	60
61	2.27	2.26	2.24	2.23	2.22	2.20	2.19	2.18	2.16	2.15	2.14	2.13	2.12	2.10	2.09	2.08	61
62	2.37	2.35	2.34	2.32	2.31	2.30	2.28	2.27	2.26	2.24	2.23	2.22	2.21	2.19	2.18	2.17	62
63	2.47	2.46	2.44	2.43	2.41	2.40	2.38	2.37	2.35	2.34	2.33	2.31	2.30	2.29	2.28	2.27	63
DEC.	127½ 232½	127° 233	126½ 233½	126° 234	125½ 234½	125° 235	124½ 235½	124° 236	123½ 236½	123° 237	122½ 237½	122° 238	121½ 238½	121° 239	120½ 239½	120° 240	DEC.

Table 29

A   If entered with H.A. at **top**,   Sign **+**

     „   „   „   „   **foot**,   „   **–**

4 hrs.

HOUR ANGLE or DIFF. LONG.

LAT.	00m	04m	08m	12m	16m	20m	24m	28m	32m	36m	40m	44m	48m	52m	56m	60m	LAT.
	60° 300	61° 299	62° 298	63° 297	64° 296	65° 295	66° 294	67° 293	68° 292	69° 291	70° 290	71° 289	72° 288	73° 287	74° 286	75° 285	
0°	.000	.000	.000	.000	.000	.000	.000	.000	.000	.000	.000	.000	.000	.000	.000	.000	0°
1	.010	.010	.009	.009	.009	.008	.008	.007	.007	.007	.006	.006	.006	.005	.005	.005	1
2	.020	.019	.019	.018	.017	.016	.016	.015	.014	.013	.013	.012	.011	.011	.010	.009	2
3	.030	.029	.028	.027	.026	.024	.023	.022	.021	.020	.019	.018	.017	.016	.015	.014	3
4	.040	.039	.037	.036	.034	.033	.031	.030	.028	.027	.026	.024	.023	.021	.020	.019	4
5	.051	.048	.047	.045	.043	.041	.039	.037	.035	.034	.032	.030	.028	.027	.025	.023	5
6	.061	.058	.056	.054	.051	.049	.047	.045	.043	.040	.038	.036	.034	.032	.030	.028	6
7	.071	.068	.065	.063	.060	.057	.055	.052	.050	.047	.045	.042	.040	.038	.035	.033	7
8	.081	.078	.075	.072	.069	.066	.063	.060	.057	.054	.051	.048	.046	.043	.040	.038	8
9	.091	.088	.084	.081	.077	.074	.071	.067	.064	.061	.058	.055	.051	.048	.045	.042	9
10	.102	.098	.094	.090	.086	.082	.079	.075	.071	.068	.064	.061	.057	.054	.051	.047	10
11	.112	.108	.103	.099	.095	.091	.087	.083	.079	.075	.071	.067	.063	.059	.056	.052	11
12	.123	.118	.113	.108	.104	.099	.095	.090	.086	.082	.077	.073	.069	.065	.061	.057	12
13	.133	.128	.123	.118	.113	.108	.103	.098	.093	.089	.084	.079	.075	.071	.066	.062	13
14	.144	.138	.133	.127	.122	.116	.111	.106	.101	.096	.091	.086	.081	.076	.071	.067	14
15	.155	.149	.142	.137	.131	.125	.119	.114	.108	.103	.098	.092	.087	.082	.077	.072	15
16	.166	.159	.152	.146	.140	.134	.128	.122	.116	.110	.104	.099	.093	.088	.082	.077	16
17	.177	.169	.163	.156	.149	.143	.136	.130	.124	.117	.111	.105	.099	.093	.088	.082	17
18	.188	.180	.173	.166	.158	.152	.145	.138	.131	.125	.118	.112	.106	.099	.093	.087	18
19	.199	.191	.183	.175	.168	.161	.153	.146	.139	.132	.125	.119	.112	.105	.099	.092	19
20	.210	.202	.194	.185	.178	.170	.162	.154	.147	.140	.132	.125	.118	.111	.104	.098	20
21	.222	.213	.204	.196	.187	.179	.171	.163	.155	.147	.140	.132	.125	.117	.110	.103	21
22	.233	.224	.215	.206	.197	.188	.180	.171	.163	.155	.147	.139	.131	.124	.116	.108	22
23	.245	.235	.226	.216	.207	.198	.189	.180	.171	.163	.154	.146	.138	.130	.122	.114	23
24	.257	.247	.237	.227	.217	.208	.198	.189	.180	.171	.162	.153	.145	.136	.128	.119	24
25	.269	.258	.248	.238	.227	.217	.208	.198	.188	.179	.170	.161	.152	.143	.134	.125	25
26	.282	.270	.259	.249	.238	.227	.217	.207	.197	.187	.178	.168	.158	.149	.140	.131	26
27	.294	.282	.271	.260	.249	.238	.227	.216	.206	.196	.185	.175	.166	.156	.146	.137	27
28	.307	.295	.283	.271	.259	.248	.237	.226	.215	.204	.194	.183	.173	.163	.152	.142	28
29	.320	.307	.295	.282	.270	.258	.247	.235	.224	.213	.202	.191	.180	.169	.159	.149	29
30	.333	.320	.307	.294	.282	.269	.257	.245	.233	.222	.210	.199	.188	.177	.166	.155	30
31	.347	.333	.319	.306	.293	.280	.268	.255	.243	.231	.219	.207	.195	.184	.172	.161	31
32	.361	.346	.332	.318	.305	.291	.278	.265	.252	.240	.227	.215	.203	.191	.179	.167	32
33	.375	.360	.345	.331	.317	.303	.289	.276	.262	.249	.236	.224	.211	.199	.186	.174	33
34	.389	.374	.359	.344	.329	.315	.300	.286	.273	.259	.246	.232	.219	.206	.193	.181	34
35	.404	.388	.372	.357	.342	.327	.312	.297	.283	.269	.255	.241	.228	.214	.201	.188	35
36	.419	.403	.386	.370	.354	.339	.323	.308	.294	.279	.264	.250	.236	.222	.208	.195	36
37	.435	.418	.401	.384	.368	.351	.336	.320	.304	.289	.274	.259	.245	.230	.216	.202	37
38	.451	.433	.415	.398	.381	.364	.348	.332	.316	.300	.284	.269	.254	.239	.224	.209	38
39	.468	.449	.431	.413	.395	.378	.361	.344	.327	.311	.295	.279	.263	.248	.232	.217	39
40	.484	.465	.446	.428	.409	.391	.374	.356	.339	.322	.305	.289	.273	.257	.241	.225	40
41	.502	.482	.462	.443	.424	.405	.387	.369	.351	.334	.316	.299	.282	.266	.249	.233	41
42	.520	.499	.479	.459	.439	.420	.401	.382	.364	.346	.328	.310	.293	.275	.258	.241	42
43	.538	.517	.496	.475	.455	.435	.415	.396	.377	.358	.339	.321	.303	.285	.267	.250	43
44	.558	.535	.513	.492	.471	.450	.430	.410	.390	.371	.351	.333	.314	.295	.277	.259	44
45	.577	.554	.532	.510	.488	.466	.445	.424	.404	.384	.364	.344	.325	.306	.287	.268	45
46	.598	.574	.551	.528	.505	.483	.461	.440	.418	.398	.377	.357	.336	.317	.297	.277	46
47	.619	.594	.570	.546	.523	.500	.477	.455	.433	.412	.390	.369	.348	.328	.307	.287	47
48	.641	.616	.591	.566	.542	.518	.494	.471	.449	.426	.404	.382	.361	.340	.318	.298	48
49	.664	.638	.612	.586	.561	.536	.512	.488	.465	.442	.419	.396	.374	.352	.330	.308	49
50	.688	.661	.634	.607	.581	.556	.531	.506	.481	.457	.434	.410	.387	.364	.342	.319	50
51	.713	.685	.657	.629	.602	.576	.550	.524	.499	.474	.449	.425	.401	.378	.354	.331	51
52	.739	.709	.681	.652	.624	.597	.570	.543	.517	.491	.466	.441	.416	.391	.367	.343	52
53	.766	.736	.706	.676	.647	.619	.591	.563	.536	.509	.483	.457	.431	.406	.381	.356	53
54	.795	.763	.732	.701	.671	.642	.613	.584	.556	.528	.501	.474	.447	.421	.395	.369	54
55	.825	.792	.759	.728	.697	.666	.636	.606	.577	.548	.520	.492	.464	.437	.410	.383	55
56	.856	.822	.788	.755	.723	.691	.660	.629	.599	.569	.540	.510	.482	.453	.425	.397	56
57	.889	.854	.819	.785	.751	.718	.686	.654	.622	.591	.560	.530	.500	.471	.442	.413	57
58	.924	.887	.851	.815	.781	.746	.713	.679	.647	.614	.582	.551	.520	.489	.459	.429	58
59	.961	.923	.885	.848	.812	.776	.741	.706	.672	.639	.606	.573	.541	.509	.477	.446	59
60	1.00	.960	.921	.883	.845	.808	.771	.735	.700	.665	.630	.596	.563	.530	.497	.464	60
LAT.	120° 240	119° 241	118° 242	117° 243	116° 244	115° 245	114° 246	113° 247	112° 248	111° 249	110° 250	109° 251	108° 252	107° 253	106° 254	105° 255	LAT.

Table 29

B

4 hrs.

Lat. and Dec. SAME name, Sign —
Lat. and Dec. CONTRARY names, Sign +

HOUR ANGLE or DIFF. LONG.

DEC.	00m	04m	08m	12m	16m	20m	24m	28m	32m	36m	40m	44m	48m	52m	56m	60m	DEC.
	60° 300	61° 299	62° 298	63° 297	64° 296	65° 295	66° 294	67° 293	68° 292	69° 291	70° 290	71° 289	72° 288	73° 287	74° 286	75° 285	
0°	.000	.000	.000	.000	.000	.000	.000	.000	.000	.000	.000	.000	.000	.000	.000	.000	0°
1	.020	.020	.020	.020	.019	.019	.019	.019	.019	.019	.019	.018	.018	.018	.018	.018	1
2	.040	.040	.040	.039	.039	.039	.038	.038	.038	.037	.037	.037	.037	.037	.036	.036	2
3	.061	.060	.059	.059	.058	.058	.057	.057	.057	.056	.056	.055	.055	.055	.055	.054	3
4	.081	.080	.079	.078	.078	.077	.077	.076	.075	.075	.074	.074	.074	.073	.073	.072	4
5	.101	.100	.099	.098	.097	.097	.096	.095	.094	.094	.093	.093	.092	.091	.091	.091	5
6	.121	.120	.119	.118	.117	.116	.115	.114	.113	.113	.112	.111	.111	.110	.109	.109	6
7	.142	.140	.139	.138	.137	.135	.134	.133	.132	.132	.131	.130	.129	.128	.128	.127	7
8	.162	.161	.159	.158	.156	.155	.154	.153	.152	.151	.150	.149	.148	.147	.146	.145	8
9	.183	.181	.179	.178	.176	.175	.173	.172	.171	.170	.169	.168	.167	.166	.165	.164	9
10	.204	.202	.200	.198	.196	.195	.193	.192	.190	.189	.188	.186	.185	.184	.183	.183	10
11	.224	.222	.220	.218	.216	.214	.213	.211	.210	.208	.207	.206	.204	.203	.202	.201	11
12	.245	.243	.241	.239	.236	.235	.233	.231	.229	.228	.226	.225	.223	.222	.221	.220	12
13	.267	.264	.261	.259	.257	.255	.253	.251	.249	.247	.246	.244	.243	.241	.240	.239	13
14	.288	.285	.282	.280	.277	.275	.273	.271	.269	.267	.265	.264	.262	.261	.259	.258	14
15	.309	.306	.303	.301	.298	.296	.293	.291	.289	.287	.285	.283	.282	.280	.279	.277	15
16	.331	.328	.325	.322	.319	.316	.314	.312	.309	.307	.305	.303	.302	.300	.298	.297	16
17	.353	.350	.346	.343	.340	.337	.335	.332	.330	.327	.325	.323	.321	.320	.318	.317	17
18	.375	.371	.368	.365	.362	.359	.356	.353	.350	.348	.346	.344	.342	.340	.338	.336	18
19	.398	.394	.390	.386	.383	.380	.377	.374	.371	.369	.366	.364	.362	.360	.358	.356	19
20	.420	.416	.412	.408	.405	.402	.398	.395	.393	.390	.387	.385	.383	.381	.379	.377	20
21	.443	.439	.435	.431	.427	.424	.420	.417	.414	.411	.408	.406	.404	.401	.399	.397	21
22	.467	.462	.458	.453	.450	.446	.442	.439	.436	.433	.430	.427	.425	.422	.420	.418	22
23	.490	.485	.481	.476	.472	.468	.465	.461	.458	.455	.452	.449	.446	.444	.442	.439	23
24	.514	.509	.504	.500	.495	.491	.487	.484	.480	.477	.474	.471	.468	.466	.463	.461	24
25	.538	.533	.528	.523	.519	.515	.510	.507	.503	.499	.496	.493	.490	.488	.485	.483	25
26	.563	.558	.552	.547	.543	.538	.534	.530	.526	.522	.519	.516	.513	.510	.507	.505	26
27	.588	.583	.577	.572	.567	.562	.558	.554	.550	.546	.542	.539	.536	.533	.530	.527	27
28	.614	.608	.602	.597	.592	.587	.582	.578	.573	.570	.566	.562	.559	.556	.553	.550	28
29	.640	.634	.628	.622	.617	.612	.607	.602	.598	.594	.590	.586	.583	.580	.577	.574	29
30	.667	.660	.654	.648	.642	.637	.632	.627	.623	.618	.614	.611	.607	.604	.601	.598	30
31	.694	.687	.681	.674	.669	.663	.658	.653	.648	.644	.639	.635	.632	.628	.625	.622	31
32	.722	.714	.708	.701	.695	.689	.684	.679	.674	.669	.665	.661	.657	.653	.650	.647	32
33	.750	.743	.735	.729	.723	.717	.711	.705	.700	.696	.691	.687	.683	.679	.676	.672	33
34	.779	.771	.764	.757	.750	.744	.738	.733	.727	.722	.718	.713	.709	.705	.702	.698	34
35	.809	.801	.793	.786	.779	.773	.766	.761	.755	.750	.745	.741	.736	.732	.728	.725	35
36	.839	.831	.823	.815	.808	.802	.795	.789	.784	.778	.773	.768	.764	.760	.756	.752	36
37	.870	.862	.853	.846	.838	.831	.825	.819	.813	.807	.802	.797	.792	.788	.784	.780	37
38	.902	.893	.885	.877	.869	.862	.855	.849	.843	.837	.831	.826	.821	.817	.813	.809	38
39	.935	.926	.917	.909	.901	.893	.886	.880	.873	.867	.862	.856	.851	.847	.842	.838	39
40	.969	.959	.950	.942	.934	.926	.919	.912	.905	.899	.893	.887	.882	.877	.873	.869	40
41	1.00	.994	.985	.976	.967	.959	.952	.944	.938	.931	.925	.919	.914	.909	.904	.900	41
42	1.04	1.03	1.02	1.01	1.00	.993	.986	.978	.971	.964	.958	.952	.947	.942	.937	.932	42
43	1.08	1.07	1.06	1.05	1.04	1.03	1.02	1.01	1.01	.999	.992	.986	.981	.975	.970	.965	43
44	1.12	1.10	1.09	1.08	1.07	1.07	1.06	1.05	1.04	1.03	1.03	1.02	1.02	1.01	1.00	1.00	44
45	1.15	1.14	1.13	1.12	1.11	1.10	1.09	1.09	1.08	1.07	1.06	1.06	1.05	1.05	1.04	1.04	45
46	1.20	1.18	1.17	1.16	1.15	1.14	1.13	1.12	1.12	1.11	1.10	1.10	1.09	1.08	1.08	1.07	46
47	1.24	1.23	1.21	1.20	1.19	1.18	1.17	1.16	1.16	1.15	1.14	1.13	1.13	1.12	1.12	1.11	47
48	1.28	1.27	1.26	1.25	1.24	1.23	1.22	1.21	1.20	1.19	1.18	1.17	1.17	1.16	1.16	1.15	48
49	1.33	1.32	1.30	1.29	1.28	1.27	1.26	1.25	1.24	1.23	1.22	1.22	1.21	1.20	1.20	1.19	49
50	1.38	1.36	1.35	1.34	1.33	1.31	1.30	1.29	1.29	1.28	1.27	1.26	1.25	1.25	1.24	1.23	50
51	1.43	1.41	1.40	1.39	1.37	1.36	1.35	1.34	1.33	1.32	1.31	1.31	1.30	1.29	1.28	1.28	51
52	1.48	1.46	1.45	1.44	1.42	1.41	1.40	1.39	1.38	1.37	1.36	1.35	1.35	1.34	1.33	1.33	52
53	1.53	1.52	1.50	1.49	1.48	1.46	1.45	1.44	1.43	1.42	1.41	1.40	1.40	1.39	1.38	1.37	53
54	1.59	1.57	1.56	1.54	1.53	1.52	1.51	1.50	1.48	1.47	1.46	1.46	1.45	1.44	1.43	1.42	54
55	1.65	1.63	1.62	1.60	1.59	1.58	1.56	1.55	1.54	1.53	1.52	1.51	1.50	1.49	1.49	1.48	55
56	1.71	1.70	1.68	1.66	1.65	1.64	1.62	1.61	1.60	1.59	1.58	1.57	1.56	1.55	1.54	1.53	56
57	1.78	1.76	1.74	1.73	1.71	1.70	1.69	1.67	1.66	1.65	1.64	1.63	1.62	1.61	1.60	1.59	57
58	1.85	1.83	1.81	1.80	1.78	1.77	1.75	1.74	1.73	1.71	1.70	1.69	1.68	1.67	1.66	1.66	58
59	1.92	1.90	1.88	1.87	1.85	1.84	1.82	1.81	1.79	1.78	1.77	1.76	1.75	1.74	1.73	1.72	59
60	2.00	1.98	1.96	1.94	1.93	1.91	1.90	1.88	1.87	1.86	1.84	1.83	1.82	1.81	1.80	1.79	60
61	2.08	2.06	2.04	2.02	2.01	1.99	1.97	1.96	1.95	1.93	1.92	1.91	1.90	1.89	1.88	1.87	61
62	2.17	2.15	2.13	2.11	2.09	2.08	2.06	2.04	2.03	2.01	2.00	1.99	1.98	1.97	1.96	1.95	62
63	2.27	2.24	2.22	2.20	2.18	2.17	2.15	2.13	2.12	2.10	2.09	2.08	2.06	2.05	2.04	2.03	63
DEC.	120° 240	119° 241	118° 242	117° 243	116° 244	115° 245	114° 246	113° 247	112° 248	111° 249	110° 250	109° 251	108° 252	107° 253	106° 254	105° 255	DEC.

Table 29

A

5 hrs.

If entered with H.A. at **top**, Sign **+**
„ „ „ „ **foot**, „ **—**

HOUR ANGLE or DIFF. LONG.

LAT.	00m	04m	08m	12m	16m	20m	24m	28m	32m	36m	40m	44m	48m	52m	56m	60m	LAT.
	75° 285	76° 284	77° 283	78° 282	79° 281	80° 280	81° 279	82° 278	83° 277	84° 276	85° 275	86° 274	87° 273	88° 272	89° 271	90° 270	
0°	.000	.000	.000	.000	.000	.000	.000	.000	.000	.000	.000	.000	.000	.000	.000	.000	0°
1	.005	.004	.004	.004	.003	.003	.003	.003	.002	.002	.002	.001	.001	.001	.000	.000	1
2	.009	.009	.008	.007	.007	.006	.006	.005	.004	.004	.003	.002	.002	.001	.001	.000	2
3	.014	.013	.012	.011	.010	.009	.008	.007	.006	.006	.005	.004	.003	.002	.001	.000	3
4	.019	.017	.016	.015	.014	.012	.011	.010	.009	.007	.006	.005	.004	.002	.001	.000	4
5	.023	.022	.020	.019	.017	.015	.014	.012	.011	.009	.008	.006	.005	.003	.002	.000	5
6	.028	.026	.024	.022	.020	.019	.017	.015	.013	.011	.009	.007	.006	.004	.002	.000	6
7	.033	.031	.028	.026	.024	.022	.019	.017	.015	.013	.011	.009	.006	.004	.002	.000	7
8	.038	.035	.032	.030	.027	.025	.022	.020	.017	.015	.012	.010	.007	.005	.003	.000	8
9	.042	.039	.037	.034	.031	.028	.025	.022	.019	.017	.014	.011	.008	.006	.003	.000	9
10	.047	.044	.041	.037	.034	.031	.028	.025	.022	.019	.015	.012	.009	.006	.003	.000	10
11	.052	.048	.045	.041	.038	.034	.031	.027	.024	.020	.017	.014	.010	.007	.003	.000	11
12	.057	.053	.049	.045	.041	.037	.034	.030	.026	.022	.019	.015	.011	.007	.004	.000	12
13	.062	.058	.053	.049	.045	.041	.037	.032	.028	.024	.020	.016	.012	.008	.004	.000	13
14	.067	.062	.058	.053	.048	.044	.039	.035	.031	.026	.022	.017	.013	.009	.004	.000	14
15	.072	.067	.062	.057	.052	.047	.042	.038	.033	.028	.023	.019	.014	.009	.005	.000	15
16	.077	.071	.066	.061	.056	.051	.045	.040	.035	.030	.025	.020	.015	.010	.005	.000	16
17	.082	.076	.071	.065	.059	.054	.048	.043	.038	.032	.027	.021	.016	.011	.005	.000	17
18	.087	.081	.075	.069	.063	.057	.051	.046	.040	.034	.028	.023	.017	.011	.006	.000	18
19	.092	.086	.079	.073	.067	.061	.055	.048	.042	.036	.030	.024	.018	.012	.006	.000	19
20	.098	.091	.084	.077	.071	.064	.058	.051	.045	.038	.032	.025	.019	.013	.006	.000	20
21	.103	.096	.089	.082	.075	.068	.061	.054	.047	.040	.034	.027	.020	.013	.007	.000	21
22	.108	.101	.093	.086	.079	.071	.064	.057	.050	.042	.035	.028	.021	.014	.007	.000	22
23	.114	.106	.098	.090	.083	.075	.067	.060	.052	.045	.037	.030	.022	.015	.007	.000	23
24	.119	.111	.103	.095	.087	.079	.071	.063	.055	.047	.039	.031	.023	.016	.008	.000	24
25	.125	.116	.108	.099	.091	.082	.074	.066	.057	.049	.041	.033	.024	.016	.008	.000	25
26	.131	.122	.113	.104	.095	.086	.077	.069	.060	.051	.043	.034	.026	.017	.009	.000	26
27	.137	.127	.118	.108	.099	.090	.081	.072	.063	.054	.045	.036	.027	.018	.009	.000	27
28	.142	.133	.123	.113	.103	.094	.084	.075	.065	.056	.047	.037	.028	.019	.009	.000	28
29	.149	.138	.128	.118	.108	.098	.088	.078	.068	.058	.049	.039	.029	.019	.010	.000	29
30	.155	.144	.133	.123	.112	.102	.091	.081	.071	.061	.051	.040	.030	.020	.010	.000	30
31	.161	.150	.139	.128	.117	.106	.095	.084	.074	.063	.053	.042	.031	.021	.010	.000	31
32	.167	.156	.144	.133	.121	.110	.099	.088	.077	.066	.055	.044	.033	.022	.011	.000	32
33	.174	.162	.150	.138	.126	.115	.103	.091	.080	.068	.057	.045	.034	.023	.011	.000	33
34	.181	.168	.156	.143	.131	.119	.107	.095	.083	.071	.059	.047	.035	.024	.012	.000	34
35	.188	.175	.162	.149	.136	.123	.111	.098	.086	.074	.061	.049	.037	.024	.012	.000	35
36	.195	.181	.168	.154	.141	.128	.115	.102	.089	.076	.064	.051	.038	.025	.013	.000	36
37	.202	.188	.174	.160	.146	.133	.119	.106	.093	.079	.066	.053	.039	.026	.013	.000	37
38	.209	.195	.180	.166	.152	.138	.124	.110	.096	.082	.068	.055	.041	.027	.014	.000	38
39	.217	.202	.187	.172	.157	.143	.128	.114	.099	.085	.071	.057	.042	.028	.014	.000	39
40	.225	.209	.194	.178	.163	.148	.133	.118	.103	.088	.073	.059	.044	.029	.015	.000	40
41	.233	.217	.201	.185	.169	.153	.138	.122	.107	.091	.076	.061	.046	.030	.015	.000	41
42	.241	.224	.208	.191	.175	.159	.143	.127	.111	.095	.079	.063	.047	.031	.016	.000	42
43	.250	.233	.215	.198	.181	.164	.148	.131	.114	.098	.082	.065	.049	.033	.016	.000	43
44	.259	.241	.223	.205	.188	.170	.153	.136	.119	.101	.085	.068	.051	.034	.017	.000	44
45	.268	.249	.231	.213	.194	.176	.158	.141	.123	.105	.088	.070	.052	.035	.017	.000	45
46	.277	.258	.239	.220	.201	.183	.164	.146	.127	.109	.091	.072	.054	.036	.018	.000	46
47	.287	.267	.248	.228	.208	.189	.170	.151	.132	.113	.094	.075	.056	.037	.019	.000	47
48	.298	.277	.256	.236	.216	.196	.176	.156	.136	.117	.097	.078	.058	.039	.019	.000	48
49	.308	.287	.266	.245	.224	.203	.182	.162	.141	.121	.101	.080	.060	.040	.020	.000	49
50	.319	.297	.275	.253	.232	.210	.189	.167	.146	.125	.104	.083	.062	.042	.021	.000	50
51	.331	.308	.285	.262	.240	.218	.196	.174	.152	.130	.108	.086	.065	.043	.022	.000	51
52	.343	.319	.295	.272	.249	.226	.203	.180	.157	.135	.112	.090	.067	.045	.022	.000	52
53	.356	.331	.306	.282	.258	.234	.210	.187	.163	.139	.116	.093	.070	.046	.023	.000	53
54	.369	.343	.318	.293	.268	.243	.218	.193	.169	.145	.120	.096	.072	.048	.024	.000	54
55	.383	.356	.330	.304	.278	.252	.226	.201	.175	.150	.125	.100	.075	.050	.025	.000	55
56	.397	.370	.342	.315	.288	.261	.235	.208	.182	.156	.130	.104	.078	.052	.026	.000	56
57	.413	.384	.356	.327	.299	.272	.244	.216	.189	.162	.135	.108	.081	.054	.027	.000	57
58	.429	.399	.369	.340	.311	.282	.253	.225	.196	.168	.140	.112	.084	.056	.028	.000	58
59	.446	.415	.384	.354	.324	.293	.264	.234	.204	.175	.146	.116	.087	.058	.029	.000	59
60	.464	.432	.400	.368	.337	.305	.274	.243	.213	.182	.152	.121	.091	.060	.030	.000	60
LAT.	105° 255	104° 256	103° 257	102° 258	101° 259	100° 260	99° 261	98° 262	97° 263	96° 264	95° 265	94° 266	93° 267	92° 268	91° 269	90° 270	LAT.

Table 29   B

5 hrs.

Lat. and Dec. SAME name, Sign —
Lat. and Dec. CONTRARY names, Sign +

HOUR ANGLE or DIFF. LONG.

DEC.	00m	04m	08m	12m	16m	20m	24m	28m	32m	36m	40m	44m	48m	52m	56m	60m	DEC.
	75° 285	76° 284	77° 283	78° 282	79° 281	80° 280	81° 279	82° 278	83° 277	84° 276	85° 275	86° 274	87° 273	88° 272	89° 271	90° 270	
0°	.000	.000	.000	.000	.000	.000	.000	.000	.000	.000	.000	.000	.000	.000	.000	.000	0°
1	.018	.018	.018	.018	.018	.018	.018	.018	.018	.018	.018	.017	.017	.017	.017	.017	1
2	.036	.036	.036	.036	.036	.035	.035	.035	.035	.035	.035	.035	.035	.035	.035	.035	2
3	.054	.054	.054	.054	.053	.053	.053	.053	.053	.053	.053	.053	.052	.052	.052	.052	3
4	.072	.072	.072	.071	.071	.071	.071	.071	.071	.070	.070	.070	.070	.070	.070	.070	4
5	.091	.090	.090	.089	.089	.089	.089	.088	.088	.088	.088	.088	.088	.088	.088	.087	5
6	.109	.108	.108	.107	.107	.107	.106	.106	.106	.106	.106	.105	.105	.105	.105	.105	6
7	.127	.127	.126	.126	.125	.125	.124	.124	.124	.123	.123	.123	.123	.123	.123	.123	7
8	.145	.145	.144	.144	.143	.143	.142	.142	.142	.141	.141	.141	.141	.141	.141	.141	8
9	.164	.163	.163	.162	.161	.161	.160	.160	.160	.159	.159	.159	.159	.158	.158	.158	9
10	.183	.182	.181	.180	.180	.179	.179	.178	.178	.177	.177	.177	.177	.176	.176	.176	10
11	.201	.200	.199	.199	.198	.197	.197	.196	.196	.195	.195	.195	.195	.194	.194	.194	11
12	.220	.219	.218	.217	.217	.216	.215	.215	.214	.214	.213	.213	.213	.213	.213	.213	12
13	.239	.238	.237	.236	.235	.234	.234	.233	.233	.232	.232	.231	.231	.231	.231	.231	13
14	.258	.257	.256	.255	.254	.253	.252	.252	.251	.251	.250	.250	.250	.249	.249	.249	14
15	.277	.276	.275	.274	.273	.272	.271	.271	.270	.269	.269	.269	.268	.268	.268	.268	15
16	.297	.296	.294	.293	.292	.291	.290	.290	.289	.288	.288	.287	.287	.287	.287	.287	16
17	.317	.315	.314	.313	.311	.310	.310	.309	.308	.307	.307	.306	.306	.306	.306	.306	17
18	.336	.335	.333	.332	.331	.330	.329	.328	.327	.327	.326	.326	.325	.325	.325	.325	18
19	.356	.355	.353	.352	.351	.350	.349	.348	.347	.346	.346	.345	.345	.345	.344	.344	19
20	.377	.375	.374	.372	.371	.370	.369	.368	.367	.366	.365	.365	.364	.364	.364	.364	20
21	.397	.396	.394	.392	.391	.390	.389	.388	.387	.386	.385	.385	.384	.384	.384	.384	21
22	.418	.416	.415	.413	.412	.410	.409	.408	.407	.406	.406	.405	.405	.404	.404	.404	22
23	.439	.437	.436	.434	.432	.431	.430	.429	.428	.427	.426	.426	.425	.425	.425	.424	23
24	.461	.459	.457	.455	.454	.452	.451	.450	.449	.448	.447	.446	.446	.446	.445	.445	24
25	.483	.481	.479	.477	.475	.474	.472	.471	.470	.469	.468	.467	.467	.467	.466	.466	25
26	.505	.503	.501	.499	.497	.495	.494	.493	.491	.490	.490	.489	.488	.488	.488	.488	26
27	.527	.525	.523	.521	.519	.517	.516	.515	.513	.512	.511	.511	.510	.510	.510	.510	27
28	.550	.548	.546	.544	.542	.540	.538	.537	.536	.535	.534	.533	.532	.532	.532	.532	28
29	.574	.571	.569	.567	.565	.563	.561	.560	.558	.557	.556	.556	.555	.555	.554	.554	29
30	.598	.595	.593	.590	.588	.586	.585	.583	.582	.581	.580	.579	.578	.578	.577	.577	30
31	.622	.619	.617	.614	.612	.610	.608	.607	.605	.604	.603	.602	.602	.601	.601	.601	31
32	.647	.644	.641	.639	.637	.635	.633	.631	.630	.628	.627	.626	.626	.625	.625	.625	32
33	.672	.669	.666	.664	.662	.659	.658	.656	.654	.653	.652	.651	.650	.650	.650	.649	33
34	.698	.695	.692	.690	.687	.685	.683	.681	.680	.678	.677	.676	.675	.675	.675	.675	34
35	.725	.722	.719	.716	.713	.711	.709	.707	.705	.704	.703	.702	.701	.701	.700	.700	35
36	.752	.749	.746	.743	.740	.738	.736	.734	.732	.731	.729	.728	.728	.727	.727	.727	36
37	.780	.777	.773	.770	.768	.765	.763	.761	.759	.758	.756	.755	.755	.754	.754	.754	37
38	.809	.805	.802	.799	.796	.793	.791	.789	.787	.786	.784	.783	.782	.782	.781	.781	38
39	.838	.835	.831	.828	.825	.822	.820	.818	.816	.814	.813	.812	.811	.810	.810	.810	39
40	.869	.865	.861	.858	.855	.852	.850	.847	.845	.844	.842	.841	.840	.840	.839	.839	40
41	.900	.896	.892	.889	.886	.883	.880	.878	.876	.874	.873	.871	.870	.870	.869	.869	41
42	.932	.928	.924	.921	.917	.914	.912	.909	.907	.905	.904	.903	.902	.901	.901	.900	42
43	.965	.961	.957	.953	.950	.947	.944	.942	.940	.938	.936	.935	.934	.933	.933	.933	43
44	1.00	.995	.991	.987	.984	.981	.978	.975	.973	.971	.969	.968	.967	.966	.966	.966	44
45	1.04	1.03	1.03	1.02	1.02	1.02	1.01	1.01	1.01	1.01	1.00	1.00	1.00	1.00	1.00	1.00	45
46	1.07	1.07	1.06	1.06	1.05	1.05	1.05	1.05	1.04	1.04	1.04	1.04	1.04	1.04	1.04	1.04	46
47	1.11	1.11	1.10	1.10	1.09	1.09	1.09	1.08	1.08	1.08	1.08	1.07	1.07	1.07	1.07	1.07	47
48	1.15	1.14	1.14	1.14	1.13	1.13	1.12	1.12	1.12	1.12	1.11	1.11	1.11	1.11	1.11	1.11	48
49	1.19	1.19	1.18	1.18	1.17	1.17	1.16	1.16	1.16	1.16	1.15	1.15	1.15	1.15	1.15	1.15	49
50	1.23	1.23	1.22	1.22	1.21	1.21	1.21	1.20	1.20	1.20	1.20	1.19	1.19	1.19	1.19	1.19	50
51	1.28	1.27	1.27	1.26	1.26	1.25	1.25	1.25	1.24	1.24	1.24	1.24	1.24	1.24	1.24	1.23	51
52	1.33	1.32	1.31	1.31	1.30	1.30	1.30	1.29	1.29	1.29	1.28	1.28	1.28	1.28	1.28	1.28	52
53	1.37	1.37	1.36	1.36	1.35	1.35	1.34	1.34	1.34	1.33	1.33	1.33	1.33	1.33	1.33	1.33	53
54	1.42	1.42	1.41	1.41	1.40	1.40	1.39	1.39	1.39	1.38	1.38	1.38	1.38	1.38	1.38	1.38	54
55	1.48	1.47	1.47	1.46	1.46	1.45	1.45	1.44	1.44	1.44	1.43	1.43	1.43	1.43	1.43	1.43	55
56	1.53	1.53	1.52	1.52	1.51	1.51	1.50	1.50	1.49	1.49	1.49	1.49	1.48	1.48	1.48	1.48	56
57	1.59	1.59	1.58	1.57	1.57	1.56	1.56	1.55	1.55	1.55	1.55	1.54	1.54	1.54	1.54	1.54	57
58	1.66	1.65	1.64	1.64	1.63	1.63	1.62	1.62	1.61	1.61	1.61	1.60	1.60	1.60	1.60	1.60	58
59	1.72	1.72	1.71	1.70	1.70	1.69	1.69	1.68	1.68	1.67	1.67	1.67	1.67	1.67	1.66	1.66	59
60	1.79	1.79	1.78	1.77	1.76	1.76	1.75	1.75	1.75	1.74	1.74	1.74	1.73	1.73	1.73	1.73	60
61	1.87	1.86	1.85	1.84	1.84	1.83	1.83	1.82	1.82	1.81	1.81	1.81	1.81	1.81	1.80	1.80	61
62	1.95	1.94	1.93	1.92	1.92	1.91	1.90	1.90	1.89	1.89	1.89	1.89	1.88	1.88	1.88	1.88	62
63	2.03	2.02	2.01	2.01	2.00	1.99	1.99	1.98	1.98	1.97	1.97	1.97	1.97	1.96	1.96	1.96	63
DEC.	105° 255	104° 256	103° 257	102° 258	101° 259	100° 260	99° 261	98° 262	97° 263	96° 264	95° 265	94° 266	93° 267	92° 268	91° 269	90° 270	DEC.

Table 30

North Lat.　South Lat.

C

Body **RISING** (H.A. greater than 180°)　{ Sign − Az. in **NE** Qdt. **SE** Qdt.
　　　　　　　　　　　　　　　　　　　　{ " + " **SE** " **NE** "

Body **SETTING** (H.A. less than 180°)　{ Sign + Az. in **SW** Qdt. **NW** Qdt.
　　　　　　　　　　　　　　　　　　　　{ " − " **NW** " **SW** "

(Longitude Correction)

Qdt. 1st 2nd 3rd 4th	½° 179½ 180½ 359½	1° 179 181 359	1½° 178½ 181½ 358½	2° 178 182 358	2½° 177½ 182½ 357½	3° 177 183 357	3½° 176½ 183½ 356½	4° 176 184 356	4½° 175½ 184½ 355½	5° 175 185 355	5½° 174½ 185½ 354½	6° 174 186 354	6½° 173½ 186½ 353½	7° 173 187 353	7½° 172½ 187½ 352½	Qdt. NE SE SW NW
LAT. 0°	115.	57.3	38.2	28.6	22.9	19.1	16.4	14.3	12.7	11.4	10.4	9.51	8.78	8.14	7.60	**LAT. 0°**
1	115.	57.3	38.2	28.6	22.9	19.1	16.4	14.3	12.7	11.4	10.4	9.52	8.78	8.15	7.60	1
2	115.	57.3	38.2	28.7	22.9	19.1	16.4	14.3	12.7	11.4	10.4	9.52	8.78	8.15	7.60	2
3	115.	57.4	38.2	28.7	22.9	19.1	16.4	14.3	12.7	11.5	10.4	9.53	8.79	8.16	7.61	3
4	115.	57.4	38.3	28.7	23.0	19.1	16.4	14.3	12.7	11.5	10.4	9.54	8.80	8.16	7.61	4
5	115.	57.5	38.3	28.8	23.0	19.2	16.4	14.4	12.8	11.5	10.4	9.55	8.81	8.18	7.63	5
6	115.	57.6	38.4	28.8	23.0	19.2	16.4	14.4	12.8	11.5	10.4	9.57	8.83	8.19	7.64	6
7	115.	57.7	38.5	28.9	23.1	19.2	16.5	14.4	12.8	11.5	10.5	9.59	8.84	8.21	7.65	7
8	116.	57.9	38.6	28.9	23.1	19.3	16.5	14.4	12.8	11.5	10.5	9.61	8.86	8.22	7.67	8
9	116.	58.0	38.7	29.0	23.2	19.3	16.6	14.5	12.9	11.6	10.5	9.63	8.89	8.25	7.69	9
10	116.	58.2	38.8	29.1	23.3	19.4	16.6	14.5	12.9	11.6	10.6	9.66	8.91	8.27	7.71	10
11	117.	58.4	38.9	29.2	23.3	19.4	16.7	14.6	12.9	11.6	10.6	9.69	8.94	8.30	7.74	11
12	117.	58.6	39.0	29.3	23.4	19.5	16.7	14.6	13.0	11.7	10.6	9.73	8.97	8.33	7.77	12
13	118.	58.8	39.2	29.4	23.5	19.6	16.8	14.7	13.0	11.7	10.7	9.77	9.01	8.36	7.80	13
14	118.	59.0	39.4	29.5	23.6	19.7	16.9	14.7	13.1	11.8	10.7	9.81	9.05	8.39	7.83	14
15	119.	59.3	39.5	29.7	23.7	19.8	16.9	14.8	13.2	11.8	10.8	9.85	9.09	8.43	7.86	15
16	119.	59.6	39.7	29.8	23.8	19.9	17.0	14.9	13.2	11.9	10.8	9.90	9.13	8.47	7.90	16
17	120.	59.9	39.9	29.9	24.0	20.0	17.1	15.0	13.3	12.0	10.9	9.95	9.18	8.52	7.94	17
18	121.	60.2	40.2	30.1	24.1	20.1	17.2	15.0	13.4	12.0	10.9	10.0	9.23	8.56	7.99	18
19	121.	60.6	40.4	30.3	24.2	20.2	17.3	15.1	13.4	12.1	11.0	10.1	9.28	8.61	8.03	19
20	122.	61.0	40.6	30.5	24.4	20.3	17.4	15.2	13.5	12.2	11.1	10.1	9.34	8.67	8.08	20
21	123.	61.4	40.9	30.7	24.5	20.4	17.5	15.3	13.6	12.2	11.1	10.2	9.40	8.72	8.14	21
22	124.	61.8	41.2	30.9	24.7	20.6	17.6	15.4	13.7	12.3	11.2	10.3	9.47	8.78	8.19	22
23	125.	62.2	41.5	31.1	24.9	20.7	17.8	15.5	13.8	12.4	11.3	10.3	9.54	8.85	8.25	23
24	125.	62.7	41.8	31.4	25.1	20.9	17.9	15.7	13.9	12.5	11.4	10.4	9.61	8.92	8.32	24
25	126.	63.2	42.1	31.6	25.3	21.1	18.0	15.8	14.0	12.6	11.5	10.5	9.68	8.99	8.38	25
26	128.	63.7	42.5	31.9	25.5	21.2	18.2	15.9	14.1	12.7	11.6	10.6	9.77	9.06	8.45	26
27	129.	64.3	42.9	32.1	25.7	21.4	18.4	16.1	14.3	12.8	11.7	10.7	9.85	9.14	8.53	27
28	130.	64.9	43.4	32.4	25.9	21.6	18.5	16.2	14.4	13.0	11.8	10.8	9.94	9.22	8.60	28
29	131.	65.5	43.7	32.7	26.2	21.8	18.7	16.4	14.5	13.1	11.9	10.9	10.0	9.31	8.69	29
30	132.	66.2	44.1	33.1	26.5	22.0	18.9	16.5	14.7	13.2	12.0	11.0	10.1	9.40	8.77	30
31	134.	66.8	44.6	33.4	26.7	22.3	19.1	16.7	14.8	13.3	12.1	11.1	10.2	9.50	8.86	31
32	135.	67.6	45.0	33.8	27.0	22.5	19.3	16.9	15.0	13.5	12.3	11.2	10.4	9.60	8.96	32
33	137.	68.3	45.5	34.1	27.3	22.8	19.5	17.1	15.2	13.6	12.4	11.3	10.5	9.71	9.06	33
34	138.	69.1	46.1	34.5	27.6	23.0	19.7	17.3	15.3	13.8	12.5	11.5	10.6	9.82	9.16	34
35	140.	69.9	46.6	35.0	28.0	23.3	20.0	17.5	15.5	14.0	12.7	11.6	10.7	9.94	9.27	35
36	142.	70.8	47.2	35.4	28.3	23.6	20.2	17.7	15.7	14.1	12.8	11.8	10.9	10.1	9.39	36
37	144.	71.7	47.8	35.9	28.7	23.9	20.5	17.9	15.9	14.3	13.0	11.9	11.0	10.2	9.51	37
38	145.	72.7	48.5	36.3	29.1	24.2	20.8	18.2	16.1	14.5	13.2	12.1	11.1	10.3	9.64	38
39	147.	73.7	49.1	36.9	29.5	24.6	21.0	18.4	16.4	14.7	13.4	12.2	11.3	10.5	9.77	39
40	150.	74.8	49.9	37.4	29.9	24.9	21.3	18.7	16.6	14.9	13.6	12.4	11.5	10.6	9.92	40
41	152.	75.9	50.6	37.9	30.4	25.3	21.7	19.0	16.8	15.1	13.8	12.6	11.6	10.8	10.1	41
42	154.	77.1	51.4	38.5	30.8	25.7	22.0	19.2	17.1	15.4	14.0	12.8	11.8	11.0	10.2	42
43	157.	78.3	52.2	39.2	31.3	26.1	22.4	19.6	17.4	15.6	14.2	13.0	12.0	11.1	10.4	43
44	159.	79.6	53.1	39.8	31.8	26.5	22.7	19.9	17.7	15.9	14.4	13.2	12.2	11.3	10.6	44
45	162.	81.0	54.0	40.5	32.4	27.0	23.1	20.2	18.0	16.2	14.7	13.5	12.4	11.5	10.7	45
46	165.	82.5	55.0	41.2	33.0	27.5	23.5	20.6	18.3	16.5	15.0	13.7	12.6	11.7	10.9	46
47	168.	84.0	56.0	42.0	33.6	28.0	24.0	21.0	18.6	16.8	15.2	14.0	12.9	11.9	11.1	47
48	171.	85.6	57.1	42.8	34.2	28.5	24.4	21.4	19.0	17.1	15.5	14.2	13.1	12.2	11.4	48
49	175.	87.3	58.2	43.7	34.9	29.1	24.9	21.8	19.4	17.4	15.8	14.5	13.4	12.4	11.6	49
50	178.	89.1	59.4	44.6	35.6	29.7	25.4	22.3	19.8	17.8	16.2	14.8	13.7	12.7	11.8	50
51	182.	91.0	60.7	45.5	36.4	30.3	26.0	22.7	20.2	18.2	16.5	15.1	14.0	12.9	12.1	51
52	186.	93.1	62.0	46.5	37.2	31.0	26.6	23.2	20.6	18.6	16.9	15.5	14.3	13.2	12.3	52
53	190.	95.2	63.5	47.6	38.1	31.7	27.2	23.8	21.1	19.0	17.3	15.8	14.6	13.5	12.6	53
54	195.	97.5	65.0	48.7	39.0	32.5	27.8	24.3	21.6	19.5	17.7	16.2	14.9	13.9	12.9	54
55	200.	99.9	66.6	49.9	39.9	33.3	28.5	24.9	22.2	19.9	18.1	16.6	15.3	14.2	13.2	55
56	205.	103.	68.3	51.2	41.0	34.1	29.2	25.6	22.7	20.4	18.6	17.0	15.7	14.6	13.6	56
57	210.	105.	70.1	52.6	42.1	35.0	30.0	26.3	23.3	21.0	19.1	17.5	16.1	15.0	14.0	57
58	216.	108.	72.1	54.0	43.2	36.0	30.9	27.0	24.0	21.6	19.6	18.0	16.6	15.4	14.3	58
59	223.	111.	74.2	55.6	44.5	37.1	31.7	27.8	24.7	22.2	20.2	18.5	17.0	15.8	14.8	59
60	229.	115.	76.4	57.3	45.8	38.2	32.7	28.6	25.4	22.9	20.8	19.0	17.6	16.3	15.2	60

For quadrantal compass graduation readings the degrees are to be taken as for 1st Quadrant (0° to 90°). The azimuth is then named in accordance with the precepts above.

Table 30

C

(Longitude Correction)

Body **RISING** (H.A. greater than 180°)
North Lat. / South Lat.
{ Sign − Az. in **NE** Qdt. **SE** Qdt.
{ „ + „ **SE** „ **NE** „

Body **SETTING** (H.A. less than 180°)
{ Sign + Az. in **SW** Qdt. **NW** Qdt.
{ „ − „ **NW** „ **SW** „

Qdt. 1st	7½°	8°	8½°	9°	9½°	10°	10½°	11°	11½°	12°	12½°	13°	13½°	14°	14½°	15°	Qdt. NE
2nd	172½	172	171½	171	170½	170	169½	169	168½	168	167½	167	166½	166	165½	165	SE
3rd	187½	188	188½	189	189½	190	190½	191	191½	192	192½	193	193½	194	194½	195	SW
4th	352½	352	351½	351	350½	350	349½	349	348½	348	347½	347	346½	346	345½	345	NW
LAT.																	**LAT.**
0°	7·60	7·12	6·69	6·31	5·98	5·67	5·40	5·15	4·92	4·71	4·51	4·33	4·17	4·01	3·87	3·73	0°
1	7·60	7·12	6·69	6·32	5·98	5·67	5·40	5·15	4·92	4·71	4·51	4·33	4·17	4·01	3·87	3·73	1
2	7·60	7·12	6·70	6·32	5·98	5·68	5·40	5·15	4·92	4·71	4·51	4·33	4·17	4·01	3·87	3·73	2
3	7·61	7·13	6·70	6·32	5·98	5·68	5·40	5·15	4·92	4·71	4·52	4·34	4·17	4·02	3·87	3·74	3
4	7·61	7·13	6·71	6·33	5·99	5·69	5·41	5·16	4·93	4·72	4·52	4·34	4·18	4·02	3·88	3·74	4
5	7·63	7·14	6·72	6·34	6·00	5·69	5·42	5·16	4·93	4·72	4·53	4·35	4·18	4·03	3·88	3·75	5
6	7·64	7·16	6·73	6·35	6·01	5·70	5·43	5·17	4·94	4·73	4·54	4·36	4·19	4·03	3·89	3·75	6
7	7·65	7·17	6·74	6·36	6·02	5·71	5·44	5·18	4·95	4·74	4·55	4·36	4·20	4·04	3·90	3·76	7
8	7·67	7·19	6·76	6·38	6·03	5·73	5·45	5·20	4·96	4·75	4·56	4·37	4·21	4·05	3·91	3·77	8
9	7·69	7·20	6·78	6·39	6·05	5·74	5·46	5·21	4·98	4·76	4·57	4·39	4·22	4·06	3·92	3·78	9
10	7·71	7·23	6·79	6·41	6·07	5·76	5·48	5·22	4·99	4·78	4·58	4·40	4·23	4·07	3·93	3·79	10
11	7·74	7·25	6·82	6·43	6·09	5·78	5·50	5·24	5·01	4·79	4·60	4·41	4·24	4·09	3·94	3·80	11
12	7·77	7·27	6·84	6·46	6·11	5·80	5·52	5·26	5·03	4·81	4·61	4·43	4·26	4·10	3·95	3·82	12
13	7·80	7·30	6·87	6·48	6·13	5·82	5·54	5·28	5·04	4·83	4·63	4·45	4·28	4·12	3·97	3·83	13
14	7·83	7·33	6·90	6·51	6·16	5·85	5·56	5·30	5·07	4·85	4·65	4·46	4·29	4·13	3·99	3·85	14
15	7·86	7·37	6·93	6·54	6·19	5·87	5·59	5·33	5·09	4·87	4·67	4·48	4·31	4·15	4·00	3·86	15
16	7·90	7·40	6·96	6·57	6·22	5·90	5·61	5·35	5·11	4·89	4·69	4·51	4·33	4·17	4·02	3·88	16
17	7·94	7·44	7·00	6·60	6·25	5·93	5·64	5·38	5·14	4·92	4·72	4·53	4·36	4·19	4·04	3·90	17
18	7·99	7·48	7·04	6·64	6·28	5·96	5·67	5·41	5·17	4·95	4·74	4·55	4·38	4·22	4·07	3·92	18
19	8·03	7·53	7·08	6·68	6·32	6·00	5·71	5·44	5·20	4·98	4·77	4·58	4·41	4·24	4·09	3·95	19
20	8·08	7·57	7·12	6·72	6·36	6·04	5·74	5·48	5·23	5·01	4·80	4·61	4·43	4·27	4·12	3·97	20
21	8·14	7·62	7·17	6·76	6·40	6·08	5·78	5·51	5·27	5·04	4·83	4·64	4·46	4·30	4·14	4·00	21
22	8·19	7·67	7·22	6·81	6·45	6·12	5·82	5·55	5·30	5·07	4·87	4·67	4·49	4·33	4·17	4·03	22
23	8·25	7·73	7·27	6·86	6·49	6·16	5·86	5·59	5·34	5·11	4·90	4·71	4·53	4·36	4·20	4·05	23
24	8·32	7·79	7·32	6·91	6·54	6·21	5·91	5·63	5·38	5·15	4·94	4·74	4·56	4·39	4·23	4·09	24
25	8·38	7·85	7·38	6·97	6·59	6·26	5·95	5·68	5·42	5·19	4·98	4·78	4·60	4·43	4·27	4·12	25
26	8·45	7·92	7·45	7·03	6·65	6·31	6·00	5·72	5·47	5·23	5·02	4·82	4·63	4·46	4·30	4·15	26
27	8·53	7·99	7·51	7·09	6·71	6·37	6·06	5·77	5·52	5·28	5·06	4·86	4·68	4·50	4·34	4·19	27
28	8·60	8·06	7·58	7·15	6·77	6·42	6·11	5·83	5·57	5·33	5·11	4·91	4·72	4·54	4·38	4·23	28
29	8·69	8·14	7·65	7·22	6·83	6·48	6·17	5·88	5·62	5·38	5·16	4·95	4·76	4·59	4·42	4·27	29
30	8·77	8·22	7·73	7·29	6·90	6·55	6·23	5·94	5·68	5·43	5·21	5·00	4·81	4·63	4·47	4·31	30
31	8·86	8·30	7·81	7·37	6·97	6·62	6·30	6·00	5·73	5·49	5·26	5·05	4·86	4·68	4·51	4·35	31
32	8·96	8·39	7·89	7·45	7·05	6·69	6·36	6·07	5·80	5·55	5·32	5·11	4·91	4·73	4·56	4·40	32
33	9·06	8·48	7·98	7·53	7·13	6·76	6·43	6·13	5·86	5·61	5·38	5·17	4·97	4·78	4·61	4·45	33
34	9·16	8·58	8·07	7·62	7·21	6·84	6·51	6·21	5·93	5·68	5·44	5·23	5·02	4·84	4·66	4·50	34
35	9·27	8·69	8·17	7·71	7·30	6·92	6·59	6·28	6·00	5·74	5·51	5·29	5·09	4·90	4·72	4·56	35
36	9·39	8·80	8·27	7·80	7·39	7·01	6·67	6·36	6·08	5·82	5·58	5·35	5·15	4·96	4·78	4·61	36
37	9·51	8·91	8·38	7·91	7·48	7·10	6·76	6·44	6·15	5·89	5·65	5·42	5·22	5·02	4·84	4·67	37
38	9·64	9·03	8·49	8·01	7·58	7·20	6·85	6·53	6·24	5·97	5·72	5·50	5·29	5·09	4·91	4·74	38
39	9·77	9·16	8·61	8·12	7·69	7·30	6·94	6·62	6·33	6·05	5·80	5·57	5·36	5·16	4·98	4·80	39
40	9·92	9·29	8·74	8·24	7·80	7·40	7·04	6·72	6·42	6·14	5·89	5·65	5·44	5·24	5·05	4·87	40
41	10·1	9·43	8·87	8·37	7·92	7·52	7·15	6·82	6·51	6·23	5·98	5·74	5·52	5·31	5·12	4·95	41
42	10·2	9·58	9·00	8·50	8·04	7·63	7·26	6·92	6·61	6·33	6·07	5·83	5·61	5·40	5·20	5·02	42
43	10·4	9·73	9·15	8·63	8·17	7·75	7·38	7·03	6·72	6·43	6·17	5·92	5·70	5·48	5·29	5·10	43
44	10·6	9·89	9·30	8·78	8·31	7·88	7·50	7·15	6·83	6·54	6·27	6·02	5·79	5·58	5·38	5·19	44
45	10·7	10·1	9·46	8·93	8·45	8·02	7·63	7·28	6·95	6·65	6·38	6·13	5·89	5·67	5·47	5·28	45
46	10·9	10·2	9·63	9·09	8·60	8·16	7·77	7·41	7·08	6·77	6·49	6·24	6·00	5·77	5·57	5·37	46
47	11·1	10·4	9·81	9·26	8·76	8·32	7·91	7·54	7·21	6·90	6·61	6·35	6·11	5·88	5·67	5·47	47
48	11·4	10·6	10·0	9·44	8·93	8·48	8·06	7·69	7·35	7·03	6·74	6·47	6·23	5·99	5·78	5·58	48
49	11·6	10·9	10·2	9·62	9·11	8·64	8·22	7·84	7·49	7·17	6·88	6·60	6·35	6·11	5·89	5·69	49
50	11·8	11·1	10·4	9·82	9·30	8·82	8·39	8·00	7·65	7·32	7·02	6·74	6·48	6·24	6·02	5·81	50
51	12·1	11·3	10·6	10·0	9·50	9·01	8·57	8·18	7·81	7·48	7·17	6·88	6·62	6·37	6·14	5·93	51
52	12·3	11·6	10·9	10·3	9·71	9·21	8·76	8·36	7·98	7·64	7·33	7·04	6·77	6·52	6·28	6·06	52
53	12·6	11·8	11·1	10·5	9·93	9·42	8·97	8·55	8·17	7·82	7·50	7·20	6·92	6·66	6·43	6·20	53
54	12·9	12·1	11·4	10·7	10·2	9·65	9·18	8·75	8·36	8·00	7·67	7·37	7·09	6·82	6·58	6·35	54
55	13·2	12·4	11·7	11·0	10·4	9·89	9·41	8·97	8·57	8·20	7·86	7·55	7·26	6·99	6·74	6·51	55
56	13·6	12·7	12·0	11·3	10·7	10·1	9·65	9·20	8·79	8·41	8·07	7·75	7·45	7·17	6·92	6·67	56
57	14·0	13·1	12·3	11·6	11·0	10·4	9·91	9·45	9·03	8·64	8·28	7·95	7·65	7·36	7·10	6·85	57
58	14·3	13·4	12·6	11·9	11·3	10·7	10·2	9·71	9·28	8·88	8·51	8·17	7·86	7·57	7·30	7·04	58
59	14·8	13·8	13·0	12·3	11·6	11·0	10·5	9·99	9·54	9·14	8·76	8·41	8·09	7·79	7·51	7·25	59
60	15·2	14·2	13·4	12·6	12·0	11·3	10·8	10·3	9·83	9·41	9·02	8·66	8·33	8·02	7·73	7·46	60

For quadrantal compass graduation readings the degrees are to be taken as for 1st Quadrant (0° to 90°). The azimuth is then named in accordance with the precepts above.

Table 30

C

Body RISING (H.A. greater than 180°)

Body SETTING (H.A. less than 180°)

(Longitude Correction)

	North Lat.	South Lat.
Sign −	Az. in **NE** Qdt.	**SE** Qdt.
„ +	„ **SE** „	**NE** „
Sign +	Az. in **SW** Qdt.	**NW** Qdt.
„ −	„ **NW** „	**SW** „

AZIMUTH or Course (according to Quadrant)

Qdt. 1st 2nd 3rd 4th	15° 165 195 345	15½° 164½ 195½ 344½	16° 164 196 344	16½° 163½ 196½ 343½	17° 163 197 343	17½° 162½ 197½ 342½	18° 162 198 342	18½° 161½ 198½ 341½	19° 161 199 341	19½° 160½ 199½ 340½	20° 160 200 340	20½° 159½ 200½ 339½	21° 159 201 339	21½° 158½ 201½ 338½	22° 158 202 338	22½° 157½ 202½ 337½	Qdt. NE SE SW NW
LAT.																	**LAT.**
0°	3.73	3.61	3.49	3.38	3.27	3.17	3.08	2.99	2.90	2.82	2.75	2.68	2.61	2.54	2.48	2.41	0°
1	3.73	3.61	3.49	3.38	3.27	3.17	3.08	2.99	2.91	2.82	2.75	2.68	2.61	2.54	2.48	2.42	1
2	3.73	3.61	3.49	3.38	3.27	3.17	3.08	2.99	2.91	2.83	2.75	2.68	2.61	2.54	2.48	2.42	2
3	3.74	3.61	3.49	3.38	3.28	3.18	3.08	2.99	2.91	2.83	2.75	2.68	2.61	2.54	2.48	2.42	3
4	3.74	3.62	3.50	3.38	3.28	3.18	3.09	3.00	2.91	2.83	2.75	2.68	2.61	2.55	2.48	2.42	4
5	3.75	3.62	3.50	3.39	3.28	3.18	3.09	3.00	2.92	2.84	2.76	2.69	2.62	2.55	2.49	2.42	5
6	3.75	3.63	3.51	3.40	3.29	3.19	3.10	3.01	2.92	2.84	2.76	2.69	2.62	2.55	2.49	2.43	6
7	3.76	3.63	3.51	3.40	3.30	3.20	3.10	3.01	2.93	2.85	2.77	2.70	2.63	2.56	2.49	2.43	7
8	3.77	3.64	3.52	3.41	3.30	3.20	3.11	3.02	2.93	2.85	2.77	2.70	2.63	2.56	2.50	2.44	8
9	3.78	3.65	3.53	3.42	3.31	3.21	3.12	3.03	2.94	2.86	2.78	2.71	2.64	2.57	2.51	2.44	9
10	3.79	3.66	3.54	3.43	3.32	3.22	3.13	3.04	2.95	2.87	2.79	2.72	2.65	2.58	2.51	2.45	10
11	3.80	3.67	3.55	3.44	3.33	3.23	3.14	3.05	2.96	2.88	2.80	2.73	2.65	2.59	2.52	2.46	11
12	3.82	3.69	3.57	3.45	3.34	3.24	3.15	3.06	2.97	2.89	2.81	2.73	2.66	2.60	2.53	2.47	12
13	3.83	3.70	3.58	3.47	3.36	3.26	3.16	3.07	2.98	2.90	2.82	2.75	2.67	2.61	2.54	2.48	13
14	3.85	3.72	3.59	3.48	3.37	3.27	3.17	3.08	2.99	2.91	2.83	2.76	2.69	2.62	2.55	2.49	14
15	3.86	3.73	3.61	3.50	3.39	3.28	3.19	3.09	3.01	2.92	2.84	2.77	2.70	2.63	2.56	2.50	15
16	3.88	3.75	3.63	3.51	3.40	3.30	3.20	3.11	3.02	2.94	2.86	2.78	2.71	2.64	2.58	2.51	16
17	3.90	3.77	3.65	3.53	3.42	3.32	3.22	3.13	3.04	2.95	2.87	2.80	2.72	2.66	2.59	2.53	17
18	3.92	3.79	3.67	3.55	3.44	3.34	3.24	3.14	3.05	2.97	2.89	2.81	2.74	2.67	2.60	2.54	18
19	3.95	3.81	3.69	3.57	3.46	3.35	3.26	3.16	3.07	2.99	2.91	2.83	2.76	2.69	2.62	2.55	19
20	3.97	3.84	3.71	3.59	3.48	3.38	3.28	3.18	3.09	3.01	2.92	2.85	2.77	2.70	2.63	2.57	20
21	4.00	3.86	3.74	3.62	3.50	3.40	3.30	3.20	3.11	3.03	2.94	2.87	2.79	2.72	2.65	2.59	21
22	4.03	3.89	3.76	3.64	3.53	3.42	3.32	3.22	3.13	3.05	2.96	2.89	2.81	2.74	2.67	2.60	22
23	4.05	3.92	3.79	3.67	3.55	3.45	3.34	3.25	3.16	3.07	2.99	2.91	2.83	2.76	2.69	2.62	23
24	4.09	3.95	3.82	3.70	3.58	3.47	3.37	3.27	3.18	3.09	3.01	2.93	2.85	2.78	2.71	2.64	24
25	4.12	3.98	3.85	3.73	3.61	3.50	3.40	3.30	3.20	3.12	3.03	2.95	2.87	2.80	2.73	2.66	25
26	4.15	4.01	3.88	3.76	3.64	3.53	3.42	3.33	3.23	3.14	3.06	2.98	2.90	2.83	2.75	2.69	26
27	4.19	4.05	3.91	3.79	3.67	3.56	3.45	3.35	3.26	3.17	3.08	3.00	2.92	2.85	2.78	2.71	27
28	4.23	4.08	3.95	3.82	3.70	3.59	3.49	3.39	3.29	3.20	3.11	3.03	2.95	2.88	2.80	2.73	28
29	4.27	4.12	3.99	3.86	3.74	3.63	3.52	3.42	3.32	3.23	3.14	3.06	2.98	2.90	2.83	2.76	29
30	4.31	4.16	4.03	3.90	3.78	3.66	3.55	3.45	3.35	3.26	3.17	3.09	3.01	2.93	2.86	2.79	30
31	4.35	4.21	4.07	3.94	3.82	3.70	3.59	3.49	3.39	3.29	3.21	3.12	3.04	2.96	2.89	2.82	31
32	4.40	4.25	4.11	3.98	3.86	3.74	3.63	3.52	3.43	3.33	3.24	3.15	3.07	2.99	2.92	2.85	32
33	4.45	4.30	4.16	4.03	3.90	3.78	3.67	3.56	3.46	3.37	3.28	3.19	3.11	3.03	2.95	2.88	33
34	4.50	4.35	4.21	4.07	3.95	3.83	3.71	3.61	3.50	3.41	3.31	3.23	3.14	3.06	2.99	2.91	34
35	4.56	4.40	4.26	4.12	3.99	3.87	3.76	3.65	3.55	3.45	3.35	3.27	3.18	3.10	3.02	2.95	35
36	4.61	4.46	4.31	4.17	4.04	3.92	3.80	3.69	3.59	3.49	3.40	3.31	3.22	3.14	3.06	2.98	36
37	4.67	4.52	4.37	4.23	4.10	3.97	3.85	3.74	3.64	3.54	3.44	3.35	3.26	3.18	3.10	3.02	37
38	4.74	4.58	4.43	4.28	4.15	4.03	3.91	3.79	3.69	3.58	3.49	3.39	3.31	3.22	3.14	3.06	38
39	4.80	4.64	4.49	4.34	4.21	4.08	3.96	3.85	3.74	3.63	3.54	3.44	3.35	3.27	3.19	3.11	39
40	4.87	4.71	4.55	4.41	4.27	4.14	4.02	3.90	3.79	3.69	3.59	3.49	3.40	3.31	3.23	3.15	40
41	4.95	4.78	4.62	4.47	4.33	4.20	4.08	3.96	3.85	3.74	3.64	3.54	3.45	3.36	3.28	3.20	41
42	5.02	4.85	4.69	4.54	4.40	4.27	4.14	4.02	3.91	3.80	3.70	3.60	3.51	3.42	3.33	3.25	42
43	5.10	4.93	4.77	4.62	4.47	4.34	4.21	4.09	3.97	3.86	3.76	3.66	3.56	3.47	3.38	3.30	43
44	5.19	5.01	4.85	4.69	4.55	4.41	4.28	4.16	4.04	3.93	3.82	3.72	3.62	3.53	3.44	3.36	44
45	5.28	5.10	4.93	4.77	4.63	4.49	4.35	4.23	4.11	3.99	3.89	3.78	3.68	3.59	3.50	3.41	45
46	5.37	5.19	5.02	4.86	4.71	4.57	4.43	4.30	4.18	4.07	3.96	3.85	3.75	3.66	3.56	3.48	46
47	5.47	5.29	5.11	4.95	4.80	4.65	4.51	4.38	4.26	4.14	4.03	3.92	3.82	3.72	3.63	3.54	47
48	5.58	5.39	5.21	5.05	4.89	4.74	4.60	4.47	4.34	4.22	4.11	4.00	3.89	3.79	3.70	3.61	48
49	5.69	5.50	5.32	5.15	4.99	4.83	4.69	4.56	4.43	4.30	4.19	4.08	3.97	3.87	3.77	3.68	49
50	5.81	5.61	5.43	5.25	5.09	4.93	4.79	4.65	4.52	4.39	4.27	4.16	4.05	3.95	3.85	3.76	50
51	5.93	5.73	5.54	5.36	5.20	5.04	4.89	4.75	4.62	4.49	4.37	4.25	4.14	4.03	3.93	3.84	51
52	6.06	5.86	5.67	5.48	5.31	5.15	5.00	4.85	4.72	4.59	4.46	4.34	4.23	4.12	4.02	3.92	52
53	6.20	5.99	5.80	5.61	5.44	5.27	5.11	4.97	4.83	4.69	4.57	4.44	4.33	4.22	4.11	4.01	53
54	6.35	6.14	5.93	5.74	5.57	5.40	5.24	5.09	4.94	4.80	4.67	4.55	4.43	4.32	4.21	4.11	54
55	6.51	6.29	6.08	5.89	5.70	5.53	5.37	5.21	5.06	4.92	4.79	4.66	4.54	4.43	4.32	4.21	55
56	6.67	6.45	6.24	6.04	5.85	5.67	5.50	5.35	5.19	5.05	4.91	4.78	4.66	4.54	4.43	4.32	56
57	6.85	6.62	6.40	6.20	6.01	5.82	5.65	5.49	5.33	5.19	5.05	4.91	4.78	4.66	4.54	4.43	57
58	7.04	6.81	6.58	6.37	6.17	5.99	5.81	5.64	5.48	5.33	5.19	5.05	4.92	4.79	4.67	4.56	58
59	7.25	7.00	6.77	6.56	6.35	6.16	5.98	5.80	5.64	5.48	5.34	5.19	5.06	4.93	4.81	4.69	59
60	7.46	7.21	6.98	6.75	6.54	6.34	6.16	5.98	5.81	5.65	5.50	5.35	5.21	5.08	4.95	4.83	60

For quadrantal compass graduation readings the degrees are to be taken as for 1st Quadrant (0° to 90°). The azimuth is then named in accordance with the precepts above.

Table 30

C
(Longitude Correction)

Body **RISING** (H.A. greater than 180°)
Body **SETTING** (H.A. less than 180°)

	North Lat.	South Lat.
Body **RISING**	Sign − Az. in **NE** Qdt. **SE** Qdt.	
	„ + „ **SE** „ **NE** „	
Body **SETTING**	Sign + Az. in **SW** Qdt. **NW** Qdt.	
	„ − „ **NW** „ **SW** „	

AZIMUTH or Course (according to Quadrant)

Qdt.	22½°	23°	23½°	24°	24½°	25°	25½°	26°	26½°	27°	27½°	28°	28½°	29°	29½°	30°	Qdt.
1st	22½	23	23½	24	24½	25	25½	26	26½	27	27½	28	28½	29	29½	30	NE
2nd	157½	157	156½	156	155½	155	154½	154	153½	153	152½	152	151½	151	150½	150	SE
3rd	202½	203	203½	204	204½	205	205½	206	206½	207	207½	208	208½	209	209½	210	SW
4th	337½	337	336½	336	335½	335	334½	334	333½	333	332½	332	331½	331	330½	330	NW

LAT.																	LAT.
0°	2.41	2.36	2.30	2.25	2.19	2.15	2.10	2.05	2.01	1.96	1.92	1.88	1.84	1.80	1.77	1.73	0°
1	2.42	2.36	2.30	2.25	2.20	2.15	2.10	2.05	2.01	1.96	1.92	1.88	1.84	1.80	1.77	1.73	1
2	2.42	2.36	2.30	2.25	2.20	2.15	2.10	2.05	2.01	1.96	1.92	1.88	1.84	1.81	1.77	1.73	2
3	2.42	2.36	2.30	2.25	2.20	2.15	2.10	2.05	2.01	1.97	1.92	1.88	1.84	1.81	1.77	1.73	3
4	2.42	2.36	2.31	2.25	2.20	2.15	2.10	2.06	2.01	1.97	1.93	1.89	1.85	1.81	1.77	1.74	4
5	2.42	2.37	2.31	2.26	2.20	2.15	2.11	2.06	2.01	1.97	1.93	1.89	1.85	1.81	1.77	1.74	5
6	2.43	2.37	2.31	2.26	2.21	2.16	2.11	2.06	2.02	1.97	1.93	1.89	1.85	1.81	1.78	1.74	6
7	2.43	2.37	2.32	2.26	2.21	2.16	2.11	2.07	2.02	1.98	1.94	1.90	1.86	1.82	1.78	1.75	7
8	2.44	2.38	2.32	2.27	2.22	2.17	2.12	2.07	2.03	1.98	1.94	1.90	1.86	1.82	1.79	1.75	8
9	2.44	2.39	2.33	2.27	2.22	2.17	2.12	2.08	2.03	1.99	1.95	1.90	1.87	1.83	1.79	1.75	9
10	2.45	2.39	2.34	2.28	2.23	2.18	2.13	2.08	2.04	1.99	1.95	1.91	1.87	1.83	1.80	1.76	10
11	2.46	2.40	2.34	2.29	2.24	2.19	2.14	2.09	2.04	2.00	1.96	1.92	1.88	1.84	1.80	1.76	11
12	2.47	2.41	2.35	2.30	2.24	2.19	2.14	2.10	2.05	2.01	1.96	1.92	1.88	1.84	1.81	1.77	12
13	2.48	2.42	2.36	2.31	2.25	2.20	2.15	2.10	2.06	2.01	1.97	1.93	1.89	1.85	1.81	1.78	13
14	2.49	2.43	2.37	2.32	2.26	2.21	2.16	2.11	2.07	2.02	1.98	1.94	1.90	1.86	1.82	1.79	14
15	2.50	2.44	2.38	2.33	2.27	2.22	2.17	2.12	2.08	2.03	1.99	1.95	1.91	1.87	1.83	1.79	15
16	2.51	2.45	2.39	2.34	2.28	2.23	2.18	2.13	2.09	2.04	2.00	1.96	1.92	1.88	1.84	1.80	16
17	2.53	2.46	2.41	2.35	2.30	2.24	2.19	2.14	2.10	2.05	2.01	1.97	1.93	1.89	1.85	1.81	17
18	2.54	2.48	2.42	2.36	2.31	2.26	2.20	2.16	2.11	2.06	2.02	1.98	1.94	1.90	1.86	1.82	18
19	2.55	2.49	2.43	2.38	2.32	2.27	2.22	2.17	2.12	2.08	2.03	1.99	1.95	1.91	1.87	1.83	19
20	2.57	2.51	2.45	2.39	2.34	2.28	2.23	2.18	2.13	2.09	2.04	2.00	1.96	1.92	1.88	1.84	20
21	2.59	2.52	2.46	2.41	2.35	2.30	2.25	2.20	2.15	2.10	2.06	2.02	1.97	1.93	1.89	1.86	21
22	2.60	2.54	2.48	2.42	2.37	2.31	2.26	2.21	2.16	2.12	2.07	2.03	1.99	1.95	1.91	1.87	22
23	2.62	2.56	2.50	2.44	2.38	2.33	2.28	2.23	2.18	2.13	2.09	2.04	2.00	1.96	1.92	1.88	23
24	2.64	2.58	2.52	2.46	2.40	2.35	2.30	2.24	2.20	2.15	2.10	2.06	2.02	1.98	1.94	1.90	24
25	2.66	2.60	2.54	2.48	2.42	2.37	2.31	2.26	2.21	2.17	2.12	2.08	2.03	1.99	1.95	1.91	25
26	2.69	2.62	2.56	2.50	2.44	2.39	2.33	2.28	2.23	2.18	2.14	2.09	2.05	2.01	1.97	1.93	26
27	2.71	2.64	2.58	2.52	2.46	2.41	2.35	2.30	2.25	2.20	2.16	2.11	2.07	2.03	1.98	1.94	27
28	2.73	2.67	2.61	2.54	2.49	2.43	2.37	2.32	2.27	2.22	2.18	2.13	2.09	2.04	2.00	1.96	28
29	2.76	2.69	2.63	2.57	2.51	2.45	2.40	2.34	2.29	2.24	2.20	2.15	2.11	2.06	2.02	1.98	29
30	2.79	2.72	2.66	2.59	2.53	2.48	2.42	2.37	2.32	2.27	2.22	2.17	2.13	2.08	2.04	2.00	30
31	2.82	2.75	2.68	2.62	2.56	2.50	2.45	2.39	2.34	2.29	2.24	2.19	2.15	2.11	2.06	2.02	31
32	2.85	2.78	2.71	2.65	2.59	2.53	2.47	2.42	2.37	2.31	2.27	2.22	2.17	2.13	2.08	2.04	32
33	2.88	2.81	2.74	2.68	2.62	2.56	2.50	2.45	2.39	2.34	2.29	2.24	2.20	2.15	2.11	2.07	33
34	2.91	2.84	2.77	2.71	2.65	2.59	2.53	2.47	2.42	2.37	2.32	2.27	2.22	2.18	2.13	2.09	34
35	2.95	2.88	2.81	2.74	2.68	2.62	2.56	2.50	2.45	2.40	2.35	2.30	2.25	2.20	2.16	2.11	35
36	2.98	2.91	2.84	2.78	2.71	2.65	2.59	2.53	2.48	2.43	2.37	2.33	2.28	2.23	2.19	2.14	36
37	3.02	2.95	2.88	2.81	2.75	2.69	2.63	2.57	2.51	2.46	2.41	2.36	2.31	2.26	2.21	2.17	37
38	3.06	2.99	2.92	2.85	2.79	2.72	2.66	2.60	2.55	2.49	2.44	2.39	2.34	2.29	2.24	2.20	38
39	3.11	3.03	2.96	2.89	2.82	2.76	2.70	2.64	2.58	2.53	2.47	2.42	2.37	2.32	2.27	2.23	39
40	3.15	3.08	3.00	2.93	2.86	2.80	2.74	2.68	2.62	2.56	2.51	2.46	2.40	2.36	2.31	2.26	40
41	3.20	3.12	3.05	2.98	2.91	2.84	2.78	2.72	2.66	2.60	2.55	2.49	2.44	2.39	2.34	2.30	41
42	3.25	3.17	3.10	3.02	2.95	2.89	2.82	2.76	2.70	2.64	2.59	2.53	2.48	2.43	2.38	2.33	42
43	3.30	3.22	3.15	3.07	3.00	2.93	2.87	2.80	2.74	2.68	2.63	2.57	2.52	2.47	2.42	2.37	43
44	3.36	3.28	3.20	3.12	3.05	2.98	2.92	2.85	2.79	2.73	2.67	2.62	2.56	2.51	2.46	2.41	44
45	3.41	3.33	3.25	3.18	3.10	3.03	2.97	2.90	2.84	2.78	2.72	2.66	2.61	2.55	2.50	2.45	45
46	3.48	3.39	3.31	3.23	3.16	3.09	3.02	2.95	2.89	2.83	2.77	2.71	2.65	2.60	2.54	2.49	46
47	3.54	3.45	3.37	3.29	3.22	3.14	3.07	3.01	2.94	2.88	2.82	2.76	2.70	2.65	2.59	2.54	47
48	3.61	3.52	3.44	3.36	3.28	3.21	3.13	3.06	3.00	2.93	2.87	2.81	2.75	2.70	2.64	2.59	48
49	3.68	3.59	3.51	3.42	3.35	3.27	3.20	3.13	3.06	2.99	2.93	2.87	2.81	2.75	2.69	2.64	49
50	3.76	3.67	3.58	3.49	3.41	3.34	3.26	3.19	3.12	3.05	2.99	2.93	2.87	2.81	2.75	2.70	50
51	3.84	3.74	3.65	3.57	3.49	3.41	3.33	3.26	3.19	3.12	3.05	2.99	2.93	2.87	2.81	2.75	51
52	3.92	3.83	3.74	3.65	3.56	3.48	3.41	3.33	3.26	3.19	3.12	3.06	2.99	2.93	2.87	2.81	52
53	4.01	3.92	3.82	3.73	3.65	3.56	3.48	3.41	3.33	3.26	3.19	3.13	3.06	3.00	2.94	2.88	53
54	4.11	4.01	3.91	3.82	3.73	3.65	3.57	3.49	3.41	3.34	3.27	3.20	3.13	3.07	3.01	2.95	54
55	4.21	4.11	4.01	3.92	3.83	3.74	3.66	3.58	3.50	3.42	3.35	3.28	3.21	3.15	3.08	3.02	55
56	4.32	4.21	4.11	4.02	3.92	3.84	3.75	3.67	3.59	3.51	3.44	3.36	3.29	3.23	3.16	3.10	56
57	4.43	4.33	4.22	4.12	4.03	3.94	3.85	3.77	3.68	3.60	3.53	3.45	3.38	3.31	3.25	3.18	57
58	4.56	4.45	4.34	4.24	4.14	4.05	3.96	3.87	3.79	3.70	3.63	3.55	3.48	3.40	3.34	3.27	58
59	4.69	4.57	4.47	4.36	4.26	4.16	4.07	3.98	3.89	3.81	3.73	3.65	3.58	3.50	3.43	3.36	59
60	4.83	4.71	4.60	4.49	4.39	4.29	4.19	4.10	4.01	3.93	3.84	3.76	3.68	3.61	3.54	3.46	60

For quadrantal compass graduation readings the degrees are to be taken as for 1st Quadrant (0° to 90°). The azimuth is then named in accordance with the precepts above.

Table 30

C

Body RISING (H.A. greater than 180°)

Body SETTING (H.A. less than 180°)

(Longitude Correction)

	North Lat.	South Lat.
Body RISING	Sign − Az. in **NE** Qdt.	**SE** Qdt.
	" + " **SE** "	**NE** "
Body SETTING	Sign + Az. in **SW** Qdt.	**NW** Qdt.
	" − " **NW** "	**SW** "

AZIMUTH or Course (according to Quadrant)

Qdt. 1st	30°	30½°	31°	31½°	32°	32½°	33°	33½°	34°	34½°	35°	35½°	36°	36½°	37°	37½°	NE
2nd	150	149½	149	148½	148	147½	147	146½	146	145½	145	144½	144	143½	143	142½	SE
3rd	210	210½	211	211½	212	212½	213	213½	214	214½	215	215½	216	216½	217	217½	SW
4th	330	329½	329	328½	328	327½	327	326½	326	325½	325	324½	324	323½	323	322½	NW

LAT.																	LAT.
0°	1.73	1.70	1.66	1.63	1.60	1.57	1.54	1.51	1.48	1.45	1.43	1.40	1.38	1.35	1.33	1.30	0°
1	1.73	1.70	1.67	1.63	1.60	1.57	1.54	1.51	1.48	1.46	1.43	1.40	1.38	1.35	1.33	1.30	1
2	1.73	1.70	1.67	1.63	1.60	1.57	1.54	1.51	1.48	1.46	1.43	1.40	1.38	1.35	1.33	1.30	2
3	1.73	1.70	1.67	1.63	1.60	1.57	1.54	1.51	1.49	1.46	1.43	1.40	1.38	1.35	1.33	1.31	3
4	1.74	1.70	1.67	1.64	1.60	1.57	1.54	1.52	1.49	1.46	1.43	1.41	1.38	1.36	1.33	1.31	4
5	1.74	1.70	1.67	1.64	1.61	1.58	1.55	1.52	1.49	1.46	1.43	1.41	1.38	1.36	1.33	1.31	5
6	1.74	1.71	1.67	1.64	1.61	1.58	1.55	1.52	1.49	1.46	1.44	1.41	1.38	1.36	1.33	1.31	6
7	1.75	1.71	1.68	1.64	1.61	1.58	1.55	1.52	1.49	1.47	1.44	1.41	1.39	1.36	1.34	1.31	7
8	1.75	1.71	1.68	1.65	1.62	1.59	1.56	1.53	1.50	1.47	1.44	1.42	1.39	1.37	1.34	1.32	8
9	1.75	1.72	1.69	1.65	1.62	1.59	1.56	1.53	1.50	1.47	1.45	1.42	1.39	1.37	1.34	1.32	9
10	1.76	1.72	1.69	1.66	1.63	1.59	1.56	1.53	1.51	1.48	1.45	1.42	1.40	1.37	1.35	1.32	10
11	1.76	1.73	1.70	1.66	1.63	1.60	1.57	1.54	1.51	1.48	1.46	1.43	1.40	1.38	1.35	1.33	11
12	1.77	1.74	1.70	1.67	1.64	1.61	1.57	1.54	1.52	1.49	1.46	1.43	1.41	1.38	1.36	1.33	12
13	1.78	1.74	1.71	1.68	1.64	1.61	1.58	1.55	1.52	1.49	1.47	1.44	1.41	1.39	1.36	1.34	13
14	1.79	1.75	1.72	1.68	1.65	1.62	1.59	1.56	1.53	1.50	1.47	1.45	1.42	1.39	1.37	1.34	14
15	1.79	1.76	1.72	1.69	1.66	1.63	1.59	1.56	1.54	1.51	1.48	1.45	1.43	1.40	1.37	1.35	15
16	1.80	1.77	1.73	1.70	1.67	1.63	1.60	1.57	1.54	1.51	1.49	1.46	1.43	1.41	1.38	1.36	16
17	1.81	1.78	1.74	1.71	1.67	1.64	1.61	1.58	1.55	1.52	1.49	1.47	1.44	1.41	1.39	1.36	17
18	1.82	1.79	1.75	1.72	1.68	1.65	1.62	1.59	1.56	1.53	1.50	1.47	1.45	1.42	1.40	1.37	18
19	1.83	1.80	1.76	1.73	1.69	1.66	1.63	1.60	1.57	1.54	1.51	1.48	1.46	1.43	1.40	1.38	19
20	1.84	1.81	1.77	1.74	1.70	1.67	1.64	1.61	1.58	1.55	1.52	1.49	1.47	1.44	1.41	1.39	20
21	1.86	1.82	1.78	1.75	1.71	1.68	1.65	1.62	1.59	1.56	1.53	1.50	1.47	1.45	1.42	1.40	21
22	1.87	1.83	1.80	1.76	1.73	1.69	1.66	1.63	1.60	1.57	1.54	1.51	1.48	1.46	1.43	1.41	22
23	1.88	1.84	1.81	1.77	1.74	1.71	1.67	1.64	1.61	1.58	1.55	1.52	1.50	1.47	1.44	1.42	23
24	1.90	1.86	1.82	1.79	1.75	1.72	1.69	1.65	1.62	1.59	1.56	1.54	1.51	1.48	1.45	1.43	24
25	1.91	1.87	1.84	1.80	1.77	1.73	1.70	1.67	1.64	1.61	1.58	1.55	1.52	1.49	1.46	1.44	25
26	1.93	1.89	1.85	1.82	1.78	1.75	1.71	1.68	1.65	1.62	1.59	1.56	1.53	1.50	1.48	1.45	26
27	1.94	1.91	1.87	1.83	1.80	1.76	1.73	1.70	1.66	1.63	1.60	1.57	1.55	1.52	1.49	1.46	27
28	1.96	1.92	1.89	1.85	1.81	1.78	1.74	1.71	1.68	1.65	1.62	1.59	1.56	1.53	1.50	1.48	28
29	1.98	1.94	1.90	1.87	1.83	1.80	1.76	1.73	1.70	1.66	1.63	1.60	1.57	1.55	1.52	1.49	29
30	2.00	1.96	1.92	1.88	1.85	1.81	1.78	1.75	1.71	1.68	1.65	1.62	1.59	1.56	1.53	1.51	30
31	2.02	1.98	1.94	1.90	1.87	1.83	1.80	1.76	1.73	1.70	1.67	1.64	1.61	1.58	1.55	1.52	31
32	2.04	2.00	1.96	1.92	1.89	1.85	1.82	1.78	1.75	1.72	1.68	1.65	1.62	1.59	1.57	1.54	32
33	2.07	2.02	1.98	1.95	1.91	1.87	1.84	1.80	1.77	1.74	1.70	1.67	1.64	1.61	1.58	1.55	33
34	2.09	2.05	2.01	1.97	1.93	1.89	1.86	1.82	1.79	1.76	1.72	1.69	1.66	1.63	1.60	1.57	34
35	2.11	2.07	2.03	1.99	1.95	1.92	1.88	1.84	1.81	1.78	1.74	1.71	1.68	1.65	1.62	1.59	35
36	2.14	2.10	2.06	2.02	1.98	1.94	1.90	1.87	1.83	1.80	1.77	1.73	1.70	1.67	1.64	1.61	36
37	2.17	2.13	2.08	2.04	2.00	1.97	1.93	1.89	1.86	1.82	1.79	1.76	1.72	1.69	1.66	1.63	37
38	2.20	2.15	2.11	2.07	2.03	1.99	1.95	1.92	1.88	1.85	1.81	1.78	1.75	1.72	1.68	1.65	38
39	2.23	2.18	2.14	2.10	2.06	2.02	1.98	1.94	1.91	1.87	1.84	1.80	1.77	1.74	1.71	1.68	39
40	2.26	2.22	2.17	2.13	2.09	2.05	2.01	1.97	1.94	1.90	1.86	1.83	1.80	1.76	1.73	1.70	40
41	2.30	2.25	2.21	2.16	2.12	2.08	2.04	2.00	1.96	1.93	1.89	1.86	1.82	1.79	1.76	1.73	41
42	2.33	2.28	2.24	2.20	2.15	2.11	2.07	2.03	2.00	1.96	1.92	1.89	1.85	1.82	1.79	1.75	42
43	2.37	2.32	2.28	2.23	2.19	2.15	2.11	2.07	2.03	1.99	1.95	1.92	1.88	1.85	1.82	1.78	43
44	2.41	2.36	2.31	2.27	2.23	2.18	2.14	2.10	2.06	2.02	1.99	1.95	1.91	1.88	1.85	1.81	44
45	2.45	2.40	2.35	2.31	2.26	2.22	2.18	2.14	2.10	2.06	2.02	1.98	1.95	1.91	1.88	1.84	45
46	2.49	2.44	2.40	2.35	2.30	2.26	2.22	2.18	2.13	2.10	2.06	2.02	1.98	1.95	1.91	1.88	46
47	2.54	2.49	2.44	2.39	2.35	2.30	2.26	2.22	2.17	2.13	2.09	2.06	2.02	1.98	1.95	1.91	47
48	2.59	2.54	2.49	2.44	2.39	2.35	2.30	2.26	2.22	2.17	2.13	2.10	2.06	2.02	1.98	1.95	48
49	2.64	2.59	2.54	2.49	2.44	2.39	2.35	2.30	2.26	2.22	2.18	2.14	2.10	2.06	2.02	1.99	49
50	2.70	2.64	2.59	2.54	2.49	2.44	2.40	2.35	2.31	2.26	2.22	2.18	2.14	2.10	2.07	2.03	50
51	2.75	2.70	2.65	2.59	2.54	2.49	2.45	2.40	2.36	2.31	2.27	2.23	2.19	2.15	2.11	2.07	51
52	2.81	2.76	2.70	2.65	2.60	2.55	2.50	2.45	2.41	2.36	2.32	2.28	2.24	2.20	2.16	2.12	52
53	2.88	2.82	2.77	2.71	2.66	2.61	2.56	2.51	2.46	2.42	2.37	2.33	2.29	2.25	2.21	2.17	53
54	2.95	2.89	2.83	2.78	2.72	2.67	2.62	2.57	2.52	2.48	2.43	2.39	2.34	2.30	2.26	2.22	54
55	3.02	2.96	2.90	2.85	2.79	2.74	2.69	2.63	2.59	2.54	2.49	2.44	2.40	2.36	2.31	2.27	55
56	3.10	3.04	2.98	2.92	2.86	2.81	2.75	2.70	2.65	2.60	2.55	2.51	2.46	2.42	2.37	2.33	56
57	3.18	3.12	3.06	3.00	2.94	2.88	2.83	2.77	2.72	2.67	2.62	2.57	2.53	2.48	2.44	2.39	57
58	3.27	3.20	3.14	3.08	3.02	2.96	2.91	2.85	2.80	2.75	2.70	2.65	2.60	2.55	2.50	2.46	58
59	3.36	3.30	3.23	3.17	3.11	3.05	2.99	2.93	2.88	2.83	2.77	2.72	2.67	2.62	2.58	2.53	59
60	3.46	3.40	3.33	3.26	3.20	3.14	3.08	3.02	2.97	2.91	2.86	2.80	2.75	2.70	2.65	2.61	60

For quadrantal compass graduation readings the degrees are to be taken as for 1st Quadrant (0° to 90°). The azimuth is then named in accordance with the precepts above.

Table 30

C

(Longitude Correction)

Body **RISING** (H.A. greater than 180°)

Body **SETTING** (H.A. less than 180°)

	North Lat.	South Lat.	
Sign −	Az. in **NE** Qdt.	**SE**	Qdt.
" +	" **SE** "	**NE**	"
Sign +	Az. in **SW** Qdt.	**NW**	Qdt.
" −	" **NW** "	**SW**	"

AZIMUTH or Course (according to Quadrant)

Qdt. 1st	$37\frac{1}{2}°$	38°	$38\frac{1}{2}°$	39°	$39\frac{1}{2}°$	40°	$40\frac{1}{2}°$	41°	$41\frac{1}{2}°$	42°	$42\frac{1}{2}°$	43°	$43\frac{1}{2}°$	44°	$44\frac{1}{2}°$	45°	Qdt. NE
2nd	$142\frac{1}{2}$	142	$141\frac{1}{2}$	141	$140\frac{1}{2}$	140	$139\frac{1}{2}$	139	$138\frac{1}{2}$	138	$137\frac{1}{2}$	137	$136\frac{1}{2}$	136	$135\frac{1}{2}$	135	SE
3rd	$217\frac{1}{2}$	218	$218\frac{1}{2}$	219	$219\frac{1}{2}$	220	$220\frac{1}{2}$	221	$221\frac{1}{2}$	222	$222\frac{1}{2}$	223	$223\frac{1}{2}$	224	$224\frac{1}{2}$	225	SW
4th	$322\frac{1}{2}$	322	$321\frac{1}{2}$	321	$320\frac{1}{2}$	320	$319\frac{1}{2}$	319	$318\frac{1}{2}$	318	$317\frac{1}{2}$	317	$316\frac{1}{2}$	316	$315\frac{1}{2}$	315	NW

LAT.																	LAT.
0°	1.30	1.28	1.26	1.24	1.21	1.19	1.17	1.15	1.13	1.11	1.09	1.07	1.05	1.04	1.02	1.00	0°
1	1.30	1.28	1.26	1.24	1.21	1.19	1.17	1.15	1.13	1.11	1.09	1.07	1.05	1.04	1.02	1.00	1
2	1.30	1.28	1.26	1.24	1.21	1.19	1.17	1.15	1.13	1.11	1.09	1.07	1.05	1.04	1.02	1.00	2
3	1.31	1.28	1.26	1.24	1.22	1.19	1.17	1.15	1.13	1.11	1.09	1.07	1.06	1.04	1.02	1.00	3
4	1.31	1.28	1.26	1.24	1.22	1.20	1.17	1.15	1.13	1.11	1.09	1.08	1.06	1.04	1.02	1.00	4
5	1.31	1.29	1.26	1.24	1.22	1.20	1.18	1.16	1.14	1.12	1.10	1.08	1.06	1.04	1.02	1.00	5
6	1.31	1.29	1.26	1.24	1.22	1.20	1.18	1.16	1.14	1.12	1.10	1.08	1.06	1.04	1.02	1.01	6
7	1.31	1.29	1.27	1.24	1.22	1.20	1.18	1.16	1.14	1.12	1.10	1.08	1.06	1.04	1.03	1.01	7
8	1.32	1.29	1.27	1.25	1.23	1.20	1.18	1.16	1.14	1.12	1.10	1.08	1.06	1.05	1.03	1.01	8
9	1.32	1.30	1.27	1.25	1.23	1.21	1.19	1.17	1.14	1.12	1.11	1.09	1.07	1.05	1.03	1.01	9
10	1.32	1.30	1.28	1.25	1.23	1.21	1.19	1.17	1.15	1.13	1.11	1.09	1.07	1.05	1.03	1.02	10
11	1.33	1.30	1.28	1.26	1.24	1.21	1.19	1.17	1.15	1.13	1.11	1.09	1.07	1.06	1.04	1.02	11
12	1.33	1.31	1.29	1.26	1.24	1.22	1.20	1.18	1.16	1.14	1.12	1.10	1.08	1.06	1.04	1.02	12
13	1.34	1.31	1.29	1.27	1.25	1.22	1.20	1.18	1.16	1.14	1.12	1.10	1.08	1.06	1.04	1.03	13
14	1.34	1.32	1.30	1.27	1.25	1.23	1.21	1.19	1.17	1.15	1.13	1.11	1.09	1.07	1.05	1.03	14
15	1.35	1.33	1.30	1.28	1.26	1.23	1.21	1.19	1.17	1.15	1.13	1.11	1.09	1.07	1.05	1.04	15
16	1.36	1.33	1.31	1.29	1.26	1.24	1.22	1.20	1.18	1.16	1.14	1.12	1.10	1.08	1.06	1.04	16
17	1.36	1.34	1.32	1.29	1.27	1.25	1.22	1.20	1.18	1.16	1.14	1.12	1.10	1.08	1.06	1.05	17
18	1.37	1.35	1.32	1.30	1.28	1.25	1.23	1.21	1.19	1.17	1.15	1.13	1.11	1.09	1.07	1.05	18
19	1.38	1.35	1.33	1.31	1.28	1.26	1.24	1.22	1.20	1.18	1.15	1.13	1.11	1.10	1.08	1.06	19
20	1.39	1.36	1.34	1.31	1.29	1.27	1.25	1.22	1.20	1.18	1.16	1.14	1.12	1.10	1.08	1.06	20
21	1.40	1.37	1.35	1.32	1.30	1.28	1.25	1.23	1.21	1.19	1.17	1.15	1.13	1.11	1.09	1.07	21
22	1.41	1.38	1.36	1.33	1.31	1.29	1.26	1.24	1.22	1.20	1.18	1.16	1.14	1.12	1.10	1.08	22
23	1.42	1.39	1.37	1.34	1.32	1.30	1.27	1.25	1.23	1.21	1.19	1.17	1.15	1.13	1.11	1.09	23
24	1.43	1.40	1.38	1.35	1.33	1.31	1.28	1.26	1.24	1.22	1.20	1.17	1.15	1.13	1.11	1.10	24
25	1.44	1.41	1.39	1.36	1.34	1.32	1.29	1.27	1.25	1.23	1.20	1.18	1.16	1.14	1.12	1.10	25
26	1.45	1.42	1.40	1.37	1.35	1.33	1.30	1.28	1.26	1.24	1.21	1.19	1.17	1.15	1.13	1.11	26
27	1.46	1.44	1.41	1.39	1.36	1.34	1.31	1.29	1.27	1.25	1.23	1.20	1.18	1.16	1.14	1.12	27
28	1.48	1.45	1.42	1.40	1.37	1.35	1.33	1.30	1.28	1.26	1.24	1.22	1.19	1.17	1.15	1.13	28
29	1.49	1.46	1.44	1.41	1.39	1.36	1.34	1.32	1.29	1.27	1.25	1.23	1.21	1.18	1.16	1.14	29
30	1.51	1.48	1.45	1.43	1.40	1.38	1.35	1.33	1.31	1.28	1.26	1.24	1.22	1.20	1.18	1.16	30
31	1.52	1.49	1.47	1.44	1.42	1.39	1.37	1.34	1.32	1.30	1.27	1.25	1.23	1.21	1.19	1.17	31
32	1.54	1.51	1.48	1.46	1.43	1.41	1.38	1.36	1.33	1.31	1.29	1.27	1.24	1.22	1.20	1.18	32
33	1.55	1.53	1.50	1.47	1.45	1.42	1.40	1.37	1.35	1.32	1.30	1.28	1.26	1.24	1.21	1.19	33
34	1.57	1.54	1.52	1.49	1.46	1.44	1.41	1.39	1.36	1.34	1.32	1.29	1.27	1.25	1.23	1.21	34
35	1.59	1.56	1.54	1.51	1.48	1.46	1.43	1.40	1.38	1.36	1.33	1.31	1.29	1.26	1.24	1.22	35
36	1.61	1.58	1.55	1.53	1.50	1.47	1.45	1.42	1.40	1.37	1.35	1.33	1.30	1.28	1.26	1.24	36
37	1.63	1.60	1.57	1.55	1.52	1.49	1.47	1.44	1.42	1.39	1.37	1.34	1.32	1.30	1.27	1.25	37
38	1.65	1.62	1.60	1.57	1.54	1.51	1.49	1.46	1.43	1.41	1.39	1.36	1.34	1.31	1.29	1.27	38
39	1.68	1.65	1.62	1.59	1.56	1.53	1.51	1.48	1.45	1.43	1.40	1.38	1.36	1.33	1.31	1.29	39
40	1.70	1.67	1.64	1.61	1.58	1.56	1.53	1.50	1.48	1.45	1.43	1.40	1.38	1.35	1.33	1.31	40
41	1.73	1.70	1.67	1.64	1.61	1.58	1.55	1.52	1.50	1.47	1.45	1.42	1.40	1.37	1.35	1.33	41
42	1.75	1.72	1.69	1.66	1.63	1.60	1.58	1.55	1.52	1.49	1.47	1.44	1.42	1.39	1.37	1.35	42
43	1.78	1.75	1.72	1.69	1.66	1.63	1.60	1.57	1.55	1.52	1.49	1.47	1.44	1.42	1.39	1.37	43
44	1.81	1.78	1.75	1.72	1.69	1.66	1.63	1.60	1.57	1.54	1.52	1.49	1.47	1.44	1.42	1.39	44
45	1.84	1.81	1.78	1.75	1.72	1.69	1.66	1.63	1.60	1.57	1.54	1.52	1.49	1.46	1.44	1.41	45
46	1.88	1.84	1.81	1.78	1.75	1.72	1.69	1.66	1.63	1.60	1.57	1.54	1.52	1.49	1.47	1.44	46
47	1.91	1.88	1.84	1.81	1.78	1.75	1.72	1.69	1.66	1.63	1.60	1.57	1.55	1.52	1.49	1.47	47
48	1.95	1.91	1.88	1.85	1.81	1.78	1.75	1.72	1.69	1.66	1.63	1.60	1.58	1.55	1.52	1.49	48
49	1.99	1.95	1.92	1.88	1.85	1.82	1.79	1.75	1.72	1.69	1.66	1.64	1.61	1.58	1.55	1.52	49
50	2.03	1.99	1.96	1.92	1.89	1.85	1.82	1.79	1.76	1.73	1.70	1.67	1.64	1.61	1.58	1.56	50
51	2.07	2.03	2.00	1.96	1.93	1.89	1.86	1.83	1.80	1.77	1.73	1.70	1.67	1.65	1.62	1.59	51
52	2.12	2.08	2.04	2.01	1.97	1.94	1.90	1.87	1.84	1.80	1.77	1.74	1.71	1.68	1.65	1.62	52
53	2.17	2.13	2.09	2.05	2.02	1.98	1.95	1.91	1.88	1.85	1.81	1.78	1.75	1.72	1.69	1.66	53
54	2.22	2.18	2.14	2.10	2.06	2.03	1.99	1.96	1.92	1.89	1.86	1.82	1.79	1.76	1.73	1.70	54
55	2.27	2.23	2.19	2.15	2.12	2.08	2.04	2.01	1.97	1.94	1.90	1.87	1.84	1.81	1.77	1.74	55
56	2.33	2.29	2.25	2.21	2.17	2.13	2.09	2.06	2.02	1.99	1.95	1.92	1.88	1.85	1.82	1.79	56
57	2.39	2.35	2.31	2.27	2.23	2.19	2.15	2.11	2.08	2.04	2.00	1.97	1.94	1.90	1.87	1.84	57
58	2.46	2.42	2.37	2.33	2.29	2.25	2.21	2.17	2.13	2.10	2.06	2.02	1.99	1.95	1.92	1.89	58
59	2.53	2.49	2.44	2.40	2.36	2.31	2.27	2.23	2.20	2.16	2.12	2.08	2.05	2.01	1.98	1.94	59
60	2.61	2.56	2.51	2.47	2.43	2.38	2.34	2.30	2.26	2.22	2.18	2.15	2.11	2.07	2.04	2.00	60

For quadrantal compass graduation readings the degrees are to be taken as for 1st Quadrant (0° to 90°). The azimuth is then named in accordance with the precepts above.

Table 30

C

(Longitude Correction)

Body **RISING** (H.A. greater than 180°)

Body **SETTING** (H.A. less than 180°)

North Lat. | South Lat.

{ Sign − Az. in **NE** Qdt. **SE** Qdt.
{ " + " **SE** " **NE** "
{ Sign + Az. in **SW** Qdt. **NW** Qdt.
{ " − " **NW** " **SW** "

AZIMUTH or Course (according to Quadrant)

Qdt. 1st	45°	45½°	46°	46½°	47°	47½°	48°	48½°	49°	49½°	50°	50½°	51°	51½°	52°	52½°	Qdt. NE
2nd	135	134½	134	133½	133	132½	132	131½	131	130½	130	129½	129	128½	128	127½	SE
3rd	225	225½	226	226½	227	227½	228	228½	229	229½	230	230½	231	231½	232	232½	SW
4th	315	314½	314	313½	313	312½	312	311½	311	310½	310	309½	309	308½	308	307½	NW

LAT.	45°	45½°	46°	46½°	47°	47½°	48°	48½°	49°	49½°	50°	50½°	51°	51½°	52°	52½°	LAT.
0°	1.00	.983	.966	.949	.933	.916	.900	.885	.869	.854	.839	.824	.810	.795	.781	.767	0°
1	1.00	.983	.966	.949	.933	.916	.901	.885	.869	.854	.839	.824	.810	.796	.781	.767	1
2	1.00	.983	.966	.950	.933	.917	.901	.885	.870	.855	.840	.825	.810	.796	.782	.768	2
3	1.00	.984	.967	.950	.934	.918	.902	.886	.870	.855	.840	.825	.811	.797	.782	.768	3
4	1.00	.985	.968	.951	.935	.919	.903	.887	.871	.856	.841	.826	.812	.797	.783	.769	4
5	1.00	.986	.969	.953	.936	.920	.904	.888	.873	.857	.842	.827	.813	.798	.784	.770	5
6	1.01	.988	.971	.954	.938	.921	.905	.890	.874	.859	.844	.829	.814	.800	.786	.772	6
7	1.01	.990	.973	.956	.940	.923	.907	.891	.876	.860	.845	.831	.816	.801	.787	.773	7
8	1.01	.992	.975	.958	.942	.925	.909	.893	.878	.862	.847	.832	.818	.803	.789	.775	8
9	1.01	.995	.978	.961	.944	.928	.912	.896	.880	.865	.850	.835	.820	.805	.791	.777	9
10	1.02	.998	.981	.964	.947	.930	.914	.898	.883	.867	.852	.837	.822	.808	.793	.779	10
11	1.02	1.00	.984	.967	.950	.933	.917	.901	.886	.870	.855	.840	.825	.810	.796	.782	11
12	1.02	1.01	.987	.970	.953	.937	.921	.904	.889	.873	.858	.843	.828	.813	.799	.784	12
13	1.03	1.01	.991	.974	.957	.940	.924	.908	.892	.877	.861	.846	.831	.816	.802	.788	13
14	1.03	1.01	.995	.978	.961	.944	.928	.912	.896	.880	.865	.850	.835	.820	.805	.791	14
15	1.04	1.02	1.00	.982	.965	.949	.932	.916	.900	.884	.869	.853	.838	.823	.809	.794	15
16	1.04	1.02	1.01	.987	.970	.953	.937	.920	.904	.888	.873	.858	.842	.827	.813	.798	16
17	1.05	1.03	1.01	.992	.975	.958	.942	.925	.909	.893	.877	.862	.847	.832	.817	.802	17
18	1.05	1.03	1.02	.998	.981	.963	.947	.930	.914	.898	.882	.867	.851	.836	.821	.807	18
19	1.06	1.04	1.02	1.00	.986	.969	.952	.936	.919	.903	.887	.872	.856	.841	.826	.812	19
20	1.06	1.05	1.03	1.01	.992	.975	.958	.942	.925	.909	.893	.877	.862	.846	.831	.817	20
21	1.07	1.05	1.03	1.02	.999	.982	.964	.948	.931	.915	.899	.883	.867	.852	.837	.822	21
22	1.08	1.06	1.04	1.02	1.01	.988	.971	.954	.938	.921	.905	.889	.873	.858	.843	.828	22
23	1.09	1.07	1.05	1.03	1.01	.995	.978	.961	.944	.928	.912	.896	.880	.864	.849	.834	23
24	1.10	1.08	1.06	1.04	1.02	1.00	.986	.968	.952	.935	.919	.902	.886	.871	.855	.840	24
25	1.10	1.08	1.07	1.05	1.03	1.01	.993	.976	.959	.942	.926	.910	.893	.878	.862	.847	25
26	1.11	1.09	1.07	1.06	1.04	1.02	1.00	.984	.967	.950	.934	.917	.901	.885	.869	.854	26
27	1.12	1.10	1.08	1.07	1.05	1.03	1.01	.993	.976	.959	.942	.925	.909	.893	.877	.861	27
28	1.13	1.11	1.09	1.08	1.06	1.04	1.02	1.00	.985	.967	.950	.934	.917	.901	.885	.869	28
29	1.14	1.12	1.10	1.09	1.07	1.05	1.03	1.01	.994	.977	.959	.943	.926	.909	.893	.877	29
30	1.16	1.14	1.12	1.10	1.08	1.06	1.04	1.02	1.00	.986	.969	.952	.935	.918	.902	.886	30
31	1.17	1.15	1.13	1.11	1.09	1.07	1.05	1.03	1.01	.996	.979	.962	.945	.928	.911	.895	31
32	1.18	1.16	1.14	1.12	1.10	1.08	1.06	1.04	1.03	1.01	.989	.972	.955	.938	.921	.905	32
33	1.19	1.17	1.15	1.13	1.11	1.09	1.07	1.06	1.04	1.02	1.00	.983	.966	.948	.932	.915	33
34	1.21	1.19	1.17	1.15	1.13	1.11	1.09	1.07	1.05	1.03	1.01	.994	.977	.959	.942	.926	34
35	1.22	1.20	1.18	1.16	1.14	1.12	1.10	1.08	1.06	1.04	1.02	1.01	.989	.971	.954	.937	35
36	1.24	1.22	1.19	1.17	1.15	1.13	1.11	1.09	1.07	1.06	1.04	1.02	1.00	.983	.966	.948	36
37	1.25	1.23	1.21	1.19	1.17	1.15	1.13	1.11	1.09	1.07	1.05	1.03	1.01	.996	.978	.961	37
38	1.27	1.25	1.23	1.20	1.18	1.16	1.14	1.12	1.10	1.08	1.07	1.05	1.03	1.01	.991	.974	38
39	1.29	1.26	1.24	1.22	1.20	1.18	1.16	1.14	1.12	1.10	1.08	1.06	1.04	1.02	1.01	.987	39
40	1.31	1.28	1.26	1.24	1.22	1.20	1.18	1.16	1.14	1.12	1.10	1.08	1.06	1.04	1.02	1.00	40
41	1.33	1.30	1.28	1.26	1.24	1.21	1.19	1.17	1.15	1.13	1.11	1.09	1.07	1.05	1.04	1.02	41
42	1.35	1.32	1.30	1.28	1.26	1.23	1.21	1.19	1.17	1.15	1.13	1.11	1.09	1.07	1.05	1.03	42
43	1.37	1.34	1.32	1.30	1.28	1.25	1.23	1.21	1.19	1.17	1.15	1.13	1.11	1.09	1.07	1.05	43
44	1.39	1.37	1.34	1.32	1.30	1.27	1.25	1.23	1.21	1.19	1.17	1.15	1.13	1.11	1.09	1.07	44
45	1.41	1.39	1.37	1.34	1.32	1.30	1.27	1.25	1.23	1.21	1.19	1.17	1.15	1.13	1.11	1.09	45
46	1.44	1.42	1.39	1.37	1.34	1.32	1.30	1.27	1.25	1.23	1.21	1.19	1.17	1.15	1.13	1.11	46
47	1.47	1.44	1.42	1.39	1.37	1.34	1.32	1.30	1.28	1.25	1.23	1.21	1.19	1.17	1.15	1.13	47
48	1.49	1.47	1.44	1.42	1.39	1.37	1.35	1.32	1.30	1.28	1.25	1.23	1.21	1.19	1.17	1.15	48
49	1.52	1.50	1.47	1.45	1.42	1.40	1.37	1.35	1.33	1.30	1.28	1.26	1.23	1.21	1.19	1.17	49
50	1.56	1.53	1.50	1.48	1.45	1.43	1.40	1.38	1.35	1.33	1.31	1.28	1.26	1.24	1.22	1.19	50
51	1.59	1.56	1.53	1.51	1.48	1.46	1.43	1.41	1.38	1.36	1.33	1.31	1.29	1.26	1.24	1.22	51
52	1.62	1.60	1.57	1.54	1.52	1.49	1.46	1.44	1.41	1.39	1.36	1.34	1.32	1.29	1.27	1.25	52
53	1.66	1.63	1.61	1.58	1.55	1.52	1.50	1.47	1.44	1.42	1.39	1.37	1.35	1.32	1.30	1.28	53
54	1.70	1.67	1.64	1.61	1.59	1.56	1.53	1.51	1.48	1.45	1.43	1.40	1.38	1.35	1.33	1.31	54
55	1.74	1.71	1.68	1.65	1.63	1.60	1.57	1.54	1.52	1.49	1.46	1.44	1.41	1.39	1.36	1.34	55
56	1.79	1.76	1.73	1.70	1.67	1.64	1.61	1.58	1.56	1.53	1.50	1.47	1.45	1.42	1.40	1.37	56
57	1.84	1.80	1.77	1.74	1.71	1.68	1.65	1.62	1.60	1.57	1.54	1.51	1.49	1.46	1.44	1.41	57
58	1.89	1.85	1.82	1.79	1.76	1.73	1.70	1.67	1.64	1.61	1.58	1.56	1.53	1.50	1.47	1.45	58
59	1.94	1.91	1.88	1.84	1.81	1.78	1.75	1.72	1.69	1.66	1.63	1.60	1.57	1.54	1.52	1.49	59
60	2.00	1.97	1.93	1.90	1.87	1.83	1.80	1.77	1.74	1.71	1.68	1.65	1.62	1.59	1.56	1.54	60

For quadrantal compass graduation readings the degrees are to be taken as for 1st Quadrant (0° to 90°). The azimuth is then named in accordance with the precepts above.

Table 30

C (Longitude Correction)

	North Lat.	South Lat.
Body **RISING** (H.A. greater than 180°)	Sign **−** Az. in **NE** Qdt. **SE** Qdt.	" **+** " **SE** " **NE** "
Body **SETTING** (H.A. less than 180°)	Sign **+** Az. in **SW** Qdt. **NW** Qdt.	" **−** " **NW** " **SW** "

AZIMUTH or Course (according to Quadrant)

Qdt.																	Qdt.
1st	52½°	53°	53½°	54°	54½°	55°	55½°	56°	56½°	57°	57½°	58°	58½°	59°	59½°	60°	NE
2nd	127½	127	126½	126	125½	125	124½	124	123½	123	122½	122	121½	121	120½	120	SE
3rd	232½	233	233½	234	234½	235	235½	236	236½	237	237½	238	238½	239	239½	240	SW
4th	307½	307	306½	306	305½	305	304½	304	303½	303	302½	302	301½	301	300½	300	NW

LAT.	52½°	53°	53½°	54°	54½°	55°	55½°	56°	56½°	57°	57½°	58°	58½°	59°	59½°	60°	LAT.
0°	.767	.754	.740	.727	.713	.700	.687	.675	.662	.649	.637	.625	.613	.601	.589	.577	0°
1	.767	.754	.740	.727	.713	.700	.687	.675	.662	.650	.637	.625	.613	.601	.589	.577	1
2	.768	.754	.740	.727	.714	.701	.688	.675	.662	.650	.637	.625	.613	.601	.589	.578	2
3	.768	.755	.741	.728	.714	.701	.688	.675	.663	.650	.638	.626	.614	.602	.590	.578	3
4	.769	.755	.742	.728	.715	.702	.689	.676	.664	.651	.639	.626	.614	.602	.590	.579	4
5	.770	.756	.743	.729	.716	.703	.690	.677	.664	.652	.640	.627	.615	.603	.591	.580	5
6	.772	.758	.744	.731	.717	.704	.691	.678	.666	.653	.641	.628	.616	.604	.592	.581	6
7	.773	.759	.746	.732	.719	.705	.692	.680	.667	.654	.642	.630	.617	.605	.593	.582	7
8	.775	.761	.747	.734	.720	.707	.694	.681	.668	.656	.643	.631	.619	.607	.595	.583	8
9	.777	.763	.749	.736	.722	.709	.696	.683	.670	.658	.645	.633	.620	.608	.596	.585	9
10	.779	.765	.751	.738	.724	.711	.698	.685	.672	.659	.647	.635	.622	.610	.598	.586	10
11	.782	.768	.754	.740	.727	.713	.700	.687	.674	.662	.649	.637	.624	.612	.600	.588	11
12	.784	.770	.756	.743	.729	.716	.703	.690	.677	.664	.651	.639	.626	.614	.602	.590	12
13	.788	.773	.759	.746	.732	.719	.705	.692	.679	.666	.654	.641	.629	.617	.605	.593	13
14	.791	.777	.763	.749	.735	.722	.708	.695	.682	.669	.657	.644	.632	.619	.607	.595	14
15	.794	.780	.766	.752	.738	.725	.712	.698	.685	.672	.660	.647	.634	.622	.610	.598	15
16	.798	.784	.770	.756	.742	.728	.715	.702	.689	.676	.663	.650	.637	.625	.613	.601	16
17	.802	.788	.774	.760	.746	.732	.719	.705	.692	.679	.666	.653	.641	.628	.616	.604	17
18	.807	.792	.778	.764	.750	.736	.723	.709	.696	.683	.670	.657	.644	.632	.619	.607	18
19	.812	.797	.783	.768	.754	.741	.727	.713	.700	.687	.674	.661	.648	.635	.623	.611	19
20	.817	.802	.787	.773	.759	.745	.731	.718	.704	.691	.678	.665	.652	.639	.627	.614	20
21	.822	.807	.793	.778	.764	.750	.736	.722	.709	.696	.682	.669	.656	.644	.631	.618	21
22	.828	.813	.798	.784	.769	.755	.741	.727	.714	.700	.687	.674	.661	.648	.635	.623	22
23	.834	.819	.804	.789	.775	.761	.747	.733	.719	.705	.692	.679	.666	.653	.640	.627	23
24	.840	.825	.810	.795	.781	.766	.752	.738	.725	.711	.697	.684	.671	.658	.645	.632	24
25	.847	.831	.816	.802	.787	.773	.758	.744	.730	.717	.703	.689	.676	.663	.650	.637	25
26	.854	.838	.823	.808	.794	.779	.765	.750	.736	.723	.709	.695	.682	.669	.655	.642	26
27	.861	.846	.830	.815	.801	.786	.771	.757	.743	.729	.715	.701	.688	.674	.661	.648	27
28	.869	.853	.838	.823	.808	.793	.778	.764	.750	.736	.722	.708	.694	.681	.667	.654	28
29	.877	.862	.846	.831	.816	.801	.786	.771	.757	.743	.728	.714	.701	.687	.673	.660	29
30	.886	.870	.854	.839	.824	.809	.794	.779	.764	.750	.736	.722	.708	.694	.680	.667	30
31	.895	.879	.863	.848	.832	.817	.802	.787	.772	.758	.743	.729	.715	.701	.687	.674	31
32	.905	.889	.873	.857	.841	.826	.810	.795	.780	.766	.751	.737	.723	.709	.695	.681	32
33	.915	.899	.882	.866	.851	.835	.819	.804	.789	.774	.760	.745	.731	.716	.702	.688	33
34	.926	.909	.893	.876	.860	.845	.829	.814	.798	.783	.768	.754	.739	.725	.711	.696	34
35	.937	.920	.903	.887	.871	.855	.839	.823	.808	.793	.778	.763	.748	.734	.719	.705	35
36	.948	.931	.915	.898	.882	.866	.850	.834	.818	.803	.787	.772	.757	.743	.728	.714	36
37	.961	.944	.927	.910	.893	.877	.861	.845	.829	.813	.798	.782	.767	.752	.738	.723	37
38	.974	.956	.939	.922	.905	.889	.872	.856	.840	.824	.808	.793	.778	.763	.748	.733	38
39	.987	.970	.952	.935	.918	.901	.884	.868	.852	.836	.820	.804	.789	.773	.758	.743	39
40	1.00	.984	.966	.948	.931	.914	.897	.881	.864	.848	.832	.816	.800	.784	.769	.754	40
41	1.02	.998	.980	.963	.945	.928	.911	.894	.877	.860	.844	.828	.812	.796	.780	.765	41
42	1.03	1.01	.996	.978	.960	.942	.925	.908	.891	.874	.857	.841	.825	.809	.793	.777	42
43	1.05	1.03	1.01	.993	.975	.957	.940	.922	.905	.888	.871	.854	.838	.822	.805	.789	43
44	1.07	1.05	1.03	1.01	.992	.973	.955	.938	.920	.903	.886	.869	.852	.835	.819	.803	44
45	1.09	1.07	1.05	1.03	1.01	.990	.972	.954	.936	.918	.901	.884	.867	.850	.833	.817	45
46	1.11	1.09	1.07	1.05	1.03	1.01	.989	.971	.953	.935	.917	.900	.882	.865	.848	.831	46
47	1.13	1.11	1.09	1.07	1.05	1.03	1.01	.989	.971	.952	.934	.916	.899	.881	.864	.847	47
48	1.15	1.13	1.11	1.09	1.07	1.05	1.03	1.01	.989	.971	.952	.934	.916	.898	.880	.863	48
49	1.17	1.15	1.13	1.11	1.09	1.07	1.05	1.03	1.01	.990	.971	.952	.934	.916	.898	.880	49
50	1.19	1.17	1.15	1.13	1.11	1.09	1.07	1.05	1.03	1.01	.991	.972	.953	.935	.916	.898	50
51	1.22	1.20	1.18	1.15	1.13	1.11	1.09	1.07	1.05	1.03	1.01	.993	.974	.955	.936	.917	51
52	1.25	1.22	1.20	1.18	1.16	1.14	1.12	1.10	1.08	1.06	1.04	1.02	.995	.976	.957	.938	52
53	1.28	1.25	1.23	1.21	1.19	1.16	1.14	1.12	1.10	1.08	1.06	1.04	1.02	.998	.979	.959	53
54	1.31	1.28	1.26	1.24	1.21	1.19	1.17	1.15	1.13	1.11	1.08	1.06	1.04	1.02	1.00	.982	54
55	1.34	1.31	1.29	1.27	1.24	1.22	1.20	1.18	1.15	1.13	1.11	1.09	1.07	1.05	1.03	1.01	55
56	1.37	1.35	1.32	1.30	1.28	1.25	1.23	1.21	1.18	1.16	1.14	1.12	1.10	1.08	1.05	1.03	56
57	1.41	1.38	1.36	1.33	1.31	1.29	1.26	1.24	1.22	1.19	1.17	1.15	1.13	1.10	1.08	1.06	57
58	1.45	1.42	1.40	1.37	1.35	1.32	1.30	1.27	1.25	1.23	1.20	1.18	1.16	1.13	1.11	1.09	58
59	1.49	1.46	1.44	1.41	1.39	1.36	1.33	1.31	1.29	1.26	1.24	1.21	1.19	1.17	1.14	1.12	59
60	1.54	1.51	1.48	1.45	1.43	1.40	1.38	1.35	1.32	1.30	1 27	1.25	1.23	1.20	1.18	1.16	60

For quadrantal compass graduation readings the degrees are to be taken as for 1st Quadrant (0° to 90°). The azimuth is then named in accordance with the precepts above.

Table 30

							North Lat.	South Lat.

C

(Longitude Correction)

Body **RISING** (H.A. greater than 180°)
Body **SETTING** (H.A. less than 180°)

Sign	−	Az. in **NE** Qdt.	**SE**	Qdt.
"	+	" **SE**	" **NE**	"
Sign	+	Az. in **SW** Qdt.	**NW** Qdt.
"	−	" **NW**	" **SW**	"

Qdt. 1st	60°	60½°	61°	61½°	62°	62½°	63°	63½°	64°	64½°	65°	65½°	66°	66½°	67°	67½°	Qdt. NE
2nd	120	119½	119	118½	118	117½	117	116½	116	115½	115	114½	114	113½	113	112½	SE
3rd	240	240½	241	241½	242	242½	243	243½	244	244½	245	245½	246	246½	247	247½	SW
4th	300	299½	299	298½	298	297½	297	296½	296	295½	295	294½	294	293½	293	292½	NW

AZIMUTH or Course (according to Quadrant)

LAT.	60°	60½°	61°	61½°	62°	62½°	63°	63½°	64°	64½°	65°	65½°	66°	66½°	67°	67½°	LAT.
0°	.577	.566	.554	.543	.532	.521	.510	.499	.488	.477	.466	.456	.445	.435	.424	.414	0°
1	.577	.566	.554	.543	.532	.521	.510	.499	.488	.477	.466	.456	.445	.435	.425	.414	1
2	.578	.566	.555	.543	.532	.521	.510	.499	.488	.477	.467	.456	.446	.435	.425	.414	2
3	.578	.567	.555	.544	.532	.521	.510	.499	.488	.478	.467	.456	.446	.435	.425	.415	3
4	.579	.567	.556	.544	.533	.522	.511	.500	.489	.478	.467	.457	.446	.436	.426	.415	4
5	.580	.568	.556	.545	.534	.523	.511	.500	.490	.479	.468	.457	.447	.436	.426	.416	5
6	.581	.569	.557	.546	.535	.523	.512	.501	.490	.480	.469	.458	.448	.437	.427	.416	6
7	.582	.570	.558	.547	.536	.524	.513	.502	.491	.481	.470	.459	.449	.438	.428	.417	7
8	.583	.571	.560	.548	.537	.526	.515	.503	.493	.482	.471	.460	.450	.439	.429	.418	8
9	.585	.573	.561	.550	.538	.527	.516	.505	.494	.483	.472	.461	.451	.440	.430	.419	9
10	.586	.575	.563	.551	.540	.529	.517	.506	.495	.484	.474	.463	.452	.442	.431	.421	10
11	.588	.576	.565	.553	.542	.530	.519	.508	.497	.486	.475	.464	.454	.443	.432	.422	11
12	.590	.578	.567	.555	.544	.532	.521	.510	.499	.488	.477	.466	.455	.445	.434	.423	12
13	.593	.581	.569	.557	.546	.534	.523	.512	.501	.490	.479	.468	.457	.446	.436	.425	13
14	.595	.583	.571	.560	.548	.537	.525	.514	.503	.492	.481	.470	.459	.448	.437	.427	14
15	.598	.586	.574	.562	.550	.539	.527	.516	.505	.494	.483	.472	.461	.450	.439	.429	15
16	.601	.589	.577	.565	.553	.542	.530	.519	.507	.496	.485	.474	.463	.452	.442	.431	16
17	.604	.592	.580	.568	.556	.544	.533	.521	.510	.499	.488	.477	.466	.455	.444	.433	17
18	.607	.595	.583	.571	.559	.547	.536	.524	.513	.502	.490	.479	.468	.457	.446	.436	18
19	.611	.598	.586	.574	.562	.551	.539	.527	.516	.504	.493	.482	.471	.460	.449	.438	19
20	.614	.602	.590	.578	.566	.554	.542	.531	.519	.508	.496	.485	.474	.463	.452	.441	20
21	.618	.606	.594	.582	.570	.558	.546	.534	.522	.511	.499	.488	.477	.466	.455	.444	21
22	.623	.610	.598	.586	.573	.561	.550	.538	.526	.514	.503	.492	.480	.469	.458	.447	22
23	.627	.615	.602	.590	.578	.566	.554	.542	.530	.518	.507	.495	.484	.472	.461	.450	23
24	.632	.619	.607	.594	.582	.570	.558	.546	.534	.522	.510	.499	.487	.476	.465	.453	24
25	.637	.624	.612	.599	.587	.574	.562	.550	.538	.526	.515	.503	.491	.480	.468	.457	25
26	.642	.629	.617	.604	.592	.579	.567	.555	.543	.531	.519	.507	.495	.484	.472	.461	26
27	.648	.635	.622	.609	.597	.584	.572	.560	.547	.535	.523	.511	.500	.488	.476	.465	27
28	.654	.641	.628	.615	.602	.590	.577	.565	.552	.540	.528	.516	.504	.492	.481	.469	28
29	.660	.647	.634	.621	.608	.595	.583	.570	.558	.545	.533	.521	.509	.497	.485	.474	29
30	.667	.653	.640	.627	.614	.601	.588	.576	.563	.551	.538	.526	.514	.502	.490	.478	30
31	.674	.660	.647	.633	.620	.607	.594	.582	.569	.556	.544	.532	.519	.507	.495	.483	31
32	.681	.667	.654	.640	.627	.614	.601	.588	.575	.562	.550	.537	.525	.513	.501	.488	32
33	.688	.675	.661	.647	.634	.621	.608	.594	.582	.569	.556	.543	.531	.518	.506	.494	33
34	.696	.682	.669	.655	.641	.628	.615	.601	.588	.575	.562	.550	.537	.524	.512	.500	34
35	.705	.691	.677	.663	.649	.635	.622	.609	.595	.582	.569	.556	.544	.531	.518	.506	35
36	.714	.699	.685	.671	.657	.643	.630	.616	.603	.590	.576	.563	.550	.537	.525	.512	36
37	.723	.708	.694	.680	.666	.652	.638	.624	.611	.597	.584	.571	.557	.544	.532	.519	37
38	.733	.718	.703	.689	.675	.661	.647	.633	.619	.605	.592	.578	.565	.552	.539	.526	38
39	.743	.728	.713	.699	.684	.670	.656	.642	.628	.614	.600	.586	.573	.559	.546	.533	39
40	.754	.739	.724	.709	.694	.680	.665	.651	.637	.623	.609	.595	.581	.568	.554	.541	40
41	.765	.750	.734	.719	.705	.690	.675	.661	.646	.632	.618	.604	.590	.576	.562	.549	41
42	.777	.761	.746	.731	.715	.700	.686	.671	.656	.642	.627	.613	.599	.585	.571	.557	42
43	.789	.774	.758	.742	.727	.712	.697	.682	.667	.652	.638	.623	.609	.595	.580	.566	43
44	.803	.787	.771	.755	.739	.724	.708	.693	.678	.663	.648	.634	.619	.604	.590	.576	44
45	.817	.800	.784	.768	.752	.736	.721	.705	.690	.675	.659	.644	.630	.615	.600	.586	45
46	.831	.814	.798	.782	.765	.749	.733	.718	.702	.687	.671	.656	.641	.626	.611	.596	46
47	.847	.830	.813	.796	.780	.763	.747	.731	.715	.699	.684	.668	.653	.638	.622	.607	47
48	.863	.846	.828	.811	.795	.778	.761	.745	.729	.713	.697	.681	.665	.650	.634	.619	48
49	.880	.862	.845	.828	.810	.793	.777	.760	.743	.727	.711	.695	.679	.663	.647	.631	49
50	.898	.880	.862	.845	.827	.810	.793	.776	.759	.742	.725	.709	.693	.676	.660	.644	50
51	.917	.899	.881	.863	.845	.827	.810	.792	.775	.758	.741	.724	.707	.691	.674	.658	51
52	.938	.919	.900	.882	.864	.846	.828	.810	.792	.775	.757	.740	.723	.706	.689	.673	52
53	.959	.940	.921	.902	.884	.865	.847	.828	.810	.793	.775	.757	.740	.723	.705	.688	53
54	.982	.963	.943	.924	.905	.886	.867	.848	.830	.811	.793	.775	.757	.740	.722	.705	54
55	1.01	.986	.966	.947	.927	.908	.888	.869	.850	.832	.813	.795	.776	.758	.740	.722	55
56	1.03	1.01	.991	.971	.951	.931	.911	.892	.872	.853	.834	.815	.796	.778	.759	.741	56
57	1.06	1.04	1.02	.997	.976	.956	.936	.915	.896	.876	.856	.837	.817	.798	.779	.761	57
58	1.09	1.07	1.05	1.03	1.00	.982	.962	.941	.920	.900	.880	.860	.840	.821	.801	.782	58
59	1.12	1.10	1.08	1.05	1.03	1.01	.989	.968	.947	.926	.905	.885	.864	.844	.824	.804	59
60	1.16	1.13	1.11	1.09	1.06	1.04	1.02	.997	.975	.954	.933	.911	.890	.870	.849	.828	60

For quadrantal compass graduation readings the degrees are to be taken as for 1st Quadrant (0° to 90°). The azimuth is then named in accordance with the precepts above.

Table 30

C

(Longitude Correction)

Body **RISING** (H.A. greater than 180°)

Body **SETTING** (H.A. less than 180°)

North Lat.　South Lat.

	Sign − Az. in **NE** Qdt. **SE** Qdt.
	„ + „ **SE** „ **NE** „
	Sign + Az. in **SW** Qdt. **NW** Qdt.
	„ − „ **NW** „ **SW** „

AZIMUTH or Course (according to Quadrant)

Qdt. 1st	67½°	68°	68½°	69°	69½°	70°	70½°	71°	71½°	72°	72½°	73°	73½°	74°	74½°	75°	Qdt.
2nd	112½	112	111½	111	110½	110	109½	109	108½	108	107½	107	106½	106	105½	105	NE
3rd	247½	248	248½	249	249½	250	250½	251	251½	252	252½	253	253½	254	254½	255	SE
4th	292½	292	291½	291	290½	290	289½	289	288½	288	287½	287	286½	286	285½	285	SW NW
LAT.																	**LAT.**
0°	.414	.404	.394	.384	.374	.364	.354	.344	.335	.325	.315	.306	.296	.287	.277	.268	0°
1	.414	.404	.394	.384	.374	.364	.354	.344	.335	.325	.315	.306	.296	.287	.277	.268	1
2	.414	.404	.394	.384	.374	.364	.354	.345	.335	.325	.315	.306	.296	.287	.277	.268	2
3	.415	.405	.394	.384	.374	.364	.355	.345	.335	.325	.316	.306	.297	.287	.278	.268	3
4	.415	.405	.395	.385	.375	.365	.355	.345	.335	.326	.316	.306	.297	.287	.278	.269	4
5	.416	.406	.395	.385	.375	.365	.355	.346	.336	.326	.317	.307	.297	.288	.278	.269	5
6	.416	.406	.396	.386	.376	.366	.356	.346	.336	.327	.317	.307	.298	.288	.279	.269	6
7	.417	.407	.397	.387	.377	.367	.357	.347	.337	.327	.318	.308	.298	.289	.279	.270	7
8	.418	.408	.398	.388	.378	.368	.358	.348	.338	.328	.318	.309	.299	.290	.280	.271	8
9	.419	.409	.399	.389	.379	.369	.359	.349	.339	.329	.319	.310	.300	.290	.281	.271	9
10	.421	.410	.400	.390	.380	.370	.360	.350	.340	.330	.320	.310	.301	.291	.282	.272	10
11	.422	.412	.401	.391	.381	.371	.361	.351	.341	.331	.321	.311	.302	.292	.283	.273	11
12	.423	.413	.403	.392	.382	.372	.362	.352	.342	.332	.322	.313	.303	.293	.284	.274	12
13	.425	.415	.404	.394	.384	.374	.363	.353	.343	.333	.324	.314	.304	.294	.285	.275	13
14	.427	.416	.406	.396	.385	.375	.365	.355	.345	.335	.325	.315	.305	.296	.286	.276	14
15	.429	.418	.408	.397	.387	.377	.367	.356	.346	.336	.326	.317	.307	.297	.287	.277	15
16	.431	.420	.410	.399	.389	.379	.368	.358	.348	.338	.328	.318	.308	.298	.289	.279	16
17	.433	.422	.412	.401	.391	.381	.370	.360	.350	.340	.330	.320	.310	.300	.290	.280	17
18	.436	.425	.414	.404	.393	.383	.372	.362	.352	.342	.332	.321	.311	.302	.292	.282	18
19	.438	.427	.417	.406	.395	.385	.375	.364	.354	.344	.333	.323	.313	.303	.293	.283	19
20	.441	.430	.419	.408	.398	.387	.377	.366	.356	.346	.336	.325	.315	.305	.295	.285	20
21	.444	.433	.422	.411	.400	.390	.379	.369	.358	.348	.338	.327	.317	.307	.297	.287	21
22	.447	.436	.425	.414	.403	.393	.382	.371	.361	.350	.340	.330	.319	.309	.299	.289	22
23	.450	.439	.428	.417	.406	.395	.385	.374	.363	.353	.343	.332	.322	.312	.301	.291	23
24	.453	.442	.431	.420	.409	.398	.388	.377	.366	.356	.345	.335	.324	.314	.304	.293	24
25	.457	.446	.435	.424	.413	.402	.391	.380	.369	.359	.348	.337	.327	.316	.306	.296	25
26	.461	.450	.438	.427	.416	.405	.394	.383	.372	.362	.351	.340	.330	.319	.309	.298	26
27	.465	.453	.442	.431	.420	.408	.397	.386	.376	.365	.354	.343	.332	.322	.311	.302	27
28	.469	.458	.446	.435	.423	.412	.401	.390	.379	.368	.357	.346	.335	.325	.314	.303	28
29	.474	.462	.450	.439	.427	.416	.405	.394	.383	.371	.360	.350	.339	.328	.317	.306	29
30	.478	.467	.455	.443	.432	.420	.409	.398	.386	.375	.364	.353	.342	.331	.320	.309	30
31	.483	.471	.460	.448	.436	.425	.413	.402	.390	.379	.368	.357	.346	.335	.324	.313	31
32	.488	.476	.464	.453	.441	.429	.418	.406	.395	.383	.372	.361	.349	.338	.327	.316	32
33	.494	.482	.470	.458	.446	.434	.422	.411	.399	.387	.376	.365	.353	.342	.331	.319	33
34	.500	.487	.475	.463	.451	.439	.427	.415	.404	.392	.380	.369	.357	.346	.335	.323	34
35	.506	.493	.481	.469	.456	.444	.432	.420	.408	.397	.385	.373	.362	.350	.339	.327	35
36	.512	.499	.487	.474	.462	.450	.438	.426	.414	.402	.390	.378	.366	.354	.343	.331	36
37	.519	.506	.493	.481	.468	.456	.443	.431	.419	.407	.395	.383	.371	.359	.347	.336	37
38	.526	.513	.500	.487	.474	.462	.449	.437	.425	.412	.400	.388	.376	.364	.352	.340	38
39	.533	.520	.507	.494	.481	.468	.456	.443	.431	.418	.406	.393	.381	.369	.357	.345	39
40	.541	.527	.514	.501	.488	.475	.462	.449	.437	.424	.412	.399	.387	.374	.362	.350	40
41	.549	.535	.522	.509	.495	.482	.469	.456	.443	.431	.418	.405	.392	.380	.367	.355	41
42	.557	.544	.530	.517	.503	.490	.477	.463	.450	.437	.424	.411	.399	.386	.373	.361	42
43	.566	.552	.539	.525	.511	.498	.484	.471	.458	.444	.431	.418	.405	.392	.379	.366	43
44	.576	.562	.548	.534	.520	.506	.492	.479	.465	.452	.438	.425	.412	.399	.386	.372	44
45	.586	.571	.557	.543	.529	.515	.501	.487	.473	.460	.446	.432	.419	.406	.392	.379	45
46	.596	.582	.567	.553	.538	.524	.510	.496	.482	.468	.454	.440	.426	.413	.399	.386	46
47	.607	.592	.578	.563	.548	.534	.519	.505	.491	.476	.462	.448	.434	.420	.407	.393	47
48	.619	.604	.589	.574	.559	.545	.529	.515	.500	.486	.471	.457	.443	.429	.414	.400	48
49	.631	.616	.600	.585	.570	.555	.540	.525	.510	.495	.481	.466	.452	.437	.423	.408	49
50	.644	.629	.613	.597	.582	.566	.551	.536	.521	.505	.491	.476	.461	.446	.431	.417	50
51	.658	.642	.626	.610	.594	.578	.563	.547	.532	.516	.501	.486	.471	.456	.441	.426	51
52	.673	.656	.640	.623	.607	.591	.575	.559	.543	.528	.512	.497	.481	.466	.450	.435	52
53	.688	.671	.655	.638	.621	.605	.588	.572	.556	.540	.524	.508	.492	.476	.461	.445	53
54	.705	.687	.670	.653	.636	.619	.602	.586	.569	.553	.536	.520	.504	.488	.472	.456	54
55	.722	.704	.687	.669	.652	.635	.617	.600	.583	.566	.550	.533	.516	.500	.484	.467	55
56	.741	.723	.704	.686	.669	.651	.633	.616	.598	.581	.564	.547	.530	.513	.496	.479	56
57	.761	.742	.723	.705	.686	.668	.650	.632	.614	.597	.579	.561	.544	.526	.509	.492	57
58	.782	.762	.743	.724	.706	.687	.668	.650	.631	.613	.595	.577	.559	.541	.523	.506	58
59	.804	.784	.765	.745	.726	.707	.688	.669	.650	.631	.612	.594	.575	.557	.538	.520	59
60	.828	.808	.788	.768	.748	.728	.708	.689	.669	.650	.631	.611	.592	.573	.555	.536	60

For quadrantal compass graduation readings the degrees are to be taken as for 1st Quadrant 0° to 90°). The azimuth is then named in accordance with the precepts above.

Table 30

C
(Longitude Correction)

Body **RISING** (H.A. greater than 180°)

Body **SETTING** (H.A. less than 180°)

	North Lat.	South Lat.	
Sign − Az. in **NE** Qdt.	**SE** Qdt.
" + " **SE** "	**NE** "
Sign + Az. in **SW** Qdt.	**NW** Qdt.
" − " **NW** "	**SW** "

AZIMUTH or Course (according to Quadrant)

Qdt. 1st 2nd 3rd 4th	75° 105 255 285	75½° 104½ 255½ 284½	76° 104 256 284	76½° 103½ 256½ 283½	77° 103 257 283	77½° 102½ 257½ 282½	78° 102 258 282	78½° 101½ 258½ 281½	79° 101 259 281	79½° 100½ 259½ 280½	80° 100 260 280	80½° 99½ 260½ 279½	81° 99 261 279	81½° 98½ 261½ 278½	82° 98 262 278	82½° 97½ 262½ 277½	Qdt. NE SE SW NW
LAT. 0°	.268	.259	.249	.240	.231	.222	.213	.203	.194	.185	.176	.167	.158	.149	.141	.132	**LAT. 0°**
1	.268	.259	.249	.240	.231	.222	.213	.203	.194	.185	.176	.167	.158	.149	.141	.132	1
2	.268	.259	.249	.240	.231	.222	.213	.204	.194	.185	.176	.167	.158	.150	.141	.132	2
3	.268	.259	.250	.240	.231	.222	.213	.204	.195	.186	.177	.168	.159	.150	.141	.132	3
4	.269	.259	.250	.241	.231	.222	.213	.204	.195	.186	.177	.168	.159	.150	.141	.132	4
5	.269	.260	.250	.241	.232	.223	.213	.204	.195	.186	.177	.168	.159	.150	.141	.132	5
6	.269	.260	.251	.241	.232	.223	.214	.205	.195	.186	.177	.168	.159	.150	.141	.132	6
7	.270	.261	.251	.242	.233	.223	.214	.205	.196	.187	.178	.169	.160	.151	.142	.133	7
8	.271	.261	.252	.242	.233	.224	.215	.205	.196	.187	.178	.169	.160	.151	.142	.133	8
9	.271	.262	.252	.243	.234	.224	.215	.206	.197	.188	.179	.169	.160	.151	.142	.133	9
10	.272	.263	.253	.244	.234	.225	.216	.207	.197	.188	.179	.170	.161	.152	.143	.134	10
11	.273	.263	.254	.245	.235	.226	.217	.207	.198	.189	.180	.170	.161	.152	.143	.134	11
12	.274	.264	.255	.245	.236	.227	.217	.208	.199	.189	.180	.171	.162	.153	.144	.135	12
13	.275	.265	.256	.246	.237	.228	.218	.209	.199	.190	.181	.172	.163	.153	.144	.135	13
14	.276	.267	.257	.247	.238	.228	.219	.210	.200	.191	.182	.172	.163	.154	.145	.136	14
15	.277	.268	.258	.249	.239	.230	.220	.211	.201	.192	.183	.173	.164	.155	.145	.136	15
16	.279	.269	.259	.250	.240	.231	.221	.212	.202	.193	.183	.174	.165	.155	.146	.137	16
17	.280	.270	.261	.251	.241	.232	.222	.213	.203	.194	.184	.175	.166	.156	.147	.138	17
18	.282	.272	.262	.252	.243	.233	.223	.214	.204	.195	.185	.176	.167	.157	.148	.138	18
19	.283	.274	.264	.254	.244	.234	.225	.215	.206	.196	.186	.177	.168	.158	.149	.139	19
20	.285	.275	.265	.255	.246	.236	.226	.217	.207	.197	.188	.178	.169	.159	.150	.140	20
21	.287	.277	.267	.257	.247	.237	.228	.218	.208	.199	.189	.179	.170	.160	.151	.141	21
22	.289	.279	.269	.259	.249	.239	.229	.219	.210	.200	.190	.180	.171	.161	.152	.142	22
23	.291	.281	.271	.261	.251	.241	.231	.221	.211	.201	.192	.182	.172	.162	.153	.143	23
24	.293	.283	.273	.263	.253	.243	.233	.223	.213	.203	.193	.183	.173	.164	.154	.144	24
25	.296	.285	.275	.265	.255	.245	.235	.224	.214	.204	.195	.185	.175	.165	.155	.145	25
26	.298	.288	.277	.267	.257	.247	.236	.226	.216	.206	.196	.186	.176	.166	.156	.146	26
27	.302	.290	.280	.269	.259	.249	.239	.228	.218	.208	.198	.188	.178	.168	.158	.148	27
28	.303	.293	.282	.272	.261	.251	.241	.230	.220	.210	.200	.190	.179	.169	.159	.149	28
29	.306	.296	.285	.274	.264	.253	.243	.233	.222	.212	.202	.191	.181	.171	.161	.151	29
30	.309	.299	.288	.277	.267	.256	.245	.235	.224	.214	.204	.193	.183	.173	.162	.152	30
31	.313	.302	.291	.280	.269	.259	.248	.237	.227	.216	.206	.195	.185	.174	.164	.154	31
32	.316	.305	.294	.283	.272	.261	.251	.240	.229	.219	.208	.197	.187	.176	.166	.155	32
33	.319	.308	.297	.286	.275	.264	.253	.243	.232	.221	.210	.200	.189	.178	.168	.157	33
34	.323	.312	.301	.290	.278	.267	.256	.245	.234	.224	.213	.202	.191	.180	.170	.159	34
35	.327	.316	.304	.293	.282	.271	.259	.248	.237	.226	.215	.204	.193	.182	.172	.161	35
36	.331	.320	.308	.297	.285	.274	.263	.251	.240	.229	.218	.207	.196	.185	.174	.163	36
37	.336	.324	.312	.301	.289	.278	.266	.255	.243	.232	.221	.210	.198	.187	.176	.165	37
38	.340	.328	.316	.305	.293	.281	.270	.258	.247	.235	.224	.212	.201	.190	.178	.167	38
39	.345	.333	.321	.309	.297	.285	.274	.262	.250	.238	.227	.215	.204	.192	.181	.169	39
40	.350	.338	.325	.313	.301	.289	.277	.266	.254	.242	.230	.218	.207	.195	.183	.172	40
41	.355	.343	.330	.318	.306	.294	.282	.270	.258	.246	.234	.222	.210	.198	.186	.174	41
42	.361	.348	.336	.323	.311	.298	.286	.274	.262	.249	.237	.225	.213	.201	.189	.177	42
43	.366	.354	.341	.328	.316	.303	.291	.278	.266	.253	.241	.229	.217	.204	.192	.180	43
44	.372	.360	.347	.334	.321	.308	.295	.283	.270	.258	.245	.233	.220	.208	.195	.183	44
45	.379	.366	.353	.340	.326	.314	.301	.288	.275	.262	.249	.237	.224	.211	.199	.186	45
46	.386	.372	.359	.346	.333	.320	.306	.293	.280	.267	.254	.241	.228	.215	.202	.190	46
47	.393	.379	.366	.352	.339	.325	.312	.298	.285	.272	.259	.245	.232	.219	.206	.193	47
48	.400	.386	.373	.359	.345	.331	.318	.304	.290	.277	.264	.250	.237	.223	.210	.197	48
49	.408	.394	.380	.366	.352	.338	.324	.310	.296	.283	.269	.255	.241	.228	.214	.201	49
50	.417	.402	.388	.373	.359	.345	.331	.317	.302	.288	.274	.260	.246	.233	.219	.205	50
51	.426	.411	.396	.381	.367	.352	.338	.323	.309	.295	.280	.266	.252	.237	.223	.209	51
52	.435	.420	.405	.390	.375	.360	.345	.330	.316	.301	.286	.272	.257	.243	.228	.214	52
53	.445	.430	.414	.399	.384	.368	.353	.338	.323	.308	.293	.278	.263	.248	.234	.219	53
54	.456	.440	.424	.408	.393	.377	.362	.346	.331	.315	.300	.285	.269	.254	.239	.224	54
55	.467	.451	.435	.419	.403	.387	.371	.355	.339	.323	.307	.292	.276	.261	.245	.230	55
56	.479	.462	.446	.429	.413	.396	.380	.364	.348	.331	.315	.299	.283	.267	.251	.235	56
57	.492	.475	.458	.441	.424	.407	.390	.374	.357	.340	.324	.307	.291	.274	.258	.242	57
58	.506	.488	.471	.453	.436	.418	.401	.384	.367	.350	.333	.316	.299	.282	.265	.248	58
59	.520	.502	.484	.466	.448	.430	.413	.395	.377	.360	.342	.325	.308	.290	.273	.256	59
60	.536	.517	.499	.480	.462	.443	.425	.407	.389	.371	.353	.335	.317	.299	.281	.263	60

For quadrantal compass graduation readings the degrees are to be taken as for 1st Quadrant (0° to 90°). The azimuth is then named in accordance with the precepts above.

Table 30

C

(Longitude Correction)

	North Lat.	South Lat.
Body **RISING** (H.A. greater than 180°)	Sign − Az. in **NE** Qdt.	**SE** Qdt.
	„ + „ **SE** „	**NE** „
Body **SETTING** (H.A. less than 180°)	Sign + Az. in **SW** Qdt.	**NW** Qdt.
	„ − „ **NW** „	**SW** „

AZIMUTH or Course (according to Quadrant)

Qdt. 1st	82½°	83°	83½°	84°	84½°	85°	85½°	86°	86½°	87°	87½°	88°	88½°	89°	89½°	90°	Qdt.
2nd	97½	97	96½	96	95½	95	94½	94	93½	93	92½	92	91½	91	90½	90	NE
3rd	262½	263	263½	264	264½	265	265½	266	266½	267	267½	268	268½	269	269½	270	SE
4th	277½	277	276½	276	275½	275	274½	274	273½	273	272½	272	271½	271	270½	270	SW/NW

LAT.																	LAT.
0°	.132	.123	.114	.105	.096	.087	.079	.070	.061	.052	.044	.035	.026	.017	.009	.000	0°
1	.132	.123	.114	.105	.096	.088	.079	.070	.061	.052	.044	.035	.026	.017	.009	.000	1
2	.132	.123	.114	.105	.096	.088	.079	.070	.061	.052	.044	.035	.026	.017	.009	.000	2
3	.132	.123	.114	.105	.096	.088	.079	.070	.061	.052	.044	.035	.026	.017	.009	.000	3
4	.132	.123	.114	.105	.097	.088	.079	.070	.061	.053	.044	.035	.026	.017	.009	.000	4
5	.132	.123	.114	.106	.097	.088	.079	.070	.061	.053	.044	.035	.026	.018	.009	.000	5
6	.132	.123	.115	.106	.097	.088	.079	.070	.062	.053	.044	.035	.026	.018	.009	.000	6
7	.133	.124	.115	.106	.097	.088	.079	.070	.062	.053	.044	.035	.026	.018	.009	.000	7
8	.133	.124	.115	.106	.097	.088	.079	.071	.062	.053	.044	.035	.026	.018	.009	.000	8
9	.133	.124	.115	.106	.097	.089	.080	.071	.062	.053	.044	.035	.027	.018	.009	.000	9
10	.134	.125	.116	.107	.098	.089	.080	.071	.062	.053	.044	.035	.027	.018	.009	.000	10
11	.134	.125	.116	.107	.098	.089	.080	.071	.062	.053	.044	.036	.027	.018	.009	.000	11
12	.135	.126	.116	.107	.098	.089	.080	.071	.063	.054	.045	.036	.027	.018	.009	.000	12
13	.135	.126	.117	.108	.099	.090	.081	.072	.063	.054	.045	.036	.027	.018	.009	.000	13
14	.136	.127	.117	.108	.099	.090	.081	.072	.063	.054	.045	.036	.027	.018	.009	.000	14
15	.136	.127	.118	.109	.100	.091	.081	.072	.063	.054	.045	.036	.027	.018	.009	.000	15
16	.137	.128	.119	.109	.100	.091	.082	.073	.064	.055	.045	.036	.027	.018	.009	.000	16
17	.138	.128	.119	.110	.101	.091	.082	.073	.064	.055	.046	.037	.027	.018	.009	.000	17
18	.138	.129	.120	.111	.101	.092	.083	.074	.064	.055	.046	.037	.028	.018	.009	.000	18
19	.139	.130	.121	.111	.102	.093	.083	.074	.065	.055	.046	.037	.028	.018	.009	.000	19
20	.140	.131	.121	.112	.102	.093	.084	.074	.065	.056	.046	.037	.028	.019	.009	.000	20
21	.141	.132	.122	.113	.103	.094	.084	.075	.066	.056	.047	.037	.028	.019	.009	.000	21
22	.142	.132	.123	.113	.104	.094	.085	.075	.066	.057	.047	.038	.028	.019	.009	.000	22
23	.143	.133	.124	.114	.105	.095	.085	.076	.066	.057	.047	.038	.028	.019	.009	.000	23
24	.144	.134	.125	.115	.105	.096	.086	.077	.067	.057	.048	.038	.029	.019	.010	.000	24
25	.145	.135	.126	.116	.106	.097	.087	.077	.067	.058	.048	.039	.029	.019	.010	.000	25
26	.146	.137	.127	.117	.107	.097	.088	.078	.068	.058	.049	.039	.029	.019	.010	.000	26
27	.148	.138	.128	.118	.108	.098	.088	.078	.069	.059	.049	.039	.029	.020	.010	.000	27
28	.149	.139	.129	.119	.109	.099	.089	.079	.069	.059	.049	.040	.030	.020	.010	.000	28
29	.151	.140	.130	.120	.110	.100	.090	.080	.070	.060	.050	.040	.030	.020	.010	.000	29
30	.152	.142	.132	.121	.111	.101	.091	.081	.071	.061	.050	.040	.030	.020	.010	.000	30
31	.154	.143	.133	.123	.112	.102	.092	.082	.071	.061	.051	.041	.031	.020	.010	.000	31
32	.155	.145	.134	.124	.114	.103	.093	.082	.072	.062	.051	.041	.031	.021	.010	.000	32
33	.157	.146	.136	.125	.115	.104	.094	.083	.073	.062	.052	.042	.031	.021	.010	.000	33
34	.159	.148	.137	.127	.116	.106	.095	.084	.074	.063	.053	.042	.032	.021	.011	.000	34
35	.161	.150	.139	.128	.118	.107	.096	.085	.075	.064	.053	.043	.032	.021	.011	.000	35
36	.163	.152	.141	.130	.119	.108	.097	.086	.076	.065	.054	.043	.032	.022	.011	.000	36
37	.165	.154	.143	.132	.121	.110	.099	.088	.077	.066	.055	.044	.033	.022	.011	.000	37
38	.167	.156	.145	.133	.122	.111	.100	.089	.078	.067	.055	.044	.033	.022	.011	.000	38
39	.169	.158	.147	.135	.124	.113	.101	.090	.079	.067	.056	.045	.034	.022	.011	.000	39
40	.172	.160	.149	.137	.126	.114	.103	.091	.080	.068	.057	.046	.034	.023	.011	.000	40
41	.174	.163	.151	.139	.128	.116	.104	.093	.081	.069	.058	.046	.035	.023	.012	.000	41
42	.177	.165	.153	.141	.130	.118	.106	.094	.082	.071	.059	.047	.035	.023	.012	.000	42
43	.180	.168	.156	.144	.132	.120	.108	.096	.084	.072	.060	.048	.036	.024	.012	.000	43
44	.183	.171	.158	.146	.134	.122	.109	.097	.085	.073	.061	.049	.036	.024	.012	.000	44
45	.186	.174	.161	.149	.136	.124	.111	.099	.086	.074	.062	.049	.037	.025	.012	.000	45
46	.190	.177	.164	.151	.139	.126	.113	.101	.088	.075	.063	.050	.038	.025	.013	.000	46
47	.193	.180	.167	.154	.141	.128	.115	.103	.090	.077	.064	.051	.038	.026	.013	.000	47
48	.197	.183	.170	.157	.144	.131	.118	.105	.091	.078	.065	.052	.039	.026	.013	.000	48
49	.201	.187	.174	.160	.147	.133	.120	.107	.093	.080	.067	.053	.040	.027	.013	.000	49
50	.205	.191	.177	.164	.150	.136	.122	.109	.095	.082	.068	.054	.041	.027	.014	.000	50
51	.209	.195	.181	.167	.153	.139	.125	.111	.097	.083	.069	.055	.042	.028	.014	.000	51
52	.214	.199	.185	.171	.156	.142	.128	.114	.099	.085	.071	.057	.043	.028	.014	.000	52
53	.219	.204	.189	.175	.160	.145	.131	.116	.102	.087	.073	.058	.044	.029	.015	.000	53
54	.224	.209	.194	.179	.164	.149	.134	.119	.104	.089	.074	.059	.045	.030	.015	.000	54
55	.230	.214	.199	.183	.168	.153	.137	.122	.107	.091	.076	.061	.046	.030	.015	.000	55
56	.235	.220	.204	.188	.172	.156	.141	.125	.109	.094	.078	.062	.047	.031	.016	.000	56
57	.242	.225	.209	.193	.177	.161	.145	.128	.112	.096	.080	.064	.048	.032	.016	.000	57
58	.248	.232	.215	.198	.182	.165	.149	.132	.115	.099	.082	.066	.049	.033	.016	.000	58
59	.256	.238	.221	.204	.187	.170	.153	.136	.119	.102	.085	.068	.051	.034	.017	.000	59
60	.263	.246	.228	.210	.193	.175	.157	.140	.122	.105	.087	.070	.052	.035	.017	.000	60

For quadrantal compass graduation readings the degrees are to be taken as for 1st Quadrant (0° to 90°). The azimuth is then named in accordance with the precepts above.

Table 29 (H.L.)

A

0 hrs.

If entered with H.A. at **top,** Sign **+**
„   „   „   „ **foot,** „ **—**

HOUR ANGLE or DIFF. LONG.

LAT.	01m	02m	03m	04m	05m	06m	07m	08m	09m	10m	11m	12m	13m	14m	15m	LAT.
	$\frac{1}{4}°$ 359¾	$\frac{1}{2}°$ 359½	$\frac{3}{4}°$ 359¼	**1°** 359	1¼° 358¾	1½° 358½	1¾° 358¼	**2°** 358	2¼° 357¾	2½° 357½	2¾° 357¼	**3°** 357	3¼° 356¾	3½° 356½	3¾° 356¼	
60°	397.	198.	132.	99.2	79.4	66.1	56.7	49.6	44.1	39.7	36.1	33.0	30.5	28.3	26.4	60°
61	414.	207.	138.	103.	82.7	68.9	59.1	51.7	45.9	41.3	37.6	34.4	31.8	29.5	27.5	61
62	431.	216.	144.	108.	86.2	71.8	61.6	53.9	47.9	43.1	39.2	35.9	33.1	30.8	28.7	62
63	450.	225.	150.	112.	90.0	75.0	64.2	56.2	50.0	45.0	40.9	37.4	34.6	32.1	29.9	63
64	470.	235.	157.	117.	94.0	78.3	67.1	58.7	52.2	47.0	42.7	39.1	36.1	33.5	31.3	64
65	492.	246.	164.	123.	98.3	81.9	70.2	61.4	54.6	49.1	44.7	40.9	37.8	35.1	32.7	65
66	515.	257.	172.	129.	103.	85.8	73.5	64.3	57.2	51.4	46.8	42.9	39.6	36.7	34.3	66
67	540.	270.	180.	135.	108.	90.0	77.1	67.5	60.0	54.0	49.1	45.0	41.5	38.5	35.9	67
68	567.	284.	189.	142.	113.	94.5	81.0	70.9	63.0	56.7	51.5	47.2	43.6	40.5	37.8	68
69	597.	299.	199.	149.	119.	99.5	85.3	74.6	66.3	59.7	54.2	49.7	45.9	42.6	39.8	69
70	630.	315.	210.	157.	126.	105.	89.9	78.7	69.9	62.9	57.2	52.4	48.4	44.9	41.9	70
71	666.	333.	222.	166.	133.	111.	95.1	83.2	73.9	66.5	60.5	55.4	51.1	47.5	44.3	71
72	705.	353.	235.	176.	141.	118.	101.	88.1	78.3	70.5	64.1	58.7	54.2	50.3	47.0	72
73	750.	375.	250.	187.	150.	125.	107.	93.7	83.3	74.9	68.1	62.4	57.6	53.5	49.9	73
74	799.	400.	266.	200.	160.	133.	114.	99.9	88.8	79.9	72.6	66.5	61.4	57.0	53.2	74
75	855.	428.	285.	214.	171.	143.	122.	107.	95.0	85.5	77.7	71.2	65.7	61.0	56.9	75
76	919.	460.	306.	230.	184.	153.	131.	115.	102.	91.9	83.5	76.5	70.6	65.6	61.2	76
77	993.	496.	331.	248.	199.	165.	142.	124.	110.	99.2	90.2	82.7	76.3	70.8	66.1	77
78	1078.	539.	359.	270.	216.	180.	154.	135.	120.	108.	98.0	89.8	82.9	76.9	71.8	78
79	1179.	590.	393.	295.	236.	197.	168.	147.	131.	118.	107.	98.2	90.6	84.1	78.5	79
80	1300.	650.	433.	325.	260.	217.	186.	162.	144.	130.	118.	108.	99.9	92.7	86.5	80
81	1447.	723.	482.	362.	289.	241.	207.	181.	161.	145.	131.	120.	111.	103.	96.3	81
82	1631.	815.	544.	408.	326.	272.	233.	204.	181.	163.	148.	136.	125.	116.	109.	82
LAT.	179¾ 180¼	179½ 180½	179¼ 180¾	**179°** **181**	178¾ 181¼	178½ 181½	178¼ 181¾	**178°** **182**	177¾ 182¼	177½ 182½	177¼ 182¾	**177°** **183**	176¾ 183¼	176½ 183½	176¼ 183¾	LAT.

(S.W. Qdt.) **180°**—→**270°**   (S.E. Qdt.) **180°**←—**90°**

0°—→90° (N.E. Qdt.) 360°←—270° (N.W. Qdt.)

Table 29 (H.L.)

B

0 hrs.

Lat. and Dec. SAME name, Sign **—**
Lat. and Dec. CONTRARY names, Sign **+**

HOUR ANGLE or DIFF. LONG.

DEC.	01m	02m	03m	04m	05m	06m	07m	08m	09m	10m	11m	12m	13m	14m	15m	DEC.
	$\frac{1}{4}°$ 359¾	$\frac{1}{2}°$ 359½	$\frac{3}{4}°$ 359¼	**1°** 359	1¼° 358¾	1½° 358½	1¾° 358¼	**2°** 358	2¼° 357¾	2½° 357½	2¾° 357¼	**3°** 357	3¼° 356¾	3½° 356½	3¾° 356¼	
68°	567.	284.	189.	142.	113.	94.5	81.0	70.9	63.1	56.7	51.6	47.3	43.7	40.5	37.8	68°
69	597.	298.	199.	149.	119.	99.5	85.3	74.7	66.4	59.7	54.3	49.8	46.0	42.7	39.8	69
70	629.	315.	210.	157.	126.	105.	90.0	78.7	70.0	63.0	57.3	52.5	48.5	45.0	42.0	70
74	799.	400.	266.	200.	160.	133.	114.	99.9	88.8	80.0	72.7	66.6	61.5	57.1	53.3	74
75	855.	428.	285.	214.	171.	143.	122.	107.	95.1	85.6	77.8	71.3	65.8	61.1	57.1	75
DEC.	179¾ 180¼	179½ 180½	179¼ 180¾	**179°** **181**	178¾ 181¼	178½ 181½	178¼ 181¾	**178°** **182**	177¾ 182¼	177½ 182½	177¼ 182¾	**177°** **183**	176¾ 183¼	176½ 183½	176¼ 183¾	DEC.

(S.W. Qdt.) **180°**—→**270°**   (S.E. Qdt.) **180°**←—**90°**

Table 29 (H.L.) B — 0 hrs.

Lat. and Dec. SAME name, Sign —
Lat. and Dec. CONTRARY names, Sign +

HOUR ANGLE or DIFF. LONG.

DEC.	01m $\frac{1}{4}°$ 359$\frac{3}{4}$	02m $\frac{1}{2}°$ 359$\frac{1}{2}$	03m $\frac{3}{4}°$ 359$\frac{1}{4}$	04m 1° 359	05m 1$\frac{1}{4}°$ 358$\frac{3}{4}$	06m 1$\frac{1}{2}°$ 358$\frac{1}{2}$	07m 1$\frac{3}{4}°$ 358$\frac{1}{4}$	08m 2° 358	09m 2$\frac{1}{4}°$ 357$\frac{3}{4}$	10m 2$\frac{1}{2}°$ 357$\frac{1}{2}$	11m 2$\frac{3}{4}°$ 357$\frac{1}{4}$	12m 3° 357	13m 3$\frac{1}{4}°$ 356$\frac{3}{4}$	14m 3$\frac{1}{2}°$ 356$\frac{1}{2}$	15m 3$\frac{3}{4}°$ 356$\frac{1}{4}$	DEC.
0	.000	.000	.000	.000	.000	.000	.000	.000	.000	.000	.000	.000	.000	.000	.000	0
1	4.00	2.00	1.33	1.00	.800	.667	.572	.500	.445	.400	.364	.334	.308	.286	.267	1
2	8.00	4.00	2.67	2.00	1.60	1.33	1.14	1.00	.889	.801	.728	.667	.616	.572	.534	2
3	12.0	6.01	4.00	3.00	2.40	2.00	1.72	1.50	1.34	1.20	1.09	1.00	.924	.858	.801	3
4	16.0	8.01	5.34	4.01	3.21	2.67	2.29	2.00	1.78	1.60	1.46	1.34	1.23	1.15	1.07	4
5	20.1	10.0	6.68	5.01	4.01	3.34	2.87	2.51	2.23	2.01	1.82	1.67	1.54	1.43	1.34	5
6	24.1	12.0	8.03	6.02	4.82	4.02	3.44	3.01	2.68	2.41	2.19	2.01	1.85	1.72	1.61	6
7	28.1	14.1	9.38	7.04	5.63	4.69	4.02	3.52	3.13	2.81	2.56	2.35	2.17	2.01	1.88	7
8	32.2	16.1	10.7	8.05	6.44	5.37	4.60	4.03	3.58	3.22	2.93	2.69	2.48	2.30	2.15	8
9	36.3	18.2	12.1	9.08	7.26	6.05	5.19	4.54	4.03	3.63	3.30	3.03	2.79	2.59	2.42	9
10	40.4	20.2	13.5	10.1	8.08	6.74	5.77	5.05	4.49	4.04	3.68	3.37	3.11	2.89	2.70	10
11	44.6	22.3	14.9	11.1	8.91	7.43	6.37	5.57	4.95	4.46	4.05	3.71	3.43	3.18	2.97	11
12	48.7	24.4	16.2	12.2	9.74	8.12	6.96	6.09	5.41	4.87	4.43	4.06	3.75	3.48	3.25	12
13	52.9	26.5	17.6	13.2	10.6	8.82	7.56	6.62	5.88	5.29	4.81	4.41	4.07	3.78	3.53	13
14	57.1	28.6	19.1	14.3	11.4	9.52	8.16	7.14	6.35	5.72	5.20	4.76	4.40	4.08	3.81	14
15	61.4	30.7	20.5	15.4	12.3	10.2	8.77	7.68	6.83	6.14	5.59	5.12	4.73	4.39	4.10	15
16	65.7	32.9	21.9	16.4	13.1	11.0	9.39	8.22	7.30	6.57	5.98	5.48	5.06	4.70	4.38	16
17	70.1	35.0	23.4	17.5	14.0	11.7	10.0	8.76	7.79	7.01	6.37	5.84	5.39	5.01	4.68	17
18	74.5	37.2	24.8	18.6	14.9	12.4	10.6	9.31	8.28	7.45	6.77	6.21	5.73	5.32	4.97	18
19	78.9	39.5	26.3	19.7	15.8	13.2	11.3	9.87	8.77	7.89	7.18	6.58	6.07	5.64	5.27	19
20	83.4	41.7	27.8	20.9	16.7	13.9	11.9	10.4	9.27	8.34	7.59	6.95	6.42	5.96	5.57	20
21	88.0	44.0	29.3	22.0	17.6	14.7	12.6	11.0	9.78	8.80	8.00	7.34	6.77	6.29	5.87	21
22	92.6	46.3	30.9	23.2	18.5	15.4	13.2	11.6	10.3	9.26	8.42	7.72	7.13	6.62	6.18	22
23	97.3	48.6	32.4	24.3	19.5	16.2	13.9	12.2	10.8	9.73	8.85	8.11	7.49	6.95	6.49	23
24	102.	51.0	34.0	25.5	20.4	17.0	14.6	12.8	11.3	10.2	9.28	8.51	7.85	7.29	6.81	24
25	107.	53.4	35.6	26.7	21.4	17.8	15.3	13.4	11.9	10.7	9.72	8.91	8.23	7.64	7.13	25
26	112.	55.9	37.3	27.9	22.4	18.6	16.0	14.0	12.4	11.2	10.2	9.32	8.60	7.99	7.46	26
27	117.	58.4	38.9	29.2	23.4	19.5	16.7	14.6	13.0	11.7	10.6	9.74	8.99	8.35	7.79	27
28	122.	60.9	40.6	30.5	24.4	20.3	17.4	15.2	13.5	12.2	11.1	10.2	9.38	8.71	8.13	28
29	127.	63.5	42.4	31.8	25.4	21.2	18.2	15.9	14.1	12.7	11.6	10.6	9.78	9.08	8.48	29
30	132.	66.2	44.1	33.1	26.5	22.1	18.9	16.5	14.7	13.2	12.0	11.0	10.2	9.46	8.83	30
31	138.	68.9	45.9	34.4	27.5	23.0	19.7	17.2	15.3	13.8	12.5	11.5	10.6	9.84	9.19	31
32	143.	71.6	47.7	35.8	28.6	23.9	20.5	17.9	15.9	14.3	13.0	11.9	11.0	10.2	9.55	32
33	149.	74.4	49.6	37.2	29.8	24.8	21.3	18.6	16.5	14.9	13.5	12.4	11.5	10.6	9.93	33
34	155.	77.3	51.5	38.6	30.9	25.8	22.1	19.3	17.2	15.5	14.1	12.9	11.9	11.0	10.3	34
35	161.	80.2	53.5	40.1	32.1	26.7	22.9	20.1	17.8	16.1	14.6	13.4	12.4	11.5	10.7	35
36	167.	83.3	55.5	41.6	33.3	27.8	23.8	20.8	18.5	16.7	15.1	13.9	12.8	11.9	11.1	36
37	173.	86.4	57.6	43.2	34.5	28.8	24.7	21.6	19.2	17.3	15.7	14.4	13.3	12.3	11.5	37
38	179.	89.5	59.7	44.8	35.8	29.8	25.6	22.4	19.9	17.9	16.3	14.9	13.8	12.8	12.0	38
39	186.	92.8	61.9	46.4	37.1	30.9	26.5	23.2	20.6	18.6	16.9	15.5	14.3	13.3	12.4	39
40	192.	96.2	64.1	48.1	38.5	32.1	27.5	24.0	21.4	19.2	17.5	16.0	14.8	13.7	12.8	40
41	199.	99.6	66.4	49.8	39.9	33.2	28.5	24.9	22.1	19.9	18.1	16.6	15.3	14.2	13.3	41
42	206.	103.	68.8	51.6	41.3	34.4	29.5	25.8	22.9	20.6	18.8	17.2	15.9	14.7	13.8	42
43	214.	107.	71.2	53.4	42.8	35.6	30.5	26.7	23.8	21.4	19.4	17.8	16.5	15.3	14.3	43
44	221.	111.	73.8	55.3	44.3	36.9	31.6	27.7	24.6	22.1	20.1	18.5	17.0	15.8	14.8	44
45	229.	115.	76.4	57.3	45.8	38.2	32.8	28.7	25.5	22.9	20.8	19.1	17.6	16.4	15.3	45
46	237.	119.	79.1	59.3	47.5	39.6	33.9	29.7	26.4	23.7	21.6	19.8	18.3	17.0	15.8	46
47	246.	123.	81.9	61.5	49.2	41.0	35.1	30.7	27.3	24.6	22.4	20.5	18.9	17.6	16.4	47
48	255.	127.	84.9	63.6	50.9	42.4	36.4	31.8	28.3	25.5	23.2	21.2	19.6	18.2	17.0	48
49	264.	132.	87.9	65.9	52.7	43.9	37.7	33.0	29.3	26.4	24.0	22.0	20.3	18.8	17.6	49
50	273.	137.	91.1	68.3	54.6	45.5	39.0	34.1	30.4	27.3	24.8	22.8	21.0	19.5	18.2	50
51	283.	142.	94.3	70.8	56.6	47.2	40.4	35.4	31.5	28.3	25.7	23.6	21.8	20.2	18.9	51
52	293.	147.	97.8	73.3	58.7	48.9	41.9	36.7	32.6	29.3	26.7	24.5	22.6	21.0	19.6	52
53	304.	152.	101.	76.0	60.8	50.7	43.5	38.0	33.8	30.4	27.7	25.4	23.4	21.7	20.3	53
54	315.	158.	105.	78.9	63.1	52.6	45.1	39.4	35.1	31.6	28.7	26.3	24.3	22.5	21.0	54
55	327.	164.	109.	81.8	65.5	54.6	46.8	40.9	36.4	32.7	29.8	27.3	25.2	23.4	21.8	55
56	340.	170.	113.	84.9	68.0	56.6	48.6	42.5	37.8	34.0	30.9	28.3	26.2	24.3	22.7	56
57	353.	176.	118.	88.2	70.6	58.8	50.4	44.1	39.2	35.3	32.1	29.4	27.2	25.2	23.5	57
58	367.	183.	122.	91.7	73.4	61.1	52.4	45.9	40.8	36.7	33.4	30.6	28.2	26.2	24.5	58
59	381.	191.	127.	95.4	76.3	63.6	54.5	47.7	42.4	38.2	34.7	31.8	29.4	27.3	25.5	59
60	397.	198.	132.	99.2	79.4	66.2	56.7	49.6	44.1	39.7	36.1	33.1	30.6	28.4	26.5	60
61	414.	207.	138.	103.	82.7	68.9	59.1	51.7	46.0	41.4	37.6	34.5	31.8	29.6	27.6	61
62	431.	216.	144.	108.	86.2	71.9	61.6	53.9	47.9	43.1	39.2	35.9	33.2	30.8	28.8	62
63	450.	225.	150.	112.	90.0	75.0	64.3	56.2	50.0	45.0	40.9	37.5	34.6	32.1	30.0	63

| DEC. | 179$\frac{3}{4}$ 180$\frac{1}{4}$ | 179$\frac{1}{2}$ 180$\frac{1}{2}$ | 179$\frac{1}{4}$ 180$\frac{3}{4}$ | 179° 181 | 178$\frac{3}{4}$ 181$\frac{1}{4}$ | 178$\frac{1}{2}$ 181$\frac{1}{2}$ | 178$\frac{1}{4}$ 181$\frac{3}{4}$ | 178° 182 | 177$\frac{3}{4}$ 182$\frac{1}{4}$ | 177$\frac{1}{2}$ 182$\frac{1}{2}$ | 177$\frac{1}{4}$ 182$\frac{3}{4}$ | 177° 183 | 176$\frac{3}{4}$ 183$\frac{1}{4}$ | 176$\frac{1}{2}$ 183$\frac{1}{2}$ | 176$\frac{1}{4}$ 183$\frac{3}{4}$ | DEC. |

Table 29 (H.L.)

A

0 hrs.

If entered with H.A. at **top**, Sign **+**
„ „ „ „ **foot**, „ **—**

HOUR ANGLE or DIFF. LONG.

LAT.	15m	16m	17m	18m	19m	20m	21m	22m	23m	24m	25m	26m	27m	28m	29m	30m	LAT.
	3¾° 356¼	4° 356	4¼° 355¾	4½° 355½	4¾° 355¼	5° 355	5¼° 354¾	5½° 354½	5¾° 354¼	6° 354	6¼° 353¾	6½° 353½	6¾° 353¼	7° 353	7¼° 352¾	7½° 352½	
60°	26.4	24.8	23.3	22.0	20.8	19.8	18.9	18.0	17.2	16.5	15.8	15.2	14.6	14.1	13.6	13.2	60°
61	27.5	25.8	24.3	22.9	21.7	20.6	19.6	18.7	17.9	17.2	16.5	15.8	15.2	14.7	14.2	13.7	61
62	28.7	26.9	25.3	23.9	22.6	21.5	20.5	19.5	18.7	17.9	17.2	16.5	15.9	15.3	14.8	14.3	62
63	29.9	28.1	26.4	24.9	23.6	22.4	21.4	20.4	19.5	18.7	17.9	17.2	16.6	16.0	15.4	14.9	63
64	31.3	29.3	27.6	26.1	24.7	23.4	22.3	21.3	20.4	19.5	18.7	18.0	17.3	16.7	16.1	15.6	64
65	32.7	30.7	28.9	27.3	25.8	24.5	23.3	22.3	21.3	20.4	19.6	18.8	18.1	17.5	16.9	16.3	65
66	34.3	32.1	30.2	28.5	27.0	25.7	24.4	23.3	22.3	21.4	20.5	19.7	19.0	18.3	17.7	17.1	66
67	35.9	33.7	31.7	29.9	28.4	26.9	25.6	24.5	23.4	22.4	21.5	20.7	19.9	19.2	18.5	17.9	67
68	37.8	35.4	33.3	31.4	29.8	28.3	26.9	25.7	24.6	23.5	22.6	21.7	20.9	20.2	19.5	18.8	68
69	39.8	37.3	35.1	33.1	31.4	29.8	28.4	27.1	25.9	24.8	23.8	22.9	22.0	21.2	20.5	19.8	69
70	41.9	39.3	37.0	34.9	33.1	31.4	29.9	28.5	27.3	26.1	25.1	24.1	23.2	22.4	21.6	20.9	70
71	44.3	41.5	39.1	36.9	35.0	33.2	31.6	30.2	28.8	27.6	26.5	25.5	24.5	23.7	22.8	22.1	71
72	47.0	44.0	41.4	39.1	37.0	35.2	33.5	32.0	30.6	29.3	28.1	27.0	26.0	25.1	24.2	23.4	72
73	49.9	46.8	44.0	41.6	39.4	37.4	35.6	34.0	32.5	31.1	29.9	28.7	27.6	26.6	25.7	24.8	73
74	53.2	49.9	46.9	44.3	42.0	39.9	38.0	36.2	34.6	33.2	31.8	30.6	29.5	28.4	27.4	26.5	74
75	56.9	53.4	50.2	47.4	44.9	42.7	40.6	38.8	37.1	35.5	34.1	32.8	31.5	30.4	29.3	28.3	75
76	61.2	57.4	54.0	51.0	48.3	45.8	43.6	41.7	39.8	38.2	36.6	35.2	33.9	32.7	31.5	30.5	76
77	66.1	61.9	58.3	55.0	52.1	49.5	47.1	45.0	43.0	41.2	39.5	38.0	36.6	35.3	34.0	32.9	77
78	71.8	67.3	63.3	59.8	56.6	53.8	51.2	48.9	46.7	44.8	43.0	41.3	39.7	38.3	37.0	35.7	78
79	78.5	73.6	69.2	65.4	61.9	58.8	56.0	53.4	51.1	48.9	47.0	45.2	43.5	41.9	40.4	39.1	79
80	86.5	81.1	76.3	72.1	68.3	64.8	61.7	58.9	56.3	54.0	51.8	49.8	47.9	46.2	44.6	43.1	80
81	96.3	90.3	85.0	80.2	76.0	72.2	68.7	65.6	62.7	60.1	57.7	55.4	53.3	51.4	49.6	48.0	81
82	109.	102.	95.7	90.4	85.6	81.3	77.4	73.9	70.7	67.7	64.9	62.5	60.1	58.0	55.9	54.0	82
LAT.	176¼ 183¾	176° 184	175¾ 184¼	175½ 184½	175¼ 184¾	175° 185	174¾ 185¼	174½ 185½	174¼ 185¾	174° 186	173¾ 186¼	173½ 186½	173¼ 186¾	173° 187	172¾ 187¼	172½ 187½	LAT.

Table 29 (H.L.)

B

0 hrs.

Lat. and Dec. SAME name, Sign **—**
Lat. and Dec. CONTRARY names, Sign **+**

HOUR ANGLE or DIFF. LONG.

DEC.	15m	16m	17m	18m	19m	20m	21m	22m	23m	24m	25m	26m	27m	28m	29m	30m	DEC.
	3¾° 356·	4° 356	4¼° 355¾	4½° 355½	4¾° 355¼	5° 355	5¼° 354¾	5½° 354½	5¾° 354¼	6° 354	6¼° 353¾	6½° 353½	6¾° 353¼	7° 353	7¼° 352¾	7½° 352½	
68°	37.8	35.5	33.4	31.6	29.9	28.4	27.1	25.8	24.7	23.7	22.7	21.9	21.1	20.3	19.6	19.0	68°
69	39.8	37.3	35.2	33.2	31.5	29.9	28.5	27.2	26.0	24.9	23.9	23.0	22.2	21.4	20.6	20.0	69
70	42.0	39.4	37.1	35.0	33.2	31.5	30.0	28.7	27.4	26.3	25.2	24.3	23.4	22.5	21.7	21.0	70
74	53.3	50.0	47.1	44.4	42.1	40.0	38.1	36.4	34.8	33.4	32.0	30.8	29.7	28.6	27.6	26.7	74
75	57.1	53.5	50.4	47.6	45.1	42.8	40.8	38.9	37.3	35.7	34.3	33.0	31.8	30.6	29.6	28.6	75
DEC.	176¼ 183¾	176° 184	175¾ 184¼	175½ 184½	175¼ 184¾	175° 185	174¾ 185¼	174½ 185½	174¼ 185¾	174° 186	173¾ 186¼	173½ 186½	173¼ 186¾	173° 187	172¾ 187¼	172½ 187½	DEC.

Table 29 (H.L.) B — 0 hrs.

Lat. and Dec. SAME name, Sign −
Lat. and Dec. CONTRARY names, Sign +

HOUR ANGLE or DIFF. LONG.

DEC.	15m	16m	17m	18m	19m	20m	21m	22m	23m	24m	25m	26m	27m	28m	29m	30m	DEC.
	3¾° 356¼	4° 356	4¼° 355¾	4½° 355½	4¾° 355¼	5° 355	5¼° 354¾	5½° 354½	5¾° 354¼	6° 354	6¼° 353¾	6½° 353½	6¾° 353¼	7° 353	7¼° 352¾	7½° 352½	
0°	.000	.000	.000	.000	.000	.000	.000	.000	.000	.000	.000	.000	.000	.000	.000	.000	0°
1	.267	.250	.236	.222	.211	.200	.191	.182	.174	.167	.160	.154	.149	.143	.138	.134	1
2	.534	.501	.471	.445	.422	.401	.382	.364	.349	.334	.321	.308	.297	.287	.277	.268	2
3	.801	.751	.707	.668	.633	.601	.573	.547	.523	.501	.481	.463	.446	.430	.414	.402	3
4	1.07	1.00	.944	.891	.844	.802	.764	.730	.698	.669	.642	.618	.595	.574	.554	.536	4
5	1.34	1.25	1.18	1.12	1.06	1.00	.956	.913	.873	.837	.804	.773	.744	.718	.693	.670	5
6	1.61	1.51	1.42	1.34	1.27	1.21	1.15	1.10	1.05	1.01	.965	.928	.894	.862	.833	.805	6
7	1.88	1.76	1.66	1.57	1.48	1.41	1.34	1.28	1.23	1.17	1.13	1.08	1.05	1.01	.973	.941	7
8	2.15	2.01	1.90	1.79	1.70	1.61	1.54	1.47	1.40	1.34	1.29	1.24	1.20	1.15	1.11	1.08	8
9	2.42	2.27	2.14	2.02	1.91	1.82	1.73	1.65	1.58	1.52	1.46	1.40	1.35	1.30	1.26	1.21	9
10	2.70	2.53	2.38	2.25	2.13	2.02	1.93	1.84	1.76	1.69	1.62	1.56	1.50	1.45	1.40	1.35	10
11	2.97	2.79	2.62	2.48	2.35	2.23	2.12	2.03	1.94	1.86	1.79	1.72	1.65	1.60	1.54	1.49	11
12	3.25	3.05	2.87	2.71	2.57	2.44	2.32	2.22	2.12	2.03	1.95	1.88	1.81	1.74	1.68	1.63	12
13	3.53	3.31	3.12	2.94	2.79	2.65	2.52	2.41	2.30	2.21	2.12	2.04	1.96	1.89	1.83	1.77	13
14	3.81	3.57	3.36	3.18	3.01	2.86	2.73	2.60	2.49	2.39	2.29	2.20	2.12	2.05	1.98	1.91	14
15	4.10	3.84	3.62	3.42	3.24	3.07	2.93	2.80	2.67	2.56	2.46	2.37	2.28	2.20	2.12	2.05	15
16	4.38	4.11	3.87	3.65	3.46	3.29	3.13	2.99	2.86	2.74	2.63	2.53	2.44	2.35	2.27	2.20	16
17	4.68	4.38	4.13	3.90	3.69	3.51	3.34	3.19	3.05	2.92	2.81	2.70	2.60	2.51	2.42	2.34	17
18	4.97	4.66	4.38	4.14	3.92	3.73	3.55	3.39	3.24	3.11	2.99	2.87	2.76	2.67	2.58	2.49	18
19	5.27	4.94	4.65	4.39	4.16	3.95	3.76	3.59	3.44	3.29	3.16	3.04	2.93	2.83	2.73	2.64	19
20	5.57	5.22	4.91	4.64	4.40	4.18	3.98	3.80	3.63	3.48	3.34	3.22	3.10	2.99	2.88	2.79	20
21	5.87	5.50	5.18	4.89	4.64	4.40	4.20	4.01	3.83	3.67	3.53	3.39	3.27	3.15	3.04	2.94	21
22	6.18	5.79	5.45	5.15	4.88	4.64	4.42	4.22	4.03	3.87	3.71	3.57	3.44	3.32	3.20	3.10	22
23	6.49	6.09	5.73	5.41	5.13	4.87	4.64	4.43	4.24	4.06	3.90	3.75	3.61	3.48	3.36	3.25	23
24	6.81	6.38	6.01	5.67	5.38	5.11	4.87	4.65	4.44	4.26	4.09	3.93	3.79	3.65	3.53	3.41	24
25	7.13	6.68	6.29	5.94	5.63	5.35	5.10	4.87	4.65	4.46	4.28	4.12	3.97	3.83	3.70	3.57	25
26	7.46	6.99	6.58	6.22	5.89	5.60	5.33	5.09	4.87	4.67	4.48	4.31	4.15	4.00	3.87	3.74	26
27	7.79	7.30	6.88	6.49	6.15	5.85	5.57	5.32	5.09	4.87	4.68	4.50	4.34	4.18	4.04	3.90	27
28	8.13	7.62	7.18	6.78	6.42	6.10	5.81	5.55	5.31	5.09	4.88	4.70	4.52	4.36	4.21	4.07	28
29	8.48	7.95	7.48	7.06	6.69	6.36	6.06	5.78	5.53	5.30	5.09	4.90	4.72	4.55	4.39	4.25	29
30	8.83	8.28	7.79	7.36	6.97	6.62	6.31	6.02	5.76	5.52	5.30	5.10	4.91	4.74	4.58	4.42	30
31	9.19	8.61	8.11	7.66	7.26	6.89	6.57	6.27	6.00	5.75	5.52	5.31	5.11	4.93	4.76	4.60	31
32	9.55	8.96	8.43	7.96	7.55	7.17	6.83	6.52	6.24	5.98	5.74	5.52	5.32	5.13	4.95	4.79	32
33	9.93	9.31	8.76	8.28	7.84	7.45	7.10	6.78	6.48	6.21	5.97	5.74	5.53	5.33	5.15	4.98	33
34	10.3	9.67	9.10	8.60	8.15	7.74	7.37	7.04	6.73	6.45	6.20	5.96	5.74	5.53	5.35	5.17	34
35	10.7	10.0	9.45	8.92	8.46	8.03	7.65	7.31	6.99	6.70	6.43	6.19	5.96	5.75	5.55	5.36	35
36	11.1	10.4	9.80	9.26	8.77	8.34	7.94	7.58	7.25	6.95	6.67	6.42	6.18	5.96	5.76	5.57	36
37	11.5	10.8	10.2	9.60	9.10	8.65	8.24	7.86	7.52	7.21	6.92	6.66	6.41	6.18	5.97	5.77	37
38	12.0	11.2	10.5	9.96	9.44	8.96	8.54	8.15	7.80	7.47	7.18	6.90	6.65	6.41	6.19	5.99	38
39	12.4	11.6	10.9	10.3	9.78	9.29	8.85	8.45	8.08	7.75	7.44	7.15	6.89	6.64	6.42	6.20	39
40	12.8	12.0	11.3	10.7	10.1	9.63	9.17	8.75	8.38	8.03	7.71	7.41	7.14	6.89	6.65	6.43	40
41	13.3	12.5	11.7	11.1	10.5	9.97	9.50	9.07	8.68	8.32	7.99	7.68	7.40	7.13	6.89	6.66	41
42	13.8	12.9	12.2	11.5	10.9	10.3	9.84	9.39	8.99	8.61	8.27	7.95	7.66	7.39	7.14	6.90	42
43	14.3	13.4	12.6	11.9	11.3	10.7	10.2	9.73	9.31	8.92	8.57	8.24	7.93	7.65	7.39	7.14	43
44	14.8	13.8	13.0	12.3	11.7	11.1	10.6	10.1	9.64	9.24	8.87	8.53	8.22	7.92	7.65	7.40	44
45	15.3	14.3	13.5	12.7	12.1	11.5	10.9	10.4	9.98	9.57	9.19	8.83	8.51	8.21	7.92	7.66	45
46	15.8	14.8	14.0	13.2	12.5	11.9	11.3	10.8	10.3	9.91	9.51	9.15	8.81	8.50	8.21	7.93	46
47	16.4	15.4	14.5	13.7	13.0	12.3	11.7	11.2	10.7	10.3	9.85	9.47	9.12	8.80	8.50	8.22	47
48	17.0	15.9	15.0	14.2	13.4	12.7	12.1	11.6	11.1	10.6	10.2	9.81	9.45	9.11	8.80	8.51	48
49	17.6	16.5	15.5	14.7	13.9	13.2	12.6	12.0	11.5	11.0	10.6	10.2	9.79	9.44	9.12	8.81	49
50	18.2	17.1	16.1	15.2	14.4	13.7	13.0	12.4	11.9	11.4	11.0	10.5	10.1	9.78	9.44	9.13	50
51	18.9	17.7	16.7	15.7	14.9	14.2	13.5	12.9	12.3	11.8	11.3	10.9	10.5	10.1	9.79	9.46	51
52	19.6	18.3	17.3	16.3	15.5	14.7	14.0	13.4	12.8	12.2	11.8	11.3	10.9	10.5	10.1	9.81	52
53	20.3	19.0	17.9	16.9	16.0	15.2	14.5	13.9	13.3	12.7	12.2	11.7	11.3	10.9	10.5	10.2	53
54	21.0	19.7	18.6	17.5	16.6	15.8	15.0	14.4	13.7	13.2	12.6	12.2	11.7	11.3	10.9	10.5	54
55	21.8	20.5	19.3	18.2	17.3	16.4	15.6	14.9	14.3	13.7	13.1	12.6	12.2	11.7	11.3	10.9	55
56	22.7	21.3	20.0	18.9	17.9	17.0	16.2	15.5	14.8	14.2	13.6	13.1	12.6	12.2	11.8	11.4	56
57	23.5	22.1	20.8	19.6	18.6	17.7	16.8	16.1	15.4	14.7	14.1	13.6	13.1	12.6	12.2	11.8	57
58	24.5	22.9	21.6	20.4	19.3	18.4	17.5	16.7	16.0	15.3	14.7	14.1	13.6	13.1	12.7	12.3	58
59	25.5	23.9	22.5	21.2	20.1	19.1	18.2	17.4	16.6	15.9	15.3	14.7	14.2	13.7	13.2	12.8	59
60	26.5	24.8	23.4	22.1	20.9	19.9	18.9	18.1	17.3	16.6	15.9	15.3	14.7	14.2	13.7	13.3	60
61	27.6	25.9	24.3	23.0	21.8	20.7	19.7	18.8	18.0	17.3	16.6	15.9	15.4	14.8	14.3	13.8	61
62	28.8	27.0	25.4	24.0	22.7	21.6	20.6	19.6	18.8	18.0	17.3	16.6	16.0	15.4	14.9	14.4	62
63	30.0	28.1	26.5	25.0	23.7	22.5	21.5	20.5	19.6	18.8	18.0	17.3	16.7	16.1	15.6	15.0	63
DEC.	176¼ 183¾	176° 184	175¾ 184¼	175½ 184½	175¼ 184¾	175° 185	174¾ 185¼	174½ 185½	174¼ 185¾	174° 186	173¾ 186¼	173½ 186½	173¼ 186¾	173° 187	172¾ 187¼	172½ 187½	DEC.

0°⟶90° (N.E. Qdt.) 360°⟵270° (N.W. Qdt.)

Table 29 (H.L.) A

0 hrs.

If entered with H.A. at **top**, Sign **+**
„ „ „ „ **foot**, „ **−**

HOUR ANGLE or DIFF. LONG.

LAT.	30m	31m	32m	33m	34m	35m	36m	37m	38m	39m	40m	41m	42m	43m	44m	45m	LAT.
	7½° 352½	7¾° 352¼	**8°** **352**	8¼° 351¾	8½° 351½	8¾° 351¼	**9°** **351**	9¼° 350¾	9½° 350½	9¾° 350¼	**10°** **350**	10¼° 349¾	10½° 349½	10¾° 349¼	**11°** **349**	11¼° 348¾	
60°	13.2	12.7	12.3	12.0	11.6	11.3	10.9	10.6	10.4	10.1	9.82	9.58	9.35	9.12	8.91	8.71	60°
61	13.7	13.3	12.8	12.4	12.1	11.7	11.4	11.1	10.8	10.5	10.2	9.98	9.73	9.50	9.28	9.07	61
62	14.3	13.8	13.4	13.0	12.6	12.2	11.9	11.6	11.2	11.0	10.7	10.4	10.2	9.91	9.68	9.46	62
63	14.9	14.4	14.0	13.5	13.1	12.8	12.4	12.1	11.7	11.4	11.1	10.9	10.6	10.3	10.1	9.87	63
64	15.6	15.1	14.6	14.1	13.7	13.3	13.0	12.6	12.3	11.9	11.6	11.3	11.1	10.8	10.6	10.3	64
65	16.3	15.8	15.3	14.8	14.4	13.9	13.5	13.2	12.8	12.5	12.2	11.9	11.6	11.3	11.0	10.8	65
66	17.1	16.5	16.0	15.5	15.0	14.6	14.2	13.8	13.4	13.1	12.7	12.4	12.1	11.8	11.6	11.3	66
67	17.9	17.3	16.8	16.2	15.8	15.3	14.9	14.5	14.1	13.7	13.4	13.0	12.7	12.4	12.1	11.8	67
68	18.8	18.2	17.6	17.1	16.6	16.1	15.6	15.2	14.8	14.4	14.0	13.7	13.4	13.0	12.7	12.4	68
69	19.8	19.1	18.5	18.0	17.4	16.9	16.4	16.0	15.6	15.2	14.8	14.4	14.1	13.7	13.4	13.1	69
70	20.9	20.2	19.5	18.9	18.4	17.9	17.3	16.9	16.4	16.0	15.6	15.2	14.8	14.5	14.1	13.8	70
71	22.1	21.3	20.7	20.0	19.4	18.9	18.3	17.8	17.4	16.9	16.5	16.1	15.7	15.3	14.9	14.6	71
72	23.4	22.6	21.9	21.2	20.6	20.0	19.4	18.9	18.4	17.9	17.5	17.0	16.6	16.2	15.8	15.5	72
73	24.8	24.0	23.3	22.6	21.9	21.3	20.7	20.1	19.5	19.0	18.5	18.1	17.6	17.2	16.8	16.4	73
74	26.5	25.6	24.8	24.1	23.3	22.7	22.0	21.4	20.8	20.3	19.8	19.3	18.8	18.4	17.9	17.5	74
75	28.3	27.4	26.6	25.7	25.0	24.2	23.6	22.9	22.3	21.7	21.2	20.6	20.1	19.7	19.2	18.8	75
76	30.5	29.5	28.5	27.7	26.8	26.1	25.3	24.6	24.0	23.3	22.7	22.2	21.6	21.1	20.6	20.2	76
77	32.9	31.8	30.8	29.9	29.0	28.1	27.3	26.6	25.9	25.2	24.6	24.0	23.4	22.8	22.3	21.8	77
78	35.7	34.6	33.5	32.4	31.5	30.6	29.7	28.9	28.1	27.4	26.7	26.0	25.4	24.8	24.2	23.7	78
79	39.1	37.8	36.6	35.5	34.4	33.4	32.5	31.6	30.7	29.9	29.2	28.4	27.8	27.1	26.5	25.9	79
80	43.1	41.7	40.4	39.1	37.9	36.8	35.8	34.8	33.9	33.0	32.2	31.4	30.6	29.9	29.2	28.5	80
81	48.0	46.4	44.9	43.5	42.3	41.0	39.9	38.8	37.7	36.7	35.8	34.9	34.1	33.3	32.5	31.7	81
82	54.0	52.3	50.6	49.1	47.6	46.2	44.9	43.7	42.5	41.4	40.4	39.3	38.3	37.5	36.6	35.8	82
LAT.	172½ 187½	172¼ 187¾	**172°** **188**	171¾ 188¼	171½ 188½	171¼ 188¾	**171°** **189**	170¾ 189¼	170½ 189½	170¼ 189¾	**170°** **190**	169¾ 190¼	169½ 190½	169¼ 190¾	**169°** **191**	168¾ 191¼	LAT.

(S.W. Qdt.) 180°⟶270° (S.E. Qdt.) 180°⟵90°

0°⟶90° (N.E. Qdt.) 360°⟵270° (N.W. Qdt.)

Table 29 (H.L.) B

0 hrs.

Lat. and Dec. SAME name, Sign **−**
Lat. and Dec. CONTRARY names, Sign **+**

HOUR ANGLE or DIFF. LONG.

DEC.	30m	31m	32m	33m	34m	35m	36m	37m	38m	39m	40m	41m	42m	43m	44m	45m	DEC.
	7½° 352½	7¾° 352¼	**8°** **352**	8¼° 351¾	8½° 351½	8¾° 351¼	**9°** **351**	9¼° 350¾	9½° 350½	9¾° 350¼	**10°** **350**	10¼° 349¾	10½° 349½	10¾° 349¼	**11°** **349**	11¼° 348¾	
68°	19.0	18.4	17.8	17.3	16.7	16.3	15.8	15.4	15.0	14.6	14.3	13.9	13.6	13.3	13.0	12.7	68°
69	20.0	19.3	18.8	18.2	17.6	17.1	16.7	16.2	15.8	15.4	15.0	14.6	14.3	14.0	13.7	13.4	69
70	21.0	20.4	19.7	19.1	18.6	18.1	17.6	17.1	16.6	16.2	15.8	15.4	15.1	14.7	14.4	14.1	70
74	26.7	25.9	25.1	24.3	23.6	22.9	22.3	21.7	21.1	20.6	20.1	19.6	19.1	18.7	18.3	17.9	74
75	28.6	27.7	26.8	26.0	25.2	24.5	23.9	23.2	22.6	22.0	21.5	21.0	20.5	20.0	19.6	19.1	75
DEC.	172½ 187½	172¼ 187¾	**172°** **188**	171¾ 188¼	171½ 188½	171¼ 188¾	**171°** **189**	170¾ 189¼	170½ 189½	170¼ 189¾	**170°** **190**	169¾ 190¼	169½ 190½	169¼ 190¾	**169°** **191**	168¾ 191¼	DEC.

(S.W. Qdt.) 180°⟶270° (S.E. Qdt.) 180°⟵90°

Table 29 (H.L.) **B**   0 hrs.

Lat. and Dec. SAME name, Sign —
Lat. and Dec. CONTRARY names, Sign +

HOUR ANGLE or DIFF. LONG.

DEC.	30m	31m	32m	33m	34m	35m	36m	37m	38m	39m	40m	41m	42m	43m	44m	45m	DEC.
	7½°	7¾°	8°	8¼°	8½°	8¾°	9°	9¼°	9½°	9¾°	10°	10¼°	10½°	10¾°	11°	11¼°	
	352½	352¼	352	351¾	351½	351¼	351	350¾	350½	350¼	350	349¾	349½	349¼	349	348¾	
0°	.000	.000	.000	.000	.000	.000	.000	.000	.000	.000	.000	.000	.000	.000	.000	.000	0°
1	.134	.129	.125	.122	.118	.115	.112	.109	.106	.103	.101	.098	.096	.094	.091	.089	1
2	.268	.259	.251	.243	.236	.230	.223	.217	.212	.206	.201	.196	.192	.187	.183	.179	2
3	.402	.389	.377	.365	.355	.345	.335	.326	.318	.309	.302	.295	.288	.281	.275	.269	3
4	.536	.519	.502	.487	.473	.460	.447	.435	.424	.413	.403	.393	.384	.375	.366	.358	4
5	.670	649	.629	.610	.592	.575	.559	.544	.530	.517	.504	.492	.480	.469	.459	.448	5
6	.805	.779	.755	.732	.711	.691	.672	.654	.637	.621	.605	.591	.577	.563	.551	.539	6
7	.941	.911	.882	.856	.831	.807	.785	.764	.744	.725	.707	.690	.674	.658	.643	.629	7
8	1.08	1.04	1.01	.979	.951	.924	.898	.874	.852	.830	.809	.790	.771	.753	.737	.720	8
9	1.21	1.18	1.14	1.10	1.07	1.04	1.01	.985	.960	.935	.912	.890	.869	.849	.830	.812	9
10	1.35	1.31	1.27	1.23	1.19	1.16	1.13	1.10	1.07	1.04	1.02	.991	.968	.945	.924	.904	10
11	1.49	1.44	1.40	1.36	1.32	1.28	1.24	1.21	1.18	1.15	1.12	1.09	1.07	1.04	1.02	.996	11
12	1.63	1.58	1.53	1.48	1.44	1.40	1.36	1.32	1.29	1.26	1.22	1.20	1.17	1.14	1.11	1.09	12
13	1.77	1.71	1.66	1.61	1.56	1.52	1.48	1.44	1.40	1.36	1.33	1.30	1.27	1.24	1.21	1.18	13
14	1.91	1.85	1.79	1.74	1.69	1.64	1.59	1.55	1.51	1.47	1.44	1.40	1.37	1.34	1.31	1.28	14
15	2.05	1.99	1.93	1.87	1.81	1.76	1.71	1.67	1.62	1.58	1.54	1.51	1.47	1.44	1.40	1.37	15
16	2.20	2.13	2.06	2.00	1.94	1.89	1.83	1.78	1.74	1.69	1.65	1.61	1.57	1.54	1.50	1.47	16
17	2.34	2.27	2.20	2.13	2.07	2.01	1.95	1.90	1.85	1.81	1.76	1.72	1.68	1.64	1.60	1.57	17
18	2.49	2.41	2.33	2.26	2.20	2.14	2.08	2.02	1.97	1.92	1.87	1.83	1.78	1.74	1.70	1.67	18
19	2.64	2.55	2.47	2.40	2.33	2.26	2.20	2.14	2.09	2.03	1.98	1.94	1.89	1.85	1.80	1.77	19
20	2.79	2.70	2.62	2.54	2.46	2.39	2.33	2.26	2.21	2.15	2.10	2.05	2.00	1.95	1.91	1.87	20
21	2.94	2.85	2.76	2.68	2.60	2.52	2.45	2.39	2.33	2.27	2.21	2.16	2.11	2.06	2.01	1.97	21
22	3.10	3.00	2.90	2.82	2.73	2.66	2.58	2.51	2.45	2.39	2.33	2.27	2.22	2.17	2.12	2.07	22
23	3.25	3.15	3.05	2.96	2.87	2.79	2.71	2.64	2.57	2.51	2.44	2.39	2.33	2.28	2.22	2.18	23
24	3.41	3.30	3.20	3.10	3.01	2.93	2.85	2.77	2.70	2.63	2.56	2.50	2.44	2.39	2.33	2.28	24
25	3.57	3.46	3.35	3.25	3.15	3.07	2.98	2.90	2.83	2.75	2.69	2.62	2.56	2.50	2.44	2.39	25
26	3.74	3.62	3.50	3.40	3.30	3.21	3.12	3.03	2.96	2.88	2.81	2.74	2.68	2.62	2.56	2.50	26
27	3.90	3.78	3.66	3.55	3.45	3.35	3.26	3.17	3.09	3.01	2.93	2.86	2.80	2.73	2.67	2.61	27
28	4.07	3.94	3.82	3.71	3.60	3.50	3.40	3.31	3.22	3.14	3.06	2.99	2.92	2.85	2.79	2.73	28
29	4.25	4.11	3.98	3.86	3.75	3.64	3.54	3.45	3.36	3.27	3.19	3.12	3.04	2.97	2.91	2.84	29
30	4.42	4.28	4.15	4.02	3.91	3.80	3.69	3.59	3.50	3.41	3.32	3.25	3.17	3.10	3.03	2.96	30
31	4.60	4.46	4.32	4.19	4.07	3.95	3.84	3.74	3.64	3.55	3.46	3.38	3.30	3.22	3.15	3.08	31
32	4.79	4.63	4.49	4.36	4.23	4.11	3.99	3.89	3.79	3.69	3.60	3.51	3.43	3.35	3.27	3.20	32
33	4.98	4.82	4.67	4.53	4.39	4.27	4.15	4.04	3.93	3.84	3.74	3.65	3.56	3.48	3.40	3.33	33
34	5.17	5.00	4.85	4.70	4.56	4.43	4.31	4.20	4.09	3.98	3.88	3.79	3.70	3.62	3.54	3.46	34
35	5.36	5.19	5.03	4.88	4.74	4.60	4.48	4.36	4.24	4.14	4.03	3.94	3.84	3.75	3.67	3.59	35
36	5.57	5.39	5.22	5.06	4.92	4.78	4.64	4.52	4.40	4.29	4.18	4.08	3.99	3.90	3.81	3.72	36
37	5.77	5.59	5.41	5.25	5.10	4.95	4.82	4.69	4.57	4.45	4.34	4.24	4.14	4.04	3.95	3.86	37
38	5.99	5.79	5.61	5.45	5.29	5.14	4.99	4.86	4.73	4.61	4.50	4.39	4.29	4.19	4.10	4.01	38
39	6.20	6.01	5.82	5.64	5.48	5.32	5.18	5.04	4.91	4.78	4.66	4.55	4.44	4.34	4.24	4.15	39
40	6.43	6.22	6.03	5.85	5.68	5.52	5.36	5.22	5.08	4.96	4.83	4.72	4.60	4.50	4.40	4.30	40
41	6.66	6.45	6.25	6.06	5.88	5.71	5.56	5.41	5.27	5.13	5.01	4.89	4.77	4.66	4.56	4.46	41
42	6.90	6.68	6.47	6.28	6.09	5.92	5.76	5.60	5.46	5.32	5.19	5.06	4.94	4.83	4.72	4.62	42
43	7.14	6.92	6.70	6.50	6.31	6.13	5.96	5.80	5.65	5.51	5.37	5.24	5.12	5.00	4.89	4.78	43
44	7.40	7.16	6.94	6.73	6.53	6.35	6.17	6.01	5.85	5.70	5.56	5.43	5.30	5.18	5.06	4.95	44
45	7.66	7.42	71.9	6.97	6.77	6.57	6.39	6.22	6.06	5.91	5.76	5.62	5.49	5.36	5.24	5.13	45
46	7.93	7.68	7.44	7.22	7.01	6.81	6.62	6.44	6.27	6.12	5.96	5.82	5.68	5.55	5.43	5.31	46
47	8.22	7.95	7.71	7.47	7.26	7.05	6.86	6.67	6.50	6.33	6.18	6.03	5.89	5.75	5.62	5.50	47
48	8.51	8.24	7.98	7.74	7.51	7.30	7.10	6.91	6.73	6.56	6.40	6.24	6.09	5.95	5.82	5.69	48
49	8.81	8.53	8.27	8.02	7.78	7.56	7.35	7.16	6.97	6.79	6.62	6.47	6.31	6.17	6.03	5.90	49
50	9.13	8.84	8.56	8.31	8.06	7.83	7.62	7.41	7.22	7.04	6.86	6.70	6.54	6.39	6.25	6.11	50
51	9.46	9.16	8.87	8.61	8.35	8.12	7.89	7.68	7.48	7.29	7.11	6.94	6.78	6.62	6.47	6.33	51
52	9.81	9.49	9.20	8.92	8.66	8.41	8.18	7.96	7.76	7.56	7.37	7.19	7.02	6.86	6.71	6.56	52
53	10.2	9.84	9.54	9.25	8.98	8.72	8.48	8.26	8.04	7.84	7.64	7.46	7.28	7.12	6.95	6.80	53
54	10.5	10.2	9.89	9.59	9.31	9.05	8.80	8.56	8.34	8.13	7.93	7.74	7.55	7.38	7.21	7.06	54
55	10.9	10.6	10.3	9.95	9.66	9.39	9.13	8.89	8.65	8.43	8.22	8.03	7.84	7.66	7.48	7.32	55
56	11.4	11.0	10.7	10.3	10.0	9.75	9.48	9.22	8.98	8.75	8.54	8.33	8.14	7.95	7.77	7.60	56
57	11.8	11.4	11.1	10.7	10.4	10.1	9.84	9.58	9.33	9.09	8.87	8.65	8.45	8.26	8.07	7.89	57
58	12.3	11.9	11.5	11.2	10.8	10.5	10.2	9.96	9.70	9.45	9.22	8.99	8.78	8.58	8.39	8.20	58
59	12.8	12.3	12.0	11.6	11.3	10.9	10.6	10.4	10.1	9.83	9.58	9.35	9.13	8.92	8.72	8.53	59
60	13.3	12.8	12.5	12.1	11.7	11.4	11.1	10.8	10.5	10.2	9.97	9.73	9.50	9.29	9.08	8.88	60
61	13.8	13.4	13.0	12.6	12.2	11.9	11.5	11.2	10.9	10.7	10.4	10.1	9.90	9.67	9.45	9.25	61
62	14.4	14.0	13.5	13.1	12.7	12.4	12.0	11.7	11.4	11.1	10.8	10.6	10.3	10.1	9.86	9.64	62
63	15.0	14.6	14.1	13.7	13.3	12.9	12.5	12.2	11.9	11.6	11.3	11.0	10.8	10.5	10.3	10.1	63
DEC.	172½	172¼	172°	171¾	171½	171¼	171°	170¾	170½	170¼	170°	169¾	169½	169¼	169°	168¾	DEC.
	187½	187¾	188	188¼	188½	188¾	189	189¼	189½	189¾	190	190¼	190½	190¾	191	191¼	

0°⟶90° (N.E. Qdt.) 360°⟵270° (N.W. Qdt.)

Table 29 (H.L.)

A

0 hrs.

If entered with H.A. at **top,** Sign **+**
„ „ „ „ **foot,** „ **−**

HOUR ANGLE or DIFF. LONG.

LAT.	45m	46m	47m	48m	49m	50m	51m	52m	53m	54m	55m	56m	57m	58m	59m	60m	LAT.
	11¼° 348¾	11½° 348½	11¾° 348¼	**12°** **348**	12¼° 347¾	12½° 347½	12¾° 347¼	**13°** **347**	13¼° 346¾	13½° 346½	13¾° 346¼	**14°** **346**	14¼° 345¾	14½° 345½	14¾° 345¼	**15°** **345**	
60°	8.71	8.51	8.33	8.15	7.98	7.81	7.66	7.50	7.36	7.22	7.08	6.95	6.82	6.70	6.58	6.46	**60°**
61	9.07	8.87	8.67	8.49	8.31	8.14	7.97	7.81	7.66	7.51	7.37	7.24	7.10	6.98	6.85	6.73	**61**
62	9.46	9.24	9.04	8.85	8.66	8.48	8.31	8.15	7.99	7.83	7.69	7.54	7.41	7.27	7.14	7.02	**62**
63	9.87	9.65	9.44	9.23	9.04	8.85	8.67	8.50	8.34	8.18	8.02	7.87	7.73	7.59	7.46	7.33	**63**
64	10.3	10.1	9.86	9.65	9.44	9.25	9.06	8.88	8.71	8.54	8.38	8.22	8.07	7.93	7.79	7.65	**64**
65	10.8	10.5	10.3	10.1	9.88	9.67	9.48	9.29	9.11	8.93	8.76	8.60	8.44	8.29	8.15	8.00	**65**
66	11.3	11.0	10.8	10.6	10.3	10.1	9.93	9.72	9.54	9.36	9.18	9.01	8.84	8.68	8.53	8.38	**66**
67	11.8	11.6	11.3	11.1	10.9	10.6	10.4	10.2	10.0	9.81	9.63	9.45	9.28	9.11	8.95	8.79	**67**
68	12.4	12.2	11.9	11.6	11.4	11.2	10.9	10.7	10.5	10.4	10.1	9.93	9.75	9.57	9.40	9.24	**68**
69	13.1	12.8	12.5	12.3	12.0	11.8	11.5	11.3	11.1	10.9	10.6	10.4	10.3	10.1	9.89	9.72	**69**
70	13.8	13.5	13.2	12.9	12.7	12.4	12.1	11.9	11.7	11.4	11.2	11.0	10.8	10.6	10.4	10.3	**70**
71	14.6	14.3	14.0	13.7	13.4	13.1	12.8	12.6	12.3	12.1	11.9	11.6	11.4	11.2	11.0	10.8	**71**
72	15.5	15.1	14.8	14.5	14.2	13.9	13.6	13.3	13.1	12.8	12.6	12.3	12.1	11.9	11.7	11.5	**72**
73	16.4	16.1	15.7	15.4	15.1	14.8	14.5	14.2	13.9	13.6	13.4	13.1	12.9	12.6	12.4	12.2	**73**
74	17.5	17.1	16.8	16.4	16.1	15.7	15.4	15.1	14.8	14.5	14.3	14.0	13.7	13.5	13.2	13.0	**74**
75	18.8	18.3	17.9	17.6	17.2	16.8	16.5	16.2	15.8	15.6	15.3	15.0	14.7	14.4	14.2	13.9	**75**
76	20.2	19.7	19.3	18.9	18.5	18.1	17.7	17.4	17.0	16.7	16.4	16.1	15.8	15.5	15.2	15.0	**76**
77	21.8	21.3	20.8	20.4	19.9	19.5	19.1	18.8	18.4	18.0	17.7	17.4	17.1	16.7	16.5	16.2	**77**
78	23.7	23.1	22.6	22.1	21.7	21.2	20.8	20.4	20.0	19.6	19.2	18.9	18.5	18.2	17.9	17.6	**78**
79	25.9	25.3	24.7	24.2	23.7	23.1	22.7	22.2	21.8	21.4	21.0	20.6	20.3	19.9	19.5	19.2	**79**
80	28.5	27.9	27.3	26.7	26.1	25.6	25.1	24.6	24.1	23.6	23.2	22.7	22.3	21.9	21.5	21.1	**80**
81	31.7	31.0	30.4	29.7	29.1	28.5	27.9	27.3	26.8	26.3	25.8	25.3	24.9	24.4	24.0	23.6	**81**
82	35.8	35.0	34.2	33.5	32.8	32.1	31.5	30.8	30.2	29.6	29.1	28.5	28.0	27.5	27.0	26.6	**82**
LAT.	168¾ 191¼	168½ 191½	168¼ 191¾	**168°** **192**	167¾ 192¼	167½ 192½	167¼ 192¾	**167°** **193**	166¾ 193¼	166½ 193½	166¼ 193¾	**166°** **194**	165¾ 194¼	165½ 194½	165¼ 194¾	**165°** **195**	LAT.

(S.W. Qdt.) 180°⟶270° (S.E. Qdt.) 180°⟵90°

0°⟶90° (N.E. Qdt.) 360°⟵270° (N.W. Qdt.)

Table 29 (H.L.)

B

0 hrs.

Lat. and Dec. SAME name, Sign **−**
Lat. and Dec. CONTRARY names, Sign **+**

HOUR ANGLE or DIFF. LONG.

DEC.	45m	46m	47m	48m	49m	50m	51m	52m	53m	54m	55m	56m	57m	58m	59m	60m	DEC.
	11¼° 348¾	11½° 348½	11¾° 348¼	**12°** **348**	12¼° 347¾	12½° 347½	12¾° 347¼	**13°** **347**	13¼° 346¾	13½° 346½	13¾° 346¼	**14°** **346**	14¼° 345¾	14½° 345½	14¾° 345¼	**15°** **345**	
68°	12.7	12.4	12.2	11.9	11.7	11.4	11.2	11.0	10.8	10.6	10.4	10.2	10.1	9.89	9.72	9.56	**68°**
69	13.4	13.1	12.8	12.5	12.3	12.0	11.8	11.6	11.4	11.2	11.0	10.8	10.6	10.4	10.2	10.1	**69**
70	14.1	13.8	13.5	13.2	12.9	12.7	12.4	12.2	12.0	11.8	11.6	11.4	11.2	11.0	10.8	10.6	**70**
74	17.9	17.5	17.1	16.8	16.4	16.1	15.8	15.5	15.2	14.9	14.7	14.4	14.2	13.9	13.7	13.5	**74**
75	19.1	18.7	18.3	18.0	17.6	17.2	16.9	16.6	16.3	16.0	15.7	15.4	15.2	14.9	14.7	14.4	**75**
DEC.	168¾ 191¼	168½ 191½	168¼ 191¾	**168°** **192**	167¾ 192¼	167½ 192½	167¼ 192¾	**167°** **193**	166¾ 193¼	166½ 193½	166¼ 193¾	**166°** **194**	165¾ 194¼	165½ 194½	165¼ 194¾	**165°** **195**	DEC.

(S.W. Qdt.) 180°⟶270° (S.E. Qdt.) 180°⟵90°

Table 29 (H.L.) **B** 0 hrs.

Lat. and Dec. SAME name, Sign **−**
Lat. and Dec. CONTRARY names, Sign **+**

HOUR ANGLE or DIFF. LONG.

DEC.	45m 11¼° 348¾	46m 11½° 348½	47m 11¾° 348¼	48m 12° 348	49m 12¼° 347¾	50m 12½° 347½	51m 12¾° 347¼	52m 13° 347	53m 13¼° 346¾	54m 13½° 346½	55m 13¾° 346¼	56m 14° 346	57m 14¼° 345¾	58m 14½° 345½	59m 14¾° 345¼	60m 15° 345	DEC.
0°	.000	.000	.000	.000	.000	.000	.000	.000	.000	.000	.000	.000	.000	.000	.000	.000	0°
1	.089	.088	.086	.084	.082	.081	.079	.078	.076	.075	.073	.072	.071	.070	.069	.067	1
2	.179	.175	.171	.168	.165	.161	.158	.155	.152	.150	.147	.144	.142	.140	.137	.135	2
3	.269	.263	.257	.252	.247	.242	.237	.233	.229	.224	.220	.217	.213	.209	.206	.202	3
4	.358	.351	.343	.336	.330	.323	.317	.311	.305	.300	.294	.289	.284	.279	.275	.270	4
5	.448	.439	.430	.421	.412	.404	.396	.389	.382	.375	.368	.362	.355	.349	.344	.338	5
6	.539	.527	.516	.506	.495	.486	.476	.467	.459	.450	.442	.434	.427	.420	.413	.406	6
7	.629	.616	.603	.591	.579	.567	.556	.546	.536	.526	.517	.508	.499	.490	.482	.474	7
8	.720	.705	.690	.676	.662	.649	.637	.625	.613	.602	.591	.581	.571	.561	.552	.543	8
9	.812	.794	.778	.762	.746	.732	.718	.704	.691	.678	.666	.655	.643	.633	.622	.612	9
10	.904	.884	.866	.848	.831	.815	.799	.784	.769	.755	.742	.729	.716	.704	.693	.681	10
11	.996	.975	.955	.935	.916	.898	.881	.864	.848	.833	.818	.803	.790	.776	.763	.751	11
12	1.09	1.07	1.04	1.02	1.00	.982	.963	.945	.927	.911	.894	.879	.864	.849	.835	.821	12
13	1.18	1.16	1.13	1.11	1.09	1.07	1.05	1.03	1.01	.989	.971	.954	.938	.922	.907	.892	13
14	1.28	1.25	1.22	1.20	1.18	1.15	1.13	1.11	1.09	1.07	1.05	1.03	1.01	.996	.979	.963	14
15	1.37	1.34	1.32	1.29	1.26	1.24	1.21	1.19	1.17	1.15	1.13	1.11	1.09	1.07	1.05	1.04	15
16	1.47	1.44	1.41	1.38	1.35	1.32	1.30	1.27	1.25	1.23	1.21	1.19	1.17	1.15	1.13	1.11	16
17	1.57	1.53	1.50	1.47	1.44	1.41	1.39	1.36	1.33	1.31	1.29	1.26	1.24	1.22	1.20	1.18	17
18	1.67	1.63	1.60	1.56	1.53	1.50	1.47	1.44	1.42	1.39	1.37	1.34	1.32	1.30	1.28	1.26	18
19	1.77	1.73	1.69	1.66	1.62	1.59	1.56	1.53	1.50	1.48	1.45	1.42	1.40	1.38	1.35	1.33	19
20	1.87	1.83	1.79	1.75	1.72	1.68	1.65	1.62	1.59	1.56	1.53	1.50	1.48	1.45	1.43	1.41	20
21	1.97	1.93	1.89	1.85	1.81	1.77	1.74	1.71	1.68	1.64	1.62	1.59	1.56	1.53	1.51	1.48	21
22	2.07	2.03	1.98	1.94	1.90	1.87	1.83	1.80	1.76	1.73	1.70	1.67	1.64	1.61	1.59	1.56	22
23	2.18	2.13	2.08	2.04	2.00	1.96	1.92	1.89	1.85	1.82	1.79	1.75	1.72	1.70	1.67	1.64	23
24	2.28	2.23	2.19	2.14	2.10	2.06	2.02	1.98	1.94	1.91	1.87	1.84	1.81	1.78	1.75	1.72	24
25	2.39	2.34	2.29	2.24	2.20	2.15	2.11	2.07	2.03	2.00	1.96	1.93	1.89	1.86	1.83	1.80	25
26	2.50	2.45	2.40	2.35	2.30	2.25	2.21	2.17	2.13	2.09	2.05	2.02	1.98	1.95	1.92	1.88	26
27	2.61	2.56	2.50	2.45	2.40	2.35	2.31	2.27	2.22	2.18	2.14	2.11	2.07	2.04	2.00	1.97	27
28	2.73	2.67	2.61	2.56	2.51	2.46	2.41	2.36	2.32	2.28	2.24	2.20	2.16	2.12	2.09	2.05	28
29	2.84	2.78	2.72	2.67	2.61	2.56	2.51	2.46	2.42	2.37	2.33	2.29	2.25	2.21	2.18	2.14	29
30	2.96	2.90	2.84	2.78	2.72	2.67	2.62	2.57	2.52	2.47	2.43	2.39	2.35	2.31	2.27	2.23	30
31	3.08	3.01	2.95	2.89	2.83	2.78	2.72	2.67	2.62	2.57	2.53	2.48	2.44	2.40	2.36	2.32	31
32	3.20	3.13	3.07	3.01	2.95	2.89	2.83	2.78	2.73	2.68	2.63	2.58	2.54	2.50	2.45	2.41	32
33	3.33	3.26	3.19	3.12	3.06	3.00	2.94	2.89	2.83	2.78	2.73	2.68	2.64	2.59	2.55	2.51	33
34	3.46	3.38	3.31	3.24	3.18	3.12	3.06	3.00	2.94	2.89	2.84	2.79	2.74	2.69	2.65	2.61	34
35	3.59	3.51	3.44	3.37	3.30	3.24	3.17	3.11	3.06	3.00	2.95	2.89	2.85	2.80	2.75	2.71	35
36	3.72	3.64	3.57	3.49	3.42	3.36	3.29	3.23	3.17	3.11	3.06	3.00	2.95	2.90	2.85	2.81	36
37	3.86	3.78	3.70	3.62	3.55	3.48	3.41	3.35	3.29	3.23	3.17	3.11	3.06	3.01	2.96	2.91	37
38	4.01	3.92	3.84	3.76	3.68	3.61	3.54	3.47	3.41	3.35	3.29	3.23	3.17	3.12	3.07	3.02	38
39	4.15	4.06	3.98	3.89	3.82	3.74	3.67	3.60	3.53	3.47	3.41	3.35	3.29	3.23	3.18	3.13	39
40	4.30	4.21	4.12	4.04	3.96	3.88	3.80	3.73	3.66	3.59	3.53	3.47	3.41	3.35	3.30	3.24	40
41	4.46	4.36	4.27	4.18	4.10	4.02	3.94	3.86	3.79	3.72	3.66	3.59	3.53	3.47	3.41	3.36	41
42	4.62	4.52	4.42	4.33	4.24	4.16	4.08	4.00	3.93	3.86	3.79	3.72	3.66	3.60	3.54	3.48	42
43	4.78	4.68	4.58	4.49	4.40	4.31	4.23	4.15	4.07	3.99	3.92	3.85	3.79	3.72	3.66	3.60	43
44	4.95	4.84	4.74	4.64	4.55	4.46	4.38	4.29	4.21	4.14	4.06	3.99	3.92	3.86	3.79	3.73	44
45	5.13	5.02	4.91	4.81	4.71	4.62	4.53	4.45	4.36	4.28	4.21	4.13	4.06	3.99	3.93	3.86	45
46	5.31	5.19	5.09	4.98	4.88	4.78	4.69	4.60	4.52	4.44	4.36	4.28	4.21	4.14	4.07	4.00	46
47	5.50	5.38	5.27	5.16	5.05	4.95	4.86	4.77	4.68	4.59	4.51	4.43	4.36	4.28	4.21	4.14	47
48	5.69	5.57	5.45	5.34	5.23	5.13	5.03	4.94	4.85	4.76	4.67	4.59	4.51	4.44	4.36	4.29	48
49	5.90	5.77	5.65	5.53	5.42	5.32	5.21	5.11	5.02	4.93	4.84	4.76	4.67	4.59	4.52	4.44	49
50	6.11	5.98	5.85	5.73	5.62	5.51	5.40	5.30	5.20	5.11	5.01	4.93	4.84	4.76	4.68	4.60	50
51	6.33	6.19	6.06	5.94	5.82	5.71	5.60	5.49	5.39	5.29	5.20	5.10	5.02	4.93	4.85	4.77	51
52	6.56	6.42	6.29	6.16	6.03	5.91	5.80	5.69	5.58	5.48	5.39	5.29	5.20	5.11	5.03	4.95	52
53	6.80	6.66	6.52	6.38	6.25	6.13	6.01	5.90	5.79	5.68	5.58	5.49	5.39	5.30	5.21	5.13	53
54	7.06	6.90	6.76	6.62	6.49	6.36	6.24	6.12	6.01	5.90	5.79	5.69	5.59	5.50	5.41	5.32	54
55	7.32	7.16	7.01	6.87	6.73	6.60	6.47	6.35	6.23	6.12	6.01	5.90	5.80	5.70	5.61	5.52	55
56	7.60	7.44	7.28	7.13	6.99	6.85	6.72	6.59	6.47	6.35	6.24	6.13	6.02	5.92	5.82	5.73	56
57	7.89	7.72	7.56	7.41	7.26	7.11	6.98	6.85	6.72	6.60	6.48	6.37	6.26	6.15	6.05	5.95	57
58	8.20	8.03	7.86	7.70	7.54	7.39	7.25	7.11	6.98	6.86	6.73	6.62	6.50	6.39	6.29	6.18	58
59	8.53	8.35	8.17	8.00	7.84	7.69	7.54	7.40	7.26	7.13	7.00	6.88	6.76	6.65	6.54	6.43	59
60	8.88	8.69	8.51	8.33	8.16	8.00	7.85	7.70	7.56	7.42	7.29	7.16	7.04	6.92	6.80	6.69	60
61	9.25	9.05	8.86	8.68	8.50	8.34	8.17	8.02	7.87	7.73	7.59	7.46	7.33	7.21	7.09	6.97	61
62	9.64	9.43	9.24	9.05	8.86	8.69	8.52	8.36	8.21	8.06	7.91	7.77	7.64	7.51	7.39	7.27	62
63	10.1	9.84	9.64	9.44	9.25	9.07	8.89	8.72	8.56	8.41	8.26	8.11	7.97	7.84	7.71	7.58	63
DEC.	168¾ 191¼	168½ 191½	168¼ 191¾	168° 192	167¾ 192¼	167½ 192½	167¼ 192¾	167° 193	166¾ 193¼	166½ 193½	166¼ 193¾	166° 194	165¾ 194¼	165½ 194½	165¼ 194¾	165° 195	DEC.

Table 29 (H.L.)

A If entered with H.A. at **top**, Sign **+**

"   "   "   "   **foot**, " **−**

1 hr.

HOUR ANGLE or DIFF. LONG.

LAT.	00m	01m	02m	03m	04m	05m	06m	07m	08m	09m	10m	11m	12m	13m	14m	15m	LAT.
	15° 345	15¼° 344¾	15½° 344½	15¾° 344¼	16° 344	16¼° 343¾	16½° 343½	16¾° 343¼	17° 343	17¼° 342¾	17½° 342½	17¾° 342¼	18° 342	18¼° 341¾	18½° 341½	18¾° 341¼	
60°	6.46	6.35	6.25	6.14	6.04	5.94	5.85	5.76	5.67	5.58	5.49	5.41	5.33	5.25	5.18	5.10	60°
61	6.73	6.62	6.51	6.40	6.29	6.19	6.09	5.99	5.90	5.81	5.72	5.64	5.55	5.47	5.39	5.31	61
62	7.02	6.90	6.78	6.67	6.56	6.45	6.35	6.25	6.15	6.06	5.97	5.88	5.79	5.70	5.62	5.54	62
63	7.33	7.20	7.08	6.96	6.84	6.73	6.63	6.52	6.42	6.32	6.23	6.13	6.04	5.95	5.87	5.78	63
64	7.65	7.52	7.39	7.27	7.15	7.03	6.92	6.81	6.71	6.60	6.50	6.41	6.31	6.22	6.13	6.04	64
65	8.00	7.87	7.73	7.60	7.48	7.36	7.24	7.13	7.01	6.91	6.80	6.70	6.60	6.50	6.41	6.32	65
66	8.38	8.24	8.10	7.96	7.83	7.71	7.58	7.46	7.35	7.23	7.12	7.02	6.91	6.81	6.71	6.62	66
67	8.79	8.64	8.49	8.35	8.22	8.08	7.95	7.83	7.71	7.59	7.47	7.36	7.25	7.14	7.04	6.94	67
68	9.24	9.08	8.92	8.78	8.63	8.49	8.36	8.22	8.10	7.97	7.85	7.73	7.62	7.51	7.40	7.29	68
69	9.72	9.56	9.39	9.24	9.09	8.94	8.79	8.66	8.52	8.39	8.26	8.14	8.02	7.90	7.79	7.67	69
70	10.3	10.1	9.91	9.74	9.58	9.43	9.28	9.13	8.99	8.85	8.71	8.58	8.46	8.33	8.21	8.09	70
71	10.8	10.7	10.5	10.3	10.1	9.96	9.80	9.65	9.50	9.35	9.21	9.07	8.94	8.81	8.68	8.56	71
72	11.5	11.3	11.1	10.9	10.7	10.6	10.4	10.2	10.1	9.91	9.76	9.61	9.47	9.33	9.20	9.07	72
73	12.2	12.0	11.8	11.6	11.4	11.2	11.0	10.9	10.7	10.5	10.4	10.2	10.1	9.92	9.78	9.64	73
74	13.0	12.8	12.6	12.4	12.2	12.0	11.8	11.6	11.4	11.2	11.1	10.9	10.7	10.6	10.4	10.3	74
75	13.9	13.7	13.5	13.2	13.0	12.8	12.6	12.4	12.2	12.0	11.8	11.7	11.5	11.3	11.2	11.0	75
76	15.0	14.7	14.5	14.2	14.0	13.8	13.5	13.3	13.1	12.9	12.7	12.5	12.3	12.2	12.0	11.8	76
77	16.2	15.9	15.6	15.4	15.1	14.9	14.6	14.4	14.2	13.9	13.7	13.5	13.3	13.1	12.9	12.8	77
78	17.6	17.3	17.0	16.7	16.4	16.1	15.9	15.6	15.4	15.2	14.9	14.7	14.5	14.3	14.1	13.9	78
79	19.2	18.9	18.6	18.2	17.9	17.7	17.4	17.1	16.8	16.6	16.3	16.1	15.8	15.6	15.4	15.1	79
80	21.1	20.8	20.5	20.1	19.8	19.5	19.1	18.8	18.5	18.3	18.0	17.7	17.5	17.2	16.9	16.7	80
81	23.6	23.2	22.8	22.4	22.0	21.7	21.3	21.0	20.7	20.3	20.0	19.7	19.4	19.1	18.9	18.6	81
82	26.6	26.1	25.7	25.2	24.8	24.4	24.0	23.6	23.3	22.9	22.6	22.2	21.9	21.6	21.3	21.0	82
LAT.	165° 195	164¾ 195¼	164½ 195½	164¼ 195¾	164° 196	163¾ 196¼	163½ 196½	163¼ 196¾	163° 197	162¾ 197¼	162½ 197½	162¼ 197¾	162° 198	161¾ 198¼	161½ 198½	161¼ 198¾	LAT.

(S.W. Qdt.) **180°—→270°**   (S.E. Qdt.) **180°←—90°**

Table 29 (H.L.)

B Lat. and Dec. SAME name, Sign **−**

Lat. and Dec. CONTRARY names, Sign **+**

1 hr.

HOUR ANGLE or DIFF. LONG.

DEC.	00m	01m	02m	03m	04m	05m	06m	07m	08m	09m	10m	11m	12m	13m	14m	15m	DEC.
	15° 345	15¼° 344¾	15½° 344½	15¾° 344¼	16° 344	16¼° 343¾	16½° 343½	16¾° 343¼	17° 343	17¼° 342¾	17½° 342½	17¾° 342¼	18° 342	18¼° 341¾	18½° 341½	18¾° 341¼	
68°	9.56	9.41	9.26	9.12	8.98	8.85	8.72	8.59	8.47	8.35	8.23	8.12	8.01	7.90	7.80	7.70	68°
69	10.1	9.90	9.75	9.60	9.45	9.31	9.17	9.04	8.91	8.79	8.66	8.55	8.43	8.32	8.21	8.10	69
70	10.6	10.4	10.2	10.1	9.97	9.82	9.67	9.54	9.40	9.27	9.14	9.01	8.89	8.77	8.66	8.55	70
74	13.5	13.3	13.0	12.8	12.7	12.5	12.3	12.1	11.9	11.8	11.6	11.4	11.3	11.1	11.0	10.8	74
75	14.4	14.2	14.0	13.7	13.5	13.3	13.1	12.9	12.8	12.6	12.4	12.2	12.1	11.9	11.8	11.6	75
DEC.	165° 195	164¾ 195¼	164½ 195½	164¼ 195¾	164° 196	163¾ 196¼	163½ 196½	163¼ 196¾	163° 197	162¾ 197¼	162½ 197½	162¼ 197¾	162° 198	161¾ 198¼	161½ 198½	161¼ 198¾	DEC.

(S.W. Qdt.) **180°—→270°**   S.E. Qdt.) **180°←—90°**

Table 29 (H.L.) — B — 1 hr.

Lat. and Dec. SAME name, Sign −
Lat. and Dec. CONTRARY names, Sign +

HOUR ANGLE or DIFF. LONG.

DEC.	00m	01m	02m	03m	04m	05m	06m	07m	08m	09m	10m	11m	12m	13m	14m	15m	DEC.
	15° 345	15¼° 344¾	15½° 344½	15¾° 344¼	16° 344	16¼° 343¾	16½° 343½	16¾° 343¼	17° 343	17¼° 342¾	17½° 342½	17¾° 342¼	18° 342	18¼° 341¾	18½° 341½	18¾° 341¼	
0°	.000	.000	.000	.000	.000	.000	.000	.000	.000	.000	.000	.000	.000	.000	.000	.000	0°
1	.067	.066	.065	.064	.063	.062	.061	.061	.060	.059	.058	.057	.057	.056	.055	.054	1
2	.135	.133	.131	.129	.127	.125	.123	.121	.119	.118	.116	.115	.113	.112	.110	.109	2
3	.202	.199	.196	.193	.190	.187	.185	.182	.179	.177	.174	.172	.170	.167	.165	.163	3
4	.270	.266	.262	.258	.254	.250	.246	.243	.239	.236	.233	.229	.226	.223	.220	.218	4
5	.338	.333	.327	.322	.317	.313	.308	.304	.299	.295	.291	.287	.283	.279	.276	.272	5
6	.406	.400	.393	.387	.381	.376	.370	.365	.359	.354	.350	.345	.340	.336	.331	.327	6
7	.474	.467	.459	.452	.445	.439	.432	.426	.420	.414	.408	.403	.397	.392	.387	.382	7
8	.543	.534	.526	.518	.510	.502	.495	.488	.481	.474	.467	.461	.455	.449	.443	.437	8
9	.612	.602	.593	.584	.575	.566	.558	.550	.542	.534	.527	.520	.513	.506	.499	.493	9
10	.681	.670	.660	.650	.640	.630	.621	.612	.603	.595	.586	.578	.571	.563	.556	.549	10
11	.751	.739	.727	.716	.705	.694	.684	.675	.665	.656	.646	.638	.629	.621	.613	.605	11
12	.821	.808	.795	.783	.771	.760	.748	.738	.727	.717	.707	.697	.688	.679	.670	.661	12
13	.892	.878	.864	.851	.838	.825	.813	.801	.790	.779	.768	.757	.747	.737	.728	.718	13
14	.963	.948	.933	.919	.905	.891	.878	.865	.853	.841	.829	.818	.807	.796	.786	.776	14
15	1.04	1.02	1.00	.987	.972	.958	.943	.930	.916	.904	.891	.879	.867	.856	.844	.834	15
16	1.11	1.09	1.07	1.06	1.04	1.02	1.01	.995	.981	.967	.954	.941	.928	.916	.904	.892	16
17	1.18	1.16	1.14	1.13	1.11	1.09	1.08	1.06	1.05	1.03	1.02	1.00	.989	.976	.964	.951	17
18	1.26	1.24	1.22	1.20	1.18	1.16	1.14	1.13	1.11	1.10	1.08	1.07	1.05	1.04	1.02	1.01	18
19	1.33	1.31	1.29	1.27	1.25	1.23	1.21	1.19	1.18	1.16	1.15	1.13	1.11	1.10	1.09	1.07	19
20	1.41	1.38	1.36	1.34	1.32	1.30	1.28	1.26	1.24	1.23	1.21	1.19	1.18	1.16	1.15	1.13	20
21	1.48	1.46	1.44	1.41	1.39	1.37	1.35	1.33	1.31	1.29	1.28	1.26	1.24	1.23	1.21	1.19	21
22	1.56	1.54	1.51	1.49	1.47	1.44	1.42	1.40	1.38	1.36	1.34	1.33	1.31	1.29	1.27	1.26	22
23	1.64	1.61	1.59	1.56	1.54	1.52	1.49	1.47	1.45	1.43	1.41	1.39	1.37	1.36	1.34	1.32	23
24	1.72	1.69	1.67	1.64	1.62	1.59	1.57	1.55	1.52	1.50	1.48	1.46	1.44	1.42	1.40	1.39	24
25	1.80	1.77	1.74	1.72	1.69	1.67	1.64	1.62	1.59	1.57	1.55	1.53	1.51	1.49	1.47	1.45	25
26	1.88	1.85	1.83	1.80	1.77	1.74	1.72	1.69	1.67	1.64	1.62	1.60	1.58	1.56	1.54	1.52	26
27	1.97	1.94	1.91	1.88	1.85	1.82	1.79	1.77	1.74	1.72	1.69	1.67	1.65	1.63	1.61	1.59	27
28	2.05	2.02	1.99	1.96	1.93	1.90	1.87	1.85	1.82	1.79	1.77	1.74	1.72	1.70	1.68	1.65	28
29	2.14	2.10	2.07	2.04	2.01	1.98	1.95	1.92	1.90	1.87	1.84	1.82	1.79	1.77	1.75	1.72	29
30	2.23	2.20	2.16	2.13	2.09	2.06	2.03	2.00	1.97	1.95	1.92	1.89	1.87	1.84	1.82	1.80	30
31	2.32	2.28	2.25	2.21	2.18	2.15	2.12	2.09	2.06	2.03	2.00	1.97	1.94	1.92	1.89	1.87	31
32	2.41	2.38	2.34	2.30	2.27	2.23	2.20	2.17	2.14	2.11	2.08	2.05	2.02	2.00	1.97	1.94	32
33	2.51	2.47	2.43	2.39	2.36	2.32	2.29	2.25	2.22	2.19	2.16	2.13	2.10	2.07	2.05	2.02	33
34	2.61	2.56	2.52	2.49	2.45	2.41	2.37	2.34	2.31	2.27	2.24	2.21	2.18	2.15	2.13	2.10	34
35	2.71	2.66	2.62	2.58	2.54	2.50	2.47	2.43	2.39	2.36	2.33	2.30	2.27	2.24	2.21	2.18	35
36	2.81	2.76	2.72	2.68	2.64	2.60	2.56	2.52	2.48	2.45	2.42	2.38	2.35	2.32	2.29	2.26	36
37	2.91	2.87	2.82	2.78	2.73	2.69	2.65	2.61	2.58	2.54	2.51	2.47	2.44	2.41	2.37	2.34	37
38	3.02	2.97	2.92	2.88	2.83	2.79	2.75	2.71	2.67	2.63	2.60	2.56	2.53	2.49	2.46	2.43	38
39	3.13	3.08	3.03	2.98	2.94	2.89	2.85	2.81	2.77	2.73	2.69	2.66	2.62	2.59	2.55	2.52	39
40	3.24	3.19	3.14	3.09	3.04	3.00	2.95	2.91	2.87	2.83	2.79	2.75	2.72	2.68	2.64	2.61	40
41	3.36	3.31	3.25	3.20	3.15	3.11	3.06	3.02	2.97	2.93	2.89	2.85	2.81	2.78	2.74	2.70	41
42	3.48	3.42	3.37	3.32	3.27	3.22	3.17	3.12	3.08	3.04	2.99	2.95	2.91	2.88	2.84	2.80	42
43	3.60	3.55	3.49	3.44	3.38	3.33	3.28	3.24	3.19	3.15	3.10	3.06	3.02	2.98	2.94	2.90	43
44	3.73	3.67	3.61	3.56	3.50	3.45	3.40	3.35	3.30	3.26	3.21	3.17	3.13	3.08	3.04	3.00	44
45	3.86	3.80	3.74	3.68	3.63	3.57	3.52	3.47	3.42	3.37	3.33	3.28	3.24	3.19	3.15	3.11	45
46	4.00	3.94	3.87	3.82	3.76	3.70	3.65	3.59	3.54	3.49	3.44	3.40	3.35	3.31	3.26	3.22	46
47	4.14	4.08	4.01	3.95	3.89	3.83	3.78	3.72	3.67	3.62	3.57	3.52	3.47	3.42	3.38	3.34	47
48	4.29	4.22	4.16	4.09	4.03	3.97	3.91	3.85	3.80	3.75	3.69	3.64	3.59	3.55	3.50	3.46	48
49	4.44	4.37	4.30	4.24	4.17	4.11	4.05	3.99	3.93	3.88	3.83	3.77	3.72	3.67	3.63	3.58	49
50	4.60	4.53	4.46	4.39	4.32	4.26	4.20	4.14	4.08	4.02	3.96	3.91	3.86	3.81	3.76	3.71	50
51	4.77	4.70	4.62	4.55	4.48	4.41	4.35	4.28	4.22	4.16	4.11	4.05	4.00	3.94	3.89	3.84	51
52	4.95	4.87	4.79	4.72	4.64	4.57	4.51	4.44	4.38	4.32	4.26	4.20	4.14	4.09	4.03	3.98	52
53	5.13	5.05	4.97	4.89	4.81	4.74	4.67	4.61	4.54	4.48	4.41	4.35	4.29	4.24	4.18	4.13	53
54	5.32	5.23	5.15	5.07	4.99	4.92	4.85	4.78	4.71	4.64	4.58	4.51	4.45	4.39	4.34	4.28	54
55	5.52	5.43	5.34	5.26	5.18	5.10	5.03	4.96	4.88	4.82	4.75	4.69	4.62	4.56	4.50	4.44	55
56	5.73	5.64	5.55	5.46	5.38	5.30	5.22	5.14	5.07	5.00	4.93	4.86	4.80	4.73	4.67	4.61	56
57	5.95	5.86	5.76	5.67	5.59	5.50	5.42	5.34	5.27	5.19	5.12	5.05	4.98	4.92	4.85	4.79	57
58	6.18	6.08	5.99	5.90	5.81	5.72	5.63	5.55	5.47	5.40	5.32	5.25	5.18	5.11	5.04	4.98	58
59	6.43	6.33	6.23	6.13	6.04	5.95	5.86	5.77	5.69	5.61	5.53	5.46	5.39	5.31	5.25	5.18	59
60	6.69	6.59	6.48	6.38	6.28	6.19	6.10	6.01	5.92	5.84	5.76	5.68	5.61	5.53	5.46	5.39	60
61	6.97	6.86	6.75	6.65	6.55	6.45	6.35	6.26	6.17	6.08	6.00	5.92	5.84	5.76	5.69	5.61	61
62	7.27	7.15	7.04	6.93	6.82	6.72	6.62	6.53	6.43	6.34	6.25	6.17	6.09	6.01	5.93	5.85	62
63	7.58	7.46	7.34	7.23	7.12	7.01	6.91	6.81	6.71	6.62	6.53	6.44	6.35	6.27	6.19	6.11	63
DEC.	165° 195	164¾ 195¼	164½ 195½	164¼ 195¾	164° 196	163¾ 196¼	163½ 196½	163¼ 196¾	163° 197	162¾ 197¼	162½ 197½	162¼ 197¾	162° 198	161¾ 198¼	161½ 198½	161¼ 198¾	DEC.

Table 29 (H.L.)

A

I hr.

If entered with H.A. at **top**, Sign **+**
„　　„　　„　„ **foot,** „　**−**

HOUR ANGLE or DIFF. LONG.

LAT.	15m	16m	17m	18m	19m	20m	21m	22m	23m	24m	25m	26m	27m	28m	29m	30m	LAT.
	18¾° 341¼	19° 341	19¼° 340¾	19½° 340½	19¾° 340¼	20° 340	20¼° 339¾	20½° 339½	20¾° 339¼	21° 339	21¼° 338¾	21½° 338½	21¾° 338¼	22° 338	22¼° 337¾	22½° 337½	
60°	5.10	5.03	4.96	4.89	4.82	4.76	4.69	4.63	4.57	4.51	4.45	4.40	4.34	4.29	4.23	4.18	60°
61	5.31	5.24	5.17	5.09	5.02	4.96	4.89	4.83	4.76	4.70	4.64	4.58	4.52	4.47	4.41	4.36	61
62	5.54	5.46	5.39	5.31	5.24	5.17	5.10	5.03	4.96	4.90	4.84	4.78	4.71	4.66	4.60	4.54	62
63	5.78	5.70	5.62	5.54	5.47	5.39	5.32	5.25	5.18	5.11	5.05	4.98	4.92	4.86	4.80	4.74	63
64	6.04	5.96	5.87	5.79	5.71	5.63	5.56	5.48	5.41	5.34	5.27	5.21	5.14	5.08	5.01	4.95	64
65	6.32	6.23	6.14	6.06	5.97	5.89	5.81	5.74	5.66	5.59	5.51	5.44	5.38	5.31	5.24	5.18	65
66	6.62	6.52	6.43	6.34	6.26	6.17	6.09	6.01	5.93	5.85	5.78	5.70	5.63	5.56	5.49	5.42	66
67	6.94	6.84	6.75	6.65	6.56	6.47	6.39	6.30	6.22	6.14	6.06	5.98	5.90	5.83	5.76	5.69	67
68	7.29	7.19	7.09	6.99	6.89	6.80	6.71	6.62	6.53	6.45	6.36	6.28	6.20	6.13	6.05	5.98	68
69	7.67	7.57	7.46	7.36	7.26	7.16	7.06	6.97	6.88	6.79	6.70	6.61	6.53	6.45	6.37	6.29	69
70	8.09	7.98	7.87	7.76	7.65	7.55	7.45	7.35	7.25	7.16	7.07	6.97	6.89	6.80	6.72	6.63	70
71	8.56	8.43	8.32	8.20	8.09	7.98	7.87	7.77	7.67	7.57	7.47	7.37	7.28	7.19	7.10	7.01	71
72	9.07	8.94	8.81	8.69	8.57	8.46	8.34	8.23	8.12	8.02	7.91	7.81	7.71	7.62	7.52	7.43	72
73	9.64	9.50	9.37	9.24	9.11	8.99	8.87	8.75	8.63	8.52	8.41	8.30	8.20	8.10	8.00	7.90	73
74	10.3	10.1	9.99	9.85	9.71	9.59	9.45	9.33	9.20	9.09	8.97	8.85	8.74	8.63	8.52	8.42	74
75	11.0	10.8	10.7	10.5	10.4	10.3	10.1	9.98	9.85	9.72	9.60	9.47	9.35	9.24	9.12	9.01	75
76	11.8	11.6	11.5	11.3	11.2	11.0	10.9	10.7	10.6	10.4	10.3	10.2	10.1	9.93	9.80	9.68	76
77	12.8	12.6	12.4	12.2	12.1	11.9	11.7	11.6	11.4	11.3	11.1	11.0	10.9	10.7	10.6	10.5	77
78	13.9	13.7	13.5	13.3	13.1	12.9	12.8	12.6	12.4	12.3	12.1	11.9	11.8	11.6	11.5	11.4	78
79	15.1	14.9	14.7	14.5	14.3	14.1	13.9	13.8	13.6	13.4	13.2	13.1	12.9	12.7	12.6	12.4	79
80	16.7	16.5	16.2	16.0	15.8	15.6	15.4	15.2	15.0	14.8	14.6	14.4	14.2	14.0	13.9	13.7	80
81	18.6	18.3	18.1	17.8	17.6	17.3	17.1	16.9	16.7	16.4	16.2	16.0	15.8	15.6	15.4	15.2	81
82	21.0	20.7	20.4	20.1	19.8	19.5	19.3	19.0	18.8	18.5	18.3	18.1	17.8	17.6	17.4	17.2	82
LAT.	161¼ 198¾	161° 199	160¾ 199¼	160½ 199½	160¼ 199¾	160° 200	159¾ 200¼	159½ 200½	159¼ 200¾	159° 201	158¾ 201¼	158½ 201½	158¼ 201¾	158° 202	157¾ 202¼	157½ 202½	LAT.

(S.W. Qdt.) **180°**——→**270°**　　　　　　　　　　　(S.E. Qdt.) **180°**←——**90°**

Table 29 (H.L.)

B

I hr.

Lat. and Dec. SAME name, Sign **−**
Lat. and Dec. CONTRARY names, Sign **+**

HOUR ANGLE or DIFF. LONG.

DEC.	15m	16m	17m	18m	19m	20m	21m	22m	23m	24m	25m	26m	27m	28m	29m	30m	DEC.
	18¾° 341¼	19° 341	19¼° 340¾	19½° 340½	19¾° 340¼	20° 340	20¼° 339¾	20½° 339½	20¾° 339¼	21° 339	21¼° 338¾	21½° 338½	21¾° 338¼	22° 338	22¼° 337¾	22½° 337½	
68°	7.70	7.60	7.51	7.42	7.33	7.24	7.15	7.07	6.99	6.91	6.83	6.75	6.68	6.61	6.54	6.47	68°
69	8.10	8.00	7.90	7.80	7.71	7.62	7.53	7.44	7.35	7.27	7.19	7.11	7.03	6.95	6.88	6.81	69
70	8.55	8.44	8.33	8.23	8.13	8.03	7.94	7.85	7.75	7.67	7.58	7.50	7.41	7.33	7.26	7.18	70
74	10.8	10.7	10.6	10.4	10.3	10.2	10.1	9.96	9.84	9.73	9.62	9.52	9.41	9.31	9.21	9.11	74
75	11.6	11.5	11.3	11.2	11.0	10.9	10.8	10.7	10.5	10.4	10.3	10.2	10.1	9.96	9.86	9.75	75
DEC.	161¼ 198¾	161° 199	160¾ 199¼	160½ 199½	160¼ 199¾	160° 200	159¾ 200¼	159½ 200½	159¼ 200¾	159° 201	158¾ 201¼	158½ 201½	158¼ 201¾	158° 202	157¾ 202¼	157½ 202½	DEC.

(S.W. Qdt.) **180°**——→**270°**　　　　　　　　　　　(S.E. Qdt.) **180°**←——**90°**

Table 29 (H.L.)   B   1 hr.

Lat. and Dec. SAME name, Sign —
Lat. and Dec. CONTRARY names, Sign +

HOUR ANGLE or DIFF. LONG.

DEC.	15m	16m	17m	18m	19m	20m	21m	22m	23m	24m	25m	26m	27m	28m	29m	30m	DEC.
	18¾° 341¼	19° 341	19¼° 340¾	19½° 340½	19¾° 340¼	20° 340	20¼° 339¾	20½° 339½	20¾° 339¼	21° 339	21¼° 338¾	21½° 338½	21¾° 338¼	22° 338	22¼° 337¾	22½° 337½	
0°	.000	.000	.000	.000	.000	.000	.000	.000	.000	.000	.000	.000	.000	.000	.000	.000	0°
1	.054	.054	.053	.052	.052	.051	.050	.050	.049	.049	.048	.048	.047	.047	.046	.046	1
2	.109	.107	.106	.105	.103	.102	.101	.100	.099	.097	.096	.095	.094	.093	.092	.091	2
3	.163	.161	.159	.157	.155	.153	.151	.150	.148	.146	.145	.143	.141	.140	.138	.137	3
4	.218	.215	.212	.209	.207	.204	.202	.200	.197	.195	.193	.191	.189	.187	.185	.183	4
5	.272	.269	.265	.262	.259	.256	.253	.250	.247	.244	.241	.239	.236	.234	.231	.229	5
6	.327	.323	.319	.315	.311	.307	.304	.300	.297	.293	.290	.287	.284	.281	.278	.275	6
7	.382	.377	.372	.368	.363	.359	.355	.351	.347	.343	.339	.335	.331	.328	.324	.321	7
8	.437	.432	.426	.421	.416	.411	.406	.401	.397	.392	.388	.383	.379	.375	.371	.367	8
9	.493	.486	.480	.474	.469	.463	.458	.452	.447	.442	.437	.432	.427	.423	.418	.414	9
10	.549	.542	.535	.528	.522	.516	.510	.504	.498	.492	.487	.481	.476	.471	.466	.461	10
11	.605	.597	.590	.582	.575	.568	.561	.555	.549	.542	.536	.530	.525	.519	.514	.508	11
12	.661	.653	.645	.637	.629	.621	.614	.607	.600	.593	.587	.580	.574	.567	.561	.555	12
13	.718	.709	.700	.692	.683	.675	.667	.659	.652	.644	.637	.630	.623	.616	.610	.603	13
14	.776	.766	.756	.747	.738	.729	.721	.712	.704	.696	.688	.680	.673	.666	.659	.652	14
15	.834	.823	.813	.803	.793	.783	.774	.765	.756	.748	.740	.731	.723	.715	.708	.700	15
16	.892	.881	.870	.859	.849	.838	.829	.819	.809	.800	.791	.782	.774	.765	.757	.749	16
17	.951	.939	.927	.916	.905	.894	.883	.873	.863	.853	.844	.834	.825	.816	.808	.799	17
18	1.01	.998	.986	.973	.962	.950	.939	.928	.917	.907	.897	.887	.877	.867	.858	.849	18
19	1.07	1.06	1.04	1.03	1.02	1.01	.995	.983	.972	.961	.950	.939	.929	.919	.910	.900	19
20	1.13	1.12	1.10	1.09	1.08	1.06	1.05	1.04	1.03	1.02	1.00	.993	.982	.972	.962	.951	20
21	1.19	1.18	1.16	1.15	1.14	1.12	1.11	1.10	1.08	1.07	1.06	1.05	1.04	1.02	1.01	1.00	21
22	1.26	1.24	1.23	1.21	1.20	1.18	1.17	1.15	1.14	1.13	1.11	1.10	1.09	1.08	1.07	1.06	22
23	1.32	1.30	1.29	1.27	1.26	1.24	1.23	1.21	1.20	1.18	1.17	1.16	1.15	1.13	1.12	1.11	23
24	1.39	1.37	1.35	1.33	1.32	1.30	1.29	1.27	1.26	1.24	1.23	1.21	1.20	1.19	1.18	1.16	24
25	1.45	1.43	1.41	1.40	1.38	1.36	1.35	1.33	1.32	1.30	1.29	1.27	1.26	1.24	1.23	1.22	25
26	1.52	1.50	1.48	1.46	1.44	1.43	1.41	1.39	1.38	1.36	1.35	1.33	1.32	1.30	1.29	1.27	26
27	1.59	1.57	1.55	1.53	1.51	1.49	1.47	1.45	1.44	1.42	1.41	1.39	1.38	1.36	1.35	1.33	27
28	1.65	1.63	1.61	1.59	1.57	1.55	1.54	1.52	1.50	1.48	1.47	1.45	1.43	1.42	1.40	1.39	28
29	1.72	1.70	1.68	1.66	1.64	1.62	1.60	1.58	1.56	1.55	1.53	1.51	1.50	1.48	1.46	1.45	29
30	1.80	1.77	1.75	1.73	1.71	1.69	1.67	1.65	1.63	1.61	1.59	1.58	1.56	1.54	1.52	1.51	30
31	1.87	1.85	1.82	1.80	1.78	1.76	1.74	1.72	1.70	1.68	1.66	1.64	1.62	1.60	1.59	1.57	31
32	1.94	1.92	1.90	1.87	1.85	1.83	1.81	1.78	1.76	1.74	1.72	1.71	1.69	1.67	1.65	1.63	32
33	2.02	1.99	1.97	1.95	1.92	1.90	1.88	1.85	1.83	1.81	1.79	1.77	1.75	1.73	1.72	1.70	33
34	2.10	2.07	2.05	2.02	2.00	1.97	1.95	1.93	1.90	1.88	1.86	1.84	1.82	1.80	1.78	1.76	34
35	2.18	2.15	2.12	2.10	2.07	2.05	2.02	2.00	1.98	1.95	1.93	1.91	1.89	1.87	1.85	1.83	35
36	2.26	2.23	2.20	2.18	2.15	2.12	2.10	2.08	2.05	2.03	2.01	1.98	1.96	1.94	1.92	1.90	36
37	2.34	2.31	2.29	2.26	2.23	2.20	2.18	2.15	2.13	2.10	2.08	2.06	2.03	2.01	1.99	1.97	37
38	2.43	2.40	2.37	2.34	2.31	2.28	2.26	2.23	2.21	2.18	2.16	2.13	2.11	2.09	2.06	2.04	38
39	2.52	2.49	2.46	2.43	2.40	2.37	2.34	2.31	2.29	2.26	2.23	2.21	2.19	2.16	2.14	2.12	39
40	2.61	2.58	2.55	2.51	2.48	2.45	2.42	2.40	2.37	2.34	2.32	2.29	2.26	2.24	2.22	2.19	40
41	2.70	2.67	2.64	2.60	2.57	2.54	2.51	2.48	2.45	2.43	2.40	2.37	2.35	2.32	2.30	2.27	41
42	2.80	2.77	2.73	2.70	2.66	2.63	2.60	2.57	2.54	2.51	2.48	2.46	2.43	2.40	2.38	2.35	42
43	2.90	2.86	2.83	2.79	2.76	2.73	2.69	2.66	2.63	2.60	2.57	2.54	2.52	2.49	2.46	2.44	43
44	3.00	2.97	2.93	2.89	2.86	2.82	2.79	2.76	2.73	2.69	2.66	2.64	2.61	2.58	2.55	2.52	44
45	3.11	3.07	3.03	3.00	2.96	2.92	2.89	2.86	2.82	2.79	2.76	2.73	2.70	2.67	2.64	2.61	45
46	3.22	3.18	3.14	3.10	3.07	3.03	2.99	2.96	2.92	2.89	2.86	2.83	2.79	2.76	2.74	2.71	46
47	3.34	3.29	3.25	3.21	3.17	3.14	3.10	3.06	3.03	2.99	2.96	2.93	2.89	2.86	2.83	2.80	47
48	3.46	3.41	3.37	3.33	3.29	3.25	3.21	3.17	3.14	3.10	3.07	3.03	3.00	2.97	2.93	2.90	48
49	3.58	3.53	3.49	3.45	3.40	3.36	3.32	3.28	3.25	3.21	3.17	3.14	3.10	3.07	3.04	3.01	49
50	3.71	3.66	3.62	3.57	3.53	3.48	3.44	3.40	3.36	3.33	3.29	3.25	3.22	3.18	3.15	3.11	50
51	3.84	3.79	3.75	3.70	3.65	3.61	3.57	3.53	3.49	3.45	3.41	3.37	3.33	3.30	3.26	3.23	51
52	3.98	3.93	3.88	3.83	3.79	3.74	3.70	3.65	3.61	3.57	3.53	3.49	3.45	3.42	3.38	3.34	52
53	4.13	4.08	4.03	3.98	3.93	3.88	3.83	3.79	3.75	3.70	3.66	3.62	3.58	3.54	3.51	3.47	53
54	4.28	4.23	4.17	4.12	4.07	4.02	3.98	3.93	3.88	3.84	3.80	3.76	3.71	3.67	3.64	3.60	54
55	4.44	4.39	4.33	4.28	4.23	4.18	4.13	4.08	4.03	3.99	3.94	3.90	3.85	3.81	3.77	3.73	55
56	4.61	4.55	4.50	4.44	4.39	4.33	4.28	4.23	4.18	4.14	4.09	4.05	4.00	3.96	3.92	3.87	56
57	4.79	4.73	4.67	4.61	4.56	4.50	4.45	4.40	4.35	4.30	4.25	4.20	4.16	4.11	4.07	4.02	57
58	4.98	4.92	4.85	4.79	4.74	4.68	4.62	4.57	4.52	4.47	4.42	4.37	4.32	4.27	4.23	4.18	58
59	5.18	5.11	5.05	4.99	4.93	4.87	4.81	4.75	4.70	4.64	4.59	4.54	4.49	4.44	4.40	4.35	59
60	5.39	5.32	5.25	5.19	5.13	5.06	5.01	4.95	4.89	4.83	4.78	4.73	4.67	4.62	4.58	4.53	60
61	5.61	5.54	5.47	5.40	5.34	5.27	5.21	5.15	5.09	5.03	4.98	4.92	4.87	4.82	4.76	4.71	61
62	5.85	5.78	5.70	5.63	5.57	5.50	5.43	5.37	5.31	5.25	5.19	5.13	5.08	5.02	4.97	4.91	62
63	6.11	6.03	5.95	5.88	5.81	5.74	5.67	5.60	5.54	5.48	5.42	5.36	5.30	5.24	5.18	5.13	63
DEC.	161¼° 198¾	161° 199	160¾° 199¼	160½° 199½	160¼° 199¾	160° 200	159¾° 200¼	159½° 200½	159¼° 200¾	159° 201	158¾° 201¼	158½° 201½	158¼° 201¾	158° 202	157¾° 202¼	157½° 202½	DEC.

Table 29 (H.L.) A

If entered with H.A. at top, Sign +
„ „ „ „ foot, „ −

1 hr.

HOUR ANGLE or DIFF. LONG.

LAT.	30m	31m	32m	33m	34m	35m	36m	37m	38m	39m	40m	41m	42m	43m	44m	45m	LAT.
	22½° 337½	22¾° 337¼	23° 337	23¼° 336¾	23½° 336½	23¾° 336¼	24° 336	24¼° 335¾	24½° 335½	24¾° 335¼	25° 335	25¼° 334¾	25½° 334½	25¾° 334¼	26° 334	26¼° 333¾	
60°	4.18	4.13	4.08	4.03	3.98	3.94	3.89	3.85	3.80	3.76	3.71	3.67	3.63	3.59	3.55	3.51	60°
61	4.36	4.30	4.25	4.20	4.15	4.10	4.05	4.00	3.96	3.91	3.87	3.83	3.78	3.74	3.70	3.66	61
62	4.54	4.49	4.43	4.38	4.33	4.27	4.22	4.18	4.13	4.08	4.03	3.99	3.94	3.90	3.86	3.81	62
63	4.74	4.68	4.62	4.57	4.51	4.46	4.41	4.36	4.31	4.26	4.21	4.16	4.12	4.07	4.02	3.98	63
64	4.95	4.89	4.83	4.77	4.72	4.66	4.61	4.55	4.50	4.45	4.40	4.35	4.30	4.25	4.20	4.16	64
65	5.18	5.11	5.05	4.99	4.93	4.87	4.82	4.77	4.71	4.65	4.60	4.55	4.50	4.45	4.40	4.35	65
66	5.42	5.36	5.29	5.23	5.17	5.10	5.04	4.99	4.93	4.87	4.82	4.76	4.71	4.66	4.61	4.55	66
67	5.69	5.62	5.55	5.48	5.42	5.35	5.29	5.23	5.17	5.11	5.05	5.00	4.94	4.88	4.83	4.78	67
68	5.98	5.90	5.83	5.76	5.69	5.63	5.56	5.49	5.43	5.37	5.31	5.25	5.19	5.13	5.07	5.02	68
69	6.29	6.21	6.14	6.06	5.99	5.92	5.85	5.78	5.72	5.65	5.59	5.52	5.46	5.40	5.34	5.28	69
70	6.63	6.55	6.47	6.39	6.32	6.24	6.17	6.10	6.03	5.96	5.89	5.83	5.76	5.70	5.63	5.57	70
71	7.01	6.93	6.84	6.76	6.68	6.60	6.52	6.45	6.37	6.30	6.23	6.16	6.09	6.02	5.95	5.89	71
72	7.43	7.34	7.25	7.16	7.08	6.99	6.91	6.83	6.75	6.68	6.60	6.53	6.45	6.38	6.31	6.24	72
73	7.90	7.80	7.71	7.61	7.52	7.43	7.35	7.26	7.18	7.10	7.01	6.94	6.86	6.78	6.71	6.63	73
74	8.42	8.32	8.22	8.12	8.02	7.93	7.83	7.74	7.65	7.56	7.48	7.39	7.31	7.23	7.15	7.07	74
75	9.01	8.90	8.79	8.69	8.58	8.48	8.38	8.28	8.19	8.10	8.00	7.91	7.82	7.74	7.65	7.57	75
76	9.68	9.56	9.45	9.34	9.22	9.12	9.01	8.90	8.80	8.70	8.60	8.50	8.41	8.32	8.22	8.13	76
77	10.5	10.3	10.2	10.1	9.96	9.84	9.73	9.62	9.50	9.40	9.29	9.18	9.08	8.98	8.88	8.78	77
78	11.4	11.2	11.1	10.9	10.8	10.7	10.6	10.4	10.3	10.2	10.1	9.98	9.86	9.75	9.65	9.54	78
79	12.4	12.3	12.1	12.0	11.8	11.7	11.6	11.4	11.3	11.2	11.0	10.9	10.8	10.7	10.5	10.4	79
80	13.7	13.5	13.4	13.2	13.0	12.9	12.7	12.6	12.4	12.3	12.2	12.0	11.9	11.8	11.6	11.5	80
81	15.2	15.1	14.9	14.7	14.5	14.3	14.2	14.0	13.9	13.7	13.5	13.4	13.2	13.1	12.9	12.8	81
82	17.2	17.0	16.8	16.6	16.4	16.2	16.0	15.8	15.6	15.4	15.3	15.1	14.9	14.8	14.6	14.4	82
LAT.	157½ 202½	157¼ 202¾	157° 203	156¾ 203¼	156½ 203½	156¼ 203¾	156° 204	155¾ 204¼	155½ 204½	155¼ 204¾	155° 205	154¾ 205¼	154½ 205½	154¼ 205¾	154° 206	153¾ 206¼	LAT.

Table 29 (H.L.) B

1 hr.

Lat. and Dec. SAME name, Sign −
Lat. and Dec. CONTRARY names, Sign +

HOUR ANGLE or DIFF. LONG.

DEC.	30m	31m	32m	33m	34m	35m	36m	37m	38m	39m	40m	41m	42m	43m	44m	45m	DEC.
	22½° 337½	22¾° 337¼	23° 337	23¼° 336¾	23½° 336½	23¾° 336¼	24° 336	24¼° 335¾	24½° 335½	24¾° 335¼	25° 335	25¼° 334¾	25½° 334½	25¾° 334¼	26° 334	26¼° 333¾	
68°	6.47	6.40	5.34	6.27	6.21	6.15	6.09	6.03	5.97	5.91	5.86	5.80	5.75	5.70	5.65	5.60	68°
69	6.81	6.74	6.67	6.60	6.53	6.47	6.41	6.34	6.28	6.22	6.17	6.11	6.05	6.00	5.94	5.89	69
70	7.18	7.10	7.03	6.96	6.89	6.82	6.76	6.70	6.63	6.56	6.50	6.44	6.38	6.32	6.27	6.21	70
74	9.11	9.02	8.93	8.83	8.75	8.66	8.57	8.49	8.41	8.33	8.25	8.18	8.10	8.03	7.96	7.88	74
75	9.75	9.65	9.55	9.45	9.36	9.27	9.18	9.09	9.00	8.91	8.83	8.75	8.67	8.59	8.51	8.44	75
DEC.	157½ 202½	157¼ 202¾	157° 203	156¾ 203¼	156½ 203½	156¼ 203¾	156° 204	155¾ 204¼	155½ 204½	155¼ 204¾	155° 205	154¾ 205¼	154½ 205½	154¼ 205¾	154° 206	153¾ 206¼	DEC.

| Table 29 (H.L.) | **B** | Lat. and Dec. SAME name, Sign — |
| 1 hr. | | Lat. and Dec. CONTRARY names, Sign + |

HOUR ANGLE or DIFF. LONG.

DEC.	30m	31m	32m	33m	34m	35m	36m	37m	38m	39m	40m	41m	42m	43m	44m	45m	DEC.
	22½° 337½	22¾° 337¼	23° 337	23¼° 336¾	23½° 336½	23¾° 336¼	24° 336	24¼° 335¾	24½° 335½	24¾° 335¼	25° 335	25¼° 334¾	25½° 334½	25¾° 334¼	26° 334	26¼° 333¾	
0°	.000	.000	.000	.000	.000	.000	.000	.000	.000	.000	.000	.000	.000	.000	.000	.000	0°
1	.046	.045	.045	.044	.044	.043	.043	.043	.042	.042	.041	.041	.041	.040	.040	.040	1
2	.091	.090	.089	.089	.088	.087	.086	.085	.084	.083	.083	.082	.081	.080	.080	.079	2
3	.137	.136	.134	.133	.131	.130	.129	.128	.126	.125	.124	.123	.122	.121	.120	.119	3
4	.183	.181	.179	.177	.175	.174	.172	.170	.169	.167	.165	.164	.162	.161	.160	.158	4
5	.229	.226	.224	.222	.219	.217	.215	.213	.211	.209	.207	.205	.203	.201	.200	.198	5
6	.275	.272	.269	.266	.264	.261	.258	.256	.253	.251	.249	.246	.244	.242	.240	.238	6
7	.321	.318	.314	.311	.308	.305	.302	.299	.296	.293	.291	.288	.285	.283	.280	.278	7
8	.367	.363	.360	.356	.352	.349	.346	.342	.339	.336	.333	.329	.326	.324	.321	.318	8
9	.414	.410	.405	.401	.397	.393	.389	.386	.382	.378	.375	.371	.368	.365	.361	.358	9
10	.461	.456	.451	.447	.442	.438	.434	.429	.425	.421	.417	.413	.410	.406	.402	.399	10
11	.508	.503	.497	.492	.487	.483	.478	.473	.469	.464	.460	.456	.452	.448	.443	.439	11
12	.555	.550	.544	.539	.533	.528	.523	.518	.513	.508	.503	.498	.494	.489	.485	.481	12
13	.603	.597	.591	.585	.579	.573	.568	.562	.557	.552	.546	.541	.536	.532	.527	.522	13
14	.652	.645	.638	.632	.625	.619	.613	.607	.601	.596	.590	.585	.579	.574	.569	.564	14
15	.700	.693	.686	.679	.672	.666	.659	.653	.646	.640	.634	.628	.622	.617	.611	.606	15
16	.749	.742	.734	.727	.719	.712	.705	.698	.691	.685	.678	.672	.666	.660	.654	.648	16
17	.799	.791	.782	.775	.767	.759	.752	.744	.737	.730	.723	.717	.710	.704	.697	.691	17
18	.849	.840	.832	.823	.815	.807	.799	.791	.784	.776	.769	.762	.755	.748	.741	.735	18
19	.900	.891	.881	.872	.864	.855	.847	.839	.830	.823	.815	.807	.800	.793	.785	.779	19
20	.951	.941	.932	.922	.913	.904	.895	.886	.878	.869	.861	.853	.845	.838	.830	.823	20
21	1.00	.993	.982	.973	.963	.953	.944	.935	.926	.917	.908	.900	.892	.884	.876	.868	21
22	1.06	1.04	1.03	1.02	1.01	1.00	.993	.984	.974	.965	.956	.947	.938	.930	.922	.914	22
23	1.11	1.10	1.09	1.08	1.06	1.05	1.04	1.03	1.02	1.01	1.00	.995	.986	.977	.968	.960	23
24	1.16	1.15	1.14	1.13	1.12	1.11	1.09	1.08	1.07	1.06	1.05	1.04	1.03	1.03	1.02	1.01	24
25	1.22	1.21	1.19	1.18	1.17	1.16	1.15	1.14	1.12	1.11	1.10	1.09	1.08	1.07	1.06	1.05	25
26	1.27	1.26	1.25	1.24	1.22	1.21	1.20	1.19	1.18	1.17	1.15	1.14	1.13	1.12	1.11	1.10	26
27	1.33	1.32	1.30	1.29	1.28	1.27	1.25	1.24	1.23	1.22	1.21	1.19	1.18	1.17	1.16	1.15	27
28	1.39	1.38	1.36	1.35	1.33	1.32	1.31	1.29	1.28	1.27	1.26	1.25	1.24	1.22	1.21	1.20	28
29	1.45	1.43	1.42	1.40	1.39	1.38	1.36	1.35	1.34	1.32	1.31	1.30	1.29	1.28	1.26	1.25	29
30	1.51	1.49	1.48	1.46	1.45	1.43	1.42	1.41	1.39	1.38	1.37	1.35	1.34	1.33	1.32	1.31	30
31	1.57	1.55	1.54	1.52	1.51	1.49	1.48	1.46	1.45	1.44	1.42	1.41	1.40	1.38	1.37	1.36	31
32	1.63	1.62	1.60	1.58	1.57	1.55	1.54	1.52	1.51	1.49	1.48	1.47	1.45	1.44	1.43	1.41	32
33	1.70	1.68	1.66	1.65	1.63	1.61	1.60	1.58	1.57	1.55	1.54	1.52	1.51	1.50	1.48	1.47	33
34	1.76	1.74	1.73	1.71	1.69	1.68	1.66	1.64	1.63	1.61	1.60	1.58	1.57	1.55	1.54	1.53	34
35	1.83	1.81	1.79	1.77	1.76	1.74	1.72	1.71	1.69	1.67	1.66	1.64	1.63	1.61	1.60	1.58	35
36	1.90	1.88	1.86	1.84	1.82	1.80	1.79	1.77	1.75	1.74	1.72	1.70	1.69	1.67	1.66	1.64	36
37	1.97	1.95	1.93	1.91	1.89	1.87	1.85	1.84	1.82	1.80	1.78	1.77	1.75	1.73	1.72	1.70	37
38	2.04	2.02	2.00	1.98	1.96	1.94	1.92	1.90	1.88	1.87	1.85	1.83	1.81	1.80	1.78	1.77	38
39	2.12	2.09	2.07	2.05	2.03	2.01	1.99	1.97	1.95	1.93	1.92	1.90	1.88	1.86	1.85	1.83	39
40	2.19	2.17	2.15	2.13	2.10	2.08	2.06	2.04	2.02	2.00	1.99	1.97	1.95	1.93	1.91	1.90	40
41	2.27	2.25	2.22	2.20	2.18	2.16	2.14	2.12	2.10	2.08	2.06	2.04	2.02	2.00	1.98	1.97	41
42	2.35	2.33	2.30	2.28	2.26	2.24	2.21	2.19	2.17	2.15	2.13	2.11	2.09	2.07	2.05	2.04	42
43	2.44	2.41	2.39	2.36	2.34	2.32	2.29	2.27	2.25	2.23	2.21	2.19	2.17	2.15	2.13	2.11	43
44	2.52	2.50	2.47	2.45	2.42	2.40	2.37	2.35	2.33	2.31	2.29	2.26	2.24	2.22	2.20	2.18	44
45	2.61	2.59	2.56	2.53	2.51	2.48	2.46	2.44	2.41	2.39	2.37	2.34	2.32	2.30	2.28	2.26	45
46	2.71	2.68	2.65	2.62	2.60	2.57	2.55	2.52	2.50	2.47	2.45	2.43	2.41	2.38	2.36	2.34	46
47	2.80	2.77	2.74	2.72	2.69	2.66	2.64	2.61	2.59	2.56	2.54	2.51	2.49	2.47	2.45	2.42	47
48	2.90	2.87	2.84	2.81	2.79	2.76	2.73	2.70	2.68	2.65	2.63	2.60	2.58	2.56	2.53	2.51	48
49	3.01	2.97	2.94	2.91	2.88	2.86	2.83	2.80	2.77	2.75	2.72	2.70	2.67	2.65	2.62	2.60	49
50	3.11	3.08	3.05	3.02	2.99	2.96	2.93	2.90	2.87	2.85	2.82	2.79	2.77	2.74	2.72	2.69	50
51	3.23	3.19	3.16	3.13	3.10	3.07	3.04	3.01	2.98	2.95	2.92	2.90	2.87	2.84	2.82	2.79	51
52	3.34	3.31	3.28	3.24	3.21	3.18	3.15	3.12	3.09	3.06	3.03	3.00	2.97	2.95	2.92	2.89	52
53	3.47	3.43	3.40	3.36	3.33	3.30	3.26	3.23	3.20	3.17	3.14	3.11	3.08	3.06	3.03	3.00	53
54	3.60	3.56	3.52	3.49	3.45	3.42	3.38	3.35	3.32	3.29	3.26	3.23	3.20	3.17	3.14	3.11	54
55	3.73	3.69	3.66	3.62	3.58	3.55	3.51	3.48	3.44	3.41	3.38	3.35	3.32	3.29	3.26	3.23	55
56	3.87	3.83	3.79	3.76	3.72	3.68	3.65	3.61	3.58	3.54	3.51	3.48	3.44	3.41	3.38	3.35	56
57	4.02	3.98	3.94	3.90	3.86	3.82	3.79	3.75	3.71	3.68	3.64	3.61	3.58	3.55	3.51	3.48	57
58	4.18	4.14	4.10	4.05	4.01	3.97	3.93	3.90	3.86	3.82	3.79	3.75	3.72	3.68	3.65	3.62	58
59	4.35	4.30	4.26	4.22	4.17	4.13	4.09	4.05	4.01	3.98	3.94	3.90	3.87	3.83	3.80	3.76	59
60	4.53	4.48	4.43	4.39	4.34	4.30	4.26	4.22	4.18	4.14	4.10	4.06	4.02	3.99	3.95	3.92	60
61	4.71	4.67	4.62	4.57	4.52	4.48	4.44	4.39	4.35	4.31	4.27	4.23	4.19	4.15	4.12	4.08	61
62	4.91	4.86	4.81	4.76	4.72	4.67	4.62	4.58	4.54	4.49	4.45	4.41	4.37	4.33	4.29	4.25	62
63	5.13	5.08	5.02	4.97	4.92	4.87	4.83	4.78	4.73	4.69	4.64	4.60	4.56	4.52	4.48	4.44	63
DEC.	157½ 202½	157¼ 202¾	157° 203	156¾ 203¼	156½ 203½	156¼ 203¾	156° 204	155¾ 204¼	155½ 204½	155¼ 204¾	155° 205	154¾ 205¼	154½ 205½	154¼ 205¾	154° 206	153¾ 206¼	DEC.

Table 29 (H.L.)

A — If entered with H.A. at **top**, Sign **+**
   „   „   „ „ **foot**, „   **−**

1 hr.

HOUR ANGLE or DIFF. LONG.

LAT.	45m	46m	47m	48m	49m	50m	51m	52m	53m	54m	55m	56m	57m	58m	59m	60m	LAT.
	26¼° 333¾	26½° 333½	26¾° 333¼	**27° 333**	27¼° 332¾	27½° 332½	27¾° 332¼	**28° 332**	28¼° 331¾	28½° 331½	28¾° 331¼	**29° 331**	29¼° 330¾	29½° 330½	29¾° 330¼	**30° 330**	
60°	3.51	3.47	3.44	3.40	3.36	3.33	3.29	3.26	3.22	3.19	3.16	3.12	3.09	3.06	3.03	3.00	60°
61	3.66	3.62	3.58	3.54	3.50	3.47	3.43	3.39	3.36	3.32	3.29	3.26	3.22	3.19	3.16	3.13	61
62	3.81	3.77	3.73	3.69	3.65	3.61	3.57	3.54	3.50	3.46	3.43	3.39	3.36	3.32	3.29	3.26	62
63	3.98	3.94	3.89	3.85	3.81	3.77	3.73	3.69	3.65	3.62	3.58	3.54	3.50	3.47	3.43	3.40	63
64	4.16	4.11	4.07	4.02	3.98	3.94	3.90	3.86	3.82	3.78	3.74	3.70	3.66	3.62	3.59	3.55	64
65	4.35	4.30	4.25	4.21	4.16	4.12	4.08	4.03	3.99	3.95	3.91	3.87	3.83	3.79	3.75	3.71	65
66	4.55	4.50	4.46	4.41	4.36	4.31	4.27	4.22	4.18	4.14	4.09	4.05	4.01	3.97	3.93	3.89	66
67	4.78	4.73	4.67	4.62	4.57	4.53	4.48	4.43	4.38	4.34	4.29	4.25	4.21	4.16	4.12	4.08	67
68	5.02	4.96	4.91	4.86	4.81	4.75	4.70	4.65	4.61	4.56	4.51	4.47	4.42	4.37	4.33	4.29	68
69	5.28	5.23	5.17	5.11	5.06	5.00	4.95	4.90	4.85	4.80	4.75	4.70	4.65	4.60	4.56	4.51	69
70	5.57	5.51	5.45	5.39	5.33	5.28	5.22	5.17	5.11	5.06	5.01	4.96	4.91	4.86	4.81	4.76	70
71	5.89	5.82	5.76	5.70	5.64	5.58	5.52	5.46	5.40	5.35	5.29	5.24	5.19	5.13	5.08	5.03	71
72	6.24	6.17	6.11	6.04	5.98	5.91	5.85	5.79	5.73	5.67	5.61	5.55	5.50	5.44	5.38	5.33	72
73	6.63	6.56	6.49	6.42	6.35	6.28	6.22	6.15	6.09	6.02	5.96	5.90	5.84	5.78	5.72	5.67	73
74	7.07	6.99	6.92	6.84	6.77	6.70	6.63	6.56	6.49	6.42	6.36	6.29	6.23	6.16	6.10	6.04	74
75	7.57	7.49	7.40	7.32	7.25	7.17	7.09	7.02	6.95	6.87	6.80	6.73	6.66	6.60	6.53	6.46	75
76	8.13	8.04	7.96	7.87	7.79	7.70	7.62	7.54	7.46	7.39	7.31	7.24	7.16	7.09	7.02	6.95	76
77	8.78	8.69	8.59	8.50	8.41	8.32	8.23	8.15	8.06	7.98	7.90	7.81	7.73	7.66	7.58	7.50	77
78	9.54	9.44	9.33	9.23	9.13	9.04	8.94	8.85	8.76	8.66	8.58	8.49	8.40	8.32	8.23	8.15	78
79	10.4	10.3	10.2	10.1	9.99	9.88	9.78	9.68	9.57	9.48	9.38	9.28	9.19	9.09	9.00	8.91	79
80	11.5	11.4	11.3	11.1	11.0	10.9	10.8	10.7	10.6	10.4	10.3	10.2	10.1	10.0	9.92	9.82	80
81	12.8	12.7	12.5	12.4	12.3	12.1	12.0	11.9	11.8	11.6	11.5	11.4	11.3	11.2	11.0	10.9	81
82	14.4	14.3	14.1	14.0	13.8	13.7	13.5	13.4	13.2	13.1	13.0	12.8	12.7	12.6	12.4	12.3	82
LAT.	153¾ 206¼	153½ 206½	153¼ 206¾	**153° 207**	152¾ 207¼	152½ 207½	152¼ 207¾	**152° 208**	151¾ 208¼	151½ 208½	151¼ 208¾	**151° 209**	150¾ 209¼	150½ 209½	150¼ 209¾	**150° 210**	LAT.

Table 29 (H.L.)

B — Lat. and Dec. SAME name, Sign **−**
Lat. and Dec. CONTRARY names, Sign **+**

1 hr.

HOUR ANGLE or DIFF. LONG.

DEC.	45m	46m	47m	48m	49m	50m	51m	52m	53m	54m	55m	56m	57m	58m	59m	60m	DEC.
	26¼° 333¾	26½° 333½	26¾° 333¼	**27° 333**	27¼° 332¾	27½° 332½	27¾° 332¼	**28° 332**	28¼° 331¾	28½° 331½	28¾° 331¼	**29° 331**	29¼° 330¾	29½° 330½	29¾° 330¼	**30° 330**	
68°	5.60	5.55	5.50	5.45	5.41	5.36	5.32	5.27	5.23	5.19	5.15	5.11	5.07	5.03	4.99	4.95	68°
69	5.89	5.84	5.79	5.74	5.69	5.64	5.60	5.55	5.50	5.46	5.42	5.37	5.33	5.29	5.25	5.21	69
70	6.21	6.16	6.10	6.05	6.00	5.95	5.90	5.85	5.80	5.76	5.71	5.67	5.62	5.58	5.54	5.49	70
74	7.88	7.82	7.75	7.68	7.62	7.55	7.49	7.43	7.37	7.31	7.25	7.19	7.14	7.08	7.03	6.97	74
75	8.44	8.36	8.29	8.22	8.15	8.08	8.02	7.95	7.88	7.82	7.76	7.70	7.64	7.58	7.52	7.46	75
DEC.	153¾ 206¼	153½ 206½	153¼ 206¾	**153° 207**	152¾ 207¼	152½ 207½	152¼ 207¾	**152° 208**	151¾ 208¼	151½ 208½	151¼ 208¾	**151° 209**	150¾ 209¼	150½ 209½	150¼ 209¾	**150° 210**	DEC.

Table 29 (H.L.)	**B**	Lat. and Dec. SAME name, Sign —
1 hr.		Lat. and Dec. CONTRARY names, Sign **+**

HOUR ANGLE or DIFF. LONG.

DEC.	45m	46m	47m	48m	49m	50m	51m	52m	53m	54m	55m	56m	57m	58m	59m	60m	DEC.
	26¼° 333¾	26½° 333½	26¾° 333¼	**27°** **333**	27¼° 332¾	27½° 332½	27¾° 332¼	**28°** **332**	28¼° 331¾	28½° 331½	28¾° 331¼	**29°** **331**	29¼° 330¾	29½° 330½	29¾° 330¼	**30°** **330**	
0°	.000	.000	.000	.000	.000	.000	.000	.000	.000	.000	.000	.000	.000	.000	.000	.000	0°
1	.040	.039	.039	.038	.038	.038	.038	.037	.037	.037	.036	.036	.036	.035	.035	.035	1
2	.079	.078	.078	.077	.076	.076	.075	.074	.074	.073	.073	.072	.072	.071	.070	.070	2
3	.119	.117	.116	.115	.114	.113	.113	.112	.111	.110	.109	.108	.107	.106	.106	.105	3
4	.158	.157	.155	.154	.152	.151	.150	.149	.148	.147	.145	.144	.143	.142	.141	.140	4
5	.198	.196	.194	.193	.191	.189	.188	.186	.185	.183	.182	.180	.179	.178	.176	.175	5
6	.238	.236	.234	.232	.230	.228	.226	.224	.222	.220	.219	.217	.215	.213	.212	.210	6
7	.278	.275	.273	.270	.268	.266	.264	.262	.259	.257	.255	.253	.251	.249	.247	.246	7
8	.318	.315	.312	.310	.307	.304	.302	.299	.297	.295	.292	.290	.288	.285	.283	.281	8
9	.358	.355	.352	.349	.346	.343	.340	.337	.335	.332	.329	.327	.324	.322	.319	.317	9
10	.399	.395	.392	.388	.385	.382	.379	.376	.373	.370	.367	.364	.361	.358	.355	.353	10
11	.439	.436	.432	.428	.425	.421	.418	.414	.411	.407	.404	.401	.398	.395	.392	.389	11
12	.481	.476	.472	.468	.464	.460	.457	.453	.449	.445	.442	.438	.435	.432	.428	.425	12
13	.522	.517	.513	.509	.504	.500	.496	.492	.488	.484	.480	.476	.473	.469	.465	.462	13
14	.564	.559	.554	.549	.545	.540	.536	.531	.527	.523	.519	.514	.510	.506	.503	.499	14
15	.606	.601	.595	.590	.585	.580	.576	.571	.566	.562	.557	.553	.548	.544	.540	.536	15
16	.648	.643	.637	.632	.626	.621	.616	.611	.606	.601	.596	.591	.587	.582	.578	.573	16
17	.691	.685	.679	.673	.668	.662	.657	.651	.646	.641	.636	.631	.626	.621	.616	.611	17
18	.735	.728	.722	.716	.710	.704	.698	.692	.687	.681	.676	.670	.665	.660	.655	.650	18
19	.779	.772	.765	.758	.752	.746	.740	.733	.728	.722	.716	.710	.705	.699	.694	.689	19
20	.823	.816	.809	.802	.795	.788	.782	.775	.769	.763	.757	.751	.745	.739	.734	.728	20
21	.868	.860	.853	.846	.839	.831	.825	.818	.811	.804	.798	.792	.786	.780	.774	.768	21
22	.914	.905	.898	.890	.883	.875	.868	.861	.854	.847	.840	.833	.827	.820	.814	.808	22
23	.960	.951	.943	.935	.927	.919	.912	.904	.897	.890	.883	.876	.869	.862	.856	.849	23
24	1.01	.998	.989	.981	.973	.964	.956	.948	.941	.933	.926	.918	.911	.904	.897	.890	24
25	1.05	1.05	1.04	1.03	1.02	1.01	1.00	.993	.985	.977	.970	.962	.954	.947	.940	.933	25
26	1.10	1.09	1.08	1.07	1.07	1.06	1.05	1.04	1.03	1.02	1.01	1.01	.998	.990	.983	.975	26
27	1.15	1.14	1.13	1.12	1.11	1.10	1.09	1.09	1.08	1.07	1.06	1.05	1.04	1.03	1.02	1.02	27
28	1.20	1.19	1.18	1.17	1.16	1.15	1.14	1.13	1.12	1.11	1.11	1.10	1.09	1.08	1.07	1.06	28
29	1.25	1.24	1.23	1.22	1.21	1.20	1.19	1.18	1.17	1.16	1.15	1.14	1.13	1.13	1.12	1.11	29
30	1.31	1.29	1.28	1.27	1.26	1.25	1.24	1.23	1.22	1.21	1.20	1.19	1.18	1.17	1.16	1.15	30
31	1.36	1.35	1.34	1.32	1.31	1.30	1.29	1.28	1.27	1.26	1.25	1.24	1.23	1.22	1.21	1.20	31
32	1.41	1.40	1.39	1.38	1.37	1.35	1.34	1.33	1.32	1.31	1.30	1.29	1.28	1.27	1.26	1.25	32
33	1.47	1.46	1.44	1.43	1.42	1.41	1.39	1.38	1.37	1.36	1.35	1.34	1.33	1.32	1.31	1.30	33
34	1.53	1.51	1.50	1.49	1.48	1.46	1.45	1.44	1.43	1.41	1.40	1.39	1.38	1.37	1.36	1.35	34
35	1.58	1.57	1.56	1.54	1.53	1.52	1.50	1.49	1.48	1.47	1.46	1.44	1.43	1.42	1.41	1.40	35
36	1.64	1.63	1.61	1.60	1.59	1.57	1.56	1.55	1.54	1.52	1.51	1.50	1.49	1.48	1.46	1.45	36
37	1.70	1.69	1.67	1.66	1.65	1.63	1.62	1.61	1.59	1.58	1.57	1.55	1.54	1.53	1.52	1.51	37
38	1.77	1.75	1.74	1.72	1.71	1.69	1.68	1.66	1.65	1.64	1.62	1.61	1.60	1.59	1.57	1.56	38
39	1.83	1.81	1.80	1.78	1.77	1.75	1.74	1.72	1.71	1.70	1.68	1.67	1.66	1.64	1.63	1.62	39
40	1.90	1.88	1.86	1.85	1.83	1.82	1.80	1.79	1.77	1.76	1.74	1.73	1.72	1.70	1.69	1.68	40
41	1.97	1.95	1.93	1.91	1.90	1.88	1.87	1.85	1.84	1.82	1.81	1.79	1.78	1.77	1.75	1.74	41
42	2.04	2.02	2.00	1.98	1.97	1.95	1.93	1.92	1.90	1.89	1.87	1.86	1.84	1.83	1.81	1.80	42
43	2.11	2.09	2.07	2.05	2.04	2.02	2.00	1.99	1.97	1.95	1.94	1.92	1.91	1.89	1.88	1.87	43
44	2.18	2.16	2.15	2.13	2.11	2.09	2.07	2.06	2.04	2.02	2.01	1.99	1.98	1.96	1.95	1.93	44
45	2.26	2.24	2.22	2.20	2.18	2.17	2.15	2.13	2.11	2.10	2.08	2.06	2.05	2.03	2.02	2.00	45
46	2.34	2.32	2.30	2.28	2.26	2.24	2.22	2.21	2.19	2.17	2.15	2.14	2.12	2.10	2.09	2.07	46
47	2.42	2.40	2.38	2.36	2.34	2.32	2.30	2.28	2.27	2.25	2.23	2.21	2.19	2.18	2.16	2.14	47
48	2.51	2.49	2.47	2.45	2.43	2.41	2.39	2.37	2.35	2.33	2.31	2.29	2.27	2.26	2.24	2.22	48
49	2.60	2.58	2.56	2.53	2.51	2.49	2.47	2.45	2.43	2.41	2.39	2.37	2.35	2.34	2.32	2.30	49
50	2.69	2.67	2.65	2.63	2.60	2.58	2.56	2.54	2.52	2.50	2.48	2.46	2.44	2.42	2.40	2.38	50
51	2.79	2.77	2.74	2.72	2.70	2.67	2.65	2.63	2.61	2.59	2.57	2.55	2.53	2.51	2.49	2.47	51
52	2.89	2.87	2.84	2.82	2.80	2.77	2.75	2.73	2.70	2.68	2.66	2.64	2.62	2.60	2.58	2.56	52
53	3.00	2.97	2.95	2.92	2.90	2.87	2.85	2.83	2.80	2.78	2.76	2.74	2.72	2.69	2.67	2.65	53
54	3.11	3.08	3.06	3.03	3.01	2.98	2.96	2.93	2.91	2.89	2.86	2.84	2.82	2.80	2.77	2.75	54
55	3.23	3.20	3.17	3.15	3.12	3.09	3.07	3.04	3.02	2.99	2.97	2.95	2.92	2.90	2.88	2.86	55
56	3.35	3.32	3.29	3.27	3.24	3.21	3.18	3.16	3.13	3.11	3.08	3.06	3.03	3.01	2.99	2.97	56
57	3.48	3.45	3.42	3.39	3.36	3.33	3.31	3.28	3.25	3.23	3.20	3.18	3.15	3.13	3.10	3.08	57
58	3.62	3.59	3.56	3.53	3.50	3.47	3.44	3.41	3.38	3.35	3.33	3.30	3.28	3.25	3.23	3.20	58
59	3.76	3.73	3.70	3.67	3.64	3.60	3.57	3.55	3.52	3.49	3.46	3.43	3.40	3.38	3.35	3.33	59
60	3.92	3.88	3.85	3.82	3.78	3.75	3.72	3.69	3.66	3.63	3.60	3.57	3.55	3.52	3.49	3.46	60
61	4.08	4.04	4.01	3.97	3.94	3.91	3.87	3.84	3.81	3.78	3.75	3.72	3.69	3.66	3.64	3.61	61
62	4.25	4.22	4.18	4.14	4.11	4.07	4.04	4.01	3.97	3.94	3.91	3.88	3.85	3.82	3.79	3.76	62
63	4.44	4.40	4.36	4.32	4.29	4.25	4.22	4.18	4.15	4.11	4.08	4.05	4.02	3.99	3.96	3.93	63
DEC.	153¾ 206¼	153½ 206½	153¼ 206¾	**153°** **207**	152¾ 207¼	152½ 207½	152¼ 207¾	**152°** **208**	151¾ 208¼	151½ 208½	151¼ 208¾	**151°** **209**	150¾ 209¼	150½ 209½	150¼ 209¾	**150°** **210**	DEC.

Table 29 (H.L.)

A — If entered with H.A. at **top**, Sign **+**
„ „ „ „ **foot**, „ **−**

2 hrs.

HOUR ANGLE or DIFF. LONG.

LAT.	00m	02m	04m	06m	08m	10m	12m	14m	16m	18m	20m	22m	24m	26m	28m	30m	LAT.
	30°	30½°	31°	31½°	32°	32½°	33°	33½°	34°	34½°	35°	35½°	36°	36½°	37°	37½°	
	330	329½	329	328½	328	327½	327	326½	326	325½	325	324½	324	323½	323	322½	
60°	3.00	2.94	2.88	2.83	2.77	2.72	2.67	2.62	2.57	2.52	2.47	2.43	2.38	2.34	2.30	2.26	60°
61	3.13	3.06	3.00	2.94	2.89	2.83	2.78	2.73	2.68	2.63	2.58	2.53	2.48	2.44	2.39	2.35	61
62	3.26	3.19	3.13	3.07	3.01	2.95	2.90	2.84	2.79	2.74	2.69	2.64	2.59	2.54	2.50	2.45	62
63	3.40	3.33	3.27	3.20	3.14	3.08	3.02	2.97	2.91	2.86	2.80	2.75	2.70	2.65	2.60	2.56	63
64	3.55	3.48	3.41	3.35	3.28	3.22	3.16	3.10	3.04	2.98	2.93	2.87	2.82	2.77	2.72	2.67	64
65	3.71	3.64	3.57	3.50	3.43	3.37	3.30	3.24	3.18	3.12	3.06	3.01	2.95	2.90	2.85	2.80	65
66	3.89	3.81	3.74	3.67	3.59	3.53	3.46	3.39	3.33	3.27	3.21	3.15	3.09	3.04	2.98	2.93	66
67	4.08	4.00	3.92	3.84	3.77	3.70	3.63	3.56	3.49	3.43	3.36	3.30	3.24	3.18	3.13	3.07	67
68	4.29	4.20	4.12	4.04	3.96	3.89	3.81	3.74	3.67	3.60	3.53	3.47	3.41	3.35	3.28	3.23	68
69	4.51	4.42	4.34	4.25	4.17	4.09	4.01	3.94	3.86	3.79	3.72	3.65	3.59	3.52	3.46	3.40	69
70	4.76	4.66	4.57	4.48	4.40	4.31	4.23	4.15	4.07	4.00	3.92	3.85	3.78	3.71	3.65	3.58	70
71	5.03	4.93	4.83	4.74	4.65	4.56	4.47	4.39	4.31	4.23	4.15	4.07	4.00	3.92	3.85	3.78	71
72	5.33	5.22	5.12	5.02	4.93	4.83	4.74	4.65	4.56	4.48	4.40	4.31	4.24	4.16	4.08	4.01	72
73	5.67	5.55	5.44	5.34	5.23	5.13	5.04	4.94	4.85	4.76	4.67	4.59	4.50	4.42	4.34	4.26	73
74	6.04	5.92	5.80	5.69	5.58	5.47	5.37	5.27	5.17	5.07	4.98	4.89	4.80	4.71	4.63	4.54	74
75	6.46	6.34	6.21	6.09	5.97	5.86	5.75	5.64	5.53	5.43	5.33	5.23	5.14	5.04	4.95	4.86	75
76	6.95	6.81	6.68	6.55	6.42	6.30	6.18	6.06	5.95	5.84	5.73	5.62	5.52	5.42	5.32	5.23	76
77	7.50	7.35	7.21	7.07	6.93	6.80	6.67	6.54	6.42	6.30	6.19	6.07	5.96	5.85	5.75	5.65	77
78	8.15	7.99	7.83	7.68	7.53	7.38	7.24	7.11	6.97	6.85	6.72	6.60	6.48	6.36	6.24	6.13	78
79	8.91	8.73	8.56	8.40	8.23	8.08	7.92	7.77	7.63	7.49	7.35	7.21	7.08	6.95	6.83	6.70	79
80	9.82	9.63	9.44	9.25	9.08	8.90	8.73	8.57	8.41	8.25	8.10	7.95	7.81	7.66	7.53	7.39	80
81	10.9	10.7	10.5	10.3	10.1	9.91	9.72	9.54	9.36	9.19	9.02	8.85	8.69	8.53	8.38	8.23	81
82	12.3	12.1	11.8	11.6	11.4	11.2	11.0	10.8	10.5	10.4	10.2	9.98	9.79	9.62	9.44	9.27	82
LAT.	150°	149½	149°	148½	148°	147½	147°	146½	146°	145½	145°	144½	144°	143½	143°	142½	LAT.
	210	210½	211	211½	212	212½	213	213½	214	214½	215	215½	216	216½	217	217½	

(S.W. Qdt.) **180°——→270°**   (S.E. Qdt.) **180°←——90°**

Table 29 (H.L.)

B — Lat. and Dec. SAME name, Sign **−**
Lat. and Dec. CONTRARY names, Sign **+**

2 hrs.

HOUR ANGLE or DIFF. LONG.

DEC.	00m	02m	04m	06m	08m	10m	12m	14m	16m	18m	20m	22m	24m	26m	28m	30m	DEC.
	30°	30½°	31°	31½°	32°	32½°	33°	33½°	34°	34½°	35°	35½°	36°	36½°	3°	37½°	
	330	329½	329	328½	328	327½	327	326½	326	325½	325	324½	324	323½	323	322½	
68°	4.95	4.88	4.81	4.74	4.67	4.61	4.55	4.48	4.43	4.37	4.32	4.26	4.21	4.16	4.11	4.07	68°
69	5.21	5.13	5.05	4.99	4.92	4.85	4.78	4.72	4.66	4.60	4.54	4.49	4.43	4.38	4.33	4.28	69
70	5.49	5.41	5.34	5.26	5.19	5.11	5.04	4.98	4.91	4.85	4.79	4.73	4.67	4.62	4.57	4.51	70
74	6.97	6.87	6.77	6.67	6.58	6.49	6.40	6.32	6.24	6.16	6.08	6.01	5.93	5.86	5.79	5.73	74
75	7.46	7.35	7.25	7.14	7.04	6.95	6.85	6.76	6.67	6.59	6.51	6.43	6.35	6.27	6.20	6.13	75
DEC.	150°	149½	149°	148½	148°	147½	147°	146½	146°	145½	145°	144½	144°	143½	143°	142½	DEC.
	210	210½	211	211½	212	212½	213	213½	214	214½	215	215½	216	216½	217	217½	

(S.W. Qdt.) **180°——→270°**   (S.E. Qdt.) **180°←——90°**

Table 29 (H.L.) 2 hrs. **B**

Lat. and Dec. SAME name, Sign −
Lat. and Dec. CONTRARY names, Sign +

HOUR ANGLE or DIFF. LONG.

DEC.	00m 30° 330	02m 30½° 329½	04m 31° 329	06m 31½° 328½	08m 32° 328	10m 32½° 327½	12m 33° 327	14m 33½° 326½	16m 34° 326	18m 34½° 325½	20m 35° 325	22m 35½° 324½	24m 36° 324	26m 36½° 323½	28m 37° 323	30m 37½° 322½	DEC.
0°	.000	.000	.000	.000	.000	.000	.000	.000	.000	.000	.000	.000	.000	.000	.000	.000	0°
1	.035	.034	.034	.033	.033	.032	.032	.032	.031	.031	.030	.030	.030	.029	.029	.029	1
2	.070	.069	.068	.067	.066	.065	.064	.063	.062	.062	.061	.060	.059	.059	.058	.057	2
3	.105	.103	.102	.100	.099	.098	.096	.095	.094	.093	.091	.090	.089	.088	.087	.086	3
4	.140	.138	.136	.134	.132	.130	.128	.127	.125	.123	.122	.120	.119	.118	.116	.115	4
5	.175	.172	.170	.167	.165	.163	.161	.159	.157	.154	.153	.151	.149	.147	.145	.144	5
6	.210	.207	.204	.201	.198	.196	.193	.190	.188	.186	.183	.181	.179	.177	.175	.173	6
7	.246	.242	.238	.235	.232	.229	.225	.222	.220	.217	.214	.211	.209	.206	.204	.202	7
8	.281	.277	.273	.269	.265	.262	.258	.255	.251	.248	.245	.242	.239	.236	.234	.231	8
9	.317	.312	.308	.303	.299	.295	.291	.287	.283	.280	.276	.273	.269	.266	.263	.260	9
10	.353	.347	.342	.337	.333	.328	.324	.319	.315	.311	.307	.304	.300	.296	.293	.290	10
11	.389	.383	.377	.372	.367	.362	.357	.352	.348	.343	.339	.335	.331	.327	.323	.319	11
12	.425	.419	.413	.407	.401	.396	.390	.385	.380	.375	.371	.366	.362	.357	.353	.349	12
13	.462	.455	.448	.442	.436	.430	.424	.418	.413	.408	.403	.398	.393	.388	.384	.379	13
14	.499	.491	.484	.477	.471	.464	.458	.452	.446	.440	.435	.429	.424	.419	.414	.410	14
15	.536	.528	.520	.513	.506	.499	.492	.485	.479	.473	.467	.461	.456	.450	.445	.440	15
16	.573	.565	.557	.549	.541	.534	.527	.520	.513	.506	.500	.494	.488	.482	.476	.471	16
17	.611	.602	.594	.585	.577	.569	.561	.554	.547	.540	.533	.526	.520	.514	.508	.502	17
18	.650	.640	.631	.622	.613	.605	.597	.589	.581	.574	.566	.560	.553	.546	.540	.534	18
19	.689	.678	.669	.659	.650	.641	.632	.624	.616	.608	.600	.593	.586	.579	.572	.566	19
20	.728	.717	.707	.697	.687	.677	.668	.659	.651	.643	.635	.627	.619	.612	.605	.598	20
21	.768	.756	.745	.735	.724	.714	.705	.695	.686	.678	.669	.661	.653	.645	.638	.631	21
22	.808	.796	.784	.773	.762	.752	.742	.732	.723	.713	.704	.696	.687	.679	.671	.664	22
23	.849	.836	.824	.812	.801	.790	.779	.769	.759	.749	.740	.731	.722	.714	.705	.697	23
24	.890	.877	.864	.852	.840	.829	.817	.807	.796	.786	.776	.767	.757	.749	.740	.731	24
25	.933	.919	.905	.892	.880	.868	.856	.845	.834	.823	.813	.803	.793	.784	.775	.766	25
26	.975	.961	.947	.933	.920	.908	.896	.884	.872	.861	.850	.840	.830	.820	.810	.801	26
27	1.02	1.00	.989	.975	.962	.948	.936	.923	.911	.900	.888	.877	.867	.857	.847	.837	27
28	1.06	1.05	1.03	1.02	1.00	.990	.976	.963	.951	.939	.927	.916	.905	.894	.884	.873	28
29	1.11	1.09	1.08	1.06	1.05	1.03	1.02	1.00	.991	.979	.966	.955	.943	.932	.921	.911	29
30	1.15	1.14	1.12	1.11	1.09	1.08	1.06	1.05	1.03	1.02	1.01	.994	.982	.971	.959	.948	30
31	1.20	1.18	1.17	1.15	1.13	1.12	1.10	1.09	1.07	1.06	1.05	1.04	1.02	1.01	.998	.987	31
32	1.25	1.23	1.21	1.20	1.18	1.16	1.15	1.13	1.12	1.10	1.09	1.08	1.06	1.05	1.04	1.03	32
33	1.30	1.28	1.26	1.24	1.23	1.21	1.19	1.18	1.16	1.15	1.13	1.12	1.10	1.09	1.08	1.07	33
34	1.35	1.33	1.31	1.29	1.27	1.26	1.24	1.22	1.21	1.19	1.18	1.16	1.15	1.13	1.12	1.11	34
35	1.40	1.38	1.36	1.34	1.32	1.30	1.29	1.27	1.25	1.24	1.22	1.21	1.19	1.18	1.16	1.15	35
36	1.45	1.43	1.41	1.39	1.37	1.35	1.33	1.32	1.30	1.28	1.27	1.25	1.24	1.22	1.21	1.19	36
37	1.51	1.49	1.46	1.44	1.42	1.40	1.38	1.37	1.35	1.33	1.31	1.30	1.28	1.27	1.25	1.24	37
38	1.56	1.54	1.52	1.50	1.47	1.45	1.43	1.42	1.40	1.38	1.36	1.35	1.33	1.31	1.30	1.28	38
39	1.62	1.60	1.57	1.55	1.53	1.51	1.49	1.47	1.45	1.43	1.41	1.39	1.38	1.36	1.35	1.33	39
40	1.68	1.65	1.63	1.61	1.58	1.56	1.54	1.52	1.50	1.48	1.46	1.45	1.43	1.41	1.39	1.38	40
41	1.74	1.71	1.69	1.66	1.64	1.62	1.60	1.58	1.55	1.54	1.52	1.50	1.48	1.46	1.44	1.43	41
42	1.80	1.77	1.75	1.72	1.70	1.68	1.65	1.63	1.61	1.59	1.57	1.55	1.53	1.51	1.50	1.48	42
43	1.87	1.84	1.81	1.79	1.76	1.74	1.71	1.69	1.67	1.65	1.63	1.61	1.59	1.57	1.55	1.53	43
44	1.93	1.90	1.88	1.85	1.82	1.80	1.77	1.75	1.73	1.71	1.68	1.66	1.64	1.62	1.60	1.59	44
45	2.00	1.97	1.94	1.91	1.89	1.86	1.84	1.81	1.79	1.77	1.74	1.72	1.70	1.68	1.66	1.64	45
46	2.07	2.04	2.01	1.98	1.95	1.93	1.90	1.88	1.85	1.83	1.81	1.78	1.76	1.74	1.72	1.70	46
47	2.14	2.11	2.08	2.05	2.02	2.00	1.97	1.94	1.92	1.89	1.87	1.85	1.82	1.80	1.78	1.76	47
48	2.22	2.19	2.16	2.13	2.10	2.07	2.04	2.01	1.99	1.96	1.94	1.91	1.89	1.87	1.85	1.82	48
49	2.30	2.27	2.23	2.20	2.17	2.14	2.11	2.08	2.06	2.03	2.01	1.98	1.96	1.93	1.91	1.89	49
50	2.38	2.35	2.31	2.28	2.25	2.22	2.19	2.16	2.13	2.10	2.08	2.05	2.03	2.00	1.98	1.96	50
51	2.47	2.43	2.40	2.36	2.33	2.30	2.27	2.24	2.21	2.18	2.15	2.13	2.10	2.08	2.05	2.03	51
52	2.56	2.52	2.49	2.45	2.42	2.38	2.35	2.32	2.29	2.26	2.23	2.20	2.18	2.15	2.13	2.10	52
53	2.65	2.62	2.58	2.54	2.50	2.47	2.44	2.40	2.37	2.34	2.31	2.29	2.26	2.23	2.21	2.18	53
54	2.75	2.71	2.67	2.63	2.60	2.56	2.53	2.49	2.46	2.43	2.40	2.37	2.34	2.31	2.29	2.26	54
55	2.86	2.81	2.77	2.73	2.70	2.66	2.62	2.59	2.55	2.52	2.49	2.46	2.43	2.40	2.37	2.35	55
56	2.97	2.92	2.88	2.84	2.80	2.76	2.72	2.69	2.65	2.62	2.58	2.55	2.52	2.49	2.46	2.44	56
57	3.08	3.03	2.99	2.95	2.91	2.87	2.83	2.79	2.75	2.72	2.68	2.65	2.62	2.59	2.56	2.53	57
58	3.20	3.15	3.11	3.06	3.02	2.98	2.94	2.90	2.86	2.83	2.79	2.76	2.72	2.69	2.66	2.63	58
59	3.33	3.28	3.23	3.19	3.14	3.10	3.06	3.02	2.98	2.94	2.90	2.87	2.83	2.80	2.77	2.73	59
60	3.46	3.41	3.36	3.32	3.27	3.22	3.18	3.14	3.10	3.06	3.02	2.98	2.95	2.91	2.88	2.85	60
61	3.61	3.56	3.50	3.45	3.40	3.36	3.31	3.27	3.23	3.19	3.15	3.11	3.07	3.03	3.00	2.96	61
62	3.76	3.71	3.65	3.60	3.55	3.50	3.45	3.41	3.36	3.32	3.28	3.24	3.20	3.16	3.13	3.09	62
63	3.93	3.87	3.81	3.76	3.70	3.65	3.60	3.56	3.51	3.47	3.42	3.38	3.34	3.30	3.26	3.22	63
DEC.	150° 210	149½ 210½	149° 211	148½ 211½	148° 212	147½ 212½	147° 213	146½ 213½	146° 214	145½ 214½	145° 215	144½ 215½	144° 216	143½ 216½	143° 217	142½ 217½	DEC.

Table 29 (H.L.)

A

If entered with H.A. at **top**, Sign **+**

„   „   „   „ **foot**, „   **—**

2 hrs.

HOUR ANGLE or DIFF. LONG.

LAT.	30m	32m	34m	36m	38m	40m	42m	44m	46m	48m	50m	52m	54m	56m	58m	60m	LAT.
	37½°/322½	38°/322	38½°/321½	39°/321	39½°/320½	40°/320	40½°/319½	41°/319	41½°/318½	42°/318	42½°/317½	43°/317	43½°/316½	44°/316	44½°/315½	45°/315	
60°	2.26	2.22	2.18	2.14	2.10	2.07	2.03	1.99	1.96	1.92	1.89	1.86	1.83	1.79	1.76	1.73	60°
61	2.35	2.31	2.27	2.23	2.19	2.15	2.11	2.08	2.04	2.00	1.97	1.94	1.90	1.87	1.84	1.80	61
62	2.45	2.41	2.36	2.32	2.28	2.24	2.20	2.16	2.13	2.09	2.05	2.02	1.98	1.95	1.91	1.88	62
63	2.56	2.51	2.47	2.42	2.38	2.34	2.30	2.26	2.22	2.18	2.14	2.11	2.07	2.03	2.00	1.96	63
64	2.67	2.62	2.58	2.53	2.49	2.44	2.40	2.36	2.32	2.28	2.24	2.20	2.16	2.12	2.09	2.05	64
65	2.80	2.75	2.70	2.65	2.60	2.56	2.51	2.47	2.42	2.38	2.34	2.30	2.26	2.22	2.18	2.15	65
66	2.93	2.87	2.82	2.77	2.72	2.68	2.63	2.58	2.54	2.49	2.45	2.41	2.37	2.33	2.29	2.25	66
67	3.07	3.02	2.96	2.91	2.86	2.81	2.76	2.71	2.66	2.62	2.57	2.53	2.48	2.44	2.40	2.36	67
68	3.23	3.17	3.11	3.06	3.00	2.95	2.90	2.85	2.80	2.75	2.70	2.65	2.61	2.56	2.52	2.48	68
69	3.40	3.33	3.28	3.22	3.16	3.10	3.05	3.00	2.94	2.89	2.84	2.79	2.75	2.70	2.65	2.61	69
70	3.58	3.52	3.45	3.39	3.33	3.27	3.22	3.16	3.11	3.05	3.00	2.95	2.90	2.85	2.80	2.75	70
71	3.78	3.72	3.65	3.59	3.52	3.46	3.40	3.34	3.28	3.23	3.17	3.11	3.06	3.01	2.96	2.90	71
72	4.01	3.94	3.87	3.80	3.73	3.67	3.60	3.54	3.48	3.42	3.36	3.30	3.24	3.19	3.13	3.08	72
73	4.26	4.19	4.11	4.04	3.97	3.90	3.83	3.76	3.70	3.63	3.57	3.51	3.45	3.39	3.33	3.27	73
74	4.54	4.46	4.38	4.31	4.23	4.16	4.08	4.01	3.94	3.87	3.81	3.74	3.67	3.61	3.55	3.49	74
75	4.86	4.78	4.69	4.61	4.53	4.45	4.37	4.29	4.22	4.14	4.07	4.00	3.93	3.86	3.80	3.73	75
76	5.23	5.13	5.04	4.95	4.87	4.78	4.70	4.61	4.53	4.45	4.38	4.30	4.23	4.15	4.08	4.01	76
77	5.65	5.54	5.45	5.35	5.25	5.16	5.07	4.98	4.90	4.81	4.73	4.64	4.56	4.49	4.41	4.33	77
78	6.13	6.02	5.91	5.81	5.71	5.61	5.51	5.41	5.32	5.23	5.13	5.05	4.96	4.87	4.79	4.70	78
79	6.70	6.58	6.47	6.35	6.24	6.13	6.02	5.92	5.81	5.71	5.61	5.52	5.42	5.33	5.24	5.14	79
80	7.39	7.26	7.13	7.00	6.88	6.76	6.64	6.52	6.41	6.30	6.19	6.08	5.98	5.87	5.77	5.67	80
81	8.23	8.08	7.94	7.80	7.66	7.52	7.39	7.26	7.14	7.01	6.89	6.77	6.65	6.54	6.42	6.31	81
82	9.27	9.11	8.95	8.79	8.63	8.48	8.33	8.19	8.04	7.90	7.77	7.63	7.50	7.37	7.24	7.12	82
LAT.	142½/217½	142°/218	141½/218½	141°/219	140½/219½	140°/220	139½/220½	139°/221	138½/221½	138°/222	137½/222½	137°/223	136½/223½	136°/224	135½/224½	135°/225	LAT.

Table 29 (H.L.)

B

Lat. and Dec. SAME name, Sign **—**

Lat. and Dec. CONTRARY names, Sign **+**

2 hrs.

HOUR ANGLE or DIFF. LONG.

DEC.	30m	32m	34m	36m	38m	40m	42m	44m	46m	48m	50m	52m	54m	56m	58m	60m	DEC.
	37½°/322½	38°/322	38½°/321½	39°/321	39½°/320½	40°/320	40½°/319½	41°/319	41½°/318½	42°/318	42½°/317½	43°/317	43½°/316½	44°/316	44½°/315½	45°/315	
68°	4.07	4.02	3.98	3.93	3.89	3.85	3.81	3.77	3.74	3.70	3.66	3.63	3.60	3.56	3.53	3.50	68°
69	4.28	4.23	4.19	4.14	4.10	4.05	4.01	3.97	3.93	3.89	3.86	3.82	3.78	3.75	3.72	3.68	69
70	4.51	4.46	4.41	4.37	4.32	4.27	4.23	4.19	4.15	4.11	4.07	4.03	3.99	3.96	3.92	3.89	70
74	5.73	5.66	5.60	5.54	5.48	5.42	5.37	5.32	5.26	5.21	5.16	5.11	5.07	5.02	4.98	4.93	74
75	6.13	6.06	6.00	5.93	5.87	5.81	5.75	5.69	5.63	5.58	5.52	5.47	5.42	5.37	5.32	5.28	75
DEC.	142½/217½	142°/218	141½/218½	141°/219	140½/219½	140°/220	139½/220½	139°/221	138½/221½	138°/222	137½/222½	137°/223	136½/223½	136°/224	135½/224½	135°/225	DEC.

Table 29 (H.L.) — B — 2 hrs.

Lat. and Dec. SAME name, sign —
Lat. and Dec. CONTRARY names, Sign +

HOUR ANGLE or DIFF. LONG.

DEC.	30m	32m	34m	36m	38m	40m	42m	44m	46m	48m	50m	52m	54m	56m	58m	60m	DEC.
	37½° 322½	38° 322	38½° 321½	39° 321	39½° 320½	40° 320	40½° 319½	41° 319	41½° 318½	42° 318	42½° 317½	43° 317	43½° 316½	44° 316	44½° 315½	45° 315	
0°	.000	.000	.000	.000	.000	.000	.000	.000	.000	.000	.000	.000	.000	.000	.000	.000	0°
1	.029	.028	.028	.028	.027	.027	.027	.027	.026	.026	.026	.026	.025	.025	.025	.025	1
2	.057	.057	.056	.055	.055	.054	.054	.053	.053	.052	.052	.051	.051	.050	.050	.049	2
3	.086	.085	.084	.083	.082	.082	.081	.080	.079	.078	.078	.077	.076	.075	.075	.074	3
4	.115	.114	.112	.111	.110	.109	.108	.107	.106	.105	.104	.103	.102	.101	.100	.099	4
5	.144	.142	.141	.139	.138	.136	.135	.133	.132	.131	.129	.128	.127	.126	.125	.124	5
6	.173	.171	.169	.167	.165	.164	.162	.160	.159	.157	.156	.154	.153	.151	.150	.149	6
7	.202	.199	.197	.195	.193	.191	.189	.187	.185	.183	.182	.180	.178	.177	.175	.174	7
8	.231	.228	.226	.223	.221	.219	.216	.214	.212	.210	.208	.206	.204	.202	.201	.199	8
9	.260	.257	.254	.252	.249	.246	.244	.241	.239	.237	.234	.232	.230	.228	.226	.224	9
10	.290	.286	.283	.280	.277	.274	.272	.269	.266	.264	.261	.259	.256	.254	.252	.249	10
11	.319	.316	.312	.309	.306	.302	.299	.296	.293	.290	.288	.285	.282	.280	.277	.275	11
12	.349	.345	.341	.338	.334	.331	.327	.324	.321	.318	.315	.312	.309	.306	.303	.301	12
13	.379	.375	.371	.367	.363	.359	.355	.352	.348	.345	.342	.339	.335	.332	.329	.326	13
14	.410	.405	.401	.396	.392	.388	.384	.380	.376	.373	.369	.366	.362	.359	.356	.353	14
15	.440	.435	.430	.426	.421	.417	.413	.408	.404	.400	.397	.393	.389	.386	.382	.379	15
16	.471	.466	.461	.456	.451	.446	.442	.437	.433	.429	.424	.420	.417	.413	.409	.406	16
17	.502	.497	.491	.486	.481	.476	.471	.466	.461	.457	.453	.448	.444	.440	.436	.432	17
18	.534	.528	.522	.516	.511	.505	.500	.495	.490	.486	.481	.476	.472	.468	.464	.460	18
19	.566	.559	.553	.547	.541	.536	.530	.525	.520	.515	.510	.505	.500	.496	.491	.487	19
20	.598	.591	.585	.578	.572	.566	.560	.555	.549	.544	.539	.534	.529	.524	.519	.515	20
21	.631	.623	.617	.610	.603	.597	.591	.585	.579	.574	.568	.563	.558	.553	.548	.543	21
22	.664	.656	.649	.642	.635	.629	.622	.616	.610	.604	.598	.592	.587	.582	.576	.571	22
23	.697	.689	.682	.674	.667	.660	.654	.647	.641	.634	.628	.622	.617	.611	.606	.600	23
24	.731	.723	.715	.707	.700	.693	.686	.679	.672	.665	.659	.653	.647	.641	.635	.630	24
25	.766	.757	.749	.741	.733	.725	.718	.711	.704	.697	.690	.684	.677	.671	.665	.659	25
26	.801	.792	.783	.775	.767	.759	.751	.743	.736	.729	.722	.715	.709	.702	.696	.690	26
27	.837	.828	.818	.810	.801	.793	.785	.777	.769	.761	.754	.747	.740	.733	.727	.721	27
28	.873	.864	.854	.845	.836	.827	.819	.810	.802	.795	.787	.780	.772	.765	.759	.752	28
29	.911	.900	.890	.881	.871	.862	.854	.845	.837	.828	.820	.813	.805	.798	.791	.784	29
30	.948	.938	.927	.917	.908	.898	.889	.880	.871	.863	.855	.847	.839	.831	.824	.816	30
31	.987	.976	.965	.955	.945	.935	.925	.916	.907	.898	.889	.881	.873	.865	.857	.850	31
32	1.03	1.02	1.00	.993	.982	.972	.962	.952	.943	.934	.925	.916	.908	.900	.892	.884	32
33	1.07	1.06	1.04	1.03	1.02	1.01	1.00	.990	.980	.971	.961	.952	.943	.935	.927	.918	33
34	1.11	1.10	1.08	1.07	1.06	1.05	1.04	1.03	1.02	1.01	.998	.989	.980	.971	.962	.954	34
35	1.15	1.14	1.13	1.11	1.10	1.09	1.08	1.07	1.06	1.05	1.04	1.03	1.02	1.01	.999	.990	35
36	1.19	1.18	1.17	1.15	1.14	1.13	1.12	1.11	1.10	1.09	1.08	1.07	1.06	1.05	1.04	1.03	36
37	1.24	1.22	1.21	1.20	1.19	1.17	1.16	1.15	1.14	1.13	1.12	1.11	1.10	1.09	1.08	1.07	37
38	1.28	1.27	1.26	1.24	1.23	1.22	1.20	1.19	1.18	1.17	1.16	1.15	1.14	1.13	1.12	1.11	38
39	1.33	1.32	1.30	1.29	1.27	1.26	1.25	1.23	1.22	1.21	1.20	1.19	1.18	1.17	1.16	1.15	39
40	1.38	1.36	1.35	1.33	1.32	1.31	1.29	1.28	1.27	1.25	1.24	1.23	1.22	1.21	1.20	1.19	40
41	1.43	1.41	1.40	1.38	1.37	1.35	1.34	1.33	1.31	1.30	1.29	1.27	1.26	1.25	1.24	1.23	41
42	1.48	1.46	1.45	1.43	1.42	1.40	1.39	1.37	1.36	1.35	1.33	1.32	1.31	1.30	1.29	1.27	42
43	1.53	1.51	1.50	1.48	1.47	1.45	1.44	1.42	1.41	1.39	1.38	1.37	1.36	1.34	1.33	1.32	43
44	1.59	1.57	1.55	1.53	1.52	1.50	1.49	1.47	1.46	1.44	1.43	1.42	1.40	1.39	1.38	1.37	44
45	1.64	1.62	1.61	1.59	1.57	1.56	1.54	1.52	1.51	1.49	1.48	1.47	1.45	1.44	1.43	1.41	45
46	1.70	1.68	1.66	1.65	1.63	1.61	1.59	1.58	1.56	1.55	1.53	1.52	1.50	1.49	1.48	1.46	46
47	1.76	1.74	1.72	1.70	1.69	1.67	1.65	1.63	1.62	1.60	1.59	1.57	1.56	1.54	1.53	1.52	47
48	1.82	1.80	1.78	1.77	1.75	1.73	1.71	1.69	1.68	1.66	1.64	1.63	1.61	1.60	1.59	1.57	48
49	1.89	1.87	1.85	1.83	1.81	1.79	1.77	1.75	1.74	1.72	1.70	1.69	1.67	1.66	1.64	1.63	49
50	1.96	1.94	1.91	1.89	1.87	1.85	1.84	1.82	1.80	1.78	1.76	1.75	1.73	1.72	1.70	1.69	50
51	2.03	2.01	1.98	1.96	1.94	1.92	1.90	1.88	1.86	1.85	1.83	1.81	1.79	1.78	1.76	1.75	51
52	2.10	2.08	2.06	2.03	2.01	1.99	1.97	1.95	1.93	1.91	1.90	1.88	1.86	1.84	1.83	1.81	52
53	2.18	2.16	2.13	2.11	2.09	2.06	2.04	2.02	2.00	1.98	1.96	1.95	1.93	1.91	1.89	1.88	53
54	2.26	2.24	2.21	2.19	2.16	2.14	2.12	2.10	2.08	2.06	2.04	2.02	2.00	1.98	1.96	1.95	54
55	2.35	2.32	2.29	2.27	2.25	2.22	2.20	2.18	2.16	2.13	2.11	2.09	2.08	2.06	2.04	2.02	55
56	2.44	2.41	2.38	2.36	2.33	2.31	2.28	2.26	2.24	2.22	2.19	2.17	2.15	2.13	2.12	2.10	56
57	2.53	2.50	2.47	2.45	2.42	2.40	2.37	2.35	2.32	2.30	2.28	2.26	2.24	2.22	2.20	2.18	57
58	2.63	2.60	2.57	2.54	2.52	2.49	2.46	2.44	2.42	2.39	2.37	2.35	2.33	2.30	2.28	2.26	58
59	2.73	2.70	2.67	2.65	2.62	2.59	2.56	2.54	2.51	2.49	2.46	2.44	2.42	2.40	2.37	2.35	59
60	2.85	2.81	2.78	2.75	2.72	2.69	2.67	2.64	2.61	2.59	2.56	2.54	2.52	2.49	2.47	2.45	60
61	2.96	2.93	2.90	2.87	2.84	2.81	2.78	2.75	2.72	2.70	2.67	2.65	2.62	2.60	2.57	2.55	61
62	3.09	3.05	3.02	2.99	2.96	2.93	2.90	2.87	2.84	2.81	2.78	2.76	2.73	2.71	2.68	2.66	62
63	3.22	3.19	3.15	3.12	3.09	3.05	3.02	2.99	2.96	2.93	2.91	2.88	2.85	2.83	2.80	2.78	63
DEC.	142½° 217½	142° 218	141½° 218½	141° 219	140½° 219½	140° 220	139½° 220½	139° 221	138½° 221½	138° 222	137½° 222½	137° 223	136½° 223½	136° 224	135½° 224½	135° 225	DEC.

Table 29 (H.L.) — A

3 hrs.

If entered with H.A. at **top**, Sign **+**
„ „ „ „ **foot**, „ **−**

HOUR ANGLE or DIFF. LONG.

LAT.	00m	02m	04m	06m	08m	10m	12m	14m	16m	18m	20m	22m	24m	26m	28m	30m	LAT.
	45° 315	45½° 314½	46° 314	46½° 313½	47° 313	47½° 312½	48° 312	48½° 311½	49° 311	49½° 310½	50° 310	50½° 309½	51° 309	51½° 308½	52° 308	52½° 307½	
60°	1.73	1.70	1.67	1.64	1.62	1.59	1.56	1.53	1.51	1.48	1.45	1.43	1.40	1.38	1.35	1.33	60°
61	1.80	1.77	1.74	1.71	1.68	1.65	1.62	1.60	1.57	1.54	1.51	1.49	1.46	1.44	1.41	1.38	61
62	1.88	1.85	1.82	1.79	1.75	1.72	1.69	1.66	1.64	1.61	1.58	1.55	1.52	1.50	1.47	1.44	62
63	1.96	1.93	1.90	1.86	1.83	1.80	1.77	1.74	1.71	1.68	1.65	1.62	1.59	1.56	1.53	1.51	63
64	2.05	2.02	1.98	1.95	1.91	1.88	1.85	1.81	1.78	1.75	1.72	1.69	1.66	1.63	1.60	1.57	64
65	2.15	2.11	2.07	2.04	2.00	1.97	1.93	1.90	1.86	1.83	1.80	1.77	1.74	1.71	1.68	1.65	65
66	2.25	2.21	2.17	2.13	2.09	2.06	2.02	1.99	1.95	1.92	1.88	1.85	1.82	1.79	1.75	1.72	66
67	2.36	2.32	2.28	2.24	2.20	2.16	2.12	2.08	2.05	2.01	1.98	1.94	1.91	1.87	1.84	1.81	67
68	2.48	2.43	2.39	2.35	2.31	2.27	2.23	2.19	2.15	2.11	2.08	2.04	2.00	1.97	1.93	1.90	68
69	2.61	2.56	2.52	2.47	2.43	2.39	2.35	2.31	2.26	2.22	2.19	2.15	2.11	2.07	2.04	2.00	69
70	2.75	2.70	2.65	2.61	2.56	2.52	2.47	2.43	2.39	2.35	2.31	2.26	2.22	2.19	2.15	2.11	70
71	2.90	2.85	2.80	2.76	2.71	2.66	2.61	2.57	2.52	2.48	2.44	2.39	2.35	2.31	2.27	2.23	71
72	3.08	3.02	2.97	2.92	2.87	2.82	2.77	2.72	2.68	2.63	2.58	2.54	2.49	2.45	2.40	2.36	72
73	3.27	3.21	3.16	3.10	3.05	3.00	2.95	2.89	2.84	2.79	2.74	2.70	2.65	2.60	2.56	2.51	73
74	3.49	3.43	3.37	3.31	3.25	3.20	3.14	3.09	3.03	2.98	2.93	2.87	2.82	2.77	2.72	2.68	74
75	3.73	3.67	3.60	3.54	3.48	3.42	3.36	3.30	3.24	3.19	3.13	3.08	3.02	2.97	2.92	2.86	75
76	4.01	3.94	3.87	3.81	3.74	3.68	3.61	3.55	3.49	3.43	3.37	3.31	3.25	3.19	3.13	3.08	76
77	4.33	4.26	4.18	4.11	4.04	3.97	3.90	3.83	3.77	3.70	3.63	3.57	3.51	3.45	3.38	3.32	77
78	4.70	4.62	4.54	4.46	4.39	4.31	4.24	4.16	4.09	4.02	3.95	3.88	3.81	3.74	3.68	3.61	78
79	5.14	5.06	4.97	4.88	4.80	4.71	4.63	4.55	4.47	4.39	4.32	4.24	4.17	4.09	4.02	3.95	79
80	5.67	5.57	5.48	5.38	5.29	5.20	5.11	5.02	4.93	4.84	4.76	4.68	4.59	4.51	4.43	4.35	80
81	6.31	6.20	6.10	5.99	5.89	5.79	5.68	5.59	5.49	5.39	5.30	5.20	5.11	5.02	4.93	4.84	81
82	7.12	6.99	6.87	6.75	6.64	6.52	6.41	6.30	6.19	6.08	5.97	5.87	5.76	5.66	5.56	5.46	82
LAT.	135° 225	134½ 225½	134° 226	133½ 226½	133° 227	132½ 227½	132° 228	131½ 228½	131° 229	130½ 229½	130° 230	129½ 230½	129° 231	128½ 231½	128° 232	127½ 232½	LAT.

Table 29 (H.L.) — B

3 hrs.

Lat. and Dec. SAME name, Sign **−**
Lat. and Dec. CONTRARY names, Sign **+**

HOUR ANGLE or DIFF. LONG.

DEC.	00m	02m	04m	06m	08m	10m	12m	14m	16m	18m	20m	22m	24m	26m	28m	30m	DEC.
	45° 315	45½° 314½	46° 314	46½° 313½	47° 313	47½° 312½	48° 312	48½° 311½	49° 311	49½° 310½	50° 310	50½° 309½	51° 309	51½° 308½	52° 308	52½° 307½	
68°	3.50	3.47	3.44	3.41	3.38	3.36	3.33	3.30	3.28	3.26	3.23	3.21	3.19	3.16	3.14	3.12	68°
69	3.68	3.65	3.62	3.59	3.56	3.53	3.51	3.48	3.45	3.43	3.40	3.38	3.35	3.33	3.31	3.28	69
70	3.89	3.85	3.82	3.79	3.76	3.73	3.70	3.67	3.64	3.61	3.59	3.56	3.54	3.51	3.49	3.46	70
74	4.93	4.89	4.85	4.81	4.77	4.73	4.69	4.66	4.62	4.59	4.55	4.52	4.49	4.46	4.43	4.40	74
75	5.28	5.23	5.19	5.15	5.10	5.06	5.02	4.98	4.95	4.91	4.87	4.84	4.80	4.77	4.74	4.70	75
DEC.	135° 225	134½ 225½	134° 226	133½ 226½	133° 227	132½ 227½	132° 228	131½ 228½	131° 229	130½ 229½	130° 230	129½ 230½	129° 231	128½ 231½	128° 232	127½ 232½	DEC.

Table 29 (H.L.) **3 hrs.**

B

Lat. and Dec. SAME name, sign −

Lat. and Dec. CONTRARY names, sign +

HOUR ANGLE or DIFF. LONG.

DEC.	00m	02m	04m	06m	08m	10m	12m	14m	16m	18m	20m	22m	24m	26m	28m	30m	DEC.
	45° 315	45½° 314½	46° 314	46½° 313½	47° 313	47½° 312½	48° 312	48½° 311½	49° 311	49½° 310½	50° 310	50½° 309½	51° 309	51½° 308½	52° 308	52½° 307½	
0°	.000	.000	.000	.000	.000	.000	.000	.000	.000	.000	.000	.000	.000	.000	.000	.000	0°
1	.025	.024	.024	.024	.024	.024	.023	.023	.023	.023	.023	.023	.023	.022	.022	.022	1
2	.049	.049	.049	.048	.048	.047	.047	.047	.046	.046	.046	.045	.045	.045	.044	.044	2
3	.074	.073	.073	.072	.072	.071	.071	.070	.069	.069	.068	.068	.067	.067	.067	.066	3
4	.099	.098	.097	.096	.096	.095	.094	.093	.093	.092	.091	.091	.090	.089	.089	.088	4
5	.124	.123	.122	.121	.120	.119	.118	.117	.116	.115	.114	.113	.113	.112	.111	.110	5
6	.149	.147	.146	.145	.144	.143	.141	.140	.139	.138	.137	.136	.135	.134	.133	.132	6
7	.174	.172	.171	.169	.168	.167	.165	.164	.163	.161	.160	.159	.158	.157	.156	.155	7
8	.199	.197	.195	.194	.192	.191	.189	.188	.186	.185	.183	.182	.181	.180	.178	.177	8
9	.224	.222	.220	.218	.217	.215	.213	.211	.210	.208	.207	.205	.204	.202	.201	.200	9
10	.249	.247	.245	.243	.241	.239	.237	.235	.234	.232	.230	.229	.227	.225	.224	.222	10
11	.275	.273	.270	.268	.266	.264	.262	.260	.258	.256	.254	.252	.250	.248	.247	.245	11
12	.301	.298	.295	.293	.291	.288	.286	.284	.282	.280	.277	.275	.274	.272	.270	.268	12
13	.326	.324	.321	.318	.316	.313	.311	.308	.306	.304	.301	.299	.297	.295	.293	.291	13
14	.353	.350	.347	.344	.341	.338	.336	.333	.330	.328	.325	.323	.321	.319	.316	.314	14
15	.379	.376	.372	.369	.366	.363	.361	.358	.355	.352	.350	.347	.345	.342	.340	.338	15
16	.406	.402	.399	.395	.392	.389	.386	.383	.380	.377	.374	.372	.369	.366	.364	.361	16
17	.432	.429	.425	.421	.418	.415	.411	.408	.405	.402	.399	.396	.393	.391	.388	.385	17
18	.460	.456	.452	.448	.444	.441	.437	.434	.431	.427	.424	.421	.418	.415	.412	.410	18
19	.487	.483	.479	.475	.471	.467	.463	.460	.456	.453	.449	.446	.443	.440	.437	.434	19
20	.515	.510	.506	.502	.498	.494	.490	.486	.482	.479	.475	.472	.468	.465	.462	.459	20
21	.543	.538	.534	.529	.525	.521	.517	.513	.509	.505	.501	.497	.494	.490	.487	.484	21
22	.571	.566	.562	.557	.552	.548	.544	.539	.535	.531	.527	.524	.520	.516	.513	.509	22
23	.600	.595	.590	.585	.580	.576	.571	.567	.562	.558	.554	.550	.546	.542	.539	.535	23
24	.630	.624	.619	.614	.609	.604	.599	.594	.590	.586	.581	.577	.573	.569	.565	.561	24
25	.659	.654	.648	.643	.638	.632	.627	.623	.618	.613	.609	.604	.600	.596	.592	.588	25
26	.690	.684	.678	.672	.667	.662	.656	.651	.646	.641	.637	.632	.628	.623	.619	.615	26
27	.721	.714	.708	.702	.697	.691	.686	.680	.675	.670	.665	.660	.656	.651	.647	.642	27
28	.752	.745	.739	.733	.727	.721	.715	.710	.705	.699	.694	.689	.684	.679	.675	.670	28
29	.784	.777	.771	.764	.758	.752	.746	.740	.734	.729	.724	.718	.713	.708	.703	.699	29
30	.816	.809	.803	.796	.789	.783	.777	.771	.765	.759	.754	.748	.743	.738	.733	.728	30
31	.850	.842	.835	.828	.822	.815	.809	.802	.796	.790	.784	.779	.773	.768	.763	.757	31
32	.884	.876	.869	.861	.851	.848	.841	.834	.828	.822	.816	.810	.804	.798	.793	.788	32
33	.918	.910	.903	.895	.888	.881	.874	.867	.860	.854	.848	.842	.836	.830	.824	.819	33
34	.954	.946	.938	.930	.922	.915	.908	.901	.894	.887	.881	.874	.868	.862	.856	.850	34
35	.990	.982	.973	.965	.957	.950	.942	.935	.928	.921	.914	.907	.901	.895	.889	.883	35
36	1.03	1.02	1.01	1.00	.993	.985	.978	.970	.963	.955	.948	.942	.935	.928	.922	.916	36
37	1.07	1.06	1.05	1.04	1.03	1.02	1.01	1.01	.998	.991	.984	.977	.970	.963	.956	.950	37
38	1.11	1.10	1.09	1.08	1.07	1.06	1.05	1.04	1.04	1.03	1.02	1.01	1.01	.998	.991	.985	38
39	1.15	1.14	1.13	1.12	1.11	1.10	1.09	1.08	1.07	1.07	1.06	1.05	1.04	1.04	1.03	1.02	39
40	1.19	1.18	1.17	1.16	1.15	1.14	1.13	1.12	1.11	1.10	1.10	1.09	1.08	1.07	1.06	1.06	40
41	1.23	1.22	1.21	1.20	1.19	1.18	1.17	1.16	1.15	1.14	1.13	1.13	1.12	1.11	1.10	1.10	41
42	1.27	1.26	1.25	1.24	1.23	1.22	1.21	1.20	1.19	1.18	1.18	1.17	1.16	1.15	1.14	1.14	42
43	1.32	1.31	1.30	1.29	1.28	1.27	1.26	1.25	1.24	1.23	1.22	1.21	1.20	1.19	1.18	1.18	43
44	1.37	1.35	1.34	1.33	1.32	1.31	1.30	1.29	1.28	1.27	1.26	1.25	1.24	1.23	1.23	1.22	44
45	1.41	1.40	1.39	1.38	1.37	1.36	1.35	1.34	1.33	1.32	1.31	1.30	1.29	1.28	1.27	1.26	45
46	1.46	1.45	1.44	1.43	1.42	1.41	1.39	1.38	1.37	1.36	1.35	1.34	1.33	1.32	1.31	1.31	46
47	1.52	1.50	1.49	1.48	1.47	1.45	1.44	1.43	1.42	1.41	1.40	1.39	1.38	1.37	1.36	1.35	47
48	1.57	1.56	1.54	1.53	1.52	1.51	1.49	1.48	1.47	1.46	1.45	1.44	1.43	1.42	1.41	1.40	48
49	1.63	1.61	1.60	1.59	1.57	1.56	1.55	1.54	1.52	1.51	1.50	1.49	1.48	1.47	1.46	1.45	49
50	1.69	1.67	1.66	1.64	1.63	1.62	1.60	1.59	1.58	1.57	1.56	1.54	1.53	1.52	1.51	1.50	50
51	1.75	1.73	1.72	1.70	1.69	1.68	1.66	1.65	1.64	1.62	1.61	1.60	1.59	1.58	1.57	1.56	51
52	1.81	1.80	1.78	1.77	1.75	1.74	1.72	1.71	1.70	1.68	1.67	1.66	1.65	1.64	1.62	1.61	52
53	1.88	1.86	1.84	1.83	1.81	1.80	1.79	1.77	1.76	1.75	1.73	1.72	1.71	1.70	1.68	1.67	53
54	1.95	1.93	1.91	1.90	1.88	1.87	1.85	1.84	1.82	1.81	1.80	1.78	1.77	1.76	1.75	1.74	54
55	2.02	2.00	1.99	1.97	1.95	1.94	1.92	1.91	1.89	1.88	1.86	1.85	1.84	1.83	1.81	1.80	55
56	2.10	2.08	2.06	2.04	2.03	2.01	2.00	1.98	1.96	1.95	1.94	1.92	1.91	1.89	1.88	1.87	56
57	2.18	2.16	2.14	2.12	2.11	2.09	2.07	2.06	2.04	2.03	2.01	2.00	1.98	1.97	1.95	1.94	57
58	2.26	2.24	2.22	2.21	2.19	2.17	2.15	2.14	2.12	2.11	2.09	2.07	2.06	2.05	2.03	2.02	58
59	2.35	2.33	2.31	2.29	2.28	2.26	2.24	2.22	2.21	2.19	2.17	2.16	2.14	2.13	2.11	2.10	59
60	2.45	2.43	2.41	2.39	2.37	2.35	2.33	2.31	2.29	2.28	2.26	2.25	2.23	2.21	2.20	2.18	60
61	2.55	2.53	2.51	2.49	2.47	2.45	2.43	2.41	2.39	2.37	2.36	2.34	2.32	2.31	2.29	2.27	61
62	2.66	2.64	2.62	2.59	2.57	2.55	2.53	2.51	2.49	2.47	2.46	2.44	2.42	2.40	2.39	2.37	62
63	2.78	2.75	2.73	2.71	2.68	2.66	2.64	2.62	2.60	2.58	2.56	2.54	2.53	2.51	2.49	2.47	63
DEC.	135° 225	134½ 225½	134° 226	133½ 226½	133° 227	132½ 227½	132° 228	131½ 228½	131° 229	130½ 229½	130° 230	129½ 230½	129° 231	128½ 231½	128° 232	127½ 232½	DEC.

Table 29 (H.L.) — A

3 hrs.

If entered with H.A. at **top**, Sign **+**
„ „ „ „ **foot**, „ **−**

HOUR ANGLE or DIFF. LONG.

LAT.	30m	32m	34m	36m	38m	40m	42m	44m	46m	48m	50m	52m	54m	56m	58m	60m	LAT.
	52½° 307½	53° 307	53½° 306½	54° 306	54½° 305½	55° 305	55½° 304½	56° 304	56½° 303½	57° 303	57½° 302½	58° 302	58½° 301½	59° 301	59½° 300½	60° 300	
60°	1.33	1.31	1.28	1.26	1.24	1.21	1.19	1.17	1.15	1.13	1.10	1.08	1.06	1.04	1.02	1.00	60°
61	1.38	1.36	1.34	1.31	1.29	1.26	1.24	1.22	1.19	1.17	1.15	1.13	1.11	1.08	1.06	1.04	61
62	1.44	1.42	1.39	1.37	1.34	1.32	1.29	1.27	1.25	1.22	1.20	1.18	1.15	1.13	1.11	1.09	62
63	1.51	1.48	1.45	1.43	1.40	1.37	1.35	1.32	1.30	1.28	1.25	1.23	1.20	1.18	1.16	1.13	63
64	1.57	1.55	1.52	1.49	1.46	1.44	1.41	1.38	1.36	1.33	1.31	1.28	1.26	1.23	1.21	1.18	64
65	1.65	1.62	1.59	1.56	1.53	1.50	1.47	1.45	1.42	1.39	1.37	1.34	1.31	1.29	1.26	1.24	65
66	1.72	1.69	1.66	1.63	1.60	1.57	1.54	1.51	1.49	1.46	1.43	1.40	1.38	1.35	1.32	1.30	66
67	1.81	1.78	1.74	1.71	1.68	1.65	1.62	1.59	1.56	1.53	1.50	1.47	1.44	1.42	1.39	1.36	67
68	1.90	1.87	1.83	1.80	1.77	1.73	1.70	1.67	1.64	1.61	1.58	1.55	1.52	1.49	1.46	1.43	68
69	2.00	1.96	1.93	1.89	1.86	1.82	1.79	1.76	1.72	1.69	1.66	1.63	1.60	1.57	1.53	1.50	69
70	2.11	2.07	2.03	2.00	1.96	1.92	1.89	1.85	1.82	1.78	1.75	1.72	1.68	1.65	1.62	1.59	70
71	2.23	2.19	2.15	2.11	2.07	2.03	2.00	1.96	1.92	1.89	1.85	1.81	1.78	1.75	1.71	1.68	71
72	2.36	2.32	2.28	2.24	2.20	2.15	2.12	2.08	2.04	2.00	1.96	1.92	1.89	1.85	1.81	1.78	72
73	2.51	2.46	2.42	2.38	2.33	2.29	2.25	2.21	2.16	2.12	2.08	2.04	2.00	1.97	1.93	1.89	73
74	2.68	2.63	2.58	2.53	2.49	2.44	2.40	2.35	2.31	2.26	2.22	2.18	2.14	2.10	2.05	2.01	74
75	2.86	2.81	2.76	2.71	2.66	2.61	2.56	2.52	2.47	2.42	2.38	2.33	2.29	2.24	2.20	2.15	75
76	3.08	3.02	2.97	2.91	2.86	2.81	2.76	2.71	2.65	2.60	2.56	2.51	2.46	2.41	2.36	2.32	76
77	3.32	3.26	3.21	3.15	3.09	3.03	2.98	2.92	2.87	2.81	2.76	2.71	2.65	2.60	2.55	2.50	77
78	3.61	3.55	3.48	3.42	3.36	3.29	3.23	3.17	3.11	3.06	3.00	2.94	2.88	2.83	2.77	2.72	78
79	3.95	3.88	3.81	3.74	3.67	3.60	3.54	3.47	3.41	3.34	3.28	3.21	3.15	3.09	3.03	2.97	79
80	4.35	4.27	4.20	4.12	4.05	3.97	3.90	3.83	3.75	3.68	3.61	3.54	3.48	3.41	3.34	3.27	80
81	4.84	4.76	4.67	4.59	4.50	4.42	4.34	4.26	4.18	4.10	4.02	3.95	3.87	3.79	3.72	3.65	81
82	5.46	5.36	5.27	5.17	5.08	4.98	4.89	4.80	4.71	4.62	4.53	4.45	4.36	4.28	4.19	4.11	82
LAT.	127½ 232½	127° 233	126½ 233½	126° 234	125½ 234½	125° 235	124½ 235½	124° 236	123½ 236½	123° 237	122½ 237½	122° 238	121½ 238½	121° 239	120½ 239½	120° 240	LAT.

(S.W. Qdt.) 180°—→270°   (S.E. Qdt.) 180°←—90°

Table 29 (H.L.) — B

3 hrs.

Lat. and Dec. SAME name, Sign **−**
Lat. and Dec. CONTRARY names, Sign **+**

HOUR ANGLE or DIFF. LONG.

DEC.	30m	32m	34m	36m	38m	40m	42m	44m	46m	48m	50m	52m	54m	56m	58m	60m	DEC.
	52½° 307½	53° 307	53½° 306½	54° 306	54½° 305½	55° 305	55½° 304½	56° 304	56½° 303½	57° 303	57½° 302½	58° 302	58½° 301½	59° 301	59½° 300½	60° 300	
68°	3.12	3.10	3.08	3.06	3.04	3.02	3.00	2.99	2.97	2.95	2.94	2.92	2.90	2.89	2.87	2.86	68°
69	3.28	3.26	3.24	3.22	3.20	3.18	3.16	3.14	3.12	3.11	3.09	3.07	3.06	3.04	3.02	3.01	69
70	3.46	3.44	3.42	3.40	3.37	3.35	3.33	3.31	3.29	3.28	3.26	3.24	3.22	3.21	3.19	3.17	70
74	4.40	4.37	4.34	4.31	4.28	4.26	4.23	4.21	4.18	4.16	4.14	4.11	4.09	4.07	4.05	4.03	74
75	4.70	4.67	4.64	4.61	4.58	4.56	4.53	4.50	4.48	4.45	4.43	4.40	4.38	4.35	4.33	4.31	75
DEC.	127½ 232½	127° 233	126½ 233½	126° 234	125½ 234½	125° 235	124½ 235½	124° 236	123½ 236½	123° 237	122½ 237½	122° 238	121½ 238½	121° 239	120½ 239½	120° 240	DEC.

(S.W. Qdt.) 180°—→270°   (S.E. Qdt.) 180°←—90°

Table 29 (H.L.) **B**
3 hrs.

Lat. and Dec. SAME name, sign **—**
Lat. and Dec. CONTRARY names, sign **+**

HOUR ANGLE or DIFF. LONG.

DEC.	30m	32m	34m	36m	38m	40m	42m	44m	46m	48m	50m	52m	54m	56m	58m	60m	DEC.
	52½° 307½	53° 307	53½° 306½	54° 306	54½° 305½	55° 305	55½° 304½	56° 304	56½° 303½	57° 303	57½° 302½	58° 302	58½° 301½	59° 301	59½° 300½	60° 300	
0°	.000	.000	.000	.000	.000	.000	.000	.000	.000	.000	.000	.000	.000	.000	.000	.000	0°
1	.022	.022	.022	.022	.021	.021	.021	.021	.021	.021	.021	.021	.020	.020	.020	.020	1
2	.044	.044	.043	.043	.043	.043	.042	.042	.042	.042	.041	.041	.041	.041	.041	.040	2
3	.066	.066	.065	.065	.064	.064	.064	.063	.063	.062	.062	.062	.061	.061	.061	.061	3
4	.088	.088	.087	.086	.086	.085	.085	.084	.084	.083	.083	.083	.082	.082	.081	.081	4
5	.110	.110	.109	.108	.107	.107	.106	.106	.105	.104	.104	.103	.103	.102	.102	.101	5
6	.132	.132	.131	.130	.129	.128	.128	.127	.126	.125	.125	.124	.123	.123	.122	.121	6
7	.155	.154	.153	.152	.151	.150	.149	.148	.147	.146	.146	.145	.144	.143	.143	.142	7
8	.177	.176	.175	.174	.173	.172	.171	.170	.169	.168	.167	.166	.165	.164	.163	.162	8
9	.200	.198	.197	.196	.195	.193	.192	.191	.190	.189	.188	.187	.186	.185	.184	.183	9
10	.222	.221	.219	.218	.217	.215	.214	.213	.211	.210	.209	.208	.207	.206	.205	.204	10
11	.245	.243	.242	.240	.239	.237	.236	.234	.233	.232	.230	.229	.228	.227	.226	.224	11
12	.268	.266	.264	.263	.261	.259	.258	.256	.255	.253	.252	.251	.249	.248	.247	.245	12
13	.291	.289	.287	.285	.284	.282	.280	.278	.277	.275	.274	.272	.271	.269	.268	.267	13
14	.314	.312	.310	.308	.306	.304	.303	.301	.299	.297	.296	.294	.292	.291	.289	.288	14
15	.338	.336	.333	.331	.329	.327	.325	.323	.321	.319	.318	.316	.314	.313	.311	.309	15
16	.361	.359	.357	.354	.352	.350	.348	.346	.344	.342	.340	.338	.336	.335	.333	.331	16
17	.385	.383	.380	.378	.376	.373	.371	.369	.367	.365	.363	.361	.359	.357	.355	.353	17
18	.410	.407	.404	.402	.399	.397	.394	.392	.390	.387	.385	.383	.381	.379	.377	.375	18
19	.434	.431	.428	.426	.423	.420	.418	.415	.413	.411	.408	.406	.404	.402	.400	.398	19
20	.459	.456	.453	.450	.447	.444	.442	.439	.436	.434	.432	.429	.427	.425	.422	.420	20
21	.484	.481	.478	.474	.472	.469	.466	.463	.460	.458	.455	.453	.450	.448	.446	.443	21
22	.509	.506	.503	.499	.496	.493	.490	.487	.485	.482	.479	.476	.474	.471	.469	.467	22
23	.535	.532	.528	.525	.521	.518	.515	.512	.509	.506	.503	.501	.498	.495	.493	.490	23
24	.561	.557	.554	.550	.547	.544	.540	.537	.534	.531	.528	.525	.522	.519	.517	.514	24
25	.588	.584	.580	.576	.573	.569	.566	.562	.559	.556	.553	.550	.547	.544	.541	.538	25
26	.615	.611	.607	.603	.599	.595	.592	.588	.585	.582	.578	.575	.572	.569	.566	.563	26
27	.642	.638	.634	.630	.626	.622	.618	.615	.611	.608	.604	.601	.598	.594	.591	.588	27
28	.670	.666	.661	.657	.653	.649	.645	.641	.638	.634	.630	.627	.624	.620	.617	.614	28
29	.699	.694	.690	.685	.681	.677	.673	.669	.665	.661	.657	.654	.650	.647	.643	.640	29
30	.728	.723	.718	.714	.709	.705	.701	.696	.692	.688	.685	.681	.677	.674	.670	.667	30
31	.757	.752	.747	.743	.738	.734	.729	.725	.721	.716	.712	.709	.705	.701	.697	.694	31
32	.788	.782	.777	.772	.768	.763	.758	.754	.749	.745	.741	.737	.733	.729	.725	.722	32
33	.819	.813	.808	.803	.798	.793	.788	.783	.779	.774	.770	.766	.762	.758	.754	.750	33
34	.850	.845	.839	.834	.829	.823	.818	.814	.809	.804	.800	.795	.791	.787	.783	.779	34
35	.883	.877	.871	.866	.860	.855	.850	.845	.840	.835	.830	.826	.821	.817	.813	.809	35
36	.916	.910	.904	.898	.892	.887	.882	.876	.871	.866	.861	.857	.852	.848	.843	.839	36
37	.950	.944	.937	.931	.926	.920	.914	.909	.904	.899	.893	.889	.884	.879	.875	.870	37
38	.985	.978	.972	.966	.960	.954	.948	.942	.937	.932	.926	.921	.916	.911	.907	.902	38
39	1.02	1.01	1.01	1.00	.995	.989	.983	.977	.971	.966	.960	.955	.950	.945	.940	.935	39
40	1.06	1.05	1.04	1.04	1.03	1.02	1.02	1.01	1.01	1.00	.995	.989	.984	.979	.974	.969	40
41	1.10	1.09	1.08	1.07	1.07	1.06	1.06	1.05	1.04	1.04	1.03	1.03	1.02	1.01	1.01	1.00	41
42	1.14	1.13	1.12	1.11	1.11	1.10	1.09	1.09	1.08	1.07	1.07	1.06	1.06	1.05	1.05	1.04	42
43	1.18	1.17	1.16	1.15	1.15	1.14	1.13	1.12	1.12	1.11	1.11	1.10	1.09	1.09	1.08	1.08	43
44	1.22	1.21	1.20	1.19	1.19	1.18	1.17	1.16	1.16	1.15	1.15	1.14	1.13	1.13	1.12	1.12	44
45	1.26	1.25	1.24	1.24	1.23	1.22	1.21	1.21	1.20	1.19	1.19	1.18	1.17	1.17	1.16	1.15	45
46	1.31	1.30	1.29	1.28	1.27	1.26	1.26	1.25	1.24	1.23	1.23	1.22	1.21	1.21	1.20	1.20	46
47	1.35	1.34	1.33	1.33	1.32	1.31	1.30	1.29	1.29	1.28	1.27	1.26	1.26	1.25	1.25	1.24	47
48	1.40	1.39	1.38	1.37	1.36	1.36	1.35	1.34	1.33	1.32	1.32	1.31	1.30	1.30	1.29	1.28	48
49	1.45	1.44	1.43	1.42	1.41	1.40	1.40	1.39	1.38	1.37	1.36	1.36	1.35	1.34	1.34	1.33	49
50	1.50	1.49	1.48	1.47	1.46	1.46	1.45	1.44	1.43	1.42	1.41	1.41	1.40	1.39	1.38	1.38	50
51	1.56	1.55	1.54	1.53	1.52	1.51	1.50	1.49	1.48	1.47	1.46	1.46	1.45	1.44	1.43	1.43	51
52	1.61	1.60	1.59	1.58	1.57	1.56	1.55	1.54	1.54	1.53	1.52	1.51	1.50	1.49	1.49	1.48	52
53	1.67	1.66	1.65	1.64	1.63	1.62	1.61	1.60	1.59	1.58	1.57	1.56	1.56	1.55	1.54	1.53	53
54	1.74	1.72	1.71	1.70	1.69	1.68	1.67	1.66	1.65	1.64	1.63	1.62	1.61	1.61	1.60	1.59	54
55	1.80	1.79	1.78	1.77	1.75	1.74	1.73	1.72	1.71	1.70	1.69	1.68	1.68	1.67	1.66	1.65	55
56	1.87	1.86	1.84	1.83	1.82	1.81	1.80	1.79	1.78	1.77	1.76	1.75	1.74	1.73	1.72	1.71	56
57	1.94	1.93	1.92	1.90	1.89	1.88	1.87	1.86	1.85	1.84	1.83	1.82	1.81	1.80	1.79	1.78	57
58	2.02	2.00	1.99	1.98	1.97	1.95	1.94	1.93	1.92	1.91	1.90	1.89	1.88	1.87	1.86	1.85	58
59	2.10	2.08	2.07	2.06	2.04	2.03	2.02	2.01	2.00	1.98	1.97	1.96	1.95	1.94	1.93	1.92	59
60	2.18	2.17	2.16	2.14	2.13	2.11	2.10	2.09	2.08	2.07	2.05	2.04	2.03	2.02	2.01	2.00	60
61	2.27	2.26	2.24	2.23	2.22	2.20	2.19	2.18	2.16	2.15	2.14	2.13	2.12	2.10	2.09	2.08	61
62	2.37	2.35	2.34	2.32	2.31	2.30	2.28	2.27	2.26	2.24	2.23	2.22	2.21	2.19	2.18	2.17	62
63	2.47	2.46	2.44	2.43	2.41	2.40	2.38	2.37	2.35	2.34	2.33	2.31	2.30	2.29	2.28	2.27	63
DEC.	127½ 232½	127° 233	126½ 233½	126° 234	125½ 234½	125° 235	124½ 235½	124° 236	123½ 236½	123° 237	122½ 237½	122° 238	121½ 238½	121° 239	120½ 239½	120° 240	DEC.

Table 29 (H.L.)　　A

4 hrs.

If entered with H.A. at **top**, Sign **+**
„　„　„　„ **foot**, „　**−**

HOUR ANGLE or DIFF. LONG.

LAT.	00m 60° 300	04m 61° 299	08m 62° 298	12m 63° 297	16m 64° 296	20m 65° 295	24m 66° 294	28m 67° 293	32m 68° 292	36m 69° 291	40m 70° 290	44m 71° 289	48m 72° 288	52m 73° 287	56m 74° 286	60m 75° 285	LAT.
60°	1.00	.960	.921	.883	.845	.808	.771	.735	.700	.665	.630	.596	.563	.530	.497	.464	60°
61	1.04	1.00	.959	.919	.880	.841	.803	.766	.729	.693	.657	.621	.586	.552	.517	.483	61
62	1.09	1.04	1.00	.958	.917	.877	.837	.798	.760	.722	.685	.648	.611	.575	.539	.504	62
63	1.13	1.09	1.04	1.00	.957	.915	.874	.833	.793	.753	.714	.676	.638	.600	.563	.526	63
64	1.18	1.14	1.09	1.05	1.00	.956	.913	.870	.828	.787	.746	.706	.666	.627	.588	.549	64
65	1.24	1.19	1.14	1.09	1.05	1.00	.955	.910	.866	.823	.781	.738	.697	.656	.615	.575	65
66	1.30	1.25	1.19	1.14	1.10	1.05	1.00	.953	.907	.862	.817	.773	.730	.687	.644	.602	66
67	1.36	1.31	1.25	1.20	1.15	1.10	1.05	1.00	.952	.904	.857	.811	.766	.720	.676	.631	67
68	1.43	1.37	1.32	1.26	1.21	1.15	1.09	1.05	1.00	.950	.901	.852	.804	.757	.710	.663	68
69	1.50	1.44	1.39	1.33	1.27	1.21	1.16	1.11	1.05	1.00	.948	.897	.846	.796	.747	.698	69
70	1.59	1.52	1.46	1.40	1.34	1.28	1.22	1.17	1.11	1.05	1.00	.946	.893	.840	.788	.736	70
71	1.68	1.61	1.54	1.48	1.42	1.35	1.29	1.23	1.17	1.11	1.06	1.00	.944	.888	.833	.778	71
72	1.78	1.71	1.64	1.57	1.50	1.44	1.37	1.31	1.24	1.18	1.12	1.06	1.00	.941	.883	.825	72
73	1.89	1.81	1.74	1.67	1.60	1.53	1.46	1.39	1.32	1.26	1.19	1.13	1.06	1.00	.938	.876	73
74	2.01	1.93	1.85	1.78	1.70	1.63	1.55	1.48	1.41	1.34	1.27	1.20	1.13	1.07	1.00	.934	74
75	2.15	2.07	1.98	1.90	1.82	1.74	1.66	1.58	1.51	1.43	1.36	1.29	1.21	1.14	1.07	1.00	75
76	2.32	2.22	2.13	2.04	1.96	1.87	1.79	1.70	1.62	1.54	1.46	1.38	1.30	1.23	1.15	1.07	76
77	2.50	2.40	2.30	2.21	2.11	2.02	1.93	1.85	1.75	1.66	1.58	1.49	1.41	1.32	1.24	1.16	77
78	2.72	2.61	2.50	2.40	2.29	2.19	2.09	2.00	1.90	1.81	1.71	1.62	1.53	1.44	1.35	1.26	78
79	2.97	2.85	2.74	2.62	2.51	2.40	2.29	2.18	2.08	1.97	1.87	1.77	1.67	1.57	1.48	1.38	79
80	3.27	3.14	3.02	2.89	2.77	2.64	2.53	2.41	2.29	2.18	2.06	1.95	1.84	1.73	1.63	1.52	80
81	3.65	3.50	3.36	3.22	3.08	2.94	2.81	2.68	2.55	2.42	2.30	2.17	2.05	1.93	1.81	1.69	81
82	4.11	3.94	3.78	3.63	3.47	3.32	3.17	3.02	2.87	2.73	2.59	2.45	2.31	2.18	2.04	1.91	82
LAT.	120° 240	119° 241	118° 242	117° 243	116° 244	115° 245	114° 246	113° 247	112° 248	111° 249	110° 250	109° 251	108° 252	107° 253	106° 254	105° 255	LAT.

Table 29 (H.L.)　　B

4 hrs.

Lat. and Dec. SAME name, Sign **−**
Lat. and Dec. CONTRARY names, Sign **+**

HOUR ANGLE or DIFF. LONG.

DEC.	00m 60° 300	04m 61° 299	08m 62° 298	12m 63° 297	16m 64° 296	20m 65° 295	24m 66° 294	28m 67° 293	32m 68° 292	36m 69° 291	40m 70° 290	44m 71° 289	48m 72° 288	52m 73° 287	56m 74° 286	60m 75° 285	DEC.
68°	2.86	2.83	2.80	2.78	2.75	2.73	2.71	2.69	2.67	2.65	2.63	2.62	2.60	2.59	2.58	2.56	68°
69	3.01	2.98	2.95	2.92	2.90	2.87	2.85	2.83	2.81	2.79	2.77	2.76	2.74	2.72	2.71	2.70	69
70	3.17	3.14	3.11	3.08	3.06	3.03	3.01	2.99	2.96	2.94	2.92	2.91	2.89	2.87	2.86	2.84	70
74	4.03	3.99	3.95	3.91	3.88	3.85	3.82	3.79	3.76	3.74	3.71	3.69	3.67	3.65	3.63	3.61	74
75	4.31	4.27	4.23	4.19	4.15	4.12	4.09	4.05	4.03	4.00	3.97	3.95	3.92	3.90	3.88	3.86	75
DEC.	120° 240	119° 241	118° 242	117° 243	116° 244	115° 245	114° 246	113° 247	112° 248	111° 249	110° 250	109° 251	108° 252	107° 253	106° 254	105° 255	DEC.

Table 29 (H.L.) **B** Lat. and Dec. SAME name, Sign —
4 hrs. Lat. and Dec. CONTRARY names, Sign +

HOUR ANGLE or DIFF. LONG.

DEC.	00m	04m	08m	12m	16m	20m	24m	28m	32m	36m	40m	44m	48m	52m	56m	60m	DEC.
	60° 300	61° 299	62° 298	63° 297	64° 296	65° 295	66° 294	67° 293	68° 292	69° 291	70° 290	71° 289	72° 288	73° 287	74° 286	75° 285	
0°	.000	.000	.000	.000	.000	.000	.000	.000	.000	.000	.000	.000	.000	.000	.000	.000	0°
1	.020	.020	.020	.020	.019	.019	.019	.019	.019	.019	.019	.018	.018	.018	.018	.018	1
2	.040	.040	.040	.039	.039	.039	.038	.038	.038	.037	.037	.037	.037	.037	.036	.036	2
3	.061	.060	.059	.059	.058	.058	.057	.057	.057	.056	.056	.055	.055	.055	.055	.054	3
4	.081	.080	.079	.078	.078	.077	.077	.076	.075	.075	.074	.074	.074	.073	.073	.072	4
5	.101	.100	.099	.098	.097	.097	.096	.095	.094	.094	.093	.093	.092	.091	.091	.091	5
6	.121	.120	.119	.118	.117	.116	.115	.114	.113	.113	.112	.111	.111	.110	.109	.109	6
7	.142	.140	.139	.138	.137	.135	.134	.133	.132	.132	.131	.130	.129	.128	.128	.127	7
8	.162	.161	.159	.158	.156	.155	.154	.153	.152	.151	.150	.149	.148	.147	.146	.145	8
9	.183	.181	.179	.178	.176	.175	.173	.172	.171	.170	.169	.168	.167	.166	.165	.164	9
10	.204	.202	.200	.198	.196	.195	.193	.192	.190	.189	.188	.186	.185	.184	.183	.183	10
11	.224	.222	.220	.218	.216	.214	.213	.211	.210	.208	.207	.206	.204	.203	.202	.201	11
12	.245	.243	.241	.239	.236	.235	.233	.231	.229	.228	.226	.225	.223	.222	.221	.220	12
13	.267	.264	.261	.259	.257	.255	.253	.251	.249	.247	.246	.244	.243	.241	.240	.239	13
14	.288	.285	.282	.280	.277	.275	.273	.271	.269	.267	.265	.264	.262	.261	.259	.258	14
15	.309	.306	.303	.301	.298	.296	.293	.291	.289	.287	.285	.283	.282	.280	.279	.277	15
16	.331	.328	.325	.322	.319	.316	.314	.312	.309	.307	.305	.303	.302	.300	.298	.297	16
17	.353	.350	.346	.343	.340	.337	.335	.332	.330	.327	.325	.323	.321	.320	.318	.317	17
18	.375	.371	.368	.365	.362	.359	.356	.353	.350	.348	.346	.344	.342	.340	.338	.336	18
19	.398	.394	.390	.386	.383	.380	.377	.374	.371	.369	.366	.364	.362	.360	.358	.356	19
20	.420	.416	.412	.408	.405	.402	.398	.395	.393	.390	.387	.385	.383	.381	.379	.377	20
21	.443	.439	.435	.431	.427	.424	.420	.417	.414	.411	.408	.406	.404	.401	.399	.397	21
22	.467	.462	.458	.453	.450	.446	.442	.439	.436	.433	.430	.427	.425	.422	.420	.418	22
23	.490	.485	.481	.476	.472	.468	.465	.461	.458	.455	.452	.449	.446	.444	.442	.439	23
24	.514	.509	.504	.500	.495	.491	.487	.484	.480	.477	.474	.471	.468	.466	.463	.461	24
25	.538	.533	.528	.523	.519	.515	.510	.507	.503	.499	.496	.493	.490	.488	.485	.483	25
26	.563	.558	.552	.547	.543	.538	.534	.530	.526	.522	.519	.516	.513	.510	.507	.505	26
27	.588	.583	.577	.572	.567	.562	.558	.554	.550	.546	.542	.539	.536	.533	.530	.527	27
28	.614	.608	.602	.597	.592	.587	.582	.578	.573	.570	.566	.562	.559	.556	.553	.550	28
29	.640	.634	.628	.622	.617	.612	.607	.602	.598	.594	.590	.586	.583	.580	.577	.574	29
30	.667	.660	.654	.648	.642	.637	.632	.627	.623	.618	.614	.611	.607	.604	.601	.598	30
31	.694	.687	.681	.674	.669	.663	.658	.653	.648	.644	.639	.635	.632	.628	.625	.622	31
32	.722	.714	.708	.701	.695	.689	.684	.679	.674	.669	.665	.661	.657	.653	.650	.647	32
33	.750	.743	.735	.729	.723	.717	.711	.705	.700	.696	.691	.687	.683	.679	.676	.672	33
34	.779	.771	.764	.757	.750	.744	.738	.733	.727	.722	.718	.713	.709	.705	.702	.698	34
35	.809	.801	.793	.786	.779	.773	.766	.761	.755	.750	.745	.741	.736	.732	.728	.725	35
36	.839	.831	.823	.815	.808	.802	.795	.789	.784	.778	.773	.768	.764	.760	.756	.752	36
37	.870	.862	.853	.846	.838	.831	.825	.819	.813	.807	.802	.797	.792	.788	.784	.780	37
38	.902	.893	.885	.877	.869	.862	.855	.849	.843	.837	.831	.826	.821	.817	.813	.809	38
39	.935	.926	.917	.909	.901	.893	.886	.880	.873	.867	.862	.856	.851	.847	.842	.838	39
40	.969	.959	.950	.942	.934	.926	.919	.912	.905	.899	.893	.887	.882	.877	.873	.869	40
41	1.00	.994	.985	.976	.967	.959	.952	.944	.938	.931	.925	.919	.914	.909	.904	.900	41
42	1.04	1.03	1.02	1.01	1.00	.993	.986	.978	.971	.964	.958	.952	.947	.942	.937	.932	42
43	1.08	1.07	1.06	1.05	1.04	1.03	1.02	1.01	1.01	.999	.992	.986	.981	.975	.970	.965	43
44	1.12	1.10	1.09	1.08	1.07	1.06	1.05	1.05	1.04	1.03	1.03	1.02	1.02	1.01	1.00	1.00	44
45	1.15	1.14	1.13	1.12	1.11	1.10	1.09	1.09	1.08	1.07	1.06	1.06	1.05	1.05	1.04	1.04	45
46	1.20	1.18	1.17	1.16	1.15	1.14	1.13	1.12	1.12	1.11	1.10	1.10	1.09	1.08	1.08	1.07	46
47	1.24	1.23	1.21	1.20	1.19	1.18	1.17	1.16	1.16	1.15	1.14	1.13	1.13	1.12	1.12	1.11	47
48	1.28	1.27	1.26	1.25	1.24	1.23	1.22	1.21	1.20	1.19	1.18	1.17	1.17	1.16	1.16	1.15	48
49	1.33	1.32	1.30	1.29	1.28	1.27	1.26	1.25	1.24	1.23	1.22	1.22	1.21	1.20	1.20	1.19	49
50	1.38	1.36	1.35	1.34	1.33	1.31	1.30	1.29	1.29	1.28	1.27	1.26	1.25	1.25	1.24	1.23	50
51	1.43	1.41	1.40	1.39	1.37	1.36	1.35	1.34	1.33	1.32	1.31	1.31	1.30	1.29	1.28	1.28	51
52	1.48	1.46	1.45	1.44	1.42	1.41	1.40	1.39	1.38	1.37	1.36	1.35	1.35	1.34	1.33	1.33	52
53	1.53	1.52	1.50	1.49	1.48	1.46	1.45	1.44	1.43	1.42	1.41	1.40	1.40	1.39	1.38	1.37	53
54	1.59	1.57	1.56	1.54	1.53	1.52	1.51	1.50	1.48	1.47	1.46	1.46	1.45	1.44	1.43	1.42	54
55	1.65	1.63	1.62	1.60	1.59	1.58	1.56	1.55	1.54	1.53	1.52	1.51	1.50	1.49	1.49	1.48	55
56	1.71	1.70	1.68	1.66	1.65	1.64	1.62	1.61	1.60	1.59	1.58	1.57	1.56	1.55	1.54	1.53	56
57	1.78	1.76	1.74	1.73	1.71	1.70	1.69	1.67	1.66	1.65	1.64	1.63	1.62	1.61	1.60	1.59	57
58	1.85	1.83	1.81	1.80	1.78	1.77	1.75	1.74	1.73	1.71	1.70	1.69	1.68	1.67	1.66	1.66	58
59	1.92	1.90	1.88	1.87	1.85	1.84	1.82	1.81	1.79	1.78	1.77	1.76	1.75	1.74	1.73	1.72	59
60	2.00	1.98	1.96	1.94	1.93	1.91	1.90	1.88	1.87	1.86	1.84	1.83	1.82	1.81	1.80	1.79	60
61	2.08	2.06	2.04	2.02	2.01	1.99	1.97	1.96	1.95	1.93	1.92	1.91	1.90	1.89	1.88	1.87	61
62	2.17	2.15	2.13	2.11	2.09	2.08	2.06	2.04	2.03	2.01	2.00	1.99	1.98	1.97	1.96	1.95	62
63	2.27	2.24	2.22	2.20	2.18	2.17	2.15	2.13	2.12	2.10	2.09	2.08	2.06	2.05	2.04	2.03	63
DEC.	120° 240	119° 241	118° 242	117° 243	116° 244	115° 245	114° 246	113° 247	112° 248	111° 249	110° 250	109° 251	108° 252	107° 253	106° 254	105° 255	DEC.

Table 29 (H.L.)

A

5 hrs.

If entered with H.A. at **top**, Sign **+**
,,   ,,   ,,   ,,   **foot**, ,,   **—**

HOUR ANGLE or DIFF. LONG.

LAT.	00m	04m	08m	12m	16m	20m	24m	28m	32m	36m	40m	44m	48m	52m	56m	60m	LAT.
	75° 285	76° 284	77° 283	78° 282	79° 281	80° 280	81° 279	82° 278	83° 277	84° 276	85° 275	86° 274	87° 273	88° 272	89° 271	90° 270	
60°	.464	.432	.400	.368	.337	.305	.274	.243	.213	.182	.152	.121	.091	.060	.030	.000	60°
61	.483	.450	.416	.383	.351	.318	.286	.254	.222	.190	.158	.126	.095	.063	.031	.000	61
62	.504	.469	.434	.400	.366	.332	.298	.264	.231	.198	.165	.132	.099	.066	.033	.000	62
63	.526	.489	.453	.417	.381	.346	.311	.276	.241	.206	.172	.137	.103	.069	.034	.000	63
64	.549	.511	.473	.436	.399	.362	.325	.288	.252	.215	.179	.143	.107	.072	.036	.000	64
65	.575	.535	.495	.456	.417	.378	.340	.301	.263	.225	.188	.150	.112	.075	.037	.000	65
66	.602	.560	.519	.477	.437	.396	.356	.316	.276	.236	.197	.157	.118	.078	.039	.000	66
67	.631	.587	.544	.501	.458	.415	.373	.331	.289	.248	.206	.165	.123	.082	.041	.000	67
68	.663	.617	.571	.526	.481	.436	.392	.348	.304	.260	.217	.173	.130	.086	.043	.000	68
69	.698	.650	.601	.554	.506	.459	.413	.366	.320	.274	.228	.182	.137	.090	.045	.000	69
70	.736	.685	.634	.584	.534	.484	.435	.386	.337	.289	.240	.192	.144	.096	.048	.000	70
71	.778	.724	.670	.617	.565	.512	.460	.408	.357	.305	.254	.203	.152	.101	.051	.000	71
72	.825	.767	.711	.654	.598	.543	.487	.433	.378	.323	.269	.215	.161	.107	.054	.000	72
73	.876	.816	.755	.695	.636	.577	.518	.460	.402	.344	.286	.229	.171	.114	.057	.000	73
74	.934	.870	.805	.741	.678	.615	.552	.490	.428	.367	.305	.244	.183	.122	.061	.000	74
75	1.00	.931	.862	.793	.725	.658	.591	.525	.458	.392	.327	.261	.196	.130	.065	.000	75
76	1.07	1.00	.926	.853	.780	.707	.635	.564	.492	.422	.351	.280	.210	.140	.070	.000	76
77	1.16	1.08	1.00	.921	.842	.764	.686	.609	.532	.455	.379	.303	.227	.151	.076	.000	77
78	1.26	1.17	1.09	1.00	.914	.830	.745	.661	.578	.494	.412	.329	.247	.164	.082	.000	78
79	1.38	1.28	1.19	1.09	1.00	.907	.815	.723	.632	.541	.450	.360	.270	.180	.090	.000	79
80	1.52	1.41	1.31	1.21	1.10	1.00	.898	.797	.696	.596	.496	.397	.297	.198	.099	.000	80
81	1.69	1.57	1.46	1.34	1.23	1.11	1.00	.887	.775	.664	.552	.442	.331	.220	.110	.000	81
82	1.91	1.77	1.64	1.51	1.38	1.25	1.13	1.00	.874	.748	.623	.498	.373	.248	.124	.000	82
LAT.	105° 255	104° 256	103° 257	102° 258	101° 259	100° 260	99° 261	98° 262	97° 263	96° 264	95° 265	94° 266	93° 267	92° 268	91° 269	90° 270	LAT.

(S.W. Qdt.) **180°——→270°**   (S.E. Qdt.) **180°←——90°**

Table 29 (H.L.)

5 hrs.

B

Lat. and Dec. SAME name, Sign —
Lat. and Dec. CONTRARY names, Sign +

HOUR ANGLE or DIFF. LONG.

DEC.	00m	04m	08m	12m	16m	20m	24m	28m	32m	36m	40m	44m	48m	52m	56m	60m	DEC.
	75° 285	76° 284	77° 283	78° 282	79° 281	80° 280	81° 279	82° 278	83° 277	84° 276	85° 275	86° 274	87° 273	88° 272	89° 271	90° 270	
68°	2.56	2.55	2.54	2.53	2.52	2.51	2.51	2.50	2.49	2.49	2.49	2.48	2.48	2.48	2.48	2.48	68°
69	2.70	2.69	2.67	2.66	2.65	2.65	2.64	2.63	2.62	2.62	2.62	2.61	2.61	2.61	2.61	2.61	69
70	2.84	2.83	2.82	2.81	2.80	2.79	2.78	2.77	2.77	2.76	2.76	2.75	2.75	2.75	2.75	2.75	70
74	3.61	3.59	3.58	3.57	3.55	3.54	3.53	3.52	3.51	3.51	3.50	3.50	3.49	3.49	3.49	3.49	74
75	3.86	3.85	3.83	3.82	3.80	3.79	3.78	3.77	3.76	3.75	3.75	3.74	3.74	3.73	3.73	3.73	75
DEC.	105° 255	104° 256	103° 257	102° 258	101° 259	100° 260	99° 261	98° 262	97° 263	96° 264	95° 265	94° 266	93° 267	92° 268	91° 269	90° 270	DEC.

(S.W. Qdt.) **180°——→270°**   (S.E. Qdt.) **180°←——90°**

Table 29 (H.L.)   **B**   5 hrs.

Lat. and Dec. SAME name, Sign **—**
Lat. and Dec. CONTRARY names, Sign **+**

HOUR ANGLE or DIFF. LONG.

DEC.	00m	04m	08m	12m	16m	20m	24m	28m	32m	36m	40m	44m	48m	52m	56m	60m	DEC.
	75°/285	76°/284	77°/283	78°/282	79°/281	80°/280	81°/279	82°/278	83°/277	84°/276	85°/275	86°/274	87°/273	88°/272	89°/271	90°/270	
0°	.000	.000	.000	.000	.000	.000	.000	.000	.000	.000	.000	.000	.000	.000	.000	.000	0°
1	.018	.018	.018	.018	.018	.018	.018	.018	.018	.018	.018	.017	.017	.017	.017	.017	1
2	.036	.036	.036	.036	.036	.035	.035	.035	.035	.035	.035	.035	.035	.035	.035	.035	2
3	.054	.054	.054	.054	.053	.053	.053	.053	.053	.053	.053	.053	.052	.052	.052	.052	3
4	.072	.072	.072	.071	.071	.071	.071	.071	.071	.070	.070	.070	.070	.070	.070	.070	4
5	.091	.090	.090	.089	.089	.089	.089	.088	.088	.088	.088	.088	.088	.088	.088	.087	5
6	.109	.108	.108	.107	.107	.107	.106	.106	.106	.106	.106	.105	.105	.105	.105	.105	6
7	.127	.127	.126	.126	.125	.125	.124	.124	.124	.123	.123	.123	.123	.123	.123	.123	7
8	.145	.145	.144	.144	.143	.143	.142	.142	.142	.141	.141	.141	.141	.141	.141	.141	8
9	.164	.163	.163	.162	.161	.161	.160	.160	.160	.159	.159	.159	.159	.158	.158	.158	9
10	.183	.182	.181	.180	.180	.179	.179	.178	.178	.177	.177	.177	.177	.176	.176	.176	10
11	.201	.200	.199	.199	.198	.197	.197	.196	.196	.195	.195	.195	.195	.194	.194	.194	11
12	.220	.219	.218	.217	.217	.216	.215	.215	.214	.214	.213	.213	.213	.213	.213	.213	12
13	.239	.238	.237	.236	.235	.234	.234	.233	.233	.232	.232	.231	.231	.231	.231	.231	13
14	.258	.257	.256	.255	.254	.253	.252	.252	.251	.251	.250	.250	.250	.249	.249	.249	14
15	.277	.276	.275	.274	.273	.272	.271	.271	.270	.269	.269	.269	.268	.268	.268	.268	15
16	.297	.296	.294	.293	.292	.291	.290	.290	.289	.288	.288	.287	.287	.287	.287	.287	16
17	.317	.315	.314	.313	.311	.310	.310	.309	.308	.307	.307	.306	.306	.306	.306	.306	17
18	.336	.335	.333	.332	.331	.330	.329	.328	.327	.327	.326	.326	.325	.325	.325	.325	18
19	.356	.355	.353	.352	.351	.350	.349	.348	.347	.346	.346	.345	.345	.345	.344	.344	19
20	.377	.375	.374	.372	.371	.370	.369	.368	.367	.366	.365	.365	.364	.364	.364	.364	20
21	.397	.396	.394	.392	.391	.390	.389	.388	.387	.386	.385	.385	.384	.384	.384	.384	21
22	.418	.416	.415	.413	.412	.410	.409	.408	.407	.406	.406	.405	.405	.404	.404	.404	22
23	.439	.437	.436	.434	.432	.431	.430	.429	.428	.427	.426	.426	.425	.425	.425	.424	23
24	.461	.459	.457	.455	.454	.452	.451	.450	.449	.448	.447	.446	.446	.446	.445	.445	24
25	.483	.481	.479	.477	.475	.474	.472	.471	.470	.469	.468	.467	.467	.467	.466	.466	25
26	.505	.503	.501	.499	.497	.495	.494	.493	.491	.490	.490	.489	.488	.488	.488	.488	26
27	.527	.525	.523	.521	.519	.517	.516	.515	.513	.512	.511	.511	.510	.510	.510	.510	27
28	.550	.548	.546	.544	.542	.540	.538	.537	.536	.535	.534	.533	.532	.532	.532	.532	28
29	.574	.571	.569	.567	.565	.563	.561	.560	.558	.557	.556	.556	.555	.555	.554	.554	29
30	.598	.595	.593	.590	.588	.586	.585	.583	.582	.581	.580	.579	.578	.578	.577	.577	30
31	.622	.619	.617	.614	.612	.610	.608	.607	.605	.604	.603	.602	.602	.601	.601	.601	31
32	.647	.644	.641	.639	.637	.635	.633	.631	.630	.628	.627	.626	.626	.625	.625	.625	32
33	.672	.669	.666	.664	.662	.659	.658	.656	.654	.653	.652	.651	.650	.650	.650	.649	33
34	.698	.695	.692	.690	.687	.685	.683	.681	.680	.678	.677	.676	.675	.675	.675	.675	34
35	.725	.722	.719	.716	.713	.711	.709	.707	.705	.704	.703	.702	.701	.701	.700	.700	35
36	.752	.749	.746	.743	.740	.738	.736	.734	.732	.731	.729	.728	.728	.727	.727	.727	36
37	.780	.777	.773	.770	.768	.765	.763	.761	.759	.758	.756	.755	.755	.754	.754	.754	37
38	.809	.805	.802	.799	.796	.793	.791	.789	.787	.786	.784	.783	.782	.782	.781	.781	38
39	.838	.835	.831	.828	.825	.822	.820	.818	.816	.814	.813	.812	.811	.810	.810	.810	39
40	.869	.865	.861	.858	.855	.852	.850	.847	.845	.844	.842	.841	.840	.840	.839	.839	40
41	.900	.896	.892	.889	.886	.883	.880	.878	.876	.874	.873	.871	.870	.870	.869	.869	41
42	.932	.928	.924	.921	.917	.914	.912	.909	.907	.905	.904	.903	.902	.901	.901	.900	42
43	.965	.961	.957	.953	.950	.947	.944	.942	.940	.938	.936	.935	.934	.933	.933	.933	43
44	1.00	.995	.991	.987	.984	.981	.978	.975	.973	.971	.969	.968	.967	.966	.966	.966	44
45	1.04	1.03	1.03	1.02	1.02	1.02	1.01	1.01	1.01	1.01	1.00	1.00	1.00	1.00	1.00	1.00	45
46	1.07	1.07	1.06	1.06	1.05	1.05	1.05	1.05	1.04	1.04	1.04	1.04	1.04	1.04	1.04	1.04	46
47	1.11	1.11	1.10	1.10	1.09	1.09	1.09	1.08	1.08	1.08	1.08	1.07	1.07	1.07	1.07	1.07	47
48	1.15	1.14	1.14	1.14	1.13	1.13	1.12	1.12	1.12	1.12	1.11	1.11	1.11	1.11	1.11	1.11	48
49	1.19	1.19	1.18	1.18	1.17	1.17	1.16	1.16	1.16	1.16	1.15	1.15	1.15	1.15	1.15	1.15	49
50	1.23	1.23	1.22	1.22	1.21	1.21	1.21	1.20	1.20	1.20	1.20	1.19	1.19	1.19	1.19	1.19	50
51	1.28	1.27	1.27	1.26	1.26	1.25	1.25	1.25	1.24	1.24	1.24	1.24	1.24	1.24	1.24	1.23	51
52	1.33	1.32	1.31	1.31	1.30	1.30	1.30	1.29	1.29	1.29	1.28	1.28	1.28	1.28	1.28	1.28	52
53	1.37	1.37	1.36	1.36	1.35	1.35	1.34	1.34	1.34	1.33	1.33	1.33	1.33	1.33	1.33	1.33	53
54	1.42	1.42	1.41	1.41	1.40	1.40	1.39	1.39	1.39	1.38	1.38	1.38	1.38	1.38	1.38	1.38	54
55	1.48	1.47	1.47	1.46	1.46	1.45	1.45	1.44	1.44	1.44	1.43	1.43	1.43	1.43	1.43	1.43	55
56	1.53	1.53	1.52	1.52	1.51	1.51	1.50	1.50	1.49	1.49	1.49	1.49	1.48	1.48	1.48	1.48	56
57	1.59	1.59	1.58	1.57	1.57	1.56	1.56	1.55	1.55	1.55	1.55	1.54	1.54	1.54	1.54	1.54	57
58	1.66	1.65	1.64	1.64	1.63	1.63	1.62	1.62	1.61	1.61	1.61	1.60	1.60	1.60	1.60	1.60	58
59	1.72	1.72	1.71	1.70	1.70	1.69	1.69	1.68	1.68	1.67	1.67	1.67	1.67	1.67	1.66	1.66	59
60	1.79	1.79	1.78	1.77	1.76	1.76	1.75	1.75	1.75	1.74	1.74	1.74	1.73	1.73	1.73	1.73	60
61	1.87	1.86	1.85	1.84	1.84	1.83	1.83	1.82	1.82	1.81	1.81	1.81	1.81	1.81	1.80	1.80	61
62	1.95	1.94	1.93	1.92	1.92	1.91	1.90	1.90	1.89	1.89	1.89	1.89	1.88	1.88	1.88	1.88	62
63	2.03	2.02	2.01	2.01	2.00	1.99	1.99	1.98	1.98	1.97	1.97	1.97	1.97	1.96	1.96	1.96	63
DEC.	105°/255	104°/256	103°/257	102°/258	101°/259	100°/260	99°/261	98°/262	97°/263	96°/264	95°/265	94°/266	93°/267	92°/268	91°/269	90°/270	DEC.

Table 30 (H.L.)

C

(Longitude Correction)

			North Lat.		South Lat.	
Body **RISING** (H.A. greater than 180°)	Sign	**−**	Az. in **NE**	Qdt.	**SE**	Qdt.
	„	**+**	„ **SE**	„	**NE**	„
Body **SETTING** (H.A. less than 180°)	Sign	**+**	Az. in **SW**	Qdt.	**NW**	Qdt.
	„	**−**	„ **NW**	„	**SW**	„

AZIMUTH or Course (according to Quadrant)

Qdt.																Qdt.
1st	½°	**1**°	1½°	**2**°	2½°	**3**°	3½°	**4**°	4½°	**5**°	5½°	**6**°	6½°	**7**°	7½	NE
2nd	179½	179	178½	178	177½	177	176½	176	175½	175	174½	174	173½	173	172½	SE
3rd	180½	181	181½	182	182½	183	183½	184	184½	185	185½	186	186½	187	187½	SW
4th	359½	359	358½	358	357½	357	356½	356	355½	355	354½	354	353½	353	352½	NW
LAT.																LAT.
60°	229.	115.	76.4	57.3	45.8	38.2	32.7	28.6	25.4	22.9	20.8	19.0	17.6	16.3	15.2	**60**°
61	236.	118.	78.8	59.1	47.2	39.4	33.7	29.5	26.2	23.6	21.4	19.6	18.1	16.8	15.7	**61**
62	244.	122.	81.3	61.0	48.8	40.6	34.8	30.5	27.1	24.4	22.1	20.3	18.7	17.4	16.2	**62**
63	252.	126.	84.1	63.1	50.5	42.0	36.0	31.5	28.0	25.2	22.9	21.0	19.3	17.9	16.7	**63**
64	261.	131.	87.1	65.3	52.3	43.5	37.3	32.6	29.0	26.1	23.7	21.7	20.0	18.6	17.3	**64**
65	271.	136.	90.4	67.8	54.2	45.2	38.7	33.8	30.1	27.1	24.6	22.5	20.8	19.3	18.0	**65**
66	282.	141.	93.9	70.4	56.3	46.9	40.2	35.2	31.2	28.1	25.5	23.4	21.6	20.0	18.7	**66**
67	293.	147.	97.7	73.3	58.6	48.8	41.8	36.6	32.5	29.2	26.6	24.3	22.5	20.8	19.4	**67**
68	306.	153.	102.	76.4	61.1	50.9	43.6	38.2	33.9	30.5	27.7	25.4	23.4	21.7	20.3	**68**
69	320.	160.	107.	79.9	63.9	53.2	45.6	39.9	35.5	31.9	29.0	26.6	24.5	22.7	21.2	**69**
70	335.	168.	112.	83.7	67.0	55.8	47.8	41.8	37.2	33.4	30.4	27.8	25.7	23.8	22.2	**70**
71	352.	176.	117.	88.0	70.4	58.6	50.2	43.9	39.0	35.1	31.9	29.2	27.0	25.0	23.3	**71**
72	371.	185.	124.	92.7	74.1	61.7	52.9	46.3	41.1	37.0	33.6	30.8	28.4	26.4	24.6	**72**
73	392.	196.	131.	97.9	78.3	65.3	55.9	48.9	43.5	39.1	35.5	32.5	30.0	27.9	26.0	**73**
74	416.	208.	139.	104.	83.1	69.2	59.3	51.9	46.1	41.5	37.7	34.5	31.8	29.6	27.6	**74**
75	443.	221.	148.	111.	88.5	73.7	63.2	55.3	49.1	44.2	40.1	36.8	33.9	31.5	29.3	**75**
76	474.	237.	158.	118.	94.7	78.9	67.6	59.1	52.5	47.2	42.9	39.3	36.3	33.7	31.4	**76**
77	509.	255.	170.	127.	102.	84.8	72.7	63.6	56.5	50.8	46.2	42.3	39.0	36.2	33.8	**77**
78	551.	276.	184.	138.	110.	91.8	78.6	68.8	61.1	55.0	50.0	45.8	42.2	39.2	36.5	**78**
79	601.	300.	200.	150.	120.	100.	85.7	74.9	66.6	59.9	54.4	49.9	46.0	42.7	39.8	**79**
80	660.	330.	220.	165.	132.	110.	94.2	82.4	73.2	65.8	59.8	54.8	50.5	46.9	43.7	**80**
81	733.	366.	244.	183.	146.	122.	105.	91.4	81.2	73.0	66.4	60.8	56.1	52.1	48.6	**81**
82	823.	412.	274.	206.	165.	137.	117.	103.	91.3	82.1	74.6	68.4	63.1	58.5	54.6	**82**

AZIMUTH or Course (according to Quadrant)

Qdt.																	Qdt.
1st	7½°	**8**°	8½°	**9**°	9½°	**10**°	10½°	**11**°	11½°	**12**°	12½°	**13**°	13½°	**14**°	14½°	**15**°	NE
2nd	172½	172	171½	171	170½	170	169½	169	168½	168	167½	167	166½	166	165½	165	SE
3rd	187½	188	188½	189	189½	190	190½	191	191½	192	192½	193	193½	194	194½	195	SW
4th	352½	352	351½	351	350½	350	349½	349	348½	348	347½	347	346½	346	345½	345	NW
LAT.																	LAT.
60°	15.2	14.2	13.4	12.6	12.0	11.3	10.8	10.3	9.83	9.41	9.02	8.66	8.33	8.02	7.73	7.46	**60**°
61	15.7	14.7	13.8	13.0	12.3	11.7	11.1	10.6	10.1	9.70	9.30	8.93	8.59	8.27	7.98	7.70	**61**
62	16.2	15.2	14.3	13.5	12.7	12.1	11.5	11.0	10.5	10.0	9.61	9.23	8.87	8.54	8.24	7.95	**62**
63	16.7	15.7	14.7	13.9	13.2	12.5	11.9	11.3	10.8	10.4	9.94	9.54	9.18	8.84	8.52	8.22	**63**
64	17.3	16.2	15.3	14.4	13.6	12.9	12.3	11.7	11.2	10.7	10.3	9.88	9.50	9.15	8.82	8.51	**64**
65	18.0	16.8	15.8	14.9	14.1	13.4	12.8	12.2	11.6	11.1	10.7	10.2	9.86	9.49	9.15	8.83	**65**
66	18.7	17.5	16.5	15.5	14.7	13.9	13.3	12.6	12.1	11.6	11.1	10.6	10.2	9.86	9.51	9.18	**66**
67	19.4	18.2	17.1	16.2	15.3	14.5	13.8	13.2	12.6	12.0	11.5	11.1	10.7	10.3	9.90	9.55	**67**
68	20.3	19.0	17.9	16.9	16.0	15.1	14.4	13.7	13.1	12.6	12.0	11.6	11.1	10.7	10.3	9.96	**68**
69	21.2	19.9	18.7	17.6	16.7	15.8	15.1	14.4	13.7	13.1	12.6	12.1	11.6	11.2	10.8	10.4	**69**
70	22.2	20.8	19.6	18.5	17.5	16.6	15.8	15.0	14.4	13.8	13.2	12.7	12.2	11.7	11.3	10.9	**70**
71	23.3	21.9	20.6	19.4	18.4	17.4	16.6	15.8	15.1	14.5	13.9	13.3	12.8	12.3	11.9	11.5	**71**
72	24.6	23.0	21.7	20.4	19.3	18.4	17.5	16.6	15.9	15.2	14.6	14.0	13.5	13.0	12.5	12.1	**72**
73	26.0	24.3	22.9	21.6	20.4	19.4	18.5	17.6	16.8	16.1	15.4	14.8	14.2	13.7	13.2	12.8	**73**
74	27.6	25.8	24.3	22.9	21.7	20.6	19.6	18.7	17.8	17.1	16.4	15.7	15.1	14.6	14.0	13.5	**74**
75	29.3	27.5	25.9	24.4	23.1	21.9	20.8	19.9	19.0	18.2	17.4	16.7	16.1	15.5	14.9	14.4	**75**
76	31.4	29.4	27.7	26.1	24.7	23.4	22.3	21.3	20.3	19.4	18.6	17.9	17.2	16.6	16.0	15.4	**76**
77	33.8	31.6	29.7	28.1	26.6	25.1	24.0	22.9	21.9	20.9	20.1	19.3	18.5	17.8	17.2	16.6	**77**
78	36.5	34.2	32.2	30.4	28.7	27.3	26.0	24.7	23.6	22.6	21.7	20.8	20.0	19.3	18.2	18.0	**78**
79	39.8	37.3	35.1	33.1	31.3	29.7	28.3	27.0	25.8	24.7	23.6	22.7	21.8	21.0	20.3	19.6	**79**
80	43.7	41.0	38.5	36.4	34.4	32.7	31.1	29.6	28.3	27.1	26.0	24.9	24.0	23.1	22.3	21.5	**80**
81	48.6	45.5	42.8	40.4	38.2	36.3	34.5	32.9	21.4	30.1	28.8	27.7	26.6	25.6	24.7	23.9	**81**
82	54.6	51.1	48.1	45.4	42.9	40.7	38.8	37.0	35.3	33.8	32.4	31.1	29.9	28.8	27.8	26.8	**82**

For quadrantal compass graduation readings the degrees are to be taken as for 1st Quadrant (0° to 90°). The azimuth is then named in accordance with the precepts above.

Table 30 (H.L.)

C
(Longitude Correction)

Body **RISING** (H.A. greater than 180°)
Body **SETTING** (H.A. less than 180°)

	North Lat.	South Lat.	
Sign −	Az. in NE Qdt.	SE Qdt.	
" +	" SE	" NE "	
Sign +	Az. in SW Qdt.	NW Qdt.	
" −	" NW	" SW "	

AZIMUTH or Course (according to Quadrant)

Qdt.																	Qdt.
1st	15°	15½°	16°	16½°	17°	17½°	18°	18½°	19°	19½°	20°	20½°	21°	21½°	22°	22½°	NE
2nd	165	164½	164	163½	163	162½	162	161½	161	160½	160	159½	159	158½	158	157½	SE
3rd	195	195½	196	196½	197	197½	198	198½	199	199½	200	200½	201	201½	202	202½	SW
4th	345	344½	344	343½	343	342½	342	341½	341	340½	340	339½	339	338½	338	337½	NW
LAT.																	**LAT.**
60°	7.46	7.21	6.98	6.75	6.54	6.34	6.16	5.98	5.81	5.65	5.50	5.35	5.21	5.08	4.95	4.83	60°
61	7.70	7.44	7.19	6.96	6.75	6.54	6.35	6.17	5.99	5.83	5.67	5.52	5.37	5.24	5.11	4.98	61
62	7.95	7.68	7.43	7.19	6.97	6.76	6.56	6.37	6.19	6.02	5.85	5.70	5.55	5.41	5.27	5.14	62
63	8.22	7.94	7.68	7.44	7.21	6.99	6.78	6.58	6.40	6.22	6.05	5.89	5.74	5.59	5.45	5.32	63
64	8.51	8.23	7.96	7.70	7.46	7.24	7.02	6.82	6.63	6.44	6.27	6.10	5.94	5.79	5.65	5.51	64
65	8.83	8.53	8.25	7.99	7.74	7.51	7.28	7.07	6.87	6.68	6.50	6.33	6.16	6.01	5.86	5.71	65
66	9.18	8.87	8.57	8.30	8.04	7.80	7.57	7.35	7.14	6.94	6.75	6.58	6.40	6.24	6.09	5.94	66
67	9.55	9.23	8.93	8.64	8.37	8.12	7.88	7.65	7.43	7.23	7.03	6.85	6.67	6.50	6.33	6.18	67
68	9.96	9.63	9.31	9.01	8.73	8.47	8.22	7.98	7.75	7.54	7.33	7.14	6.95	6.78	6.61	6.44	68
69	10.4	10.1	9.73	9.42	9.13	8.85	8.59	8.34	8.10	7.88	7.67	7.46	7.27	7.08	6.91	6.74	69
70	10.9	10.5	10.2	9.87	9.56	9.27	9.00	8.74	8.49	8.26	8.03	7.82	7.62	7.42	7.24	7.06	70
71	11.5	11.1	10.7	10.4	10.0	9.74	9.45	9.18	8.92	8.67	8.44	8.22	8.00	7.80	7.60	7.42	71
72	12.1	11.7	11.3	10.9	10.6	10.3	9.96	9.67	9.40	9.14	8.89	8.66	8.43	8.22	8.01	7.81	72
73	12.8	12.3	11.9	11.5	11.2	10.8	10.5	10.2	9.93	9.66	9.40	9.15	8.91	8.68	8.47	8.26	73
74	13.5	13.1	12.7	12.2	11.9	11.5	11.2	10.8	10.5	10.2	9.97	9.70	9.45	9.21	8.98	8.76	74
75	14.4	13.9	13.5	13.0	12.6	12.3	11.9	11.5	11.2	10.9	10.6	10.3	10.1	9.81	9.56	9.33	75
76	15.4	14.9	14.4	14.0	13.5	13.1	12.7	12.4	12.0	11.7	11.4	11.1	10.8	10.5	10.2	9.98	76
77	16.6	16.0	15.5	15.0	14.5	14.1	13.7	13.3	12.9	12.6	12.2	11.9	11.6	11.3	11.0	10.7	77
78	18.0	17.3	16.8	16.2	15.7	15.3	14.8	14.4	14.0	13.6	13.2	12.9	12.5	12.2	11.9	11.6	78
79	19.6	18.9	18.3	17.7	17.1	16.6	16.1	15.7	15.2	14.8	14.4	14.0	13.7	13.3	13.0	12.7	79
80	21.5	20.8	20.1	19.4	18.8	18.3	17.7	17.2	16.7	16.3	15.8	15.4	15.0	14.6	14.3	13.9	80
81	23.9	23.1	22.3	21.6	20.9	20.3	19.7	19.1	18.6	18.1	17.6	17.1	16.7	16.2	15.8	15.4	81
82	26.8	25.9	25.1	24.3	23.5	22.8	22.1	21.5	20.9	20.3	19.7	19.2	18.7	18.2	17.8	17.3	82

AZIMUTH or Course (according to Quadrant)

Qdt.																	Qdt.
1st	22½°	23°	23½°	24°	24½°	25°	25½°	26°	26½°	27°	27½°	28°	28½°	29°	29½°	30°	NE
2nd	157½	157	156½	156	155½	155	154½	154	153½	153	152½	152	151½	151	150½	150	SE
3rd	202½	203	203½	204	204½	205	205½	206	206½	207	207½	208	208½	209	209½	210	SW
4th	337½	337	336½	336	335½	335	334½	334	333½	333	332½	332	331½	331	330½	330	NW
LAT.																	**LAT.**
60°	4.83	4.71	4.60	4.49	4.39	4.29	4.19	4.10	4.01	3.93	3.84	3.76	3.68	3.61	3.54	3.46	60°
61	4.98	4.86	4.74	4.63	4.53	4.42	4.32	4.23	4.14	4.05	3.96	3.88	3.80	3.72	3.65	3.57	61
62	5.14	5.02	4.90	4.78	4.67	4.57	4.47	4.37	4.27	4.18	4.09	4.01	3.92	3.84	3.77	3.69	62
63	5.32	5.19	5.07	4.95	4.83	4.72	4.62	4.52	4.42	4.32	4.23	4.14	4.06	3.97	3.89	3.82	63
64	5.51	5.37	5.25	5.12	5.01	4.89	4.78	4.68	4.58	4.48	4.38	4.29	4.20	4.12	4.03	3.95	64
65	5.71	5.57	5.44	5.32	5.19	5.07	4.96	4.85	4.75	4.64	4.55	4.45	4.36	4.27	4.18	4.10	65
66	5.94	5.79	5.65	5.52	5.39	5.27	5.15	5.04	4.93	4.83	4.72	4.62	4.53	4.44	4.35	4.26	66
67	6.18	6.03	5.89	5.75	5.62	5.49	5.37	5.25	5.13	5.02	4.92	4.81	4.71	4.62	4.52	4.43	67
68	6.44	6.29	6.14	6.00	5.86	5.72	5.60	5.47	5.35	5.24	5.13	5.02	4.92	4.82	4.72	4.62	68
69	6.74	6.57	6.42	6.27	6.12	5.98	5.85	5.72	5.60	5.48	5.36	5.25	5.14	5.03	4.93	4.83	69
70	7.06	6.89	6.72	6.57	6.42	6.27	6.13	5.99	5.86	5.74	5.62	5.50	5.39	5.27	5.17	5.06	70
71	7.42	7.24	7.06	6.90	6.74	6.59	6.44	6.30	6.16	6.03	5.90	5.78	5.66	5.54	5.43	5.32	71
72	7.81	7.62	7.44	7.26	7.10	6.94	6.78	6.64	6.49	6.35	6.22	6.09	5.96	5.84	5.72	5.60	72
73	8.26	8.06	7.87	7.68	7.51	7.33	7.17	7.01	6.86	6.71	6.57	6.43	6.30	6.17	6.05	5.92	73
74	8.76	8.55	8.34	8.15	7.96	7.78	7.61	7.44	7.28	7.12	6.97	6.82	6.68	6.54	6.41	6.28	74
75	9.33	9.10	8.89	8.68	8.48	8.29	8.10	7.92	7.75	7.58	7.42	7.27	7.12	6.97	6.83	6.69	75
76	9.98	9.74	9.51	9.28	9.07	8.86	8.67	8.48	8.29	8.11	7.94	7.77	7.61	7.46	7.31	7.16	76
77	10.7	10.5	10.2	9.98	9.75	9.53	9.32	9.11	8.92	8.72	8.54	8.36	8.19	8.02	7.86	7.70	77
78	11.6	11.3	11.1	10.8	10.6	10.2	10.1	9.86	9.65	9.44	9.24	9.05	8.86	8.68	8.50	8.33	78
79	12.7	12.3	12.1	11.8	11.5	11.2	11.0	10.7	10.5	10.3	10.1	9.86	9.65	9.45	9.26	9.08	79
80	13.9	13.6	13.2	12.9	12.6	12.3	12.1	11.8	11.6	11.3	11.1	10.8	10.6	10.4	10.2	9.97	80
81	15.4	15.1	14.7	14.4	14.0	13.7	13.4	13.1	12.8	12.5	12.3	12.0	11.8	11.5	11.3	11.1	81
82	17.3	16.9	16.5	16.1	15.8	15.4	15.1	14.7	14.4	14.1	13.8	13.5	13.2	13.0	12.7	12.4	82

For quadrantal compass graduation readings the degrees are to be taken as for 1st Quadrant (0° to 90°). The azimuth is then named in accordance with the precepts above.

Table 30 (H.L.)

C

Body RISING (H.A. greater than 180°)

Body SETTING (H.A. less than 180°)

(Longitude Correction)

	North Lat.		South Lat.	
Sign −	Az. in **NE** Qdt.		**SE** Qdt.	
" +	" **SE** "		**NE** "	
Sign +	Az. in **SW** Qdt.		**NW** Qdt.	
" −	" **NW** "		**SW** "	

AZIMUTH or Course (according to Quadrant)

Qdt.	30°	30½°	31°	31½°	32°	32½°	33°	33½°	34°	34½°	35°	35½°	36°	36½°	37°	37½°	Qdt.
1st	30°	30½°	31°	31½°	32°	32½°	33°	33½°	34°	34½°	35°	35½°	36°	36½°	37°	37½°	NE
2nd	150	149½	149	148½	148	147½	147	146½	146	145½	145	144½	144	143½	143	142½	SE
3rd	210	210½	211	211½	212	212½	213	213½	214	214½	215	215½	216	216½	217	217½	SW
4th	330	329½	329	328½	328	327½	327	326½	326	325½	325	324½	324	323½	323	322½	NW
LAT.																	**LAT.**
60°	3.46	3.40	3.33	3.26	3.20	3.14	3.08	3.02	2.97	2.91	2.86	2.80	2.75	2.70	2.65	2.61	60°
61	3.57	3.50	3.43	3.37	3.30	3.24	3.18	3.12	3.06	3.00	2.95	2.89	2.84	2.79	2.74	2.69	61
62	3.69	3.62	3.55	3.48	3.41	3.34	3.29	3.22	3.16	3.10	3.04	2.99	2.93	2.88	2.83	2.78	62
63	3.82	3.74	3.67	3.59	3.53	3.46	3.39	3.33	3.27	3.21	3.15	3.09	3.03	2.98	2.92	2.87	63
64	3.95	3.87	3.80	3.72	3.65	3.58	3.51	3.45	3.38	3.32	3.26	3.20	3.14	3.08	3.03	2.97	64
65	4.10	4.02	3.94	3.86	3.79	3.71	3.64	3.58	3.51	3.44	3.38	3.32	3.26	3.20	3.14	3.08	65
66	4.26	4.17	4.09	4.01	3.93	3.86	3.79	3.71	3.64	3.58	3.51	3.45	3.38	3.32	3.26	3.20	66
67	4.43	4.34	4.26	4.18	4.10	4.02	3.94	3.87	3.79	3.72	3.65	3.59	3.52	3.46	3.40	3.34	67
68	4.62	4.53	4.44	4.36	4.27	4.19	4.11	4.03	3.96	3.88	3.81	3.74	3.67	3.61	3.54	3.48	68
69	4.83	4.74	4.64	4.55	4.47	4.38	4.30	4.22	4.14	4.06	3.99	3.91	3.84	3.77	3.70	3.64	69
70	5.06	4.96	4.87	4.77	4.68	4.59	4.50	4.42	4.33	4.25	4.18	4.10	4.02	3.95	3.88	3.81	70
71	5.32	5.21	5.11	5.01	4.92	4.82	4.73	4.64	4.55	4.47	4.39	4.31	4.23	4.15	4.08	4.00	71
72	5.60	5.49	5.39	5.28	5.18	5.08	4.98	4.89	4.80	4.71	4.62	4.54	4.45	4.37	4.29	4.22	72
73	5.92	5.81	5.69	5.58	5.47	5.37	5.27	5.17	5.07	4.98	4.88	4.80	4.71	4.62	4.54	4.46	73
74	6.28	6.16	6.04	5.92	5.81	5.69	5.59	5.48	5.38	5.28	5.18	5.09	4.99	4.90	4.81	4.73	74
75	6.69	6.56	6.43	6.31	6.18	6.06	5.95	5.84	5.73	5.62	5.52	5.42	5.32	5.22	5.13	5.04	75
76	7.16	7.02	6.88	6.75	6.62	6.49	6.36	6.25	6.13	6.01	5.90	5.80	5.69	5.59	5.49	5.39	76
77	7.70	7.55	7.40	7.25	7.11	6.98	6.85	6.72	6.59	6.47	6.35	6.23	6.12	6.01	5.90	5.79	77
78	8.33	8.17	8.00	7.85	7.70	7.55	7.41	7.27	7.13	7.00	6.87	6.74	6.62	6.50	6.38	6.27	78
79	9.08	8.90	8.72	8.55	8.39	8.23	8.07	7.92	7.77	7.63	7.48	7.35	7.21	7.08	6.95	6.83	79
80	9.97	9.78	9.58	9.40	9.22	9.04	8.87	8.70	8.54	8.38	8.22	8.07	7.93	7.78	7.64	7.51	80
81	11.1	10.9	10.6	10.4	10.2	10.0	9.84	9.66	9.48	9.30	9.13	8.96	8.80	8.64	8.48	8.33	81
82	12.4	12.2	12.0	11.7	11.5	11.3	11.1	10.9	10.7	10.5	10.3	10.1	9.89	9.71	9.54	9.36	82

AZIMUTH or Course (according to Quadrant)

Qdt.	37½°	38°	38½°	39°	39½°	40°	40½°	41°	41½°	42°	42½°	43°	43½°	44°	44½°	45°	Qdt.
1st	37½°	38°	38½°	39°	39½°	40°	40½°	41°	41½°	42°	42½°	43°	43½°	44°	44½°	45°	NE
2nd	142½	142	141½	141	140½	140	139½	139	138½	138	137½	137	136½	136	135½	135	SE
3rd	217½	218	218½	219	219½	220	220½	221	221½	222	222½	223	223½	224	224½	225	SW
4th	322½	322	321½	321	320½	320	319½	319	318½	318	317½	317	316½	316	315½	315	NW
LAT.																	**LAT.**
60°	2.61	2.56	2.51	2.47	2.43	2.38	2.34	2.30	2.26	2.22	2.18	2.15	2.11	2.07	2.04	2.00	60°
61	2.69	2.64	2.59	2.55	2.50	2.46	2.42	2.37	2.33	2.29	2.25	2.21	2.17	2.14	2.10	2.06	61
62	2.78	2.73	2.68	2.63	2.58	2.54	2.49	2.45	2.41	2.37	2.33	2.28	2.25	2.21	2.17	2.13	62
63	2.87	2.82	2.77	2.72	2.67	2.63	2.58	2.53	2.49	2.45	2.40	2.36	2.32	2.28	2.24	2.20	63
64	2.97	2.92	2.87	2.82	2.77	2.72	2.67	2.62	2.58	2.53	2.49	2.45	2.40	2.36	2.32	2.28	64
65	3.08	3.03	2.98	2.92	2.87	2.82	2.77	2.72	2.68	2.63	2.58	2.54	2.49	2.45	2.41	2.37	65
66	3.20	3.15	3.09	3.04	2.98	2.93	2.88	2.83	2.78	2.73	2.68	2.64	2.59	2.55	2.50	2.46	66
67	3.34	3.28	3.22	3.16	3.10	3.05	3.00	2.94	2.89	2.84	2.79	2.74	2.70	2.65	2.60	2.56	67
68	3.48	3.42	3.36	3.30	3.24	3.18	3.13	3.07	3.02	2.96	2.91	2.86	2.81	2.76	2.72	2.67	68
69	3.64	3.57	3.51	3.45	3.39	3.33	3.27	3.21	3.15	3.10	3.05	2.99	2.94	2.89	2.84	2.79	69
70	3.81	3.74	3.68	3.61	3.55	3.48	3.42	3.36	3.30	3.25	3.19	3.14	3.08	3.03	2.98	2.92	70
71	4.00	3.93	3.86	3.79	3.73	3.66	3.60	3.53	3.47	3.41	3.35	3.29	3.24	3.18	3.13	3.07	71
72	4.22	4.14	4.07	4.00	3.93	3.86	3.79	3.72	3.66	3.59	3.53	3.47	3.41	3.35	3.29	3.24	72
73	4.46	4.38	4.30	4.22	4.15	4.08	4.00	3.93	3.87	3.80	3.73	3.67	3.60	3.54	3.48	3.42	73
74	4.73	4.64	4.56	4.48	4.40	4.32	4.25	4.17	4.10	4.03	3.96	3.89	3.82	3.76	3.69	3.63	74
75	5.04	4.95	4.86	4.77	4.69	4.60	4.52	4.44	4.37	4.29	4.22	4.14	4.07	4.00	3.93	3.86	75
76	5.39	5.29	5.20	5.10	5.01	4.93	4.84	4.76	4.67	4.59	4.51	4.43	4.36	4.28	4.21	4.13	76
77	5.79	5.69	5.59	5.49	5.39	5.30	5.20	5.11	5.02	4.94	4.85	4.77	4.68	4.60	4.52	4.45	77
78	6.27	6.16	6.05	5.94	5.83	5.73	5.63	5.53	5.44	5.34	5.25	5.16	5.07	4.98	4.89	4.81	78
79	6.83	6.71	6.59	6.47	6.36	6.25	6.14	6.03	5.92	5.82	5.72	5.62	5.52	5.43	5.33	5.24	79
80	7.51	7.37	7.24	7.11	6.99	6.86	6.74	6.62	6.51	6.40	6.28	6.18	6.07	5.96	5.86	5.76	80
81	8.33	8.18	8.04	7.89	7.75	7.62	7.48	7.35	7.23	7.10	6.98	6.85	6.74	6.62	6.51	6.39	81
82	9.36	9.20	9.03	8.87	8.72	8.56	8.41	8.27	8.12	7.98	7.84	7.70	7.57	7.44	7.31	7.19	82

For quadrantal compass graduation readings the degrees are to be taken as for 1st Quadrant (0° to 90°). The azimuth is then named in accordance with the precepts above.

Table 30 (H.L.)

C

(Longitude Correction)

	North Lat.	South Lat.
Body **RISING** (H.A. greater than 180°)	Sign — Az. in **NE** Qdt. **SE** Qdt.	" + " **SE** " **NE** "
Body **SETTING** (H.A. less than 180°)	Sign + Az. in **SW** Qdt. **NW** Qdt.	" — " **NW** " **SW** "

AZIMUTH or Course (according to Quadrant)

Qdt. 1st	45°	45½°	46°	46½°	47°	47½°	48°	48½°	49°	49½°	50°	50½°	51°	51½°	52°	52½°	Qdt. NE
2nd	135	134½	134	133½	133	132½	132	131½	131	130½	130	129½	129	128½	128	127½	SE
3rd	225	225½	226	226½	227	227½	228	228½	229	229½	230	230½	231	231½	232	232½	SW
4th	315	314½	314	313½	313	312½	312	311½	311	310½	310	309½	309	308½	308	307½	NW
LAT. 60°	2.00	1.97	1.93	1.90	1.87	1.83	1.80	1.77	1.74	1.71	1.68	1.65	1.62	1.59	1.56	1.54	LAT. 60°
61	2.06	2.03	1.99	1.96	1.92	1.89	1.86	1.83	1.79	1.76	1.73	1.70	1.67	1.64	1.61	1.58	61
62	2.13	2.09	2.06	2.02	1.99	1.95	1.92	1.89	1.85	1.82	1.79	1.76	1.73	1.69	1.66	1.63	62
63	2.20	2.17	2.13	2.09	2.05	2.02	1.98	1.95	1.92	1.88	1.85	1.82	1.78	1.75	1.72	1.69	63
64	2.28	2.24	2.20	2.17	2.13	2.09	2.05	2.02	1.98	1.95	1.91	1.88	1.85	1.82	1.78	1.75	64
65	2.37	2.33	2.29	2.25	2.21	2.17	2.13	2.09	2.06	2.02	1.99	1.95	1.92	1.88	1.85	1.82	65
66	2.46	2.42	2.37	2.33	2.29	2.25	2.21	2.18	2.14	2.10	2.06	2.03	1.99	1.96	1.92	1.89	66
67	2.56	2.52	2.47	2.43	2.39	2.35	2.31	2.26	2.22	2.19	2.15	2.11	2.07	2.04	2.00	1.96	67
68	2.67	2.62	2.58	2.53	2.49	2.45	2.40	2.36	2.32	2.28	2.24	2.20	2.16	2.12	2.09	2.05	68
69	2.79	2.74	2.69	2.65	2.60	2.56	2.51	2.47	2.43	2.38	2.34	2.30	2.26	2.22	2.18	2.14	69
70	2.92	2.87	2.82	2.77	2.73	2.68	2.63	2.59	2.54	2.50	2.45	2.41	2.37	2.33	2.28	2.24	70
71	3.07	3.02	2.97	2.91	2.86	2.81	2.77	2.72	2.67	2.62	2.58	2.53	2.49	2.44	2.40	2.36	71
72	3.24	3.18	3.13	3.07	3.02	2.97	2.91	2.86	2.81	2.76	2.72	2.67	2.62	2.57	2.53	2.48	72
73	3.42	3.36	3.30	3.25	3.19	3.13	3.08	3.03	2.97	2.92	2.87	2.82	2.77	2.72	2.67	2.62	73
74	3.63	3.57	3.50	3.44	3.39	3.32	3.27	3.21	3.15	3.10	3.04	2.99	2.94	2.89	2.83	2.78	74
75	3.86	3.80	3.72	3.67	3.60	3.54	3.48	3.42	3.35	3.30	3.24	3.19	3.13	3.07	3.02	2.96	75
76	4.13	4.06	3.99	3.92	3.85	3.79	3.72	3.66	3.59	3.53	3.47	3.41	3.35	3.29	3.22	3.17	76
77	4.45	4.37	4.29	4.22	4.15	4.07	4.00	3.93	3.86	3.80	3.73	3.66	3.60	3.54	3.47	3.41	77
78	4.81	4.73	4.64	4.56	4.49	4.41	4.33	4.26	4.18	4.11	4.04	3.96	3.90	3.83	3.76	3.69	78
79	5.24	5.15	5.06	4.97	4.89	4.80	4.72	4.64	4.56	4.48	4.40	4.32	4.24	4.17	4.09	4.02	79
80	5.76	5.66	5.56	5.46	5.37	5.28	5.19	5.09	5.01	4.92	4.83	4.75	4.66	4.58	4.50	4.42	80
81	6.39	6.28	6.17	6.07	5.96	5.86	5.76	5.66	5.56	5.46	5.36	5.27	5.18	5.08	4.99	4.91	81
82	7.19	7.06	6.94	6.82	6.70	6.58	6.47	6.36	6.25	6.14	6.03	5.92	5.82	5.72	5.61	5.51	82

AZIMUTH or Course (according to Quadrant)

Qdt. 1st	52½°	53°	53½°	54°	54½°	55°	55½°	56°	56½°	57°	57½°	58°	58½°	59°	59½°	60°	Qdt. NE
2nd	127½	127	126½	126	125½	125	124½	124	123½	123	122½	122	121½	121	120½	120	SE
3rd	232½	233	233½	234	234½	235	235½	236	236½	237	237½	238	238½	239	239½	240	SW
4th	307½	307	306½	306	305½	305	304½	304	303½	303	302½	302	301½	301	300½	300	NW
LAT. 60°	1.54	1.51	1.48	1.45	1.43	1.40	1.38	1.35	1.32	1.30	1.27	1.25	1.23	1.20	1.18	1.16	LAT. 60°
61	1.58	1.55	1.53	1.50	1.47	1.44	1.42	1.39	1.37	1.34	1.31	1.29	1.26	1.24	1.22	1.19	61
62	1.63	1.61	1.58	1.55	1.52	1.49	1.46	1.44	1.41	1.38	1.36	1.33	1.31	1.28	1.26	1.23	62
63	1.69	1.66	1.63	1.60	1.57	1.54	1.51	1.49	1.46	1.42	1.40	1.38	1.35	1.32	1.30	1.27	63
64	1.75	1.72	1.69	1.66	1.63	1.60	1.57	1.54	1.51	1.48	1.45	1.43	1.40	1.37	1.34	1.32	64
65	1.82	1.78	1.75	1.72	1.69	1.66	1.63	1.60	1.57	1.54	1.51	1.48	1.45	1.42	1.39	1.37	65
66	1.89	1.85	1.82	1.79	1.75	1.72	1.69	1.66	1.63	1.60	1.57	1.54	1.51	1.48	1.45	1.42	66
67	1.96	1.93	1.89	1.86	1.83	1.79	1.76	1.73	1.69	1.66	1.63	1.60	1.57	1.54	1.51	1.48	67
68	2.05	2.01	1.98	1.94	1.90	1.87	1.83	1.80	1.77	1.73	1.70	1.67	1.64	1.60	1.57	1.54	68
69	2.14	2.10	2.06	2.03	1.99	1.95	1.92	1.88	1.85	1.81	1.78	1.74	1.71	1.68	1.64	1.61	69
70	2.24	2.20	2.16	2.12	2.09	2.05	2.01	1.97	1.94	1.90	1.86	1.83	1.79	1.76	1.72	1.69	70
71	2.36	2.31	2.27	2.23	2.19	2.15	2.11	2.07	2.03	1.99	1.96	1.92	1.88	1.85	1.81	1.77	71
72	2.48	2.44	2.39	2.35	2.31	2.27	2.22	2.18	2.14	2.10	2.06	2.02	1.98	1.94	1.91	1.87	72
73	2.62	2.58	2.53	2.48	2.44	2.39	2.35	2.31	2.26	2.22	2.18	2.14	2.10	2.06	2.01	1.97	73
74	2.78	2.73	2.68	2.64	2.59	2.54	2.49	2.45	2.40	2.36	2.31	2.27	2.22	2.18	2.14	2.09	74
75	2.96	2.91	2.86	2.81	2.76	2.71	2.66	2.61	2.56	2.51	2.46	2.41	2.37	2.32	2.28	2.23	75
76	3.17	3.11	3.06	3.00	2.95	2.89	2.84	2.79	2.74	2.68	2.63	2.58	2.53	2.48	2.43	2.39	76
77	3.41	3.35	3.29	3.23	3.17	3.11	3.06	3.00	2.94	2.89	2.83	2.78	2.72	2.67	2.62	2.57	77
78	3.69	3.62	3.56	3.49	3.43	3.37	3.31	3.24	3.18	3.12	3.06	3.01	2.95	2.89	2.83	2.78	78
79	4.02	3.95	3.88	3.81	3.74	3.67	3.60	3.54	3.47	3.40	3.34	3.27	3.21	3.15	3.09	3.03	79
80	4.42	4.34	4.26	4.18	4.11	4.03	3.96	3.89	3.81	3.74	3.67	3.60	3.53	3.46	3.39	3.32	80
81	4.91	4.82	4.73	4.64	4.56	4.48	4.39	4.31	4.23	4.15	4.07	3.99	3.92	3.84	3.77	3.69	81
82	5.51	5.41	5.32	5.22	5.13	5.03	4.94	4.85	4.76	4.67	4.58	4.49	4.40	4.32	4.23	4.15	82

For quadrantal compass graduation readings the degrees are to be taken as for 1st Quadrant (0° to 90°). The azimuth is then named in accordance with the precepts above.

Table 30 (H.L.)

C

(Longitude Correction)

Body **RISING** (H.A. greater than 180°)
Body **SETTING** (H.A. less than 180°)

North Lat.　South Lat.

	Sign − Az. in **NE** Qdt. **SE** Qdt.
	„ + „ **SE** „ **NE** „
	Sign + Az. in **SW** Qdt. **NW** Qdt.
	„ − „ **NW** „ **SW** „

AZIMUTH or Course (according to Quadrant)

Qdt. 1st	60°	60½°	61°	61½°	62°	62½°	63°	63½°	64°	64½°	65°	65½°	66°	66½°	67°	67½°	Qdt. NE
2nd	120	119½	119	118½	118	117½	117	116½	116	115½	115	114½	114	113½	113	112½	SE
3rd	240	240½	241	241½	242	242½	243	243½	244	244½	245	245½	246	246½	247	247½	SW
4th	300	299½	299	298½	298	297½	297	296½	296	295½	295	294½	294	293½	293	292½	NW
LAT.																	**LAT.**
60°	1.16	1.13	1.11	1.09	1.06	1.04	1.02	.997	.975	.954	.933	.911	.890	.870	.849	.828	60°
61	1.19	1.17	1.14	1.12	1.10	1.07	1.05	1.03	1.01	.984	.962	.940	.918	.897	.876	.854	61
62	1.23	1.21	1.18	1.16	1.13	1.11	1.09	1.06	1.04	1.02	.993	.971	.948	.926	.904	.882	62
63	1.27	1.25	1.22	1.20	1.17	1.15	1.12	1.10	1.07	1.05	1.03	1.00	.981	.958	.935	.912	63
64	1.32	1.29	1.26	1.24	1.21	1.19	1.16	1.14	1.11	1.09	1.06	1.04	1.02	.992	.968	.945	64
65	1.37	1.34	1.31	1.29	1.26	1.23	1.21	1.18	1.15	1.13	1.10	1.08	1.05	1.03	1.00	.980	65
66	1.42	1.39	1.36	1.33	1.31	1.28	1.25	1.23	1.20	1.17	1.15	1.12	1.09	1.07	1.04	1.02	66
67	1.48	1.45	1.42	1.39	1.36	1.33	1.30	1.28	1.25	1.22	1.19	1.17	1.14	1.11	1.09	1.06	67
68	1.54	1.51	1.48	1.45	1.42	1.39	1.36	1.33	1.30	1.27	1.24	1.22	1.19	1.16	1.13	1.11	68
69	1.61	1.58	1.55	1.52	1.48	1.45	1.42	1.39	1.36	1.33	1.30	1.27	1.24	1.21	1.18	1.16	69
70	1.69	1.65	1.62	1.59	1.55	1.52	1.49	1.46	1.43	1.39	1.36	1.33	1.30	1.27	1.24	1.21	70
71	1.77	1.74	1.70	1.67	1.63	1.60	1.57	1.53	1.50	1.46	1.43	1.40	1.37	1.34	1.30	1.27	71
72	1.87	1.83	1.79	1.76	1.72	1.68	1.65	1.61	1.58	1.54	1.51	1.47	1.44	1.41	1.37	1.34	72
73	1.97	1.94	1.90	1.86	1.82	1.78	1.74	1.71	1.67	1.63	1.59	1.56	1.52	1.49	1.45	1.42	73
74	2.09	2.05	2.01	1.97	1.93	1.89	1.85	1.81	1.77	1.73	1.69	1.65	1.62	1.58	1.54	1.50	74
75	2.23	2.19	2.14	2.10	2.05	2.01	1.97	1.93	1.88	1.84	1.80	1.76	1.72	1.68	1.64	1.60	75
76	2.39	2.34	2.29	2.24	2.20	2.15	2.11	2.06	2.02	1.97	1.93	1.88	1.84	1.80	1.75	1.71	76
77	2.57	2.52	2.46	2.41	2.36	2.31	2.27	2.22	2.17	2.12	2.07	2.03	1.98	1.93	1.89	1.84	77
78	2.78	2.72	2.67	2.61	2.56	2.50	2.45	2.40	2.35	2.29	2.24	2.19	2.14	2.09	2.04	1.99	78
79	3.03	2.97	2.90	2.85	2.79	2.73	2.67	2.61	2.56	2.50	2.44	2.39	2.33	2.28	2.22	2.17	79
80	3.32	3.26	3.19	3.13	3.06	3.00	2.93	2.87	2.81	2.75	2.69	2.62	2.56	2.50	2.44	2.39	80
81	3.69	3.62	3.54	3.47	3.40	3.33	3.26	3.19	3.12	3.05	2.98	2.91	2.85	2.78	2.71	2.65	81
82	4.15	4.07	3.98	3.90	3.82	3.74	3.66	3.58	3.50	3.43	3.35	3.27	3.20	3.12	3.05	2.98	82

AZIMUTH or Course (according to Quadrant)

Qdt. 1st	67½°	68°	68½°	69°	69½°	70°	70½°	71°	71½°	72°	72½°	73°	73½°	74°	74½°	75°	Qdt. NE
2nd	112½	112	111½	111	110½	110	109½	109	108½	108	107½	107	106½	106	105½	105	SE
3rd	247½	248	248½	249	249½	250	250½	251	251½	252	252½	253	253½	254	254½	255	SW
4th	292½	292	291½	291	290½	290	289½	289	288½	288	287½	287	286½	286	285½	285	NW
LAT.																	**LAT.**
60°	.828	.808	.788	.768	.748	.728	.708	.689	.669	.650	.631	.611	.592	.573	.555	.536	60°
61	.854	.833	.813	.792	.771	.751	.730	.710	.690	.670	.650	.631	.611	.591	.572	.553	61
62	.882	.861	.839	.818	.796	.775	.754	.733	.713	.692	.672	.651	.631	.611	.591	.571	62
63	.912	.890	.868	.846	.824	.802	.780	.758	.737	.716	.695	.673	.652	.632	.611	.590	63
64	.945	.922	.899	.876	.853	.830	.808	.785	.763	.741	.719	.697	.676	.654	.633	.611	64
65	.980	.956	.932	.908	.885	.861	.838	.815	.792	.769	.746	.723	.701	.678	.656	.634	65
66	1.02	.993	.968	.944	.919	.895	.871	.847	.823	.799	.775	.752	.728	.705	.682	.659	66
67	1.06	1.03	1.01	.982	.957	.932	.906	.881	.856	.832	.807	.782	.758	.734	.710	.686	67
68	1.11	1.08	1.05	1.02	.998	.972	.945	.919	.893	.867	.842	.816	.791	.765	.740	.715	68
69	1.16	1.13	1.10	1.07	1.04	1.02	.988	.961	.934	.907	.880	.853	.827	.800	.774	.748	69
70	1.21	1.18	1.15	1.12	1.09	1.06	1.04	1.01	.978	.950	.922	.894	.866	.838	.811	.783	70
71	1.27	1.24	1.21	1.18	1.15	1.12	1.09	1.06	1.03	1.00	.968	.939	.910	.881	.852	.823	71
72	1.34	1.31	1.27	1.24	1.21	1.18	1.15	1.11	1.08	1.05	1.02	.989	.959	.928	.897	.867	72
73	1.42	1.38	1.35	1.31	1.28	1.24	1.21	1.18	1.14	1.11	1.08	1.05	1.01	.981	.949	.916	73
74	1.50	1.47	1.43	1.39	1.36	1.32	1.28	1.25	1.21	1.18	1.14	1.11	1.07	1.04	1.01	.972	74
75	1.60	1.56	1.52	1.48	1.44	1.41	1.37	1.33	1.29	1.26	1.22	1.18	1.14	1.11	1.07	1.04	75
76	1.71	1.67	1.63	1.59	1.55	1.50	1.46	1.42	1.38	1.34	1.30	1.26	1.22	1.19	1.15	1.11	76
77	1.84	1.80	1.75	1.71	1.66	1.62	1.57	1.53	1.49	1.44	1.40	1.36	1.32	1.27	1.23	1.19	77
78	1.99	1.94	1.89	1.85	1.80	1.75	1.70	1.66	1.61	1.56	1.52	1.47	1.42	1.38	1.33	1.29	78
79	2.17	2.12	2.06	2.01	1.96	1.91	1.86	1.80	1.75	1.70	1.65	1.60	1.55	1.50	1.45	1.40	79
80	2.39	2.33	2.27	2.21	2.15	2.10	2.04	1.98	1.93	1.87	1.82	1.76	1.71	1.65	1.60	1.54	80
81	2.65	2.58	2.52	2.45	2.39	2.33	2.26	2.20	2.14	2.08	2.02	1.95	1.89	1.83	1.77	1.71	81
82	2.98	2.90	2.83	2.76	2.69	2.62	2.54	2.47	2.40	2.33	2.27	2.20	2.13	2.06	1.99	1.93	82

For quadrantal compass graduation readings the degrees are to be taken as for 1st Quadrant (0° to 90°). The azimuth is then named in accordance with the precepts above.

Table 30 (H.L.)

C

(Longitude Correction)

	North Lat.	South Lat.
Body **RISING** (H.A. greater than 180°)	Sign − Az. in **NE** Qdt. / " + " **SE** "	**SE** Qdt. / **NE** "
Body **SETTING** (H.A. less than 180°)	Sign + Az. in **SW** Qdt. / " − " **NW** "	**NW** Qdt. / **SW** "

AZIMUTH or Course (according to Quadrant)

Qdt.	75°	75½°	76°	76½°	77°	77½°	78°	78½°	79°	79½°	80°	80½°	81°	81½°	82°	82½°	Qdt.
1st	75	75½	76	76½	77	77½	78	78½	79	79½	80	80½	81	81½	82	82½	NE
2nd	105	104½	104	103½	103	102½	102	101½	101	100½	100	99½	99	98½	98	97½	SE
3rd	255	255½	256	256½	257	257½	258	258½	259	259½	260	260½	261	261½	262	262½	SW
4th	285	284½	284	283½	283	282½	282	281½	281	280½	280	279½	279	278½	278	277½	NW
LAT.																	LAT.
60°	.536	.517	.499	.480	.462	.443	.425	.407	.389	.371	.353	.335	.317	.299	.281	.263	60°
61	.553	.533	.514	.495	.476	.457	.438	.420	.401	.382	.364	.345	.327	.308	.290	.272	61
62	.571	.551	.531	.511	.492	.472	.453	.433	.414	.395	.376	.356	.337	.318	.299	.280	62
63	.590	.570	.549	.529	.509	.488	.468	.448	.428	.408	.388	.369	.349	.329	.310	.290	63
64	.611	.590	.569	.548	.527	.506	.485	.464	.443	.423	.402	.382	.361	.341	.321	.300	64
65	.634	.612	.590	.568	.546	.525	.503	.481	.460	.439	.417	.396	.375	.354	.333	.312	65
66	.659	.636	.613	.590	.568	.545	.523	.500	.478	.456	.434	.411	.389	.367	.346	.324	66
67	.686	.662	.638	.614	.591	.567	.544	.521	.497	.474	.451	.428	.405	.382	.360	.337	67
68	.715	.690	.666	.641	.616	.592	.567	.543	.519	.495	.471	.447	.423	.399	.375	.351	68
69	.748	.722	.696	.670	.644	.619	.593	.568	.542	.517	.492	.467	.442	.417	.392	.367	69
70	.783	.756	.729	.702	.675	.648	.621	.595	.568	.542	.516	.489	.463	.437	.411	.385	70
71	.823	.794	.766	.737	.709	.681	.653	.625	.597	.569	.542	.514	.486	.459	.432	.404	71
72	.867	.837	.807	.777	.747	.717	.688	.658	.629	.600	.571	.542	.513	.484	.455	.426	72
73	.916	.885	.853	.821	.790	.758	.727	.696	.665	.634	.603	.572	.542	.511	.481	.450	73
74	.972	.938	.905	.871	.838	.804	.771	.738	.705	.672	.640	.607	.575	.542	.510	.478	74
75	1.04	.999	.963	.928	.892	.857	.821	.786	.751	.716	.681	.647	.612	.577	.543	.509	75
76	1.11	1.07	1.03	.992	.954	.916	.879	.841	.803	.766	.729	.692	.655	.618	.581	.544	76
77	1.19	1.15	1.11	1.07	1.03	.986	.945	.904	.864	.824	.784	.744	.704	.664	.625	.585	77
78	1.29	1.24	1.20	1.15	1.11	1.07	1.02	.979	.935	.891	.848	.805	.762	.719	.676	.633	78
79	1.40	1.36	1.31	1.26	1.21	1.16	1.11	1.07	1.02	.971	.924	.877	.830	.783	.737	.690	79
80	1.54	1.49	1.44	1.38	1.33	1.28	1.22	1.17	1.12	1.07	1.02	.964	.912	.861	.809	.758	80
81	1.71	1.65	1.59	1.53	1.48	1.42	1.36	1.30	1.24	1.18	1.13	1.07	1.01	.955	.898	.842	81
82	1.93	1.86	1.79	1.73	1.66	1.59	1.53	1.46	1.40	1.33	1.27	1.20	1.14	1.07	1.01	.946	82

AZIMUTH or Course (according to Quadrant)

Qdt.	82½°	83°	83½°	84°	84½°	85°	85½°	86°	86½°	87°	87½°	88°	88½°	89°	89½°	90°	Qdt.
1st	82½	83	83½	84	84½	85	85½	86	86½	87	87½	88	88½	89	89½	90	NE
2nd	97½	97	96½	96	95½	95	94½	94	93½	93	92½	92	91½	91	90½	90	SE
3rd	262½	263	263½	264	264½	265	265½	266	266½	267	267½	268	268½	269	269½	270	SW
4th	277½	277	276½	276	275½	275	274½	274	273½	273	272½	272	271½	271	270½	270	NW
LAT.																	LAT.
60°	.263	.246	.228	.210	.193	.175	.157	.140	.122	.105	.087	.070	.052	.035	.017	.000	60°
61	.272	.253	.235	.217	.199	.180	.162	.144	.126	.108	.090	.072	.054	.036	.018	.000	61
62	.280	.262	.243	.224	.205	.186	.168	.149	.130	.112	.093	.074	.056	.037	.019	.000	62
63	.290	.270	.251	.232	.212	.193	.173	.154	.135	.115	.096	.077	.058	.038	.019	.000	63
64	.300	.280	.260	.240	.220	.200	.180	.160	.140	.120	.100	.080	.060	.040	.020	.000	64
65	.312	.291	.270	.249	.228	.207	.186	.165	.145	.124	.103	.083	.062	.041	.021	.000	65
66	.324	.302	.280	.258	.237	.215	.193	.172	.150	.129	.107	.086	.064	.043	.022	.000	66
67	.337	.314	.292	.269	.246	.224	.201	.179	.157	.134	.112	.089	.067	.045	.022	.000	67
68	.351	.328	.304	.281	.257	.234	.210	.187	.163	.140	.117	.093	.070	.047	.023	.000	68
69	.367	.343	.318	.293	.269	.244	.220	.195	.171	.146	.122	.097	.073	.049	.024	.000	69
70	.385	.359	.333	.307	.282	.256	.230	.204	.179	.153	.128	.102	.077	.051	.026	.000	70
71	.404	.377	.350	.323	.296	.269	.242	.215	.188	.161	.134	.107	.080	.054	.027	.000	71
72	.426	.397	.369	.340	.312	.283	.255	.226	.198	.170	.141	.113	.085	.057	.028	.000	72
73	.450	.420	.390	.359	.329	.299	.269	.239	.209	.179	.149	.119	.090	.060	.030	.000	73
74	.478	.445	.413	.381	.349	.317	.286	.254	.222	.190	.158	.127	.095	.063	.032	.000	74
75	.509	.474	.440	.406	.372	.338	.304	.270	.236	.202	.169	.135	.101	.067	.034	.000	75
76	.544	.508	.471	.434	.398	.362	.325	.289	.253	.217	.180	.144	.108	.072	.036	.000	76
77	.585	.546	.506	.467	.428	.389	.350	.311	.272	.233	.194	.155	.116	.078	.039	.000	77
78	.633	.591	.548	.506	.463	.421	.379	.336	.294	.252	.210	.168	.126	.084	.042	.000	78
79	.690	.643	.597	.551	.505	.459	.412	.366	.321	.275	.229	.183	.137	.092	.046	.000	79
80	.758	.707	.656	.605	.555	.504	.453	.403	.352	.302	.251	.201	.151	.101	.050	.000	80
81	.842	.785	.728	.672	.616	.559	.503	.447	.391	.335	.279	.223	.167	.112	.056	.000	81
82	.946	.882	.819	.755	.692	.629	.565	.502	.439	.377	.314	.251	.188	.125	.063	.000	82

For quadrantal compass graduation readings the degrees are to be taken as for 1st Quadrant (0° to 90°). The azimuth is then named in accordance with the precepts above.

Diff. per Degree	Minutes of Latitude, Declination or Azimuth											Diff. per Degree
	5	10	15	20	25	30	35	40	45	50	55	
2	0	0	0	1	1	1	1	1	1	2	2	2
4	0	1	1	1	1	2	2	3	3	3	4	4
6	0	1	1	2	2	3	3	4	4	5	6	6
8	1	1	2	3	3	4	5	5	6	7	7	8
10	1	2	2	3	4	5	6	7	7	8	9	10
12	1	2	3	4	5	6	7	8	9	10	11	12
14	1	2	3	5	6	7	8	9	10	12	13	14
16	1	3	4	5	7	8	9	11	12	13	15	16
18	1	3	4	6	7	9	10	12	13	15	16	18
20	2	3	5	7	8	10	12	13	15	17	18	20
22	2	4	5	7	9	11	13	15	16	18	20	22
24	2	4	6	8	10	12	14	16	18	20	22	24
26	2	4	6	9	11	13	15	17	19	22	24	26
28	2	5	7	9	12	14	16	19	21	23	25	28
30	2	5	7	10	12	15	17	20	22	25	27	30
32	3	5	8	10	13	16	19	21	24	27	29	32
34	3	6	8	11	14	17	20	23	25	28	31	34
36	3	6	9	12	15	18	21	24	27	30	33	36
38	3	6	9	13	16	19	22	25	28	32	35	38
40	3	7	10	13	17	20	23	27	30	33	37	40
42	3	7	10	14	17	21	24	28	31	35	38	42
44	4	7	11	15	18	22	26	29	33	37	40	44
46	4	8	11	15	19	23	27	31	34	38	42	46
48	4	8	12	16	20	24	28	32	36	40	44	48
50	4	8	12	17	21	25	29	33	37	42	46	50
Diff. per 4m	20s	40s	1m	20s	40s	2m	20s	40s	3m	20s	40s	Diff. per 4m
	Minutes and Seconds of Time											

For the general purposes of navigation it will be found sufficiently accurate to employ two decimal places only, when working the A, B and C Tables; in which case interpolation presents no difficulty, and can generally be done at a glance.

Where, however, for academic or other purposes, a more exact result is required, the process of interpolation can be greatly facilitated by the use of the above table. The figures in the body of this table represent differences in the values A, B or C between the tabulated values and the actual values.

Example:

Given H.A. 4h46m   Lat 67° 15' N.   Dec. 40° 20' N.

From Tables

A				B		
Lat.	44m	48m		Dec.	44m	48m
67°	.811	.766		40°	.887	.882
68	.852	.804		41	.919	.914

Then, reckoning from H.A. 4h 44m, Lat 67° Dec. 40°
A = .811 + 10 (for 15') — 22 (for 2m) = .799 +
B = .887 + 10 (for 20') — 2 (for 2m) = .895 —

C = .096 — = Az. N88° —

In the above case C requires no interpolation. In cases where C does, however, the process is slightly different. Thus, the actual "Value C" must first be adjusted (by the Table) so as to correspond to an even degree of latitude. It is then easily interpolated for Azimuth.

Example:
Given Lat. 77° 25',   C = 3.88

From Tables

Lat.	49°	50°
77°	3.86	3.73
78	4.18	4.04

First adjust C for Lat. 77°—
    Thus 3.88—13 (for 25') = 3.75 (C for Lat. 77°).
    Thence in Lat. 77°,   3.75 = 50° — 10' = Az. 49° 50'

Table 31

DISTANCE by VERTICAL SEXTANT ANGLE

Dist. M	HEIGHT OF OBJECT IN FEET																Dist. M
	35	40	45	50	55	60	65	70	75	80	85	90	95	100	105	110	
	° ′	° ′	° ′	° ′	° ′	° ′	° ′	° ′	° ′	° ′	° ′	° ′	° ′	° ′	° ′	° ′	
.1	3.18	3.46	4.14	4.42	5.10	5.38	6.06	6.34	7.02	7.30	7.58	8.25	8.53	9.20	9.48	10.15	.1
.2	1.39	1.53	2.07	2.21	2.35	2.49	3.04	3.18	3.32	3.46	4.00	4.14	4.28	4.42	4.56	5.10	.2
.3	1.06	1.15	1.25	1.34	1.44	1.53	2.02	2.12	2.21	2.31	2.40	2.49	2.59	3.08	3.18	3.27	.3
.4	0.49	0.57	1.04	1.11	1.18	1.25	1.32	1.39	1.46	1.53	2.00	2.07	2.14	2.21	2.28	2.35	.4
.5	0.40	0.45	0.51	0.57	1.02	1.08	1.14	1.19	1.25	1.30	1.36	1.42	1.47	1.53	1.59	2.04	.5
.6	0.33	0.38	0.42	0.47	0.52	0.57	1.01	1.06	1.11	1.15	1.20	1.25	1.30	1.34	1.39	1.44	.6
.7	0.28	0.32	0.36	0.40	0.44	0.48	0.52	0.57	1.01	1.05	1.09	1.13	1.17	1.21	1.25	1.29	.7
.8	0.25	0.28	0.32	0.35	0.39	0.42	0.46	0.49	0.53	0.57	1.00	1.04	1.07	1.11	1.14	1.18	.8
.9	0.22	0.25	0.28	0.31	0.35	0.38	0.41	0.44	0.47	0.50	0.53	0.57	1.00	1.03	1.06	1.09	.9
1.0	0.20	0.23	0.25	0.28	0.31	0.34	0.37	0.40	0.42	0.45	0.48	0.51	0.54	0.57	0.59	1.02	1.0
1.1	0.18	0.21	0.23	0.26	0.28	0.31	0.33	0.36	0.39	0.41	0.44	0.46	0.49	0.51	0.54	0.57	1.1
1.2	0.16	0.19	0.21	0.24	0.26	0.28	0.31	0.33	0.35	0.38	0.40	0.42	0.45	0.47	0.49	0.52	1.2
1.3	0.15	0.17	0.20	0.22	0.24	0.26	0.28	0.30	0.33	0.35	0.37	0.39	0.41	0.44	0.46	0.48	1.3
1.4	0.14	0.16	0.18	0.20	0.22	0.24	0.26	0.28	0.30	0.32	0.34	0.36	0.38	0.40	0.42	0.44	1.4
1.5	0.13	0.15	0.17	0.19	0.21	0.23	0.25	0.26	0.28	0.30	0.32	0.34	0.36	0.38	0.40	0.41	1.5
1.6	0.12	0.14	0.16	0.18	0.19	0.21	0.23	0.25	0.27	0.28	0.30	0.32	0.34	0.35	0.37	0.39	1.6
1.7	0.12	0.13	0.15	0.17	0.18	0.20	0.22	0.23	0.25	0.27	0.28	0.30	0.32	0.33	0.35	0.37	1.7
1.8	0.11	0.13	0.14	0.16	0.17	0.19	0.20	0.22	0.24	0.25	0.27	0.28	0.30	0.31	0.33	0.35	1.8
1.9	0.10	0.12	0.13	0.15	0.16	0.18	0.19	0.21	0.22	0.24	0.25	0.27	0.28	0.30	0.31	0.33	1.9
2.0	0.10	0.11	0.13	0.14	0.16	0.17	0.18	0.20	0.21	0.23	0.24	0.25	0.27	0.28	0.30	0.31	2.0
2.1	–	0.11	0.12	0.13	0.15	0.16	0.18	0.19	0.20	0.22	0.23	0.24	0.26	0.27	0.28	0.30	2.1
2.2	–	0.10	0.12	0.13	0.14	0.15	0.17	0.18	0.19	0.21	0.22	0.23	0.24	0.26	0.27	0.28	2.2
2.3	–	0.10	0.11	0.12	0.14	0.15	0.16	0.17	0.18	0.20	0.21	0.22	0.23	0.25	0.26	0.27	2.3
2.4	–	–	0.11	0.12	0.13	0.14	0.15	0.16	0.18	0.19	0.20	0.21	0.22	0.24	0.25	0.26	2.4
2.5	–	–	0.10	0.11	0.12	0.14	0.15	0.16	0.17	0.18	0.19	0.20	0.21	0.23	0.24	0.25	2.5
2.6	–	–	0.10	0.11	0.12	0.13	0.14	0.15	0.16	0.17	0.18	0.20	0.21	0.22	0.23	0.24	2.6
2.7	–	–	–	0.10	0.12	0.13	0.14	0.15	0.16	0.17	0.18	0.19	0.20	0.21	0.22	0.23	2.7
2.8	–	–	–	0.10	0.11	0.12	0.13	0.14	0.15	0.16	0.17	0.18	0.19	0.20	0.21	0.22	2.8
2.9	–	–	–	0.10	0.11	0.12	0.13	0.14	0.15	0.16	0.17	0.18	0.19	0.19	0.20	0.21	2.9
3.0	–	–	–	–	0.10	0.11	0.12	0.13	0.14	0.15	0.16	0.17	0.18	0.19	0.20	0.21	3.0
3.1	–	–	–	–	0.10	0.11	0.12	0.13	0.14	0.15	0.16	0.16	0.17	0.18	0.19	0.20	3.1
3.2	–	–	–	–	0.10	0.11	0.11	0.12	0.13	0.14	0.15	0.16	0.17	0.18	0.19	0.19	3.2
3.3	–	–	–	–	–	0.10	0.11	0.12	0.13	0.14	0.15	0.15	0.16	0.17	0.18	0.19	3.3
3.4	–	–	–	–	–	0.10	0.11	0.12	0.12	0.13	0.14	0.15	0.16	0.17	0.17	0.18	3.4
3.5	–	–	–	–	–	0.10	0.11	0.11	0.12	0.13	0.14	0.15	0.15	0.16	0.17	0.18	3.5
3.6	–	–	–	–	–	–	0.10	0.11	0.12	0.13	0.13	0.14	0.15	0.16	0.16	0.17	3.6
3.7	–	–	–	–	–	–	0.10	0.11	0.11	0.12	0.13	0.14	0.15	0.16	0.16	0.17	3.7
3.8	–	–	–	–	–	–	0.10	0.10	0.11	0.12	0.13	0.13	0.14	0.15	0.16	0.16	3.8
3.9	–	–	–	–	–	–	–	0.10	0.11	0.12	0.12	0.13	0.14	0.14	0.15	0.16	3.9
4.0	–	–	–	–	–	–	–	0.10	0.11	0.11	0.12	0.13	0.13	0.14	0.15	0.16	4.0
4.2	–	–	–	–	–	–	–	–	0.10	0.11	0.11	0.12	0.13	0.13	0.14	0.15	4.2
4.4	–	–	–	–	–	–	–	–	0.10	0.10	0.11	0.12	0.12	0.13	0.13	0.14	4.4
4.6	–	–	–	–	–	–	–	–	–	0.10	0.10	0.11	0.12	0.12	0.13	0.14	4.6
4.8	–	–	–	–	–	–	–	–	–	–	0.10	0.11	0.11	0.12	0.12	0.13	4.8
5.0	–	–	–	–	–	–	–	–	–	–	0.10	0.10	0.11	0.11	0.12	0.12	5.0
5.2	–	–	–	–	–	–	–	–	–	–	–	0.10	0.10	0.11	0.11	0.12	5.2
5.4	–	–	–	–	–	–	–	–	–	–	–	–	0.10	0.10	0.11	0.12	5.4
5.6	–	–	–	–	–	–	–	–	–	–	–	–	0.10	0.10	0.11	0.11	5.6
5.8	–	–	–	–	–	–	–	–	–	–	–	–	–	0.10	0.10	0.11	5.8
6.0	–	–	–	–	–	–	–	–	–	–	–	–	–	–	0.10	0.10	6.0
6.5	–	–	–	–	–	–	–	–	–	–	–	–	–	–	–	0.10	6.5
7.0	–	–	–	–	–	–	–	–	–	–	–	–	–	–	–	–	7.0
7.5	–	–	–	–	–	–	–	–	–	–	–	–	–	–	–	–	7.5
8.0	–	–	–	–	–	–	–	–	–	–	–	–	–	–	–	–	8.0

Table 31
DISTANCE by VERTICAL SEXTANT ANGLE

Skerries Lt. 117

Dist. M	115	120	125	130	135	140	145	150	155	160	165	170	175	180	185	190	Dist. M
	° ′	° ′	° ′	° ′	° ′	° ′	° ′	° ′	° ′	° ′	° ′	° ′	° ′	° ′	° ′	° ′	
.1	10.43	11.10	11.37	12.04	12.31	12.58	13.25	13.52	14.18	14.45	15.11	15.37	16.03	16.29	16.55	17.21	.1
.2	5.24	5.38	5.52	6.06	6.20	6.34	6.48	7.02	7.16	7.30	7.44	7.58	8.11	8.25	8.39	8.53	.2
.3	3.36	3.46	3.55	4.05	4.14	4.23	4.33	4.42	4.51	5.01	5.10	5.19	5.29	5.38	5.47	5.57	.3
.4	2.42	2.49	2.57	3.04	3.11	3.18	3.25	3.32	3.39	3.46	3.53	4.00	4.07	4.14	4.21	4.28	.4
.5	2.10	2.16	2.21	2.27	2.33	2.38	2.44	2.49	2.55	3.01	3.06	3.12	3.18	3.23	3.29	3.35	.5
.6	1.48	1.53	1.58	2.02	2.07	2.12	2.17	2.21	2.26	2.31	2.35	2.40	2.45	2.49	2.54	2.59	.6
.7	1.33	1.37	1.41	1.45	1.49	1.53	1.57	2.01	2.05	2.09	2.13	2.17	2.21	2.25	2.29	2.33	.7
.8	1.21	1.25	1.28	1.32	1.35	1.39	1.42	1.46	1.50	1.53	1.57	2.00	2.04	2.07	2.11	2.14	.8
.9	1.12	1.15	1.19	1.22	1.25	1.28	1.31	1.34	1.37	1.40	1.44	1.47	1.50	1.53	1.56	1.59	.9
1.0	1.05	1.08	1.11	1.14	1.16	1.19	1.22	1.25	1.28	1.30	1.33	1.36	1.39	1.42	1.45	1.47	1.0
1.1	0.59	1.02	1.04	1.07	1.09	1.12	1.15	1.17	1.20	1.22	1.25	1.27	1.30	1.33	1.35	1.38	1.1
1.2	0.54	0.57	0.59	1.01	1.04	1.06	1.08	1.11	1.13	1.15	1.18	1.20	1.22	1.25	1.27	1.30	1.2
1.3	0.50	0.52	0.54	0.57	0.59	1.01	1.03	1.05	1.07	1.10	1.12	1.14	1.16	1.18	1.20	1.23	1.3
1.4	0.46	0.48	0.51	0.53	0.55	0.57	0.59	1.01	1.03	1.05	1.07	1.09	1.11	1.13	1.15	1.17	1.4
1.5	0.43	0.45	0.47	0.49	0.51	0.53	0.55	0.57	0.58	1.00	1.02	1.04	1.06	1.08	1.10	1.12	1.5
1.6	0.41	0.42	0.44	0.46	0.48	0.49	0.51	0.53	0.55	0.57	0.58	1.00	1.02	1.04	1.05	1.07	1.6
1.7	0.38	0.40	0.42	0.43	0.45	0.47	0.48	0.50	0.52	0.53	0.55	0.57	0.58	1.00	1.02	1.03	1.7
1.8	0.36	0.38	0.39	0.41	0.42	0.44	0.46	0.47	0.49	0.50	0.52	0.53	0.55	0.57	0.58	1.00	1.8
1.9	0.34	0.36	0.37	0.39	0.40	0.42	0.43	0.45	0.46	0.48	0.49	0.51	0.52	0.54	0.55	0.57	1.9
2.0	0.33	0.34	0.35	0.37	0.38	0.40	0.41	0.42	0.44	0.45	0.47	0.48	0.49	0.51	0.52	0.54	2.0
2.1	0.31	0.32	0.34	0.35	0.36	0.38	0.39	0.40	0.42	0.43	0.44	0.46	0.47	0.48	0.50	0.51	2.1
2.2	0.30	0.31	0.32	0.33	0.35	0.36	0.37	0.39	0.40	0.41	0.42	0.44	0.45	0.46	0.48	0.49	2.2
2.3	0.28	0.29	0.31	0.32	0.33	0.34	0.36	0.37	0.38	0.39	0.41	0.42	0.43	0.44	0.45	0.47	2.3
2.4	0.27	0.28	0.29	0.31	0.32	0.33	0.34	0.35	0.37	0.38	0.39	0.40	0.41	0.42	0.44	0.45	2.4
2.5	0.26	0.27	0.28	0.29	0.31	0.32	0.33	0.34	0.35	0.36	0.37	0.38	0.40	0.41	0.42	0.43	2.5
2.6	0.25	0.26	0.27	0.28	0.29	0.30	0.32	0.33	0.34	0.35	0.36	0.37	0.38	0.39	0.40	0.41	2.6
2.7	0.24	0.25	0.26	0.27	0.28	0.29	0.30	0.31	0.32	0.34	0.35	0.36	0.37	0.38	0.39	0.40	2.7
2.8	0.23	0.24	0.25	0.26	0.27	0.28	0.29	0.30	0.31	0.32	0.33	0.34	0.35	0.36	0.37	0.38	2.8
2.9	0.22	0.23	0.24	0.25	0.26	0.27	0.28	0.29	0.30	0.31	0.32	0.33	0.34	0.35	0.36	0.37	2.9
3.0	0.22	0.23	0.24	0.25	0.25	0.26	0.27	0.28	0.29	0.30	0.31	0.32	0.33	0.34	0.35	0.36	3.0
3.1	0.21	0.22	0.23	0.24	0.25	0.26	0.26	0.27	0.28	0.29	0.30	0.31	0.32	0.33	0.34	0.35	3.1
3.2	0.20	0.21	0.22	0.23	0.24	0.25	0.26	0.27	0.27	0.28	0.29	0.30	0.31	0.32	0.33	0.34	3.2
3.3	0.20	0.21	0.21	0.22	0.23	0.24	0.25	0.26	0.27	0.27	0.28	0.29	0.30	0.31	0.32	0.33	3.3
3.4	0.19	0.20	0.21	0.22	0.22	0.23	0.24	0.25	0.26	0.27	0.27	0.28	0.29	0.30	0.31	0.32	3.4
3.5	0.19	0.19	0.20	0.21	0.22	0.23	0.23	0.24	0.25	0.26	0.27	0.27	0.28	0.29	0.30	0.31	3.5
3.6	0.18	0.19	0.20	0.20	0.21	0.22	0.23	0.24	0.24	0.25	0.26	0.27	0.27	0.28	0.29	0.30	3.6
3.7	0.18	0.18	0.19	0.20	0.21	0.21	0.22	0.23	0.24	0.24	0.25	0.26	0.27	0.28	0.28	0.29	3.7
3.8	0.17	0.18	0.19	0.19	0.20	0.21	0.22	0.22	0.23	0.24	0.25	0.25	0.26	0.27	0.28	0.28	3.8
3.9	0.17	0.17	0.18	0.19	0.20	0.20	0.21	0.22	0.22	0.23	0.24	0.25	0.25	0.26	0.27	0.28	3.9
4.0	0.16	0.17	0.18	0.18	0.19	0.20	0.20	0.21	0.22	0.23	0.23	0.24	0.25	0.25	0.26	0.27	4.0
4.2	0.15	0.16	0.17	0.18	0.18	0.19	0.20	0.20	0.21	0.22	0.22	0.23	0.24	0.24	0.25	0.26	4.2
4.4	0.15	0.15	0.16	0.17	0.17	0.18	0.19	0.19	0.20	0.21	0.21	0.22	0.22	0.23	0.24	0.24	4.4
4.6	0.14	0.15	0.15	0.16	0.17	0.17	0.18	0.18	0.19	0.20	0.20	0.21	0.22	0.22	0.23	0.23	4.6
4.8	0.14	0.14	0.15	0.15	0.16	0.16	0.17	0.18	0.18	0.19	0.19	0.20	0.21	0.21	0.22	0.22	4.8
5.0	0.13	0.14	0.14	0.15	0.15	0.16	0.16	0.17	0.18	0.18	0.19	0.19	0.20	0.20	0.21	0.21	5.0
5.2	0.13	0.13	0.14	0.14	0.15	0.15	0.16	0.16	0.17	0.17	0.18	0.18	0.19	0.20	0.20	0.21	5.2
5.4	0.12	0.13	0.13	0.14	0.14	0.15	0.15	0.16	0.16	0.17	0.17	0.18	0.18	0.19	0.19	0.20	5.4
5.6	0.12	0.12	0.13	0.13	0.14	0.14	0.15	0.15	0.16	0.16	0.17	0.17	0.18	0.18	0.19	0.19	5.6
5.8	0.11	0.12	0.12	0.13	0.13	0.14	0.14	0.15	0.15	0.16	0.16	0.17	0.17	0.18	0.18	0.19	5.8
6.0	0.11	0.11	0.12	0.12	0.13	0.13	0.14	0.14	0.15	0.15	0.16	0.16	0.16	0.17	0.17	0.18	6.0
6.5	0.10	0.10	0.11	0.11	0.12	0.12	0.13	0.13	0.13	0.14	0.14	0.15	0.15	0.16	0.16	0.17	6.5
7.0	–	–	0.10	0.10	0.11	0.11	0.12	0.12	0.13	0.13	0.13	0.14	0.14	0.15	0.15	0.15	7.0
7.5	–	–	–	0.10	0.10	0.11	0.11	0.11	0.12	0.12	0.12	0.13	0.13	0.14	0.14	0.14	7.5
8.0	–	–	–	–	0.10	0.10	0.10	0.11	0.11	0.11	0.12	0.12	0.12	0.13	0.13	0.13	8.0

Table 31

DISTANCE by VERTICAL SEXTANT ANGLE

C. St. Vincent Lt. 221

Dist. M	HEIGHT OF OBJECT IN FEET																Dist. M
	200	210	220	230	240	250	260	270	280	290	300	310	320	330	340	350	
	o '	o '	o '	o '	o '	o '	o '	o '	o '	o '	o '	o '	o '	o '	o '	o '	
.1	18.13	19.03	19.54	20.43	21.32	22.21	23.09	23.57	24.44	25.30	26.16	27.01	27.46	28.29	29.13	29.56	.1
.2	9.20	9.48	10.15	10.43	11.10	11.37	12.04	12.31	12.58	13.25	13.52	14.18	14.45	15.11	15.37	16.03	.2
.3	6.15	6.34	6.53	7.11	7.30	7.48	8.07	8.25	8.44	9.02	9.20	9.39	9.57	10.15	10.34	10.52	.3
.4	4.42	4.56	5.10	5.24	5.38	5.52	6.06	6.20	6.34	6.48	7.02	7.16	7.30	7.44	7.58	8.11	.4
.5	3.46	3.57	4.08	4.20	4.31	4.42	4.53	5.05	5.16	5.27	5.38	5.49	6.01	6.12	6.23	6.34	.5
.6	3.08	3.18	3.27	3.36	3.46	3.55	4.05	4.14	4.23	4.33	4.42	4.51	5.01	5.10	5.19	5.29	.6
.7	2.41	2.49	2.58	3.06	3.14	3.22	3.30	3.38	3.46	3.54	4.02	4.10	4.18	4.26	4.34	4.42	.7
.8	2.21	2.28	2.35	2.42	2.49	2.57	3.04	3.11	3.18	3.25	3.32	3.39	3.46	3.53	4.00	4.07	.8
.9	2.06	2.12	2.18	2.24	2.31	2.37	2.43	2.49	2.56	3.02	3.08	3.15	3.21	3.27	3.33	3.40	.9
1.0	1.53	1.59	2.04	2.10	2.16	2.21	2.27	2.33	2.38	2.44	2.49	2.55	3.01	3.06	3.12	3.18	1.0
1.1	1.43	1.48	1.53	1.58	2.03	2.08	2.14	2.19	2.24	2.29	2.34	2.39	2.44	2.49	2.55	3.00	1.1
1.2	1.34	1.39	1.44	1.48	1.53	1.58	2.02	2.07	2.12	2.17	2.21	2.26	2.31	2.35	2.40	2.45	1.2
1.3	1.27	1.31	1.36	1.40	1.44	1.49	1.53	1.57	2.02	2.06	2.10	2.15	2.19	2.23	2.28	2.32	1.3
1.4	1.21	1.25	1.29	1.33	1.37	1.41	1.45	1.49	1.53	1.57	2.01	2.05	2.09	2.13	2.17	2.21	1.4
1.5	1.15	1.19	1.23	1.27	1.30	1.34	1.38	1.42	1.46	1.49	1.53	1.57	2.01	2.04	2.08	2.12	1.5
1.6	1.11	1.14	1.18	1.21	1.25	1.28	1.32	1.35	1.39	1.42	1.46	1.50	1.53	1.57	2.00	2.04	1.6
1.7	1.07	1.10	1.13	1.16	1.20	1.23	1.26	1.30	1.33	1.36	1.40	1.43	1.46	1.50	1.53	1.56	1.7
1.8	1.03	1.06	1.09	1.12	1.15	1.19	1.22	1.25	1.28	1.31	1.34	1.37	1.40	1.44	1.47	1.50	1.8
1.9	1.00	1.02	1.05	1.08	1.11	1.14	1.17	1.20	1.23	1.26	1.29	1.32	1.35	1.38	1.41	1.44	1.9
2.0	0.57	0.59	1.02	1.05	1.08	1.11	1.14	1.16	1.19	1.22	1.25	1.28	1.30	1.33	1.36	1.39	2.0
2.1	0.54	0.57	0.59	1.02	1.05	1.07	1.10	1.13	1.15	1.18	1.21	1.23	1.26	1.29	1.32	1.34	2.1
2.2	0.51	0.54	0.57	0.59	1.02	1.04	1.07	1.09	1.12	1.15	1.17	1.20	1.22	1.25	1.27	1.30	2.2
2.3	0.49	0.52	0.54	0.57	0.59	1.01	1.04	1.06	1.09	1.11	1.14	1.16	1.19	1.21	1.24	1.26	2.3
2.4	0.47	0.49	0.52	0.54	0.57	0.59	1.01	1.04	1.06	1.08	1.11	1.13	1.15	1.18	1.20	1.22	2.4
2.5	0.45	0.48	0.50	0.52	0.54	0.57	0.59	1.01	1.03	1.06	1.08	1.10	1.12	1.15	1.17	1.19	2.5
2.6	0.44	0.46	0.48	0.50	0.52	0.54	0.57	0.59	1.01	1.03	1.05	1.07	1.10	1.12	1.14	1.16	2.6
2.7	0.42	0.44	0.46	0.48	0.50	0.52	0.54	0.57	0.59	1.01	1.03	1.05	1.07	1.09	1.11	1.13	2.7
2.8	0.40	0.42	0.44	0.46	0.48	0.50	0.53	0.55	0.57	0.59	1.01	1.03	1.05	1.07	1.09	1.11	2.8
2.9	0.39	0.41	0.43	0.45	0.47	0.49	0.51	0.53	0.55	0.57	0.58	1.00	1.02	1.04	1.06	1.08	2.9
3.0	0.38	0.40	0.41	0.43	0.45	0.47	0.49	0.51	0.53	0.55	0.57	0.58	1.00	1.02	1.04	1.06	3.0
3.1	0.36	0.38	0.40	0.42	0.44	0.46	0.47	0.49	0.51	0.53	0.55	0.57	0.58	1.00	1.02	1.04	3.1
3.2	0.35	0.37	0.39	0.41	0.42	0.44	0.46	0.48	0.49	0.51	0.53	0.55	0.57	0.58	1.00	1.02	3.2
3.3	0.34	0.36	0.38	0.39	0.41	0.43	0.45	0.46	0.48	0.50	0.51	0.53	0.55	0.57	0.58	1.00	3.3
3.4	0.33	0.35	0.37	0.38	0.40	0.42	0.43	0.45	0.47	0.48	0.50	0.52	0.53	0.55	0.57	0.58	3.4
3.5	0.32	0.34	0.36	0.37	0.39	0.40	0.42	0.44	0.45	0.47	0.48	0.50	0.52	0.53	0.55	0.57	3.5
3.6	0.31	0.33	0.35	0.36	0.38	0.39	0.41	0.42	0.44	0.46	0.47	0.49	0.50	0.52	0.53	0.55	3.6
3.7	0.31	0.32	0.34	0.35	0.37	0.38	0.40	0.41	0.43	0.44	0.46	0.47	0.49	0.50	0.52	0.53	3.7
3.8	0.30	0.31	0.33	0.34	0.36	0.37	0.39	0.40	0.42	0.43	0.45	0.46	0.48	0.49	0.51	0.52	3.8
3.9	0.29	0.30	0.32	0.33	0.35	0.36	0.38	0.39	0.41	0.42	0.43	0.45	0.46	0.48	0.49	0.51	3.9
4.0	0.28	0.30	0.31	0.33	0.34	0.35	0.37	0.38	0.40	0.41	0.42	0.44	0.45	0.47	0.48	0.49	4.0
4.2	0.27	0.28	0.30	0.31	0.32	0.34	0.35	0.36	0.38	0.39	0.40	0.42	0.43	0.44	0.46	0.47	4.2
4.4	0.26	0.27	0.28	0.30	0.31	0.32	0.33	0.35	0.36	0.37	0.39	0.40	0.41	0.42	0.44	0.45	4.4
4.6	0.25	0.26	0.27	0.28	0.30	0.31	0.32	0.33	0.34	0.36	0.37	0.38	0.39	0.41	0.42	0.43	4.6
4.8	0.24	0.25	0.26	0.27	0.28	0.29	0.31	0.32	0.33	0.34	0.35	0.37	0.38	0.39	0.40	0.41	4.8
5.0	0.23	0.24	0.25	0.26	0.27	0.28	0.29	0.31	0.32	0.33	0.34	0.35	0.36	0.37	0.38	0.40	5.0
5.2	0.22	0.23	0.24	0.25	0.26	0.27	0.28	0.29	0.30	0.32	0.33	0.34	0.35	0.36	0.37	0.38	5.2
5.4	0.21	0.22	0.23	0.24	0.25	0.26	0.27	0.28	0.29	0.30	0.31	0.32	0.34	0.35	0.36	0.37	5.4
5.6	0.20	0.21	0.22	0.23	0.24	0.25	0.26	0.27	0.28	0.29	0.30	0.31	0.32	0.33	0.34	0.35	5.6
5.8	0.19	0.20	0.21	0.22	0.23	0.24	0.25	0.26	0.27	0.28	0.29	0.30	0.31	0.32	0.33	0.34	5.8
6.0	0.19	0.20	0.21	0.22	0.23	0.24	0.25	0.25	0.26	0.27	0.28	0.29	0.30	0.31	0.32	0.33	6.0
6.5	0.17	0.18	0.19	0.20	0.21	0.22	0.23	0.23	0.24	0.25	0.26	0.27	0.28	0.29	0.30	0.30	6.5
7.0	0.16	0.17	0.18	0.19	0.19	0.20	0.21	0.22	0.23	0.23	0.24	0.25	0.26	0.27	0.27	0.28	7.0
7.5	0.15	0.16	0.17	0.17	0.18	0.19	0.20	0.20	0.21	0.22	0.23	0.23	0.24	0.25	0.26	0.26	7.5
8.0	0.14	0.15	0.16	0.16	0.17	0.18	0.18	0.19	0.20	0.20	0.21	0.22	0.23	0.23	0.24	0.25	8.0

Table 31

DISTANCE by VERTICAL SEXTANT ANGLE

Burlings Lt. 365

Dist. M	HEIGHT OF OBJECT IN FEET																Dist. M
	360	370	380	390	400	410	420	430	440	450	460	470	480	490	500	520	
	° ′	° ′	° ′	° ′	° ′	° ′	° ′	° ′	° ′	° ′	° ′	° ′	° ′	° ′	° ′	° ′	
.1	30.38	31.19	32.00	32.41	33.20	34.00	34.38	35.16	35.54	36.30	37.07	37.42	38.17	38.52	39.26	40.32	.1
.2	16.29	16.55	17.21	17.47	18.13	18.38	19.03	19.28	19.54	20.18	20.43	21.08	21.32	21.57	22.21	23.09	.2
.3	11.10	11.28	11.46	12.04	12.22	12.40	12.58	13.16	13.34	13.52	14.09	14.27	14.45	15.02	15.20	15.55	.3
.4	8.25	8.39	8.53	9.07	9.20	9.34	9.48	10.02	10.15	10.29	10.43	10.56	11.10	11.23	11.37	12.04	.4
.5	6.45	6.56	7.08	7.19	7.30	7.41	7.52	8.03	8.14	8.25	8.36	8.47	8.58	9.09	9.20	9.42	.5
.6	5.38	5.47	5.57	6.06	6.15	6.25	6.34	6.43	6.53	7.02	7.11	7.20	7.30	7.39	7.48	8.07	.6
.7	4.50	4.58	5.06	5.14	5.22	5.30	5.38	5.46	5.54	6.02	6.10	6.18	6.26	6.34	6.42	6.58	.7
.8	4.14	4.21	4.28	4.35	4.42	4.49	4.56	5.03	5.10	5.17	5.24	5.31	5.38	5.45	5.52	6.06	.8
.9	3.46	3.52	3.58	4.05	4.11	4.17	4.23	4.30	4.36	4.42	4.48	4.55	5.01	5.07	5.13	5.26	.9
1.0	3.23	3.29	3.35	3.40	3.46	3.51	3.57	4.03	4.08	4.14	4.20	4.25	4.31	4.36	4.42	4.53	1.0
1.1	3.05	3.10	3.15	3.20	3.25	3.30	3.36	3.41	3.46	3.51	3.56	4.01	4.06	4.11	4.17	4.27	1.1
1.2	2.49	2.54	2.59	3.04	3.08	3.13	3.18	3.22	3.27	3.32	3.36	3.41	3.46	3.51	3.55	4.05	1.2
1.3	2.36	2.41	2.45	2.49	2.54	2.58	3.03	3.07	3.11	3.16	3.20	3.24	3.29	3.33	3.37	3.46	1.3
1.4	2.25	2.29	2.33	2.37	2.41	2.45	2.49	2.54	2.58	3.02	3.06	3.10	3.14	3.18	3.22	3.30	1.4
1.5	2.16	2.19	2.23	2.27	2.31	2.34	2.38	2.42	2.46	2.49	2.53	2.57	3.01	3.05	3.08	3.16	1.5
1.6	2.07	2.11	2.14	2.18	2.21	2.25	2.28	2.32	2.35	2.39	2.42	2.46	2.49	2.53	2.57	3.04	1.6
1.7	2.00	2.03	2.06	2.10	2.13	2.16	2.20	2.23	2.26	2.30	2.33	2.36	2.40	2.43	2.46	2.53	1.7
1.8	1.53	1.56	1.59	2.02	2.06	2.09	2.12	2.15	2.18	2.21	2.24	2.28	2.31	2.34	2.37	2.43	1.8
1.9	1.47	1.50	1.53	1.56	1.59	2.02	2.05	2.08	2.11	2.14	2.17	2.20	2.23	2.26	2.29	2.35	1.9
2.0	1.42	1.45	1.47	1.50	1.53	1.56	1.59	2.02	2.04	2.07	2.10	2.13	2.16	2.18	2.21	2.27	2.0
2.1	1.37	1.40	1.42	1.45	1.48	1.50	1.53	1.56	1.58	2.01	2.04	2.06	2.09	2.12	2.15	2.20	2.1
2.2	1.33	1.35	1.38	1.40	1.43	1.45	1.48	1.50	1.53	1.56	1.58	2.01	2.03	2.06	2.08	2.14	2.2
2.3	1.29	1.31	1.33	1.36	1.38	1.41	1.43	1.46	1.48	1.51	1.53	1.55	1.58	2.00	2.03	2.08	2.3
2.4	1.25	1.27	1.30	1.32	1.34	1.37	1.39	1.41	1.44	1.46	1.48	1.51	1.53	1.55	1.58	2.02	2.4
2.5	1.21	1.24	1.26	1.28	1.30	1.33	1.35	1.37	1.39	1.42	1.44	1.46	1.49	1.51	1.53	1.58	2.5
2.6	1.18	1.20	1.23	1.25	1.27	1.29	1.31	1.33	1.36	1.38	1.40	1.42	1.44	1.47	1.49	1.53	2.6
2.7	1.15	1.17	1.20	1.22	1.24	1.26	1.28	1.30	1.32	1.34	1.36	1.38	1.40	1.43	1.45	1.49	2.7
2.8	1.13	1.15	1.17	1.19	1.21	1.23	1.25	1.27	1.29	1.31	1.33	1.35	1.37	1.39	1.41	1.45	2.8
2.9	1.10	1.12	1.14	1.16	1.18	1.20	1.22	1.24	1.26	1.28	1.30	1.32	1.34	1.36	1.37	1.41	2.9
3.0	1.08	1.10	1.12	1.14	1.15	1.17	1.19	1.21	1.23	1.25	1.27	1.29	1.30	1.32	1.34	1.38	3.0
3.1	1.06	1.07	1.09	1.11	1.13	1.15	1.17	1.18	1.20	1.22	1.24	1.26	1.28	1.29	1.31	1.35	3.1
3.2	1.04	1.05	1.07	1.09	1.11	1.12	1.14	1.16	1.18	1.19	1.21	1.23	1.25	1.27	1.28	1.32	3.2
3.3	1.02	1.03	1.05	1.07	1.09	1.10	1.12	1.14	1.15	1.17	1.19	1.21	1.22	1.24	1.26	1.29	3.3
3.4	1.00	1.02	1.03	1.05	1.07	1.08	1.10	1.12	1.13	1.15	1.16	1.18	1.20	1.21	1.23	1.26	3.4
3.5	0.58	1.00	1.01	1.03	1.05	1.06	1.08	1.09	1.11	1.13	1.14	1.16	1.18	1.19	1.21	1.24	3.5
3.6	0.57	0.58	1.00	1.01	1.03	1.04	1.06	1.08	1.09	1.11	1.12	1.14	1.15	1.17	1.19	1.22	3.6
3.7	0.55	0.57	0.58	1.00	1.01	1.03	1.04	1.06	1.07	1.09	1.10	1.12	1.13	1.15	1.16	1.19	3.7
3.8	0.54	0.55	0.57	0.58	1.00	1.01	1.02	1.04	1.05	1.07	1.08	1.10	1.11	1.13	1.14	1.17	3.8
3.9	0.52	0.54	0.55	0.57	0.58	0.59	1.01	1.02	1.04	1.05	1.07	1.08	1.10	1.11	1.12	1.15	3.9
4.0	0.51	0.52	0.54	0.55	0.57	0.58	0.59	1.01	1.02	1.04	1.05	1.06	1.08	1.09	1.11	1.13	4.0
4.2	0.48	0.50	0.51	0.52	0.54	0.55	0.57	0.58	0.59	1.01	1.02	1.03	1.05	1.06	1.07	1.10	4.2
4.4	0.46	0.48	0.49	0.50	0.51	0.53	0.54	0.55	0.57	0.58	0.59	1.00	1.02	1.03	1.04	1.07	4.4
4.6	0.44	0.45	0.47	0.48	0.49	0.50	0.52	0.53	0.54	0.55	0.57	0.58	0.59	1.00	1.01	1.04	4.6
4.8	0.42	0.44	0.45	0.46	0.47	0.48	0.49	0.51	0.52	0.53	0.54	0.55	0.57	0.58	0.59	1.01	4.8
5.0	0.41	0.42	0.43	0.44	0.45	0.46	0.47	0.49	0.50	0.51	0.52	0.53	0.54	0.55	0.57	0.59	5.0
5.2	0.39	0.40	0.41	0.42	0.43	0.45	0.46	0.47	0.48	0.49	0.50	0.51	0.52	0.53	0.54	0.57	5.2
5.4	0.38	0.39	0.40	0.41	0.42	0.43	0.44	0.45	0.46	0.47	0.48	0.49	0.50	0.51	0.52	0.54	5.4
5.6	0.36	0.37	0.38	0.39	0.40	0.41	0.42	0.43	0.44	0.45	0.46	0.47	0.48	0.49	0.50	0.52	5.6
5.8	0.35	0.36	0.37	0.38	0.39	0.40	0.41	0.42	0.43	0.44	0.45	0.46	0.47	0.48	0.49	0.51	5.8
6.0	0.34	0.35	0.36	0.37	0.38	0.39	0.40	0.41	0.41	0.42	0.43	0.44	0.45	0.46	0.47	0.49	6.0
6.5	0.31	0.32	0.33	0.34	0.35	0.36	0.37	0.37	0.38	0.39	0.40	0.41	0.42	0.43	0.43	0.45	6.5
7.0	0.29	0.30	0.31	0.32	0.32	0.33	0.34	0.35	0.36	0.36	0.37	0.38	0.39	0.40	0.40	0.42	7.0
7.5	0.27	0.28	0.29	0.29	0.30	0.31	0.32	0.32	0.33	0.34	0.35	0.35	0.36	0.37	0.38	0.39	7.5
8.0	0.25	0.26	0.27	0.28	0.28	0.29	0.30	0.30	0.31	0.32	0.33	0.33	0.34	0.35	0.35	0.37	8.0

Table 31

DISTANCE by VERTICAL SEXTANT ANGLE

Gavdo Lt. 1181

Dist. M	HEIGHT OF OBJECT IN FEET								Dist. M
	540 560	580 600	620 640	660 680	700 750	800 850	900 1000	1100 1200	
	° ′ ° ′	° ′ ° ′	° ′ ° ′	° ′ ° ′	° ′ ° ′	° ′ ° ′	° ′ ° ′	° ′ ° ′	
.1	41.37 42.39	43.39 44.37							.1
.2	23.57 24.44	25.30 26.16	27.01 27.46	28.29 29.13	29.56 31.40	33.20 34.57	36.30 39.26		.2
.3	16.29 17.04	17.38 18.13	18.46 19.20	19.54 20.27	21.00 22.21	23.41 24.59	26.16 28.44	31.06	.3
.4	12.31 12.58	13.25 13.52	14.18 14.45	15.11 15.37	16.03 17.08	18.13 19.16	20.18 22.21	24.20 26.16	.4
.5	10.04 10.26	10.48 11.10	11.32 11.53	12.15 12.37	12.58 13.52	14.45 15.37	16.29 18.13	19.54 21.32	.5
.6	8.25 8.44	9.02 9.20	9.39 9.57	10.15 10.34	10.52 11.37	12.22 13.07	13.52 15.20	16.47 18.13	.6
.7	7.14 7.30	7.46 8.01	8.17 8.33	8.49 9.05	9.20 10.00	10.39 11.18	11.56 13.13	14.29 15.45	.7
.8	6.20 6.34	6.48 7.02	7.16 7.30	7.44 7.58	8.11 8.46	9.20 9.55	10.29 11.37	12.45 13.52	.8
.9	5.38 5.51	6.03 6.15	6.28 6.40	6.53 7.05	7.17 7.48	8.19 8.50	9.20 10.21	11.22 12.22	.9
1.0	5.05 5.16	5.27 5.38	5.49 6.01	6.12 6.23	6.34 7.02	7.30 7.58	8.25 9.20	10.15 11.10	1.0
1.1	4.37 4.47	4.57 5.08	5.18 5.28	5.38 5.48	5.59 6.24	6.49 7.15	7.40 8.30	9.20 10.10	1.1
1.2	4.14 4.23	4.33 4.42	4.51 5.01	5.10 5.19	5.29 5.52	6.15 6.39	7.02 7.48	8.34 9.20	1.2
1.3	3.55 4.03	4.12 4.20	4.29 4.38	4.46 4.55	5.04 5.25	5.47 6.08	6.30 7.13	7.55 8.38	1.3
1.4	3.38 3.46	3.54 4.02	4.10 4.18	4.26 4.34	4.42 5.02	5.22 5.42	6.02 6.42	7.22 8.01	1.4
1.5	3.23 3.31	3.38 3.46	3.53 4.01	4.08 4.16	4.23 4.42	5.01 5.19	5.38 6.15	6.53 7.30	1.5
1.6	3.11 3.18	3.25 3.32	3.39 3.46	3.53 4.00	4.07 4.25	4.42 5.00	5.17 5.52	6.27 7.02	1.6
1.7	2.59 3.06	3.13 3.19	3.26 3.33	3.39 3.46	3.52 4.09	4.26 4.42	4.59 5.32	6.04 6.38	1.7
1.8	2.49 2.56	3.02 3.08	3.15 3.21	3.27 3.33	3.40 3.55	4.11 4.26	4.42 5.13	5.44 6.15	1.8
1.9	2.41 2.47	2.52 2.58	3.04 3.10	3.16 3.22	3.28 3.43	3.58 4.13	4.27 4.57	5.26 5.56	1.9
2.0	2.33 2.38	2.44 2.49	2.55 3.01	3.06 3.12	3.18 3.32	3.46 4.00	4.14 4.42	5.10 5.38	2.0
2.1	2.25 2.31	2.36 2.41	2.47 2.52	2.58 3.03	3.08 3.22	3.35 3.49	4.02 4.29	4.55 5.22	2.1
2.2	2.19 2.24	2.29 2.34	2.39 2.44	2.49 2.55	3.00 3.13	3.25 3.38	3.51 4.17	4.42 5.08	2.2
2.3	2.13 2.18	2.23 2.27	2.32 2.37	2.42 2.47	2.52 3.04	3.16 3.29	3.41 4.05	4.30 4.55	2.3
2.4	2.07 2.12	2.17 2.21	2.26 2.31	2.35 2.40	2.45 2.57	3.08 3.20	3.32 3.55	4.19 4.42	2.4
2.5	2.02 2.07	2.11 2.16	2.20 2.25	2.29 2.34	2.38 2.49	3.01 3.12	3.23 3.46	4.08 4.31	2.5
2.6	1.57 2.02	2.06 2.10	2.15 2.19	2.23 2.28	2.32 2.43	2.54 3.05	3.16 3.37	3.59 4.20	2.6
2.7	1.53 1.57	2.01 2.06	2.10 2.14	2.18 2.22	2.27 2.37	2.47 2.58	3.08 3.29	3.50 4.11	2.7
2.8	1.49 1.53	1.57 2.01	2.05 2.09	2.13 2.17	2.21 2.31	2.41 2.52	3.02 3.22	3.42 4.02	2.8
2.9	1.45 1.49	1.53 1.57	2.01 2.05	2.09 2.13	2.16 2.26	2.36 2.46	2.55 3.15	3.34 3.54	2.9
3.0	1.42 1.46	1.49 1.53	1.57 2.01	2.04 2.08	2.12 2.21	2.31 2.40	2.49 3.08	3.27 3.46	3.0
3.1	1.38 1.42	1.46 1.49	1.53 1.57	2.00 2.04	2.08 2.17	2.26 2.35	2.44 3.03	3.20 3.39	3.1
3.2	1.35 1.39	1.42 1.46	1.50 1.53	1.57 2.00	2.04 2.12	2.21 2.30	2.39 2.57	3.14 3.32	3.2
3.3	1.33 1.36	1.39 1.43	1.46 1.50	1.53 1.56	2.00 2.08	2.17 2.26	2.34 2.51	3.08 3.25	3.3
3.4	1.30 1.33	1.36 1.40	1.43 1.46	1.50 1.53	1.56 2.05	2.13 2.21	2.30 2.46	3.03 3.19	3.4
3.5	1.27 1.30	1.34 1.37	1.40 1.43	1.47 1.50	1.53 2.01	2.09 2.17	2.25 2.41	2.58 3.14	3.5
3.6	1.25 1.28	1.31 1.34	1.37 1.40	1.44 1.47	1.50 1.58	2.06 2.13	2.21 2.37	2.53 3.08	3.6
3.7	1.23 1.26	1.29 1.32	1.35 1.38	1.41 1.44	1.47 1.55	2.02 2.10	2.17 2.33	2.48 3.03	3.7
3.8	1.20 1.23	1.26 1.29	1.32 1.35	1.38 1.41	1.44 1.52	1.59 2.06	2.14 2.29	2.44 2.58	3.8
3.9	1.18 1.21	1.24 1.27	1.30 1.33	1.36 1.39	1.41 1.49	1.56 2.03	2.10 2.25	2.39 2.54	3.9
4.0	1.16 1.19	1.22 1.25	1.28 1.30	1.33 1.36	1.39 1.46	1.53 2.00	2.07 2.21	2.35 2.49	4.0
4.2	1.13 1.15	1.18 1.21	1.23 1.26	1.29 1.32	1.34 1.41	1.48 1.54	2.01 2.15	2.28 2.41	4.2
4.4	1.09 1.12	1.15 1.17	1.20 1.22	1.25 1.27	1.30 1.36	1.43 1.49	1.56 2.08	2.21 2.34	4.4
4.6	1.06 1.09	1.11 1.14	1.16 1.19	1.21 1.24	1.26 1.32	1.38 1.44	1.51 2.03	2.15 2.27	4.6
4.8	1.04 1.06	1.08 1.11	1.13 1.15	1.18 1.20	1.22 1.28	1.34 1.40	1.46 1.58	2.10 2.21	4.8
5.0	1.01 1.03	1.06 1.08	1.10 1.12	1.15 1.17	1.19 1.25	1.30 1.36	1.42 1.53	2.04 2.16	5.0
5.2	0.59 1.01	1.03 1.05	1.07 1.10	1.12 1.14	1.16 1.22	1.27 1.33	1.38 1.49	2.00 2.11	5.2
5.4	0.57 0.59	1.01 1.03	1.05 1.07	1.09 1.11	1.13 1.19	1.24 1.29	1.34 1.45	1.55 2.06	5.4
5.6	0.55 0.57	0.59 1.01	1.03 1.05	1.07 1.09	1.11 1.16	1.21 1.26	1.31 1.41	1.51 2.01	5.6
5.8	0.53 0.55	0.57 0.58	1.00 1.02	1.04 1.06	1.08 1.13	1.18 1.23	1.28 1.37	1.47 1.57	5.8
6.0	0.51 0.53	0.55 0.57	0.58 1.00	1.02 1.04	1.06 1.11	1.15 1.20	1.25 1.34	1.44 1.53	6.0
6.5	0.47 0.49	0.50 0.52	0.54 0.56	0.57 0.59	1.01 1.05	1.10 1.14	1.18 1.27	1.36 1.44	6.5
7.0	0.44 0.45	0.47 0.48	0.50 0.52	0.53 0.55	0.57 1.01	1.05 1.09	1.13 1.21	1.29 1.37	7.0
7.5	0.41 0.42	0.44 0.45	0.47 0.48	0.50 0.51	0.53 0.57	1.00 1.04	1.08 1.15	1.23 1.30	7.5
8.0	0.38 0.40	0.41 0.42	0.44 0.45	0.47 0.48	0.49 0.53	0.57 1.00	1.04 1.11	1.18 1.25	8.0

Table 32

NATURAL SINES

/	0°	1°	2°	3°	4°	5°	6°	7°	8°	9°	10°	11°	12°	13°	14°	
	0.	0.	0.	0.	0.	0.	0.	0.	0.	0.	0.	0.	0.	0.	0.	
0	0000	0175	0349	0523	0698	0872	1045	1219	1392	1564	1736	1908	2079	2250	2419	60
1	0003	0177	0352	0526	0700	0874	1048	1222	1395	1567	1739	1911	2082	2252	2422	59
2	0006	0180	0355	0529	0703	0877	1051	1224	1397	1570	1742	1914	2085	2255	2425	58
3	0009	0183	0358	0532	0706	0880	1054	1227	1400	1573	1745	1917	2088	2258	2428	57
4	0012	0186	0361	0535	0709	0883	1057	1230	1403	1576	1748	1920	2090	2261	2431	56
5	0015	0189	0364	0538	0712	0886	1060	1233	1406	1579	1751	1922	2093	2264	2433	55
6	0017	0192	0366	0541	0715	0889	1063	1236	1409	1582	1754	1925	2096	2267	2436	54
7	0020	0195	0369	0544	0718	0892	1066	1239	1412	1584	1757	1928	2099	2269	2439	53
8	0023	0198	0372	0547	0721	0895	1068	1242	1415	1587	1759	1931	2102	2272	2442	52
9	0026	0201	0375	0550	0724	0898	1071	1245	1418	1590	1762	1934	2105	2275	2445	51
10	0029	0204	0378	0552	0727	0901	1074	1248	1421	1593	1765	1937	2108	2278	2447	50
11	0032	0207	0381	0555	0729	0903	1077	1250	1423	1596	1768	1939	2110	2281	2450	49
12	0035	0209	0384	0558	0732	0906	1080	1253	1426	1599	1771	1942	2113	2284	2453	48
13	0038	0212	0387	0561	0735	0909	1083	1256	1429	1602	1774	1945	2116	2286	2456	47
14	0041	0215	0390	0564	0738	0912	1086	1259	1432	1605	1777	1948	2119	2289	2459	46
15	0044	0218	0393	0567	0741	0915	1089	1262	1435	1607	1779	1951	2122	2292	2462	45
16	0047	0221	0396	0570	0744	0918	1092	1265	1438	1610	1782	1954	2125	2295	2464	44
17	0049	0224	0398	0573	0747	0921	1094	1268	1441	1613	1785	1957	2127	2298	2467	43
18	0052	0227	0401	0576	0750	0924	1097	1271	1444	1616	1788	1959	2130	2300	2470	42
19	0055	0230	0404	0579	0753	0927	1100	1274	1446	1619	1791	1962	2133	2303	2473	41
20	0058	0233	0407	0581	0756	0929	1103	1276	1449	1622	1794	1965	2136	2306	2476	40
21	0061	0236	0410	0584	0758	0932	1106	1279	1452	1625	1797	1968	2139	2309	2478	39
22	0064	0239	0413	0587	0761	0935	1109	1282	1455	1628	1799	1971	2142	2312	2481	38
23	0067	0241	0416	0590	0764	0938	1112	1285	1458	1630	1802	1974	2145	2315	2484	37
24	0070	0244	0419	0593	0767	0941	1115	1288	1461	1633	1805	1977	2147	2317	2487	36
25	0073	0247	0422	0596	0770	0944	1118	1291	1464	1636	1808	1979	2150	2320	2490	35
26	0076	0250	0425	0599	0773	0947	1120	1294	1467	1639	1811	1982	2153	2323	2493	34
27	0079	0253	0427	0602	0776	0950	1123	1297	1469	1642	1814	1985	2156	2326	2495	33
28	0081	0256	0430	0605	0779	0953	1126	1299	1472	1645	1817	1988	2159	2329	2498	32
29	0084	0259	0433	0608	0782	0956	1129	1302	1475	1648	1819	1991	2162	2332	2501	31
30	0087	0262	0436	0610	0785	0958	1132	1305	1478	1650	1822	1994	2164	2334	2504	30
31	0090	0265	0439	0613	0787	0961	1135	1308	1481	1653	1825	1997	2167	2337	2507	29
32	0093	0268	0442	0616	0790	0964	1138	1311	1484	1656	1828	1999	2170	2340	2509	28
33	0096	0270	0445	0619	0793	0967	1141	1314	1487	1659	1831	2002	2173	2343	2512	27
34	0099	0273	0448	0622	0796	0970	1144	1317	1490	1662	1834	2005	2176	2346	2515	26
35	0102	0276	0451	0625	0799	0973	1146	1320	1492	1665	1837	2008	2179	2349	2518	25
36	0105	0279	0454	0628	0802	0976	1149	1323	1495	1668	1840	2011	2181	2351	2521	24
37	0108	0282	0457	0631	0805	0979	1152	1325	1498	1671	1842	2014	2184	2354	2524	23
38	0111	0285	0459	0634	0808	0982	1155	1328	1501	1673	1845	2016	2187	2357	2526	22
39	0113	0288	0462	0637	0811	0985	1158	1331	1504	1676	1848	2019	2190	2360	2529	21
40	0116	0291	0465	0640	0814	0987	1161	1334	1507	1679	1851	2022	2193	2363	2532	20
41	0119	0294	0468	0642	0816	0990	1164	1337	1510	1682	1854	2025	2196	2366	2535	19
42	0122	0297	0471	0645	0819	0993	1167	1340	1513	1685	1857	2028	2198	2368	2538	18
43	0125	0300	0474	0648	0822	0996	1170	1343	1515	1688	1860	2031	2201	2371	2540	17
44	0128	0302	0477	0651	0825	0999	1172	1346	1518	1691	1862	2034	2204	2374	2543	16
45	0131	0305	0480	0654	0828	1002	1175	1349	1521	1693	1865	2036	2207	2377	2546	15
46	0134	0308	0483	0657	0831	1005	1178	1351	1524	1696	1868	2039	2210	2380	2549	14
47	0137	0311	0486	0660	0834	1008	1181	1354	1527	1699	1871	2042	2213	2383	2552	13
48	0140	0314	0488	0663	0837	1011	1184	1357	1530	1702	1874	2045	2215	2385	2554	12
49	0143	0317	0491	0666	0840	1013	1187	1360	1533	1705	1877	2048	2218	2388	2557	11
50	0145	0320	0494	0669	0843	1016	1190	1363	1536	1708	1880	2051	2221	2391	2560	10
51	0148	0323	0497	0671	0845	1019	1193	1366	1538	1711	1882	2054	2224	2394	2563	9
52	0151	0326	0500	0674	0848	1022	1196	1369	1541	1714	1885	2056	2227	2397	2566	8
53	0154	0329	0503	0677	0851	1025	1198	1372	1544	1716	1888	2059	2230	2399	2569	7
54	0157	0332	0506	0680	0854	1028	1201	1374	1547	1719	1891	2062	2233	2402	2571	6
55	0160	0334	0509	0683	0857	1031	1204	1377	1550	1722	1894	2065	2235	2405	2574	5
56	0163	0337	0512	0686	0860	1034	1207	1380	1553	1725	1897	2068	2238	2408	2577	4
57	0166	0340	0515	0689	0863	1037	1210	1383	1556	1728	1900	2071	2241	2411	2580	3
58	0169	0343	0518	0692	0866	1039	1213	1386	1559	1731	1902	2073	2244	2414	2583	2
59	0172	0346	0520	0695	0869	1042	1216	1389	1561	1734	1905	2076	2247	2416	2585	1
60	0175	0349	0523	0698	0872	1045	1219	1392	1564	1736	1908	2079	2250	2419	2588	0
	0.	0.	0.	0.	0.	0.	0.	0.	0.	0.	0.	0.	0.	0.	0.	
	89°	88°	87°	86°	85°	84°	83°	82°	81°	80°	79°	78°	77°	76°	75°	/

NATURAL COSINES

Table 32

NATURAL SINES

′	15°	16°	17°	18°	19°	20°	21°	22°	23°	24°	25°	26°	27°	28°	29°	
	0.	0.	0.	0.	0.	0.	0.	0.	0.	0.	0.	0.	0.	0.	0.	
0	2588	2756	2924	3090	3256	3420	3584	3746	3907	4067	4226	4384	4540	4695	4848	60
1	2591	2759	2926	3093	3258	3423	3586	3749	3910	4070	4229	4386	4542	4697	4851	59
2	2594	2762	2929	3096	3261	3426	3589	3751	3913	4073	4231	4389	4545	4700	4853	58
3	2597	2765	2932	3098	3264	3428	3592	3754	3915	4075	4234	4392	4548	4702	4856	57
4	2599	2768	2935	3101	3267	3431	3595	3757	3918	4078	4237	4394	4550	4705	4858	56
5	2602	2770	2938	3104	3269	3434	3597	3760	3921	4081	4239	4397	4553	4708	4861	55
6	2605	2773	2940	3107	3272	3437	3600	3762	3923	4083	4242	4399	4555	4710	4863	54
7	2608	2776	2943	3110	3275	3439	3603	3765	3926	4086	4245	4402	4558	4713	4866	53
8	2611	2779	2946	3112	3278	3442	3605	3768	3929	4089	4247	4405	4561	4715	4868	52
9	2613	2782	2949	3115	3280	3445	3608	3770	3931	4091	4250	4407	4563	4718	4871	51
10	2616	2784	2952	3118	3283	3448	3611	3773	3934	4094	4253	4410	4566	4720	4874	50
11	2619	2787	2954	3121	3286	3450	3614	3776	3937	4097	4255	4412	4568	4723	4876	49
12	2622	2790	2957	3123	3289	3453	3616	3778	3939	4099	4258	4415	4571	4726	4879	48
13	2625	2793	2960	3126	3291	3456	3619	3781	3942	4102	4260	4418	4574	4728	4881	47
14	2628	2795	2963	3129	3294	3458	3622	3784	3945	4105	4263	4420	4576	4731	4884	46
15	2630	2798	2965	3132	3297	3461	3624	3786	3947	4107	4266	4423	4579	4733	4886	45
16	2633	2801	2968	3134	3300	3464	3627	3789	3950	4110	4268	4425	4581	4736	4889	44
17	2636	2804	2971	3137	3302	3467	3630	3792	3953	4112	4271	4428	4584	4738	4891	43
18	2639	2807	2974	3140	3305	3469	3633	3795	3955	4115	4274	4431	4586	4741	4894	42
19	2642	2809	2977	3143	3308	3472	3635	3797	3958	4118	4276	4433	4589	4743	4896	41
20	2644	2812	2979	3145	3311	3475	3638	3800	3961	4120	4279	4436	4592	4746	4899	40
21	2647	2815	2982	3148	3313	3478	3641	3803	3963	4123	4281	4439	4594	4749	4901	39
22	2650	2818	2985	3151	3316	3480	3643	3805	3966	4126	4284	4441	4597	4751	4904	38
23	2653	2821	2988	3154	3319	3483	3646	3808	3969	4128	4287	4444	4599	4754	4907	37
24	2656	2823	2990	3156	3322	3486	3649	3811	3971	4131	4289	4446	4602	4756	4909	36
25	2658	2826	2993	3159	3324	3488	3651	3813	3974	4134	4292	4449	4605	4759	4912	35
26	2661	2829	2996	3162	3327	3491	3654	3816	3977	4136	4295	4452	4607	4761	4914	34
27	2664	2832	2999	3165	3330	3494	3657	3819	3979	4139	4297	4454	4610	4764	4917	33
28	2667	2835	3002	3168	3333	3497	3660	3821	3982	4142	4300	4457	4612	4766	4919	32
29	2670	2837	3004	3170	3335	3499	3662	3824	3985	4144	4302	4459	4615	4769	4922	31
30	2672	2840	3007	3173	3338	3502	3665	3827	3987	4147	4305	4462	4617	4772	4924	30
31	2675	2843	3010	3176	3341	3505	3668	3830	3990	4150	4308	4465	4620	4774	4927	29
32	2678	2846	3013	3179	3344	3508	3670	3832	3993	4152	4310	4467	4623	4777	4929	28
33	2681	2849	3015	3181	3346	3510	3673	3835	3995	4155	4313	4470	4625	4779	4932	27
34	2684	2851	3018	3184	3349	3513	3676	3838	3998	4158	4316	4472	4628	4782	4934	26
35	2686	2854	3021	3187	3352	3516	3679	3840	4001	4160	4318	4475	4630	4784	4937	25
36	2689	2857	3024	3190	3355	3518	3681	3843	4003	4163	4321	4478	4633	4787	4939	24
37	2692	2860	3026	3192	3357	3521	3684	3846	4006	4165	4323	4480	4636	4789	4942	23
38	2695	2862	3029	3195	3360	3524	3687	3848	4009	4168	4326	4483	4638	4792	4944	22
39	2698	2865	3032	3198	3363	3527	3689	3851	4011	4171	4329	4485	4641	4795	4947	21
40	2700	2868	3035	3201	3365	3529	3692	3854	4014	4173	4331	4488	4643	4797	4950	20
41	2703	2871	3038	3203	3368	3532	3695	3856	4017	4176	4334	4491	4646	4800	4952	19
42	2706	2874	3040	3206	3371	3535	3697	3859	4019	4179	4337	4493	4648	4802	4955	18
43	2709	2876	3043	3209	3374	3537	3700	3862	4022	4181	4339	4496	4651	4805	4957	17
44	2712	2879	3046	3212	3376	3540	3703	3864	4025	4184	4342	4498	4654	4807	4960	16
45	2714	2882	3049	3214	3379	3543	3706	3867	4027	4187	4344	4501	4656	4810	4962	15
46	2717	2885	3051	3217	3382	3546	3708	3870	4030	4189	4347	4504	4659	4812	4965	14
47	2720	2888	3054	3220	3385	3548	3711	3872	4033	4192	4350	4506	4661	4815	4967	13
48	2723	2890	3057	3223	3387	3551	3714	3875	4035	4195	4352	4509	4664	4818	4970	12
49	2726	2893	3060	3225	3390	3554	3716	3878	4038	4197	4355	4511	4666	4820	4972	11
50	2728	2896	3062	3228	3393	3557	3719	3881	4041	4200	4358	4514	4669	4823	4975	10
51	2731	2899	3065	3231	3396	3559	3722	3883	4043	4202	4360	4517	4672	4825	4977	9
52	2734	2901	3068	3234	3398	3562	3724	3886	4046	4205	4363	4519	4674	4828	4980	8
53	2737	2904	3071	3236	3401	3565	3727	3889	4049	4208	4365	4522	4677	4830	4982	7
54	2740	2907	3074	3239	3404	3567	3730	3891	4051	4210	4368	4524	4679	4833	4985	6
55	2742	2910	3076	3242	3407	3570	3733	3894	4054	4213	4371	4527	4682	4835	4987	5
56	2745	2913	3079	3245	3409	3573	3735	3897	4057	4216	4373	4530	4684	4838	4990	4
57	2748	2915	3082	3247	3412	3576	3738	3899	4059	4218	4376	4532	4687	4840	4992	3
58	2751	2918	3085	3250	3415	3578	3741	3902	4062	4221	4378	4535	4690	4843	4995	2
59	2754	2921	3087	3253	3417	3581	3743	3905	4065	4224	4381	4537	4692	4846	4997	1
60	2756	2924	3090	3256	3420	3584	3746	3907	4067	4226	4384	4540	4695	4848	5000	0
	0.	0.	0.	0.	0.	0.	0.	0.	0.	0.	0.	0.	0.	0.	0.	
	74°	73°	72°	71°	70°	69°	68°	67°	66°	65°	64°	63°	62°	61°	60°	′

NATURAL COSINES

Table 32

NATURAL SINES

/	30°	31°	32°	33°	34°	35°	36°	37°	38°	39°	40°	41°	42°	43°	44°	
	0.	0.	0.	0.	0.	0.	0.	0.	0.	0.	0.	0.	0.	0.	0.	
0	5000	5150	5299	5446	5592	5736	5878	6018	6157	6293	6428	6561	6691	6820	6947	60
1	5003	5153	5302	5449	5594	5738	5880	6020	6159	6295	6430	6563	6693	6822	6949	59
2	5005	5155	5304	5451	5597	5741	5883	6023	6161	6298	6432	6565	6696	6824	6951	58
3	5008	5158	5307	5454	5599	5743	5885	6025	6163	6300	6435	6567	6698	6826	6953	57
4	5010	5160	5309	5456	5602	5745	5887	6027	6166	6302	6437	6569	6700	6828	6955	56
5	5013	5163	5312	5459	5604	5748	5890	6030	6168	6305	6439	6572	6702	6831	6957	55
6	5015	5165	5314	5461	5606	5750	5892	6032	6170	6307	6441	6574	6704	6833	6959	54
7	5018	5168	5316	5463	5609	5752	5894	6034	6173	6309	6443	6576	6706	6835	6961	53
8	5020	5170	5319	5466	5611	5755	5897	6037	6175	6311	6446	6578	6709	6837	6963	52
9	5023	5173	5321	5468	5614	5757	5899	6039	6177	6314	6448	6580	6711	6839	6965	51
10	5025	5175	5324	5471	5616	5760	5901	6041	6180	6316	6450	6583	6713	6841	6967	50
11	5028	5178	5326	5473	5618	5762	5904	6044	6182	6318	6452	6585	6715	6843	6970	49
12	5030	5180	5329	5476	5621	5764	5906	6046	6184	6320	6455	6587	6717	6845	6972	48
13	5033	5183	5331	5478	5623	5767	5908	6048	6186	6323	6457	6589	6719	6848	6974	47
14	5035	5185	5334	5480	5626	5769	5911	6051	6189	6325	6459	6591	6722	6850	6976	46
15	5038	5188	5336	5483	5628	5771	5913	6053	6191	6327	6461	6593	6724	6852	6978	45
16	5040	5190	5339	5485	5630	5774	5915	6055	6193	6329	6463	6596	6726	6854	6980	44
17	5043	5193	5341	5488	5633	5776	5918	6058	6196	6332	6466	6598	6728	6856	6982	43
18	5045	5195	5344	5490	5635	5779	5920	6060	6198	6334	6468	6600	6730	6858	6984	42
19	5048	5198	5346	5493	5638	5781	5922	6062	6200	6336	6470	6602	6732	6860	6986	41
20	5050	5200	5348	5495	5640	5783	5925	6065	6202	6338	6472	6604	6734	6862	6988	40
21	5053	5203	5351	5498	5642	5786	5927	6067	6205	6341	6475	6607	6737	6865	6990	39
22	5055	5205	5353	5500	5645	5788	5930	6069	6207	6343	6477	6609	6739	6867	6992	38
23	5058	5208	5356	5502	5647	5790	5932	6071	6209	6345	6479	6611	6741	6869	6995	37
24	5060	5210	5358	5505	5650	5793	5934	6074	6211	6347	6481	6613	6743	6871	6997	36
25	5063	5213	5361	5507	5652	5795	5937	6076	6214	6350	6483	6615	6745	6873	6999	35
26	5065	5215	5363	5510	5654	5798	5939	6078	6216	6352	6486	6617	6747	6875	7001	34
27	5068	5218	5366	5512	5657	5800	5941	6081	6218	6354	6488	6620	6749	6877	7003	33
28	5070	5220	5368	5515	5659	5802	5944	6083	6221	6356	6490	6622	6752	6879	7005	32
29	5073	5223	5371	5517	5662	5805	5946	6085	6223	6359	6492	6624	6754	6881	7007	31
30	5075	5225	5373	5519	5664	5807	5948	6088	6225	6361	6494	6626	6756	6884	7009	30
31	5078	5227	5375	5522	5666	5809	5951	6090	6227	6363	6497	6628	6758	6886	7011	29
32	5080	5230	5378	5524	5669	5812	5953	6092	6230	6365	6499	6631	6760	6888	7013	28
33	5083	5232	5380	5527	5671	5814	5955	6095	6232	6368	6501	6633	6762	6890	7015	27
34	5085	5235	5383	5529	5674	5816	5958	6097	6234	6370	6503	6635	6764	6892	7017	26
35	5088	5237	5385	5531	5676	5819	5960	6099	6237	6372	6506	6637	6767	6894	7019	25
36	5090	5240	5388	5534	5678	5821	5962	6101	6239	6374	6508	6639	6769	6896	7022	24
37	5093	5242	5390	5536	5681	5824	5965	6104	6241	6376	6510	6641	6771	6898	7024	23
38	5095	5245	5393	5539	5683	5826	5967	6106	6243	6379	6512	6644	6773	6900	7026	22
39	5098	5247	5395	5541	5686	5828	5969	6108	6246	6381	6514	6646	6775	6903	7028	21
40	5100	5250	5398	5544	5688	5831	5972	6111	6248	6383	6517	6648	6777	6905	7030	20
41	5103	5252	5400	5546	5690	5833	5974	6113	6250	6385	6519	6650	6779	6907	7032	19
42	5105	5255	5402	5548	5693	5835	5976	6115	6252	6388	6521	6652	6782	6909	7034	18
43	5108	5257	5405	5551	5695	5838	5979	6118	6255	6390	6523	6654	6784	6911	7036	17
44	5110	5260	5407	5553	5698	5840	5981	6120	6257	6392	6525	6657	6786	6913	7038	16
45	5113	5262	5410	5556	5700	5842	5983	6122	6259	6394	6528	6659	6788	6915	7040	15
46	5115	5265	5412	5558	5702	5845	5986	6124	6262	6397	6530	6661	6790	6917	7042	14
47	5118	5267	5415	5561	5705	5847	5988	6127	6264	6399	6532	6663	6792	6919	7044	13
48	5120	5270	5417	5563	5707	5850	5990	6129	6266	6401	6534	6665	6794	6921	7046	12
49	5123	5272	5420	5565	5710	5852	5993	6131	6268	6403	6536	6667	6797	6924	7048	11
50	5125	5275	5422	5568	5712	5854	5995	6134	6271	6406	6539	6670	6799	6926	7050	10
51	5128	5277	5424	5570	5714	5857	5997	6136	6273	6408	6541	6672	6801	6928	7053	9
52	5130	5279	5427	5573	5717	5859	6000	6138	6275	6410	6543	6674	6803	6930	7055	8
53	5133	5282	5429	5575	5719	5861	6002	6141	6277	6412	6545	6676	6805	6932	7057	7
54	5135	5284	5432	5577	5721	5864	6004	6143	6280	6414	6547	6678	6807	6934	7059	6
55	5138	5287	5434	5580	5724	5866	6007	6145	6282	6417	6550	6680	6809	6936	7061	5
56	5140	5289	5437	5582	5726	5868	6009	6147	6284	6419	6552	6683	6811	6938	7063	4
57	5143	5292	5439	5585	5729	5871	6011	6150	6286	6421	6554	6685	6814	6940	7065	3
58	5145	5294	5442	5587	5731	5873	6014	6152	6289	6423	6556	6687	6816	6942	7067	2
59	5148	5297	5444	5590	5733	5875	6016	6154	6291	6426	6558	6689	6818	6944	7069	1
60	5150	5299	5446	5592	5736	5878	6018	6157	6293	6428	6561	6691	6820	6947	7071	0
	0.	0.	0.	0.	0.	0.	0.	0.	0.	0.	0.	0.	0.	0.	0.	
	59°	58°	57°	56°	55°	54°	53°	52°	51°	50°	49°	48°	47°	46°	45°	/

NATURAL COSINES

Table 32

NATURAL SINES

∕	45°	46°	47°	48°	49°	50°	51°	52°	53°	54°	55°	56°	57°	58°	59°	
	0.	0.	0.	0.	0.	0.	0.	0.	0.	0.	0.	0.	0.	0.	0.	
0	7071	7193	7314	7431	7547	7660	7771	7880	7986	8090	8192	8290	8387	8480	8572	60
1	7073	7195	7316	7433	7549	7662	7773	7882	7988	8092	8193	8292	8388	8482	8573	59
2	7075	7197	7318	7435	7551	7664	7775	7884	7990	8094	8195	8294	8390	8484	8575	58
3	7077	7199	7319	7437	7553	7666	7777	7885	7992	8095	8197	8295	8391	8485	8576	57
4	7079	7201	7321	7439	7555	7668	7779	7887	7993	8097	8198	8297	8393	8487	8578	56
5	7081	7203	7323	7441	7557	7670	7781	7889	7995	8099	8200	8298	8395	8488	8579	55
6	7083	7206	7325	7443	7559	7672	7782	7891	7997	8100	8202	8300	8396	8490	8581	54
7	7085	7208	7327	7445	7560	7674	7784	7893	7999	8102	8203	8302	8398	8491	8582	53
8	7088	7210	7329	7447	7562	7675	7786	7894	8000	8104	8205	8303	8399	8493	8584	52
9	7090	7212	7331	7449	7564	7677	7788	7896	8002	8106	8207	8305	8401	8494	8585	51
10	7092	7214	7333	7451	7566	7679	7790	7898	8004	8107	8208	8307	8403	8496	8587	50
11	7094	7216	7335	7453	7568	7681	7792	7900	8006	8109	8210	8308	8404	8497	8588	49
12	7096	7218	7337	7455	7570	7683	7793	7902	8007	8111	8211	8310	8406	8499	8590	48
13	7098	7220	7339	7457	7572	7685	7795	7903	8009	8112	8213	8311	8407	8500	8591	47
14	7100	7222	7341	7459	7574	7687	7797	7905	8011	8114	8215	8313	8409	8502	8593	46
15	7102	7224	7343	7461	7576	7688	7799	7907	8013	8116	8216	8315	8410	8504	8594	45
16	7104	7226	7345	7463	7578	7690	7801	7909	8014	8117	8218	8316	8412	8505	8596	44
17	7106	7228	7347	7464	7579	7692	7802	7910	8016	8119	8220	8318	8414	8507	8597	43
18	7108	7230	7349	7466	7581	7694	7804	7912	8018	8121	8221	8320	8415	8508	8599	42
19	7110	7232	7351	7468	7583	7696	7806	7914	8019	8123	8223	8321	8417	8510	8600	41
20	7112	7234	7353	7470	7585	7698	7808	7916	8021	8124	8225	8323	8418	8511	8601	40
21	7114	7236	7355	7472	7587	7700	7810	7918	8023	8126	8226	8324	8420	8513	8603	39
22	7116	7238	7357	7474	7589	7701	7812	7919	8025	8128	8228	8326	8421	8514	8604	38
23	7118	7240	7359	7476	7591	7703	7813	7921	8026	8129	8230	8328	8423	8516	8606	37
24	7120	7242	7361	7478	7593	7705	7815	7923	8028	8131	8231	8329	8425	8517	8607	36
25	7122	7244	7363	7480	7595	7707	7817	7925	8030	8133	8233	8331	8426	8519	8609	35
26	7124	7246	7365	7482	7596	7709	7819	7926	8032	8134	8235	8332	8428	8520	8610	34
27	7126	7248	7367	7484	7598	7711	7821	7928	8033	8136	8236	8334	8429	8522	8612	33
28	7128	7250	7369	7486	7600	7713	7822	7930	8035	8138	8238	8336	8431	8523	8613	32
29	7130	7252	7371	7488	7602	7714	7824	7932	8037	8139	8240	8337	8432	8525	8615	31
30	7133	7254	7373	7490	7604	7716	7826	7934	8039	8141	8241	8339	8434	8526	8616	30
31	7135	7256	7375	7491	7606	7718	7828	7935	8040	8143	8243	8340	8435	8528	8618	29
32	7137	7258	7377	7493	7608	7720	7830	7937	8042	8145	8245	8342	8437	8529	8619	28
33	7139	7260	7379	7495	7610	7722	7832	7939	8044	8146	8246	8344	8439	8531	8621	27
34	7141	7262	7381	7497	7612	7724	7833	7941	8045	8148	8248	8345	8440	8532	8622	26
35	7143	7264	7383	7499	7613	7725	7835	7942	8047	8150	8249	8347	8442	8534	8624	25
36	7145	7266	7385	7501	7615	7727	7837	7944	8049	8151	8251	8348	8443	8536	8625	24
37	7147	7268	7387	7503	7617	7729	7839	7946	8051	8153	8253	8350	8445	8537	8627	23
38	7149	7270	7388	7505	7619	7731	7841	7948	8052	8155	8254	8352	8446	8539	8628	22
39	7151	7272	7390	7507	7621	7733	7842	7949	8054	8156	8256	8353	8448	8540	8630	21
40	7153	7274	7392	7509	7623	7735	7844	7951	8056	8158	8258	8355	8450	8542	8631	20
41	7155	7276	7394	7511	7625	7737	7846	7953	8058	8160	8259	8356	8451	8543	8632	19
42	7157	7278	7396	7513	7627	7738	7848	7955	8059	8161	8261	8358	8453	8545	8634	18
43	7159	7280	7398	7515	7629	7740	7850	7956	8061	8163	8263	8360	8454	8546	8635	17
44	7161	7282	7400	7516	7630	7742	7851	7958	8063	8165	8264	8361	8456	8548	8637	16
45	7163	7284	7402	7518	7632	7744	7853	7960	8064	8166	8266	8363	8457	8549	8638	15
46	7165	7286	7404	7520	7634	7746	7855	7962	8066	8168	8268	8364	8459	8551	8640	14
47	7167	7288	7406	7522	7636	7748	7857	7964	8068	8170	8269	8366	8460	8552	8641	13
48	7169	7290	7408	7524	7638	7749	7859	7965	8070	8171	8271	8368	8462	8554	8643	12
49	7171	7292	7410	7526	7640	7751	7860	7967	8071	8173	8272	8369	8463	8555	8644	11
50	7173	7294	7412	7528	7642	7753	7862	7969	8073	8175	8274	8371	8465	8557	8646	10
51	7175	7296	7414	7530	7644	7755	7864	7971	8075	8176	8276	8372	8467	8558	8647	9
52	7177	7298	7416	7532	7645	7757	7866	7972	8076	8178	8277	8374	8468	8560	8649	8
53	7179	7300	7418	7534	7647	7759	7868	7974	8078	8180	8279	8376	8470	8561	8650	7
54	7181	7302	7420	7536	7649	7760	7869	7976	8080	8181	8281	8377	8471	8563	8652	6
55	7183	7304	7422	7538	7651	7762	7871	7978	8082	8183	8282	8379	8473	8564	8653	5
56	7185	7306	7424	7539	7653	7764	7873	7979	8083	8185	8284	8380	8474	8566	8654	4
57	7187	7308	7426	7541	7655	7766	7875	7981	8085	8187	8285	8382	8476	8567	8656	3
58	7189	7310	7428	7543	7657	7768	7877	7983	8087	8188	8287	8384	8477	8569	8657	2
59	7191	7312	7430	7545	7659	7770	7878	7985	8088	8190	8289	8385	8479	8570	8659	1
60	7193	7314	7431	7547	7660	7771	7880	7986	8090	8192	8290	8387	8480	8572	8660	0
	0.	0.	0.	0.	0.	0.	0.	0.	0.	0.	0.	0.	0.	0.	0.	
	44°	43°	42°	41°	40°	39°	38°	37°	36°	35°	34°	33°	32°	31°	30°	∕

NATURAL COSINES

Table 32

NATURAL SINES

/	60°	61°	62°	63°	64°	65°	66°	67°	68°	69°	70°	71°	72°	73°	74°	
	0.	0.	0.	0.	0.	0.	0.			0.			0.	0.	0.	
0	8660	8746	8829	8910	8988	9063	9135	9205	9272	9336	9397	9455	9511	9563	9613	60
1	8662	8748	8831	8911	8989	9064	9137	9206	9273	9337	9398	9456	9511	9564	9613	59
2	8663	8749	8832	8913	8990	9066	9138	9207	9274	9338	9399	9457	9512	9565	9614	58
3	8665	8750	8834	8914	8992	9067	9139	9208	9275	9339	9400	9458	9513	9566	9615	57
4	8666	8752	8835	8915	8993	9068	9140	9210	9276	9340	9401	9459	9514	9566	9616	56
5	8668	8753	8836	8917	8994	9069	9141	9211	9277	9341	9402	9460	9515	9567	9617	55
6	8669	8755	8838	8918	8996	9070	9143	9212	9278	9342	9403	9461	9516	9568	9617	54
7	8670	8756	8839	8919	8997	9072	9144	9213	9279	9343	9404	9462	9517	9569	9618	53
8	8672	8757	8840	8921	8998	9073	9145	9214	9281	9344	9405	9463	9518	9570	9619	52
9	8673	8759	8842	8922	8999	9074	9146	9215	9282	9345	9406	9464	9519	9571	9620	51
10	8675	8760	8843	8923	9001	9075	9147	9216	9283	9346	9407	9465	9520	9572	9621	50
11	8676	8762	8844	8925	9002	9077	9148	9218	9284	9347	9408	9466	9520	9572	9621	49
12	8678	8763	8846	8926	9003	9078	9150	9219	9285	9348	9409	9466	9521	9573	9622	48
13	8679	8764	8847	8927	9004	9079	9151	9220	9286	9349	9410	9467	9522	9574	9623	47
14	8681	8766	8849	8928	9006	9080	9152	9221	9287	9350	9411	9468	9523	9575	9624	46
15	8682	8767	8850	8930	9007	9081	9153	9222	9288	9351	9412	9469	9524	9576	9625	45
16	8683	8769	8851	8931	9008	9083	9154	9223	9289	9352	9413	9470	9525	9577	9625	44
17	8685	8770	8853	8932	9010	9084	9155	9224	9290	9353	9414	9471	9526	9577	9626	43
18	8686	8771	8854	8934	9011	9085	9157	9225	9291	9354	9415	9472	9527	9578	9627	42
19	8688	8773	8855	8935	9012	9086	9158	9227	9292	9355	9416	9473	9527	9579	9628	41
20	8689	8774	8857	8936	9013	9088	9159	9228	9293	9356	9417	9474	9528	9580	9628	40
21	8691	8776	8858	8938	9015	9089	9160	9229	9295	9358	9418	9475	9529	9581	9629	39
22	8692	8777	8859	8939	9016	9090	9161	9230	9296	9359	9419	9476	9530	9582	9630	38
23	8694	8778	8861	8940	9017	9091	9162	9231	9297	9360	9420	9477	9531	9582	9631	37
24	8695	8780	8862	8942	9018	9092	9164	9232	9298	9361	9421	9478	9532	9583	9632	36
25	8696	8781	8863	8943	9020	9094	9165	9233	9299	9362	9422	9479	9533	9584	9632	35
26	8698	8783	8865	8944	9021	9095	9166	9234	9300	9363	9423	9480	9534	9585	9633	34
27	8699	8784	8866	8945	9022	9096	9167	9235	9301	9364	9423	9480	9535	9586	9634	33
28	8701	8785	8867	8947	9023	9097	9168	9237	9302	9365	9424	9481	9535	9587	9635	32
29	8702	8787	8869	8948	9025	9098	9169	9238	9303	9366	9425	9482	9536	9587	9636	31
30	8704	8788	8870	8949	9026	9100	9171	9239	9304	9367	9426	9483	9537	9588	9636	30
31	8705	8790	8871	8951	9027	9101	9172	9240	9305	9368	9427	9484	9538	9589	9637	29
32	8706	8791	8873	8952	9028	9102	9173	9241	9306	9369	9428	9485	9539	9590	9638	28
33	8708	8792	8874	8953	9030	9103	9174	9242	9307	9370	9429	9486	9540	9591	9639	27
34	8709	8794	8875	8955	9031	9104	9175	9243	9308	9371	9430	9487	9541	9591	9639	26
35	8711	8795	8877	8956	9032	9106	9176	9244	9309	9372	9431	9488	9542	9592	9640	25
36	8712	8796	8878	8957	9033	9107	9178	9245	9311	9373	9432	9489	9542	9593	9641	24
37	8714	8798	8879	8958	9035	9108	9179	9247	9312	9374	9433	9490	9543	9594	9642	23
38	8715	8799	8881	8960	9036	9109	9180	9248	9313	9375	9434	9491	9544	9595	9642	22
39	8716	8801	8882	8961	9037	9110	9181	9249	9314	9376	9435	9492	9545	9596	9643	21
40	8718	8802	8884	8962	9038	9112	9182	9250	9315	9377	9436	9492	9546	9596	9644	20
41	8719	8803	8885	8964	9040	9113	9183	9251	9316	9378	9437	9493	9547	9597	9645	19
42	8721	8805	8886	8965	9041	9114	9184	9252	9317	9379	9438	9494	9548	9598	9646	18
43	8722	8806	8888	8966	9042	9115	9186	9253	9318	9380	9439	9495	9548	9599	9646	17
44	8724	8808	8889	8967	9043	9116	9187	9254	9319	9381	9440	9496	9549	9600	9647	16
45	8725	8809	8890	8969	9045	9118	9188	9255	9320	9382	9441	9497	9550	9600	9648	15
46	8726	8810	8892	8970	9046	9119	9189	9257	9321	9383	9442	9498	9551	9601	9649	14
47	8728	8812	8893	8971	9047	9120	9190	9258	9322	9384	9443	9499	9552	9602	9649	13
48	8729	8813	8894	8973	9048	9121	9191	9259	9323	9385	9444	9500	9553	9603	9650	12
49	8731	8814	8895	8974	9050	9122	9192	9260	9324	9386	9445	9501	9554	9604	9651	11
50	8732	8816	8897	8975	9051	9124	9194	9261	9325	9387	9446	9502	9555	9605	9652	10
51	8733	8817	8898	8976	9052	9125	9195	9262	9326	9388	9447	9502	9555	9605	9652	9
52	8735	8819	8899	8978	9053	9126	9196	9263	9327	9389	9448	9503	9556	9606	9653	8
53	8736	8820	8901	8979	9054	9127	9197	9264	9328	9390	9449	9504	9557	9607	9654	7
54	8738	8821	8902	8980	9056	9128	9198	9265	9330	9391	9449	9505	9558	9608	9655	6
55	8739	8823	8903	8982	9057	9130	9199	9266	9331	9392	9450	9506	9559	9609	9655	5
56	8741	8824	8905	8983	9058	9131	9200	9267	9332	9393	9451	9507	9560	9609	9656	4
57	8742	8825	8906	8984	9059	9132	9202	9269	9333	9394	9452	9508	9560	9610	9657	3
58	8743	8827	8907	8985	9061	9133	9203	9270	9334	9395	9453	9509	9561	9611	9658	2
59	8745	8828	8909	8987	9062	9134	9204	9271	9335	9396	9454	9510	9562	9612	9659	1
60	8746	8829	8910	8988	9063	9135	9205	9272	9336	9397	9455	9511	9563	9613	9659	0
	0.	0.	0.	0.	0.	0.	0.	0.	0.	0.	0.	0.	0.	0.	0.	
	29°	28°	27°	26°	25°	24°	23°	22°	21°	20°	19°	18°	17°	16°	15°	/

NATURAL COSINES

Table 32

NATURAL SINES

/	75°	76°	77°	78°	79°	80°	81°	82°	83°	84°	85°	86°	87°	88°	89°	
	0.	0.	0.	0.	0.	0.	0.	0.	0.	0.	0.	0.	0.	0.	0./1.	
0	9659	9703	9744	9781	9816	9848	9877	9903	9925	9945	9962	9976	9986	9994	9998	60
1	9660	9704	9744	9782	9817	9849	9877	9903	9926	9946	9962	9976	9986	9994	9999	59
2	9661	9704	9745	9783	9817	9849	9878	9903	9926	9946	9962	9976	9987	9994	9999	58
3	9661	9705	9746	9783	9818	9850	9878	9904	9926	9946	9963	9976	9987	9994	9999	57
4	9662	9706	9746	9784	9818	9850	9879	9904	9927	9946	9963	9976	9987	9994	9999	56
5	9663	9706	9747	9784	9819	9851	9879	9905	9927	9947	9963	9977	9987	9994	9999	55
6	9664	9707	9748	9785	9820	9851	9880	9905	9928	9947	9963	9977	9987	9995	9999	54
7	9665	9708	9748	9786	9820	9852	9880	9905	9928	9947	9964	9977	9987	9995	9999	53
8	9665	9709	9749	9786	9821	9852	9880	9906	9928	9948	9964	9977	9987	9995	9999	52
9	9666	9709	9750	9787	9821	9853	9881	9906	9929	9948	9964	9977	9988	9995	9999	51
10	9667	9710	9750	9787	9822	9853	9881	9907	9929	9948	9964	9978	9988	9995	9999	50
11	9667	9711	9751	9788	9822	9854	9882	9907	9929	9949	9965	9978	9988	9995	9999	49
12	9668	9711	9751	9789	9823	9854	9882	9907	9930	9949	9965	9978	9988	9995	9999	48
13	9669	9712	9752	9789	9823	9855	9883	9908	9930	9949	9965	9978	9988	9995	9999	47
14	9670	9713	9753	9790	9824	9855	9883	9908	9930	9949	9965	9978	9988	9995	9999	46
15	9670	9713	9753	9790	9825	9856	9884	9909	9931	9950	9966	9979	9988	9995	9999	45
16	9671	9714	9754	9791	9825	9856	9884	9909	9931	9950	9966	9979	9989	9995	9999	44
17	9672	9715	9755	9792	9826	9857	9884	9909	9931	9950	9966	9979	9989	9996	9999	43
18	9673	9715	9755	9792	9826	9857	9885	9910	9932	9951	9966	9979	9989	9996	9999	42
19	9673	9716	9756	9793	9827	9858	9885	9910	9932	9951	9967	9979	9989	9996	9999	41
20	9674	9717	9757	9793	9827	9858	9886	9911	9932	9951	9967	9980	9989	9996	9999	40
21	9675	9718	9757	9794	9828	9859	9886	9911	9933	9951	9967	9980	9989	9996	9999	39
22	9676	9718	9758	9795	9828	9859	9887	9911	9933	9952	9967	9980	9989	9996	9999	38
23	9676	9719	9759	9795	9829	9859	9887	9912	9933	9952	9968	9980	9990	9996	9999	37
24	9677	9720	9759	9796	9829	9860	9888	9912	9934	9952	9968	9980	9990	9996	9999	36
25	9678	9720	9760	9796	9830	9860	9888	9913	9934	9953	9968	9980	9990	9996	9999	35
26	9679	9721	9760	9797	9830	9861	9888	9913	9934	9953	9968	9981	9990	9996	0000	34
27	9679	9722	9761	9798	9831	9861	9889	9913	9935	9953	9968	9981	9990	9996	0000	33
28	9680	9722	9762	9798	9831	9862	9889	9914	9935	9953	9969	9981	9990	9996	0000	32
29	9681	9723	9762	9799	9832	9862	9890	9914	9935	9954	9969	9981	9990	9996	0000	31
30	9681	9724	9763	9799	9833	9863	9890	9914	9936	9954	9969	9981	9990	9997	0000	30
31	9682	9724	9764	9800	9833	9863	9891	9915	9936	9954	9969	9982	9991	9997	0000	29
32	9683	9725	9764	9800	9834	9864	9891	9915	9936	9955	9970	9982	9991	9997	0000	28
33	9684	9726	9765	9801	9834	9864	9891	9916	9937	9955	9970	9982	9991	9997	0000	27
34	9684	9726	9765	9802	9835	9865	9892	9916	9937	9955	9970	9982	9991	9997	0000	26
35	9685	9727	9766	9802	9835	9865	9892	9916	9937	9955	9970	9982	9991	9997	0000	25
36	9686	9728	9767	9803	9836	9866	9893	9917	9938	9956	9971	9982	9991	9997	0000	24
37	9687	9728	9767	9803	9836	9866	9893	9917	9938	9956	9971	9983	9991	9997	0000	23
38	9687	9729	9768	9804	9837	9867	9894	9917	9938	9956	9971	9983	9991	9997	0000	22
39	9688	9730	9769	9804	9837	9867	9894	9918	9939	9956	9971	9983	9992	9997	0000	21
40	9689	9730	9769	9805	9838	9868	9894	9918	9939	9957	9971	9983	9992	9997	0000	20
41	9689	9731	9770	9806	9838	9868	9895	9919	9939	9957	9972	9983	9992	9997	0000	19
42	9690	9732	9770	9806	9839	9869	9895	9919	9940	9957	9972	9983	9992	9997	0000	18
43	9691	9732	9771	9807	9839	9869	9896	9919	9940	9958	9972	9984	9992	9997	0000	17
44	9692	9733	9772	9807	9840	9869	9896	9920	9940	9958	9972	9984	9992	9998	0000	16
45	9692	9734	9772	9808	9840	9870	9897	9920	9941	9958	9973	9984	9992	9998	0000	15
46	9693	9734	9773	9808	9841	9870	9897	9920	9941	9958	9973	9984	9992	9998	0000	14
47	9694	9735	9774	9809	9841	9871	9897	9921	9941	9959	9973	9984	9993	9998	0000	13
48	9694	9736	9774	9810	9842	9871	9898	9921	9942	9959	9973	9984	9993	9998	0000	12
49	9695	9736	9775	9810	9842	9872	9898	9922	9942	9959	9973	9985	9993	9998	0000	11
50	9696	9737	9775	9811	9843	9872	9899	9922	9942	9959	9974	9985	9993	9998	0000	10
51	9697	9738	9776	9811	9843	9873	9899	9922	9942	9960	9974	9985	9993	9998	0000	9
52	9697	9738	9777	9812	9844	9873	9899	9923	9943	9960	9974	9985	9993	9998	0000	8
53	9698	9739	9777	9812	9845	9874	9900	9923	9943	9960	9974	9985	9993	9998	0000	7
54	9699	9740	9778	9813	9845	9874	9900	9923	9943	9960	9974	9985	9993	9998	0000	6
55	9699	9740	9778	9813	9846	9875	9901	9924	9944	9961	9975	9986	9993	9998	0000	5
56	9700	9741	9779	9814	9846	9875	9901	9924	9944	9961	9975	9986	9993	9998	0000	4
57	9701	9742	9780	9815	9847	9876	9901	9924	9944	9961	9975	9986	9994	9998	0000	3
58	9702	9742	9780	9815	9847	9876	9902	9925	9945	9961	9975	9986	9994	9998	0000	2
59	9702	9743	9781	9816	9848	9876	9902	9925	9945	9962	9975	9986	9994	9998	0000	1
60	9703	9744	9781	9816	9848	9877	9903	9925	9945	9962	9976	9986	9994	9998	0000	0
	0.	0.	0.	0.	0.	0.	0.	0.	0.	0.	0.	0.	0.	0.	0./1.	
	14°	13°	12°	11°	10°	9°	8°	7°	6°	5°	4°	3°	2°	1°	0°	/

NATURAL COSINES

Table 33

NATURAL TANGENTS

/	0°	1°	2°	3°	4°	5°	6°	7°	8°	9°	10°	11°	12°	13°	14°	
	0.	0.	0.	0.	0.	0.	0.	0.	0.	0.	0.	0.	0.	0.	0.	
0	0000	0175	0349	0524	0699	0875	1051	1228	1405	1584	1763	1944	2126	2309	2493	60
1	0003	0177	0352	0527	0702	0878	1054	1231	1408	1587	1766	1947	2129	2312	2496	59
2	0006	0180	0355	0530	0705	0881	1057	1234	1411	1590	1769	1950	2132	2315	2499	58
3	0009	0183	0358	0533	0708	0884	1060	1237	1414	1593	1772	1953	2135	2318	2503	57
4	0012	0186	0361	0536	0711	0887	1063	1240	1417	1596	1775	1956	2138	2321	2506	56
5	0015	0189	0364	0539	0714	0890	1066	1243	1420	1599	1778	1959	2141	2324	2509	55
6	0017	0192	0367	0542	0717	0892	1069	1246	1423	1602	1781	1962	2144	2327	2512	54
7	0020	0195	0370	0544	0720	0895	1072	1249	1426	1605	1784	1965	2147	2330	2515	53
8	0023	0198	0373	0547	0723	0898	1075	1251	1429	1608	1787	1968	2150	2333	2518	52
9	0026	0201	0375	0550	0726	0901	1078	1254	1432	1611	1790	1971	2153	2336	2521	51
10	0029	0204	0378	0553	0729	0904	1080	1257	1435	1614	1793	1974	2156	2339	2524	50
11	0032	0207	0381	0556	0731	0907	1083	1260	1438	1617	1796	1977	2159	2342	2527	49
12	0035	0209	0384	0559	0734	0910	1086	1263	1441	1620	1799	1980	2162	2345	2530	48
13	0038	0212	0387	0562	0737	0913	1089	1266	1444	1623	1802	1983	2165	2349	2533	47
14	0041	0215	0390	0565	0740	0916	1092	1269	1447	1626	1805	1986	2168	2352	2537	46
15	0044	0218	0393	0568	0743	0919	1095	1272	1450	1629	1808	1989	2171	2355	2540	45
16	0047	0221	0396	0571	0746	0922	1098	1275	1453	1632	1811	1992	2174	2358	2543	44
17	0049	0224	0399	0574	0749	0925	1101	1278	1456	1635	1814	1995	2177	2361	2546	43
18	0052	0227	0402	0577	0752	0928	1104	1281	1459	1638	1817	1998	2180	2364	2549	42
19	0055	0230	0405	0580	0755	0931	1107	1284	1462	1641	1820	2001	2183	2367	2552	41
20	0058	0233	0407	0582	0758	0934	1110	1287	1465	1644	1823	2004	2186	2370	2555	40
21	0061	0236	0410	0585	0761	0936	1113	1290	1468	1647	1826	2007	2189	2373	2558	39
22	0064	0239	0413	0588	0764	0939	1116	1293	1471	1650	1829	2010	2193	2376	2561	38
23	0067	0241	0416	0591	0767	0942	1119	1296	1474	1653	1832	2013	2196	2379	2564	37
24	0070	0244	0419	0594	0769	0945	1122	1299	1477	1655	1835	2016	2199	2382	2568	36
25	0073	0247	0422	0597	0772	0948	1125	1302	1480	1658	1838	2019	2202	2385	2571	35
26	0076	0250	0425	0600	0775	0951	1128	1305	1483	1661	1841	2022	2205	2388	2574	34
27	0079	0253	0428	0603	0778	0954	1131	1308	1486	1664	1844	2025	2208	2392	2577	33
28	0081	0256	0431	0606	0781	0957	1133	1311	1489	1667	1847	2028	2211	2395	2580	32
29	0084	0259	0434	0609	0784	0960	1136	1314	1492	1670	1850	2031	2214	2398	2583	31
30	0087	0262	0437	0612	0787	0963	1139	1317	1495	1673	1853	2035	2217	2401	2586	30
31	0090	0265	0440	0615	0790	0966	1142	1319	1497	1676	1856	2038	2220	2404	2589	29
32	0093	0268	0442	0617	0793	0969	1145	1322	1500	1679	1859	2041	2223	2407	2592	28
33	0096	0271	0445	0620	0796	0972	1148	1325	1503	1682	1862	2044	2226	2410	2595	27
34	0099	0274	0448	0623	0799	0975	1151	1328	1506	1685	1865	2047	2229	2413	2599	26
35	0102	0276	0451	0626	0802	0978	1154	1331	1509	1688	1868	2050	2232	2416	2602	25
36	0105	0279	0454	0629	0805	0981	1157	1334	1512	1691	1871	2053	2235	2419	2605	24
37	0108	0282	0457	0632	0808	0983	1160	1337	1515	1694	1874	2056	2238	2422	2608	23
38	0111	0285	0460	0635	0810	0986	1163	1340	1518	1697	1877	2059	2241	2425	2611	22
39	0113	0288	0463	0638	0813	0989	1166	1343	1521	1700	1880	2062	2244	2428	2614	21
40	0116	0291	0466	0641	0816	0992	1169	1346	1524	1703	1883	2065	2247	2432	2617	20
41	0119	0294	0469	0644	0819	0995	1172	1349	1527	1706	1887	2068	2251	2435	2620	19
42	0122	0297	0472	0647	0822	0998	1175	1352	1530	1709	1890	2071	2254	2438	2623	18
43	0125	0300	0475	0650	0825	1001	1178	1355	1533	1712	1893	2074	2257	2441	2627	17
44	0128	0303	0477	0653	0828	1004	1181	1358	1536	1715	1896	2077	2260	2444	2630	16
45	0131	0306	0480	0655	0831	1007	1184	1361	1539	1718	1899	2080	2263	2447	2633	15
46	0134	0308	0483	0658	0834	1010	1187	1364	1542	1721	1902	2083	2266	2450	2636	14
47	0137	0311	0486	0661	0837	1013	1189	1367	1545	1724	1905	2086	2269	2453	2639	13
48	0140	0314	0489	0664	0840	1016	1192	1370	1548	1727	1908	2089	2272	2456	2642	12
49	0143	0317	0492	0667	0843	1019	1195	1373	1551	1730	1911	2092	2275	2459	2645	11
50	0145	0320	0495	0670	0846	1022	1198	1376	1554	1733	1914	2095	2278	2462	2648	10
51	0148	0323	0498	0673	0849	1025	1201	1379	1557	1736	1917	2098	2281	2465	2651	9
52	0151	0326	0501	0676	0851	1028	1204	1382	1560	1739	1920	2101	2284	2469	2655	8
53	0154	0329	0504	0679	0854	1030	1207	1385	1563	1742	1923	2104	2287	2472	2658	7
54	0157	0332	0507	0682	0857	1033	1210	1388	1566	1745	1926	2107	2290	2475	2661	6
55	0160	0335	0509	0685	0860	1036	1213	1391	1569	1748	1929	2110	2293	2478	2664	5
56	0163	0338	0512	0688	0863	1039	1216	1394	1572	1751	1932	2113	2296	2481	2667	4
57	0166	0340	0515	0690	0866	1042	1219	1397	1575	1754	1935	2116	2299	2484	2670	3
58	0169	0343	0518	0693	0869	1045	1222	1399	1578	1757	1938	2119	2303	2487	2673	2
59	0172	0346	0521	0696	0872	1048	1225	1402	1581	1760	1941	2123	2306	2490	2676	1
60	0175	0349	0524	0699	0875	1051	1228	1405	1584	1763	1944	2126	2309	2493	2679	0
	0.	0.	0.	0.	0.	0.	0.	0.	0.	0.	0.	0.	0.	0.	0.	
	89°	88°	87°	86°	85°	84°	83°	82°	81°	80°	79°	78°	77°	76°	75°	/

NATURAL COTANGENTS

Table 33

NATURAL TANGENTS

′	15°	16°	17°	18°	19°	20°	21°	22°	23°	24°	25°	26°	27°	28°	29°	
	0.	0.	0.	0.	0.	0.	0.	0.	0.	0.	0.	0.	0.	0.	0.	
0	2679	2867	3057	3249	3443	3640	3839	4040	4245	4452	4663	4877	5095	5317	5543	60
1	2683	2871	3060	3252	3447	3643	3842	4044	4248	4456	4667	4881	5099	5321	5547	59
2	2686	2874	3064	3256	3450	3646	3845	4047	4252	4459	4670	4885	5103	5325	5551	58
3	2689	2877	3067	3259	3453	3650	3849	4050	4255	4463	4674	4888	5106	5328	5555	57
4	2692	2880	3070	3262	3456	3653	3852	4054	4258	4466	4677	4892	5110	5332	5558	56
5	2695	2883	3073	3265	3460	3656	3855	4057	4262	4470	4681	4895	5114	5336	5562	55
6	2698	2886	3076	3269	3463	3659	3859	4061	4265	4473	4684	4899	5117	5340	5566	54
7	2701	2890	3080	3272	3466	3663	3862	4064	4269	4477	4688	4903	5121	5343	5570	53
8	2704	2893	3083	3275	3469	3666	3865	4067	4272	4480	4691	4906	5125	5347	5574	52
9	2708	2896	3086	3278	3473	3669	3869	4071	4276	4484	4695	4910	5128	5351	5577	51
10	2711	2899	3089	3281	3476	3673	3872	4074	4279	4487	4699	4913	5132	5354	5581	50
11	2714	2902	3092	3285	3479	3676	3875	4078	4283	4491	4702	4917	5136	5358	5585	49
12	2717	2905	3096	3288	3482	3679	3879	4081	4286	4494	4706	4921	5139	5362	5589	48
13	2720	2908	3099	3291	3486	3683	3882	4084	4289	4498	4709	4924	5143	5366	5593	47
14	2723	2912	3102	3294	3489	3686	3885	4088	4293	4501	4713	4928	5147	5369	5596	46
15	2726	2915	3105	3298	3492	3689	3889	4091	4296	4505	4716	4931	5150	5373	5600	45
16	2729	2918	3108	3301	3495	3693	3892	4095	4300	4508	4720	4935	5154	5377	5604	44
17	2733	2921	3111	3304	3499	3696	3895	4098	4303	4512	4723	4939	5158	5381	5608	43
18	2736	2924	3115	3307	3502	3699	3899	4101	4307	4515	4727	4942	5161	5384	5612	42
19	2739	2927	3118	3310	3505	3702	3902	4105	4310	4519	4731	4946	5165	5388	5616	41
20	2742	2931	3121	3314	3508	3706	3906	4108	4314	4522	4734	4950	5169	5392	5619	40
21	2745	2934	3124	3317	3512	3709	3909	4111	4317	4526	4738	4953	5172	5396	5623	39
22	2748	2937	3127	3320	3515	3712	3912	4115	4320	4529	4741	4957	5176	5399	5627	38
23	2751	2940	3131	3323	3518	3716	3916	4118	4324	4533	4745	4960	5180	5403	5631	37
24	2754	2943	3134	3327	3522	3719	3919	4122	4327	4536	4748	4964	5184	5407	5635	36
25	2758	2946	3137	3330	3525	3722	3922	4125	4331	4540	4752	4968	5187	5411	5639	35
26	2761	2949	3140	3333	3528	3726	3926	4129	4334	4543	4755	4971	5191	5415	5642	34
27	2764	2953	3143	3336	3531	3729	3929	4132	4338	4547	4759	4975	5195	5418	5646	33
28	2767	2956	3147	3339	3535	3732	3932	4135	4341	4550	4763	4979	5198	5422	5650	32
29	2770	2959	3150	3343	3538	3736	3936	4139	4345	4554	4766	4982	5202	5426	5654	31
30	2773	2962	3153	3346	3541	3739	3939	4142	4348	4557	4770	4986	5206	5430	5658	30
31	2776	2965	3156	3349	3544	3742	3942	4146	4352	4561	4773	4989	5209	5433	5662	29
32	2780	2968	3159	3352	3548	3745	3946	4149	4355	4564	4777	4993	5213	5437	5665	28
33	2783	2972	3163	3356	3551	3749	3949	4152	4359	4568	4780	4997	5217	5441	5669	27
34	2786	2975	3166	3359	3554	3752	3953	4156	4362	4571	4784	5000	5220	5445	5673	26
35	2789	2978	3169	3362	3558	3755	3956	4159	4365	4575	4788	5004	5224	5448	5677	25
36	2792	2981	3172	3365	3561	3759	3959	4163	4369	4578	4791	5008	5228	5452	5681	24
37	2795	2984	3175	3369	3564	3762	3963	4166	4372	4582	4795	5011	5232	5456	5685	23
38	2798	2987	3179	3372	3567	3765	3966	4169	4376	4585	4798	5015	5235	5460	5688	22
39	2801	2991	3182	3375	3571	3769	3969	4173	4379	4589	4802	5019	5239	5464	5692	21
40	2805	2994	3185	3378	3574	3772	3973	4176	4383	4592	4806	5022	5243	5467	5696	20
41	2808	2997	3188	3382	3577	3775	3976	4180	4386	4596	4809	5026	5246	5471	5700	19
42	2811	3000	3191	3385	3581	3779	3979	4183	4390	4599	4813	5029	5250	5475	5704	18
43	2814	3003	3195	3388	3584	3782	3983	4187	4393	4603	4816	5033	5254	5479	5708	17
44	2817	3006	3198	3391	3587	3785	3986	4190	4397	4607	4820	5037	5258	5482	5712	16
45	2820	3010	3201	3395	3590	3789	3990	4193	4400	4610	4823	5040	5261	5486	5715	15
46	2823	3013	3204	3398	3594	3792	3993	4197	4404	4614	4827	5044	5265	5490	5719	14
47	2827	3016	3207	3401	3597	3795	3996	4200	4407	4617	4831	5048	5269	5494	5723	13
48	2830	3019	3211	3404	3600	3799	4000	4204	4411	4621	4834	5051	5272	5498	5727	12
49	2833	3022	3214	3408	3604	3802	4003	4207	4414	4624	4838	5055	5276	5501	5731	11
50	2836	3026	3217	3411	3607	3805	4006	4210	4417	4628	4841	5059	5280	5505	5735	10
51	2839	3029	3220	3414	3610	3809	4010	4214	4421	4631	4845	5062	5284	5509	5739	9
52	2842	3032	3223	3417	3613	3812	4013	4217	4424	4635	4849	5066	5287	5513	5743	8
53	2845	3035	3227	3421	3617	3815	4017	4221	4428	4638	4852	5070	5291	5517	5746	7
54	2849	3038	3230	3424	3620	3819	4020	4224	4431	4642	4856	5073	5295	5520	5750	6
55	2852	3041	3233	3427	3623	3822	4023	4228	4435	4645	4859	5077	5298	5524	5754	5
56	2855	3045	3236	3430	3627	3825	4027	4231	4438	4649	4863	5081	5302	5528	5758	4
57	2858	3048	3240	3434	3630	3829	4030	4234	4442	4652	4867	5084	5306	5532	5762	3
58	2861	3051	3243	3437	3633	3832	4033	4238	4445	4656	4870	5088	5310	5535	5766	2
59	2864	3054	3246	3440	3636	3835	4037	4241	4449	4660	4874	5092	5313	5539	5770	1
60	2867	3057	3249	3443	3640	3839	4040	4245	4452	4663	4877	5095	5317	5543	5774	0
	0.	0.	0.	0.	0.	0.	0.	0.	0.	0.	0.	0.	0.	0.	0.	
	74°	73°	72°	71°	70°	69°	68°	67°	66°	65°	64°	63°	62°	61°	60°	′

NATURAL COTANGENTS

333

Table 33

NATURAL TANGENTS

/	30°	31°	32°	33°	34°	35°	36°	37°	38°	39°	40°	41°	42°	43°	44°	
	0.	0.	0.	0.	0.	0.	0.	0.	0.	0.	0.	0.	0.	0.	0./1.	
0	5774	6009	6249	6494	6745	7002	7265	7536	7813	8098	8391	8693	9004	9325	9657	60
1	5777	6013	6253	6498	6749	7006	7270	7540	7818	8103	8396	8698	9009	9331	9663	59
2	5781	6017	6257	6502	6754	7011	7274	7545	7822	8107	8401	8703	9015	9336	9668	58
3	5785	6020	6261	6506	6758	7015	7279	7549	7827	8112	8406	8708	9020	9341	9674	57
4	5789	6024	6265	6511	6762	7019	7283	7554	7832	8117	8411	8713	9025	9347	9679	56
5	5793	6028	6269	6515	6766	7024	7288	7558	7836	8122	8416	8718	9030	9352	9685	55
6	5797	6032	6273	6519	6771	7028	7292	7563	7841	8127	8421	8724	9036	9358	9691	54
7	5801	6036	6277	6523	6775	7032	7297	7568	7846	8132	8426	8729	9041	9363	9696	53
8	5805	6040	6281	6527	6779	7037	7301	7572	7850	8136	8431	8734	9046	9369	9702	52
9	5808	6044	6285	6531	6783	7041	7306	7577	7855	8141	8436	8739	9052	9374	9708	51
10	5812	6048	6289	6536	6787	7046	7310	7581	7860	8146	8441	8744	9057	9380	9713	50
11	5816	6052	6293	6540	6792	7050	7314	7586	7865	8151	8446	8749	9062	9385	9719	49
12	5820	6056	6297	6544	6796	7054	7319	7590	7869	8156	8451	8754	9067	9391	9725	48
13	5824	6060	6301	6548	6800	7059	7323	7595	7874	8161	8456	8759	9073	9396	9730	47
14	5828	6064	6305	6552	6805	7063	7328	7600	7879	8165	8461	8765	9078	9402	9736	46
15	5832	6068	6310	6556	6809	7067	7332	7604	7883	8170	8466	8770	9083	9407	9742	45
16	5836	6072	6314	6560	6813	7072	7337	7609	7888	8175	8471	8775	9089	9413	9747	44
17	5840	6076	6318	6565	6817	7076	7341	7613	7893	8180	8476	8780	9094	9418	9753	43
18	5844	6080	6322	6569	6822	7080	7346	7618	7898	8185	8481	8785	9099	9424	9759	42
19	5847	6084	6326	6573	6826	7085	7350	7623	7902	8190	8486	8790	9105	9429	9764	41
20	5851	6088	6330	6577	6830	7089	7355	7627	7907	8195	8491	8796	9110	9435	9770	40
21	5855	6092	6334	6581	6834	7094	7359	7632	7912	8199	8496	8801	9115	9440	9776	39
22	5859	6096	6338	6585	6839	7098	7364	7636	7916	8204	8501	8806	9121	9446	9781	38
23	5863	6100	6342	6590	6843	7102	7368	7641	7921	8209	8506	8811	9126	9451	9787	37
24	5867	6104	6346	6594	6847	7107	7373	7646	7926	8214	8511	8816	9131	9457	9793	36
25	5871	6108	6350	6598	6851	7111	7377	7650	7931	8219	8516	8821	9137	9462	9798	35
26	5875	6112	6354	6602	6856	7115	7382	7655	7935	8224	8521	8827	9142	9468	9804	34
27	5879	6116	6358	6606	6860	7120	7386	7659	7940	8229	8526	8832	9147	9473	9810	33
28	5883	6120	6363	6610	6864	7124	7391	7664	7945	8234	8531	8837	9153	9479	9816	32
29	5887	6124	6367	6615	6869	7129	7395	7669	7950	8238	8536	8842	9158	9484	9821	31
30	5890	6128	6371	6619	6873	7133	7400	7673	7954	8243	8541	8847	9163	9490	9827	30
31	5894	6132	6375	6623	6877	7137	7404	7678	7959	8248	8546	8852	9169	9495	9833	29
32	5898	6136	6379	6627	6881	7142	7409	7683	7964	8253	8551	8858	9174	9501	9838	28
33	5902	6140	6383	6631	6886	7146	7413	7687	7969	8258	8556	8863	9179	9506	9844	27
34	5906	6144	6387	6636	6890	7151	7418	7692	7973	8263	8561	8868	9185	9512	9850	26
35	5910	6148	6391	6640	6894	7155	7422	7696	7978	8268	8566	8873	9190	9517	9856	25
36	5914	6152	6395	6644	6899	7159	7427	7701	7983	8273	8571	8878	9195	9523	9861	24
37	5918	6156	6399	6648	6903	7164	7431	7706	7988	8278	8576	8884	9201	9528	9867	23
38	5922	6160	6403	6652	6907	7168	7436	7710	7992	8283	8581	8889	9206	9534	9873	22
39	5926	6164	6408	6657	6911	7173	7440	7715	7997	8287	8586	8894	9212	9540	9879	21
40	5930	6168	6412	6661	6916	7177	7445	7720	8002	8292	8591	8899	9217	9545	9884	20
41	5934	6172	6416	6665	6920	7181	7449	7724	8007	8297	8596	8904	9222	9551	9890	19
42	5938	6176	6420	6669	6924	7186	7454	7729	8012	8302	8601	8910	9228	9556	9896	18
43	5942	6180	6424	6673	6929	7190	7458	7734	8016	8307	8606	8915	9233	9562	9902	17
44	5945	6184	6428	6678	6933	7195	7463	7738	8021	8312	8611	8920	9239	9567	9907	16
45	5949	6188	6432	6682	6937	7199	7467	7743	8026	8317	8617	8925	9244	9573	9913	15
46	5953	6192	6436	6686	6942	7203	7472	7747	8031	8322	8622	8931	9249	9578	9919	14
47	5957	6196	6440	6690	6946	7208	7476	7752	8035	8327	8627	8936	9255	9584	9925	13
48	5961	6200	6445	6694	6950	7212	7481	7757	8040	8332	8632	8941	9260	9590	9930	12
49	5965	6204	6449	6699	6954	7217	7485	7761	8045	8337	8637	8946	9266	9595	9936	11
50	5969	6208	6453	6703	6959	7221	7490	7766	8050	8342	8642	8952	9271	9601	9942	10
51	5973	6212	6457	6707	6963	7226	7495	7771	8055	8346	8647	8957	9276	9606	9948	9
52	5977	6216	6461	6711	6967	7230	7499	7775	8059	8351	8652	8962	9282	9612	9954	8
53	5981	6220	6465	6716	6972	7234	7504	7780	8064	8356	8657	8967	9287	9618	9959	7
54	5985	6224	6469	6720	6976	7239	7508	7785	8069	8361	8662	8973	9293	9623	9965	6
55	5989	6228	6473	6724	6980	7243	7513	7789	8074	8366	8667	8978	9298	9629	9971	5
56	5993	6233	6478	6728	6985	7248	7517	7794	8079	8371	8672	8983	9303	9634	9977	4
57	5997	6237	6482	6732	6989	7252	7522	7799	8083	8376	8678	8988	9309	9640	9983	3
58	6001	6241	6486	6737	6993	7257	7526	7803	8088	8381	8683	8994	9314	9646	9988	2
59	6005	6245	6490	6741	6998	7261	7531	7808	8093	8386	8688	8999	9320	9651	9994	1
60	6009	6249	6494	6745	7002	7265	7536	7813	8098	8391	8693	9004	9325	9657	0000	0
	0.	0.	0.	0.	0.	0.	0.	0.	0.	0.	0.	0.	0.	0.	0./1.	
	59°	58°	57°	56°	55°	54°	53°	52°	51°	50°	49°	48°	47°	46°	45°	/

NATURAL COTANGENTS

334

Table 33

NATURAL TANGENTS

′	45°	46°	47°	48°	49°	50°	51°	52°	53°	54°	55°	56°	57°	58°	59°	
	1.	1.	1.	1.	1.	1.	1.	1.	1.	1.	1.	1.	1.	1.	1.	
0	0000	0355	0724	1106	1504	1918	2349	2799	3270	3764	4281	4826	5399	6003	6643	60
1	0006	0361	0730	1113	1510	1925	2356	2807	3278	3772	4290	4835	5408	6014	6654	59
2	0012	0367	0736	1119	1517	1932	2364	2815	3287	3781	4299	4844	5418	6024	6665	58
3	0017	0373	0742	1126	1524	1939	2371	2822	3295	3789	4308	4854	5428	6034	6676	57
4	0023	0379	0749	1132	1531	1946	2378	2830	3303	3798	4317	4863	5438	6045	6687	56
5	0029	0385	0755	1139	1538	1953	2386	2838	3311	3806	4326	4872	5448	6055	6698	55
6	0035	0392	0761	1145	1544	1960	2393	2846	3319	3814	4335	4882	5458	6066	6709	54
7	0041	0398	0768	1152	1551	1967	2401	2853	3327	3823	4344	4891	5468	6076	6720	53
8	0047	0404	0774	1158	1558	1974	2408	2861	3335	3831	4352	4900	5477	6087	6731	52
9	0052	0410	0780	1165	1565	1981	2415	2869	3343	3840	4361	4910	5487	6097	6742	51
10	0058	0416	0786	1171	1571	1988	2423	2876	3351	3848	4370	4919	5497	6107	6753	50
11	0064	0422	0793	1178	1578	1995	2430	2884	3359	3857	4379	4928	5507	6118	6764	49
12	0070	0428	0799	1184	1585	2002	2437	2892	3367	3865	4388	4938	5517	6128	6775	48
13	0076	0434	0805	1191	1592	2009	2445	2900	3375	3874	4397	4947	5527	6139	6786	47
14	0082	0440	0812	1197	1599	2017	2452	2907	3384	3882	4406	4957	5537	6149	6797	46
15	0088	0446	0818	1204	1606	2024	2460	2915	3392	3891	4415	4966	5547	6160	6808	45
16	0094	0452	0824	1211	1612	2031	2467	2923	3400	3899	4424	4975	5557	6170	6820	44
17	0099	0458	0831	1217	1619	2038	2475	2931	3408	3908	4433	4985	5567	6181	6831	43
18	0105	0464	0837	1224	1626	2045	2482	2938	3416	3916	4442	4994	5577	6191	6842	42
19	0111	0470	0843	1230	1633	2052	2489	2946	3424	3925	4451	5004	5587	6202	6853	41
20	0117	0477	0850	1237	1640	2059	2497	2954	3432	3934	4460	5013	5597	6212	6864	40
21	0123	0483	0856	1243	1647	2066	2504	2962	3440	3942	4469	5023	5607	6223	6875	39
22	0129	0489	0862	1250	1653	2074	2512	2970	3449	3951	4478	5032	5617	6234	6887	38
23	0135	0495	0869	1257	1660	2081	2519	2977	3457	3959	4487	5042	5627	6244	6898	37
24	0141	0501	0875	1263	1667	2088	2527	2985	3465	3968	4496	5051	5637	6255	6909	36
25	0147	0507	0881	1270	1674	2095	2534	2993	3473	3976	4505	5061	5647	6265	6920	35
26	0152	0513	0888	1276	1681	2102	2542	3001	3481	3985	4514	5070	5657	6276	6932	34
27	0158	0519	0894	1283	1688	2109	2549	3009	3490	3994	4523	5080	5667	6287	6943	33
28	0164	0526	0900	1290	1695	2117	2557	3017	3498	4002	4532	5089	5677	6297	6954	32
29	0170	0532	0907	1296	1702	2124	2564	3024	3506	4011	4541	5099	5687	6308	6965	31
30	0176	0538	0913	1303	1708	2131	2572	3032	3514	4019	4550	5108	5697	6319	6977	30
31	0182	0544	0919	1310	1715	2138	2579	3040	3522	4028	4559	5118	5707	6329	6988	29
32	0188	0550	0926	1316	1722	2145	2587	3048	3531	4037	4568	5127	5717	6340	6999	28
33	0194	0556	0932	1323	1729	2153	2594	3056	3539	4045	4577	5137	5727	6351	7011	27
34	0200	0562	0939	1329	1736	2160	2602	3064	3547	4054	4586	5147	5737	6361	7022	26
35	0206	0569	0945	1336	1743	2167	2609	3072	3555	4063	4596	5156	5747	6372	7033	25
36	0212	0575	0951	1343	1750	2174	2617	3079	3564	4071	4605	5166	5757	6383	7045	24
37	0218	0581	0958	1349	1757	2181	2624	3087	3572	4080	4614	5175	5768	6393	7056	23
38	0224	0587	0964	1356	1764	2189	2632	3095	3580	4089	4623	5185	5778	6404	7067	22
39	0230	0593	0971	1363	1771	2196	2640	3103	3588	4097	4632	5195	5788	6415	7079	21
40	0235	0599	0977	1369	1778	2203	2647	3111	3597	4106	4641	5204	5798	6426	7090	20
41	0241	0606	0983	1376	1785	2210	2655	3119	3605	4115	4650	5214	5808	6436	7102	19
42	0247	0612	0990	1383	1792	2218	2662	3127	3613	4124	4659	5224	5818	6447	7113	18
43	0253	0618	0996	1389	1799	2225	2670	3135	3622	4132	4669	5233	5829	6458	7124	17
44	0259	0624	1003	1396	1806	2232	2677	3143	3630	4141	4678	5243	5839	6469	7136	16
45	0265	0630	1009	1403	1812	2239	2685	3151	3638	4150	4687	5253	5849	6479	7147	15
46	0271	0637	1016	1410	1819	2247	2693	3159	3647	4158	4696	5262	5859	6490	7159	14
47	0277	0643	1022	1416	1826	2254	2700	3167	3655	4167	4705	5272	5869	6501	7170	13
48	0283	0649	1028	1423	1833	2261	2708	3175	3663	4176	4715	5282	5880	6512	7182	12
49	0289	0655	1035	1430	1840	2268	2715	3182	3672	4185	4724	5291	5890	6523	7193	11
50	0295	0661	1041	1436	1847	2276	2723	3190	3680	4193	4733	5301	5900	6534	7205	10
51	0301	0668	1048	1443	1854	2283	2731	3198	3688	4202	4742	5311	5911	6545	7216	9
52	0307	0674	1054	1450	1861	2290	2738	3206	3697	4211	4751	5320	5921	6555	7228	8
53	0313	0680	1061	1456	1868	2298	2746	3214	3705	4220	4761	5330	5931	6566	7239	7
54	0319	0686	1067	1463	1875	2305	2753	3222	3713	4229	4770	5340	5941	6577	7251	6
55	0325	0692	1074	1470	1882	2312	2761	3230	3722	4237	4779	5350	5952	6588	7262	5
56	0331	0699	1080	1477	1889	2320	2769	3238	3730	4246	4788	5359	5962	6599	7274	4
57	0337	0705	1087	1483	1896	2327	2776	3246	3739	4255	4798	5369	5972	6610	7286	3
58	0343	0711	1093	1490	1903	2334	2784	3254	3747	4264	4807	5379	5983	6621	7297	2
59	0349	0717	1100	1497	1910	2342	2792	3262	3755	4273	4816	5389	5993	6632	7309	1
60	0355	0724	1106	1504	1918	2349	2799	3270	3764	4281	4826	5399	6003	6643	7321	0
	1.	1.	1.	1.	1.	1.	1.	1.	1.	1.	1.	1.	1.	1.	1.	
	44°	43°	42°	41°	40°	39°	38°	37°	36°	35°	34°	33°	32°	31°	30°	′

NATURAL COTANGENTS

Table 33

NATURAL TANGENTS

/	60°	61°	62°	63°	64°	65°	66°	67°	68°	69°	70°	71°	72°	73°	74°	
	1.	1.	1.	1./2.	2.	2.	2.	2.	2.	2.	2.	2./3.	3.	3.	3.	
0	7321	8040	8807	9626	0503	1445	2460	3559	4751	6051	7475	9042	0777	2709	4874	60
1	7332	8053	8820	9640	0518	1461	2478	3578	4772	6074	7500	9070	0807	2743	4912	59
2	7344	8065	8834	9654	0533	1478	2496	3597	4792	6096	7525	9097	0838	2777	4951	58
3	7355	8078	8847	9669	0549	1494	2513	3616	4813	6119	7550	9125	0868	2811	4989	57
4	7367	8090	8860	9683	0564	1510	2531	3635	4834	6142	7575	9152	0899	2845	5028	56
5	7379	8103	8873	9697	0579	1527	2549	3654	4855	6165	7600	9180	0930	2879	5067	55
6	7391	8115	8887	9711	0594	1543	2566	3673	4876	6187	7625	9208	0961	2914	5105	54
7	7402	8127	8900	9725	0609	1560	2584	3693	4897	6210	7650	9235	0991	2948	5144	53
8	7414	8140	8913	9740	0625	1576	2602	3712	4918	6233	7675	9263	1022	2983	5183	52
9	7426	8152	8927	9754	0640	1592	2620	3731	4939	6256	7700	9291	1053	3017	5222	51
10	7437	8165	8940	9768	0655	1609	2637	3750	4960	6279	7725	9319	1084	3052	5261	50
11	7449	8177	8953	9782	0671	1625	2655	3770	4981	6302	7751	9347	1115	3087	5300	49
12	7461	8190	8967	9797	0686	1642	2673	3789	5002	6325	7776	9375	1146	3122	5339	48
13	7473	8202	8980	9811	0701	1659	2691	3808	5023	6348	7801	9403	1178	3156	5379	47
14	7485	8215	8993	9825	0717	1675	2709	3828	5044	6371	7827	9431	1209	3191	5418	46
15	7496	8228	9007	9840	0732	1692	2727	3847	5065	6395	7852	9459	1240	3226	5457	45
16	7508	8240	9020	9854	0748	1708	2745	3867	5086	6418	7878	9487	1271	3261	5497	44
17	7520	8253	9034	9868	0763	1725	2763	3886	5108	6441	7903	9515	1303	3297	5536	43
18	7532	8265	9047	9883	0778	1742	2781	3906	5129	6464	7929	9544	1334	3332	5576	42
19	7544	8278	9061	9897	0794	1758	2799	3925	5150	6488	7955	9572	1366	3367	5616	41
20	7556	8291	9074	9912	0809	1775	2817	3945	5172	6511	7980	9600	1397	3402	5656	40
21	7567	8303	9088	9926	0825	1792	2835	3964	5193	6534	8006	9629	1429	3438	5696	39
22	7579	8316	9101	9941	0840	1808	2853	3984	5214	6558	8032	9657	1460	3473	5736	38
23	7591	8329	9115	9955	0856	1825	2871	4004	5236	6581	8057	9686	1492	3509	5776	37
24	7603	8341	9128	9970	0872	1842	2889	4023	5257	6605	8083	9714	1524	3544	5816	36
25	7615	8354	9142	9984	0887	1859	2907	4043	5279	6628	8109	9743	1556	3580	5856	35
26	7627	8367	9155	9999	0903	1876	2925	4063	5300	6652	8135	9772	1588	3616	5897	34
27	7639	8379	9169	0013	0918	1892	2944	4083	5322	6675	8161	9800	1620	3652	5937	33
28	7651	8392	9183	0028	0934	1909	2962	4102	5343	6699	8187	9829	1652	3687	5978	32
29	7663	8405	9196	0042	0950	1926	2980	4122	5365	6723	8213	9858	1684	3723	6018	31
30	7675	8418	9210	0057	0965	1943	2998	4142	5386	6746	8239	9887	1716	3759	6059	30
31	7687	8430	9223	0072	0981	1960	3017	4162	5408	6770	8265	9916	1748	3796	6100	29
32	7699	8443	9237	0086	0997	1977	3035	4182	5430	6794	8291	9945	1780	3832	6140	28
33	7711	8456	9251	0101	1013	1994	3053	4202	5452	6818	8318	9974	1813	3868	6181	27
34	7723	8469	9265	0115	1028	2011	3072	4222	5473	6841	8344	0003	1845	3904	6222	26
35	7735	8482	9278	0130	1044	2028	3090	4242	5495	6865	8370	0032	1878	3941	6264	25
36	7747	8495	9292	0145	1060	2045	3109	4262	5517	6889	8397	0061	1910	3977	6305	24
37	7759	8507	9306	0160	1076	2062	3127	4282	5539	6913	8423	0090	1943	4014	6346	23
38	7771	8520	9319	0174	1092	2079	3146	4302	5561	6937	8449	0120	1975	4050	6387	22
39	7783	8533	9333	0189	1107	2096	3164	4322	5583	6961	8476	0149	2008	4087	6429	21
40	7796	8546	9347	0204	1123	2113	3183	4342	5605	6985	8502	0178	2041	4124	6470	20
41	7808	8559	9361	0219	1139	2130	3201	4362	5627	7009	8529	0208	2073	4160	6512	19
42	7820	8572	9375	0233	1155	2148	3220	4383	5649	7034	8556	0237	2106	4197	6554	18
43	7832	8585	9388	0248	1171	2165	3238	4403	5671	7058	8582	0267	2139	4234	6596	17
44	7844	8598	9402	0263	1187	2182	3257	4423	5693	7082	8609	0296	2172	4271	6638	16
45	7856	8611	9416	0278	1203	2199	3276	4443	5715	7106	8636	0326	2205	4308	6680	15
46	7868	8624	9430	0293	1219	2216	3294	4464	5737	7130	8662	0356	2238	4346	6722	14
47	7881	8637	9444	0308	1235	2234	3313	4484	5759	7155	8689	0385	2272	4383	6764	13
48	7893	8650	9458	0323	1251	2251	3332	4504	5782	7179	8716	0415	2305	4420	6806	12
49	7905	8663	9472	0338	1267	2268	3351	4525	5804	7204	8743	0445	2338	4458	6848	11
50	7917	8676	9486	0353	1283	2286	3369	4545	5826	7228	8770	0475	2371	4495	6891	10
51	7930	8689	9500	0368	1299	2303	3388	4566	5848	7253	8797	0505	2405	4533	6933	9
52	7942	8702	9514	0383	1315	2320	3407	4586	5871	7277	8824	0535	2438	4570	6976	8
53	7954	8715	9528	0398	1332	2338	3426	4606	5893	7302	8851	0565	2472	4608	7019	7
54	7966	8728	9542	0413	1348	2355	3445	4627	5916	7326	8878	0595	2506	4646	7062	6
55	7979	8741	9556	0428	1364	2373	3464	4648	5938	7351	8905	0625	2539	4684	7105	5
56	7991	8755	9570	0443	1380	2390	3483	4668	5961	7376	8933	0655	2573	4722	7148	4
57	8003	8768	9584	0458	1396	2408	3501	4689	5983	7400	8960	0686	2607	4760	7191	3
58	8016	8781	9598	0473	1413	2425	3520	4709	6006	7425	8987	0716	2641	4798	7234	2
59	8028	8794	9612	0488	1429	2443	3539	4730	6028	7450	9015	0746	2675	4836	7277	1
60	8040	8807	9626	0503	1445	2460	3559	4751	6051	7475	9042	0777	2709	4874	7321	0
	1.	1.	1.	1./2.	2.	2.	2.	2.	2.	2.	2.	2./3.	3.	3.	3.	
	29°	28°	27°	26°	25°	24°	23°	22°	21°	20°	19°	18°	17°	16°	15°	/

NATURAL COTANGENTS

Table 33

NATURAL TANGENTS

′	75°	76°	77°	78°	79°	80°	81°	82°	83°	84°	85°	86°	87°	88°	89°	
	3./4.	4.	4.	4./5.	5.											
0	7321	0108	3315	7046	1446	5.671	6.314	7.115	8.144	9.514	11.43	14.30	19.08	28.64	57.29	60
1	7364	0158	3372	7114	1526	5.681	6.326	7.130	8.164	9.541	11.47	14.36	19.19	28.88	58.26	59
2	7408	0207	3430	7181	1606	5.691	6.338	7.146	8.184	9.568	11.51	14.42	19.30	29.12	59.27	58
3	7451	0257	3488	7249	1686	5.700	6.350	7.161	8.204	9.595	11.55	14.48	19.41	29.37	60.31	57
4	7495	0308	3546	7317	1767	5.710	6.362	7.176	8.223	9.622	11.59	14.54	19.52	29.62	61.38	56
5	7539	0358	3604	7385	1848	5.720	6.374	7.191	8.243	9.649	11.62	14.61	19.63	29.88	62.50	55
6	7583	0408	3662	7453	1929	5.730	6.386	7.207	8.264	9.677	11.66	14.67	19.74	30.14	63.66	54
7	7627	0459	3721	7522	2011	5.740	6.398	7.222	8.284	9.704	11.70	14.73	19.85	30.41	64.86	53
8	7671	0509	3779	7591	2092	5.749	6.410	7.238	8.304	9.732	11.74	14.80	19.97	30.68	66.11	52
9	7715	0560	3838	7659	2174	5.759	6.423	7.253	8.324	9.760	11.79	14.86	20.09	30.96	67.40	51
10	7760	0611	3897	7729	2257	5.769	6.435	7.269	8.345	9.788	11.83	14.92	20.21	31.24	68.75	50
11	7804	0662	3956	7798	2339	5.779	6.447	7.284	8.366	9.816	11.87	14.99	20.33	31.53	70.15	49
12	7848	0713	4015	7867	2422	5.789	6.460	7.300	8.386	9.845	11.91	15.06	20.45	31.82	71.62	48
13	7893	0764	4075	7937	2505	5.799	6.472	7.316	8.407	9.873	11.95	15.12	20.57	32.12	73.14	47
14	7938	0815	4134	8007	2588	5.810	6.485	7.332	8.428	9.902	11.99	15.19	20.69	32.42	74.73	46
15	7983	0867	4194	8077	2672	5.820	6.497	7.348	8.449	9.931	12.03	15.26	20.82	32.73	76.39	45
16	8028	0918	4253	8147	2755	5.830	6.510	7.364	8.470	9.960	12.08	15.33	20.95	33.05	78.13	44
17	8073	0970	4313	8218	2839	5.840	6.522	7.380	8.491	9.989	12.12	15.39	21.07	33.37	79.94	43
18	8118	1022	4374	8288	2924	5.850	6.535	7.396	8.513	10.02	12.16	15.46	21.20	33.69	81.85	42
19	8163	1074	4434	8359	3008	5.861	6.548	7.412	8.534	10.05	12.21	15.53	21.34	34.03	83.84	41
20	8208	1126	4494	8430	3093	5.871	6.561	7.429	8.556	10.08	12.25	15.60	21.47	34.37	85.94	40
21	8254	1178	4555	8501	3178	5.881	6.573	7.445	8.577	10.11	12.29	15.68	21.61	34.72	88.14	39
22	8299	1230	4615	8573	3263	5.892	6.586	7.462	8.599	10.14	12.34	15.75	21.74	35.07	90.46	38
23	8345	1282	4676	8644	3349	5.902	6.599	7.478	8.621	10.17	12.38	15.82	21.88	35.43	92.91	37
24	8391	1335	4737	8716	3435	5.912	6.612	7.495	8.643	10.20	12.43	15.89	22.02	35.80	95.49	36
25	8436	1388	4799	8788	3521	5.923	6.625	7.511	8.665	10.23	12.47	15.97	22.16	36.18	98.22	35
26	8482	1441	4860	8860	3607	5.933	6.638	7.528	8.687	10.26	12.52	16.04	22.31	36.56	101.1	34
27	8528	1493	4922	8933	3694	5.944	6.651	7.545	8.709	10.29	12.57	16.12	22.45	36.96	104.2	33
28	8575	1547	4983	9006	3781	5.954	6.665	7.562	8.732	10.32	12.61	16.20	22.60	37.36	107.4	32
29	8621	1600	5045	9078	3868	5.965	6.678	7.579	8.754	10.35	12.66	16.27	22.75	37.77	110.9	31
30	8667	1653	5107	9152	3955	5.976	6.691	7.596	8.777	10.39	12.71	16.35	22.90	38.19	114.6	30
31	8714	1706	5169	9225	4043	5.986	6.704	7.613	8.800	10.42	12.75	16.43	23.06	38.62	118.5	29
32	8760	1760	5232	9298	4131	5.997	6.718	7.630	8.823	10.45	12.80	16.51	23.21	39.06	122.8	28
33	8807	1814	5294	9372	4219	6.008	6.731	7.647	8.846	10.48	12.85	16.59	23.37	39.51	127.3	27
34	8854	1868	5357	9446	4308	6.019	6.745	7.665	8.869	10.51	12.90	16.67	23.53	39.97	132.2	26
35	8900	1922	5420	9520	4397	6.030	6.758	7.682	8.892	10.55	12.95	16.75	23.69	40.44	137.5	25
36	8947	1976	5483	9594	4486	6.041	6.772	7.700	8.915	10.58	13.00	16.83	23.86	40.92	143.2	24
37	8995	2030	5546	9669	4575	6.051	6.786	7.717	8.939	10.61	13.05	16.92	24.03	41.41	149.5	23
38	9042	2084	5609	9744	4665	6.062	6.799	7.735	8.962	10.64	13.10	17.00	24.20	41.92	156.3	22
39	9089	2139	5673	9819	4755	6.073	6.813	7.753	8.986	10.68	13.15	17.08	24.37	42.43	163.7	21
40	9136	2193	5736	9894	4845	6.084	6.827	7.770	9.010	10.71	13.20	17.17	24.54	42.96	171.9	20
41	9184	2248	5800	9969	4936	6.096	6.841	7.788	9.034	10.75	13.25	17.26	24.72	43.51	180.9	19
42	9232	2303	5864	0045	5026	6.107	6.855	7.806	9.058	10.78	13.30	17.34	24.90	44.07	191.0	18
43	9279	2358	5928	0121	5118	6.118	6.869	7.824	9.082	10.81	13.35	17.43	25.08	44.64	202.2	17
44	9327	2413	5993	0197	5209	6.129	6.883	7.842	9.106	10.85	13.40	17.52	25.26	45.23	214.9	16
45	9375	2468	6057	0273	5301	6.140	6.897	7.861	9.131	10.88	13.46	17.61	25.45	45.83	229.2	15
46	9423	2524	6122	0350	5393	6.152	6.911	7.879	9.156	10.92	13.51	17.70	25.64	46.45	245.6	14
47	9471	2580	6187	0427	5485	6.163	6.925	7.897	9.180	10.95	13.56	17.79	25.83	47.09	264.4	13
48	9520	2635	6252	0504	5578	6.174	6.940	7.916	9.205	10.99	13.62	17.89	26.03	47.74	286.5	12
49	9568	2691	6317	0581	5671	6.186	6.954	7.934	9.230	11.02	13.67	17.98	26.23	48.41	312.5	11
50	9617	2747	6382	0658	5764	6.197	6.968	7.953	9.255	11.06	13.73	18.07	26.43	49.10	343.8	10
51	9665	2803	6448	0736	5857	6.209	6.983	7.972	9.281	11.10	13.78	18.17	26.64	49.82	382.0	9
52	9714	2859	6514	0814	5951	6.220	6.997	7.991	9.306	11.13	13.84	18.27	26.84	50.55	429.7	8
53	9763	2916	6580	0892	6045	6.232	7.012	8.009	9.332	11.17	13.89	18.37	27.06	51.30	491.1	7
54	9812	2972	6646	0970	6140	6.243	7.026	8.028	9.357	11.20	13.95	18.46	27.27	52.08	573.0	6
55	9861	3029	6712	1049	6234	6.255	7.041	8.048	9.383	11.24	14.01	18.56	27.49	52.88	687.5	5
56	9910	3086	6779	1128	6329	6.267	7.056	8.067	9.409	11.28	14.07	18.67	27.71	53.71	859.4	4
57	9959	3143	6845	1207	6425	6.278	7.071	8.086	9.435	11.32	14.12	18.77	27.94	54.56	1146	3
58	0009	3200	6912	1286	6521	6.290	7.085	8.105	9.461	11.35	14.18	18.87	28.17	55.44	1719	2
59	0058	3257	6979	1366	6617	6.302	7.100	8.125	9.488	11.39	14.24	18.98	28.40	56.35	3438	1
60	0108	3315	7046	1446	6713	6.314	7.115	8.144	9.514	11.43	14.30	19.08	28.64	57.29	Infinite	0
	3./4.	4.	4.	4./5.	5.											
	14°	13°	12°	11°	10°	9°	8°	7°	6°	5°	4°	3°	2°	1°	0°	′

NATURAL COTANGENTS

Table 34

NATURAL SECANTS

/	0°	1°	2°	3°	4°	5°	6°	7°	8°	9°	10°	11°	12°	13°	14°	
	1.	1.	1.	1.	1.	1.	1.	1.	1.	1.	1.	1.	1.	1.	1.	
0	0000	0002	0006	0014	0024	0038	0055	0075	0098	0125	0154	0187	0223	0263	0306	60
1	0000	0002	0006	0014	0025	0038	0055	0075	0099	0125	0155	0188	0224	0264	0307	59
2	0000	0002	0006	0014	0025	0039	0056	0076	0099	0126	0155	0188	0225	0264	0308	58
3	0000	0002	0006	0014	0025	0039	0056	0076	0100	0126	0156	0189	0225	0265	0308	57
4	0000	0002	0007	0014	0025	0039	0056	0077	0100	0127	0156	0189	0226	0266	0309	56
5	0000	0002	0007	0014	0025	0039	0057	0077	0100	0127	0157	0190	0227	0266	0310	55
6	0000	0002	0007	0015	0026	0040	0057	0077	0101	0127	0157	0191	0227	0267	0311	54
7	0000	0002	0007	0015	0026	0040	0057	0078	0101	0128	0158	0191	0228	0268	0311	53
8	0000	0002	0007	0015	0026	0040	0058	0078	0102	0128	0158	0192	0228	0269	0312	52
9	0000	0002	0007	0015	0026	0041	0058	0078	0102	0129	0159	0192	0229	0269	0313	51
10	0000	0002	0007	0015	0027	0041	0058	0079	0102	0129	0160	0193	0230	0270	0314	50
11	0000	0002	0007	0015	0027	0041	0059	0079	0103	0130	0160	0194	0230	0271	0314	49
12	0000	0002	0007	0016	0027	0041	0059	0079	0103	0130	0161	0194	0231	0271	0315	48
13	0000	0002	0007	0016	0027	0042	0059	0080	0104	0131	0161	0195	0232	0272	0316	47
14	0000	0002	0008	0016	0027	0042	0059	0080	0104	0131	0162	0195	0232	0273	0317	46
15	0000	0002	0008	0016	0028	0042	0060	0081	0105	0132	0162	0196	0233	0273	0317	45
16	0000	0002	0008	0016	0028	0042	0060	0081	0105	0132	0163	0197	0234	0274	0318	44
17	0000	0003	0008	0016	0028	0043	0060	0081	0105	0133	0163	0197	0234	0275	0319	43
18	0000	0003	0008	0017	0028	0043	0061	0082	0106	0133	0164	0198	0235	0276	0320	42
19	0000	0003	0008	0017	0028	0043	0061	0082	0106	0134	0164	0198	0236	0276	0321	41
20	0000	0003	0008	0017	0029	0043	0061	0082	0107	0134	0165	0199	0236	0277	0321	40
21	0000	0003	0008	0017	0029	0044	0062	0083	0107	0135	0165	0199	0237	0278	0322	39
22	0000	0003	0009	0017	0029	0044	0062	0083	0108	0135	0166	0200	0238	0278	0323	38
23	0000	0003	0009	0017	0029	0044	0062	0084	0108	0136	0166	0201	0238	0279	0324	37
24	0000	0003	0009	0018	0030	0045	0063	0084	0108	0136	0167	0201	0239	0280	0324	36
25	0000	0003	0009	0018	0030	0045	0063	0084	0109	0137	0168	0202	0240	0281	0325	35
26	0000	0003	0009	0018	0030	0045	0063	0085	0109	0137	0168	0202	0240	0281	0326	34
27	0000	0003	0009	0018	0030	0045	0064	0085	0110	0138	0169	0203	0241	0282	0327	33
28	0000	0003	0009	0018	0030	0046	0064	0086	0110	0138	0169	0204	0241	0283	0327	32
29	0000	0003	0009	0019	0031	0046	0064	0086	0111	0139	0170	0204	0242	0283	0328	31
30	0000	0003	0010	0019	0031	0046	0065	0086	0111	0139	0170	0205	0243	0284	0329	30
31	0000	0004	0010	0019	0031	0047	0065	0087	0112	0140	0171	0205	0243	0285	0330	29
32	0000	0004	0010	0019	0031	0047	0065	0087	0112	0140	0171	0206	0244	0286	0331	28
33	0000	0004	0010	0019	0032	0047	0066	0087	0112	0141	0172	0207	0245	0286	0331	27
34	0000	0004	0010	0019	0032	0047	0066	0088	0113	0141	0173	0207	0245	0287	0332	26
35	0001	0004	0010	0020	0032	0048	0066	0088	0113	0142	0173	0208	0246	0288	0333	25
36	0001	0004	0010	0020	0032	0048	0067	0089	0114	0142	0174	0209	0247	0288	0334	24
37	0001	0004	0010	0020	0033	0048	0067	0089	0114	0143	0174	0209	0247	0289	0334	23
38	0001	0004	0011	0020	0033	0049	0067	0089	0115	0143	0175	0210	0248	0290	0335	22
39	0001	0004	0011	0020	0033	0049	0068	0090	0115	0144	0175	0210	0249	0291	0336	21
40	0001	0004	0011	0021	0033	0049	0068	0090	0116	0144	0176	0211	0249	0291	0337	20
41	0001	0004	0011	0021	0034	0049	0068	0091	0116	0145	0176	0212	0250	0292	0338	19
42	0001	0004	0011	0021	0034	0050	0069	0091	0116	0145	0177	0212	0251	0293	0338	18
43	0001	0004	0011	0021	0034	0050	0069	0091	0117	0146	0178	0213	0251	0294	0339	17
44	0001	0005	0011	0021	0034	0050	0069	0092	0117	0146	0178	0213	0252	0294	0340	16
45	0001	0005	0012	0021	0034	0051	0070	0092	0118	0147	0179	0214	0253	0295	0341	15
46	0001	0005	0012	0022	0035	0051	0070	0093	0118	0147	0179	0215	0253	0296	0342	14
47	0001	0005	0012	0022	0035	0051	0070	0093	0119	0148	0180	0215	0254	0297	0342	13
48	0001	0005	0012	0022	0035	0051	0071	0093	0119	0148	0180	0216	0255	0297	0343	12
49	0001	0005	0012	0022	0035	0052	0071	0094	0120	0149	0181	0217	0256	0298	0344	11
50	0001	0005	0012	0022	0036	0052	0072	0094	0120	0149	0181	0217	0256	0299	0345	10
51	0001	0005	0012	0023	0036	0052	0072	0095	0120	0150	0182	0218	0257	0299	0346	9
52	0001	0005	0013	0023	0036	0053	0072	0095	0121	0150	0183	0218	0258	0300	0346	8
53	0001	0005	0013	0023	0036	0053	0073	0095	0121	0151	0183	0219	0258	0301	0347	7
54	0001	0006	0013	0023	0037	0053	0073	0096	0122	0151	0184	0220	0259	0302	0348	6
55	0001	0006	0013	0023	0037	0054	0073	0096	0122	0152	0184	0220	0260	0302	0349	5
56	0001	0006	0013	0024	0037	0054	0074	0097	0123	0152	0185	0221	0260	0303	0350	4
57	0001	0006	0013	0024	0037	0054	0074	0097	0123	0153	0185	0222	0261	0304	0350	3
58	0001	0006	0013	0024	0038	0054	0074	0097	0124	0153	0186	0222	0262	0305	0351	2
59	0001	0006	0014	0024	0038	0055	0075	0098	0124	0154	0187	0223	0262	0305	0352	1
60	0002	0006	0014	0024	0038	0055	0075	0098	0125	0154	0187	0223	0263	0306	0353	0
	1.	1.	1.	1.	1.	1.	1.	1.	1.	1.	1.	1.	1.	1.	1.	
	89°	88°	87°	86°	85°	84°	83°	82°	81°	80°	79°	78°	77°	76°	75°	/

NATURAL COSECANTS

Table 34

NATURAL SECANTS

′	15°	16°	17°	18°	19°	20°	21°	22°	23°	24°	25°	26°	27°	28°	29°	
	1.	1.	1.	1.	1.	1.	1.	1.	1.	1.	1.	1.	1.	1.	1.	
0	0353	0403	0457	0515	0576	0642	0711	0785	0864	0946	1034	1126	1223	1326	1434	60
1	0354	0404	0458	0516	0577	0643	0713	0787	0865	0948	1035	1128	1225	1327	1435	59
2	0354	0405	0459	0517	0578	0644	0714	0788	0866	0949	1037	1129	1227	1329	1437	58
3	0355	0406	0460	0518	0579	0645	0715	0789	0868	0951	1038	1131	1228	1331	1439	57
4	0356	0406	0461	0519	0580	0646	0716	0790	0869	0952	1040	1132	1230	1333	1441	56
5	0357	0407	0462	0520	0582	0647	0717	0792	0870	0953	1041	1134	1232	1334	1443	55
6	0358	0408	0463	0521	0583	0649	0719	0793	0872	0955	1043	1136	1233	1336	1445	54
7	0358	0409	0463	0522	0584	0650	0720	0794	0873	0956	1044	1137	1235	1338	1446	53
8	0359	0410	0464	0523	0585	0651	0721	0796	0874	0958	1046	1139	1237	1340	1448	52
9	0360	0411	0465	0524	0586	0652	0722	0797	0876	0959	1047	1140	1238	1342	1450	51
10	0361	0412	0466	0525	0587	0653	0723	0798	0877	0961	1049	1142	1240	1343	1452	50
11	0362	0413	0467	0526	0588	0654	0725	0799	0878	0962	1050	1143	1242	1345	1454	49
12	0363	0413	0468	0527	0589	0655	0726	0801	0880	0963	1052	1145	1243	1347	1456	48
13	0363	0414	0469	0528	0590	0657	0727	0802	0881	0965	1053	1147	1245	1349	1458	47
14	0364	0415	0470	0529	0591	0658	0728	0803	0883	0966	1055	1148	1247	1350	1460	46
15	0365	0416	0471	0530	0592	0659	0730	0804	0884	0968	1056	1150	1248	1352	1461	45
16	0366	0417	0472	0531	0593	0660	0731	0806	0885	0969	1058	1151	1250	1354	1463	44
17	0367	0418	0473	0532	0594	0661	0732	0807	0887	0971	1059	1153	1252	1356	1465	43
18	0367	0419	0474	0533	0595	0662	0733	0808	0888	0972	1061	1155	1253	1357	1467	42
19	0368	0420	0475	0534	0597	0663	0734	0810	0889	0974	1062	1156	1255	1359	1469	41
20	0369	0421	0476	0535	0598	0665	0736	0811	0891	0975	1064	1158	1257	1361	1471	40
21	0370	0421	0477	0536	0599	0666	0737	0812	0892	0976	1066	1159	1259	1363	1473	39
22	0371	0422	0478	0537	0600	0667	0738	0814	0893	0978	1067	1161	1260	1365	1474	38
23	0372	0423	0479	0538	0601	0668	0739	0815	0895	0979	1069	1163	1262	1366	1476	37
24	0372	0424	0480	0539	0602	0669	0740	0816	0896	0981	1070	1164	1264	1368	1478	36
25	0373	0425	0480	0540	0603	0670	0742	0817	0898	0982	1072	1166	1265	1370	1480	35
26	0374	0426	0481	0541	0604	0671	0743	0819	0899	0984	1073	1168	1267	1372	1482	34
27	0375	0427	0482	0542	0605	0673	0744	0820	0900	0985	1075	1169	1269	1374	1484	33
28	0376	0428	0483	0543	0606	0674	0745	0821	0902	0987	1076	1171	1270	1375	1486	32
29	0377	0429	0484	0544	0607	0675	0747	0823	0903	0988	1078	1172	1272	1377	1488	31
30	0377	0429	0485	0545	0608	0676	0748	0824	0904	0989	1079	1174	1274	1379	1490	30
31	0378	0430	0486	0546	0610	0677	0749	0825	0906	0991	1081	1176	1276	1381	1491	29
32	0379	0431	0487	0547	0611	0678	0750	0827	0907	0992	1082	1177	1277	1383	1493	28
33	0380	0432	0488	0548	0612	0680	0752	0828	0909	0994	1084	1179	1279	1384	1495	27
34	0381	0433	0489	0549	0613	0681	0753	0829	0910	0995	1085	1180	1281	1386	1497	26
35	0382	0434	0490	0550	0614	0682	0754	0830	0911	0997	1087	1182	1282	1388	1499	25
36	0382	0435	0491	0551	0615	0683	0755	0832	0913	0998	1089	1184	1284	1390	1501	24
37	0383	0436	0492	0552	0616	0684	0757	0833	0914	1000	1090	1185	1286	1392	1503	23
38	0384	0437	0493	0553	0617	0685	0758	0834	0915	1001	1092	1187	1288	1393	1505	22
39	0385	0438	0494	0554	0618	0687	0759	0836	0917	1003	1093	1189	1289	1395	1507	21
40	0386	0439	0495	0555	0619	0688	0760	0837	0918	1004	1095	1190	1291	1397	1509	20
41	0387	0439	0496	0556	0621	0689	0761	0838	0920	1006	1096	1192	1293	1399	1510	19
42	0388	0440	0497	0557	0622	0690	0763	0840	0921	1007	1098	1194	1294	1401	1512	18
43	0388	0441	0498	0558	0623	0691	0764	0841	0922	1009	1099	1195	1296	1402	1514	17
44	0389	0442	0499	0559	0624	0692	0765	0842	0924	1010	1101	1197	1298	1404	1516	16
45	0390	0443	0500	0560	0625	0694	0766	0844	0925	1011	1102	1198	1300	1406	1518	15
46	0391	0444	0501	0561	0626	0695	0768	0845	0927	1013	1104	1200	1301	1408	1520	14
47	0392	0445	0502	0563	0627	0696	0769	0846	0928	1014	1106	1202	1303	1410	1522	13
48	0393	0446	0503	0564	0628	0697	0770	0848	0929	1016	1107	1203	1305	1412	1524	12
49	0394	0447	0504	0565	0629	0698	0771	0849	0931	1017	1109	1205	1307	1413	1526	11
50	0394	0448	0505	0566	0631	0700	0773	0850	0932	1019	1110	1207	1308	1415	1528	10
51	0395	0449	0506	0567	0632	0701	0774	0852	0934	1020	1112	1208	1310	1417	1530	9
52	0396	0450	0507	0568	0633	0702	0775	0853	0935	1022	1113	1210	1312	1419	1532	8
53	0397	0450	0508	0569	0634	0703	0777	0854	0936	1023	1115	1212	1313	1421	1533	7
54	0398	0451	0509	0570	0635	0704	0778	0856	0938	1025	1117	1213	1315	1423	1535	6
55	0399	0452	0510	0571	0636	0705	0779	0857	0939	1026	1118	1215	1317	1424	1537	5
56	0400	0453	0511	0572	0637	0707	0780	0858	0941	1028	1120	1217	1319	1426	1539	4
57	0400	0454	0512	0573	0638	0708	0782	0860	0942	1029	1121	1218	1320	1428	1541	3
58	0401	0455	0513	0574	0640	0709	0783	0861	0944	1031	1123	1220	1322	1430	1543	2
59	0402	0456	0514	0575	0641	0710	0784	0862	0945	1032	1124	1222	1324	1432	1545	1
60	0403	0457	0515	0576	0642	0711	0785	0864	0946	1034	1126	1223	1326	1434	1547	0
	1.	1.	1.	1.	1.	1.	1.	1.	1.	1.	1.	1.	1.	1.	1.	
	74°	73°	72°	71°	70°	69°	68°	67°	66°	65°	64°	63°	62°	61°	60°	′

NATURAL COSECANTS

Table 34

NATURAL SECANTS

′	30°	31°	32°	33°	34°	35°	36°	37°	38°	39°	40°	41°	42°	43°	44°	
	1.	1.	1.	1.	1.	1.	1.	1.	1.	1.	1.	1.	1.	1.	1.	
0	1547	1666	1792	1924	2062	2208	2361	2521	2690	2868	3054	3250	3456	3673	3902	60
1	1549	1668	1794	1926	2065	2210	2363	2524	2693	2871	3057	3253	3460	3677	3906	59
2	1551	1670	1796	1928	2067	2213	2366	2527	2696	2874	3060	3257	3463	3681	3909	58
3	1553	1672	1798	1930	2069	2215	2369	2530	2699	2877	3064	3260	3467	3684	3913	57
4	1555	1675	1800	1933	2072	2218	2371	2532	2702	2880	3067	3264	3470	3688	3917	56
5	1557	1677	1803	1935	2074	2220	2374	2535	2705	2883	3070	3267	3474	3692	3921	55
6	1559	1679	1805	1937	2076	2223	2376	2538	2708	2886	3073	3270	3478	3696	3925	54
7	1561	1681	1807	1939	2079	2225	2379	2541	2710	2889	3076	3274	3481	3699	3929	53
8	1563	1683	1809	1942	2081	2228	2382	2543	2713	2892	3080	3277	3485	3703	3933	52
9	1565	1685	1811	1944	2084	2230	2384	2546	2716	2895	3083	3280	3488	3707	3937	51
10	1566	1687	1813	1946	2086	2233	2387	2549	2719	2898	3086	3284	3492	3711	3941	50
11	1568	1689	1815	1949	2088	2235	2390	2552	2722	2901	3089	3287	3495	3714	3945	49
12	1570	1691	1818	1951	2091	2238	2392	2554	2725	2904	3093	3291	3499	3718	3949	48
13	1572	1693	1820	1953	2093	2240	2395	2557	2728	2907	3096	3294	3502	3722	3953	47
14	1574	1695	1822	1955	2096	2243	2397	2560	2731	2910	3099	3297	3506	3726	3957	46
15	1576	1697	1824	1958	2098	2245	2400	2563	2734	2913	3102	3301	3510	3729	3961	45
16	1578	1699	1826	1960	2100	2248	2403	2566	2737	2916	3105	3304	3513	3733	3965	44
17	1580	1701	1828	1962	2103	2250	2405	2568	2740	2919	3109	3307	3517	3737	3969	43
18	1582	1703	1831	1964	2105	2253	2408	2571	2742	2923	3112	3311	3520	3741	3972	42
19	1584	1705	1833	1967	2108	2255	2411	2574	2745	2926	3115	3314	3524	3744	3976	41
20	1586	1707	1835	1969	2110	2258	2413	2577	2748	2929	3118	3318	3527	3748	3980	40
21	1588	1710	1837	1971	2112	2260	2416	2579	2751	2932	3122	3321	3531	3752	3984	39
22	1590	1712	1839	1974	2115	2263	2419	2582	2754	2935	3125	3325	3535	3756	3988	38
23	1592	1714	1842	1976	2117	2265	2421	2585	2757	2938	3128	3328	3538	3759	3992	37
24	1594	1716	1844	1978	2120	2268	2424	2588	2760	2941	3131	3331	3542	3763	3996	36
25	1596	1718	1846	1981	2122	2271	2427	2591	2763	2944	3135	3335	3545	3767	4000	35
26	1598	1720	1848	1983	2124	2273	2429	2593	2766	2947	3138	3338	3549	3771	4004	34
27	1600	1722	1850	1985	2127	2276	2432	2596	2769	2950	3141	3342	3553	3775	4008	33
28	1602	1724	1853	1987	2129	2278	2435	2599	2772	2953	3144	3345	3556	3778	4012	32
29	1604	1726	1855	1990	2132	2281	2437	2602	2775	2957	3148	3348	3560	3782	4016	31
30	1606	1728	1857	1992	2134	2283	2440	2605	2778	2960	3151	3352	3563	3786	4020	30
31	1608	1730	1859	1994	2136	2286	2443	2608	2781	2963	3154	3355	3567	3790	4024	29
32	1610	1732	1861	1997	2139	2288	2445	2610	2784	2966	3157	3359	3571	3794	4028	28
33	1612	1735	1863	1999	2141	2291	2448	2613	2787	2969	3161	3362	3574	3797	4032	27
34	1614	1737	1866	2001	2144	2293	2451	2616	2790	2972	3164	3366	3578	3801	4036	26
35	1616	1739	1868	2004	2146	2296	2453	2619	2793	2975	3167	3369	3582	3805	4040	25
36	1618	1741	1870	2006	2149	2299	2456	2622	2796	2978	3171	3373	3585	3809	4044	24
37	1620	1743	1872	2008	2151	2301	2459	2624	2799	2981	3174	3376	3589	3813	4048	23
38	1622	1745	1875	2011	2154	2304	2462	2627	2802	2985	3177	3380	3592	3817	4052	22
39	1624	1747	1877	2013	2156	2306	2464	2630	2804	2988	3180	3383	3596	3820	4057	21
40	1626	1749	1879	2015	2158	2309	2467	2633	2807	2991	3184	3386	3600	3824	4061	20
41	1628	1751	1881	2018	2161	2311	2470	2636	2810	2994	3187	3390	3603	3828	4065	19
42	1630	1753	1883	2020	2163	2314	2472	2639	2813	2997	3190	3393	3607	3832	4069	18
43	1632	1756	1886	2022	2166	2317	2475	2641	2816	3000	3194	3397	3611	3836	4073	17
44	1634	1758	1888	2025	2168	2319	2478	2644	2819	3003	3197	3400	3614	3840	4077	16
45	1636	1760	1890	2027	2171	2322	2480	2647	2822	3007	3200	3404	3618	3843	4081	15
46	1638	1762	1892	2029	2173	2324	2483	2650	2825	3010	3203	3407	3622	3847	4085	14
47	1640	1764	1895	2032	2176	2327	2486	2653	2828	3013	3207	3411	3625	3851	4089	13
48	1642	1766	1897	2034	2178	2329	2489	2656	2831	3016	3210	3414	3629	3855	4093	12
49	1644	1768	1899	2036	2181	2332	2491	2659	2834	3019	3213	3418	3633	3859	4097	11
50	1646	1770	1901	2039	2183	2335	2494	2661	2837	3022	3217	3421	3636	3863	4101	10
51	1648	1773	1903	2041	2185	2337	2497	2664	2840	3026	3220	3425	3640	3867	4105	9
52	1650	1775	1906	2043	2188	2340	2499	2667	2843	3029	3223	3428	3644	3871	4109	8
53	1652	1777	1908	2046	2190	2342	2502	2670	2846	3032	3227	3432	3647	3874	4113	7
54	1654	1779	1910	2048	2193	2345	2505	2673	2849	3035	3230	3435	3651	3878	4118	6
55	1656	1781	1912	2050	2195	2348	2508	2676	2852	3038	3233	3439	3655	3882	4122	5
56	1658	1783	1915	2053	2198	2350	2510	2679	2855	3041	3237	3442	3658	3886	4126	4
57	1660	1785	1917	2055	2200	2353	2513	2682	2859	3045	3240	3446	3662	3890	4130	3
58	1662	1788	1919	2057	2203	2355	2516	2684	2862	3048	3243	3449	3666	3894	4134	2
59	1664	1790	1921	2060	2205	2358	2519	2687	2865	3051	3247	3453	3670	3898	4138	1
60	1666	1792	1924	2062	2208	2361	2521	2690	2868	3054	3250	3456	3673	3902	4142	0
	1.	1.	1.	1.	1.	1.	1.	1.	1.	1.	1.	1.	1.	1.	1.	
	59°	58°	57°	56°	55°	54°	53°	52°	51°	50°	49°	48°	47°	46°	45°	

NATURAL COSECANTS

Table 34

NATURAL SECANTS

′	45°	46°	47°	48°	49°	50°	51°	52°	53°	54°	55°	56°	57°	58°	59°	
	1.	1.	1.	1.	1.	1.	1.	1.	1.	1.	1.	1.	1.	1.	1./2.	
0	4142	4396	4663	4945	5243	5557	5890	6243	6616	7013	7434	7883	8361	8871	9416	60
1	4146	4400	4667	4950	5248	5563	5896	6249	6623	7020	7442	7891	8369	8880	9425	59
2	4150	4404	4672	4954	5253	5568	5902	6255	6629	7027	7449	7898	8377	8888	9435	58
3	4154	4409	4677	4959	5258	5573	5907	6261	6636	7033	7456	7906	8385	8897	9444	57
4	4159	4413	4681	4964	5263	5579	5913	6267	6642	7040	7463	7914	8394	8906	9454	56
5	4163	4417	4686	4969	5268	5584	5919	6273	6649	7047	7471	7922	8402	8915	9463	55
6	4167	4422	4690	4974	5273	5590	5925	6279	6655	7054	7478	7929	8410	8924	9473	54
7	4171	4426	4695	4979	5278	5595	5930	6285	6661	7061	7485	7937	8419	8933	9482	53
8	4175	4430	4700	4984	5283	5601	5936	6291	6668	7068	7493	7945	8427	8941	9492	52
9	4179	4435	4704	4988	5289	5606	5942	6297	6674	7075	7500	7953	8435	8950	9501	51
10	4183	4439	4709	4993	5294	5611	5948	6303	6681	7081	7507	7960	8443	8959	9511	50
11	4188	4443	4713	4998	5299	5617	5953	6310	6687	7088	7515	7968	8452	8968	9520	49
12	4192	4448	4718	5003	5304	5622	5959	6316	6694	7095	7522	7976	8460	8977	9530	48
13	4196	4452	4723	5008	5309	5628	5965	6322	6700	7102	7529	7984	8468	8986	9539	47
14	4200	4457	4727	5013	5314	5633	5971	6328	6707	7109	7537	7992	8477	8995	9549	46
15	4204	4461	4732	5018	5320	5639	5976	6334	6713	7116	7544	8000	8485	9004	9558	45
16	4208	4465	4737	5023	5325	5644	5982	6340	6720	7123	7551	8007	8494	9013	9568	44
17	4213	4470	4741	5027	5330	5650	5988	6346	6726	7130	7559	8015	8502	9022	9577	43
18	4217	4474	4746	5032	5335	5655	5994	6353	6733	7137	7566	8023	8510	9031	9587	42
19	4221	4479	4750	5037	5340	5661	6000	6359	6739	7144	7573	8031	8519	9039	9597	41
20	4225	4483	4755	5042	5345	5666	6005	6365	6746	7151	7581	8039	8527	9048	9606	40
21	4229	4487	4760	5047	5351	5672	6011	6371	6753	7158	7588	8047	8535	9057	9616	39
22	4234	4492	4764	5052	5356	5677	6017	6377	6759	7165	7596	8055	8544	9066	9625	38
23	4238	4496	4769	5057	5361	5683	6023	6383	6766	7172	7603	8062	8552	9075	9635	37
24	4242	4501	4774	5062	5366	5688	6029	6390	6772	7179	7610	8070	8561	9084	9645	36
25	4246	4505	4778	5067	5372	5694	6035	6396	6779	7185	7618	8078	8569	9094	9654	35
26	4250	4510	4783	5072	5377	5699	6040	6402	6785	7192	7625	8086	8578	9103	9664	34
27	4255	4514	4788	5077	5382	5705	6046	6408	6792	7199	7633	8094	8586	9112	9674	33
28	4259	4518	4792	5082	5387	5710	6052	6414	6799	7206	7640	8102	8595	9121	9684	32
29	4263	4523	4797	5087	5392	5716	6058	6421	6805	7213	7648	8110	8603	9130	9693	31
30	4267	4527	4802	5092	5398	5721	6064	6427	6812	7221	7655	8118	8612	9139	9703	30
31	4271	4532	4807	5097	5403	5727	6070	6433	6818	7228	7663	8126	8620	9148	9713	29
32	4276	4536	4811	5102	5408	5732	6076	6439	6825	7235	7670	8134	8629	9157	9722	28
33	4280	4541	4816	5107	5413	5738	6082	6446	6832	7242	7678	8142	8637	9166	9732	27
34	4284	4545	4821	5111	5419	5744	6087	6452	6838	7249	7685	8150	8646	9175	9742	26
35	4288	4550	4825	5116	5424	5749	6093	6458	6845	7256	7693	8158	8654	9184	9752	25
36	4293	4554	4830	5121	5429	5755	6099	6464	6852	7263	7700	8166	8663	9194	9762	24
37	4297	4559	4835	5126	5435	5760	6105	6471	6858	7270	7708	8174	8671	9203	9771	23
38	4301	4563	4840	5131	5440	5766	6111	6477	6865	7277	7715	8182	8680	9212	9781	22
39	4305	4568	4844	5136	5445	5771	6117	6483	6871	7284	7723	8190	8688	9221	9791	21
40	4310	4572	4849	5141	5450	5777	6123	6489	6878	7291	7730	8198	8697	9230	9801	20
41	4314	4577	4854	5146	5456	5783	6129	6496	6885	7298	7738	8206	8706	9239	9811	19
42	4318	4581	4859	5151	5461	5788	6135	6502	6892	7305	7745	8214	8714	9249	9821	18
43	4322	4586	4863	5156	5466	5794	6141	6508	6898	7312	7753	8222	8723	9258	9830	17
44	4327	4590	4868	5162	5472	5800	6147	6515	6905	7320	7761	8230	8731	9267	9840	16
45	4331	4595	4873	5167	5477	5805	6153	6521	6912	7327	7768	8238	8740	9276	9850	15
46	4335	4599	4878	5172	5482	5811	6159	6527	6918	7334	7776	8247	8749	9285	9860	14
47	4340	4604	4882	5177	5488	5816	6165	6534	6925	7341	7783	8255	8757	9295	9870	13
48	4344	4608	4887	5182	5493	5822	6171	6540	6932	7348	7791	8263	8766	9304	9880	12
49	4348	4613	4892	5187	5498	5828	6177	6546	6939	7355	7799	8271	8775	9313	9890	11
50	4352	4617	4897	5192	5504	5833	6183	6553	6945	7362	7806	8279	8783	9323	9900	10
51	4357	4622	4901	5197	5509	5839	6189	6559	6952	7370	7814	8287	8792	9332	9910	9
52	4361	4626	4906	5202	5514	5845	6195	6565	6959	7377	7821	8295	8801	9341	9920	8
53	4365	4631	4911	5207	5520	5850	6201	6572	6966	7384	7829	8303	8810	9351	9930	7
54	4370	4635	4916	5212	5525	5856	6207	6578	6972	7391	7837	8312	8818	9360	9940	6
55	4374	4640	4921	5217	5530	5862	6213	6584	6979	7398	7844	8320	8827	9369	9950	5
56	4378	4645	4925	5222	5536	5867	6219	6591	6986	7406	7852	8328	8836	9379	9960	4
57	4383	4649	4930	5227	5541	5873	6225	6597	6993	7413	7860	8336	8844	9388	9970	3
58	4387	4654	4935	5232	5546	5879	6231	6604	6999	7420	7868	8344	8853	9397	9980	2
59	4391	4658	4940	5237	5552	5884	6237	6610	7006	7427	7875	8353	8862	9407	9990	1
60	4396	4663	4945	5243	5557	5890	6243	6616	7013	7434	7883	8361	8871	9416	0000	0
	1.	1.	1.	1.	1.	1.	1.	1.	1.	1.	1.	1.	1.	1.	1./2.	
	44°	43°	42°	41°	40°	39°	38°	37°	36°	35°	34°	33°	32°	31°	30°	′

NATURAL COSECANTS

Table 34

NATURAL SECANTS

′	60°	61°	62°	63°	64°	65°	66°	67°	68°	69°	70°	71°	72°	73°	74°	
	2.	2.	2.	2.	2.	2.	2.	2.	2.	2.	2./3.	3.	3.	3.	3.	
0	0000	0627	1301	2027	2812	3662	4586	5593	6695	7904	9238	0716	2361	4203	6280	60
1	0010	0637	1312	2039	2825	3677	4602	5611	6714	7925	9261	0742	2390	4236	6316	59
2	0020	0648	1324	2052	2839	3692	4618	5628	6733	7947	9285	0768	2419	4268	6353	58
3	0030	0659	1336	2065	2853	3706	4634	5646	6752	7968	9308	0794	2448	4301	6390	57
4	0040	0670	1347	2077	2866	3721	4650	5663	6772	7989	9332	0820	2477	4334	6427	56
5	0051	0681	1359	2090	2880	3736	4667	5681	6791	8010	9355	0846	2506	4367	6465	55
6	0061	0692	1371	2103	2894	3751	4683	5699	6811	8032	9379	0872	2535	4399	6502	54
7	0071	0703	1382	2115	2907	3766	4699	5716	6830	8053	9403	0898	2565	4432	6539	53
8	0081	0714	1394	2128	2921	3781	4715	5734	6849	8075	9426	0925	2594	4465	6576	52
9	0091	0725	1406	2141	2935	3796	4731	5752	6869	8096	9450	0951	2624	4499	6614	51
10	0101	0736	1418	2153	2949	3811	4748	5770	6888	8117	9474	0977	2653	4532	6652	50
11	0112	0747	1430	2166	2962	3826	4764	5788	6908	8139	9498	1004	2683	4565	6689	49
12	0122	0757	1441	2179	2976	3841	4780	5805	6927	8161	9521	1030	2712	4598	6727	48
13	0132	0768	1453	2192	2990	3856	4797	5823	6947	8182	9545	1057	2742	4632	6765	47
14	0142	0779	1465	2205	3004	3871	4813	5841	6967	8204	9569	1083	2772	4665	6803	46
15	0152	0791	1477	2217	3018	3886	4830	5859	6986	8225	9593	1110	2801	4699	6840	45
16	0163	0802	1489	2230	3032	3901	4846	5877	7006	8247	9617	1137	2831	4732	6879	44
17	0173	0813	1501	2243	3046	3916	4862	5895	7026	8269	9641	1163	2861	4766	6917	43
18	0183	0824	1513	2256	3060	3931	4879	5913	7046	8291	9665	1190	2891	4799	6955	42
19	0194	0835	1525	2269	3074	3946	4895	5931	7065	8312	9689	1217	2921	4833	6993	41
20	0204	0846	1537	2282	3088	3961	4912	5949	7085	8334	9713	1244	2951	4867	7032	40
21	0214	0857	1549	2295	3101	3977	4928	5967	7105	8356	9738	1271	2981	4901	7070	39
22	0225	0868	1560	2308	3115	3992	4945	5985	7125	8378	9762	1298	3012	4935	7108	38
23	0235	0879	1572	2320	3130	4007	4962	6003	7145	8400	9786	1325	3042	4969	7147	37
24	0245	0890	1584	2333	3144	4022	4978	6022	7165	8422	9811	1352	3072	5003	7186	36
25	0256	0901	1596	2346	3158	4038	4995	6040	7185	8444	9835	1379	3102	5037	7225	35
26	0266	0913	1609	2359	3172	4053	5012	6058	7205	8466	9859	1406	3133	5072	7263	34
27	0276	0924	1621	2372	3186	4068	5028	6076	7225	8488	9884	1433	3163	5106	7302	33
28	0287	0935	1633	2385	3200	4083	5045	6095	7245	8510	9908	1461	3194	5140	7341	32
29	0297	0946	1645	2399	3214	4099	5062	6113	7265	8532	9933	1488	3224	5175	7381	31
30	0308	0957	1657	2412	3228	4114	5078	6131	7285	8555	9957	1515	3255	5209	7420	30
31	0318	0969	1669	2425	3242	4130	5095	6150	7305	8577	9982	1543	3286	5244	7459	29
32	0329	0980	1681	2438	3257	4145	5112	6168	7325	8599	0007	1570	3317	5279	7498	28
33	0339	0991	1693	2451	3271	4160	5129	6186	7346	8621	0031	1598	3347	5313	7538	27
34	0350	1002	1705	2464	3285	4176	5146	6205	7366	8644	0056	1625	3378	5348	7577	26
35	0360	1014	1718	2477	3299	4191	5163	6223	7386	8666	0081	1653	3409	5383	7617	25
36	0371	1025	1730	2490	3314	4207	5180	6242	7407	8688	0106	1681	3440	5418	7657	24
37	0381	1036	1742	2504	3328	4222	5196	6260	7427	8711	0131	1708	3471	5453	7697	23
38	0392	1048	1754	2517	3342	4238	5213	6279	7447	8733	0156	1736	3502	5488	7737	22
39	0402	1059	1766	2530	3356	4254	5230	6298	7468	8756	0181	1764	3534	5523	7777	21
40	0413	1070	1779	2543	3371	4269	5247	6316	7488	8779	0206	1792	3565	5559	7817	20
41	0423	1082	1791	2556	3385	4285	5264	6335	7509	8801	0231	1820	3596	5594	7857	19
42	0434	1093	1803	2570	3400	4300	5282	6354	7529	8824	0256	1848	3628	5629	7897	18
43	0445	1105	1815	2583	3414	4316	5299	6372	7550	8846	0281	1876	3659	5665	7937	17
44	0455	1116	1828	2596	3428	4332	5316	6391	7570	8869	0306	1904	3691	5700	7978	16
45	0466	1127	1840	2610	3443	4348	5333	6410	7591	8892	0331	1932	3722	5736	8018	15
46	0476	1139	1852	2623	3457	4363	5350	6429	7612	8915	0357	1960	3754	5772	8059	14
47	0487	1150	1865	2636	3472	4379	5367	6447	7632	8938	0382	1989	3785	5808	8100	13
48	0498	1162	1877	2650	3486	4395	5384	6466	7653	8960	0407	2017	3817	5843	8140	12
49	0508	1173	1890	2663	3501	4411	5402	6485	7674	8983	0433	2045	3849	5879	8181	11
50	0519	1185	1902	2677	3515	4426	5419	6504	7695	9006	0458	2074	3881	5915	8222	10
51	0530	1196	1914	2690	3530	4442	5436	6523	7715	9029	0484	2102	3913	5951	8263	9
52	0540	1208	1927	2703	3545	4458	5454	6542	7736	9052	0509	2131	3945	5988	8304	8
53	0551	1219	1939	2717	3559	4474	5471	6561	7757	9075	0535	2159	3977	6024	8346	7
54	0562	1231	1952	2730	3574	4490	5488	6580	7778	9099	0561	2188	4009	6060	8387	6
55	0573	1242	1964	2744	3588	4506	5506	6599	7799	9122	0586	2217	4041	6097	8428	5
56	0583	1254	1977	2757	3603	4522	5523	6618	7820	9145	0612	2245	4073	6133	8470	4
57	0594	1266	1989	2771	3618	4538	5541	6637	7841	9168	0638	2274	4106	6169	8512	3
58	0605	1277	2002	2785	3633	4554	5558	6656	7862	9191	0664	2303	4138	6206	8553	2
59	0616	1289	2014	2798	3647	4570	5576	6675	7883	9215	0690	2332	4171	6243	8595	1
60	0627	1301	2027	2812	3662	4586	5593	6695	7904	9238	0716	2361	4203	6280	8637	0
	2.	2.	2.	2.	2.	2.	2.	2.	2.	2.	2./3.	3.	3.	3.	3.	
	29°	28°	27°	26°	25°	24°	23°	22°	21°	20°	19°	18°	17°	16°	15°	′

NATURAL COSECANTS

Table 34

NATURAL SECANTS

′	75°	76°	77°	78°	79°	80°	81°	82°	83°	84°	85°	86°	87°	88°	89°	
	3./4.	4.	4.	4./5.	5.	5./6.	6./7.	7./8.	8./9.							
0	8637	1336	4454	8097	2408	7588	3925	1853	2055	9.567	11.47	14.34	19.11	28.65	57.30	60
1	8679	1384	4510	8163	2487	7683	4042	2002	2250	9.593	11.51	14.40	19.21	28.89	58.27	59
2	8721	1432	4566	8229	2566	7778	4160	2152	2446	9.620	11.55	14.46	19.32	29.14	59.27	58
3	8763	1481	4623	8296	2645	7874	4279	2302	2642	9.647	11.59	14.52	19.43	29.39	60.31	57
4	8806	1529	4679	8362	2724	7970	4398	2453	2840	9.674	11.63	14.58	19.54	29.64	61.39	56
5	8848	1578	4736	8429	2804	8067	4517	2604	3039	9.701	11.67	14.64	19.65	29.90	62.51	55
6	8890	1627	4793	8496	2883	8164	4637	2757	3238	9.728	11.71	14.70	19.77	30.16	63.66	54
7	8933	1676	4850	8563	2963	8261	4757	2909	3439	9.756	11.75	14.77	19.88	30.43	64.87	53
8	8976	1725	4907	8630	3044	8358	4878	3063	3640	9.783	11.79	14.83	20.00	30.70	66.11	52
9	9018	1774	4964	8697	3124	8456	4999	3217	3843	9.811	11.83	14.89	20.11	30.98	67.41	51
10	9061	1824	5022	8765	3205	8554	5121	3372	4047	9.839	11.87	14.96	20.23	31.26	68.76	50
11	9104	1873	5079	8833	3286	8652	5243	3527	4251	9.867	11.91	15.02	20.35	31.54	70.16	49
12	9147	1923	5137	8901	3367	8751	5366	3684	4457	9.895	11.95	15.09	20.47	31.84	71.62	48
13	9190	1973	5195	8969	3449	8850	5489	3840	4663	9.924	11.99	15.16	20.59	32.13	73.15	47
14	9234	2022	5253	9037	3530	8950	5612	3998	4871	9.952	12.03	15.22	20.72	32.44	74.74	46
15	9277	2072	5311	9106	3612	9049	5736	4156	5079	9.981	12.08	15.29	20.84	32.75	76.40	45
16	9320	2122	5369	9175	3695	9150	5861	4315	5289	10.01	12.12	15.36	20.97	33.06	78.13	44
17	9364	2173	5428	9244	3777	9250	5986	4474	5500	10.04	12.16	15.43	21.10	33.38	79.95	43
18	9408	2223	5486	9313	3860	9351	6111	4635	5711	10.07	12.20	15.50	21.23	33.71	81.85	42
19	9451	2273	5545	9382	3943	9452	6237	4795	5924	10.10	12.25	15.57	21.36	34.04	83.85	41
20	9495	2324	5604	9452	4026	9554	6363	4957	6138	10.13	12.29	15.64	21.49	34.38	85.95	40
21	9539	2375	5663	9521	4110	9656	6490	5119	6353	10.16	12.34	15.71	21.63	34.73	88.15	39
22	9583	2425	5722	9591	4194	9758	6618	5282	6569	10.19	12.38	15.78	21.77	35.08	90.47	38
23	9627	2476	5782	9662	4278	9860	6745	5446	6786	10.22	12.42	15.85	21.90	35.45	92.91	37
24	9672	2527	5841	9732	4362	9963	6874	5611	7004	10.25	12.47	15.93	22.04	35.81	95.49	36
25	9716	2579	5901	9803	4447	0066	7003	5776	7223	10.28	12.51	16.00	22.19	36.19	98.22	35
26	9760	2630	5961	9873	4532	0170	7132	5942	7444	10.31	12.56	16.07	22.33	36.58	101.1	34
27	9805	2681	6021	9944	4617	0274	7262	6109	7665	10.34	12.61	16.15	22.48	36.97	104.2	33
28	9850	2733	6081	0016	4702	0379	7392	6276	7888	10.37	12.65	16.23	22.62	37.37	107.4	32
29	9894	2785	6142	0087	4788	0483	7523	6444	8112	10.40	12.70	16.30	22.77	37.78	110.9	31
30	9939	2837	6202	0159	4874	0589	7655	6613	8337	10.43	12.75	16.38	22.93	38.20	114.6	30
31	9984	2889	6263	0230	4960	0694	7787	6783	8563	10.47	12.79	16.46	23.08	38.63	118.5	29
32	0029	2941	6324	0302	5047	0800	7919	6953	8790	10.50	12.84	16.54	23.24	39.07	122.8	28
33	0075	2993	6385	0375	5134	0906	8052	7124	9019	10.53	12.89	16.62	23.39	39.52	127.3	27
34	0120	3045	6446	0447	5221	1013	8186	7296	9248	10.56	12.94	16.70	23.55	39.98	132.2	26
35	0165	3098	6507	0520	5308	1120	8320	7469	9479	10.59	12.99	16.78	23.72	40.45	137.5	25
36	0211	3150	6569	0593	5396	1227	8454	7642	9711	10.63	13.03	16.86	23.88	40.93	143.2	24
37	0256	3203	6631	0666	5484	1335	8589	7817	9944	10.66	13.08	16.94	24.05	41.42	149.5	23
38	0302	3256	6693	0739	5572	1443	8725	7992	0179	10.69	13.13	17.03	24.22	41.93	156.3	22
39	0348	3309	6755	0813	5660	1552	8861	8168	0415	10.73	13.18	17.11	24.39	42.45	163.7	21
40	0394	3362	6817	0886	5749	1661	8998	8344	0652	10.76	13.23	17.20	24.56	42.98	171.9	20
41	0440	3415	6879	0960	5838	1770	9135	8522	0890	10.79	13.29	17.28	24.74	43.52	180.9	19
42	0486	3469	6942	1034	5928	1880	9273	8700	1129	10.83	13.34	17.37	24.92	44.08	191.0	18
43	0532	3522	7004	1109	6017	1990	9411	8879	1370	10.86	13.39	17.46	25.10	44.65	202.2	17
44	0579	3576	7067	1183	6107	2100	9550	9059	1612	10.89	13.44	17.55	25.28	45.24	214.9	16
45	0625	3630	7130	1258	6198	2211	9690	9240	1855	10.93	13.49	17.64	25.47	45.84	229.2	15
46	0672	3684	7194	1333	6288	2323	9830	9422	2100	10.96	13.55	17.73	25.66	46.46	245.6	14
47	0718	3738	7257	1409	6379	2434	9971	9604	2346	11.00	13.60	17.82	25.85	47.10	264.4	13
48	0765	3792	7321	1484	6470	2546	0112	9787	2593	11.03	13.65	17.91	26.05	47.75	286.5	12
49	0812	3847	7384	1560	6562	2659	0254	9971	2842	11.07	13.71	18.01	26.25	48.42	312.5	11
50	0859	3901	7448	1636	6653	2772	0396	0156	3092	11.10	13.76	18.10	26.45	49.11	343.8	10
51	0906	3956	7512	1712	6745	2885	0539	0342	3343	11.14	13.82	18.20	26.66	49.83	382.0	9
52	0954	4011	7577	1789	6838	2999	0683	0529	3596	11.18	13.87	18.30	26.86	50.56	429.7	8
53	1001	4066	7641	1865	6930	3113	0827	0717	3850	11.21	13.93	18.39	27.08	51.31	491.1	7
54	1048	4121	7706	1942	7023	3228	0972	0905	4105	11.25	13.99	18.49	27.29	52.09	573.0	6
55	1096	4176	7771	2019	7117	3343	1117	1095	4362	11.29	14.04	18.59	27.51	52.89	687.5	5
56	1144	4231	7836	2097	7210	3458	1263	1285	4620	11.32	14.10	18.69	27.73	53.72	859.4	4
57	1191	4287	7901	2174	7304	3574	1410	1476	4880	11.36	14.16	18.79	27.96	54.57	1146	3
58	1239	4342	7966	2252	7398	3691	1557	1668	5141	11.40	14.22	18.90	28.18	55.45	1719	2
59	1287	4398	8032	2330	7493	3807	1705	1861	5404	11.44	14.28	19.00	28.42	56.36	3438	1
60	1336	4454	8097	2408	7588	3925	1853	2055	5668	11.47	14.34	19.11	28.65	57.30	Infinite	0
	3./4.	4.	4.	4./5.	5.	5./6.	6./7.	7./8.	8./9.							
	14°	13°	12°	11°	10°	9°	8°	7°	6°	5°	4°	3°	2°	1°	0°	′

NATURAL COSECANTS

343

Table 35

FOR CONVERTING
HOURS AND MINUTES
INTO THE
DECIMAL OF A DAY

Hrs.	MINUTES					
	0	**10**	**20**	**30**	**40**	**50**
0	0.000	0.007	0.014	0.021	0.028	0.035
1	.042	.049	.056	.063	.069	.076
2	.083	.090	.097	.104	.111	.118
3	.125	.132	.139	.146	.153	.160
4	.167	.174	.181	.188	.194	.201
5	.208	.215	.222	.229	.236	.243
6	.250	.257	.264	.271	.278	.285
7	.292	.299	.306	.312	.319	.326
8	.333	.340	.347	.354	.361	.368
9	.375	.382	.389	.396	.403	.410
10	.417	.424	.431	.438	.445	.451
11	.458	.465	.472	.479	.486	.493
12	.500	.507	.514	.521	.528	.535
13	.542	.549	.556	.563	.569	.576
14	.583	.590	.597	.604	.611	.618
15	.625	.632	.639	.646	.653	.660
16	.667	.674	.681	.688	.694	.701
17	.708	.715	.722	.729	.736	.743
18	.750	.757	.764	.771	.778	.785
19	.792	.799	.806	.813	.819	.826
20	.833	.840	.847	.854	.861	.868
21	.875	.882	.889	.896	.903	.910
22	.917	.924	.931	.938	.945	.951
23	.958	.965	.972	.979	.986	.993

1m = .000694 days.

Therefore, to three decimal places,

1m = .001 days.		6m = .004 days.	
2	= .001	7	= .005
3	= .002	8	= .006
4	= .003	9	= .006
5	= .003	10	= .007

Table 36

MINUTES INTO
DECIMALS OF HOUR

M.	Hrs.	M.	Hrs.	M.	Hrs.	M.	Hrs.
1	.017	16	.267	31	.517	46	.767
2	.033	17	.283	32	.533	47	.783
3	.050	18	.300	33	.550	48	.800
4	.067	19	.317	34	.567	49	.817
5	.083	20	.333	35	.583	50	.833
6	.100	21	.350	36	.600	51	.850
7	.117	22	.367	37	.617	52	.867
8	.133	23	.383	38	.633	53	.883
9	.150	24	.400	39	.650	54	.900
10	.167	25	.417	40	.667	55	.917
11	.183	26	.433	41	.683	56	.933
12	.200	27	.450	42	.700	57	.950
13	.217	28	.467	43	.717	58	.967
14	.233	29	.483	44	.733	59	.983
15	.250	30	.500	45	.750	60	1.000

Table 37

TABLE OF
CO-LOGS
FOR COMPUTING
DAILY AVERAGE SPEED

Eastbound		Westbound	
Time	Co-log.	Time	Co-log
23h 0m	63827	24h 0m	61979
1	63795	1	61948
2	63765	2	61919
3	63733	3	61888
4	63701	4	61858
5	63671	5	61829
6	63639	6	61798
7	63607	7	61768
8	63577	8	61739
9	63545	9	61708
10	63513	10	61678
11	63483	11	61649
12	63451	12	61619
13	63420	13	61588
14	63390	14	61559
15	63358	15	61529
16	63326	16	61498
17	63296	17	61470
18	63264	18	61439
19	63233	19	61410
20	63203	20	61380
21	63171	21	61350
22	63140	22	61320
23	63110	23	61291
24	63078	24	61261
25	63047	25	61231
26	63017	26	61202
27	62986	27	61172
28	62954	28	61142
29	62925	29	61114
30	62893	30	61083
31	62862	31	61053
32	62832	32	61025
33	62801	33	60995
34	62770	34	60965
35	62740	35	60936
36	62709	36	60906
37	62677	37	60877
38	62648	38	60848
39	62617	39	60818
40	62585	40	60788
41	62556	41	60760
42	62525	42	60730
43	62494	43	60700
44	62465	44	60672
45	62434	45	60642
46	62403	46	60613
47	62373	47	60585
48	62342	48	60555
49	62311	49	60525
50	62282	50	60497
51	62251	51	60467
52	62220	52	60438
53	62191	53	60410
54	62160	54	60380
55	62129	55	60350
56	62100	56	60323
57	62069	57	60293
23 58	62040	24 58	60263
23 59	62010	24 59	60236

25h 0m 60206

Log. Dist. + Co-Log. Time = Log. Speed

Table 38

Correction to be applied to W/T D.F. bearing to convert to Mercatorial Bearing
(Half-convergency* Table)

Mid Lat.	D. Long. between Station (or Beacon) and Ship																				Mid Lat.
°	1°	2°	3°	4°	5°	6°	7°	8°	9°	10°	11°	12°	13°	14°	15°	16°	17°	18°	19°	20°	°
5	0.1	0.1	0.1	0.2	0.2	0.3	0.3	0.4	0.4	0.4	0.5	0.5	0.6	0.6	0.7	0.7	0.7	0.8	0.9	0.9	5
10	0.1	0.2	0.3	0.4	0.4	0.5	0.6	0.7	0.8	0.9	1.0	1.1	1.2	1.2	1.3	1.4	1.5	1.6	1.7	1.8	10
15	0.1	0.3	0.4	0.5	0.6	0.8	0.9	1.0	1.2	1.3	1.5	1.6	1.7	1.8	2.0	2.1	2.3	2.4	2.5	2.7	15
20	0.2	0.3	0.5	0.7	0.8	1.0	1.2	1.4	1.5	1.7	1.9	2.1	2.3	2.4	2.6	2.8	3.0	3.2	3.4	3.5	20
25	0.2	0.4	0.6	0.8	1.1	1.3	1.5	1.7	1.9	2.1	2.4	2.6	2.8	3.0	3.2	3.5	3.7	3.9	4.1	4.3	25
30	0.2	0.5	0.8	1.0	1.2	1.5	1.8	2.0	2.2	2.5	2.8	3.0	3.3	3.6	3.8	4.1	4.3	4.6	4.9	5.2	30
35	0.3	0.6	0.9	1.2	1.4	1.7	2.0	2.3	2.6	2.9	3.2	3.5	3.8	4.1	4.4	4.7	5.0	5.3	5.6	5.9	35
40	0.3	0.6	1.0	1.3	1.6	1.9	2.2	2.6	2.9	3.2	3.6	3.9	4.2	4.6	4.9	5.2	5.6	5.9	6.2	6.6	40
45	0.4	0.7	1.1	1.4	1.8	2.1	2.5	2.8	3.2	3.5	3.9	4.3	4.7	5.1	5.4	5.7	6.1	6.5	6.8	7.1	45
50	0.4	0.8	1.1	1.5	1.9	2.3	2.7	3.1	3.4	3.8	4.2	4.6	5.1	5.5	5.8	6.2	6.6	7.0	7.4	7.8	50
55	0.4	0.8	1.2	1.6	2.1	2.4	2.9	3.3	3.7	4.1	4.5	4.9	5.4	5.8	6.2	6.6	7.0	7.5	7.9	8.3	55
60	0.4	0.9	1.3	1.7	2.2	2.6	3.0	3.5	3.9	4.3	4.8	5.2	5.7	6.2	6.5	7.0	7.4	7.9	8.4	8.7	60
65	0.5	0.9	1.4	1.8	2.3	2.7	3.2	3.6	4.1	4.5	5.0	5.4	5.9	6.4	6.8	7.3	7.7	8.2	8.7	9.1	65
70	0.5	0.9	1.4	1.9	2.3	2.8	3.3	3.8	4.2	4.7	5.2	5.6	6.1	6.6	7.0	7.5	8.0	8.5	9.0	9.4	70
75	0.5	1.0	1.4	1.9	2.4	2.9	3.4	3.9	4.3	4.8	5.3	5.8	6.3	6.8	7.2	7.7	8.2	8.7	9.2	9.7	75
80	0.5	1.0	1.5	2.0	2.5	3.0	3.4	3.9	4.4	4.9	5.4	5.9	6.4	6.9	7.4	7.9	8.4	8.9	9.4	9.8	80
85	0.5	1.0	1.5	2.0	2.5	3.0	3.5	4.0	4.5	5.0	5.5	6.0	6.5	7.0	7.5	8.0	8.5	9.0	9.5	10.0	85

Mid Lat.	D. Long. between Station (or Beacon) and Ship																				Mid Lat.
°	20°	21°	22°	23°	24°	25°	26°	27°	28°	29°	30°	31°	32°	33°	34°	35°	36°	37°	38°	39°	°
65	9.1	9.5	10.0	10.4	10.9	11.3	11.8	12.2	12.7	13.1	13.6	14.0	14.5	15.0	15.4	15.9	16.3	16.8	17.2	17.7	65
70	9.4	9.9	10.3	10.8	11.3	11.7	12.2	12.7	13.2	13.6	14.1	14.6	15.0	15.5	16.0	16.4	16.9	17.4	17.9	18.3	70
75	9.7	10.1	10.6	11.1	11.6	12.1	12.6	13.0	13.5	14.0	14.5	15.0	15.5	15.9	16.4	16.9	17.4	17.9	18.4	18.8	75
80	9.8	10.3	10.8	11.3	11.8	12.3	12.8	13.3	13.8	14.3	14.8	15.3	15.8	16.2	16.7	17.2	17.7	18.2	18.7	19.2	80
85	10.0	10.5	11.0	11.5	12.0	12.5	13.0	13.4	13.9	14.4	14.9	15.4	15.9	16.4	16.9	17.4	17.9	18.4	18.9	19.4	85

		North Lat.	South Lat.
*When using 360° Compass	Bearing measured Eastward,	ADD	SUBTRACT
	„ „ Westward,	SUBTRACT	ADD

i.e. The rhumb line (Mercatorial bearing) always lies on the equatorial side of the true (Great Circle) position-line.

Table 39

DISTANCE TO THE RADAR HORIZON

Approximate heights and distances at which land may be picked up by radar under conditions of standard refraction. Changes in temperature gradients, humidity and pressure will affect these values; e.g. if the temperature of the air is considerably warmer than that of the sea, the tabulated distances may be greatly increased, and *vice versa*.

Height of Aerial or Elevation of Target in Feet	Distance in Nautical Miles
18	5
24	6
32	7
42	8
54	9
66	10
80	11
96	12
112	13
130	14
150	15
170	16
190	17
215	18
240	19
265	20
320	22
380	24
450	26
520	28
600	30
680	32
770	34
860	36
960	38
1060	40
1320	45
1660	50

Example 1.

At what distance may land having an elevation of 100 feet be expected to be picked up by radar with an aerial height of 35 feet?

Height of aerial 35 feet: distance = 7 miles
Elevation 100 feet: distance = 12 miles
————————————————
distance = 19 miles (approx.)

Example 2.

A response has appeared on the radar at a range of 29 miles, the radar aerial is at 52 feet. What is the probable minimum elevation of this target?

Distance on radar   = 29 miles
Height of radar 52 feet;   distance = 9 miles
————————————————
distance = 20 miles

From table, 20 miles requires an elevation of 265 feet approx., i.e. the probable minimum.

CAUTION: At long ranges power output, set efficiency and nature of target will largely control range of detection.

Table 40 — COMPASS EQUIVALENTS

(For 360° and Quadrantal Graduations)

Error is applied to 360° Compass Directions as follows:—

COMPASS to TRUE { Error EAST **+** „ WEST **−**   TRUE to COMPASS { Error EAST **−** „ WEST **+**

N. E.				S. E.				S. W.				N. W.			
001	N1E	046	N46E	091	S89E	136	S44E	181	S1W	226	S46W	271	N89W	316	N44W
002	2	047	47	092	88	137	43	182	2	227	47	272	88	317	43
003	3	048	48	093	87	138	42	183	3	228	48	273	87	318	42
004	4	049	49	094	86	139	41	184	4	229	49	274	86	319	41
005	5	050	50	095	85	140	40	185	5	230	50	275	85	320	40
006	6	051	51	096	84	141	39	186	6	231	51	276	84	321	39
007	7	052	52	097	83	142	38	187	7	232	52	277	83	322	38
008	8	053	53	098	82	143	37	188	8	233	53	278	82	323	37
009	9	054	54	099	81	144	36	189	9	234	54	279	81	324	36
010	10	055	55	100	80	145	35	190	10	235	55	280	80	325	35
011	11	056	56	101	79	146	34	191	11	236	56	281	79	326	34
012	12	057	57	102	78	147	33	192	12	237	57	282	78	327	33
013	13	058	58	103	77	148	32	193	13	238	58	283	77	328	32
014	14	059	59	104	76	149	31	194	14	239	59	284	76	329	31
015	15	060	60	105	75	150	30	195	15	240	60	285	75	330	30
016	16	061	61	106	74	151	29	196	16	241	61	286	74	331	29
017	17	062	62	107	73	152	28	197	17	242	62	287	73	332	28
018	18	063	63	108	72	153	27	198	18	243	63	288	72	333	27
019	19	064	64	109	71	154	26	199	19	244	64	289	71	334	26
020	20	065	65	110	70	155	25	200	20	245	65	290	70	335	25
021	21	066	66	111	69	156	24	201	21	246	66	291	69	336	24
022	22	067	67	112	68	157	23	202	22	247	67	292	68	337	23
023	23	068	68	113	67	158	22	203	23	248	68	293	67	338	22
024	24	069	69	114	66	159	21	204	24	249	69	294	66	339	21
025	25	070	70	115	65	160	20	205	25	250	70	295	65	340	20
026	26	071	71	116	64	161	19	206	26	251	71	296	64	341	19
027	27	072	72	117	63	162	18	207	27	252	72	297	63	342	18
028	28	073	73	118	62	163	17	208	28	253	73	298	62	343	17
029	29	074	74	119	61	164	16	209	29	254	74	299	61	344	16
030	30	075	75	120	60	165	15	210	30	255	75	300	60	345	15
031	31	076	76	121	59	166	14	211	31	256	76	301	59	346	14
032	32	077	77	122	58	167	13	212	32	257	77	302	58	347	13
033	33	078	78	123	57	168	12	213	33	258	78	303	57	348	12
034	34	079	79	124	56	169	11	214	34	259	79	304	56	349	11
035	35	080	80	125	55	170	10	215	35	260	80	305	55	350	10
036	36	081	81	126	54	171	9	216	36	261	81	306	54	351	9
037	37	082	82	127	53	172	8	217	37	262	82	307	53	352	8
038	38	083	83	128	52	173	7	218	38	263	83	308	52	353	7
039	39	084	84	129	51	174	6	219	39	264	84	309	51	354	6
040	40	085	85	130	50	175	5	220	40	265	85	310	50	355	5
041	41	086	86	131	49	176	4	221	41	266	86	311	49	356	4
042	42	087	87	132	48	177	3	222	42	267	87	312	48	357	3
043	43	088	88	133	47	178	2	223	43	268	88	313	47	358	2
044	44	089	89	134	46	179	1	224	44	269	89	314	46	359	1
045	N45E	090	East	135	S45E	180	South	225	S45W	270	West	315	N45W	000	North

The mnemonic:

Error EAST, compass LEAST
„ WEST, „ BEST

may be found helpful in recollecting how error
is to be applied to 360° courses and bearings.

Table 41

A TABLE OF THE COMPASS ANGLES

NORTH

	357° 11′	N. ¼ W.	2° 49′	N. ¼ E.	002° 49′	
	354 23	N. ½ W.	5 37	N. ½ E.	005 37	
	351 34	N. ¾ W.	8 26	N. ¾ E.	008 26	
	348 45	**N. by W.**	**11 15**	**N. by E.**	**011 15**	
	345 56	N. by W. ¼ W.	14 04	N. by E. ¼ E.	014 04	
	343 08	N. by W. ½ W.	16 52	N. by E. ½ E.	016 52	
	340 19	N. by W. ¾ W.	19 41	N. by E. ¾ E.	019 41	
	337 30	**N. N. W.**	**22 30**	**N. N. E.**	**022 30**	
	334 41	N. W. by N. ¾ N.	25 19	N. E. by N. ¾ N.	025 19	
	331 52	N. W. by N. ½ N	28 07	N. E. by N. ½ N.	028 07	
	329 04	N. W. by N. ¼ N.	30 56	N. E. by N. ¼ N.	030 56	
	326 15	**N. W. by N.**	**33 45**	**N. E. by N.**	**033 45**	
	323 26	N. W. ¾ N.	36 34	N. E. ¾ N.	036 34	
N.W.	320 38	N. W. ½ N.	39 22	N. E. ½ N.	039 22	**N.E.**
	317 49	N. W. ¼ N.	42 11	N. E. ¼ N.	042 11	
Quadt.	**315 00**	**N. W.**	**45 00**	**N. E.**	**045 00**	Quadt.
	312 11	N. W. ¼ W.	47 49	N. E. ¼ E.	047 49	
	309 22	N. W. ½ W.	50 37	N. E. ½ E.	050 37	
	306 34	N. W. ¾ W.	53 26	N. E. ¾ E.	053 26	
	303 45	**N. W. by W.**	**56 15**	**N. E. by E.**	**056 15**	
	300 56	N.W. by W. ¼ W.	59 04	N. E. by E. ¼ E.	059 04	
	298 08	N.W. by W. ½ W.	61 52	N. E. by E. ½ E.	061 52	
	295 19	N.W. by W. ¾ W.	64 41	N. E. by E. ¾ E.	064 41	
	292 30	**W. N. W.**	**67 30**	**E. N. E.**	**067 30**	
	289 41	W. by N. ¾ N.	70 19	E. by N. ¾ N.	070 19	
	286 52	W. by N. ½ N.	73 07	E. by N. ½ N.	073 07	
	284 04	W. by N. ¼ N.	75 56	E. by N. ¼ N.	075 56	
	281 15	**W. by N.**	**78 45**	**E. by N.**	**078 45**	
	278 26	W. ¾ N.	81 34	E. ¾ N.	081 34	
	275 38	W. ½ N.	84 22	E. ½ N.	084 22	
	272 49	W. ¼ N.	87 11	E. ¼ N.	087 11	
	270 00	**WEST**	**90 00**	**EAST**	**090 00**	
	267 11	W. ¼ S.	87 11	E. ¼ S.	092 49	
	264 22	W. ½ S.	84 22	E. ½ S.	095 38	
	261 34	W. ¾ S.	81 34	E. ¾ S.	098 26	
	258 45	**W. by S.**	**78 45**	**E. by S.**	**101 15**	
	255 56	W. by S. ¼ S.	75 56	E. by S. ¼ S.	104 04	
	253 07	W. by S. ½ S.	73 07	E. by S. ½ S.	106 53	
	250 19	W. by S. ¾ S.	70 19	E. by S. ¾ S.	109 41	
	247 30	**W. S. W.**	**67 30**	**E. S. E.**	**112 30**	
	244 41	S.W. by W. ¾ W.	64 41	S. E. by E. ¾ E.	115 19	
	241 52	S.W. by W. ½ W.	61 52	S. E. by E. ½ E.	118 08	
	239 04	S.W. by W. ¼ W.	59 04	S. E. by E. ¼ E.	120 56	
S.W.	**236 15**	**S. W. by W.**	**56 15**	**S. E. by E.**	**123 45**	**S.E.**
	233 26	S. W. ¾ W.	53 26	S. E. ¾ E.	126 34	
Quadt.	230 37	S. W. ½ W.	50 37	S. E. ½ E.	129 23	Quadt.
	227 49	S. W. ¼ W.	47 49	S. E. ¼ E.	132 11	
	225 00	**S. W.**	**45 00**	**S. E.**	**135 00**	
	222 11	S. W. ¼ S.	42 11	S. E. ¼ S.	137 49	
	219 22	S. W. ½ S.	39 22	S. E. ½ S.	140 38	
	216 34	S. W. ¾ S.	36 34	S. E. ¾ S.	143 26	
	213 45	**S. W. by S.**	**33 45**	**S. E. by S.**	**146 15**	
	210 56	S. W. by S. ¼ S.	30 56	S. E. by S. ¼ S.	149 04	
	208 07	S. W. by S. ½ S.	28 07	S. E. by S. ½ S.	151 53	
	205 19	S. W. by S. ¾ S.	25 19	S. E. by S. ¾ S.	154 41	
	202 30	**S. S. W.**	**22 30**	**S. S. E.**	**157 30**	
	199 41	S. by W. ¾ W.	19 41	S. by E. ¾ E.	160 19	
	196 52	S. by W. ½ W.	16 52	S. by E. ½ E.	163 08	
	194 04	S. by W. ¼ W.	14 04	S. by E. ¼ E.	165 56	
	191 15	**S. by W.**	**11 15**	**S. by E.**	**168 45**	
	188 26	S. ¾ W.	8 26	S. ¾ E.	171 34	
	185 37	S. ½ W.	5 37	S. ½ E.	174 23	
	182 49	S. ¼ W.	2 49	S. ¼ E.	177 11	

SOUTH

Table 42

RUNNING FIX*

(FACTORS FOR CALCULATING DISTANCE OFF BY)

ANGLE BETWEEN COURSE MADE GOOD and FIRST BEARING

Change of Bearing	16°	18°	20°	22°	24°	26°	28°	30°	32°	34°	36°	38°	40°	42°	44°	46°	48°	50°	52°	54°	56°	58°	60°	62°	64°	66°	68°	70°	72°	74°	76°	78°	80°	82°	84°	86°	88°	90°
20	.47	.56	.64	.73	.83	.92	1.02	1.12	1.22	1.32	1.43	1.53	1.63	1.73	1.83	1.92	2.02	2.11	2.19	2.27	2.35	2.43	2.49	2.56	2.61	2.66	2.71	2.75	2.78	2.80	2.82	2.83	2.84	2.83	2.82	2.80	2.78	2.75
22	.45	.53	.61	.69	.78	.87	.96	1.05	1.14	1.23	1.32	1.42	1.52	1.61	1.69	1.78	1.86	1.95	2.02	2.10	2.16	2.23	2.29	2.34	2.39	2.44	2.48	2.51	2.53	2.55	2.56	2.57	2.57	2.56	2.55	2.53	2.51	2.48
24	.44	.51	.58	.66	.74	.83	.91	.99	1.08	1.17	1.25	1.34	1.42	1.50	1.58	1.66	1.74	1.81	1.88	1.95	2.01	2.06	2.12	2.17	2.21	2.25	2.28	2.30	2.33	2.34	2.35	2.35	2.35	2.34	2.33	2.30	2.28	2.25
26	.42	.49	.56	.64	.71	.79	.87	.95	1.03	1.11	1.18	1.26	1.34	1.42	1.49	1.56	1.63	1.70	1.76	1.82	1.87	1.92	1.97	2.01	2.05	2.08	2.11	2.13	2.15	2.16	2.17	2.17	2.16	2.15	2.13	2.13	2.08	2.05
28	.41	.47	.54	.61	.68	.76	.83	.90	.98	1.05	1.13	1.20	1.27	1.35	1.41	1.47	1.54	1.60	1.65	1.71	1.76	1.80	1.84	1.88	1.91	1.94	1.96	1.98	2.00	2.00	2.01	2.00	2.00	1.98	1.96	1.94	1.91	1.88
30	.40	.46	.52	.59	.66	.73	.80	.87	.94	1.01	1.07	1.14	1.21	1.27	1.34	1.40	1.45	1.51	1.56	1.61	1.65	1.70	1.73	1.76	1.79	1.82	1.84	1.85	1.86	1.87	1.87	1.86	1.85	1.84	1.82	1.79	1.76	1.73
32	.39	.45	.51	.57	.64	.70	.77	.83	.90	.96	1.03	1.09	1.15	1.21	1.27	1.33	1.38	1.43	1.48	1.52	1.56	1.60	1.63	1.66	1.69	1.71	1.72	1.73	1.74	1.74	1.74	1.73	1.72	1.71	1.69	1.66	1.63	1.60
34	.38	.44	.49	.56	.62	.68	.74	.80	.87	.93	.99	1.05	1.11	1.16	1.22	1.27	1.32	1.36	1.41	1.45	1.48	1.52	1.54	1.57	1.59	1.61	1.62	1.63	1.63	1.63	1.63	1.62	1.61	1.59	1.57	1.54	1.52	1.48
36	.37	.43	.48	.54	.60	.66	.72	.78	.84	.89	.95	1.01	1.06	1.11	1.16	1.21	1.26	1.30	1.34	1.38	1.41	1.44	1.47	1.49	1.51	1.52	1.53	1.54	1.54	1.54	1.53	1.52	1.51	1.49	1.47	1.44	1.41	1.38
38	.36	.42	.47	.53	.58	.64	.70	.75	.81	.87	.92	.97	1.01	1.07	1.12	1.16	1.20	1.24	1.28	1.31	1.34	1.37	1.39	1.41	1.43	1.44	1.45	1.45	1.45	1.45	1.44	1.43	1.41	1.39	1.37	1.34	1.31	1.28
40	.36	.41	.46	.50	.57	.62	.68	.73	.78	.84	.89	.94	.99	1.03	1.08	1.12	1.16	1.19	1.23	1.26	1.28	1.31	1.33	1.34	1.36	1.37	1.37	1.37	1.37	1.37	1.36	1.34	1.33	1.31	1.28	1.26	1.23	1.19
42	.35	.40	.45	.49	.56	.61	.66	.72	.76	.81	.86	.91	.95	.99	1.04	1.07	1.11	1.14	1.17	1.20	1.23	1.25	1.27	1.28	1.29	1.30	1.30	1.30	1.30	1.29	1.28	1.27	1.25	1.23	1.20	1.17	1.14	1.11
44	.34	.39	.44	.48	.54	.59	.64	.69	.74	.79	.83	.88	.92	.96	1.00	1.04	1.07	1.10	1.13	1.15	1.18	1.19	1.22	1.22	1.23	1.24	1.24	1.24	1.23	1.23	1.21	1.19	1.18	1.15	1.13	1.10	1.07	1.04
46	.34	.39	.43	.47	.53	.58	.63	.67	.72	.77	.81	.85	.89	.93	.97	1.00	1.03	1.06	1.09	1.11	1.13	1.14	1.16	1.17	1.17	1.18	1.18	1.17	1.17	1.17	1.14	1.13	1.11	1.08	1.06	1.03	1.00	.97
48	.33	.38	.43	.47	.52	.57	.61	.66	.70	.75	.79	.83	.86	.90	.93	.97	.99	1.02	1.04	1.06	1.08	1.10	1.11	1.12	1.12	1.12	1.12	1.12	1.11	1.10	1.08	1.06	1.04	1.02	.99	.97	.93	.90
50	.33	.37	.42	.46	.51	.56	.60	.64	.69	.73	.77	.80	.84	.87	.90	.93	.96	.98	1.01	1.02	1.04	1.05	1.06	1.07	1.07	1.07	1.07	1.06	1.05	1.04	1.02	1.01	.98	.96	.93	.90	.87	.84
52	.32	.37	.41	.45	.50	.54	.59	.63	.67	.71	.75	.78	.82	.85	.88	.90	.93	.95	.99	.99	1.00	1.01	1.02	1.02	1.02	1.02	1.01	1.01	1.00	.99	.97	.95	.92	.90	.88	.85	.82	.78
54	.32	.36	.41	.45	.49	.53	.57	.61	.65	.69	.73	.76	.79	.82	.85	.88	.90	.92	.94	.95	.96	.97	.98	.98	.98	.98	.97	.96	.95	.94	.92	.90	.88	.85	.82	.79	.76	.73
56	.31	.36	.40	.44	.48	.52	.56	.60	.64	.67	.71	.74	.78	.80	.83	.85	.87	.90	.90	.92	.93	.93	.94	.94	.94	.93	.93	.92	.90	.90	.87	.85	.83	.80	.77	.74	.71	.67
58	.31	.35	.39	.44	.47	.51	.56	.59	.62	.66	.69	.72	.75	.78	.80	.83	.84	.86	.87	.88	.89	.90	.90	.90	.90	.89	.88	.87	.86	.84	.82	.80	.78	.75	.72	.69	.66	.62
60	.31	.35	.39	.43	.47	.50	.54	.58	.61	.64	.67	.70	.73	.76	.78	.80	.82	.83	.84	.85	.86	.86	.87	.86	.86	.85	.84	.83	.82	.80	.78	.76	.73	.70	.67	.64	.61	
62	.31	.34	.38	.42	.46	.50	.53	.57	.60	.63	.66	.69	.71	.74	.76	.77	.79	.80	.82	.82	.83	.83	.83	.83	.82	.82	.80	.79	.77	.76	.74	.71	.69	.66	.63	.60		
64	.30	.34	.38	.42	.45	.49	.52	.56	.59	.62	.64	.67	.70	.72	.74	.75	.77	.78	.79	.79	.80	.80	.80	.80	.79	.78	.77	.75	.74	.72	.69	.67	.64	.62	.59			
66	.30	.33	.37	.41	.45	.48	.51	.54	.57	.60	.63	.65	.68	.70	.71	.73	.74	.75	.76	.77	.77	.77	.77	.76	.75	.75	.73	.71	.70	.68	.65	.63	.60	.57				
68	.30	.33	.37	.40	.44	.48	.50	.53	.56	.59	.62	.64	.66	.68	.69	.71	.72	.73	.74	.74	.74	.74	.74	.73	.72	.72	.69	.68	.66	.64	.62	.59	.56					
70	.29	.33	.36	.40	.43	.46	.49	.52	.55	.58	.60	.62	.64	.66	.68	.69	.70	.71	.71	.71	.71	.71	.71	.71	.69	.69	.66	.64	.62	.60	.58	.55						
72	.29	.32	.36	.39	.43	.46	.49	.51	.54	.57	.59	.61	.63	.64	.66	.67	.68	.68	.69	.69	.69	.69	.68	.68	.66	.64	.64	.61	.59	.57	.54							
74	.29	.32	.36	.39	.42	.45	.48	.50	.53	.55	.57	.59	.61	.63	.64	.65	.66	.66	.66	.66	.66	.66	.65	.64	.63	.61	.59	.57	.55	.53								

$$\left(\frac{\text{DISTANCE RUN}}{\text{BETWEEN BEARINGS}}\right) \times \text{FACTOR} = \text{DISTANCE OFF ABEAM.}$$

The factors tabulated in black faced type are those which apply when the second bearing is the beam bearing. The left hand upper part of the table therefore pertains to ante-beam fixes, and the right hand lower part to post-beam fixes.

*The navigator cannot be too frequently reminded that the reliability of a running fix depends on the course and distance over the ground being accurately known.

Table 43

Conversion TIME-ARC and ARC-TIME

HOURS (0–11)

Minutes	0	1	2	3	4	5	6	7	8	9	10	11	Minutes
0	000	015	030	045	060	075	090	105	120	135	150	165	0
2	000½	015½	030½	045½	060½	075½	090½	105½	120½	135½	150½	165½	2
4	001	016	031	046	061	076	091	106	121	136	151	166	4
6	001½	016½	031½	046½	061½	076½	091½	106½	121½	136½	151½	166½	6
8	002	017	032	047	062	077	092	107	122	137	152	167	8
10	002½	017½	032½	047½	062½	077½	092½	107½	122½	137½	152½	167½	10
12	003	018	033	048	063	078	093	108	123	138	153	168	12
14	003½	018½	033½	048½	063½	078½	093½	108½	123½	138½	153½	168½	14
16	004	019	034	049	064	079	094	109	124	139	154	169	16
18	004½	019½	034½	049½	064½	079½	094½	109½	124½	139½	154½	169½	18
20	005	020	035	050	065	080	095	110	125	140	155	170	20
22	005½	020½	035½	050½	065½	080½	095½	110½	125½	140½	155½	170½	22
24	006	021	036	051	066	081	096	111	126	141	156	171	24
26	006½	021½	036½	051½	066½	081½	096½	111½	126½	141½	156½	171½	26
28	007	022	037	052	067	082	097	112	127	142	157	172	28
30	007½	022½	037½	052½	067½	082½	097½	112½	127½	142½	157½	172½	30
32	008	023	038	053	068	083	098	113	128	143	158	173	32
34	008½	023½	038½	053½	068½	083½	098½	113½	128½	143½	158½	173½	34
36	009	024	039	054	069	084	099	114	129	144	159	174	36
38	009½	024½	039½	054½	069½	084½	099½	114½	129½	144½	159½	174½	38
40	010	025	040	055	070	085	100	115	130	145	160	175	40
42	010½	025½	040½	055½	070½	085½	100½	115½	130½	145½	160½	175½	42
44	011	026	041	056	071	086	101	116	131	146	161	176	44
46	011½	026½	041½	056½	071½	086½	101½	116½	131½	146½	161½	176½	46
48	012	027	042	057	072	087	102	117	132	147	162	177	48
50	012½	027½	042½	057½	072½	087½	102½	117½	132½	147½	162½	177½	50
52	013	028	043	058	073	088	103	118	133	148	163	178	52
54	013½	028½	043½	058½	073½	088½	103½	118½	133½	148½	163½	178½	54
56	014	029	044	059	074	089	104	119	134	149	164	179	56
58	014½	029½	044½	059½	074½	089½	104½	119½	134½	149½	164½	179½	58
60	015	030	045	060	075	090	105	120	135	150	165	180	60

HOURS (12–23)

Minutes	12	13	14	15	16	17	18	19	20	21	22	23	Minutes
0	180	195	210	225	240	255	270	285	300	315	330	345	0
2	180½	195½	210½	225½	240½	255½	270½	285½	300½	315½	330½	345½	2
4	181	196	211	226	241	256	271	286	301	316	331	346	4
6	181½	196½	211½	226½	241½	256½	271½	286½	301½	316½	331½	346½	6
8	182	197	212	227	242	257	272	287	302	317	332	347	8
10	182½	197½	212½	227½	242½	257½	272½	287½	302½	317½	332½	347½	10
12	183	198	213	228	243	258	273	288	303	318	333	348	12
14	183½	198½	213½	228½	243½	258½	273½	288½	303½	318½	333½	348½	14
16	184	199	214	229	244	259	274	289	304	319	334	349	16
18	184½	199½	214½	229½	244½	259½	274½	289½	304½	319½	334½	349½	18
20	185	200	215	230	245	260	275	290	305	320	335	350	20
22	185½	200½	215½	230½	245½	260½	275½	290½	305½	320½	335½	350½	22
24	186	201	216	231	246	261	276	291	306	321	336	351	24
26	186½	201½	216½	231½	246½	261½	276½	291½	306½	321½	336½	351½	26
28	187	202	217	232	247	262	277	292	307	322	337	352	28
30	187½	202½	217½	232½	247½	262½	277½	292½	307½	322½	337½	352½	30
32	188	203	218	233	248	263	278	293	308	323	338	353	32
34	188½	203½	218½	233½	248½	263½	278½	293½	308½	323½	338½	353½	34
36	189	204	219	234	249	264	279	294	309	324	339	354	36
38	189½	204½	219½	234½	249½	264½	279½	294½	309½	324½	339½	354½	38
40	190	205	220	235	250	265	280	295	310	325	340	355	40
42	190½	205½	220½	235½	250½	265½	280½	295½	310½	325½	340½	355½	42
44	191	206	221	236	251	266	281	296	311	326	341	356	44
46	191½	206½	221½	236½	251½	266½	281½	296½	311½	326½	341½	356½	46
48	192	207	222	237	252	267	282	297	312	327	342	357	48
50	192½	207½	222½	237½	252½	267½	282½	297½	312½	327½	342½	357½	50
52	193	208	223	238	253	268	283	298	313	328	343	358	52
54	193½	208½	223½	238½	253½	268½	283½	298½	313½	328½	343½	358½	54
56	194	209	224	239	254	269	284	299	314	329	344	359	56
58	194½	209½	224½	239½	254½	269½	284½	299½	314½	329½	344½	359½	58
60	195	210	225	240	255	270	285	300	315	330	345	360	60

Small Differences

2 min. m. s.	′ ″	½° m. s.	′ ″
0 1	0 15	1 1	15 15
2	30	2	30
3	45	3	45
4	1 00	4	16 00
5	15	5	15
6	30	6	30
7	45	7	45
8	2 00	8	17 00
9	15	9	15
10	30	10	30
11	45	11	45
12	3 00	12	18 00
13	15	13	15
14	30	14	30
15	45	15	45
16	4 00	16	19 00
17	15	17	15
18	30	18	30
19	45	19	45
20	5 00	20	20 00
21	15	21	15
22	30	22	30
23	45	23	45
24	6 00	24	21 00
25	15	25	15
26	30	26	30
27	45	27	45
28	7 00	28	22 00
29	15	29	15
30	30	30	30
31	45	31	45
32	8 00	32	23 00
33	15	33	15
34	30	34	30
35	45	35	45
36	9 00	36	24 00
37	15	37	15
38	30	38	30
39	45	39	45
40	10 00	40	25 00
41	15	41	15
42	30	42	30
43	45	43	45
44	11 00	44	26 00
45	15	45	15
46	30	46	30
47	45	47	45
48	12 00	48	27 00
49	15	49	15
50	30	50	30
51	45	51	45
52	13 00	52	28 00
53	15	53	15
54	30	54	30
55	45	55	45
56	14 00	56	29 00
57	15	57	15
58	30	58	30
59	45	59	45
60	15 00	60	30 00

LINEAR MEASURES

Metres	Feet	Fathoms	$\frac{1}{10^3}$
1	3.3	$\frac{1}{2}$	of
2	6.6	1	**Naut.**
3	9.8	$1\frac{3}{4}$	**Mile**
4	13.1	$2\frac{1}{4}$	i.e.
5	16.4	$2\frac{3}{4}$	Cables
6	19.7	$3\frac{1}{4}$	of
7	23.0	$3\frac{3}{4}$	608 ft.
8	26.2	$4\frac{1}{4}$	
9	29.5	5	
10	32.8	$5\frac{1}{2}$	
11	36.1	6	
12	39.4	$6\frac{1}{2}$	
13	42.7	7	
14	45.9	$7\frac{3}{4}$	
15	49.2	$8\frac{1}{4}$	
16	52.5	$8\frac{3}{4}$	
17	55.8	$9\frac{1}{4}$	
18	59.1	$9\frac{3}{4}$	
19	62.3	$10\frac{1}{2}$	
20	65.6	11	.1
30	98.4	16	
40	131.2	22	.2
50	164.0	27	
60	196.9	33	.3
70	229.7	38	.4
80	262.5	44	
90	295.3	49	.5
100	328.1	55	
200	656.2	109	1.1
300	984.3	164	1.6
400	1312	219	2.2
500	1640	273	2.7
600	1969	328	3.2
700	2297	383	3.8
800	2625	437	4.3
900	2953	492	4.9
1000	3281	547	5.4
1100	3609	601	5.9
1200	3937	656	6.5
1300	4265	711	7.0
1400	4593	766	7.6
1500	4921	820	8.1
1600	5249	875	8.6
1700	5578	930	9.2
1800	5906	984	9.7
1900	6234	1039	10.3
2000	6562	1094	10.8
3000	9843	1640	16.2
4000	13124	2187	21.6
5000	16404	2734	27.0
6000	19685	3281	32.4
7000	22966	3828	37.8
8000	26247	4374	43.2
9000	29528	4921	48.6
10000	32809	5468	54.0

10 Millimetres (mm.) = 1 Centim.
100 Centimetres ⎫
1000 Millimetres ⎬ = 1 Metre (m.)
1000 Metres = 1 Kilometre (Km.)

1 Metre = 39.371 inches.
,, = 3.2809 feet.
,, = 1.0936 yards.
,, = .5468 fathoms.

1 Kilometre = 3280.9 ft.
,, = 1093.6 yds.
,, = 0.621 st. mls.
,, = 0.540 M.

1 Mile (M) = 1853.15 Met.
1 ,, (St.) = 1609.32 ,,
1 Fathom = 1.829 ,,
1 Yard = .9144 ,,
1 Foot = .3048 ,,
1 Inch = { .0254 ,,
{ i.e. 25.4 mm.

"Dutch Log."
Ft. per sec. × .5921 = Knots.
Log. .5921 = 9.77240.

WEIGHTS

1 Gramme = { 15.432 Grains (Troy).
{ .0353 Ozs.
1 Kilogramme (Kg.) = 2.2046 lb.
1000 "Kilos" = .9842 Tons (Br.)

1 Ounce = 28.350 Grms.
1 Pound = .4536 Kg.
1 Hundredwt. = 50.802 ,,
1 Ton (Br.) = 1016.05 ,,

SUPERFICIAL MEASURES

1 Sq. Centimetre = .155 sq. in.
1 Sq. Metre = { 10.764 sq. ft.
{ 1.196 sq. yds.

1 Sq. Inch = 6.451 sq. cm.
1 Sq. Foot = .0929 sq. m.

VOLUME

1 Cu. Centimetre = .0610 cu. in.
1 Cu. Metre = { 35.316 cu. ft.
{ 1.308 cu. yds.

1 Cu. Inch = 16.387 cu. cm.
1 Cu. Foot = { .0283 cu. m.
{ 28.3 Litres.
{ (See below.)
1 Cu. Yd. = .765 cu. m.

CAPACITY

(1 Litre = 1000 cu. cm.)

1 Litre = { 1.76 Pints.
{ .220 Galls.

1 Pint = .568 Litres.
1 Gallon = 4.546 ,,

WATER

1 Cu. ft. = 6.25 Galls.

1 Cu. ft. **Fresh** water = 62.5 lbs.
(i.e. 1000 ozs.)
1 Cu. ft. **Salt** water = 64 lbs.
(Approx.)

1 ton **Fresh** water = { 35.8 cu. ft.
{ 224 galls.
1 ton **Salt** water = { 35 cu. ft.
{ $218\frac{1}{2}$ galls.

1 gall. **Fresh** water = { 10 lbs.
{ .1606 cu. ft.

INDEX

MEMORANDA

Table 44
SPEED, DISTANCE, AND TIME TABLE
For intervals up to 65 minutes

Mins. Time	5	6	7	8	9	Mins. Time	10	11	12	13	14	Mins. Time	15	16	17	18	19	Mins. Time
1	.1	.1	.1	.1	.2	1	.2	.2	.2	.2	.2	1	.3	.3	.3	.3	.3	1
2	.2	.2	.2	.3	.3	2	.3	.4	.4	.4	.5	2	.5	.5	.6	.6	.6	2
3	.3	.3	.4	.4	.5	3	.5	.6	.6	.7	.7	3	.8	.8	.9	.9	1.0	3
4	.3	.4	.5	.5	.6	4	.7	.7	.8	.9	.9	4	1.0	1.1	1.1	1.2	1.3	4
5	.4	.5	.6	.7	.8	5	.8	.9	1.0	1.1	1.2	5	1.3	1.3	1.4	1.5	1.6	5
6	.5	.6	.7	.8	.9	6	1.0	1.1	1.2	1.3	1.4	6	1.5	1.6	1.7	1.8	1.9	6
7	.6	.7	.8	.9	1.1	7	1.2	1.3	1.4	1.5	1.6	7	1.8	1.9	2.0	2.1	2.2	7
8	.7	.8	.9	1.1	1.2	8	1.3	1.5	1.6	1.7	1.9	8	2.0	2.1	2.3	2.4	2.5	8
9	.8	.9	1.1	1.2	1.4	9	1.5	1.7	1.8	2.0	2.1	9	2.3	2.4	2.6	2.7	2.9	9
10	.8	1.0	1.2	1.3	1.5	10	1.7	1.8	2.0	2.2	2.3	10	2.5	2.7	2.8	3.0	3.2	10
11	.9	1.1	1.3	1.5	1.7	11	1.8	2.0	2.2	2.4	2.6	11	2.8	2.9	3.1	3.3	3.5	11
12	1.0	1.2	1.4	1.6	1.8	12	2.0	2.2	2.4	2.6	2.8	12	3.0	3.2	3.4	3.6	3.8	12
13	1.1	1.3	1.5	1.7	2.0	13	2.2	2.4	2.6	2.8	3.0	13	3.3	3.5	3.7	3.9	4.1	13
14	1.2	1.4	1.6	1.9	2.1	14	2.3	2.6	2.8	3.0	3.3	14	3.5	3.7	4.0	4.2	4.4	14
15	1.3	1.5	1.8	2.0	2.3	15	2.5	2.8	3.0	3.3	3.5	15	3.8	4.0	4.3	4.5	4.8	15
16	1.3	1.6	1.9	2.1	2.4	16	2.7	2.9	3.2	3.5	3.7	16	4.0	4.3	4.5	4.8	5.1	16
17	1.4	1.7	2.0	2.3	2.6	17	2.8	3.1	3.4	3.7	4.0	17	4.3	4.5	4.8	5.1	5.4	17
18	1.5	1.8	2.1	2.4	2.7	18	3.0	3.3	3.6	3.9	4.2	18	4.5	4.8	5.1	5.4	5.7	18
19	1.6	1.9	2.2	2.5	2.9	19	3.2	3.5	3.8	4.1	4.4	19	4.8	5.1	5.4	5.7	6.0	19
20	1.7	2.0	2.3	2.7	3.0	20	3.3	3.7	4.0	4.3	4.7	20	5.0	5.3	5.7	6.0	6.3	20
21	1.8	2.1	2.5	2.8	3.2	21	3.5	3.9	4.2	4.6	4.9	21	5.3	5.6	6.0	6.3	6.7	21
22	1.8	2.2	2.6	2.9	3.3	22	3.7	4.0	4.4	4.8	5.1	22	5.5	5.9	6.2	6.6	7.0	22
23	1.9	2.3	2.7	3.1	3.5	23	3.8	4.2	4.6	5.0	5.4	23	5.8	6.1	6.5	6.9	7.3	23
24	2.0	2.4	2.8	3.2	3.6	24	4.0	4.4	4.8	5.2	5.6	24	6.0	6.4	6.8	7.2	7.6	24
25	2.1	2.5	2.9	3.3	3.8	25	4.2	4.6	5.0	5.4	5.8	25	6.3	6.7	7.1	7.5	7.9	25
26	2.2	2.6	3.0	3.5	3.9	26	4.3	4.8	5.2	5.6	6.1	26	6.5	6.9	7.4	7.8	8.2	26
27	2.3	2.7	3.2	3.6	4.1	27	4.5	5.0	5.4	5.9	6.3	27	6.8	7.2	7.7	8.1	8.6	27
28	2.3	2.8	3.3	3.7	4.2	28	4.7	5.1	5.6	6.1	6.5	28	7.0	7.5	7.9	8.4	8.9	28
29	2.4	2.9	3.4	3.9	4.4	29	4.8	5.3	5.8	6.3	6.8	29	7.3	7.7	8.2	8.7	9.2	29
30	2.5	3.0	3.5	4.0	4.5	30	5.0	5.5	6.0	6.5	7.0	30	7.5	8.0	8.5	9.0	9.5	30
31	2.6	3.1	3.6	4.1	4.7	31	5.2	5.7	6.2	6.7	7.2	31	7.8	8.3	8.8	9.3	9.8	31
32	2.7	3.2	3.7	4.3	4.8	32	5.3	5.9	6.4	6.9	7.5	32	8.0	8.5	9.1	9.6	10.2	32
33	2.8	3.3	3.9	4.4	5.0	33	5.5	6.1	6.6	7.2	7.7	33	8.3	8.8	9.4	9.9	10.5	33
34	2.8	3.4	4.0	4.5	5.1	34	5.7	6.2	6.8	7.4	7.9	34	8.5	9.1	9.6	10.2	10.8	34
35	2.9	3.5	4.1	4.7	5.3	35	5.8	6.4	7.0	7.6	8.2	35	8.8	9.3	9.9	10.5	11.1	35
36	3.0	3.6	4.2	4.8	5.4	36	6.0	6.6	7.2	7.8	8.4	36	9.0	9.6	10.2	10.8	11.4	36
37	3.1	3.7	4.3	4.9	5.6	37	6.2	6.8	7.4	8.0	8.6	37	9.3	9.9	10.5	11.1	11.7	37
38	3.2	3.8	4.4	5.1	5.7	38	6.3	7.0	7.6	8.2	8.9	38	9.5	10.1	10.8	11.4	12.0	38
39	3.3	3.9	4.6	5.2	5.9	39	6.5	7.2	7.8	8.5	9.1	39	9.8	10.4	11.0	11.7	12.4	39
40	3.3	4.0	4.7	5.3	6.0	40	6.7	7.3	8.0	8.7	9.3	40	10.0	10.7	11.3	12.0	12.7	40
41	3.4	4.1	4.8	5.5	6.2	41	6.8	7.5	8.2	8.9	9.6	41	10.3	10.9	11.6	12.3	13.0	41
42	3.5	4.2	4.9	5.6	6.3	42	7.0	7.7	8.4	9.1	9.8	42	10.5	11.2	11.9	12.6	13.3	42
43	3.6	4.3	5.0	5.7	6.5	43	7.2	7.9	8.6	9.3	10.0	43	10.8	11.5	12.2	12.9	13.6	43
44	3.7	4.4	5.1	5.9	6.6	44	7.3	8.1	8.8	9.5	10.3	44	11.0	11.7	12.5	13.2	13.9	44
45	3.8	4.5	5.3	6.0	6.8	45	7.5	8.3	9.0	9.8	10.5	45	11.3	12.0	12.8	13.5	14.3	45
46	3.8	4.6	5.4	6.1	6.9	46	7.7	8.4	9.2	10.0	10.7	46	11.5	12.3	13.0	13.8	14.6	46
47	3.9	4.7	5.5	6.3	7.1	47	7.8	8.6	9.4	10.2	11.0	47	11.8	12.5	13.3	14.1	14.9	47
48	4.0	4.8	5.6	6.4	7.2	48	8.0	8.8	9.6	10.4	11.2	48	12.0	12.8	13.6	14.4	15.2	48
49	4.1	4.9	5.7	6.5	7.4	49	8.2	9.0	9.8	10.6	11.4	49	12.3	13.1	13.9	14.7	15.5	49
50	4.2	5.0	5.8	6.7	7.5	50	8.3	9.2	10.0	10.8	11.7	50	12.5	13.3	14.2	15.0	15.8	50
51	4.3	5.1	6.0	6.8	7.7	51	8.5	9.4	10.2	11.1	11.9	51	12.8	13.6	14.5	15.3	16.2	51
52	4.3	5.2	6.1	6.9	7.8	52	8.7	9.5	10.4	11.3	12.1	52	13.0	13.9	14.7	15.6	16.5	52
53	4.4	5.3	6.2	7.1	8.0	53	8.8	9.7	10.6	11.5	12.4	53	13.3	14.1	15.0	15.9	16.8	53
54	4.5	5.4	6.3	7.2	8.1	54	9.0	9.9	10.8	11.7	12.6	54	13.5	14.4	15.3	16.2	17.1	54
55	4.6	5.5	6.4	7.3	8.3	55	9.2	10.1	11.0	11.9	12.8	55	13.8	14.7	15.6	16.5	17.4	55
56	4.7	5.6	6.5	7.5	8.4	56	9.3	10.3	11.2	12.1	13.1	56	14.0	14.9	15.9	16.8	17.7	56
57	4.8	5.7	6.7	7.6	8.6	57	9.5	10.5	11.4	12.4	13.3	57	14.3	15.2	16.2	17.1	18.1	57
58	4.8	5.8	6.8	7.7	8.7	58	9.7	10.6	11.6	12.6	13.5	58	14.5	15.5	16.4	17.4	18.4	58
59	4.9	5.9	6.9	7.9	8.9	59	9.8	10.8	11.8	12.8	13.8	59	14.8	15.7	16.7	17.7	18.7	59
60	5.0	6.0	7.0	8.0	9.0	60	10.0	11.0	12.0	13.0	14.0	60	15.0	16.0	17.0	18.0	19.0	60
61	5.1	6.1	7.1	8.1	9.2	61	10.2	11.2	12.2	13.2	14.2	61	15.3	16.3	17.3	18.3	19.3	61
62	5.2	6.2	7.2	8.3	9.3	62	10.3	11.4	12.4	13.4	14.5	62	15.5	16.5	17.6	18.6	19.6	62
63	5.3	6.3	7.4	8.4	9.5	63	10.5	11.6	12.6	13.7	14.7	63	15.8	16.8	17.9	18.9	20.0	63
64	5.3	6.4	7.5	8.5	9.6	64	10.7	11.7	12.8	13.9	14.9	64	16.0	17.1	18.1	19.2	20.3	64
65	5.4	6.5	7.6	8.7	9.8	65	10.8	11.9	13.0	14.1	15.2	65	16.3	17.3	18.4	19.5	20.6	65

Table 45
SEA HORIZON,
Distance of

Height Ft.	Dist. M	Height Ft.	Dist. M
10	3.7	610	28.9
15	4.5	620	29.1
20	5.2	630	29.4
25	5.8	640	29.4
30	6.4	650	29.8
35	6.9	660	30.1
40	7.4	670	30.3
45	7.8	680	30.5
50	8.3	690	30.7
55	8.7	700	31.0
60	9.1	710	31.2
65	9.4	720	31.4
70	9.8	730	31.6
75	10.1	740	31.8
80	10.5	750	32.0
85	10.7	760	32.3
90	11.1	770	32.5
95	11.4	780	32.7
100	11.7	790	32.9
110	12.3	800	33.1
120	12.8	810	33.3
130	13.3	820	33.5
140	13.8	830	33.7
150	14.3	840	33.9
160	14.8	850	34.1
170	15.3	860	34.3
180	15.7	870	34.5
190	16.1	880	34.7
200	16.5	890	34.9
210	17.0	900	35.1
220	17.4	910	35.3
230	17.7	920	35.5
240	18.1	930	35.7
250	18.5	940	35.9
260	18.9	950	36.1
270	19.2	960	36.3
280	19.6	970	36.4
290	19.9	980	36.6
300	20.3	990	36.8
310	20.6	1000	37.0
320	20.9	1100	38.8
330	21.3	1200	40.5
340	21.6	1300	42.2
350	21.9	1400	43.8
360	22.2	1500	45.3
370	22.5	1600	46.8
380	22.8	1700	48.2
390	23.1	1800	49.6
400	23.4	1900	51.0
410	23.7	2000	52.3
420	24.0	2100	53.6
430	24.3	2200	54.9
440	24.5	2300	56.1
450	24.8	2400	57.3
460	25.1	2500	58.5
470	25.4	2600	59.7
480	25.6	2700	60.8
490	25.9	2800	61.9
500	26.2	2900	63.0
510	26.4	3000	64.1
520	26.7	3500	69.2
530	26.9	4000	74.0
540	27.2	4500	78.5
550	27.4	5000	82.7
560	27.7	6000	90.6
570	27.9	7000	97.9
580	28.2	8000	104.6
590	28.4	9000	111.0
600	28.7	10000	117.0